SECOND SUPPLEMENT TO
THE WORLD'S ENCYCLOPÆDIA OF
RECORDED MUSIC

THE
WORLD'S ENCYCLOPÆDIA
OF RECORDED
MUSIC

SECOND
SUPPLEMENT

(1951 – 1952)

Compiled by

F. F. CLOUGH and G. J. CUMING

Associate Editor: E. A. HUGHES

LONDON RECORDS INC.

in association with
SIDGWICK AND JACKSON LIMITED

First published in 1953

This book is copyright in all countries which
are signatories to the Berne Convention

*Made and printed in Great Britain by William Clowes and Sons, Limited
London and Beccles*

FOREWORD

WE now present the **SECOND SUPPLEMENT** to THE WORLD'S ENCYCLOPÆDIA OF RECORDED MUSIC, covering the period from the close of the first Supplement in May 1951 to December 31st 1952. As before, we have also included later re-issue numbers for British, and some other, issues down to March 1953, where the original issues of such items fall within the period covered by this Second Supplement.

The volume of record publication within a period of some eighteen months is surprising, and the flood of new issues shows no signs of abating. In fact, though a number of smaller Companies in the U.S.A. has disappeared during the period under review, others have arisen to take their place; and there has been a growing tendency for American companies to find new outlets in European and other countries. To keep the size of this supplement under control, we have passed over all re-issues of American recordings in other countries which retain the original U.S.A. numbering, though exception has been made for most such re-issues in England. Similarly, small variations in the prefixes or other indications have not been re-listed where the substantive numbers remain unchanged.

On the other hand we have modified our previous rule on 45 r.p.m. discs, and have attempted to indicate wherever possible the 45 r.p.m. numbers for new issues and some older items. The position has been complicated by the recent introduction in the U.S.A. of the 45 r.p.m. "Extended Play" disc, making use of a larger playing area and of variable-grooving techniques to include much more music than the original 45 r.p.m. disc. We have retained the symbol ♭ to mark all discs played at 45 r.p.m., irrespective of the length of play. Among the tables at the end of this foreword, we list the main Extended Play series included in this Supplement. Similarly, the symbol ♯ denotes all discs played at $33\frac{1}{3}$ r.p.m.; in France, a recent innovation is a 17- or 18-cm. (nominal 7-inch) disc played at this speed, some of which, using variable-grooving techniques, play almost as long as the original 10-inch (25-cm.) LP discs. To distinguish these smaller ♯ discs, we have added a symbol **V** in front of the ♯. (All the *Oiselet* discs (Code DO.) are these small discs.) In addition to the "Variable Micrograde" 78 r.p.m. discs of Deutsche Grammophon/Polydor, and now of Telefunken and Fonodan, this supplement sees the introduction of another variety of 78 r.p.m. disc by Philips, distinguished by *PhM* in our code, meaning "78 r.p.m. Philips Minigroove". These are 17·5 cm. discs, which use the modern fine grooves and variable spacing, but play at 78 r.p.m. with a Microgroove pickup, and not with a normal pickup as do the "Variable-Micrograde" discs.

By observation of the symbols and the prefixes, we hope readers will be able to steer their way through the confusion which these rival systems have introduced into discography. This confusion has not been eased by E.M.I.'s introduction of both $33\frac{1}{3}$ and 45 r.p.m. discs to the British and European markets, the first portents of which were mentioned in the foreword to the first Supplement. It may help readers to have a table (appended at the end of this foreword) showing the letter prefixes in use at the present date by E.M.I. for these discs in various countries. We have also prepared (in response to requests) a short table of the main U.S.A. Victor numbering series at present in use or *recently* obsolete; and also an explanation of the Philips code of prefix and affix letters; the added complication that Philips have taken over the distribution of American Columbia recordings from the E.M.I. Group as from 1st January 1953 fortunately does not affect the present Supplement.

The task of preparing this Supplement has been much eased by the continued co-operation of many of those enthusiastic supporters who are mentioned, expressly or by implication, in the preface to WERM; and also of a number of new helpers whose assistance has also been invaluable. By name we wish to mention Messrs. J. London,

W. D. Kelley Jr., P. Forstall, and N. Ferber in the U.S.A.; Dr. B. Semeonoff, who has kindly translated some exceptionally complete Russian catalogues which came to hand during the year and contain many older recordings not known to us before; Miss Angela Noble, who has carried out much musical research on our behalf; and the help we have found in additional periodical sources including *Critique* (issued by The Gramophone Exchange, London, who have been most helpful), *Notes, Schwann, The Long Player*, the *American Record Letter* and *The International Record Letter*, which have joined those publications mentioned in WERM on our shelves. Our many correspondents have also greatly assisted us by sending in corrections and amplifications, and from these and our own discoveries we have compiled the Consolidated List of errata, addenda and corrigenda which precedes the Supplement proper in the following pages. In all these tasks we have again been fortunate in having the close collaboration of Mr. E. A. Hughes who has shouldered many tedious assignments with cheerfulness and even avidity; and of the same diligent typists who worked so well for us before. To all we tender renewed thanks, and express our hopes for continued co-operation from record collectors and music lovers everywhere—their expressions of goodwill are most gratifying. We wonder if there are any in South and Central America who would care to correspond with us?

The general layout of the present Supplement follows that of the first, and in general the meaning of the symbols is the same. We have however extended the meaning of ▽ to include also "correction of entry in WERM or Supplement I" as well as "entry omitted from WERM or Supplement I". In view of suggestions from collectors, we have in this supplement listed as many as possible of acoustic Vocal and a few Instrumental re-issues—mainly, apart from the H.M.V. "Archive" Series, LP "dubbings". The coverage of this type of recording—denoted by **H** in the lists—extends back to the beginning of 1951, in view of their exclusion from Supplement I, and includes so much of the H.M.V. *Archive Series* as is not already listed in WERM. It has not been possible, for reasons of space, to enter all the miscellaneous LP dubbings in detail, but a summarised list of these will be found in the *Anthologies* section under *Vocal Re-issues*, and the main items are entered under the individual headings. We must also make it clear that in a general work of this nature it is not possible to attempt any *expertise* in questions of date or place of recording, original sources, etc., of these collectors' records. This was of course also the case in WERM; both there and here our emphasis has always been rather on the music recorded than on the artist or circumstances of the recording.

In these supplements we perforce must work primarily from Press reports and the printed lists and announcements of the various manufacturers, which unfortunately are not always complete, or free from errors. These can only be detected by hearing the discs (which is possible to us in comparatively few cases), from reviews, or from the reports of our correspondents. We may therefore have listed records as existing when they do not, or omitted records which do; in which cases the makers may well be to blame for over-enthusiastic or inefficient publicity, rather than the authors. Despite certain opinions to the contrary among readers, it is only very exceptionally that we are afforded access by the manufacturers to the discs listed, by way of review copies or otherwise.

F. F. CLOUGH

G. J. CUMING

Kingswood,

Upper Colwyn Bay,

March 1953   Great Britain.

COMPOSER (Date of birth and death)
CLASSIFICATION where applicable.
GENRE or TITLE OF OPERA, etc.
Title of the individual item. Voice or instrumentation, date of composition, etc.
Name of Artist or Orch.—Conductor **Main No.**
(No. of sides, *coupling*, or anthology ref.) (Subsidiary Nos.)

▽ Omission from WERM, or corrected entry.

☆ Re-issue of recording included in WERM or Supplement I in another country, or with different nos. in country of origin, etc.

¶ Re-issue of a pre-1936 recording in **Great Britain** with same nos.

H Re-issue or dubbing of acoustic recording, or new " historical " issue.

The symbols **H**, ☆, ▽, etc., prefixed to an artist entry in large type, only refer to that particular entry, and not to any following entries, whether in large or small type. The same symbols prefixed to a number of small type entries forming a list, refer to all entries forming the list, until the appearance of a new symbol changes the description.

SONGS & ARIAS, etc., are set out:

Title, Op. no. (Author of text) Date.
(*Translation* of title, subtitles, etc.)

Singer & accompanist **Main No.**
(*Coupling*) (Subsidiary Nos.)

The language is the original unless otherwise shown, except in certain cases (e.g. USSR) where it is not possible to ascertain definitely the language used.

Excerpts from a larger work (unless it is divided into numbered or other sections) are shown:
...**Adagio** only

while an ARRANGEMENT of such an excerpt is introduced by a double dash, thus:
— — ARR VLN. & PF. Auer

while a single dash
— ARR. BAND Wright
refers to an arrangement of the whole work or section.

Where it has become the custom to record ♯ collections of songs, etc., by one composer, these have been grouped at the head of the list of such works, and individual contents not re-entered. In certain cases the sign □ is added to subsequent mention of titles which are contained in collections, to refer back to the collected entry.

In the case of there being several subsidiary numbers, the different numbers of the same make are separated by colons : and the code for the make is not repeated. Different makes are separated by semi-colons ; and the new code follows.

It can usually be assumed, in the case of 78 and 45 r.p.m. discs, that the coupling quoted applies both to main and to subsidiary numbers unless a different coupling is quoted, or the notation d.c. indicates a different coupling.
This does not apply where *no* coupling is given, as in the case of small-type entries, re-issues, etc.; or to ♯ numbers, though in this case every endeavour has been made to give as much information as space permits. In general, couplings are only given in shortened form, sufficient to guide the reader to fuller entries elsewhere. The sign † directs to the Anthology entries at the end of the book. Most composers appearing in such anthologies are listed in their alphabetical positions in the body of the Supplement; to this extent, therefore, this Supplement (unlike WERM & Supplement I) is self-indexing.
In coupling lines, the composers' names are always followed by a colon : to separate them from the titles; where there are several composers, they are divided by commas.

The name of an opera or other large work is followed by a dash — to separate it from the words of an aria or other similar excerpt. Where no composer is mentioned in the coupling line, it can be assumed that the composer of the item on the reverse is the same as that on the obverse, except where the title of an opera or other well-known work is cited, where the name of a composer would be redundant.
In the case of operatic lists, where neither composer nor opera is named in the coupling, the title will be from the same opera as the obverse.

In view of the growing practice of dubbing from older recordings, no attempt is made to separate different versions of the same item by the same artist, except where the origins are obvious. This applies in particular to LP re-issues of acoustic recordings.

LIST OF RECORD MAKES
(and abbreviations therefor)

These precede the record no. and are divided from it by a full point (.)

A.440	A.440 (U.S.A.)	EMI.	EMI Special Issues (G.B.)
AA.	Action Artistique (France—Propaganda Issue)	EPP.	Éditions phonographiques parisiennes (France)
Abb.	Abbey (U.S.A.)	Era.	Erato (France)
Acad.	Academy (U.S.A.)	Eso.	Esoteric (U.S.A.)
AF.	Addison Foster (U.S.A.)	Esq.	Esquire (G.B.)
Allo.	Allegro (U.S.A.)	Esta	Esta (Czechoslovakia)
AmC.	American Columbia (U.S.A.)	Ete.	Eterna (U.S.A.)
Amf.	Amfión (Mexico)	Etu.	Etude (U.S.A.)
AmD.	American Decca (U.S.A.)	Eur.	Eurochord (France)
AmVien.	American Viennola (U.S.A.)	EVox.	English Vox (G.B.) [1]
AmVox.	American Vox (U.S.A.)		
Amph.	Amphion (France)	FCap.	French Capitol
Antro.	Antrochord (Austria)	Felix	Felix (Denmark)
Aphe.	Audiophile (U.S.A.)	Fest.	Festival (U.S.A.)
ArgC.	Argentine Columbia (Argentine)	FestF.	French Festival
ArgOd.	Argentine Odeon (Argentine)	Fdn.	Fonodan (Denmark)
ArgV.	Argentine Victor (Argentine)	Fnt.	Fonit (Italy)
Argo.	Argo (G.B.)	FPV.	French Polydor Var. Micrograde (France)
ARS.	American Recording Society (U.S.A.)	FSor.	French Cetra-Soria
Attn.	Austroton (Germany, etc.) (issues Swiss/Austrian Elites with same numbers plus 20000 or 50000)	FT.	French Telefunken (for special numbers for local issues only)
AS.	Anthologie Sonore (France)	FV.	Fonodan Variable Micrograde (Denmark)
Atst.	Artist (U.S.A.)		
AudA.	Audio Archives (U.S.A.)	G.	H.M.V. (Gramophone Co.) (Europe, etc.) (including German Electrola)
AusT.	Austrian Telefunken (Austria)	GAR.	Golden Age Recordings (U.S.A.)
		Gco.	Grayco (H. W. Gray Inc.) (U.S.A.)
B.	Brunswick (G.B.)	GIOA	Gregorian Institute of America (U.S.A.)
BàM.	Boite à Musique (France)	GMS.	Golden Music (U.S.A.)
Ban.	Banner (U.S.A.)	Gol.	Golden Legend (U.S.A.)
BB.	Bluebird (Victor) (U.S.A.)		
Bea.	Beaver (Canada)	Harv.	Harvard University (U.S.A.)
Bib.	Bibletone (U.S.A.)	HC.	Haverford College (U.S.A.)
BlSoc.	Bloch Society (U.S.A.)	HDL.	Handel Society (U.S.A.)
Bne.	Bartone (U.S.A.)	Hma.	Harmona (Austria)
Bo.	Boston Records (U.S.A.)	HRS.	Historic Record Society (U.S.A.)
Brd.	Broadcast (G.B.)—in errata only	HS.	Haydn Society (U.S.A.) (also HSLP.)
BRS.	Bartok Recording Studio (U.S.A.)		
BrzC.	Brazilian Columbia (Brazil)	Ibe.	Iberia (Spanish Columbia) (Spain)
BrzCont.	Brazilian Continental (Brazil)	Imp.	Imperial (Germany)
BrzMGM	Brazilian MGM (Brazil)	IPV.	Polydor Variable Micrograde (Italy)
BrzOd.	Brazilian Odeon (Brazil)	IRCC	International Record Collectors Club (U.S.A.)
BrzV.	Brazilian Victor (Brazil)	Isis	Isis Recording Studios (Oxford, G.B.)
BS.	Bach Society (U.S.A.)	ISR.	International Sacred Recordings, Christian Artists' Rec. Corp. (U.S.A.)
C.	Columbia (Europe, Australia, etc.)		
Cap.	Capitol (U.S.A.)	JpC.	Japanese Columbia (Japan)
CC.	Collectors' Corner (G.B.)	JpV.	Japanese Victor (Japan)
Cdia.	Concordia (U.S.A.)		
CdM.	Chant du Monde (France)	Ken.	Kendall (U.S.A.)
CEd.	Classic Editions (U.S.A.)	KR.	Key Records (U.S.A.)
Cel.	Celson (Italy)		
CGD.	Compania Generale del Disco (Italy)	LMS.	Liberty Music Shop (U.S.A.)
Chr.	Christschall (Austria, Germany, etc.)	Lon.	London (U.S.A. issues of Eng. Decca)
CHS.	Concert Hall Society (U.S.A.)	Long.	Longines (U.S.A.)
Ch.Soc.	Cherubini Society (G.B.)	Lum.	Lumen (France)
CID.	Compagnie industrielle du disque (France)	Lyr.	Lyrichord (U.S.A.)
Circ.	Circle (U.S.A.)		
Clc.	Classic (France)	Ma. or MApp.	Musical Appreciation (U.S.A.)
CMS.	Collectors Music Shop (U.S.A.)	May.	Mayor or Nuevo Mayor (Italy)
Cmt.	Claremont (U.S.A.)	McG.	Macgregor (U.S.A.)
Coda.	Coda records of SMC (U.S.A.)	Mer.	Mercury (U.S.A.)
Conl.	Conlin (Convent) (U.S.A.)	MGM.	Metro-Goldwyn-Mayer (U.S.A. & G.B.)
Cont.	Continental (U.S.A.)	ML.	Music Library (U.S.A.)
CPf.	Command Performance (U.S.A.)	MMS.	Musical Masterworks Society (U.S.A. & Europe)
Cpt.	Contrepoint (France)		
CRG.	Children's Record Guild (U.S.A.)	Mon.	Monarch (G.B.)
Crl.	Coral (Decca) (U.S.A.)	Mrt.	Merit (U.S.A.)
Croy.	Croydon Celebrity Recording Society (G.B.)	MR.	Music Records (U.S.A.)
		MSL.	Masterseal (U.S.A.)
CRS.	Collectors Record Society (U.S.A.)	MTR.	Magic-Tone Records (U.S.A.)
Csm.	Colosseum (U.S.A.)	Mtr.	Metronome (Sweden)
Cup.	Cupol (Sweden)	Muza	Muza (Poland)
D.	Decca (Europe, Australia, etc.)	NE.	New Editions (U.S.A.)
DCap.	Capitol (G.B., pressed by Decca)	Nera	Nera (Norway)
Deci.	Decibel (G.B.)	Nix.	Nixa (G.B.)
Den.	Den Records (U.S.A.)	NRI.	New Records, Inc. (U.S.A.)
DFr.	Discophiles français (France) (In U.S.A. as AmVox.)		
Dia.	Diaphon (Australia)	Oce.	Oceanic (U.S.A.)
Dial.	Dial (U.S.A.)	Od.	Odeon (Europe, etc.)
DO.	Oiselet (OL.) (France) (all are V♯ discs)	Ofo.	Orfeo Records (U.S.A.)
Dor.	Dorian Records (U.S.A.)	OL.	Oiseau Lyre (France)
DT.	Telefunken (Decca pressings, G.B.)	Ome.	Omega (Belgium, Holland) (certain issues of CID. items with same numbers are not re-entered)
Dur.	Durium (Italy)		
EA.	English pressings of Allegro	Orf.	Orfeo Records (Argentine)
Ebor.	Eboracum Record Society (G.B.)	Ori.	Oriole (G.B.)
EdB. or EB.	Edison Bell (G.B.) inc. Winner, Velvet Face	Ox.	Oxford (G.B.)
Elec.	Electro (Finland)		
Elek.	Elektra (U.S.A.)		
Eli.	Elite (Switzerland, etc.; also a few in U.S.A.)		

[1] The 3-digit numbers in the 100, 200, 300 & 400 series have already become obsolete since going to press. English issues now use the quoted U.S.A. numbers (PL prefix) throughout.

P.   Parlophone (Europe, Australia); & Cetra (Italy)
Pac.   Pacific (France)
Parx.   Paradox (U.S.A.) (now called Pax)
Pal.   Pallas (Germany)
Pam.   Pampa (Brazil)
Pat.   Pathé (France)
PaV.   Pathé-Vox (France)
Pax.   Paxton (G.B.)
Pde.   Parade (U.S.A.)
Pem.   Pembroke (U.S.A.)
Per.   Period (U.S.A.)
Phi.   Philips (Holland & International)
Phil.   Philharmonia (U.S.A.)
PhM. Philips Minigroove, 78 r.p.m. 17-cm. discs.
Ply.   Plymouth (U.S.A.) (Only a few samples entered. The numbers in the form 12-1 or *10-1* are derived from Mrt. numbers in form 200-1 or *1-1*)
Pol.   Polydor & Deutsche Grammophon (Europe; in Denmark, etc., Polyphon)
Polym. Polymusic (U.S.A.)
Prog. Program (U.S.A.)
Pte.   Private (non-commercial, but on sale)
PV.   Polydor/Deutsche Grammophon Variable Micrograde (Germany)
Qual. Qualiton (Hungary)

REB. R. E. Blake (U.S.A.)
Rem. Remington (U.S.A.)
Ren.   Renaissance (U.S.A.)
Rgt.   Regent (U.S.A.)
RH.   Record Hunter (U.S.A.)
Rna.   Regina (U.S.A.)
Roch. Eastman-Rochester (U.S.A.
RR.   Record Rarities (U.S.A.)
RS.   Rachmaninoff Society (U.S.A
Roy.   Royale (U.S.A.)
Rtj.   Radiotjänst (Sweden)
Ryt.   Rytmi (Finland, etc.)

Sat.   Saturn (France)
Scd.   Scoladisques (France)
Sco.   Scolaphon (France)

Sel.   Selmer or Ducretet-Selmer (France)
SM.   Studio S.M. (France)
SMC. Spanish Music Centre (U.S.A.)
Son.   Sonora (Sweden)
Sor.   Cetra-Soria (U.S.A. & Italy)
SOT. Sounds of our times (U.S.A.)
SPA. Society of Participating Artists (U.S.A.)
SPAM. Society for Publication of American Music (U.S.A.)
SpC. Spanish Columbia (San Sebastian, Spain)
SpD. Spanish Decca (San Sebastian, Spain)
SRC. Sound Recording Co. (U.S.A.)
StO.   St. Olaf (U.S.A.)
Strad. Stradivari (U.S.A.)
Sup.   Supraphon (Czechoslovakia; domestic nos. & export ♯ discs)
Syc.   Symphonic (U.S.A.)
Sym. Symphony Recording Co. (U.S.A.)
Symf. Symfoni (Sweden)

T.   Telefunken (Europe)
Täh.   Tähti (Finland)
Tono Tono (Denmark)
Top. or TRC. Topic Records (G.B.)
Tpo.   Tempo (Germany)
Trla. Triola (Finland)
TV.   Telefunken Variable Micrograde (Germany)

U.   Ultraphon (export issues now labelled Supraphon) (Czechoslovakia)
UOS. University of the South (U.S.A.)
Ura.   Urania (U.S.A.)
USSR. State Music Trust (one side per no.) (Russia)
Van.   Vanguard (U.S.A.) (also Bach Guild)
Var.   Varsity (U.S.A.)
Vic.   Victor (U.S.A., Canada, South America)
Vien. Viennola (Austria)
Vienna Vienna (U.S.A.)
VIS.   Vis-Radio (Italy)
Voc.   Vocalion (G.B.)
Wald. Walden (U.S.A.)
WCFM. WCFM (U.S.A.)
Wde. World-wide (U.S.A.)

LIST OF OTHER ABBREVIATIONS

AAYO.	All-American (Youth) Orchestra
Accord.	Accordeon
A	Alto (Contralto)
B or Bar	Baritone
B & H	Breitkopf & Hartel
Bk.	Book
bsn.	Bassoon
BSO(O)	Berlin State (Opera) Orch.
Bs	Bass
CBs, Cbs.	Contra-bass
CBS.	Columbia Broadcasting Symphony Orch.
Cha.	Chamber
Cho.	Chorus or choral
Chu. or Ch.	Church
cl.	clarinet
clavi.	clavichord
Cons.	Conservatoire
cont.	continuo
C-T	Counter-tenor
CUMS.	Cambridge University Madrigal Society
Cz	Czech
D.	Deutsch references (Schubert)
d.c.	different coupling
Dan.	Danish
Ed.	Edited by, or Edition
Ens.	Ensemble
Finn	Finnish
F.O.K.	Prague Film and Concert Orch.
f.p.	First performance
Fr	French
FVB	Fitzwilliam Virginal Book
G.	Grove's No. (Beethoven, Elgar, etc.)
GA.	Gesamt-Ausgabe
G.B.	Great Britain
Ger	German
guit.	guitar
H	Vocal or other re-issue in "historical" series
hp.	harp
hpsi.	harpsichord
hrn.	horn
Icel	Icelandic
Inc. Mus.	Incidental Music
Ital	Italian
K.	Köchel Nos. (Mozart)
KFUM.	Y.M.C.A., Sweden & Denmark
L.	Longo Nos. (Scarlatti)
Latv	Latvian
Lith	Lithuanian
L.P.O.	London Philharmonic Orchestra
L.S.O.	London Symphony Orchestra
M-S or MS	Mezzo-soprano
mbrs.	members
n.d.	no data or nos. discoverable
n.n.	new number
No., Nod.	Number, Numbered
NQHO.	New Queen's Hall Orchestra
NSO	National Symphony Orchestra
NWDR	Nord-West-Deutsche-Rundfunk Orchestra (Hamburg)
NYPSO.	N.Y. Phil. Sym. Orch.
n.v.	new version
o.n.	old number (i.e. same recording has been re-numbered in the same country)
Ov.	Overture
o.v.	old version

ob.	oboe
orch.	orchestra or orchestrated
Op.	Opus, or opera
P.	Pincherle references (Vivaldi)
P.	polka (Strauss family)
pf.	piano
Pte.	Private
prep.	preparation
Q.H.O.	Queen's Hall Orchestra
Qtt.	Quartet
R.A.M.	Royal Academy of Music
RAHO.	Royal Albert Hall Orchestra
RCS	Royal Choral Society
R.I.A.S.	Berlin Radio (American Sector)
RPO	Royal Philharmonic Orchestra
rec.	recorder or recorded
ROH	Royal Opera House
r.p.m.	revolutions per minute
r.r.	re-recorded
RSCM	Royal School of Church Music
Rum	Rumanian
Russ	Russian
S or Sop	Soprano
s.c.	same coupling (this is to be understood, however, in usual cases on 78 r.p.m.)
SECM	School of English Church Music (now RSCM)
s, ss.	side(s)
signs	(see also Foreword)
†	see Anthologies section
□	see collection of this composer
‡	duplicate nos. (re-used; by G. (in Germany), DB 7600 & 5400 series)
*	non-electrical recording: or electrical re-recording from acoustic original
¶	pre-1936—re-issued in G.B. with pre-1936 number
§	pre-1936—not available in G.B. (in errata only)
▽	Omission from, or Correction of entry in, WERM and Supplement I
☆	Re-issue (re-pressing, or occasionally, dubbing) of recording to be found in WERM or Supplement I. See foreword.
♯	record played at 33⅓ r.p.m.
♭	record played at 45 r.p.m.
V♯	7-inch record played at 33⅓ r.p.m. (All records play at 78 r.p.m. unless marked as above.)
♮	Auto. couplings, 78 r.p.m.
Soc.	Society
Sp.	Special (attributed to pressings)
Sp or Span	Spanish
Swed	Swedish
T or Ten	Tenor
Tr	Treble
trs.	transcribed (*of music*)
trs.	translated (*of texts*)
tpt.	trumpet
unid.	unidentified (=heard, but not identifiable, or not included in standard lists of composers' works)
unspec.	unspecified (=not heard, and insufficient catalogue details to permit identification among several possibilities)
vlc.	violoncello
vln.	violin
v.o.v.	very old version
vla.	viola
vv.	voices
W.	Waltz (Strauss family)
W.	Wotquenne (C.P.E. Bach)

CURRENT LP PREFIXES, DECCA & ASSOCIATES

Country	Make	Label	10-inch (25 cm.)	12-inch (30 cm.)
GREAT BRITAIN & INTERNATIONAL	Decca	Gold Label Red Label Blue Label	LX LM LF	LXT LK —
GREAT BRITAIN	Brunswick Capitol (DCap.) Telefunken (DT.) London	Magenta Label Black Label Magenta Label Black Label Black Label Magenta Label	AXL LA CCL LC LGM H-APB	AXTL LAT CTL LCT LGX —
FRANCE & BELGIUM	Decca		LF, LX 133000, AK, AX 233000	AXT 233000
U.S.A.	London		LPS, now LS; LPB, now LB;	LLP, now LL

E.M.I. COMBINE NEW RECORD SERIES

Country	Make	33⅓ r.p.m. LP ♯		45 r.p.m. ♭	Normal 78 r.p.m. new series (additional to WERM)	
		10-inch (25-cm.)	12-inch (30-cm.)	7-inch (17-cm.)	10-inch (25-cm.)	12-inch (30-cm.)
GREAT BRITAIN & INTERNATIONAL	H.M.V. Columbia Parlophone MGM	BLP, DLP [33] C, S PMB, PMD MGM.D	ALP, CLP [33] CX, SX PMA, PMC —	7R, 7P, 7M SCB, SCD, SCM BSP, DSP, MSP MGM.SP	— — — MGM.500 series	— — — —
FRANCE BELGIUM SWITZERLAND }	H.M.V. Columbia Odeon Pathé	FMLP FBLP FDLP [33] FC, FS OD, OS [33] DT	FALP [33] FCX ODX [33] DTX	7BF, 7RF — — —	— — — —	— — — —
ITALY	H.M.V. Columbia Pathé	QBLP [33] QC —	QALP [33] QCX —	7BQ, 7RQ — 	— MD	— MDT
GERMANY	H.M.V. Columbia Pathé	WBLP WDLP [33] WC, WS —	WALP WCLP [33] WCX WSX —	— — —	— — PI, PK	— — PM, PN
AUSTRIA	H.M.V. Columbia	VBLP VDLP VC	VALP VCLP VCX	— —	— —	— —
DENMARK	H.M.V.	KBLP	—	—	—	—
FINLAND	H.M.V. Odeon	— —	— —	— —	TG, TJ PLE, PLD	TH PLG

NOTE: The 33 in the prefix on Columbia and French Pathé forms part of the record order no. but is omitted in our discographies, the symbol ♯ having the same meaning. The French and Italian series of ♯ and ♭ discs have so far used identical numbers, only the prefixes varying.

MGM ♯ E series is U.S.A.; four digits are 12-inch, fewer are 10-inch.

Current or Recently Obsolete record Series
(Synopsis only, of domestic series)

45 r.p.m.			Equivalent 78 r.p.m.			Equivalent 33⅓ r.p.m.		
Disc Series	Album sets	Type	Disc Series	Size	Album sets	Prefix	Series	Size
17-0000	WCT	Classical (Collectors)	15-1000 16-5000 10000, etc. & re-issues of	12	—	LCT	1 up 7000 up 1000 up 9000 up	10 12
19-0000	WOC	Original cast	14-0001	12	M, DM OC	LOC	1000 up 3000 up	12 10
27-0000	WPT	Popular (Collectors)	42-0000	10	PT	LPT	1000 up 1 up & 3000 up	12 10
41-6000	WE	Educational	45-5000	10	E	—	—	—
47-0000	WY	Childrens	45-5000 45-5800	10 12	Y	LY	1 up	10
47-2000	WP	Popular	20-0000 28-0000	10 12	P, DC	LPM	as LPT	
48-0000	WP	Pop. "Country", etc.	21-0000	10	P	—	—	—
49-0000	WDM WDC	Classical	10-1000 11, 12-0000	10 12	DM	LM	as LCT	—
149-0000	WHMV	Classical (H.M.V. recordings)	—	—	—	LHMV	1000 9000	12
249-0000	WBC	Classical (Bluebird)	—	—	—	LBC	1000	12
50-0000	—	Blues, Spirituals	22-0000	10	—	—	—	—
52-0000	WK, WDC	Popular Classics	45-0000	10	K	LK	as LPT	—
Extended play discs								
947-0000	EPBT	Popular (Collector)						
547-0000	EPB	Popular						
	EOB	Original cast						
WEPR ERA ERAT		Classical / Classical (Collectors)						
EKA		Musical Shows						
EPA		Popular						
EPAT		Popular (Collectors)						

NOTES: Additional prefix *4* added to above series indicates a "Collectors" item—thus *447-0000, 420-0000*. Additional prefix *5* added indicates Extended play 45 r.p.m., and additional prefix *9* indicates Extended play Collectors series. LCT and LM ♯ sets are numbered as follows:
12-inch: 6000 up, 2 discs; 6100, 3 discs; 6400, 4 discs.   10-inch: 6200 up, 2 discs; 6300, 3 discs; 6500, 4 discs.

OTHER NOTES

THE PHILIPS NUMBERING SYSTEM

The prefix letter refers to the price class of the record:
P = Popular
N = Medium
A = Artistic
in ascending order of price.   The suffix letter denotes the kind of record, as follows:
H = 10-inch (25 cm.) normal 78 r.p.m.
G = 12-inch (30 cm.) normal 78 r.p.m.
S = 7-inch (17·5 cm.) "minigroove" 78 r.p.m.
R = 10-inch (25 cm.) LP 33⅓ r.p.m.
L = 12-inch (30 cm.) LP 33⅓ r.p.m.
The prefix letter can change from country to country according to local price conditions, keeping the same number and suffix.

POLYDOR ♯ issues:
with five digits are German (classical called *Deutsche Grammophon*), and re-pressings with original numbers in other countries;
with six digits are French.

EXTENDED PLAY 45 r.p.m. discs (U.S.A.):
Victor: *See table above*
Columbia: ♭ *A 1500* series
Urania: ♭ *UREP*
Royale: ♭ *EP*
Capitol: ♭ *FAP*
Mercury: ♭ *EP*

CONSOLIDATED LIST
of
ERRATA, CORRIGENDA & ADDENDA
to
WERM & SUPPLEMENT I

The Authors wish to express their deep gratitude to all readers who have responded so enthusiastically to their appeal for corrections—which is, of course, still open.

This list does not contain every item reported or discovered. The following are excluded:

Purely textual errors of an obvious nature which readers will have been able to correct themselves.

Minor recordings omitted designedly, for reasons of space.

Additional numbers, omitted designedly for similar reasons, or belonging to minor obsolete series or countries.

Most alterations in designations or names of performers subsequent to the first issue of the recordings.

Alterations in couplings, numbers, status, etc., subsequent to the closing of WERM and Supplement I for press. *Important* items in this category will be found in Supplement No. II; but, as explained in the foreword to that Supplement, mere changes in prefix letters and similar matters are ignored, where the substantive part of the record number is unchanged.

Readers are recommended to carry these alterations into their copy of WERM, as it may not be possible to consolidate future lists of corrections with the present list.

Further reports of similar corrections will be gratefully received by the Authors, but it would assist them in their work if the reports could be cast in similar form to the present lists, and corrections to WERM and Supplement No. I be kept separate from those to Supplement No. II.

Page	Col.	Entry	Remarks
x	4	NORWAY	DNX should be in Roman type (12-inch).
xii	3	Table VI	Swiss Decca also KX prefix.
xiv/xv			Add to list of Record makes:
			LM. Little Master (U.S.A.)
			OUP. Oxford Univ. Press (G.B.)
			Prize Prize (U.S.A.)
			Rex Rex (G.B.)
4	1	Sevillanas	A. Rubinstein, G.DB 1257 is ¶.
			Move § down to next line.
4	2	Torre bermeja	Segovia—no. *to read* **B.04394**
5	2	ALFVÉN, line 3	*For* Kalstenius *read* Kallstenius.
6	2	ARCADELT, line 5	*For* servus *read* cervus.
6	—	Footnote	*To read* ARR. P. L. P. Dietsch from a secular madrigal: *Nous voyons que les hommes* . . .
7	2	Care flies . . .	*Voc.X 9947* is 10-inch, and should be in *italics*.
8	1	When daisies . . .	Bauman—*For* 69838D *read* 69839D♮.
9	2	AUBERT: Suite brève, Air	*Add* omission: § M. Ruff & D. Jeanès (G.W 1066).
10	2	Sonatas, G ma. & F mi.	*C.DB 830/1* are excerpts only. See WERM, p. 712.
11	1	Concerto, A major	*For* Berlin Phil. *read* Berlin State.
11	2	Symphonies	*Add* omission: No. 2, B flat major (Wind insts.) . . . **Rondeau** —ARR. Françaix, in Scuola di Ballo. *See* Boccherini.
11	2	Symphony, Op. 18, No. 2	*For* Berlin Phil. *read* Berlin Municipal. *Add* additional no.: (Fnt.90075/6).
12	1	Concerto nach . . .	*Delete* n from Allo.AL 5 and *insert* in "only" on next line.
12	2	"Vivaldi" Concerto 14	Takes only 1½ss of C.BQX 2534; the last ⅓ side contains a Fugue, so far unid.
12	2	Fantasia, C minor, BWV 906	*Delete* § H. Cohen (pf) (C.LX 400; AmC.68388D) *and transfer* to new entry: Fantasia, C minor, BWV 921.
13	2	Minuets	*AmB.15210* is 10-inch.
14	2	English Suite No. 3	Borowsky—AmVox No. should read *16011/13*.
15	1	French Suite No. 1	*D.M 494* is 10-inch.
15	1	French Suite No. 4 . . . Allemande	Ehlers—*is really from* Suite No. 6. *Transfer* entry.
16	1	W.T.C. No. 2, Fugue — ARR. ORCH.	Stokowski—*For* § G.DB 2543 *read* § G.DB 2453.
16	1	W.T.C. No. 3	Borowsky—No. *to read* : G.DA 1308.
16	2	W.T.C. Prelude 8, — ARR. ORCH.	Stokowski—Vic. no. *to read* Vic. 6786.
		Idem. — ARR. ACCORDION	*Sel.SA 5* is 10-inch.
17	1	No. 37	Key *to read* F sharp major.
18	2	Ich ruf' zu dir	Germani—MV 1109 is coupled with the *Fugue* of BWV 552, not the Prelude.
20	2	Concerto, "Vivaldi" No. 1, G major	*Add* After a concerto by Johann Ernst of Saxe-Weimar (1696–1715)
21	2	Fantasia, C minor	Dupré—*For* G.D 1536 *read* G.D 1356.
23	2	Toccata & Fugue, D minor	Stokowski—*For* AmC. 81757/8D *read* AmC. 11757/8D.
24	2	Sonata No. 3 . . . Andante	§ Huberman—No. *to read* C.LX 410.
25	1	Sonata No. 6 . . . Prelude, —ARR. STR. ORCH.	*For* G.DB 6466 *read* G.DB 6456.
25	2	Flute Sonata, G minor, BWV 1020	No. to read BàM. 86/7.
25	—	Footnote 11	*Transfer* to p. 732 where it applies to **Sonata No. 3** and not **Sonata No. 5.**
26	1	Sonata No. 3, BWV 1016	*Add* omission: § A. Busch & R. Serkin (pf) (Vic. 8412/4, set M 235).
26	2	Suite No. 3	BWV no. *should read* BWV 1009.
27	1	Brandenburg Concerto No. 1	Boyd Neel—no. *to read* D.K 1541/3.
28	1	Brandenburg Concerto No. 6	Koussevitzky—is 6ss.
			Klemperer—*add* omission: AmVox. set 623.
29	1	Concerto, E major, excerpts	*C.DB 504* is 10-inch.
30	1	Suite No. 3	Weingartner—AmC. no. *to read* AmC. 70672/4D.
		Idem, Air only	Stokowski—No. *to read* AmC. 11774D.
32	2	Cantata 68, No. 2, ARR.	*G.B 4180* is 10-inch.
33	1	Cantata 106	Tec. 1667/9 is sung in English.
33	1	Cantata 140	D.K 2292 & Lon.T 5682 are No. 4, Zion hört . . . *and not* as stated.
33	2	Cantata 147, No. 10	Temple Chu.—No. *to read* G.B 8123
			Hess—Vic. no. *read* Vic. 4538.
33	2	Cantata 151	§ Labbette is acc. fl. & orch. *not* fl. & hpsi.
35	1/2	Magnificat & Mass, B minor	*For* P. Matthew *read* P. Matthen.
37	2	No. 63, O Haupt . . .	Vocal Qtt.—*For* : G.D 9944 *read* C.D 9944.
38	2	Dir, dir, Jehova	*Lum. 2.20.038* is 10-inch.

xiii

Page	Col.	Entry	Remarks
43	1	Allegro barbaro & Burlesque No. 2 ...	Bartók—o.n. *to read* G.AM 2622
46	2	Sonata Society, Vol. XII ...	*For* G.DB 3443/8 *read* G.DB 3343/8.
46	2	Pf. Sonata No. 8 ...	Backhaus—G.DB 1031/2 *should be* ¶. *Move* § down to next line.
47	1	Sonata No. 14 ...	Paderewski — Coupling *should read* (*Paderewski : Minuet*).
47	1	Sonata No. 15 ...	Is in Soc. III and not Soc. II.
47	2	Sonata No. 22 ...	Is in Soc. VIII and not Soc. IX.
48	1	Sonata No. 30 ...	Kempff—*For* 566305/7 *read* 566305/6.
48	2	Sonata No. 31 ...	*Add to* W. Kempff, Pol. nos., *new Footnote*: 11. Originally the Polydor pressings had the same coupling, but recent re-issue (and perhaps re-recording) has the last side blank.
49	1	Quartet No. 4 ...	Rosé Qtt.—*For* G.D 1551/3 *read* G.D 1561/3.
52	1	Vlc. Sonata No. 4 ...	*Delete* note 8. The manual nos. are available.
53	2	Minuet, E flat major ...	Coates—*Add* no. G.W 759.
54	1	Concerto No. 4 ...	§ Backhaus—*For* R.A.H.O. *read* L.S.O.
54	2	Concerto No. 5 ...	Schnabel, Chicago: Vic. no. *to read* Vic. 11-8430/4.
54	—	Footnote 11 ...	Nos. *to read* 67082/6S.
55	1	Coriolan Overture ...	Vienna Phil.—Furtwängler—*Add* omitted no.: (Vic. 11-8036). § Amsterdam—Mengelberg—*Add* (& o.v. C.L 1848; AmC. 67273D).
55	1	Romances, vln. & orch. ...	Borries—No. 1 *is on* G.DB 4662 and No. 2 *is on* G.DB 4661.
55	2	Symphony No. 3 ...	Weingartner—C.LFX no. *to read* LFX 444/9.
56	1	Symphony No. 5 ...	§ L.P.O.—Koussevitzky—*For* G.DB 2238/42 *read* G.DB 2338/42. *Add* omissions: § Sym.—Weingartner (AmC. set M 178) Philadelphia—Stokowski (Vic. L 7001, LP only).
56	2	Symphony No. 7 ...	Ormandy—Set M 551 *to read* Set M 557.
56	—	Footnote 6 ...	*Add* Some German pressings have the 4th side blank, not the last side.
57	2	Egmont Overture ...	*Add* omission: § Berlin Phil.—Prüwer (D.CA 8041; Pol. 95281). *and add* (o.v. C.L 1799; AmC. 67220D) *to* Amsterdam—Mengelberg.
57	2	Egmont, Nos. 8 & 9 ...	*Add* omission: § P. Hartmann & orch.—Heger (Od. O-7682).
57	2	Fidelio Overture ...	Weingartner—French no. *to read* LFX 562.
57	2	Fidelio, No. 5 ...	Bohnen—*AmB*. 15115 is 10-inch.
58	1/2	Prometheus & Leonora, No. 3 ...	Toscanini—*For* Vic. 11-9458/9 *read* Vic. 11-9448/9.
58	1	Prometheus Overture ...	Weingartner—AmC. no. *to read* AmC. 68560D.
58	2	Leonora No. 1 ...	v. Beinum—*For* D.K 28151 *read* D.K 28154.
61	1	BELLINI: Songs—Dolente immagine ...	*For* figlia *read* Filli; *and* (Fumaroli).
61	1	Norma Overture ...	G.S 10336 is cond. Sabajno (also has o.v., G.S 10045).
62	1	A te, o cara ...	Lauri-Volpi—*For* G.DB 2936 *read* G.DB 2396.
63	1	BENDA, Jan ...	*For* ARR. VLN. & PF. *read* ARR. VLA. & PF.
63	2	BENNET, Madrigals ...	*Supply* lost l from *Madrigal*.
64	1	Lyric Suite ...	§ Galimir—Pol. no. *to read* 595135/8, o.n. 516659/62.
65	1	Marche hongroise ...	*Delete* Pol. no. from Amsterdam—v. Beinum. *Delete* entry: Berlin—Haarth (Pol. 57349). *Add* entry: Dresden Phil.—v. Kempen, Pol. 68327; & Pol. 57349, original issue.
65	1/2	Marche hongroise & Danse des sylphes	Mengelberg—*For* C.L 1818 *read* C.L 1810.
		Idem, & Menuet ...	Koussevitzky—The Vic. couplings *should read*: Menuet is on 14231 with Handel; other pieces on 14230.
67	1	Marche troyenne ...	Paris—Weingartner—*For* AmC. 72543D *read* AmC. 72634D.
67	2	BERWALD: Symphony G minor ...	N.n *should read* RE 736/9S.
		— Symphony E flat ...	In Vol. II is No. 6.
68	1	BEYDTS—Songs ...	*Add* omission: Les Boules de neige (Fort): M. Oswald & orch. (C.DF 1865; AmC. 306M).
69	2	Carmen, COMPLETE ...	Sabajno—Vic. no. *to read* Vic. 11839/57.
71	1	Parle-moi de ma mère...	*Add* omission: § (Ger.) M. Teschemacher & M. Wittrisch (G.EH 732).
71	1/2	Habanera/Seguedille ...	Onegin—*B*.15128 is 10-inch. Supervia—*Od*. 188673 is sung in *Ital. and not Span.* (also on Od. 6034M).
72	1	Chanson du Toreador ...	⊞ Ruffo—last no. *to read* G.DB 5386*
73	1	Non, tu ne m'aimes pas ...	*For* Beckman *read* Beckmann.
74	1	Finale, Act III ...	*Delete* whole entry.
74	1	Entracte, Act IV ...	Vic. Sym.—*For*: G.DA 4263 *read*: G.DA 4362.
75	1	O dieu Brahma! ...	G.DB 1316 is ¶.
75	2	Symphony, C major ...	Goehr—Vic. no. *to read* Vic. 13501/4; the nos. given are for the obsolete AM auto. set.
77	1	BLOW—A Love Song ...	*Delete* this title and *transfer* entry below—it proves to be The *Self-banished*.
77	2	Concerto, vlc. & orch....	*is edited* Grützmacher. Details at WERM, p. 747, footnote.
78	2	Sinfonia No. 2, B flat...	Is really by J. C. BACH. *Delete* the whole entry and *transfer* to p. 11. Note under *Scuola di Ballo* accordingly.
80	1	Salve Regina ...	*Add* omission: R.O.H.Cho.—Bellezza (G.D 1109). Actual performance, Covent Garden, 31-5-26.
80	2	Son lo spirito, etc. ...	G.DB 942 rec. Covent Garden, 31-5-26.
81	2	BONNAL—Noëls ...	Although labelled with orch., these have pf. accompaniment.
81	2	BORODIN ...	Date of birth to read 1833.
81	2	In the steppes ...	Mengelberg—*Add* no.: (Cap. 89-80153).
82	2	Prince Igor, No. 18 ...	L.P.O.—Beecham—ArgC. no. *to read* 264993.
83	1	Prince Igor, No. 26 ...	Sorokin Cho. no. *to read* P.R 2386.
83	1	Quartet No. 2 ...	Pro Arte—Vic. set *to read* M 255.
83	1	Quintet, C minor ...	*For* C.LZX 11/12 *read* C.LZX 13/14.
83	1	Songs ...	Maksakova—*For*: USSR. 14675 & 14676 *read*: USSR.14676 & 14677 respectively.
83	—	Footnote ...	*Supply* lost reference figure 4.
85	1	Pf. Concerto No. 2 ...	Serkin—AmC. no. *to read* AmC. 12187/92D.
86	1	Symphony No. 2 ...	*For* D minor *read* D major.
86	1	Symphony No. 3 ...	Koussevitzky—Vic. nos. *to read* 11-8832/5.
86	2	Variations, Op. 56a ...	§ Wood—Fr.Pol. no. *to read* 516726/7.
87	2	Clarinet Sonata No. 2 ...	Goodman's pianist *to read* N. Reisenberg.
88	1	Sonata No. 2, vlc. & pf. ...	*For* F minor *read* F major.
89	1	Intermezzo, Op. 118, No. 6 ...	§ Backhaus—*For* G.DB 1900 *read* G.DB 1898.
89	2	Intermezzo, Op. 119, No. 3 ...	Hess—in coupling, Op. no. of *Intermezzo* to read Op. 117-1.
90	1	Rhapsody, G minor ...	E. Fischer—no. *to read* G.DB 6437.
91	1	Hungarian Dance No. 1 ...	*Add* omission: Berlin Cha. Orch.—von Benda (Pol. 57324, recent pressings). *See* note to Svendsen, WERM, p. 609.
91 92	2 1	Hungarian Dances Nos. 5 & 6 ...	Saxon State no *to read*: G.DA 4443.
92	1	Hungarian Dance No. 6 ...	Royal Op.—Sargent—No. *to read* G.C 1874.
92	2	Waltzes, Op. 39 ...	Backhaus—Vic. no. *to read* 14131/2.

Page	Col.	Entry	Remarks
95	2	Auf dem Kirchhofe ⎫	
97	2	Sapphische Ode ⎬	*Add* omission: § S. Onegin (A) & orch. (*B.10279*).
97	2	O wüsst' ich doch	Klose—Cla.MD 9603 is 12-inch.
99	1	Wiegenlied—ARR. PF.	Rubinstein—no. *to read* G.DB 6532.
100	1	Sandmännchen	*Add* omission: § S. Onegin (A) & orch. (*B. 10219*).
101	1	Rape of Lucretia, ABRIDGED ...	*Add* additional no.: (Vic. set DM 1288).
102	2	Herbstlied	*For* Regensburg—Schrems *read* Aachen—Rehmann.
103	1	Symphony, D minor . . . Scherzo	*For* G.E 2659 *read* G.C 2659
105	2	Nun bitten wir	Spitta ref. *should read* (Pt. 2, No. 22 or 23).
105	—	Footnote 6	*Should read* Zwingli-Haus organ, Zürich. Applies to Fugue, F major (Matthaei).
108	1	CAIX d'H.—Suite	AmC. 7245M is 12-inch.
108	2	CAMPRA : Rigaudon (unspec.)	is from Opera IDOMENÉE, 1712.
109	1	EZECHIAS	*Should read* HISTORIA D'EZECHIA and the excerpt: Ezechia's Aria.
109	1	JEPHTE	Date *to read* before 1650.
112	1	Joyeuse Marche	§ Vic. Sym.—Vic. no. *to read* 36037.
112	2	Fête polonaise	*Add* omission: § Sym.—Monteux (G.L 796).
115	2	Symphony, B flat, Op. 20 ...	*Add* to Coppola: new footnote:
			3. Includes the organ interlude in the finale which the others omit.
118	2	Étude No. 10	Vondrovic—o.n. *should read* M 5186, d.c.
120	2	Impromptus—COLLECTIONS ...	Cortot—*For* G.DB 2012/3 *read* G.DB 2021/2.
123	1	Mazurka No. 31	Pachmann—No. *to read* G.DB 861.
123	2	Mazurka No. 47	Rummel—No. *to read* Pol. 68279.
125	2	Nocturne No. 19, ARR. VLN & PF.	Heifetz—*Add* omitted no.: **G.DB 6865.**
126	1	Polonaise No. 3	Gillels—No. *to read* USSR. 13299.
132	1	Variations on "La ci darem" ...	Nos. *to read* U.BP 1562/3.
132	2	Polish Songs 4 & 10 ...	Korolkiewicz—No. *to read* Muza. 1087.
133	1	Polish Songs 12 & 14 ...	Poplawsky—No. *to read* Muza. 1118.
133	1	Polish Song No. 14 ...	§ Austral, G.E. 506 is really No. 16, *below.* *Transfer.*
133	2	Sylphides	L.P.O.—Sargent—Vic. no. *to read* 11911/3.
135	2	D'une colline . . .	P. Gianotti (*sic*) is Tenor.
136	1	Psalms 42 & 69	*For* Export *read* Expert.
136	2	CLÉRAMBAULT, Suite 1, No. 7	*For* grand *read* grands.
136	2	Christmas Overture ...	*Add* omitted recording : § Sym.—Sargent (G.C 2485).
138	2	Sonata No. 5	*Delete* note 2. The manual nos. are available.
140	1	COSTELEY	*For* correct titles of madrigals on CHC 36 *see* WERM, p. 718.
148	2	L'Isle joyeuse—ARR. ORCH.	*Add* & Vic. 12033, d.c.
149	2	Preludes, Book I, COMPLETE ...	Gieseking—AmC. no. *to read* AmC. 17122/7D and is *10-inch.*
152	1	Syrinx	*Add* omission: § M. Moyse (*C.D 19056*).
152	2	Nocturnes—COMPLETE... ...	Coppola o.v.—*For* G.D 1691 *read* G.C 1691.
152	2	Nocturnes—Nuages ...	*Add* omission: ▲ Anon. orch. (MA.SR 18).
153	1	Nocturnes—Fêtes ...	*Add* omission: ▲ Anon. orch. (MA.SR 19).
153	1	Nocturnes—Sirènes ...	Stokowski—o.n. *to read* G.DB 3981/2S
153	1	Prélude à l'après midi . . .	§ Straram—LFX no. *to read* LFX 30.
157	1	Coppélia, Nos. 3 & 7 ...	§ L.P.O. *should read* L.S.O.
		Idem, Selections	C.DX 899 should be upright type—12-inch.
159	1	Sylvia—Suite ...	§ Cloez—Od. nos. *to read* Od. 165074/5.
159	2	Filles de Cadiz... ...	McDonald—*For* G.DA 1735 *read* G.DA 1739.
162	1	Ruralia Hungarica ...	The violin arr. is not by Kreisler but is by the composer, Op. 32c. Martzy is Nos. 6 & 7 (Op. 32c, Nos. 2 & 3).
162	2	Variations on a Nursery Song	Dohnányi—Vic. set no. *to read* M 162.
163	2	Seul sur la terre ...	Caruso—G.DB 700* & Vic. 15-1037* are both 12-inch and should be upright type. *Insert* "&"—these are different recordings.
164	1	Una furtiva lagrima ...	Islandi—No. *to read* G.DB 5247.
			§ Patzak—Pol. no. *to read* Pol. 25011.
166	2	Ardon gl'incensi	§ Pagliughi—*For* G.C 2090 *read* G.C 2909.
167	1	Giusto Cielo! . . .; Tu che a Dio	Gigli & Pinza—G.DB 1229 is ¶.
167	2	Come again!	Swarthout—In coupling, *for* King Arthur *read* The Libertine.
170	2	DUSSEK—Concerto ...	*Add* Op. 63.
170	2	Carnival Overture ...	Berlin Phil.—T. no. *to read* T.E 3053.
171	1	Serenade, Op. 22 ...	Lehmann—No. *to read* Od. O-7992/4.
171	2	Symphony No. 4 ...	Kubelik—Defective nos. in some copies are G.C 3852/6.
172	1	Symphony No. 5 . . .; Largo	
		—— ARR. VLN.	Menuhin—*after* Vic. 15369 *add* additional no.: G.DB 2856.
174	1	Humoresque No. 7—VOCAL ARR.	§ R. Tauber—Od. no. *to read* Od. O-4526.
177	2	Songs my mother taught me ...	*Delete* G. Farrar, IRCC. 41.
178	2	Cockaigne	L.P.O.—D.LXT no. *to read* LXT 2525.
179	1	In the South	Neel—*For* D.K 1383/3 *read* D.K 1381/3.
			Elgar—Vic. no. *to read* 11401/3.
179	2	Pomp & Circumstance, Nos. 1, 2, 3 & 4...	MacMillan—Vic. 11-8226/7 are in set M 911.
		No. 1...	Fiedler—Vic. 12-1019 is n.v.
180	1	Wand of Youth... ...	L.P.O.—D.LXT no. *to read* LXT 2525.
183	1	Care è la rosa ...	*To read* Cara è la rosa.
183	2	Folti boscetti ...	*To read* Folti boschetti.
183	2	O bellissimi . . .	Pinza—*Delete* couplings, and *see* WERM, p. 722.
183	2	AMOR BRUJO, No. 7 ...	Fiedler—*For* o.n. *read* o.v.
184	1	Canciones populares ...	Barrientos—C.D 11701 is 12-inch.
185	1	No. 5, Nana	§ Vallin—*P.RO 20065* (*see* No. 2) also includes this song.
186	1	EL SOMBRERO . . .	*For* TRE *read* TRES.
		(titles)	*For* del Molinera *read* de la Molinera.
			For Il Corregidor *read* El Corrigidor.
188	1	Nocturne No. 13 ...	*For* Op. 113 *read* Op. 119.
192	2	Tristesse	Pérugia—No. *should read* G.DB 5158.
193	2	FERROUD, Sonata ...	AmC. set *to read* X 89.
195	1	Wie freundlich strahlt . . .	Groh recording has no Cho.
198	1	FRANÇAIX, Trio ...	Philharmonic Trio—No. *should read* D.F 7053/4.
199	2	Symphony, D minor ...	Monteux—*Delete* Vic. LMX 1065; *see* WERM, p. 772, which is n.v.
202	2	Toccata, G minor ...	Sartori recording is *10-inch.*
207	1	American in Paris ...	B. nos. *to read* B. 0142/3.
207	—	Footnote ...	*Supply* lost reference figure 1.
209	1	Inno del decenniale ...	*Should read* ... Decennale.
209	2	ANDREA CHÉNIER, COMPLETE	Both are 26ss.
209	2	O pastore ...	*Should read* O pastori (Coro delle pastorelle).
210	1	La Mamma morta ...	*For* L. B. Raisa *read* R. Raisa.
211	1	O colombello ...	Capsir—*For*: C.GQ 7170 *read* C.GQ 7150.
212	1	Étude de Concert, C major ...	Barer—No. *should read* G.DB 2645.
212	2	Novellettes: No. 3	Pro Arte—*For* G.DB 7538 *read* G.DB 7358.

Page	Col.	Entry	Remarks
212	2	Polka, "Les Vendredis"	*Add* omission: § Catterall Qtt. (C. 9156).
216	1	Doubt	§ Chaliapin—*After* G.DB 1469; *entry to read:* & with vln. & pf. on Vic. 15422, d.c.).
216	2	The Northern Star	G.EK 43 is*.
216	2	Valse-fantaisie	F.O.K. Sym.—Snp. *to read* Sup.
219	2	(La) RECONTRE	*To read* (La) RENCONTRE . . . *Einem Bach der fliesst* is actually *Un ruisselet* . . . and not *C'est un torrent* . . . *Transfer* L. Lail entry. L. Fugère sings both on C.D 15178.
221	1	GOLESTAN: "Concert"	*Title should read* Arioso et Allegro de concert, vla. & pf., 1933. *Transfer to correct alphabetical position.*
223	2	GALLIA	*Delete* Le Ciel a visité la terre, and all entries attached, *except* § M. Nespoulous (*C.D 12028*), which remains here with heading Jérusalem.
224	2	Faust—Introduction	*Add* to v. Kempen, new footnote: 2. Later pressings are attrib. to Dresden Phil. Perhaps a re-recording with the same number.
224	2	Last line	*For* Lon. LLP 115 *read* Lon. LPS 115.
225	1	Avant de quitter	Christoffersen—*Pol.X 42736* is *¶*.
225	2	Salut! Demeure	Crooks—The coupling (*Roméo et Juliette*) applies only to Vic. 15542 (which is 12-inch). *Add* coupling (*Roi d'Ys*) for G.DB 3497.
225	—	Footnote 2	*Revise to read:* . . . is apparently, on *some* English pressings, a repressing of G.DB 219*; others, and the Vic. issue, appear to be electric.
229	2	Ah! lève-toi	Crooks—*Delete* no. G.DB 3497. **H** Dalmorès—No. *to read* Vic. 15-1013*.
230	2	Ave Maria	*Add* omission: ▲ C. Supervia (M-S), *P.PO 51.* J. Vincent (S)—*Add* no. C. 11805 and transfer to *¶* section.
231	1	Le Ciel a visité la terre	*Delete* reference to GALLIA. This is a separate song. Bring in here all entries deleted from p. 223.
232	2	Irish Tune from Co. Derry	*Add* omission: L. Heward Str. Orch. (C.DX 1174).
236	1	COLLECTIONS	Solesmes no. *to read* G.D 1971/82.
237	1	Cossack lullaby	This disc is **Cradle Song, Op. 1, No. 5** *below*, ARR. CHO. *Transfer* entry.
237	1	Like a sharp knife	*Delete* title and *transfer* entry to p. 238 under **The Wounded Birch.** *Add* new entry: Little flower § T. Makushina (M-S) (*EdB. 1115*).
238	1	CÉPHALE—C'est ici	*Supply* missing initial letters, C.
238	2	O Richard, O mon roi	Singher—*Delete* ML 4152. This aria is not on the LP disc.
241	2	Concerto, A minor, Op. 16	Moiséiwitsch—*For* G.DB 4125/8 *read* G.DB 4215/8. Gieseking—*Add* no. C.LWX 210/3. Schiøler—*Mer.* (LP) no. should be *italics.*
244	1	Peer Gynt Suite I—No. 3	Szreter—P. no. *to read* P.R 117.
245	2	A Hope	The title of the Alnaes song shown as coupling *should read: Friendship between two beings* . . .
251	1	Trois jours de vendange	§ N. Vallin—*Delete.* This song is not on this disc.
252	1	Entry of the Boyars	Boston—Fiedler: Vic. set no. *to read* M 552.
254	1	HERCULES—My father!	Coupling—*For* Maret *read* Moret.
256	2	L'Allegro, No. 19	§ F. Austral—No. *to read* G.D 1042.
261	2	Chaconne, G major	E. Fischer—*G.DA 4401* is *¶*.
262	2	Sonata, Op. 1, No. 3	*Add* omitted entry: W. Primrose (vla.), J. Kahn (pf.): Vic. 17478.
266	1	Fireworks Music Nos. 3, 4, 5 (2)	Benda, T.E 2353 is full orch. not str. orch. *Transfer* "— ARR. STR. ORCH." down above Stad entry.
267	2	Song for Occupations	Set no. *to read* X 50, o.n. M 226.
269	2	Vom Himmel	Coupling—*For* Othmayer *read* Othmayr; *for* Von *read* Vom.
272	1	Sonatas 7 & 11	*Should read* Sonatas 35 & 40, and *transfer* Dumont entry to col. 2 under existing headings for these Sonatas. *Delete* Rehberg under No. 40.
272	2	Sonata 36, Minuet	*Supply* missing performer: W. Landowska (hpsi.).
274	1	Penultimate line	*For* CQX *read* GQX.
275	1	Baryton Trio No. 6	*Should read* No. 107.
278	2	"Toy" Symphony	Is now attrib. to Leopold Mozart.
289	2	Istar	§ Coppola—G. no. *to read* G.DB 4850/1.
290	1	Tenebrae factae sunt	This should also have reference to footnote 1.
290	2	Bless the Lord, O my soul	*For* De Paul *read* De Paur. Remove Russian Met. Cho. entry and *transfer* to new entry at foot of column: O my soul arise!
292	2	JACQUET de la Guerre—Sarabande	The Sarabande on Pat.PAT 50 is the same as the Sarabande, D major on OL 13.
292	2	JÄRNEFELT, Berceuse	*Insert* key: G minor.
293	1	Concertino	Bakala—*Add* no.: U.H 22827/8.
293	1	Foreboding; Death	Are the titles of the movements of Sonata, 1-x-1905. *Transfer* to next page under **Sonata, 1-x-1905,** pf.
293	1	In the mist	*Add* no.: U.F 22803/4.
294	1	Sonata, vln. & pf.	*Add* no.: U.H 22801/2.
295	1	L'Eau vive	*Add* author: (J. Giono).
296	2	Colas Breugnon Ov.	Pittsburgh—Reiner is also on **C.LX 1002.**
301	2	KOŽELUH, Gavotte, ARR. VLN.	Kreisler—G. no. *to read* G.DA 777.
304	2	Sicilienne et Rigaudon	*Add* omission: § A. Catterall (C. 9610).
304	2	Variations	Neveu's pianist is G. Beck.
309	1	RENAISSANCE	*For* Neilsen *read* Nielsen, in *couplings.*
309	2	Giulio's Nocturne	Is Declamation with orch., A. Paulsen as Giulio.
311	1	R. LAPARRA	Died 1943.
313	2	LECLAIR—Sonatas	*For* Op. 2, No. 4 *read* Op. 9, No. 3.
314 to 317			*Add* Lon.LLP 8 to all mentions of D.LK 4022.
314	1	Gold und Silber W.	Léhar—Lon. set *to read* LA 10.
315	1	Frasquita, Selections	Supervia—Nos. *to read* U.AP 1020/3 & EP 1024.
320	1	Mattinata	§ Pertile—No. *to read* G.DA 1008.
324	—	Footnote 2	*Add* the following: ". . . French pressings have *Damnation de Faust—Marche hongroise* on the last side."
325	1	Les Préludes	Berlin Phil.—v. Kempen—*Add* new footnote 6: Later pressings of Pol. 67174/5 are attrib. to Dresden Phil.—v. Kempen; probably a re-recording under the same no.
325	1	Pf. Concerto No. 1	Sauer—AmC. set no. *to read* M 371.
325	2	Hungarian Fantasia	Kilenyi—AmC. no. *to read* AmC. P 69458/9D.
327	2	Gnomenreigen	W. Bohle—no. *to read* Imp. 014009.
331	1	Rigoletto Paraphrase	§ A. Cortot—*Add* no.: Vic. 6641.
332	2	Widmung	*Add* omissions: ¶ W. Backhaus (*G.DA 944; Vic. 1472*). § M. Hambourg (*G.C 2248*).

Page	Col.	Entry	Remarks
333	1	Es muss	Coupling—*For* Böhm *read* Bohm.
337	1	Des Fremden Kindes heiliger Christ ...	Erb has orch. acc. (cond. Seidler-Winkler).
338	2	Waffenschmied Ov.	Schmidt-Isserstedt—U. no. *to read* F 22576.
340	1	LOTTI	*Add* omitted entry:
		Regina coeli	§ Cho. (*P.B 3738**).
340	2	Bois épais	Singher—*Delete* ML 4152. This aria is *not* on the LP disc.
344	2	Thy beaming eyes	Tibbett—G. no. *to read* G.DA 829.
347	2	MARENZIO, Madrigal	Dispietate *to read* Dispietata.
349	1	Sonata, fl., vln., pf. ...	*Add* nos.: (Vic. 12493/4, set M 597).
350	2	Prelude & Siciliana	§ Riavez is cond. Mascagni *and not* Melichar.
352	1	Intermezzo	Vienna Phil.—Karajan—No. *should read* C.LX 1208.
352	1	Brindisi	*Add* omission: § (*Ger*) F. Völker (*Pol. 90059*).
356	2	Je suis encore	Vallin—Pat. o.v. *should read* X 7165.
358	1	Ce bruit	Vallin—Pat. o.v. *should read* X 7165.
359	2	Que te fait si sévère ...	*Transfer* to foot of p. 358—1. This is the Act I aria, not the Act II reprise.
359	2	O nature	Schipa—No. *to read*: G.DA 5420.
367	2	MENDELSSOHN	*Add* omitted entry: **March, D major, Op. 108** — ARR. ORG.
			§ A. Brown (*Brd. 5010*).
368	1	ATHALIE	Date *to read* 1834-5.
		Idem—War March	For Nat. Sym. *read* L.S.O.
372	1	Elijah, No. 39	Fullard—*RZ.MR 3237* is 10-inch.
374	2	FACKELTANZE	*Should read* FACKELTÄNZE.
377	1	Symphony No. 25	U. no. *to read* H 23915/8.
378	1	MILAN, Pavanes	Oyanguren—*For* Narbaez *read* Narvaes. *Delete* De.
379	2	Création du monde	AmC. no. *to read* AmC. 68094/5D.
380	1	Se canto	*CdM. 505* is 10-inch.
380	1	Ich knüpfte	*Supply* missing initial letter, I.
383	2	Ecco di dolci raggi ...	*Add* ref. Bk. X.
383	2	LAGRIME ... No. 1 ...	*For* a cara *read* avara.
		No. 2 ...	*For* Flauco *read* Glauco.
		No. 5 ...	*For* oro *read* or.
		LAMENTO ... No. 4 ...	*For* rispondi *read* risponde.
384	1	Maladetto	*Add* ref.: Bk. X
		Ohimé	*Add* ref. Bk. IX.
		Ballo dell' Ingrate ...	*For* Couraud *read* Conrad.
387	2	Pictures from an Exhibition ...	Kletzki—No. *to read* C.LX 1186/9.
387	2	A Tear—ARR. ORCH. ...	Coupling—*For* Leucona *read* Lecuona.
388	1	BORIS—Synthesis ...	A.A.O.—Stokowski—AmC. no. *to read* AmC. 11848/50D.
388	1	BORIS—Act I, Sc. 1 ...	*Add* omitted entry:
		Still one more page	M. Mikhailov (*USSR. 12244*).
		(Pimen's Monologue)	§ (*Ger*) B. Carmassi (Hom.E 10245).
			Ⱨ F. Chaliapin (G.DB 612*).
388	2	Come let us vote	Chaliapin does not sing.
388	2	One evening	Ⱨ Chaliapin—No. *to read* G. 022252*.
388	—	Footnote 2	*For* is the same as, *read* continues from the end of ...
389	1	BORIS—Revolutionary Scene ...	Vic. 9507/8 applies to Coates and *not* to Bellezza.
389	1	So hear ye!	*Delete*, & *see above*, p. 388 alteration.
389	1	KHOVANSHCHINA—Act III	Martha's aria is **I am a thoughtless maiden**, and comes *before* All is quiet ...
389	2	Gopak	*Delete* Leningrad—Eliasberg; *USSR. 6379* applies to Orlov. *Sup.* 40319 should be *italics*.
392	1	Mass No. 19	Sabata—*Sor.LP no.* should be italics: 40001/2.
			Philadelphia—*Soloists are*: B. Thorne (S), E. MacFarlane (A), D. Coker (T), L. Englander (Bs).
392	2	Clemenza di Tito Ov. ...	Vienna—Walter—Vic. no. *to read* 12526.
393	2	Don Giovanni Ov. ...	*Cla.M 109* is 10-inch.
393	2	No. 4, Madamina ...	¶ Chaliapin—G. no. *to read* G.DA 994.
394	1	No. 7, La ci darem ...	*Add* omissions:
			§ (*Eng*) A. Moxon & S. Robertson (*G.B 3430*).
			§ (*Ger*) F. Hüni-Mihacsek & W. Domgraf-Fassbänder (*Pol. 62699*).
394	1	No. 11, Dalla sua pace ...	H. Meyer-Welfing—No. *to read* C.DX 1385.
394	1/2	Nos. 12 & 17	Urbano—*Add* additional current no.: *Pol.* 30022.
394	2	Don Giovanni, No. 17, ARR. PF.	Backhaus—*G.DA 944* is ¶.
396	2	Idomeneo, Overture ...	Nat. Sym.—Neel—Lon. no. *to read* T 5441.
396	2	Fuor del mar ...	Is No. 12 in score, *not* No. 14.
397	1	Nozze di Figaro, Overture ...	L.P.O.—Beecham—Last line of *couplings*; amend Op. 36 *to read* Op. 56.
397/8		Nozze di Figaro	*For* Act III in headings above nos. 10 & 11 *read* Act II.
398	2	Figaro, No. 19	*Transfer* G. Farrar, IRCC 40 *from* Dove sono only *to* the complete recordings; it includes the recit.
399	1	Deh vieni	*Delete* § T. dal Monte (G.DB 831). This is *.
399	1	SCHAUSPIELDIREKTOR ...	*For* ABRIDGED *read* COMPLETE.
			♯ *Mer.MG 15025* includes the Overture cond. Leinsdorf from Sil. 19.
400	1	Zauberflöte, No. 3 ...	Meyer-Welfing—No. *to read* C.DX 1385.
			Schiøtz—No. *to read* G.DB 5265.
400	2} 401	Zauberflöte, Nos. 9 & 18 ...	Blech—*G.DA 4405* is ¶.
	1}		
402	1	Per questa bella mano... ...	*For* vlc. *read* vla.
404	1	Sonata 11, 3rd movt. ...	Mola—No. *to read* G.DA 5393.
405	1	Variations on Minuet, K 573 ...	*For* Dupont *read* Duport.
405	1	Fantasia, F minor ...	V. Fox is 3ss *not* 1½ss.
407	2	SONATAS, vln. & pf.: Soc. II	*Contains* no. 28 *and not* no. 29.
			AmD. ♯ set DX 103 is ¶.
409	2	Divertimento, K 334—Minuet	Heifetz—No. *should read* Vic. 12-0787.
410	2	Serenade No. 13	§ Ormandy—Vic. nos. *to read* (Vic. 8588 & 1698).
410	2	Concerto, K 191	Sharrow—G. no. *to read* G.DB 21082/3.
413	1	Vln. Concerto No. 7	Dubois—For 3ss. *read* 8ss.
413	2	Contretanz, K 534 ...	Fischer—*For* G.DB 4860 *read* G.DB 4680.
413	2	Sinfonia Concertante, K 364	Footnote 13 on p. 412 *applies to* Spalding recording.
415	1	Symphony No. 26	Schüler conducts Vienna Phil. *not* Berlin.
			B.B.C.—Busch—Vic. set no. *to read* M 266.
415	2	Symphony No. 39	Weingartner—o.v., Col. no. *to read* G. 9450/2.
415	2	Symphony No. 40	Footnote 4 *applies to* Pittsburgh—Reiner, and footnote 3 *applies to* E.I.A.R.—v. Karajan.
418	1	Nun eilt herbei!... ...	Cebotari—Record make is G. *not* C.
420	1	Evening Mood	*Cond. to read* Hye-Knudsen.
420	1	Farewell, my blessed native town, & Green are Spring's hedges ...	On *G.X 6988* are ½s. each *with Mortensen: You Danish Summer*. It appears that *X 6988* is a re-pressing of *X 6257*.

Page	Col.	Entry	Remarks
421 & 812		NIN Y CASTELLANOS (1879-1949)	is correct heading
422	1	NOVÁK, V.	Died 1949.
424	2	Orphée, Overture	§ D. Bela—Od. no. *to read* Od. O-6637.
426	1	Barcarolle	Schumann—*For* Böhm *read* Bohm.
430	1	Concerto No. 1, 1st movt. ...	Kreisler—Vic. set no. *to read* M 361.
430	1	Concerto No. 2...	Ronde is 3rd movement.
430	2	Le Streghe	Ricci—*Add* no.: (Pol. 566307).
435	2	PASQUINI	*Spell* first name **Bernardo.**
437	2	Stabat Mater, Excpts. ...	*MS.A 53* is 10-inch.
441	2	PIERNÉ	*Add* omitted entry: La Veillée de l'ange gardien, Op. 14, No. 3, pf. — ARR. SAX. QTT. Garde Républicaine Qtt. on *AmC. 281M,* coupled with *Chanson de la Grand'maman (see* Col. 1).
442	2	PIZZETTI	*For* (1880-1940) *read* (b. 1880). A war-time report of his death proves to have been inaccurate.
446	2	Valse	*For* ARR. Key *read* ARR. Kay.
447	1	Étude, Op. 52, No. 3	*Add* new footnote: [1]ARR. from Ballet: The Prodigal Son, Op. 46.
448	1	Sonatas, vln. & pf. ...	Oistrakh recording on USSR. 014963/70 (which is 8ss) is **Sonata No. 1, Op. 80** *and not* No. 2. *Transfer* entry.
449	2	WAR AND PEACE... ...	*Add* Op. 91.
450	2	Che gelida manina	Lugo—*Add* to no. G.DB 3276, new footnote: [1]Announced under this no. but probably not issued.
451	2	O soave fanciulla	Booth & Cross—No. *to read* G.C 3053.
451	2	Quando m'en vo	*Delete* ¶ from Borgioli & Pampanini and move § up two lines. C. Spletter—No. *to read Pol. 62863.*
452	1	Marcello! Sirena!	*Delete;* and *transfer* Pol. 66764 to Act III *below,* under **Mimi e una civetta!**—commences **Marcello! Finalmente!** *Delete* T. de Garmo entry.
452	1	Addio, dolce svegliare ...	*Insert* G.EH 813: FKX 189 from p. 453 col. 1, **Sono andati.** This disc is the Act III Qtt. and *not* the Act IV finale. The reverse contains **Donde lieta usci** sung by E. O. Förster (*Ger*).
452	—	Footnote 3	*Add* Succeeding scenes were also recorded to the end of the act (CR 413/6).
453	1	Sono andati (Duet)	*Add* omission: (*Ger*) T. Eipperle & A. Fügel (Pol. 68147).
453	2	In testa	*For* T *read* B.
454	2	Love Duet (2 sides) ...	Favero & Ziliani—No. *should read* G.DB 2894. *Add* omission: (*Ger*) T. Eipperle & A. Fügel (Pol. 68293).
455	2	Non ve l'avevo	Pertile & Fregosi—Od. no. *to read* O-8905. *Transfer* Valente from Tenor pt. only *to* duets (has Anon. B). *Add* omission: § (*Ger*) W. Ludwig & G. Hüsch (*G.EG 3035*).
456	2	Prelude, Act IV	Milan Sym.—Tansini, though labelled this, is really **Intermezzo** Act II, *above. Transfer.*
458	2	La povera mia cena	*Delete* O. Dua. The excerpt is for B solo.
458	2	Vissi d'arte	M. Cebotari—No. *to read* Pol. 67684.
459	2	E lucevan	*Delete* ¶ Caruso. *G.DA 1372.* **H** Caruso—Nos. *to read* G.VA 34*: o.n. *DA 125*;* & *DA 112*;* Vic. 511*.
459	2	Amaro sol per te	*Add* omission: § F. Austral & M. Fleta (G.DB 956).
460	1	Non piangere, Liù	§ Valente—G. no. *to read G.B 2458.*
461	1	VILLI: Intermezzo No. 2 (only)	*Add* omission: § B.B.C.—Pitt (C. 9114).
461	2	Hornpipe, E minor	*Remove* whole entry for A. Ehlers and *transfer* to next page: Suite No. 7, D minor.
466	2	QUILTER	*Add* omitted entry: Cuckoo Song, Op. 15, No. 1 (Williams). **H** G. Elwes (T) (C.L 1074*).
467	1	Fair house of joy	*Add* **H** G. Elwes (C.L 1119*).
467	1	Fill a glass	*Add* **H** G. Elwes (C.L 1101*).
472	1	(The) Soldier's Wife ...	Words *are by* Shevchenko, trs. Pleshcheev, *not* as stated.
473	1/2	Tadjik & Tartar Dances ...	*Are part of* Dance Suite. See corrected entry, *post.*
473	2	Castor et Pollux: Cho., unspec.	*Should read* Menuet chanté (Prologue, Sc. 2); Choeur des Servantes d'Hébé (Act II, Sc. 5).
477	2	Alborada del Gracioso (Orch.)	Ormandy—G. no. *to read* G.DB 2459.
477	2	Sonatina	Key *should read* F sharp minor.
479	1	Quartet, F major	§ Galimir Qtt.—Pol. no. *to read* Pol. 595102/4, o.n. 516578/80.
480	1	Rapsodie espagnole	Rodzinski—*For* ML 4093 *read* ML 4039.
483	1	Ballet Suite	Amsterdam—v. Beinum is 6ss, Pol. 68227/9.
483	2	Serenade	Cap. set no. *to read* EEL 8026.
483	2	Im Himmelreich	*For* Aachen—Thurn *read* Regensburg—Schrems.
483	2	Mariä Wiegenlied	E. Mayerhofer—No. *to read* D.M 49163.
485	2	REUSNER, Suite	Set no. *to read* M 969.
488	1	Schéhérazade, Op. 35 ...	Ansermet—Is 12ss on 78 r.p.m. D.LXT 2503 *should read* D.LXT 2508.
488	1	By the sea—excerpt ...	*Should read* excerpts. *Add* * to no.
488	1	It is not the wind, Op. 43, No. 2	USSR. 4874 is not this, but is **Op. 42, No. 3: At last the dark clouds ...** See revised entry, *post.*
489	1	Folk Song arrangements ...	Only USSR. 14919 is ARR. Rimsky-Korsakov.
491	1	SADKO—last item ...	Liubava's Recit. & aria is in fact **Ah! now I know,** Sc. 3. *Transfer* entry to p. 490. This excerpt is for M-S.
496	2	La calunnia	§ M. Journet—*Add* no.: G.DB 921.
497	2	Guillaume Tell, Overture ...	*Add* omission: La Scala—Marinuzzi (4ss). T.SKB 3213/4.
497	2	No. 2, Ah! Mathilde ...	Martinelli—G. no. *to read* G.DK 120*.
500	1	ROUSSEL: Symphony No. 3	D. no. *should read* D.CA 8199/201.
504	1	Pf. Concerto No. 5 ...	*For* Kausama *read* Kusama.
506	1	PARYSATIS—Le rossignol et la rose	*Delete* (*Eng*)—a vocalise, no words.
506	1	SAMSON ET DALILA ... Orch. Selection	§ De Groot—*For* G.D *read* G.C.
506	2	Printemps qui commence	§ S. Onegin—Vic. 7320 is in *French. Transfer.* G.DB 1420 is in *German.*
507	1	Mon coeur s'ouvre	
507	2	SAMAZEUILH—Chant d'Espagne ...	Menuhin—G.DB 1301 is ¶.
508	1	Habañera	*For* Palaikin *read* Polyakin.
512	2	L 23, E major	L. Selbiger—Coupling *to read L 422.*
516	2	SCHIASSI—Pastorale ...	*For* Boston Prom. *read* Fiedler Sinfonietta; G. no. *to read* **G.EB 351,** o.n. EB 290.
518	2	Verklärte Nacht	*Delete* note 4. The manual nos. remain current.
518	—	Footnote	*Supply* missing ref. figure [3] to last line.
519	1	Impromptus, Op. 90—COMPLETE	Fischer—G. nos. *to read* G.DB 3484/6.
519	1	Impromptu No. 2	*Add* omission: § M. Mirimanova (C.CQX 16448).

Page	Col.	Entry			Remarks
519	2	March, Op. 27, No. 3...	...	...	Symbol ▲ *should be* §.
520	2	Moment Musical No. 3,			
		— ARR. STR. QTT.			§ Virtuoso Qtt.—G. no. *to read* G.D 1209.
523	1	Sonatina No. 3, 4th movt.	...	...	Sammons—*insert* full point in *D.M 559*.
523	1	Trio No. 2, Op. 100	...	...	§ Serkin—Busch, G. no. *to read* G.DB 2676/80.
525	2	"Schubert Melodies" ...	...	...	CanC. 6233/6 are 10-inch.
528	2	Winterreise—COLLECTION	...	...	Gerhardt—*For* 21 *read* 24.
529	1	Alinde ...	...	...	Coupling *should read* (*Wer nie sein Brot . . .*).
534	1	Hirt auf dem Felsen	...	...	W. Cecil—*Delete* (*Ital*), and *for* Simonetti *read* Simonetto.
540	1	Wer sich . . . only	...	...	Schlusnus—Pol. 68241 is in fact Wer nie sein Brot . . .
543	2	Fantasia, C major	...	...	Backhaus—G. no. *to read* G.DB 3221/4.
545	1	Nachtstück, F major	...	...	Backhaus—G. no. *to read* G.DB 3224.
545	2	Romance No. 2	...	...	*Add* omission: § W. Murdoch (C.L 2185).
547	2	Sonata No. 2, Op. 121	...	...	Vic. set no. *to read* M 233.
547	2	Piano Concerto	...	...	Arrau—G. no. *to read* G.DB 6373/6.
					Rubinstein—*For* Sternberg *read* Steinberg.
					Nat—AmC. no. *to read* AmC. 68211/4D.
					Add omitted entry:
					§ A. Cortot & L.S.O.—Ronald (G.DB 1059/62; Vic. 6978/81, set M 39).
549	1	Frauenliebe und -Leben			Bettendorf—*For* P.E 10696/8 *read* P.E 10606/8.
551	2	Meine Rose ...	...	...	Ginster—*For* G.DB 2248 *read* G.DB 2482.
557	2	SHAPORIN: Songs	...	...	USSR. 14637/8 is sung by V. Davidova *not* V. Viktorova.
559	1	Song from the harbour	...	...	*Delete* whole entry. This is not by Shostakovich but is an American song.
560	1	Berceuse	...	...	Stockholm—Järnefelt—*Add* additional no.: (*P.R 2663*).
561	1	Karelia ...	...	...	Kajanus—Reference to Syms. 1 & 2 *to read* . . . as fill-ups to Syms. 2 & 1 . . . respectively.
561	2	Swanwhite, No. 3	...	...	Stokowski—Set no. *to read* MM 806.
					Koussevitzky—11-9879 is n.v.
562	2	Tapiola ...	...	...	Beecham—Vic. set *to read* M 1311.
564	2	To Evening	...	...	Op. no. *to read* Op. 17, No. 6.
566	1/2	Bartered Bride Overture	...	...	L.S.O.—Walter—No. *to read* G.DB 3652.
					Berlin—van Kempen—*For* P.OR 5058 *read* P.OR 5048.
566	2	ACT I, No. 1 ...	...	...	Volksoper—Coupling is *No. 9, not No. 11*.
574	1	Oldřich and Božena Overture...	...	...	is correct title.
574	2	SÖDERMAN: Concerto	...	...	*Delete* whole entry (is really by Stenhammar). See alteration to p. 578.
576	2	SPOHR: Rondo	...	...	Menuhin—G.DB 1301 *should be* ¶.
577	1	Shamus O'Brien, Overture	...	...	Hallé—No. *to read* C.L 1428*.
578	2	STENHAMMAR	...	...	*Add* omission:
					Concerto No. 2, D minor, Op. 23, pf. & orch.
					H. Leygraf & Goteborg Radio—Eckerberg (8ss). Rtj.RE 701/4.
578	2	Sentimental Romance ...			*For* Op. 20 *read* Op. 28, No. 1; *add* key: A major.
578	2	Symphony No. 2	...	...	*Is only* 11ss *with coupling* Lodolezzi sings, Op. 39 . . . No. 1, Elegy, only
580	1	Radetzky March	...	...	Liverpool—Sargent—*For* C.DOX 755 *read* C.DOX 758.
581 to 586		Passim ...	...	...	*Add in* Cap. set EDL 8065 *to all mentions* of Cap.(LP) P 8061.
581	1	Sans-Souci-Polka	...	...	*For* G.B. 9473 *read* G.B 9478.
582	1	An der schönen blauen Donau...			Stokowski—*For* Vic. 15423 *read* Vic. 15425.
583	2	G'schichten	...	...	Stokowski—*For* Vic. 15423 *read* Vic. 15425.
					Walter—*For* C.L 2344 *read* C.L 2334.
584	2	Künstlerleben	...	...	Vienna—Karajan—No. *to read* C.LX 1012.
587	2	Fledermaus—Vocal Selection...			*For* E. Kur *read* E. Kurz.
588	1	Fledermaus Overture	...	...	*Add to* Vienna Phil.—Krauss—(& o.v., § G.C 1755: AN 377).
588	1	Fledermaus, No. 1	...	...	In *G.EG 3870*, A. Frind sings also.
590	1	Ritter Pázmán, Czardas	...	...	Ludwig—No. *to read* Pol. 15359.
591	1	No. 7, Er ist Baron & No. 13B, Finale			Nos. *should read* P.PXO 1034 and AmD. 29013 in each case. These are only excerpts from the Finales.
594	2	Sinfonia domestica	...	...	Schuricht—*Is* 9ss *not* 10ss. No. *to read* G.DB 5418/22S.
595	2	Feuersnot, Love Scene...			G.C 1841 is cond. Heger *and not* Krauss.
596	2	Waltzes, Act III	...	...	Imp. 014113 is Berlin State—Schüler.
597	1	Hab' mir's gelobt	...	...	*Add* new footnote to G.D 1629.
					¹ B. Kemp, E. Marherr & T. de Garmo are also named by Mr. L. Riemens (*The Gramophone*, 1946).
600	2	STRAVINSKY: Études	...	...	BàM. 27 is Nos. 3 & 4 *not* as stated.
602	1/2	Firebird, Revised suite...			All Stokowski recordings abbreviate No. 5.
603	—	Footnote 1	...	...	*Supply* missing z to Radúz.
605	1	Come, Margharita	...	...	Is not a song but from Oratorio: THE MARTYR OF ANTIOCH. *Transfer* entry to p. 608.
606	2	PRINCESS IDA: Orch. Selection ...			*For* C.937 *read* C.987R.
607	1	TRIAL BY JURY, Set A	...	...	Lon. set *to read* LA 108.
608	1	LIGHT OF THE WORLD...	...	...	*Add* omission:
					Yea, though I walk . . . § Salisbury Cath. Cho. (*G.B 2814*).
609	1	Pique-Dame Overture...			Berlin Phil.—*Spell* Schmidt-Isserstedt *and add* no.: in Cap (LP) P 8108.
610	1	Variations on O Mensch			*Should read* Canon over O Mensch . . . *Transfer* entry up before Chansons. The item is only ½s.
611	2	Flesh and fantasy	...	...	Composer of coupling *should read*: Raksin. Alter Index, p. 871, accordingly.
617	—	SLEEPING BEAUTY, Table, Set A			It now appears that No. 22b is on 0194, and No. 27 on 0195.
617	1	Nos. 22 & 24 ...	...	...	C.DX 782 also includes part of No. 3, and No. 22 is abbreviated. *Delete* USSR. 15519/20 *and transfer* to new entry:
					No. 2, Scene (Entrance of fairies).
618	—	SWAN LAKE, Table			Re-number item 5 as item 26 (Act III), G.C 3823 in set C is this, Parts 1 & 2 only.
619	1	Concerto, vln. & orch....			Milstein—AmC. no. *to read* AmC. 11276/9D.
620	1	Ouverture solennelle, 1812	...	...	Mengelberg—Cap. set no. *to read* EBL 8022.
620	1	Romeo & Juliet	...	...	N.Y.P.S.O.—Stokowski—*Delete* LP only. *Add* (5ss, in set MM 898).
620	1	Russian Dance (unspec.)	...	...	Is *not* the Trepak from Nutcracker. *Delete* remark.
620	2	No. 2, Waltz ...	...	...	*Add* omissions:
					¶ Amsterdam—Mengelberg (C.D 41003: L 2182; in AmC. set M 105).
					§ Detroit Sym.—Gabrilowitsch (Vic. 6835).
621	1	Symphony No. 3	...	...	Beecham—Vic. set no. *to read* M 1279.
621	1	Symphony No. 4	...	...	§ Stokowski—G. no. *to read* G.DB 1793/7.
621	2	Symphony No. 5	...	...	Mengelberg—*Transfer* no. U.G 14214/8 to corresponding recording under Symphony No. 6.
621	2	Symphony No. 6	...	...	Albert—No. *to read* P.BB 25257/62.
622	2	No. 12, Written Words	...	...	Schlusnus—No. *to read* Pol. 67249.

Page	Col.	Entry				Remarks
622	2	No. 17	...	...	...	Lemeshev—*D.F 8154* is No. 6 above; *transfer* entry. This probably also applies to *USSR. 13996*, but *not* to *04871/2*.
625	1	Don Juan's Serenade	...	...	...	§ Henderson—*Add D.M 69* & . . .
626	1	Lullaby in a storm	...	...	...	*For* Op. 45 *read* Op. 54.
626	2	O bless you, forests	...	...	...	*Add* omission: § (*Eng*) R. Henderson (B) (*D.M 69*).
627	2	Why?	...	...	...	Obukhova—No. *should read USSR. 17151.*
630	1	Mignon, Orch. Sel.	...	...	...	§ Melichar—Pol. no. *to read Pol. 24443.*
631	1	Je suis Titania	...	...	...	§ Talley—G. no. *to read* G.DB 1142.
635	2	Wasps Overture	...	...	...	Sargent—*Add* no. AmC. 71605D.
636	1	On Wenlock Edge	...	...	...	Lon. set *to read* LA 36.
637	1	VELLONES, Pierre	...	...	...	Date of birth *to read* 1889.
638	1	Requiem, Confutatis	...	...	...	*Add* omission: § E. Pinza (G.DB 956).
638	1	Songs : Ad una stella ; Non t'accostare				*For* F. Giorgio *read* G. Favaretto.
		Lo Spazzacammino	...	...	...	*Should read* Lo Spazzacammino.
		Stornello : Tu dice . . .				*Should read* **Tu dici** . . . *Add* (Anon.).
638	1	Aïda—Set C	...	...	...	*For* C.D 14497/517 *read* C.D 14497/514.
639	1	Ritorna vincitor!				§ E. Turner—*Add* (o.v. *C.D 1578*).
639	2	Gloria all' Egitto	...	...	...	Fiedler—Vic. 12-1019 is a n.v., the others are all the o.v.
641	1	Re dell' abisso	...	...	...	Cattaneo—G. no. *to read* G.DB 1403.
642	1	La Battaglia de Legnano, Overture	...			No. *to read* C.D 12295/6 and is 10-inch.
642	1/2	DON CARLOS	...	...	...	Heading—*Add* (Later 4 acts).
						Dalberg & Harand (Od. O-3655/6)—*Delete* Mio salvator. Title *to read* **Restate!** and *transfer* to end of Act II.
						G. Bechi (G.DB 11322)—*Delete* heading and *transfer* to Per me giunto below.
643	2	Oh! de' verd' anni miei	...			Tagliabue—No. *to read* G.DB 11303.
644	1	Falstaff, Set C	...	...	...	AmC. set no. *to read* OP 16.
644	1	Signor! v'assista				DT. no. *to read* GX 61009.
645	1	Il santo nome	...	...	...	Palagi—Pol. 95279 continues to end of Act, with an anon. sop.
645	2	Auf! pazienza	...	...	...	Od. 5587F includes also **Del mondo**, *below*.
646	1	LOMBARDI, Act III				*Add* omission: **Gerusalemme . . . la grande** (Cho.): § Guido Monaco Cho.—Borgioli (G.S 10066).
646	2	Quando le sere	...	...	...	Lugo—*Add* to G.DB 3276, new footnote: ³ Announced under this no. but probably not issued.
648	2	Si, pel ciel				A. Granforte *and not* B. Franci sings on G.DB 1007.
649	1	Mia madre . . .	...	...	...	Melba—*Delete* *.
651	1	Caro nome	...	...	...	§ E. Noréna—G. no. *to read* G.DB 4892.
						L. Tetrazzini—o.v. *to read* G.DB 536*.
652	1	Tutte le feste	...	...	...	*For* L. Abott *read* B. Abott.
652	1	La donna è mobile	...	...	...	Infantino—*For*: C.GQ 7729 *read* C.GQ 7229.
652	2	La donna è mobile	...	...	...	§ Silva—No. *to read* G.DA 798.
653	2	La Traviata, Set D	...	...	...	*For* C.D 14479/83 *read* C.D 14479/93.
655	2	Addio del passato	...	...	...	*Delete* F. Hempel G.DB 272*.
657	1	Mal reggendo . . .				Brems/Islandi—No. *should read* G.DB 5279.
						Add omission: ▲ (*Ger*) G. Milinkovic & H. Taubmann (Pol. 68300)
659	2	O magnum mysterium	...			*Should precede* O quam gloriosum.
661	1	BACHIANAS BRASILEIRAS				No. 2 is for orch. 1930. No. 5 : Sayão recording is the Aria only.
663	2	Concertos, Op. 4	...	...	...	*For* Le Stravaganza *read* La Stravaganza.
663	2	Concerto, D major	...	...	...	Entered as Op. 6, No. 11.
						Transfer to next page: the work is really without Op. no.—Pincherle No. 444.
664	1	Concerto, F major (266)				Key *to read* D minor. The Largo is in F major.
665	1	Ingrata Lidia	...	...	...	Is edited V. Mortari. No evidence of origin.
666	1	5 Gedichte	...	...	...	Farrell—Vic. set no. *to read* M 1233.
666	2	(Der) FLIEGENDE HOLLÄNDER	...			Date of f.p. *to read* 1843 *and not* 1833.
669	1	Prelude & Procession	...			*Delete* § Coates entry. This is Tannhäuser—**Grand March**.
670	2	Mein lieber Schwan!	...			R. Crooks—No. *to read* G.DB 3498 and amend coupling *to read* : (*Elisir d'Amore*—Una furtiva lagrima).
671	1	Meistersinger—Orch. Suite				Reiner—Set J 79 is CanC.
674	1	Parsifal, Prelude	...	...	...	Stokowski—*Add* new footnote to G.DB 3269/70 : ¹¹ Announced with this no. but probably not issued.
						Add sign § before Muck entry.
						Add omission: § Colonne—Pierné (Od. 123744/5).
674	1	Der Glaube lebt	...	...	...	G.EG 3431 & EG 3902 are 10-inch.
677	2	Leb' wohl . . . Feuerzauber (ORCH.)				Stokowski—*Add* (LP: AmC.ML 2153).
679	2	Götterdämmerung, Set C & *passim*				*For* M. Müller *read* I. Møller.
680	1	Hoi ho!	...	...	...	Weber—AmC. no. *to read* AmC. 69047/8D.
680	1	Trauermusik	...	...	...	Nat. Sym.—Beer—D. no. *to read* D.K 1285.
						L.S.O.—Coates—Vic. no. *to read* Vic. 9049.
680	2	TANNHÄUSER				Date *to read* 1845.
681	1	Dich, teure Halle	...	...	...	*Add* omission: § M. Jeritza (*Vic. 1273*).
681	2	Fest-Marsch	...	...	...	Melichar—*For* Pol. 516712 *read* Pol. 516713.
						Coates—*Add* Vic. 9017.
683	2	Tristan, Prelude	...	...	...	*Transfer* Pol. 66832 from Original ending *to* Concert ending; & D.AK 2245/6 (& LP) *from* Concert ending *to* Original ending.
684	2	Schmied . . . Overture	...			Is 4ss on T.SK 2110/1.
685	2	España	...	...	...	§ Melichar—D. no. *to read* D.PO 5034.
687	2	Hamlet	...	...	...	G. no. *to read* G.C 3755/7.
694	1	Lost in the Stars	...	...	...	AmD. set DAU 738 is 10-inch.
695	2	Air (Aria) & Gavotte	...			{ Is by Samuel Wesley *and not* S. S. Wesley. Revise and transfer accordingly.
857						
699	1	WIKLUND—Concerto No. 1			...	*For* C minor *read* E minor.
700	1	Society Vol. V	}			
704	1	Treibt mir . . .	}			*Should read* Treibe nur . . .
705	1	Wächterlied	...	...	...	*Delete* * from Pol. 70753.
706	1	First line	...	...	...	*For* GIOIELLA *read* GIOIELLI.
708	1	Nightingale Song	...			E. Schumann also in *Ger* on § G.ER 338 : DA 6037; & probably EW 83.
708	2	ZIPOLI	...	...	...	Dates now stated to be (1688-1726).
709	2	AS. 30	...	...	...	*For* Auber *read* Aubert.
710	1	AS. 43	...	...	...	*For* Sachs *read* Cape.
714	1	MBA 13020	...	...	...	*Supply* missing letter M.
717	1	HENRY VI	...	...	...	*Add* new footnote to DX 581 & 582 : ¹ Also attributed, more probably, to Henry V.
717	2	CHARTES	...	...	...	Vic. 13555—*Delete* name and *substitute* ANON. (XIth Cent.).
722	—	Footnote	...	...	...	*Delete*.
726	1	GISELLE, Act I	...	...	...	*For* Vic. DM 1497 *read* DM 1397.
728	1	Trio-Sonata, B flat major	...			*For* W 158 *read* W 161-2.

Page	Col.	Entry	Remarks
735	2	Cantata 100, No. 3 ⎱	*Delete* (*Ital*). They are sung in German.
736	1	Cantata 208, No. 9 ⎰	
738	1/2	Rhapsody, Sonatina, etc.	*For* ♯ AmVox. PL 6140 *read* ♯ AmVox. PL 6410.
742	1	(12) Deutsche Tänze, G 140	♮ U.H 23673/4S contains nos. 1, 2, 4, 6, 8, 10, 12, only.
744	1	PURITANI, Act III	*Add* omitted entry:
			Vieni, vieni . . . (T. part only) E. Conley, in *D.LM 4534*, etc., *above.*
744	2	BERG, N.	*Add* omission:
			Aftonsång § E. Beyron (T) (*Od. O-2558*).
746	2	BJÖRKANDER, Sonatina	Is 4ss.—Symf. RT 1019/20.
		Sketches from the Archipelago	No. *should read Rtj. RA 112/3.*
747	1	BLOMDAHL: Trio	Date *to read* 1945.
748	1	BORODIN	Date of birth *to read* 1833.
749	1	Symphony No. 2	Wolff *to read* Wolf and no. *to read* ♯ Rem. 199-19.
749	2	Piano Qtt. No. 3	*Supply* missing digit, to make no. *read* Clc.C 2123/6.
750	2	Hungarian Dances—VLN. & PF.	Spalding omits Nos. 10-13, 16 & 18
753	1	Nun bitten wir . . .	The setting in ♯ Allo.AL 113 is No. 22.
753	1	Preludes & Fugues	Noehren—*For* ♯ Allo.AL 112 *read* ♯ Allo.AL 113.
753	2	BYRD—Inst. Collection	Miserere is FVB. 175.
			The Pavane & Galliard is "The Earl of Salisbury" (Allo.ALG 3021).
755	2	Ballade No. 2	Malinin—No. *to read* ♮ *Muza.* 1389/90 (3ss).
759	1	Scherzo No. 4	Arrau—No. *to read* ♮ C.LX8792/3 (No. defective in some copies only).
759	2	Valse No. 1	Ballon recording *is really* No. 14, E minor. *Transfer* entry to nex page.
759	2	Valse No. 3, A minor	*For* Op. 34, No. 8 *read* Op. 34, No. 2.
761	1/2	Sonatas, Op. 5	E minor in Allo.AL 94 *is really* No. 8.
			F major in Allo.AL 109 *is really* No. 10.
763	2	Poissons d'or	Blancard—Coupling *to read* L 475.
763	2	PRELUDES	Copeland—Bk. II, Nos. 2 & 6 are not in ♯ *MGM.E 526*, but only in omitted ♭ *set K 59*, which includes all 4 preludes.
764	1	Clair de lune	♯ AmC.ML 4311 is cond. Rodzinski.
764	1	Sonata No. 1	*For* Vic. *read* vlc.
767	1	Suite, D major, Op. 39	♯ *CHS.CHS 1069* should be *italics*—is 10-inch.
767	1	Symphony No. 5	♯ Rem. 199-4 is now stated to be cond. Singer.
769	2	EL SOMBRERO, DANCES	Iturbi—Vic. LM no. *to read* LM 1138.
770	1	Quartet, Str., Op. 121	*For* E major *read* E minor.
770	1	QUARTET, pf. & str., No. 2	♯ *Sel. LP 8004* is 10-inch.
771	1	FIBICH: In the Twilight—Lento	No. *to read Muza. 1362.*
772	2	FRANZ, Songs	Schumann collection also includes **Widmung, Op. 14, No. 1** (W. Müller).
773	1	FRUMERIE: Sonata No. 2	Violinist *is* M. Temko *and not* C. Barkel.
779	2	SERSE : Ombra mai fu	ORCH. Weldon—No. *to read* C.DX 1681.
			ORG. Asma—*Add* additional no.: Pol. 57405.
780	1	JUDAS MACCABAEUS, No. 58 & MESSIAH, No. 44	*For* T.E 3810 *read* T.E 3816.
780	1	MESSIAH, No. 47	Wishart—Coupling *to read* No. 20.
780	2	Vln. & Cont. Sonatas	Schneider—No. *to read* ♯ AmC.ML 2149/51.
780	2	Sonata, D minor (unspec.)	Is really **Concerto à 4, No. 1.** *Transfer* entry to p. 781.
781	1	Concerto grosso No. 7, B flat	CHS.D 14 is not this work. It proves to be **Op. 3, No. 2,** with 1st & 3rd movts. reversed.
782	1	Pf. Sonata No. 34	M. de la Bruchollerie—No. *to read* G.DB 21038.
782	1	Pf. Sonata No. 43 (41), 1785	*Should read* No. 46 (43), *c.* 1770.
782	1	Divertimento No. 3, B flat major	*Delete* heading. Haas plays No. 1.
783	2	No. 88	Salzburg—*Delete* (6ss). ▌
784	1	"Toy" Symphony	Is now attributed to Leopold Mozart.
785	2	Sonatas, vln.	☆ Ricci—Nos. *to read* (♮ Pol.A 6332/3).
786	2	HUMPERDINCK—Dream Pantomime	Collins—*For* ♯ D.LX *read* ♯ D.LK.
790	1	KOCH, Erland von	*Insert* omission:
			Dance No. 2, A major, vln. & pf. 1935.
			S. Karpe & E. v. Koch (*G.X 6214*).
793	1	Pagliacci Prologue	Merrill—♯ Vic. LM 1148 *should be* upright type—is 12-inch.
795	1	LOEILLET : Sonata fl., ob., & cont. (unspec.)	*Add* key: G minor (AL 69).
797	2	Adieu notre petite table	Danco—♯ No. *should read* ♯ D.LXT 2557
799	1	Symphony No. 4	Pedrotti—No. *to read* ♮U.H 23759/62.
800	1	The Consul	*For* B. 0815 *read* B. 0185. The **Frustration theme** is Magda's aria **To this we've come.**
801	1	5 Symphonies . . . No. 3, 1922.	*Delete.* WL 5051 contains the Serenade, 1920-1. *Revise* accordingly.
802	1	Magnificat No. 2	*Add* 4 vv., XV.
802	1	L'INCORONAZIONE DI POPPEA	Air of Fortune *is* **Deh, nasconditi o virtú,** from Prologue.
802	1	ORFEO, COMPLETE	E. Trötschel (S) has been omitted from the cast.
802	1	Sinfonie a ritornello	Title *should read* **Ritornelli, Sinfonie & Toccata;** which are from **ORFEO.** *Transfer* entry to follow **Tu sei morta.**
802	2	BORIS, last entry	Christoff on *G.DA 1938* sings the Act I Monologue : **Still one more page** . . . and not as shown.
803	1	Songs & Dances of Death	J. Tourel *is* acc. L. Bernstein (pf.).
803	2	Ave verum corpus	Holy Cross Cho.—no. *to read:* Imp. 19256.
		— ARR. ORG.	*Transfer* Biggs entry to Adagio, K. 580a on p. 808.
805	1	Don Giovanni, No. 4	D.KX no. *to read* D.KX 28443.
807	1	Rondo, A minor, K 511	L. Kraus—*Delete.* Never issued.
807	1	Sonata No. 2	B. Léonet—No. *to read* G.SL 161/2.
808	2	Quartets 20 & 21	*Reverse* DFr. nos. 59 & 60 and *amend* couplings to match.
812	1	(Die) LUSTIGE WEIBER	*Should read* **(Die) LUSTIGEN WEIBER** . . .
812	2	(Die) Lustigen Weiber, Overture	Olof—D.K no. *to read* D.K 28234.
812	2	NOVÁK, V.	Died 1949.
814	1	Manru, aria	No. *to read Muza.* 1124.
814	2	MOTETS, COLLECTION	Salve Regina *is for* 5 voices (IV). Several of the items are ARR. Female Cho.
817	2	Contes de la vieille grand'mère	*Insert* new line before Oborin entry: . . . **One only** (unspec.).
818	1	Overture on Hebrew themes	*Delete* Paris Cha. Orch. and *transfer* nos. to first entry. This is the same recording.
823	1	Sonata, vln. & pf. ; & Pastourelle	Nos. *to read* ♮ Pol. A 6347/9.
823	2	Shéhérazade	Tourel—♯ AmC. no. *to read* ♯ ML 4289.
824	2	Capriccio espagnol	Kostelanetz—♭ C. no. *to read* DX 8396/7.
827	1	Rouet d'Omphale	N.Y.P.S.O.—♯ No. *to read:* ML 2170.
827	1	Samson, Arias	Swarthout—♯ Vic. LM 1156 is n.v. not ☆.
829	2	Verklärte Nacht	♯ *DCap.CCL 7507* is 10-inch. Violist is A. Dinkin.
832	1	Ave Maria, ARR. ORG.	Asma—No. *to read* Pol. 57405.

833	1	SCHÜTZ	Dates *should read* (1585-1672).
		(Die) SIEBEN LETZTE WORTE ...	*Should read* (Die) SIEBEN LETZTEN WORTE.
834	1	Romance No. 2	Key *to read* F sharp minor.
836	2	Song of the Forests	USSR. and TRC. issue is 9ss (TRC 41/5), with excerpt from *Meeting on the Elbe*.
838	2	STENHAMMAR : St. Martin's Summer nights... ...	No. *should read* ♮ Symf.RT 1016/8.
839/40		Strauss Waltzes, *passim* ...	Fiedler—♮ Vic. set DM 1521 *to read* DM 1519.
842	2	Firebird Suite	Ansermet does *not* include No. 3 of orig. suite.
843	1	SONGS : (3) Songs (1908) ...	*Should read* (2) Songs, Op. 6 (Gorodetzky) 1908; Pastorale (Vocalise) 1908. (See also Section II.)
843	2	Dichter und Bauer Overture ...	Ormandy—C. no. *to read* C.LX 1369.
847	1	Concerto, 3 vlns. & orch. ...	Kaufman—Is really F major, Tafelmusik II-3.
		Concerto, vla. & orch. ...	Kromer—*Add* key: G major.
849	1	DON CARLOS, Highlights ...	The Act nos. quoted are those of the revised 4-act version. *Revise* to read Acts II & IV respectively, of the original version.
849	2	Son io dinante . . . Giustizia!...	*Transfer* above Pièta! Perdon!
852	1	Bachianas Brasileiras, No. 5 ...	Sayão is the Aria only.
		CICLO BRASILEIRO ...	COMPLETE: Ballon recording is the revised version of 1948.
852	2	VILLA-LOBOS	*Transfer* the following entries under CIRANDAS:
			No. 8, Vamos atraz . . .
			No. 10, O pintor . . .
			No. 11, N'esta rua . . .
853	1	Concerto, D major	Kaufman & Rybar—*Add* (P. 159).
853	2	Concerto (unspec.)	Kaufman—*Should read* B flat major (P. 388).
		Sonatas, Op. 14	For ♯ Allo.AL 93 read ♯ Allo.AL 95.
854	1	(Der) FLIEGENDE HOLLÄNDER...	Date of f.p. *to read* 1843 *and not* 1833.
854	1	Lohengrin, Prelude Act III ...	Swarowsky—AusT. no. *to read* E 1090.
855	1	Rienzi Overture	Swarowsky—AusT. no. *to read* E 1089/90.
855	2	Tristan—COMPLETE ...	Is cond. Konwitschny and not Schmitz. A projected recording by the latter did not appear.
860	2	Spanish Music	*For* Temperancia *read* Tempranica.
			♯ Vic. LM no. *to read* 1138.
865	1	INDEX...	*Add* entry: ERIKSSON — 493b.
867	2	INDEX...	*Add* new entry: JOHANN ERNST *of SAXE-WEIMAR* — 20b
869	3	*MOOR*, Index refs. ...	184a refers to E. MOOR
			796a refers to K. MOOR.
873	2	TIPPETT, TITELOUZE, TOCH ...	*For* 623 *read* 632.
874	2	*WILLIAMS, ALBERTO*	*Add* Index ref. 338a.
Passim		In the U.Export (auto) sets, it now appears that a fill-up backs side 1 of the main work and not the final side. The disc numbers listed for the fill-ups therefore need revision throughout.	

ABEL, Karl Friedrich (1725-1787)

Sonata, E major[1]   gamba & hpsi.
  E. Lake & D. Erhart   **Argo.S 1003**
  (2ss)

ABSIL, Jean (b. 1893)

Concerto, pf. & orch., Op. 30   1937
  A. Dumortier & Belgian Nat.—F. Quinet
                                ♯ D.LX 133013
  (*below*)

Hommage à G. Lekeu   orch.   1939
    (Andante symphonique)
  Belgian Nat.—F. Quinet   **♯ D.LX 133013**
  (*above*)

(3) MARINES   pf.   1939
… No. 2 (Andantino); No. 3 (Vivo)
  P. de Clerck (1s. each)   **C.BF 5009**

Sonatina, Op. 29   pf.   1937
  S. Cambier (2ss)   **C.DCB 57**

ADAM de la HALLE
  SEE: †XIIth & XIIIth CENTURY MUSIC

ADAM, Adolphe Charles (1803-1856)

GISELLE   Ballet   2 acts   1841
Suites, Acts I & II
  ☆ Covent Garden—Irving (♯ G.DLP 1004)

Noël—Minuit, Chrétiens (Cappeau)
  M. Anderson (A) & pf.   in ♯ **Vic. LM 7008**
                              (♭ set WDM 7008)

  G. Myers (B) & Randolph
    Singers   in ♯ **West.WL 5200**
    O. Werner (B, *Norw*), J. Øian (pf.) (*Od.ND 7046*)
  ☆ M. Lanza (T), cho. & orch. (*BrzV. 10-1582*)
  ◪ E. Caruso (T) (in ♯ Vic. LCT 1121*: ♭ set *WCT 1121**)

OPERAS

GIRALDA   3 acts   1850
Overture
    Rhineland Sym.—Federer   **♯ Rgt. 5056**
    (*Flotow*)

(Le) POSTILLON DE LONGJUMEAU   3 acts
  1836
Mes amis, écoutez l'histoire   T & cho.   (Act I)
    N. Gedda   (*Swed*)   **Od.SD 6079**
    (*Lehar: Zarewitsch—Volgalied*)

SI J'ÉTAIS ROI   3 acts   1852
Overture
    L.P.O.—Martinon   in ♯ **D.LXT 2606**
    (*Hérold & Boieldieu* (♯ Lon.LLP 351: & *LD 9011*))

    Radio Luxembourg Sym.—Pensis ♯ **FestF.FLD 3**
    (*Bizet, Boieldieu, Gounod, etc.*)

    Bamberg Sym.—Lehmann   **PV. 72257**
    (*Auber: Muette de Portici Overture*)   (♯ *Pol. 16036*)

AGAZZARI, Agostino (1578-1640)
  SEE: † ♯ AS. 2502

AGUIRRE, Juan B. (1868-1924)

Gato   pf.
    G. Cases   **ArgOd. C 57011**
    (*Cases: Habanera de organilla*)

Huella   vln. & pf.
    J. Heifetz & E. Bay (pf.)   in ♯ **B.LAT 8020**
    (*Valle, Weill, etc.*)   (♯ AmD.DL 8521)

Triste No. 4   vln. & orch.
  A. Gendelman & Argentine
    Sym.—Artola   **ArgOd. 56535**

AICHINGER, Gregor (1565–1628)
  SEE: † MONACO CATHEDRAL

---

[1] Edition privately prepared from manuscript.   It is doubtful whether this disc was ever on sale.

1

ALABIEV, Alexandre (1787-1851)

In the dance (?ARR.) cho.
State Cho.—Sveshnikov *USSR. 18202*
(Glinka: Venetian night)

Trio (unspec.) pf., vln., vlc.
E. Gilels, D. Tziganov & S. Shirinsky
(6ss) *USSR. 16324/9*

Variations on a Russian song trio
V. Berlinsky, N. Barshai & A. Dubinsky
(2ss) *USSR. 18874/5*
▽ Older recordings include many versions of *The Nightingale*

ALAIN, Jehan (1911-1944)

Chorale (Dorian) organ
▽ A. Marchal (Lum. 3.26.010, o.n. 32082)

Litanies, Op. 79 organ
C. Crozier # Ken. 2553
(† French Organ Music)
▽ E. P. Biggs (in ♮ AmC. set M 802: # ML 4195)
A. Marchal (Lum. 3.26.010, o.n. 32082)

ALBENIZ, Isaac (1860-1909)

IBERIA pf. solo 1908
Book I:
1. Evocación; 2. El Puerto; 3. El Corpus en Sevilla;
Book II:
4. Rondeña; 5. Almeria; 6. Triana;
Book III:
7. El Albaicin; 8. El Polo; 9. Lavapiés;
Book IV:
10. Malaga; 11. Jerez; 12. Eritaña
COMPLETE RECORDING
L. Querol # Sel.LPG 8557/8
(3½ss—*Navarra*)

... Nos. 1, 2, 3, 6, 7—ARR. ORCH.
Berlin Radio—Schultz # Rgt. 5023

Asturias (Leyenda) pf. (Suite española 5)
— ARR. GUITAR Segovia (*et al.*)
A. Segovia in # B.AXTL 1005
(† Segovia Recital) (# AmD.DL 9633)
L. Maravilla in # Sel.LPG 8495
(† Tañidos)
R. de la Torre in # Phil. 106
(† Guitar recital)

Cádiz pf. (Suite española 4, *q.v.*)
R. Spivak ArgV. 11-7990
(*Torre bermeja*)
— ARR. ORCH.
Madrid Iberica Orch.—Lago *Od. 184916*
(*Granados: Villanesca*)

Córdoba, Op. 232, No. 4
G. Copeland in # MGM.E 87
(♭ set K 87)
M. Regules BrzV. 11-9417
(*Triana*)
J. Bolet in # Bo.B 300
(*Falla, Granados, Lecuona; & below*)
— ARR. VLN. & PF.
A. Campoli & E. Gritton D.X 571
(*Sevillanas*)

Evocación (Iberia No. 1) pf.
M. Regules BrzV. 11-9416
(*Navarra*)

Granada (Suite española 1) pf.
R. Spivak ArgV. 11-7983
(*Mallorca*)

Love Song (unid.) — ARR. VLN. & PF.
☆ D. Oistrakh & V. Topilin (in # Csm. CRLP 105)

Malagueña, Op. 71, No. 6 (Rumores de la caleta)
C. de Groot in # Phi.A 00131R
(*below*)
☆ J. Iturbi G.DA 1987
(*Chopin: Etude, Op. 10, No. 12*)
(in # Vic.LM 1167: ♭ set WDM 1604)
— ARR. VLN. & PF.
H. Szeryng & pf. Orf. 4001
(*Falla: Paño moruno & Jota*)

Malagueña, Op. 165, No. 3
— ARR. CASTANETS & DANCING
Rosario & Antonio C.DX 1846
(*Falla: Vida Breve—Danza No. 1*)

Malagueña (unspec.) J. Bolet (in # Bo.B 300)

Mallorca, Op. 202 (Barcarolla) pf.
G. Cases ArgOd. 66010
(*Granados: La maja y el ruisenor*)
R. Spivak ArgV. 11-7983
(*Granada*)

Navarra pf. (completed by de Séverac)
L. Querol in # Sel.LPG 8557/8
(*Iberia*)
M. Regules BrzV. 11-9416
(*Evocación*)

Prelude (unspec.) J. Bolet (in # Bo.B 300)

Seguidillas (Castilla) (Suite española 7, *q.v.*)
C. Smith C.DX 1842
(*Tango*)
— ARR. CASTANETS, PF., GUITAR & DANCE
J. Toledano, P. Miguel, C. Montoya, etc.
in # SMC. 513

Sevillanas (Sevilla) (Suite española 3, *q.v.*)
— ARR. VLN. & PF.
☆ A. Campoli & E. Gritton D.X 571
(*Córdoba*)
(*Tartini: Sonata, G minor, s. 3 on K 23287*)

SUITE ESPAÑOLA pf.
... 3. Sevillanas; 4. Cádiz; 7. Seguidillas (Castilla)
C. de Groot # Phi.A 00131R
(*above*; & *Falla*) (also Phi.A 11203/4G: PhM. 09706/7S)

Tango, D major, Op. 165, No. 2 pf.
C. Smith C.DX 1842
(*Seguidillas*)
G. Copeland in # MGM.E 87
♮ set 87: ♭ K 87
C. Keene in # Mer.MG 10113
A. Földes PV. 46002
(½s.—*Thomson: Ragtime Bass & Stravinsky: Circus Polka*)
☆ E. Joyce (in # AmD.DL 9528)
— ARR. VLN. & PF. Kreisler
☆ Z. Francescatti & A. Balsam (♭ AmC.A 1533)

Torre bermeja pf.
(*Piezas caracteristicas No. 12*)
R. Spivak ArgV. 11-7990
(*Cádiz*)

= Long-playing, 33⅓ r.p.m. ♭ = 45 r.p.m. ♮ = Auto. couplings, 78 r.p.m.

Torre bermeja (*continued*)

— ARR. GUITAR
R. de la Torre   in ♯ **Phil. 106**
(† Guitar recital)

☆ A. Segovia (▽ in ♯ AmD.DL 8022)

Triana (Iberia No. 6)   pf.
M. Regules   **BrzV. 11-9417**
(*Córdoba*)
C. Keene   in ♯ **Mer.MG 10113**
(*above; & Liszt, Chopin, etc.*)

— ARR. ORCH.
☆ Boston Pops—Fiedler   ♭ *G.7BF 1026*
(*Rodriguez: La cumparsita*)

ALBERT, Eugene d' (1864-1932)

OPERAS

TIEFLAND   Prol. & 2 acts   1903
Excerpts
V. de Strozzi (S), E. Schmedes (T), R. Schubert
(T), L. Demuth (B), J. Urlus (T), M. Roth (B)
(2ss)   ♯ *Ete.ELP 456**

Orchestral Selection
☆ Berlin State Opera—Viebig (G.BB 213)

Symphonic Prelude
☆ Berlin State Op.—Ludwig (Pol. 15486)

Traumerzählung   T   (Prologue)
Wolfserzählung   T   (Act I)
☆ H. Meyer-Welfing (P.BX 607)

Ich weiss nicht wer mein Vater war   S   (Act II)
L. Rysanek   **C.LX 1559**
(*R. Strauss: Arabella—Das war sehr gut*)

(Die) TOTEN AUGEN   Prol. & 1 act   1916
Psyche wandelt durch Säulenhallen   S
☆ L. Lehmann (in ♯ AmD.DL 9523)

ALBINONI, Tommaso (1671-1750)

Adagio, G minor   Str. & org. (ed. Giazzotto)
Concerto à 5, D major, Op. 5, No. 3   1707
P. Lamacque (vln.), G. Nucci (org.), Inst.
Ensemble—Witold   ♯ **EPP.SLP 1**
(*below*)

Concerto, B flat major, Op. 7, No. 3 ob. & str. orch.
G. Tomasini & Inst. Ens.—Witold
                              in ♯ **EPP.SLP 1**
...**1st. movt., Allegro**
☆ L.Goossens & Philharmonia—Süsskind (C.GQX11458)

Concerto, C major, Op. 7, No. 11   2 ob. & str.
E. Parolari, A. Raoult & Str. Orch.
—Dahinden   ♯ **CHS.F 17**
(*Manfredini, etc.*)

Concerto, D minor, Op. 9, No. 2   ob. & str. c. 1722
Ranzani & La Scala Ens.
—Valdinoci   ♯ **Csm.CLPS 1014**
(*Monteverdi*)

Concerto, D major, Op. 9, No. 7 vln. & str. c. 1722
A. Pelliccia & Virtuosi di Roma—Fasano
                                   ♯ **AmD.DL 9598**
(*Cirri, Marcello, Pergolesi*)

Sonata, G minor, Op. 2, No. 6 str.   pub. 1694
(ed. Fasano)
Virtuosi di Roma—Fasano   ♯ **B.AXTL 1004**
(*Bach, A. Scarlatti, Tartini*)   (♯ AmD.DL 9572)
Inst. Ens.—Witold   ♯ **EPP.SLP 1**
(*above*)

ALFONSO X (the Wise) (1221-1284)

SEE : †XIIth & XIIIth CENTURY MUSIC
       † SPANISH CHORAL MUSIC

ALFVÉN, Hugo (b. 1872)

Midsommarvaka, Op. 19   orch.
Cincinnati Sym.—Johnson   **D.X 569**
(*Grieg, on* ♯ D.LXT 2630; ♯ Lon.LLP 406)

**Folk-song arrangements: Darlarna Song; Magic
strains**
▽ M. Morner (S), E. Westberg (pf.) (*C.8601*)

ALNAES, Eyvind (1872-1932)

Christiansand Song   (Krag)
L. E. Tofteland (B) & orch.   **G.AL 3131**
(*A. Hansen: Christiansand Song*)

Last voyage
M. Reizen (Bs, *Russ*)   **USSR. 017774**
(*Schubert: Aufenthalt*)

ALPAERTS, Florent (b. 1876)

Pallieter   3 Sym. episodes   Orch.[1]   1924
... **3rd episode, Wedding music**
▽ Belgian Nat. Radio—André   **T.E 2989/90**
(3ss—*A. de Boeck: Rhapsodie dahoméenne*)   (FT.T 127/8)

James Ensor Suite   orch.   1931
Belgian Nat.—Weemaels   ♯ *D.LX 133017*

ANDRICU, Mihail

(4) Rustic pictures   orch.
Rumanian Radio Sym.—Silvestri
(4ss)   ♮ *U.D 26129/30*

ANDRIESSEN, Hendrik (b. 1892)

Intermezzi   org.
▽ A. v. d. Horst   **D.X 10137**
(*Sweelinck*)

Ricercare   orch.
Residentie—v. Otterloo   **Phi.A 11141G**

Variations on a theme of Kuhnau   orch.
Residentie—v. Otterloo   **Phi.A 11243G**

---

[1] After the novel by F. Timmermans.

ANGLEBERT, Jean-Henry d' (1628-1691)

Suite No. 2, G minor hpsi. 1689
... Prelude, Allemande, Courante, Sarabande, Gigue
M. Charbonnier † AS. 163

ANTES, John (1740-1811)
SEE also : † AMERICAN MUSIC (INST. & CHA.)

▽ Go, Congregation, go in ♮ Vic. set DM 1445 : ♯ LM 57 :
♭ WDM 1445

ANTHEIL, George (b. 1900)

Sonata No. 2 vln. & pf. 1923
☆ I. Baker & Yaltah Menuhin ♯ ML. 7006

SONGS
(2) Odes (Keats)
V. Price (speaker), G. Antheil (pf.)
Songs of Experience (Blake)
V. Graf (S), G. Antheil (pf.) ♯ SPA. 1

Symphony No. 5 1945
Vienna Philharmonia—Haefner ♯ SPA. 16
(Josten)

ARBÓS, Enrique Fernandez (1863-1939)

Tango, Op. 6, No. 3 vln. & pf.
R. Posselt & A. Sly in ♯ Acad.ALP 304
(Hindemith, etc.)

ARCADELT, Jacob (c. 1514-c. 1575)

Ave Maria (ARR. Dietsch)
Vocal Qtt. in Vic. set E 101
(♭ set WE 101)

ARENSKY, Antony Stepanovitch (1861-1906)

Concerto, A minor, Op. 54 vln. & orch.
... Tempo di valse — ARR. VLN. & PF. Heifetz
☆ J. Heifetz & E. Bay (in ♯ Vic. LM 1166)

Fantasia on Russian epic themes (Ryabinin), Op. 48
pf. & orch.
M. Grünberg & USSR Radio Orch.—Samosud
(2ss) USSR. 015930/1

NAL AND DAMAYANTI Opera 1899
Damayanti's Cradle song S
A. Nezhdanova USSR. 15992
(Rimsky-Korsakov : Tsar's Bride, Martha's aria)

RAPHAEL, Op. 37 Opera, 1 act 1894
Serenade : My heart trembles with passion T
♯ L. Sobinoff (G.VB 45* : o.n. DB 893*)

SONGS
(The) Brilliant Star, Op. 60, No. 5 (Fet)
Dear pages, Op. 60, No. 6 (Fet)
A. Pirogov (B) USSR. 18378/9

Dozing, Op. 60, No. 3 (Minstein)
I. Kozlovsky (T) USSR. 20165
(Tchaikovsky : Again as before)

(The) Minstrel (Maikov)
A. Pirogov (B) (2ss) USSR. 20001/2

Weep not, my friend
A. Ivanov (B), G. Orentlichen (pf.) USSR. 21213
(Varlamoff : Sea)

SUITES 2 pfs.
No. 1, Op. 15
... Waltz only
C. Smith & P. Sellick C.DX 1806
(J. S. Bach : Cantata No. 203, excpt.)

No. 2, "Silhouettes", Op. 23
... Coquette — ARR. ORCH. Arensky
Bolshoi Theatre—Faier USSR. 15475
(Rubinstein : Toreador & Andalouse)

No. 3, Op. 33
... Valse, Minuet, Polonaise — ARR. ORCH. Arensky
USSR Radio Orch.—Gorchakov
(2ss) USSR. 18589/90

Variations on a theme of Tchaikovsky, Op. 35a
Little Orch. Soc.—Scherman ♯ AmC.ML 4526
(Rachmaninoff)
Cha. Orch.—Byrns ♯ DCap.CTL 7022
(Grieg) (♯ Cap.P 8158)
Hirsch Str. Qtt. in ♯ Argo.ARS 1002
(Debussy & Rawsthorne)

ARNE, Michael (1740-1786)

(The) Lass with a delicate air (ARR. Lehmann)
M. Morley (treb.), J. Wills (pf.) D.F 9782
(Schubert : Hark, hark the lark) (in ♯ D.LM 4543 ;
♯ Lon.LPS 399)

E. Knight (S) (in ♯ B.LA 8538 ; ♯ AmD.DL 5045 : &
AmD. 23983)

ARNE, Thomas Augustine (1710-1778)

ALFRED Masque 1740 (J. Thomson)
Rule Britannia T, cho., orch.
— ARR. BAND
Italian Carabinieri—Fantini (P.DC 5544)

AS YOU LIKE IT
Under the greenwood tree
LOVE'S LABOUR'S LOST
When daisies pied
When icicles hang by the wall
TWELFTH NIGHT
Come away, death
L. Chelsi (T), F. Kramer (pf.) in ♯ML.MLO 1010

(The) Shepherd's Song
Vocal Trio & pf. in ♯ Vic. set E 100
(♭ set WE 100)

Which is the properest day to sing?
Vocal Qtt. & pf. in ♯ Vic. set E 101
(♭ set WE 101)

♯ = Long-playing, 33⅓ r.p.m. ♭ = 45 r.p.m. ♮ = Auto. couplings, 78 r.p.m.

4

ARNELL, Richard A. S. (b. 1918)

Punch & the Child, Op. 49　Ballet Suite
☆ Royal Phil.—Beecham　　　**♯ AmC.ML 4593**
(Berners)

ARRIAGA Y BALZOLA, Juan Crisostomo Jacobo Antonio (1806-1826)

Quartets, String　1822
No. 1, D minor
No. 2, A major
☆ Guilet Qtt.　　　　　　**♯ Nix.CLP 1068**

No. 3, E flat major
Guilet Qtt.　　　　　　　**♯ CHS.F 14**
(Paganini)

ASOLA, Giovanni Matteo (fl. XVIth Cent.)

Christus factus est
Lassus Vocal Qtt.—Speyer　　　**Chr. 326B**
(Casali: Ave Maria)

ATTAIGNANT, Pierre (d.c. 1552)
SEE: † FRENCH MASTERS . . .
　　† XVITH & XVIITH CENTURY SONGS

ATTERBERG, Kurt (b. 1887)

Baroque Suite, Op. 23　　　　orch.
... Siciliana & Giga
☆ Vienna State Op.—Baltzer (Vienna. 5003)

ATTERBURY, Luffman (d. 1796)
SEE: † CATCHES & GLEES

AUBER, Daniel F. E. (1782-1871)

OPERAS
(Les) DIAMANTS DE LA COURONNE　3 acts
　　1841　*(Crown Diamonds)*
Overture
☆ Boston Pops—Fiedler (♭ G.7BF 1016)

(Le) DOMINO NOIR　3 acts　1837
Overture
Munich Phil.—Lehmann　　　**PV. 72087**
(Fra Diavolo, Overture)　　　*(♯ Pol. 16036)*
Rhineland Sym.—Federer　　　**♯ Rgt. 5054**
(Nicolai)

FRA DIAVOLO　3 acts　1830
COMPLETE RECORDING (in *German*)

Zerlina	...	...	I. Beilke (S)
Lady Pamela	...	...	M. L. Schilp (S)
Lorenzo	...	...	L. Fehenberger (T)
Fra Diavolo	...	...	H. Hopf (T)
Lord Rocburg	...	A. Schellenberg (T)
Matteo	...	...	G. Frick (Bs)
Giacomo	...	...	K. Böhme (Bs)

Dresden State Op. cho. & orch.—Elmendorff
(4ss)　　　　　　　　　**♯ Ura. set 204**

"Complete Arias"　(in *Italian*)
M. Laszlo (S), G. Prandelli (T), G. Giusti (B),
　La Scala cho. & orch.—Questa　**♯ Roy. 1207**
(Highlights from above on ♯ *Roy. 6068*)

Overture
Munich Phil.—F. Lehmann　　　**PV. 72087**
(Domino Noir, Ov.) (in ♯ *AmD.DL 4003*) (FPV. 5028)
　　　　　(♯ Pol. 16036)
F.O.K. Sym.—Strníště　　　　**U.H 23988**
(2ss)
Saxon State—Elmendorff　　**♭ Ura.UREP 3**
(Barbiere Ov.) (from set)
☆ Boston Prom.—Fiedler (G.EH 1391: ♭ *7BF 1017*)

Quel bonheur　S　(Act II)
V. Barsova (*Russ*, 2ss)　　　**USSR. 9955/6**

Je vois marcher　T　(Act III)
☆ M. Lichtegg (*Ger*) (in ♯ Lon.LLP 55)

Pour toujours, disait-elle　T　(Act III)
Ⱨ H. Jadlowker (*Ger*) (G.VB 54*: o.n. *042435**)

MANON LESCAUT　3 acts　1856

Bourbonnaise　(Act I)
L'Éclat de rire—C'est l'histoire amoureuse　S
Ⱨ A. Galli-Curci (*G.VA 8*: o.n. DA 215**)
A. Patti (*IRCC 3100**)

(La) MUETTE DE PORTICI (MASANIELLO)
　5 acts　1823
Overture
Vienna Radio—Nilius　　　　**Vien.L 6052**
(2ss)
Bamberg Sym.—Lehmann　　**PV. 72257**
(Adam: Si j'étais roi, Ov.)

O moment enchanteur　S　(Act I)
Ⱨ F. Hempel (G.VB 22*: o.n. DB 276**)

Du pauvre seul ami fidèle　T　(Act IV)
Ⱨ L. Slezak (*Ger*) (G.VA 22*: o.n. ER 6**)

AUBERT, Louis (b. 1877)

SONGS
(Les) Souliers de l'avocat
C. Panzéra (B), M. Panzéra (pf.)
　　　　　　　in ♯ **Mer.MG 10098**
(Ravel, Poulenc, etc.)

(Le) Vaincu ; (Le) Visage penché
(from *6 Poèmes arabes*) (Toussaint)
I. Kolassi (M-S), J. Bonneau (pf.)
　　　　　　　in ♯ ***D.LX 3080***
(Ravel, Fauré, etc.)　　　(in ♯ *Lon.LS 568*)

AURIC, Georges (b. 1899)

(La) Fontaine de Jouvence　Ballet Suite
Malbrouck s'en va-t-en Guerre　Ballet Suite
Paris Phil.—Leibowitz　　　**♯ Ren.X 41**
(Gradwohl)

Sonatine　pf.　1922
L. Thyrion　　　　　in ♯ ***Phi.N 00601R***
(Satie, Honegger, Poulenc)

AZZAIOLO, Filippo (fl. 1557-d. 1609)
SEE: † ITALIAN MADRIGALS (FAIT)

☆ = Re-issue of a recording to be found in WERM or Supplement I.

BABADZHANYAN, A.

Heroic Ballad   pf. & orch.
 A. Babadzhanyan & USSR. State Radio—
  Rakhlin   **USSR. 019278/83**
 (6ss)

BABBITT, Milton (b. 1916)

Composition for viola & pf.
 A. Loft & B. Weiser   **♯ NE. 4**
 (*Berger, Flanagan, Smith*)

BACH, Carl Philipp Emanuel (1714-1788)

Chromatic Fantasia (W.117-13) 1770
 D. Pinkham (hpsi.) **♯ Allo.ALG 3037**
 (*Trio*)

CONCERTOS, pf. & orch.

A minor (W.1) 1733
 ☆ F. Holletschek & Vienna Sym.— oboda
       (♯ Sel.LPG 8324)

C minor (W.31) 1753
 M. Roesgen-Champion & Paris Cons.—
  Goldschmidt   **♯ Clc. 6068**
 (*Haydn: Concerto*) (♯ Per.SPL 556)

D minor (W.23) 1748
 ☆ A. Balsam & Winterthur—Desarzens (♯ Clc. 6084)

Magnificat, D major S,A,T,B, cho. (W.215) 1749
 D. Siebert, H. Rössl-Majdan, W. Kmentt,
  H. Braun, Vienna Academy cho. & State
  Op. orch.—Prohaska **♯ Van.BG 516/7**
 (3ss.—*Suite*)

Sonata, A minor fl. & cont. (W.128) 1733
 Collegium Pro Arte   **G.DB 21304**
 [K. Redel (fl.), I. Lechner (hpsi.), M. Bochman (vlc.)]
       (♭ *G.7RF 211*)

Suite, D major (ed. Casadesus)
 — ARR. ORCH. Steinberg ("*Concerto*")
 Vienna State Op.—Prohaska **♯ Van.BG 517**
 (*Magnificat*)

SYMPHONIES

No. 2, C major (W. 174)
 Cha. Orch.—v. d. Berg **♯ CHS.G 3**
 (*J. C. Bach & W. F. Bach*)

No. 11, C major (W.182-3: "No. 3")
No. 15, D major (W.183-1: "No. 1")
 ☆ Vienna Sym.—Swoboda (♯ Sel.LPG 8324)

Trio, B flat major (W.161/2) 1751
 L. Schaefer (fl.), R. Brink (vln.),
  D. Pinkham (hpsi.) **♯ Allo.ALG 3037**
 (*W. F. Bach*)

TRIO SONATAS, cl., bsn., hpsi. (W.92)
B flat major ; E flat major
 ☆ H. Druart, M. Allard & A. v. d. Wiele (♯ Clc. 6084)

BACH, Johann Christian (1735-1782)

SONATAS, Op. 2, fl. & hpsi 1763
No. 4, C major
No. 6, E flat major
 J. P. Rampal & R. Veyron-Lacroix ♯ *DO.LD 1*

SONATAS, pf. *c.* 1770
E major, Op. 5, No. 5
C minor, Op. 5, No. 6
B flat major, Op. 17, No. 6
 M. Tolson   **♯ WCFM. 7**

SYMPHONIES

E flat major, Op. 18, No. 1
 Cincinnati Sym.—Johnson **♯ D.LXT 2604**
 (*Schubert: Sym. No. 3*) (♯ Lon.LLP 405)

B flat major & D major, Op. 18, Nos. 2 & 3
 Chamber Orch.—v. d. Berg **♯ CHS.G 3**
 (*W. F. Bach & C. P. E. Bach*)

BACH, Johann Christoph Friedrich (1732-1795)

Gigue ronde
 R. Ellsasser (org.) in **♯ MGM.E 3005**

BACH, Johann Sebastian (1685-1750)

CLASSIFIED : I. Instrumental (A. Clavier; B. Organ;
            C. Chamber; D. Orchestral;
      II. Vocal   E. Miscellaneous)

I. INSTRUMENTAL

A. CLAVIER

COLLECTIONS
 Chromatic Fantasia & Fugue, D minor (BWV 903)
 Concerto nach italienischen Gusto, F major (BWV 971)
 Fantasia, C minor   (BWV 906)
 Fantasia & Fugue, A minor (BWV 904)
 ☆ M. Meyer (pf.) (♯ *DFr. 13*)

 (6) Little Preludes : No. 1, C major (BWV 933)
 Partita No. 6 : Air, E minor (BWV 830)
 Matthäus-Passion, No. 78, q.v. *Pax.PR 486*
 Suite, E flat   (BWV 819)
 English Suite No. 6 : Gavottes 1 & 2 (BWV 811)
 Brandenburg Concerto No. 1 : Minuet, q.v. Pax.PRT 484
 (15) Two-Part Inventions : No. 13 (BWV 784)
 Partita No. 1 : Minuets 1 & 2 (BWV 818)
 English Suite No. 2 : Sarabande (BWV 807)
 Italian Concerto : Presto (BWV 971)
 P. Browne (pf.)   Pax. PRT 485

Aria variata alla maniera italiana, A minor
 (BWV 989)
 R. Tureck (pf.) in ♯ **Allo.AL 117**

Chromatic Fantasia & Fugue, D minor (BWV 903)
 ☆ L. Selbiger (hpsi.) ♮ **C.LX 8915/6**
 T. Nikolayeva (pf.) ♮ **U.H 24258/9**
 (3ss—*Shostakovich: 3 Fantastic Dances, Op. 1*)
 L. Pattison (pf.)   **♯ Cmt. 1203**
 (*Chopin*)
 J. Ching (pf.)   **♯ *Argo.ARL 1001***
 (*French Suite No. 5*)
 ☆ M. Meyer (pf.) (♯ *DFr. 13*)

CLAVIERÜBUNG
 SEE : PARTITAS, CONCERTO, OUVERTÜRE, DUETTOS,
   VARIATIONS; & ORGAN, SECTION B

Concerto nach italienischen Gusto, F major
 (*Italian Concerto*)   (BWV 971)
 L. Selbiger (hpsi.) ♮ **C.LX 8955/6**
 (*2-Part Inventions, Nos. 4, 6, 8*) (♮ LDX 7016/7)

♯ = Long-playing, 33⅓ r.p.m. ♭ = 45 r.p.m. ♮ = Auto. couplings, 78 r.p.m.

Concerto nach italienischen Gusto, F major *(continued)*

R. Kirkpatrick (hpsi.)   **# HSLP. 3059**
(French Overture & Duettos)   (& in set HSL-A)

R. Tureck (pf.)   in **# Allo.AL 117**

☆ M. Meyer (pf.) *(# DFr. 13)*

Concertos after Vivaldi
No. 1, D major   (BWV 972)
☆ W. Landowska (hpsi.) (in **#** Vic. LM 1217: ♭ *set
    WDM 1181*; ♭ *G.7RF 246*)
    R. Gerlin (hpsi.) (in † **#** *AS. 2503LD*)

(4) Duettos   (BWV 802/5)
R. Kirkpatrick (hpsi.)   **# HSLP. 3059**
(French Ov. & Italian Concerto)   (& in set HSL-A)

H. Walcha (hpsi.)   (2ss)   **PV. 1419**
(From Clavierübung collection) (in **#** AmD. set DX 115)

R. Tureck (pf.)   in **# Allo.AL 117**

☆ E. Balogh (pf.) (in **#** Lyr. set LL 3; **#** Eur.LPG 624)

FANTASIAS

A minor   (BWV 922)
R. Gianoli (pf.)   **# West.WL 5101**
(Toccata)

C minor   (BWV 919)
☆ W. Landowska (hpsi.) (in **#** Vic.LM 1217:
    ♭ *set WDM 1181*)

C minor   (BWV 906)
☆ M. Meyer (pf.) *(# DFr. 13)*

Fantasia & Fugue, A minor   (BWV 904)
☆ M. Meyer (pf.) *(# DFr. 13)*

Fugue, A minor   (BWV 947)
— ARR. STR. ORCH.   Münchinger
Stuttgart Cha.—Münchinger in **# D.LXT 2663**
(Beethoven; & Fantasia & Fugue, G minor—Fugue only)
(**#** Lon.LLP 526)   (& D.K 28597)

— ARR. BRASS INSTS.
Fodens Champion Qtt.   *(Pax.PR 579)*

INVENTIONS

(15) Two-part   (BWV 772/786)
E. Harich-Schneider (clav.)   **PV. 3406/7**
(4ss)

L. Stadelmann (clav.)   **# Mer.MG 15019**

☆ E. Balogh (pf.) (in **#** Lyr. set LL 3)
    R. Kirkpatrick (clav.) (**#** *Nix.CLPY 1088*)

... No. 4, D minor ; No. 6, E major ; No. 8, F major
L. Selbiger (hpsi.)   **C.LX 8955**
(Italian Concerto, s.1)   (LDX 7016)

(15) Three-part   (BWV 787/801)
E. Harich-Schneider (clav.)   **PV. 3408/9**
                                        (**#** *CdM.LD 8005*)

L. Foss (pf.)   **# AmD.DL 9634**

☆ E. Balogh (pf.) (in **#** Lyr. set LL 3; **#** Eur.LPG 624)

**NOTENBUCH FÜR ANNA MAGDALENA
BACH**   (BWV Anh.)
... Marches : D major (122), E flat major (127)
    Minuets : D minor (132), F major (113), G major (116)
    Musette, D major (126)
    Polonaises : F major (117a), G major (130), G minor (123)
    Prelude, C major (W.T.C.1)
    Rondo, B flat major (183)[1]
    Solo per il cembalo, E flat major (129)
K. Rapf (hpsi.)   **# Van.BG 510**
(Songs from the same ; & Chorale-Prel.)

Ouvertüre nach französischer Art   (BWV 831)
(French Overture)

R. Kirkpatrick (hpsi.)   **# HSLP. 3059**
(Duettos, Italian Concerto)   (& in set HSL-A)

[1] This is *Les Moissonneurs* by F. Couperin.

(6) PARTITAS, Op. 1   (BWV 825/830)
No. 1, B flat major   No. 2, C minor
No. 3, A minor   No. 4, D major
No. 5, G major   No. 6, E minor

COMPLETE RECORDINGS
R. Kirkpatrick (hpsi.)   **# HSLP. 3056/8**
(6ss) (Nos. 1 & 5, 3056; 2 & 4, 3057; 3 & 6, 3058)
(also with the rest of the Clavierübung in set HSL-A)

P. Badura-Skoda (pf.)   **# West.WL 5160/2**
(6ss) (Nos. 1 & 6,5160; 2 & 5,5161; 3 & 4,5162)
                                             (set WAL 303)

J. Demus, S. Biro, J. Gillespie **# Rem. set 199-108**
(Nos. 1 & 6 by J. Demus (pf.); Nos. 3, 4 & 5 by
    J. Gillespie (hpsi.); No. 2 by S. Biro (pf.))

No. 1, B flat major
☆ D. Lipatti (pf.) (C.M 15145/6)

No. 2, C minor
G. Anda (pf.)   (4ss)   **T.E 3889/90**

No. 6, E minor
J. Demus (pf.)   **# Rem. 199-92**
(Preludes & Fugues)

☆ R. Tureck (pf.) (**#** EA.ALX   67)

(6) [Little] Preludes for beginners   (BWV 933/8)
(12) Little Preludes   (BWV 924/30, 939/42, 999)
☆ E. Balogh (pf.) (in **#** Lyr. set LL 3)

... Two, unspec.   F. Kramer (in **#** *MTR.MLP 1001*)
... No. 3, C minor   (BWV 999)   orig. lute
— ARR. GUITAR   Segovia   ☆ A. Segovia (in **#** *MGM.E 123*)

Prelude & Fugue, A minor (unspec.)
☆ B. Seidlhofer   **U.H 23958**
(Handel : Concerto Grosso, Op. 3, No. 5, s.1)
(English Suite No. 5, s.1 on H 24003)

Prelude, Fugue & Allegro, E flat major (BWV 998)
F. Valenti (hpsi.)   in **# Allo.AL 118**
(Toccatas)

☆ W. Landowska (hpsi.) (in **#** Vic.LM 1217: ♭ *set
    WDM 1181*)

SUITES, English   (BWV 806/11)

Nos. 1-6, COMPLETE
E. Picht-Axenfeld (hpsi.)   **# Mer.MG 10091/3**
(6ss)   (set MGL 6)

No. 2, A minor   (BWV 807)
No. 3, G minor   (BWV 808)
☆ A. Ehlers (hpsi.)   **# EA.ALX 3017**

No. 2, A minor ... Bourrées only
☆ A. Ehlers (in **#** AmD.DL 8019)

No. 5, E minor   (BWV 810)
M. Fedorova (pf.)   ♮ **U.H 24003/5**
(5ss—Prelude & Fugue, A minor)
(Allemande & Gigue only, on *USSR. 20174/5*)

No. 6, D minor   (BWV 811)
... Gavottes only   — ARR. VLN. & PF.   Heifetz
☆ J. Heifetz & E. Bay   **G.DA 2001**
(Beethoven : Contretanz)   (in **#** Vic.LM 1166)
(Mozart, on ♭ G.7RF 249)

SUITES, French   (BWV 812/7)

No. 1, D minor ... Sarabande only
☆ A. Ehlers (in **#** AmD.DL 8019)

No. 5, G major
T. Nikolayeva (pf.)   (4ss)   ♮ **U.H 23786/7**
☆ J. Ching (pf.)   **# Argo.ARL 1001**
(Chromatic Fantasia & Fugue)

☆ W. Kempff (Pol. 15453)
... Gavotte only   ☆ A. Ehlers (in **#** AmD.DL 8019)

SUITES, French (*continued*)

No. 6, E major
R. Casadesus (pf.)   # *AmC.ML 2196*
(*Concerto, 3 claviers*)
... Allemande only ▽ A. Ehlers (in # AmD.DL 8019)

SUITES

C minor (BWV 997)
— ARR. FL. & HPSI. Veyron-Lacroix
J. P. Rampal & R. Veyron-Lacroix # *BàM.LD 01*
(*Vivaldi: Concerto & Sonata*)

E minor (BWV 996) (orig. lute)
... Sarabande & Bourrée — ARR. GUITAR
☆ A. Segovia (in # *MGM.E 123*)
... Bourrée only in † Segovia Program

TOCCATAS

D minor (BWV 913)
F. Neumeyer (hpsi.)   PV. 2436
F. Valenti (hpsi.)   in # Allo.AL 118
R. Gianoli (pf.)   # West.WL 5101
(*Chaconne*)

E minor (BWV 914)
F. Valenti (hpsi.)   in # Allo.AL 118

(30) Variations on an aria, G major
(*Goldberg Variations*) (BWV 988)
R. Kirkpatrick (hpsi.)   # HSLP. 3062
(& with rest of Clavierübung in set HSL-A)
R. Tureck (pf.) (4ss)   # Allo.ALG 3033
☆ W. Landowska (hpsi.) (2ss) # G.FALP 137

(Das) WOHLTEMPERIRTE CLAVIER
(BWV 846/93)
BOOK I: COMPLETE RECORDING
☆ W. Landowska (hpsi.)   # G.FALP 141/3
(6ss)   (QALP 141/3)

BOOK II: COMPLETE (in preparation)
Nos. 25-32
W. Landowska (hpsi.)   # Vic.LM 1152
(♭ set WDM 1552)

Nos. 33-40
W. Landowska (hpsi.)   # Vic.LM 1708
(♭ set WDM 1708)

COLLECTION
Book I: Nos. 1, 5, 6, 8, 16, 17, 24 & one unid.
Book II: Nos. 30, 36
B. Segall (pf.)   in # NRI. 103

BOOK I: No. 8, E flat minor ... Fugue
BOOK II: No. 38, F sharp minor ... Fugue
— ARR. STR. TRIO Mozart
Janssen Sym. orch.   # AmC.ML 4406
(*Mozart: Adagios & Handel*)

BOOK I

No. 1, C major (See Notenbuch, *ante*)

No. 2, C minor
F. Shapiro (pf.)   in # Ox.OR 105

No. 21, B flat major
L. Selbiger (hpsi.)   G.DB 20140
(*Brandenburg Concerto No. 1, s.1*)

No. 22, B flat minor
P. Duvauchelle (pf.)   *Lum. 2.08.019*

BOOK II

No. 26, C minor
C. Solomon (pf.)   ♭ G.7P 123
(*Couperin: Le Carillon de Cythère*)

Nos. 39 & 40, G major & G minor
J. Demus (pf.)   in # Rem. 199-92

B. ORGAN

COLLECTIONS
SET A
| | |
Prelude & Fugue, G major   (BWV 541)
Toccata, Adagio & Fugue, C major (BWV 564)
Prelude & Fugue, E minor   (BWV 548)
Ch.-Prelude: Ach bleib' bei uns (BWV 649)
Prelude & Fugue, D major ... Fugue only (BWV 532)
J. Eggington   # OL.LD 22
(Organ of Ste. Radegonde, Poitiers)

SET B [1]
Fantasia & Fugue, G minor   (BWV 542)
Prelude & Fugue, B minor   (BWV 544)
Prelude & Fugue, A minor   (BWV 543)
Ch.-Preludes: Nun freut euch   (BWV 734)
    Der Tag, der ist so
    freudenreich   (BWV 605)
J. Eggington   # OL.LD 39

BACH'S ROYAL INSTRUMENT, VOL. III
Toccata & Fugue, D minor (BWV 565)
Concerto No. 5, D minor (BWV 596)
Fugue, C major   (BWV.Anh. 90)
Fugue, G minor   (BWV 578)
Passacaglia & Fugue, C minor (BWV 582)
E. Power Biggs   # AmC.ML 4500

BACH ORGAN MUSIC
Toccata, Adagio & Fugue,
    C major   (BWV 564)
Prelude & Fugue, A minor
    ... Fugue only   (BWV 543)
Fantasia & Fugue, G minor (BWV 542) (ML 4600)
CHORALE-PRELUDES
O Mensch, bewein' dein' Sünde
    gross   (BWV 622) (2 versions)
Wenn wir in höchsten Nöten
    sein   (BWV 668)
Ich ruf' zu dir, Herr Jesu
    Christ   (BWV 639)
Gelobet seist du, Jesu Christ (BWV 604)
Herzlich tut mich verlangen (BWV 727)
Nun komm' der Heiden
    Heiland   (BWV 659) (ML 4601)
Prelude & Fugue, C major
    ... Prelude only   (BWV 531)
Prelude & Fugue, D major
    ... Prelude only   (BWV 532)
Canzona, D minor   (BWV 588) (ML 4602)
A. Schweitzer   # AmC.ML 4600/2
(5ss—*Mendelssohn: Sonata No. 6*) (also # set SL 172)
(Organ of Gunsbach Church, Alsace)

CHORALE-PRELUDES

CLAVIERÜBUNG, PART III
BWV 552, 669/89, 802/5 (Clav.)
COMPLETE RECORDINGS
H. Walcha   PV. 1413/22
(20ss)   (6ss, in # AmD. set DX 115)
    BWV 552 on St. Jakobikirche Organ, Lübeck
    (PV. 1413 & 1422)
    BWV 669, 670/1, 676, 678, 680, 682, 684, 686, 688
    (The longer settings) on St. Jakobikirche Organ
    (PV. 1414/8)
    BWV 672/4, 675, 677, 679, 681, 683, 685, 687, 689 on
    Schnitger Organ, Cappel (PV. 1420/2)
    BWV 802/5 on Ammer Harpsichord (PV. 1419)
P. Callaway (org.), R. Kirkpatrick (hpsi.,
    in 802/5)   # HSLP. 3060/1 & 3059
(4½ss)   (& in set HSL-A)

ORGELBÜCHLEIN
Herr Christ, der ein'ge Gottes Sohn
    (BWV 601-OB 3)
Der Tag, der ist so freudenreich (BWV 605-OB 7)
Lob sei dem allmächtigen Gott (BWV 602-OB 4)

[1] Early pressings were 12-inch and included Toccata, F major (BWV 540).

ORGFLBÜCHLEIN (continued)

Vom Himmel hoch (BWV 606-OB 8)
Gottes Sohn ist kommen (BWV 600-OB 2)
Lobt Gott, ihr Christen, allzugleich
 (BWV 609-OB 11) (36020)
In dir ist Freude (BWV 615-OB 17)
Christ du Lamm Gottes (BWV 619-OB 21)
O Lamm Gottes unschuldig (BWV 618-OB 20) (36021)
Christ lag in Todesbanden (BWV 625-OB 27)
Erstanden ist der heil'ge Christ (BWV 628-OB 30)
Heut' triumphieret Gottes Sohn (BWV 630-OB 32)
Liebster Jesu, wir sind hier (BWV 633-OB 35)
Es ist das Heil uns kommen her
 (BWV 638-OB 39) (36022)

H. Walcha (6ss)   *PV. 36020/2*

Vater unser in Himmelreich (BWV 636-OB 39)
Gelobet seist du, Jesu Christ (BWV 604-OB 6)
Hilf Gott, dass mir's gelinge (BWV 624-OB 26)
Heut' triumphieret Gottes Sohn (BWV 630-OB 32)
Wenn wir in höchsten Nöten sein
 (BWV 641-OB 42) (7044)
Ich ruf' zu dir (BWV 639-OB 40)
Herr Jesu Christ, dich zu uns wend'
 (BWV 632-OB 34)
Wer nur den lieben Gott lässt walten
 (BWV 642-OB 43)
O Lamm Gottes unschuldig (BWV 618-OB 20)
 (7045)

G. Krarup (4ss)   *G.Z 7044/5*

COLLECTIONS (assorted)

(6) SCHÜBLER PRELUDES (BWV 645/50)
Fuga sopra il Magnificat (BWV 733)
Vom Himmel hoch (BWV 700)
Nun freut euch (BWV 734)
An Wasserflüssen Babylon (BWV 653b)
Valet will ich dir geben (BWV 736)
☆ H. Walcha   # *AmD.DL 9569*
(Schübler Preludes on the St. Jakobikirche Organ;
others on the Schnitger Organ, Cappel)

(6) SCHÜBLER PRELUDES (BWV 645/50)
An Wasserflüssen Babylon (BWV 653b)
Ein' feste Burg (BWV 720)

C. Weinrich   # *MGM.E 99*
    (♭ set K 99)

Es ist das Heil uns kommen her (BWV 638-OB39)
Vater unser im Himmelreich (BWV 636-OB 37)
O Mensch, bewein' dein' Sünde gross
 (BWV 622-OB 24)
Heut' triumphieret Gottes Sohn (BWV 630-OB 32)
Wenn wir in höchsten Nöten sein (BWV 641-OB 42)
In dir ist Freude (BWV 615-OB 17)
Allein Gott in der Höh' sei Ehr! (BWV 663-E 13)
Von Gott will ich nicht lassen (BWV 658-E 8)
Schmücke dich, O liebe Seele (BWV 654-E 4)

F. Heitmann (2ss)   # *T.LS 6018*

Kyrie, Gott heiliger Geist (BWV 671)
Kommst du nun, Jesu (BWV 650)
Nun komm', der Heiden Heiland (BWV 599-OB 1)
Nun freut' euch, lieben Christen g'mein (BWV 734)

C. Crozier   # *Ken. 2551*
(Passacaglia & Fugue)

Nun komm' der Heiden Heiland (BWV 599-OB 1)
(Das) Alte Jahr vergangen ist (BWV 614-OB 16)
Vater unser im Himmelreich (BWV 683-CU)
Leibster Jesu, wir sind hier (BWV 706, I)
Herzlich tut mich verlangen (BWV 727)
Erstanden ist der heil'ge Christ (BWV 628-OB 30)

F. Viderø (2ss)   *FV.VME 1502*

(Das) Alte Jahr vergangen ist (BWV 614-OB 16) (1s)
Nun freut euch, lieber Christen, g'mein (BWV 734) (⅓s)
In dulci jubilo (unspec. setting)

G. Jones   *G.EG 7643*

Nun komm' der Heiden Heiland (BWV 599-OB 1)
Nun freut euch (BWV 734)
Kommst du nun . . . (BWV 650)

— ARR. ORCH. Castro
Vienna State Op.—Krueger # *NRI.103*
(W.T.C. & Pastorale)

□ See also Collections, *above.*

Ach, was ist doch unser Leben (BWV 743)
Christus, der uns selig macht (unspec.)
Vater unser im Himmelreich (unspec.)
— ARR. VLC. & PF. Kodaly
J. Scholz & M. Schwalb # **Acad.ALP 305**
(Dohnányi: Sonata)

Ach, bleib' bei uns, Herr Jesu Christ
 (BWV 649-Sch. 5) □
Kommst du nun, Jesu, vom Himmel herunter
 (BWV 650-Sch. 6) □
 ☆ E. Power Biggs (1s. each) **C.DX 1831**

Allein Gott in der Höh' sei Ehr' (unspec. setting)
 ☆ H. J. Hooper (in # Bib.TA 202)

Herzlich tut mich verlangen (BWV 727) □
 N. O. Raasted # *Mer.MG 15036*
 (below).
 H. Jensen (Felix. Ø 64)

Ich ruf' zu dir, Herr Jesu Christ (BWV 639-OB 40)□
 G. Jones **G.C 7898**
 (Prelude & Fugue, D major, s.I)
— ARR. PF. Busoni
 D. Lipatti **C.LX 1427**
 (below) (GQX 11500: LFX 992: LZX 263)
 R. Trouard # *Od.OD 1002*
 (below & Haydn)

In dir ist Freude (BWV 615-OB 17) □
 ☆ H. J. Hooper (in # Bib.TA 202)

In dulci jubilo (BWV 608-OB 10; & BWV 729)
 E. P. Biggs in # **AmC.ML 4435**

In dulci jubilo (BWV 608-OB 10)
 F. Heitmann in † # **T.LSK 7016**

In dulci jubilo (BWV 751)
 ☆ N. O. Raasted # *Mer.MG 15036*
 (above; Buxtehude & Handel)

Liebster Jesu, wir sind hier (BWV 731)
— ARR. PF. Rummel
 P. Duvauchelle *Lum. 2.08.017*
 (Concerto, F minor, s.I)

Lobt Gott, ihr Christen, allzugleich
 (BWV 609-OB 11) □
 F. Heitmann in † # **T.LSK 7016**

Meine Seele erhebt den Herren
 (BWV 648-Sch. 4) □
Wer nur den lieben Gott lässt walten
 (BWV 647-Sch. 3) □
 ☆ E. Power Biggs **C.DX 1810**
 (1s. each) (DWX 5072)

Nun freut euch, lieben Christen, g'mein
 (BWV 734) □
 E. P. Biggs in # **AmC.ML 4435**

— ARR. PF. Busoni
 R. Trouard # *Od.OD 1002*
 (above, below & Haydn)

Nun komm' der Heiden Heiland (BWV 659-E 9)
— ARR. PF. Busoni
 D. Lipatti **C.LX 1427**
 (GQX 11500: LFX 992: LZX 263)
 ☆ V. Horowitz (in # Vic.LM 1171: ♭ set WDM 1605)

— ARR. PF.
 W. Kempff **D.K 28223**
 (Fl. Sonata No. 2—Siciliano)

O Gott, du frommer Gott (Variations) (BWV 767)
R. Noehren   # Allo.AL 116
(below)

Sei gegrüsset, Jesu gütig (Variations) (BWV 768)
☆ H. Walcha   # AmD.DL 9615
(below)   *(Jakobikirche organ)*

Vom Himmel hoch (BWV 606-OB 8) □
F. Heitmann   in † # T.LSK 7016
H. Kahlhöfer   *Chr. 324A*
(⅓s.—Eccard: Vom Himmel hoch; & Praetorius)

Vom Himmel hoch (BWV 769)
(Canonische Veränderungen)
H. Walcha   PV. 1410
(Schnitger organ, Cappel)   *(# AmD.DL 9615)*
R. Noehren   # Allo.AL 116
(above)
F. Heitmann   in † # T.LSK 7016

Wachet auf! (BWV 645-Sch. 1)
— ARR. PF.   Busoni
R. Trouard   # Od.OD 1002
(above, below & Haydn)

— ARR. PF.   Kempff
☆ W. Kempff   (D.K 28224)

Wenn wir in höchsten Nöten sein (BWV 668-E 18)
(Vor deinen Thron . . .)
☆ F. Heitmann (in # T.LS 6017)

Wir glauben all' an einen Gott (BWV 680-CU 12)
— ARR. ORCH.   Stokowski
Sym. Orch.—Stokowski   in # Vic.LM 1176
(Suite No. 2, etc.)   *(♭ set WDM 1569)*

Wer nur den lieben Gott lässt walten
    (BWV 691-AMB)
K. Rapf (hpsi.)   in # Van.BG 510
(Clavier pieces & songs)

CONCERTOS after Vivaldi, et al.
No. 1, G major [1] (BWV 592)
— ARR. VLC., STR. ORCH. & HPSI.   Fasano
M. Amfitheatrov & Virtuosi di
    Roma   # B.AXTL 1004
(Tartini, Albinoni, A. Scarlatti)   *(# AmD.DL 9572)*
... **Adagio only**
R. Ellsasser   in # MGM.E 3005

No. 2, A minor (BWV 593)
C. Weinrich   # MGM.E 98
(Passacaglia & Fugue)   *(♭ set K 98)*

FANTASIAS
G major (BWV 571) *("Concerto")*
G. Krarup   G.Z 359

G major (BWV 572)
F. Heitmann   in † # T.LSK 7016
H. Walcha   Pol. 1017
(announced but perhaps not issued)

FANTASIAS & FUGUES
C minor (BWV 537)
H. Walcha   Pol. 1021
(Schnitger organ, Cappel)

G minor (BWV 542) □   1720
☆ H. J. Hooper (in # Bib.TA 202)

... **Fugue only** — ARR. STR. ORCH.   Münchinger
Stuttgart Cha.—Münchinger in # D.LXT 2668
(Beethoven, etc.)   *(# Lon.LLP 526)*
(Fugue, A minor on D.K 28597)

Fugue, F major, on the Magnificat
SEE: CHORALE-PRELUDES, COLLECTION

Fugue, G minor ("Little") (BWV 578) □
— ARR. ORCH.   Stokowski
Sym. Orch.—Stokowski   in # Vic.LM 1176
(Suite No. 2, Cantata excerpts, etc.)   *(♭ set WDM 1569)*

Passacaglia & Fugue, C minor (BWV 582) □
H. Walcha   # AmD.DL 9560
(Pastorale, etc.)
F. Asma   # Phi.N 00118L
(⅓s.—Cantata 147, excpt., & Mendelssohn, Rheinberger, etc.)
(also, 3ss, with Sonata 4, excpt., D.X 6137/8)
C. Weinrich   # MGM.E 98
(Concerto)   *(♭ set K 98)*
C. Crozier   in # Ken. 2551
(Chorale-Preludes)
☆ E. White (# Clc. 6037)

— ARR. ORCH.   Respighi
☆ San Francisco Sym.—Monteux # Vic.LM 149
(Brahms: Schicksalslied)

Pastorale, F major (BWV 590)
F. Heitmann   in † # T.LSK 7016
H. Walcha   Pol. 1018
    (in # AmD.DL 9560)
☆ E. White (# Clc. 6037)

— ARR. ORCH.   Gui
Vienna State Op.—Krueger   # NRI. 103
(W.T.C. & Chorales)

... **Aria only** — ARR. VLC. & ORCH.
P. Casals & Perpignan Fest. Orch. (in # AmC. set SL 168,
"inscription" disc)

PRELUDES & FUGUES
COLLECTION: VOLUME I—
    BWV 532, 534, 535, 536, 541, 543, 544, 545,
    546, 547, 552
    H. Walcha   # AmD. set DX 117

---

(8) "Short" Preludes & Fugues (BWV 553/60)
E. White (? n.v.)   # Mer.MG 15027

No. 3, E minor (BWV 555)
No. 6, G minor (BWV 558)
F. Viderø   FV.VME 1501

No. 3, E minor
— ARR. ORCH.   Stokowski
☆ Philadelphia—Stokowski (in ♭ set WCT 69)

No. 4, F major
G. Krarup   G.Z 7046
(Sonata No. 4, s.1)

A major (BWV 536) □
H. Walcha   Pol. 1015
(Schnitger organ, Cappel)   *(in # AmD. set DX 117)*

A minor (BWV 543) □
H. Walcha   PV. 1424
(Schnitger organ, Cappel)   *(in # AmD. set DX 117)*
F. Heitmann   in † # T.LSK 7010/1

B minor (BWV 544) □
G. Jones   ♮ G.C 7858/9
(4ss) *(Steinkirchen organ)*
H. Walcha   in # AmD. set DX 117
(St. Jakobikirche organ)

□ See also Collections, *above*.
[1] After a Concerto by Johann Ernst of Saxe-Weimar (1696-1715)

PRELUDES & FUGUES (*continued*)

C major   (BWV 545)
H. Walcha   **Pol. 1020**
(Schnitger organ, Cappel)   (in ♯ AmD. set DX 117)

C major   (BWV 547) □
☆ H. Walcha   in ♯ **AmD. set DX 117**
(St. Jakobikirche organ)

C minor   (BWV 546) □
G. Jones   *G.EG 7657/8*
(4ss) (Steinkirchen organ)
H. Walcha   in ♯ **AmD. set DX 117**
(Schnitger organ, Cappel)

D major   (BWV 532) □
G. Jones   ♮ *G.C 7898/9*
(3ss—*Ich ruf' zu dir*) (Steinkirchen organ)
H. Walcha   in ♯ **AmD. set DX 117**
(Schnitger organ, Cappel)

E minor   (BWV 533)
G. Jones   *G.EG 7597*
(2ss) (Steinkirchen organ)

E minor   (BWV 548) □
☆ F. Germani   ♯ *G.DLP 1002*
(*Franck : Choral No. 3*)

E flat major   ("*St. Anne*")   (BWV 552)
H. Walcha   in ♯ **AmD. set DX 117**
(St. Jakobikirche organ) (also in Clavierübung set, *ante*)

— ARR. PF.   Busoni
G. Gorini   (4ss)   **P.AB 30021/2**

F minor   (BWV 534)
H. Walcha   **Pol. 1022**
(Schnitger organ, Cappel)   (in ♯ AmD. set DX 117)

G major   (BWV 541)
H. Walcha   **Pol. 1016**
(Schnitger organ, Cappel)   (in ♯ AmD. set DX 117)

G minor   (BWV 535)
H. Walcha   **Pol. 1019**
(Schnitger organ, Cappel)   (in ♯ AmD. set DX 117)

... **Prelude only**   — ARR. PF. Siloti
G. Novães   in ♯ **AmVox.PL 7500**
(*Brahms, etc.*)

---

(6) SONATAS   (BWV 525-530)   1727
COMPLETE RECORDING
> No. 1, E flat major on ☆ PV. 1401
> No. 2, C minor on PV. 1409
> No. 3, D minor on Pol. 1013/4S
> No. 4, E minor on PV. 1423
> No. 5, C major not yet on Pol.
> No. 6, G major on ☆ PV. 1402

H. Walcha   (4ss)   ♯ **AmD. set DX 114**

No. 2, C minor   (BWV 526)
No. 5, C major   (BWV 529)
☆ R. Noehren   ♯ *EA.ALY 61*
                                    (♯ *CID.* & *Ome.LX 33005*)

No. 4, E minor   (BWV 528)
G. Krarup   ♮ *G.Z 7046/7*
(3ss—"*Short*" Prelude & Fugue, F major)

... **Andante only**
F. Asma   **D.XP 6138**
(*Passacaglia & Fugue, C minor, s.3*)

□ See also collections, *above.*

TOCCATAS & FUGUES

C major (Toccata, Adagio & Fugue) (BWV 564) □
F. Asma   in ♯ **Phi.N 00147L**
(*Handel, Mendelssohn, etc.*) (Amsterdam Oude Kerk organ)

... **Adagio only**   — ARR. VLC. & PF.
☆ P. Casals (in ♯ Vic.LCT 1050: ♭ *set WCT 72*)

D minor   (BWV 565) □
H. Walcha   **PV. 1411**
(2ss) (St. Jakobikirche organ, Lübeck)
F. Heitmann   in † ♯ *T.LSK 7010/1*
> ☆ F. Germani (♭ *G.7BF 1002*)
> H. J. Hooper (in ♯ Bib.TA 202)
— ARR. ORCH.   Melichar
Brussels Radio—André   **T.E 3924**
— ARR. ORCH.   Stokowski
> ☆ Orch.—Stokowski (♭ *G.7RF 136*; ♭ *Vic. 49-0263*▽)
— ARR. BAND
French Reserve—Beaufort   **V♯** *Sat.MSA 5001*
(*Beethoven*)

D minor   ("*Dorian*")   (BWV 538)
F. Germani   ♮ *G.C 7918/9*
(4ss)   (♭ *7P 126/7*)
H. Walcha   **PV. 1412**
(Schnitger organ, Cappel)

F major   (BWV 540)
... **Toccata only**
J. Ropek   ♮ **U.H 24001/2**
(3ss—*Hek : Pastorella*)

C. CHAMBER MUSIC

SONATAS, vln. unacc.   (BWV 1001/6)
COMPLETE RECORDING
J. Figueroa   ♯ **NRI. 408/11**
(Nos. 1 & 3 on 408; No. 2 on 409; No. 4 on 410; Nos. 5 & 6
on 411)

No. 1, G minor
O. Renardy   ♯ *D.LM 4542*
                                          (♯ *Lon.LPS 423*)
Y. Menuhin   **JpV.SD 3034/5**
... **Fugue only** — ARR. GUITAR
☆ A. Segovia   in ♯ *MGM.E 123*
... **Siciliano only**   — ARR. GUITAR
A. Segovia   († Segovia program)   in ♯ AmD.DL 9647

No. 2, B minor (Partita No. 1)
... **Bourrée** — ARR. GUITAR   Segovia
A. Segovia   in ♯ **B.AXTL 1010**
(† Segovia Concert)   (♯ AmD.DL 9638)

No. 4, D minor (Partita No. 2)
E. Telmanyi   ♮ **Tono. A 170/173**
(8ss)   (Played with special "Bach bow")

... **Sarabande only**
Y. Menuhin   **JpV.SD 3041**
(*below*)

... **Chaconne only**   — ARR. PF.   Busoni
R. Gianoli   ♯ **West.WL 5101**
(*Fantasia*)
☆ L. Bertolini   ♯ **Csm.CLPS 1024**
(*Chopin*)

— — ARR. GUITAR   Segovia   ☆ A. Segovia (in ♯ *MGM.E 123*)

No. 5, C major
... **Adagio & Fugue only**
V. Prihoda   **Pol. 68282/3**
(4ss)

No. 6, E major (Partita No. 3)
Y. Menuhin   **JpV.SD 3039/41**
(5ss—*above*)

... **Prelude only**   ☆ Y. Menuhin (♭ *G.7R 112*)

11

"SONATA", A minor (Suite) fl. unacc.
(BWV 1013)
☆ J. P. Rampal   # Clc. 6032
(Beethoven, Honegger, Hindemith, etc.)

SONATAS, flute & clavier
THE SIX, COMPLETE
J. Baker & S. Marlowe (hpsi.) # B.AXTL 1015/6
(4ss)   (# AmD. set DX 113)

No. 2, E flat
... Siciliana — ARR. PF. Kempff
W. Kempff   D.K 28223
(Nun komm' der Heiden Heiland)
☆ D. Lipatti (C.LF 284: GQ 7248)

SONATAS, viola da gamba & clavier (BWV 1027/9)
No. 1, G major   **No. 2, D major**
No. 3, G minor
☆ D. Soyer (vlc.), H. Chassid (hpsi.)
                                    # Nix.CLP 54

No. 1, G major
A. Wenzinger & F. Neumeyer (hpsi.) PV. 2431

No. 3, G minor . . . Adagio
☆ T. Rosenberg & A. Andersen (hpsi.) G.C 4166
(Brandenburg Concerto, No. 6, s.5)

SONATAS, vln. & clavier   (BWV 1014/9)
COLLECTION (Nos. 1-6)
Y. Menuhin & L. Kentner (pf.)
                          # Vic.LHMV 1016/7
(4ss) (For individual issue nos, *see below*; No. 1 is ☆)

No. 2, A major   ♮ G.DB 9638/9
No. 3, E major   G.DB 21435/7
No. 4, C minor   ♮ G.DB 9761/2

C minor (BWV 1024) (Doubtful)
P. Rybar, hpsi. & vlc.   # CHS. G 15
(below)

SONATAS, two vlns. & continuo
C major   (BWV 1037)
P. Rybar & A. Fietz, T. Sack (hpsi.),
& vlc.   # CHS.G 15
(above; & Concertos)

SUITES, vlc. unacc. (BWV 1007/12)
No. 1, G major
... Prelude — ARR. GUITAR Segovia
A. Segovia († Segovia Recital, in # B.AXTL 1005;
AmD.DL 9633)

No. 2, D minor — ARR. VIOLA
L. Fuchs (No. 6)   # AmD.DL 9544

... **Courante** — ARR. GUITAR
☆ A. Segovia (in # MGM.E 123)

No. 3, C major
E. Mainardi   # D.LX 3069
                                  (Lon.LPS 403)

J. Starker (No. 6)   # Nix. & Per.SPLP 543

... **Courante** — ARR. GUITAR
A. Segovia (in † Segovia Concert, # B.AXTL 1010;
AmD.DL 9638)

No. 4, E flat major
E. Mainardi   # D.LXT 2673
                                  (# Lon.LLP 404)

No. 5, C minor
A. Vlasov (6ss)   ♮ U.H 23998/24000

No. 6, D major
J. Starker (No. 3)   # Nix. & Per.SPLP 543

— ARR. VIOLA
L. Fuchs (No. 2)   # AmD.DL 9544

... **Gavottes** — ARR. GUITAR Segovia
A. Segovia († Segovia recital in # B.AXTL 1005;
AmD.DL 9633)

D. ORCHESTRAL

BRANDENBURG CONCERTOS (BWV 1046/51)
COMPLETE RECORDINGS
London Baroque Ens.—
                Haas # West. set WAL 309
(6ss) (Nos. 1 & 6 also on # WL 5172; Nos. 2 & 4 on
WL 5113; Nos. 3 & 5 on # WL 5174) [No. 5 with
R. Veyron-Lacroix (hpsi.)]

Berlin Radio Cha.—Haarth # Sat.LDG 8006/8
& [No. 2]—Rucht
(5ss—Mozart: Serenade K525)

☆ Prades Festival—Casals (# C.FCX 115/7)

No. 1, F major
Danish Radio Cha.—Wöldike ♮ G.DB 20140/2
(5ss—W.T.C.—Prelude & Fugue, No. 21)

... Minuet — ARR. PF. P. Browne (Pax.PRT 484)

No. 2, F major
Berlin Sym.—Ludwig   # Roy. 1367
(Vln. Concerto, E major)

No. 4, G major
Anon. orch.   in # Roy. 1259

No. 5, D major
E. Müller (hpsi.), J. Bopp, R. Felicani,
Basle Cha. Ens.—Wenzinger   ♮ PV. 2422/3
(4ss)
Berlin Sym.—List   # Roy. 1372
(No. 6)

No. 6, B flat major
Berlin Sym.—List   # Roy. 1372
(No. 5)
☆ Copenhagen Palace Chapel Cha.—Wöldike
                                  G.C 4164/6
(Gamba Sonata, No. 3—Adagio)
☆ Vienna Konzerthaus—Merten (Eur.TAI 732/3)

CONCERTOS, clavier & orch.
A major (BWV 1055)
K. Rapf (hpsi.) & Vienna Cha.
Orch.   # Van.BG 509
(below)
H. Schnauffer (hpsi.) & Munich Collegium
Musicum — Treiber   # Mer.MG 15033
(Handel: Suite No. 3)
H. Elsner (hpsi.) & Stuttgart Pro
Musica—R. Reinhardt   # EVox. 140
(below)   (# AmVox.PL 7260; PaV.VP 140)

D major (BWV 1054)
(From Vln. Concerto, BWV 1042)
K. Rapf (hpsi.) & Vienna Cha.
Orch.   # Van.BG 509
(above)
I. Nef (hpsi.) & Cha. Ens.—
Colombo   # OL.LD 28
(below)
M. v. d. Lyck (hpsi.) & Stuttgart Ton-Studio—
Michael   # Nix.PLP 547
(below)   (# Per.SPLP 547)

= Long-playing, 33⅓ r.p.m.   ♭ = 45 r.p.m.   ♮ = Auto. couplings, 78 r.p.m.

D minor (BWV 1052)
L. Foss (pf.) & Zimbler Sinfonietta
           ♯ **B.AXTL 1012**
(1½ss—*Concerto, F minor*)   (♯ AmD.DL 9601)

F minor (BWV 1056)
H. Elsner (hpsi.) & Stuttgart Pro Musica—
R. Reinhardt   ♯ **EVox. 140**
(*above & below*)   (♯ AmVox.PL 7260; PaV.VP 140)
I. Nef (hpsi.) & Cha. Ens.—Colombo
           ♯ **OL.LD 28**
(*above*)
P. Duvauchelle (pf.) & Paris Cha. Orch.
           ♯ *Lum.LD 103*
(*Cimarosa: Concerto*)
(also on ♮*Lum. 2.08.017/8 with Ch.-Prelude—Liebster
Jesu . . .*)
L. Foss (pf.) & Zimbler Sinfonietta
           ♯ **B.AXTL 1012**
(⅓s.—*Concerto, D minor*)   (♯ AmD.DL 9601)

G minor (BWV 1058)
(from Vln. Concerto, BWV 1041)
H. Elsner (hpsi.) & Stuttgart Pro Musica—
R. Reinhardt   ♯ **EVox. 140**
(*above*)   (♯ AmVox.PL 7260; PaV.VP 140)

CONCERTOS, 2 claviers & orch.
C major (BWV 1061)
  ☆ R. Gerlin & M. Charbonnier (hpsis.) & str. orch.—
    Sachs (in † ♯ *AS. 2503LD*)

CONCERTOS, 3 claviers & orch.
C major (BWV 1064)
  ☆ E. Fischer, D. Matthews, R. Smith (pfs.) &
    Philharmonia Orch.   ♯ **Vic.LHMV 1004**
(*Mozart*)   (♭ set WHMV 1004)
  ☆ C. Führmann, B. Seidlhofer, E. Heiller (hpsis.) &
    Vienna Cha. Orch.—A. Heiller (♯ *Era.LDE 2001*)
  G. Kuhn, G. Lasson, C. Bèche (pfs.) & Pro Musica—
    Goldschmidt (♯ *Pol. 540002*)

D minor (BWV 1063)
R., G., & J. Casadesus (pfs.) & N.Y.P.S.O.—
Mitropoulos   ♯ *AmC.ML 2196*
(*French Suite No. 6*)
Anon. pianists & Berlin Radio—Schultz [2]
           ♯ *Rgt. 5020*

CONCERTOS, 4 claviers & orch.
A minor (BWV 1065)
(After Vivaldi's Op. 3, No. 10, *q.v.*) (Ed. Fasano)
Santoliquido, Zedda-Paolone, Lessona &
Bagnoli (pfs.) & Rome Coll. Mus.—Fasano
           P.BB 25293/4
(3ss—*Respighi: Suite No. 3—Siciliana*)
  ☆ As above & K. Rapf (♯ *Era.LDE 2001*)
  As above & G. Astorg (♯ *Pol. 540002*)

CONCERTOS, vln. & orch.
A minor (BWV 1041)
S. Goldberg & Philharmonia—Süsskind
(G. Jones, hpsi.) (4ss)   ♮ **P.SW 8140/1**
  ☆ J. Bernstein & Concert Hall Ens. (♯ Clc. 6065)

E major (BWV 1042)
T. Varga & Berlin Phil.—F. Lehmann
(4ss)   ♮ **PV. 2429/30**
L. Stevens & Berlin Sym.—Ludwig ♯ **Roy. 1367**
(*Brandenburg Concerto No. 2*)
  ☆ S. Goldberg & Philharmonia—Süsskind
(*Haydn*)   ♯ **Od.ODX 104**

G minor (BWV 1056)
(restored from clav. concerto, F minor)
P. Rybar & Winterthur Sym.—Dahinden
           ♯ **CHS.G 15**
(*Vln. & ob. Concerto, & Sonatas*)

CONCERTO, 2 vlns. & orch.
D minor (BWV 1043)
H. Krebbers, T. Olof & Residentie—
v. Otterloo   ♯ **Phi.A 00140L**
(*Beethoven: Romances*)
  ☆ I. Stern, A. Schneider & Prades Festival—
Casals   ♯ **C.FCX 155**
(*below*)   (QCX 155)

CONCERTO, vln. & oboe & orch.
C minor (BWV 1060)
[1] P. Rybar, E. Parolari & Winterthur Sym.—
Dahinden   ♯ **CHS.G 15**
(*Vln. Concerto, & Sonatas*)
  ☆ I. Stern, M. Tabuteau, Prades Festival—
Casals   ♯ **C.FCX 155**
(*above*)   (QCX 155)

CONCERTO, clavier, 2 flutes & orch.
F major (BWV 1057)
(originally Brandenburg Concerto No. 4, *q.v.*)
L. Salter (hpsi.), S. & L. Taylor (recorders),
London Baroque Orch.—Haas ♮ **P.SW 8147/8**
(4ss)
M. v. d. Lyck & Stuttgart Ton-Studio—
Michael   ♯ **Nix.PLP 547**
(*above*)   (♯ Per.SPLP 547)

SUITES (BWV 1066/9)

No. 1, C major	No. 2, B minor
No. 3, D major	No. 4, D major

COMPLETE RECORDING
Hewitt Cha. Orch.   ♯ *DFr. 22/3*
(1s. each)

No. 1, C major; No. 4, D major
  ☆ Boston Sym.—Koussevitzky ♯ **G.FALP 183**

No. 2, B minor   fl. & str.
J. Baker & Sym. Orch.—Stokowski
           ♯ **Vic.LM 1176**
(*Transcriptions*)   (♭ set WDM 1569)

No. 3, D major
... **Air only**
F. Akos (vln.) & Berlin Municipal Op. Ens.
           T.A 11159
(*Handel: Serse—Largo*)   (T.TEL 585)
Pro Arte—Marrow   ♯ *MGM.E 132*
(*Handel: Water Music*)   (♭ set K 132)
  ☆ Boston Sym.—Koussevitzky (♭ Vic. 17-0419 in WCT 71)
  N.B.C.—Toscanini (♭ G.7RF 196), etc.
— ARR. ORG.   H. J. Hooper (in ♯ Bib.TA 202), etc.
— ARR. VLN. & PF.
  M. Wilk & F. Kramer (in ♯ MTR.MLP 1002)
  ☆ Y. Menuhin & M. Gazelle (♭ G.7R 112)
— ARR. VLC. & PF.
  G. Cassadò & O. Schulhof (in ♯ MSL.MW 45)

E. MISCELLANEOUS
(Die) KUNST DER FUGE (Art of Fugue)
(BWV 1080)   1749/50
... **Nos. 4, 11, 19**
  ☆ F. Heitmann (organ)   ♯ *T.LS 6017*
(*Wenn wir in höchsten Nöten . . .*)

(Ein) MUSIKALISCHES OPFER (BWV 1079)
(*A Musical Offering*)
COMPLETE RECORDING — ARR. Oubradous
  ☆ O. L. Ens.—Oubradous (♯ OL.LD 25)

Ricercari à 6 & à 3;
Sonata, C minor
  ☆ Prades Festival Soloists (♯ C.FCX 117)

(*continued on next page*)

[1] Ed. Schneider—D minor.
[2] Later announcements give Kondrashin as the conductor.

MUSIKALISCHES OPFER (continued)

Ricercare à sei voci
Stuttgart Cha.—Münchinger   in # **D.LXT 2668**
(Beethoven; & Fugues)   (D.K 28598; # Lon.LLP 526)

The Wise Virgins   Ballet Suite — ARR. Walton
No. 5 : Cantata No. 208, No. 9—Sheep may safely graze
Philharmonia—Weldon   **C.DB 3164**

MISCELLANEOUS Unidentified

Bourrée (unspec.) — ARR. HARP
V. Morgan   in # **ML. 7016**

Bourrée (unspec.) — ARR. HARP
Harpo Marx (in ♮ Vic.P 329 : # LPM 27)

"Bach, his story & his music"
Narration & orch.   # AmVox.VL 2500
(♮ set 250)

II. VOCAL

CHURCH CANTATAS

COLLECTED EXCERPTS

Sacred Arias : Aria Group—Schiede
SEE : Cantatas 7, 33, 84, 97, 101, 151 (# MGM.E 89 :
♭ K 89)
SEE : Cantatas 68, 99, 113, 157, 159, 185 (# MGM.E 115 :
♭ K 115)

No. 4, Christ lag in Todesbanden T, B, cho., orch.
H. Krebs, D. Fischer-Dieskau, Frankfurt
Hochschule Cho. & Bach Festival Orch.—
Lehmann   **PV. 2420/1**
(4ss)   (2ss, # AmD.DL 7523)

A. Uhl, H. Braun, Cho. & Orch.—Prohaska
Van.BG 511
(No. 140)   (# Nix.BLP 311)

... No. 4, Jesus Christus, Gottes Sohn T
— — ARR. ORCH. Stokowski
Sym. Orch.—Stokowski   in # **Vic.LM 1176**
(♭ set WDM 1569)

No. 6, Bleib' bei uns A, T, Bs, Cho., orch.
H. Plümacher, W. Hohmann, B. Müller,
Stuttgart Cho. Soc. & Bach Orch.—
Grischkat   # **Ren.X 34**
(No. 19)

No. 7, Christ unser Herr zum Jordan kam
... No. 6, Menschen glaubt A
M. Tobias   in # **MGM.E 89**

No. 9, Es ist das Heil uns kommen her
S, A, T, B, cho. & orch.
C. F. Luz, E. Dräger, C. Stemann, B. Müller,
Stuttgart Cho. Soc. & Bach Orch.—
Grischkat   # **Ren.X 37**
(No. 137)   (# Nix.PLP 237; # Clc. 6105)

No. 11, Lobet Gott in seinen Reichen
S, A, T, B & cho.
(Himmelfahrtsoratorium)
C. F. Luz, R. Michaelis, W. Hohmann, B. Müller
& Swabian Cho. Soc. & Stuttgart Bach
Orch.—Grischkat   # **Lyr.LL 34**

No. 19, Es erhob sich ein Streit S, T, Bs, cho. & orch.
A. Giebel, C. Stemann, B. Müller, Stuttgart
Cho. Soc. & Ton-Studio Orch.—Grischkat
Ren.X 34
(No. 6)

No. 21, Ich hatte viel Bekümmerniss 1714
... No. 3, Seufzer, Tränen, Kummer, Not S
E. Steber (Eng)   # **AmC.ML 4521**
(No. 68, excpt.; & Messiah, Creation, Elijah)

No. 22, Jesus nahm zu sich die Zwölfe
... No. 5, Ertöt uns durch dein' Güte
— — ARR. PF. Ching
J. Ching   **Argo.R 1009**
(Cantata 147, No. 10)

No. 29, Wir danken dir, Gott
... No. 1, Sinfonia
E. P. Biggs (org.) & Columbia Cha. Orch.—
Burgin   in # **AmC.ML 4435**

— — ARR. PF. Saint-Saëns
R. Trouard   **Od. 123917**
(Haydn : Sonata 23, s.3)   (in # Od.OD 1002)

No. 31, Der Himmel lacht S, T, B, Cho., orch.
A. Felbermeyer, W. Kmentt, W. Berry, Academy
Cho. & Vienna Cha. Orch.—Prohaska
Van.BG 512
(Chorales)

No. 32, Liebster Jesu mein Verlangen S, B, Cho.
A. Giebel, B. Müller, Stuttgart Pro Musica
Cho. & orch.—R. Reinhardt
AmVox.PL 7340
(No. 57)   (# BàM.LD 04)
M. Laszlo, A. Poell, Vienna Academy Cho. &
St. Op. Orch.—Scherchen # **West.WL 5122**
(No. 140)

No. 33, Allein zu dir, Herr Jesu Christ
... No. 3, Wie furchtsam wankten meine Schritte A
M. Tobias   in # **MGM.E 89**

No. 51, Jauchzet Gott in allen Landen S & orch.
M. Guilleaume & Stuttgart Bach Orch.—
Grischkat   # **Ren.X 35**
(No. 189)   (# Clc. 6096; # Nix.PLP 235)

No. 53, Schlage doch, gewünschte Stunde A & orch.
H. Hennecke & Basle Cha. Ens.—Wenzinger
PV. 2426
(Cantata 200)   (# AmD.DL 9619)

No. 56, Ich will den Kreuzstab gerne tragen
B, cho., orch.
D. Fischer-Dieskau, Berlin Motet Cho. & Cha.
Orch.—Ristenpart   **PV. 2432/3S**
(in # AmD.DL 9595)

No. 57, Selig ist der Mann S, B, cho., orch.
A. Giebel, B. Müller, Stuttgart Pro Musica Cho.
& Orch.—R. Reinhardt # **AmVox.PL 7340**
(No. 32)   (# BàM.LD 04)

... No. 8, Richte dich, Liebster (Melody : Lobe den Herrn)
Cho.—Deniau (org. acc.) (Sat. 1002)

No. 63, Christen, ätzet diesen Tag
S, A, T, B, cho., orch.
M. Opawsky, H. Rössl-Majdan, W. Kmentt,
H. Hermann & Vienna Cha. Cho. & State
Op. Orch.—Gielen   # **Van.BG 518**

No. 65, Sie werden aus Saba alle kommen 1724
... Nos. 1, 2, 6, 7 only
☆ M. Meili (T), Basle Cha. Cho. († V# AS.1801LD)

No. 68, Also hat Gott die Welt geliebt
... No. 2, Mein gläubiges Herze S
(My heart ever faithful)
E. Steber (Eng)   # **AmC.ML 4521**
(No. 21, excpt.; & Messiah, Creation, Elijah)
J. Carlton   in # **MGM.E 115**

No. 78, Jesu, der du meine Seele
☆ Soloists, Reinhart & Winterthur Chos. & orch.—
Reinhart (# Clc. 6053)

= Long-playing, 33⅓ r.p.m.   ♭ = 45 r.p.m.   ♮ = Auto. couplings, 78 r.p.m.

14

No. 79, Nun danket alle Gott
... No. 3 (Chorale)
E. P. Biggs (org.)   in ♯ AmC.ML 4435

No. 80, Ein feste Burg   S, A, T, B, cho., orch.
M. Weiss-Osborn, H. Rössl-Majdan, K. Equiluz,
W. Berry, Akademie cho. & Vienna Cha.
Orch.—Prohaska   ♯ Van.BG 508
(♯ Nix.BLP 308)

No. 82, Ich habe genug   B & orch.
D. Fischer-Dieskau & Cha. Orch.—Ristenpart
♯ AmD.DL 9595
(No. 56)

... No. 2, Ich habe genug (recit.)
... No. 3, Schlummert ein (aria)
—— VERSION in the Anna Magdalena Bach book
J. Eby (Bs), M. Hauptmann (hpsi.) & vlc.
♯ BS.LX 7001
(Songs, & Cantata 158)   (o.n. ♯ Ren.X 34)
M. Weis-Osborn (S), K. Rapf (hpsi.)
& vlc.   in ♯ Van.BG 510

No. 84, Ich bin vergnügt   S & cho.
M. Laszlo, Vienna Academy Cho. & State Op.
Orch.—Scherchen   ♯ West.WL 5125
(No. 106)

... No. 3, Ich esse mit Freuden mein weniges Brot   S
J. Carlton   in ♯ MGM.E 89

No. 97, In allen meinen Thaten
... No. 2, Nichts ist es spät und frühe   Bs
N. Farrow   in ♯ MGM.E 89

No. 99, Was Gott tut, das ist wohlgetan
... No. 5, Wenn des Kreuzes Bitterkeiten   S, A
J. Carlton, M. Tobias   in ♯ MGM.E 115

No. 101, Nimm von uns, Herr, du treuer Gott
... No. 2, Handle nicht nach deinen Rechten   T
R. Harmon   in ♯ MGM.E 89

No. 106, Gottes Zeit ist die allerbeste Zeit
A, Bs, Cho.
H. Rössl-Majdan, A. Poell, Vienna Academy
Cho. & State Op. Orch.—Scherchen
♯ West.WL 5125
(No. 84)
☆ Y. Melchior, L. Noguéra, cho. & orch.—Martin
(♯ Pat.DT 1001)
M. Torrend, P. Sandoz, Mulhouse Cho. & Inst. Ens.—
Meyer (♯ Pol. 545002)

No. 112, Der Herr ist mein getreuer Hirt
S, A, T, B, cho., orch.
C. Fassbender-Luz, H. Plümacher, C. Stemann,
B. Müller, Swabian Cho. Soc. & Stuttgart
Bach Orch.—Grischkat   ♯ Ren.X 36
(No. 185)   (♯ Nix.PLP 236; ♯ Clc. 6091)

No. 113, Herr Jesu Christ, du höchstes Gut
... No. 5, Jesus nimmt die Sünder an   T
R. Harmon   in ♯ MGM.E 115

No. 122, Das neugebor'ne Kindelein S, A, T, B, cho.
No. 133, Ich freue mich in dir   S, A, T, B, cho.
M. Opawsky, H. Rössl-Majdan, W. Kmentt,
H. Hermann & Vienna Academy Cha. Cho. &
State Op. Orch.—Gielen   ♯ Van.BG 523

No. 129, Gelobet sei der Herr
... No. 5, Dem wir das Heilig itzt
E. P. Biggs (org.) & Columbia Cha. Orch.—
Burgin   in ♯ AmC.ML 4435

No. 137, Lobe den Herren   S, A, T, B, cho., orch.
(Rathswahlkantate)
C. F. Luz, H. Plümacher, C. Stemann, B. Müller,
Stuttgart Bach Orch.—Grischkat ♯ Ren. X37
(No. 9)   (♯ Nix.PLP 237; ♯ Clc. 6105)

No. 140, Wachet auf!   S, T, Bs, cho.
M. Laszlo, W. Kmentt, A. Poell, Vienna
Academy Cho. & State Op. Orch.—
Scherchen   ♯ West.WL 5122
(No. 32)
A. Felbermeyer, A. Uhl, H. Braun, Cho. &
orch.—Prohaska   ♯ Van.BG 511
(No. 4)   (♯ Nix.BLP 311)

No. 142, Uns ist ein Kind geboren   A, T, B, cho.
... No. 1, Concerto; No. 8, Halleluja (ARR.)
E. P. Biggs (org.) & Columbia Cha. Orch.—
Burgin   in ♯ AmC.ML 4435

No. 146, Wir müssen durch viel Trübsal
S, A, T, B, cho.
... No. 7, Wie will ich mich freuen   T, B (ARR.)
E. P. Biggs (org.) & Columbia Cha. Orch.—
Burgin   in ♯ AmC.ML 4435

No. 147, Herz und Mund
... No. 10, Jesus bleibet meine Freude
St. Mark's Cha. Cho. & org. in ♯ D.LK 4039
(in English, arr. Sir H. Allen)   (♯ Lon.LLP 178)
Trapp Family Cho.—Wasner ♯ CHS.CHS 1101
—— ARR. ORCH. Stokowski
Sym. Orch.—Stokowski   ♭ G.7RF 244
(Cantata 208, excpt.)
(& in ♯ Vic.LM 1176: ♭ set WDM 1569)
—— ARR. ORGAN
H. Vollenweider   G.C 4192
(Wesley: Aria & Gavotte)
V. Fox (in ♯ AmC.ML 4401: ♭ set A 1008)
E. P. Biggs (in ♯ AmC.ML 4435)
F. Asma (in ♯ Phi.N 00118L)
—— ARR. PF. Hess   ☆ D. Lipatti (C.GQ 7248: LF 284)
—— ARR. PF.
J. Ching   Argo.R1009
(Cantata 22, No. 5)
O. Frugoni   in ♯ AmVox.PL 7700
(Beethoven, Schumann, etc.)
☆ W. Kempff (D.K 28224)
—— ARR. ORG. & PF. Mickelson & Smith in ♯ ISR. 10-003
—— ARR. HARMONICA
L. Adler   in ♯ CHS.CHS 1161
(Mozart, Vivaldi, etc.) (& with G. Moore (pf.), C.DB 3119)
—— ARR. BAND
L. Castellucci Band (in ♯ Cap.L 9011: ♭/♮ set CDF/CD 9011)

No. 151, Süsser Trost, mein Jesus kommt
... Süsser Trost   S & fl.
J. Carlton   in ♯ MGM.E 89

No. 152, Tritt auf die Glaubensbahn   S, B, orch.
☆ F. Wend, P. Sandoz & Ens.—Boncourt
♯ Pol. 545002
(No. 106)

No. 156, Ich steh' mit einem Fuss im Grabe
... Sinfonia — ARR. ORGAN   "Arioso"
H. J. Hooper   in ♯ Bib.TA 202
—— ARR. VLC. & PF.
J. Pacey & F. Kramer (in ♯ MTR.MLP 1003)
—— ARR. VLN. Franko ☆ J. Szigeti & orch. (C.GQX 11517)

No. 157, Ich lasse dich nicht
... No. 4, Ja, ja, ich halte Jesum feste   Bs
N. Farrow   in ♯ MGM.E 115

No. 158, Der Friede sei mit dir
S, Bs, cho., ob., vln., cont.
M. Hess, J. Eby, H. Gomberg, G. Osmolovsky,
hpsi., vlc. & N.Y. Bach Circle—
M. Hauptmann   ♯ BS.LX 7001
(Songs)   (o.n. ♯ Ren.X 34)

☆ = Re-issue of a recording to be found in WERM or Supplement I.

No. 159, Sehet, wir gehen hinauf 'gen Jerusalem
... No. 4, Es ist vollbracht
   N. Farrow   in ♯ *MGM.E 115*

No. 161, Komm, du süsse Todesstunde
   A, T, cho., orch.
   H. Rössl-Majdan, W. Kmentt, cho. & orch.—
   Prohaska   ♯ **Van.BG 513**
   (*No. 202*)

No. 170, Vergnügte Ruh', beliebte Seelenlust
   A, oboe d'amore, orch.
   E. Höngen, S. Hopf & Bavarian State Orch.—
   F. Lehmann   **PV. 2434/5S**

No. 182, Himmelskönig, sei willkommen
... No. 1, Sonata
   E. P. Biggs (org.) & Columbia Cha. Orch.—
   Burgin   in ♯ **AmC.ML 4435**

No. 185, Barmherziges Herze der ewigen Liebe
   S, A, T, B, cho., orch.
   C. Fassbender-Luz, H. Plümacher, W.
   Hohmann, H. Werdermann, Swabian Cho.
   Soc. & Stuttgart Bach orch.—Grischkat
   ♯ **Ren.X 36**
   (*No. 112*)   (♯ Nix.PLP 236; ♯ Clc. 6091)

... No. 3, Sei bemüht   A
   M. Tobias   in ♯ *MGM.E 115*

No. 189, Meine Seele rühmt und preist
   T, recorder, oboe, vln., cont.
   W. Ludwig, G. Scheck, H. Töttcher, R. Noll
   (hpsi.), A. Wenzinger (vlc.)   **PV. 2427/8S**
   (3ss—last blank)
   (*Nos. 53 & 200 on ♯ AmD.DL 9619*)
   C. Stemann & Stuttgart Bach Ens.—
   Grischkat   ♯ **Ren.X 35**
   (*No. 51*)   (♯ Clc. 6096; ♯ Nix.PLP 235)

... Nos. 1, 4, 5
   ☆ M. Meili, L. Moyse (fl.), L. Gromer, J. Pasquier
   hpsi. & vlc.   († **V♯** *AS. 1801LD*)

No. 198, Lass, Fürstin, lass noch einen Strahl
   S, A, T, B, orch.
   (*Trauerode*) 1727
   M. Laszlo, H. Rössl-Majdan, W. Kmentt,
   A. Poell, Vienna Academy Cho. & State Op.
   Orch.—Scherchen   ♯ **West.WL 5123**
   (2ss)

No. 200, Bekennen will ich seinen Namen
   A, 2 vlns., cont.
   H. Hennecke & Basle Cha. Ens.—Wenzinger
   PV. 2426
   (*Cantata 53*)   (♯ AmD.DL 9619)

SECULAR CANTATAS
No. 201, Der Streit zwischen Phoebus und Pan
   A. Schlemm (S), D. Eustrati (A), G. Lutze &
   H. Reinhold (T), G. Niese & K. Wolfram (Bs),
   Berlin Radio Cho. & orch.—Koch
   ♯ **CdM.LDX 8020**
   (2ss)   (♯ Van.BG 514)
   K. Nentwig (S), R. Michaelis (A), W. Hohmann
   & A. Pfeifle (T), B. Müller & F. Kelch (Bs),
   Swabian Cho. & orch.—Grischkat   (2ss)
   ♯ **Ren.X 42**

No. 202, Weichet nur, betrübte Schatten   S, orch.
   A. Felbermeyer & orch.—Prohaska
   (*No. 161*)   ♯ **Van.BG 513**

No. 205, Der zufriedengestellte Aeolus
   A. Schlemm (S), D. Eustrati (A), G. Lutze (T),
   K. Wolfram (Bs), Berlin Radio Cho. & orch.
   —Koch   ♯ **CdM.LDX 8021**
   (2ss)   (♯ Van.BG 515)
   K. Nentwig (S), R. Michaelis (A), W. Hohmann
   (T), F. Kelch (Bs), Swabian Cho. & orch.—
   Grischkat   ♯ **Ren.X 43**
   (2ss)   (♯ Nix.PLP 243)

No. 208, Was mir behagt
... No. 9, Schafe können sicher weiden   S
   — — ARR. 2 PFS.
   C. Smith & P. Sellick   **C.DX 1806**
   (*Arensky: Suite, Op. 15—Waltz*)
   — — ARR. ORCH. Stokowski
   Sym. Orch.—Stokowski   ♭ *G.7RF244*
   (*Cantata 147, excpt.*) (in ♯ Vic.LM 1176: ♭ *set WDM 1569*)
   — — ARR. ORG., 2 FL., VLC.
   E. P. Biggs   in ♯ *AmC.ML 4435*
   — — ARR. ORCH. Walton
   SEE : MISCELLANEOUS—"Wise Virgins"

No. 210, O holder Tag   S, orch.
   M. Laszlo & Vienna State Op. Orch.—
   Scherchen   ♯ **West.WL 5138**

No. 212, Mer hahn en neue Oberkeet   1742
... Excerpts — ARR. Bret (in *French*)
   ☆ J. Guyla, M. Singher & Ens.—Bret (JpV. set JAS 247)

MAGNIFICAT, D major
   ☆ Soloists, Lamy Cho. & Ansbach Orch.—Leitner
   (♯ AmD.DL 9557)
   Soloists, Reinhart & Winterthur Chos. & orch.—
   Reinhart (♯ Clc. 6052)
... No. 1, Magnificat anima mea ; No. 12, Gloria Patri
   ☆ Paris Univ. Cho. & Sym. Orch.—Gitton (Pat. PN 5020,
   from set)

MASSES
COLLECTION of the 4 Lutheran Masses
F major   (BWV 233)   A major   (BWV 234)
G minor   (BWV 235);   G major   (BWV 236)

   A. Giebel, L. Wolf-Mattheus, F. Kelch, Swabian
   Cho. & Ton-Studio Orch.—Grischkat
   ♯ **Ren.X 44/7**
   (*Sanctus with each Mass*)

F major   (BWV 233)   S, A, B, cho., orch.
   A. Gamper, G. Pfenninger, D. Olsen, Zürich
   Bach Cho. & Winterthur Sym.—Goehr
   ♯ **CHS.F 12**

A major   (BWV 234)   1737
... Qui tollis   S & 2 fls.
   M. Ritchie   *G.B 10292*

B minor   S, A, T, B, orch.   1733/7
COMPLETE RECORDINGS
   G. Heidrich, A. Brunner, C. Bochner, J. Kuntz,
   cho. & Rhineland Sym.—Federer
   (6ss)   ♯ **Rgt. set 6000**
   Anon. soloists, Berlin Cath. Cho. & Sym. Orch.
   —Balzer   ♯ **Roy. 1297/9**
   (6ss)
   ☆ E. Loose, H. Ceska, G. B. Schuster, A.
   Dermota, A. Poell, Academy Cho. & Vienna
   Sym.—Scherchen   ♯ **Sel.LPG 8251/3**
   (6ss) (A. Heiller, org.)

MOTETS
Fürchte dich nicht   (BWV 228)
   Concordia Cho.—Christiansen (*Eng*)   ♯ **Cdia. 2**
   (*Poulenc & Carols*)

(Der) Geist hilft unsrer Schwachheit auf (BWV 226)
   Leipzig Thomanerchor—Ramin   **Pol. 2016**

♯ = Long-playing, 33⅓ r.p.m.   ♭ = 45 r.p.m.   ♮ = Auto. couplings, 78 r.p.m.

Geist hilft unsrer Schwachheit auf (*continued*)
St. Olaf Cho.—O. C. Christiansen (*Eng*) in ♯StO.3
(*Grieg, Milhaud, Palestrina, etc.*)

Jesu, meine Freude (BWV 227)
Leipzig Thomanerchor—Ramin ♮ **PV. 2424/5**
(4ss)

ORATORIOS

HIMMELFAHRTSORATORIUM : *See* Cantata No. 11

OSTERN-ORATORIUM S, A, T, B, cho., orch.
(BWV 249) *c.* 1736
M. Weis-Osborn, H. Rössl-Majdan, K. Equiluz,
W. Berry, Akademie Cho. & Vienna Cha.
Orch.—Prohaska ♯ **Van.BG 507**
(♯ Nix.BLP 307)

WEIHNACHTSORATORIUM
S, A, T, B, cho., orch (BWV 248) 1734
COMPLETE RECORDINGS
E. Roon, D. Herrmann-Braun, E. Majkut,
W. Berry, Vienna Academy Cho. & Sym.
Orch.—Grossmann
(6ss) ♯ **E. & AmVox. set PL 7713**
G. Weber, L. Fischer, H. Marten, H. Gunther,
Detmold Academy Cho. & orch.—
K. Thomas ♯ **OL.LD 40/2**
(6ss) (Excerpts, on V♯ *DO.LD 7/9*)
☆ M. Schilling, R. Michaelis, W. Hohmann, B. Müller,
Stuttgart Cho. & Swabian Sym.—Grischkat (8ss—
♯ Clc. 6079/82; ♯ Rem. set 199-118)

... No. 12, Brich an, O schönes Morgenlicht cho. & orch.
R. Shaw Chorale (*Eng*) in Vic. set **DM 1711**
(♭ set *WDM 1711*: ♯ *LM 1711*)

... No. 64, Final Choral : Nun seid ihr wohl gerochen (ARR.)
E. P. Biggs (org.) & Columbia Cha. Orch.—Burgin
in ♯ AmC.**ML 4435**

PASSION MUSIC
JOHANNES-PASSION (BWV 245) 1722-3
COMPLETE RECORDINGS
R. Shaw Cho. & Collegiate Cho. & Cha. Orch.
—Shaw ♯ **Vic. set LM 6103**
(6ss) (♭ set *WDM 1587*)
Soloists: A. Addison (S), B. Thebom (A), L. Chabay &
B. Stern (T), M. Harrell (B), D. Slick, P. Ukena &
P. Matthen (Bs) (*Eng*)
(No. 68, Final Choral, also in ♯ LM 1201 ; ♭ set *WDM 1623*)
☆ G. Rathauscher (S), E. Hofstaetter (A), etc.,
Vienna Academy Cho. & Vienna Sym.—
Grossmann ♯ **EVox. 101/3**
(6ss) (♯ AmVox. set PL 6553, n.n.)(♯ PaV.VP 103-1/3)

ABRIDGED RECORDING
Soloists, cho. & Austrian Sym.—Breinfalk
♯ **Rem. 199-78**
Soloists: B. Seidl (S), H. Rössl-Majdan (A), E. Majkut
(T), W. Berry (Bs), O. Wiener (Bs)

... No. 68, Ach Herr, lass dein lieb' Engelein
Lausanne Choeur des Jeunes (*Fr*) (G.JK 44)

MATTHAEUS-PASSION (BWV 244) 1729
COMPLETE RECORDING (in *German*)
Anon. soloists, Berlin Cath. Cho. & Sym. Orch.
—Balzer (8ss) ♯ **Roy. 1290/3**
... No. 1, Kommt, ihr Töchter (Pol. 68454)
... No. 26, Ich will bei meinem Jesu wachen (68437)
... No. 35, O Mensch, bewein' dein' Sünde gross (63438)
... No. 78, Wir setzen uns mit Tränen nieder (63288)
W. Ludwig (T), Bruno Kittel Cho. & Berlin Phil. Orch.—
Kittel (☆ from set)
... No. 1, Kommt, ihr Töchter
... No. 78, Wir setzen uns mit Tränen nieder
Rotterdam Phil. Cho. & orch.—Niels Phi.N **11180/1G**
(*PhM.N 09032/3S*)
☆ Berlin Radio Chos. & orch.—F. Lehmann V♯ *DFr. 36*

... No. 47, Erbarme dich A
E. Leisner (2ss) Pol. **67791**
☆ K. Flagstad (S) (♭ *G.7R 126*: *7RF 191*)

... No. 63, O Haupt voll Blut und Wunden
Copenhagen Cha. Cho.—Bertelsen (*Dan*) (Felix. Ø 64)
... No. 78, Wir setzen uns mit Tränen nieder
Lausanne Choeur des Jeunes (*Fr*) (G.HEX 130)
— — ARR. PF. P. Browne (*Pax.PR 486*)

SANCTUS
COLLECTION
C major (BWV 237)　　　D major (BWV 238)
D minor (BWV 239)　　　G major (BWV 240)
Swabian Cho. & Ton-Studio Orch.—Grischkat
(*each with a Mass*) ♯ **Ren.X 44/7**

CHORALES S, A, T, B
Christ ist erstanden (BWV 276)
Christ lag in Todesbanden (BWV 278)
Erschienen ist der herrliche Tag (BWV 145)
Erstanden ist der heil'ge Christ (BWV 306)
Heut triumphiret Gottes Sohn (BWV 342)
Jesus Christus unser Heiland (BWV 364)
Jesus, meine Zuversicht (BWV 365)
F. Helsing, L. Kimmel, A. Planyavsky, L. Heppe
& K. Rapf (org.) ♯ **Van.BG 512**
(*Cantata 31*)
O Lamm Gottes unschuldig (BWV 401)
Herzliebster Jesu (Matthaeus-Passion, No. 3)
O Haupt voll Blut und Wunden (*idem* No. 63)
"Gesang 53" (2 verses only) (attrib. Bach)
"Gesang 61" (3 verses only) (attrib. Bach)
Netherlands Cha. & J. Jong Chos.—de Nobel
(G. Stam, org.) Phi.N **12026G**
(*PhM.N 09014S*)

In dulci jubilo (as *Now let your happy voices . . .*)
Vocal Ensemble (*Eng*) (in Vic. set E97: ♭ *WE 97*)

Freuet euch, ihr Christen alle
(Cantata 140 No. 7 ; to Eng. words—*O rejoice
ye Christians loudly*)
Cho.—Wilhousky in ♯ **DCap.LC 6576**
(*Victoria, Palestrina, Rubinstein, etc.*)
(in ♯ *Cap. L 9015* : ♭/♭ set *CD/CDF 9015*)

Nun komm' der Heiden Heiland
J. Wilson (S) & org. in ♯ AmD.**DL 9554**
(*below*)

Was Gott tut . . .
Copenhagen Cha. Cho.—Bertelsen (*Dan*) (in Felix. Ø 64)

SONGS
SONGS FROM THE NOTENBUCH FÜR A. M. BACH
Bist du bei mir (No. 25)
Gedenke doch, mein Geist (No. 41)
Ich habe genug (Cantata 82)
O Ewigkeit, du Donnerwort (No. 42)
Schlummert ein (Cantata 82)
Willst du dein Herz mir schenken (No. 37)
M. Weis-Osborn (S), K. Rapf (hpsi.), & vlc.
♯ **Van.BG 510**
(*Clavier pieces & Ch.-Prelude*)

Gedenke doch, mein Geist (No. 41)
Ich habe genug ; Schlummert ein (Cantata 82)
J. Eby (Bs), M. Hauptmann (hpsi.), & vlc.
♯ **BS.LX 7001**
(*below* ; & *Cantata 158*) (o.n. ♯ *Ren.X 34*)

Bist du bei mir (No. 25)
A. Schiøtz (T), M. Wöldike (hpsi.) *G.DA 5272*
(*below*)

SONGS FROM THE SCHEMELLI GESANGBUCH
Brunnquell aller Güter (No. 7)
Dir, dir, Jehova (No. 14)
(Der) lieben Sonne Licht und Pracht (No. 8)
J. Eby (Bs), M. Hauptmann (hpsi.), & vlc.
♯ **BS.LX 7001**
(o.n. ♯ *Ren.X 34*)

☆ = Re-issue of a recording to be found in WERM or Supplement I.

Auf, auf, mein Herz (No. 3)
A. Schiøtz (T), M. Wöldike (hpsi.) *G.DA 5272*
(*above*)

Ich steh' an deiner Krippen hier (No. 33)
E. J. Gerstein (S), W. Gerwig (lute), J. Koch
(gamba)   *Pol. 26520*
(*below*)

J. Wilson (S), R. Baker (org.) in ♯ **AmD.DL 9554**
(*above; & Bax, Holst, etc.*)

Komm, süsser Tod (No. 42)
A. Schiøtz (T), M. Wöldike (org.)   *G.DA 5271*
(*below*)

K. Flagstad (S), G. Moore (pf.)   **G.DB 21490**
(*Löhner: O Ewigkeit*)

K. Borg (Bs), H. Jensen (org.)   *Felix.F 66*
(*below*)
— ARR. ORCH.   Stokowski
Sym. Orch.—Stokowski   ♯ **Vic.LM 1176**
                              (♭ *set WDM 1569*)
— ARR. ORG.
E. P. Biggs   in ♯ **AmC.ML 4603**
(*Mattheson, Schubert, etc.*)

Liebster Herr Jesu (No. 48)
A. Schiøtz (T), M. Wöldike (org.) *G.DA 5271*
(*above*)

O Jesulein süss (No. 58)
E. J. Gerstein (S), etc.   *Pol. 26520*
(*above*)
F. Jagel (T) & org.   in *AmD. set A 883*
                              (♯ *DL 5363: ♭ set 9-272*)
K. Borg (Bs) & org.   *Felix.F 66*
(*above*)

BACH, Wilhelm Friedemann (1710-1784)

POLONAISE, No. 4, D minor clavier (F.12)
   ☆ A. Ehlers (hpsi) (in ♯ AmD.DL 8019)

SONATA No. 2, A major clavier (F.8)
F. Neumeyer (clavichord)   **PV. 3410**

Sonata, F major   fl., vln. & cont.
L. Schaefer, R. Brink & D. Pinkham (hpsi.)
                              ♯ **Allo.ALG 3037**
(*C.P.E. Bach*)

Symphony, D minor   (F.65)
Cha. Orch.—v. d. Berg   ♯ **CHS.G 3**
(*C. P. E. & J. C. Bach*)

BACKER-GRØNDAHL, Agathe
(1857-1907)

Elves' game, Op. 36, No. 10   pf.
S. Ribbing   **T.E 19807**
(½s.—*Sinding & Saeverud*)

SONGS
At eventide, Op. 42, No. 7 (*Mot Kvæld*) (Jynge)
E. Berge (S), cho. & orch.   **Felix.Ø 63**
(*Grieg: Spring*)
— ARR. VLN. & PF.   A. Brugman & B. Linderud (*Tono.K 8088*)

(The) Night is still, Op. 3, No. 1 (Bjørnson)
— ARR. ORCH.
Stavanger Ens.—Andersen   *C.GN 1150*
(*Sinding: Waltz*)

BADINGS, Henk (b. 1907)

Sonatine pf. 1936
J. Antonietti   *PV. 36019*
(*Pijper: Sonatine No. 2*)

BAINTON, Edgar Leslie (b. 1880)

Sonata, vlc. & pf. 1933
J. Kennedy & E. Bainton   **C.LOX 811/2**
(4ss)

BAIRSTOW, Edward Cuthbert
(1874-1947)

Save us, O Lord, waking   Anthem
Cho. of St. John's, Upper   Norwood—
   Betteridge (org.)   **Croy.CX 1**
(*Gibbons: Magnificat*)

BALAKIREV, Mily (1837-1910)

Islamey pf. 1869
V. Yankoff (2ss)   **Pat.PDT 265**
G. Ginsburg (2ss)   **USSR. 015798/9**

— ARR. ORCH.   Casella
USSR. State—Gauk   **USSR. 02154/5**
   ☆ L.S.O.—Weldon (in ♭ *MGM set K 58*)

King Lear, Overture 1861
USSR. Radio Sym.—L. Ginsburg
(4ss)   *USSR. 20485/8*

Sonata, B flat minor pf. 1905
L. Kentner (6ss)   **C.LX 1407/9**

SONGS
Everybody says "You're a fool"
I'm a plucky chap
   ▽ V. Rosing   (*Voc.B 3122**)

I loved him (Koltsov)
V. Viktorova (S)   *USSR. 15756*
(*Bulakhov: Gipsy song*)
Z. Dolukhanova (A)   *USSR. 18913*
(*Rubinstein: Bard*)

Lead me, O Night   (Maikov)
A. Pirogov (B)   *USSR. 14770*
(½s.—*Song of the old man & O Come to me*)

O come to me (Koltsov)
A. Pirogov (B)   *USSR. 14771*
(*Song of the old man & Lead me, O Night*)

Song (Lermontov)
M. Maksakova (S)   *USSR. 18579*
(*Tchaikovsky: As o'er the burning ashes*)

Song of the old man (Koltsov)
A. Pirogov (B)   *USSR. 14770*
(½s.—*Lead me, O night & Come to me*)

Symphony, C major 1898
   ☆ Philharmonia—von Karajan (♯ C.CX 1002)

♯ = Long-playing, 33⅓ r.p.m.   ♭ = 45 r.p.m.   ♮ = Auto. couplings, 78 r.p.m.

18

BALBÂTRE, Claude (1729-1799)
SEE: † French Masters . . .

BALDWIN, John (d. 1615)
SEE: † Catches & Glees . . .

BALFE, Michael (1808-1870)

Come into the garden, Maud　(Tennyson)
H. Nash (T), G. Moore (pf.)　　　**G.C 4186**
(*White: So we'll go no more . . .*)

BANCHIERI, Adriano (*c.* 1567-1634)

MADRIGAL COMEDIES
(II) FESTINO DELLA SERA DEL GIOVEDI GRASSO　5 voices　1608
10 Scenes
L. Marenzio Ens.—Saraceni　† ♯ *AS. 2502LD*

(La) PAZZIA SENILE　(pub. 1598)
Scenes
(La) SAVIEZZA GIOVANILE　(pub. 1628)
Io son bella e favorita
Vassar Madrigal Singers—Geer ♯ **Allo.ALG 3029**
(† Italian Madrigals)

BANTOCK, Sir Granville (1868-1946)

(The) Frogs (of Aristophanes) Overture　1936
— ARR. BAND
Fairey Aviation Works—Mortimer *Pax.PR 592/3*
(3ss—*Stewart: Trumpet Tune*)

SONGS
Dedication; Dream of Spring
(From *Lute of Jade*; L. Cranmer-Byng, from the Chinese)
☆ J. McCormack (T)　　　**G.VA 59**
Jester Songs . . . Serenade only
▽ M. Brunskill (A) (*C. 3876*)

BARBER, Samuel (b. 1910)

Concerto, vln. & orch., Op. 14　1938-9
H. Girdach & Berlin Radio—Schultz
　　　　　　　　　　　♯ Rgt. 5024

Dover Beach, Op. 3　(Arnold)　B & str. qtt.　1931
J. Langstaff & Hirsch Qtt.　　　**G.C 4201**
(2ss)
P. King & Hartt Qtt.　　　**♯ CEd. 1011**
(*below*)

Let down the bars, O Death (Dickinson) unacc. cho.
Vienna Academy Cha. Cho.—Grossmann
　　　　　　　　　　　♯ AmVox.PL 7750
(*V. Thomson, Piston, etc.*)

SONGS, Op. 10　(Joyce)
No. 1, Rain has fallen
No. 2, Sleep now
No. 3, I hear an army
P. King (B), S. Quincey (pf.)　in ♯ **CEd. 1011**

Symphony, No. 1, Op. 9　1936, rev. 1943
Stockholm Sym.—N. Lehmann in ♯ **CEd. 1011**
(*above*)

BARTLETT, John　(fl. *c.* 1600)
SEE: † XVIth & XVIIth Century Songs

BARTÓK, Bela (1881-1945)

CLASSIFIED:　I.　Orchestral
　　　　　　　II.　Chamber Music
　　　　　　　III.　Piano
　　　　　　　IV.　Vocal

I. ORCHESTRAL

CONCERTOS, pf. & orch.
No. 2　1931
☆ A. Földes & Lamoureux—Bigot
　　　　　　　(♯ EVox. 280; PaV.VP 280)

No. 3　1945
H. Reiter & Berlin Radio—Varisch ♯ *Rgt. 5028*

Concerto, vln. & orch.　1938
T. Varga & Berlin Phil.—Fricsay **PV. 72075/7**
(6ss)　　　　　(♯ Pol. 18006; AmD.DL 9545)

Concerto, viola & orch. (completed Serly)
W. Primrose & New Sym.—Serly　♯ **BRS. 309**

Divertimento for strings　1939
Minneapolis Sym.—Dorati　　　♯ **Vic.LM 1185**
(*Mozart: Symphony 31*)　　　(♭ set WDM 1596)

Music for Strings, Percussion & Celesta　1936
Chicago Sym.—Kubelik　　　♯ **Mer.MG 50001**
(*Bloch*)
☆ Philharmonia—Karajan
　　　　　　(♯ C.FC 1012; ♯ AmC.ML 4456)

(2) Portraits, Op. 5　vln. & orch.　1907/8
R. Schulz & R.I.A.S. Sym.—Fricsay **PV. 72248**
(2ss)

... No. 1 only
J. Szigeti & Philharmonia—Lambert **C.LX 1531**

(2) Rhapsodies, vln. & orch.　1928
E. Vardi & New Sym. Orch.　　　**♯ BRS. 306**
(No. 1 cond. by Serly; No. 2 by Autori)

Suite No. 1, Op. 3　1905
Salzburg Mozarteum—Fekete ♯ **Csm.CLPS 1010**
　　　　　　　　　　　(♯ Eur.LPG 615)

II. CHAMBER MUSIC

Contrasts　vln., cl. & pf.　1938
D. Guilet, H. Tichman, R. Budnevich ♯ **CHS.G 8**
(*Allegro barbaro & Suite*)
☆ J. Szigeti, B. Goodman & B. Bastole (JpC.SW 190/1)

QUARTETS, String
No. 1, A minor, Op. 7　1903
Hirsch Qtt.　　　　　　　　♯ *Argo.ATM 1001*
No. 5　☆ Hungarian Qtt. (♮ G.TH 7044/7)

Sonata, 2 pfs. & percussion　1938
E. Picht-Axenfeld & C. Seemann; L. Porth &
　K. Peinkofer　　　　　　　　**PV. 72214/5**
(4ss)　　　　　　　　　　　(♯ Pol. 16021)
☆ Bela & D. P. Bartók (♯ Clc. 6014)

☆ = Re-issue of a recording to be found in WERM or Supplement I.

CHAMBER MUSIC (*continued*)
SONATA, vln. & pf., No. 1 1921
I. Stern & A. Zakin   ♯ **AmC.ML 4376**

Sonata, vln. unacc. 1944
W. Tworek (6ss)   ♮ **Pol.HM 80062/4**

III. PIANO

COLLECTIONS
  Rondo No. 1 (1916)
  Petite Suite (1938)
  Little Piece, No. 9 (1926)
  Improvisations 1, 2, 6, 7, 8, Op. 20
  Wallachian Dance
  (3) Hungarian Folk-tunes (for Paderewski)
  Mikrokosmos, Nos. 69, 127, 145 ARR. 2 PFS.
  ☆ B. Bartók (& Mme. Bartók in duets)
                ♯ **Rem. 199-94**

  (10) Easy pieces
  ... No. 5, Evening in Transylvania
  ... No. 10, Bear Dance
  For Children ... Vol. I—Nos. 3, 4, 6, 10, 12, 13, 15, 18,
      19, 21, 26, 30, 31, 34, 35

  ☆ B. Bartók (♯ Clc. 6014)

Allegro barbaro 1911
C. de Groot   *PhM.A 11245S*
(*Khachaturian: Gayaneh excpt.*)
F. Pelleg   ♯ **CHS.G 8**
(*Suite*)
O. Frugoni   in ♯ **AmVox.PL 7700**
(*Paradies, Scarlatti, etc.*)

FOR CHILDREN 1909 rev. & re-numbered 1945
Volume I, 17 pieces (unspec.)
C. Seemann   **PV. 72266**

Vol. I, Nos. 3, 6, 31, 33, 36 ; Vol. II, Nos. 7, 8, 26.
  (old version, Vol. I, 3, 6; Vol. II, 33, 35, 38; Vol. III, 7, 8;
    Vol. IV, 28)
— ARR. VLN. & PF. Zathureczky
E. Zathureczky & M. Karin   **U.H 24263**

(15) Hungarian Peasant Songs 1917
... Nos. 7-12, 14, 15 ☆ B. Bartók (*Qual.QMN 7001*)

(9) Little Pieces 1926
... Nos. 6, 8 ☆ B. Bartók (*Qual.QKM 5001*)

Petite Suite 1938
... No. 5, Bagpipes only ☆ B. Bartók (*Qual.QKM 5001*)

MIKROKOSMOS pf. 1926/37
Nos. 97, 114, 116, 118, 125, 126, 130, 136, 139, 141,
  143, 144, 147
B. Bartók   ♯ **AmC.ML 4419**
(*below*)

Nos. 94, 100, 108, 109, 113, 120, 128, 129, 131, 133,
  138, 140, 142, 148/53
☆ B. Bartók   ♯ **AmC.ML 4419**
(*above*)

Books V & VI (Nos. 122-153) COMPLETE
J. Laforge   ♯ **Pac.LDPF 01**
(*Sonatina*)

Nos. 113, 135, 127 — ARR. 2 PFS. Bartók
A. Whittemore & J. Lowe in ♯ **Vic.LM 1705**
(*Ravel, Copland, etc.*)   (♭ set WDM 1705)

Nos. 148—153 (Bulgarian Dances)
P. Scarpini   **Dur.SA 139**
(*Stravinsky on* ♯ *Csm.CLPS 1025*)

(3) Rondos on Folk Tunes 1916/27
(6) Rumanian Folk Dances 1915
  ☆ L. Kraus   ♯ *AmD.DL 4011*
... Rondo No. 1 only. ☆ B. Bartók (*Qual.QKM 5001*)

---

(6) Rumanian Dances — ARR. VLN. & PF. Székely
D. Oistrakh & pf.   *USSR. 14653/4*
☆ Y. Menuhin & M. Gazelle (♭ *G.7RF 217*)

Sonata 1926
P. Scarpini (4ss)   **Dur.SA 140/1**
(4ss)   (in ♯ Csm.CLPS 1025)
☆ A. Földes (♯ EVox. 280; PaV.VP 280)

Sonatina 1915
J. Laforge   ♯ **Pac.LDPF 01**
(*Mikrokosmos*)

— ARR. VLN. & PF. Gertler
E. Zathureczky & M. Karin   **U.H 24262**

Suite, Op. 14 1916
F. Pelleg   ♯ **CHS.G 8**
(*Contrasts*)

IV. VOCAL

(10) Hungarian Folksongs 1906
... While walking through Kertmeg garden
    The moon shines through my window

(20) Hungarian Folksongs 1929
... An old sad song; Drinking Song;
    Slow dance of the Székelys
    Swineherd's Dance
    Complaint ; Coupling Song : There's a gay time
    Oh my dear mother
    The firm cherries are ripening
    Coupling Song : Yellow horse ...
L. Chabay (T), T. Kozma (pf.)   ♯ **BRS. 914**
(*Kodály: Folksongs*)

Hungarian Folksongs (unspec.)
L. Toth Cho. (*CdM.PA 555*)

NOTE : The following BRS. issues have been re-numbered :
Divertimento for strings	n.n.	♯ BRS. 905
Hungarian Folksongs, Vol. I	n.n.	♯ BRS. 904
Mikrokosmos, 5 pieces (—ARR. STR. QTT.)	n.n.	♯ BRS. 901
Out of Doors ; Improvisations	n.n.	♯ BRS. 902
Str. Qtt. No. 3	n.n.	♯ BRS. 901
Piano pieces (Composer	n.n.	♯ BRS. 903

BASSANI, Giovanni Battista (1657-1716)
  SEE : † ITALIAN SONGS

BATESON, Thomas (*c.* 1570-1630)
  SEE : † A TREASURY OF MADRIGALS

BATTISHILL, Jonathan (1738-1801)
  SEE : † CATCHES AND GLEES

BAX, Sir Arnold Edward Trevor (b. 1883)

(A) Christmas Carol (XVth Cent.) (ARR. Bax)
J. Wilson (S), G. Trovillo (pf.) in ♯ **AmD.DL 9554**
(*Bach, Holst, etc.*)

(A) Morning Song pf. & orch. 1947
☆ H. Cohen & orch.—Sargent   **C.DX 1838**
                (CQX 16661)

(The) Poisoned Fountain 2 pfs. 1920
A. Whittemore & J. Lowe in ♯ **Vic.LM 1705**
(*Poulenc, Stravinsky, etc*)   (in ♭ set WDM 1705)

♯ = Long-playing, 33⅓ r.p.m.   ♭ = 45 r.p.m.   ♮ = Auto. couplings, 78 r.p.m.

20

BECK, Conrad (b. 1901)

Concerto, viola & orch. 1949
W. Kägi & Suisse Romande—Meylan
♯ **D.LXT 2703**
(Reichel: Concertino, pf. & orch.) (♯ Lon.LL 601)

BEETHOVEN, Ludwig van (1770-1827)

CLASSIFIED : A. Instrumental
1. Piano, 2. Chamber Music, 3. Dances,
4. Orchestral
B. Stage Music
C. Vocal

A. INSTRUMENTAL

1. PIANO

Andante, F major (G.170) (*"Andante favori"*)
B. Moiséiwitsch (2ss) **G.C 4099**
J. Bolet in ♯ **Bo.B 301**
(St.-Saëns, Moszkowski, etc.)

BAGATELLES
Seven, Op. 33 ... **No. 1, E flat**
☆ W. Gieseking (C.GQX 11470)

Six, Op. 126
C. Seemann ♮ **PV. 72144/5**
(Variations, F major, Op. 34)

... Nos. 2 & 3 only
F. Gulda **D.KX 28560**
(Pf. Concerto No. 1, s.9)

A minor, "Für Elise" (G.173)
L. Kentner **C.DX 1775**
(Rondo, B flat) (GQX 11491)
J. Battista in ♯ *MGM.E 141*
(Brahms, Chopin, etc.)
A. Aeschbacher *Pol. 26519*
(Écossaises)
O. Frugoni in ♯ **AmVox.PL 7700**
(Schumann, Weber, etc.)
☆ W. Gieseking (C.GQX 11470)
J. Iturbi
(in ♯ Vic.LM 1167: ♭ *set WDM 1604*: in ♭ *WEPR 33*)

Polonaise, C major, Op. 89
H. Steurer ♯ **Ura. 7055**
(Sonatas 4 & 19) (♭ *UREP 15, d.c.*)

RONDOS
A major (G.164)
☆ A. Schnabel **G.DB 21343**
(Sonata No. 32, s.7)

B flat major (doubtful) [1]
L. Kentner **C.DX 1775**
(Bagatelle, A minor "Für Elise") (GQX 11491)

C major, Op. 51, No. 1
L. Rev *Pat.PD 148*
H. Steurer ♯ **Ura. 7033**
(Sonatas 13, 20, & below)
A. Aeschbacher **PV. 72260**
(Variations on "Ich bin der Schneider Kakadu," s.1)
☆ A. Schnabel (G.DB 7377)

G major, Op. 51, No. 2
L. Rev *Pat.PDT 258*
H. Steurer ♯ **Ura. 7033**
(Sonatas 13 & 20 & below)

G major, Op. 129 (*Rondo a capriccio*)
(*Wut über den verlorenen Groschen*)
H. Steurer ♯ **Ura. 7033**
(Sonatas 13, 20 & above)
P. Badura-Skoda *C.LV 14*
☆ A. Schnabel **G.DB 9748**
(Sonata No. 25, s.1)

SONATAS
THE 32 SONATAS, COMPLETE
No. 1, F minor ; No. 3, C major ♯ AmD.DL 9583
No. 2, A major ; No. 15, D major ♯ AmD.DL 9585
No. 4, E flat major ; No. 9, E major ♯ AmD.DL 9588
No. 5, C minor ; No. 32, C minor ♯ AmD.DL 9587
No. 6, F major ; No. 22, F major ; No. 30, E major ♯ AmD.DL 9591
No. 7, D major ; No. 13, E flat major ♯ AmD.DL 9584
No. 8, C minor ; No. 24, F sharp major ; No. 25, G major ♯ AmD.DL 9578
No. 9, E major : See No. 4
No. 10, G major ; No. 31, A flat major ♯ AmD.DL 9592
No. 11, B flat major ; No. 19, G minor ; No. 20, G major ♯ AmD.DL 9590
No. 12, A flat major ; No. 16, G major ♯ AmD.DL 9589
No. 13, E flat major : See No. 7
No. 14, C sharp minor ; No. 26, E flat major ♯ AmD.DL 9582
No. 15, D major : See No. 2
No. 16, G major : See No. 12
No. 17, D minor ; No. 18, E flat major ♯ AmD.DL 9586
No. 19, G minor ; No. 20, G major : See No. 11
No. 21, C major ; No. 28, A major ♯ AmD.DL 9581
No. 22, F major : See No. 6
No. 23, F minor ; No. 27, E minor ♯ AmD.DL 9580
No. 24, F sharp major ; No. 25, G major : See No. 8
No. 26, E flat major : See No. 14
No. 27, E minor : See No. 23
No. 28, A major : See No. 21
No. 29, B flat major ♯ AmD.DL 9579
No. 30, E major : See No. 6
No. 31, A flat major : See No. 10
No. 32, C minor : See No. 5

All played by W. Kempff
(Some are ☆ ; for European Nos. of those which are not,
see individual entries, *below*)

No. 1, F minor, Op. 2, No. 1
W. Kempff (4ss) ♮ *PV. 36013/4*

No. 2, A major, Op. 2, No. 2
W. Kempff (4ss) ♮ **PV. 72183/4**

No. 3, C major, Op. 2, No. 3
W. Backhaus ♯ **D.LXT 2747**
(No. 17) (♯ Lon.LL 627)
— ARR. STR. QTT. A. Brand
Pascal Qtt. ♯ **CHS.CHS 1201**
(Str. Qtt., Op. 18, No. 1) (in Qtts., complete)

No. 4, E flat major, Op. 7
W. Kempff (4ss) ♮ **PV. 72198/9**
H. Steurer ♯ **Ura. 7055**
(Sonata 19 & Polonaise)

No. 5, C minor, Op. 10, No. 1
W. Kempff (3ss) **PV. 72273/4S**

No. 7, D major, Op. 10, No. 3
C. Arrau (6ss) **C.LX 1540/2**
W. Kempff **PV. 72275/6S**
(3ss) (♯ Pol. 18019)

No. 8, C minor, Op. 13 (*"Pathétique"*)
C. Solomon **G.C 4117/9**
(5ss—Couperin: Le carillon de Cythère)
(♭ Vic. set WDM 1654)
(No. 32, on ♯ Vic. LM 1222)
O. Frugoni ♯ **E. & AmVox.PL 7160**
(Nos. 14 & 23)
T. v. d. Pas ♯ *Phi.A 00609R*
(No. 14)
A. Dorfmann ♯ **BB.LBC 1029**
(Sonata No. 14) (♭ set WBC 1029)

(continued on next page)

[1] In Köchel Anhang 284i (new K 511a); possibly by L. Kozeluch. Formerly attributed to Mozart.

No. 8, C minor, Op. 13 ("*Pathétique*")   (*continued*)

J. Páleníček   ♮ U.H 24155/6
(4ss)

☆ W. Kempff   ♯ Pol. 18019
(*Sonata No. 7*)

L. Kreutzer   (4ss)   JpC.P 37/8

☆ A. Földes   ♯ Mer.MG 10121
(*Nos. 17, 24, 25*)

... 2nd movt., Adagio, only

A. Previn (in ♯ *Vic.LPM 3045*: in ♭ *EPB 3045*)

—— ARR. ORCH.   Berlin Municipal (T.E 3913: in ♯ *LB 6022*)

No. 9, E major, Op. 14, No. 1
K. Appelbaum   ♯ West.WL 5090
(*Nos. 24 & 31*)

☆ A. Schnabel   ♮ G.DB 9729/30
          (in ♯ Vic.LCT 1110: ♭ *set WCT 1110*)

—— ARR. STR. QTT.   Beethoven (F major)
New Music Qtt.   ♯ BRS. 909
(*St. Qtt. No. 9*)

No. 10, G major, Op. 14, No. 2
W. Backhaus   ♯ D.LXT 2754
(*Nos. 22 & 24*)   (Lon.LL 603)

W. Kempff   PV. 72262

No. 11, B flat major, Op. 22
W. Kempff   ♯ Pol. 18020
(*No. 14*)

K. Appelbaum   ♯ West.WL 5078
(*No. 14*)

No. 13, E flat major, Op. 27, No. 1
H. Steurer   ♯ Ura. 7033
(*No. 20, Rondos, Variations*)

☆ A. Schnabel   ♮ G.DB 9698/9
          (in ♯ Vic.LCT 1110: ♭ *set WCT 1110*)

No. 14, C sharp minor, Op. 27, No. 2 ("*Moonlight*")
☆ W. Kempff   ♯ Pol. 18020
(*No. 11*)   (Adagio only, on PV. 72321)

W. Gieseking   (4ss)   ♮ C.LCX 5016/7

R. Serkin   (n.v.)   ♯ AmC.ML 4432
(*No. 26*)   (4ss, ♭ *set A 1014*)

O. Frugoni   ♯ E. & AmVox.PL 7160
(*Nos. 8 & 23*)

K. Appelbaum   ♯ West.WL 5078
(*No. 11*)

T. v. d. Pas   ♯ *Phi.A 00609R*
(*No. 8*)

A. Dorfmann   ♯ BB.LBC 1029
(*No. 8*)   (♭ *set WBC 1029*)

☆ B. Moiséiwitsch   G.TH 12/13
F. Gulda   D.K 28447/8
V. Schiøler   ♯ *Mer.MG 15037*
A. Jenner   ♯ Mrt. 200-16, d.c.

... **Adagio only**
E. Silver (in ♯ Var. 2008 & in ♯ Var. 6944)

—— ARR. ORCH.   Berlin Municipal (T.E 3913)

No. 16, G major, Op. 31, No. 1
K. Appelbaum   ♯ West.WL 5133
(*No. 23*)

H. Steurer   ♯ Ura. 7051
(*Nos. 22 & 27*)

No. 17, D minor, Op. 31, No. 2
W. Backhaus   ♯ D.LXT 2747
(*No. 3*)   (♯ Lon.LL 627)

M. Fedorova   ♮ U.H 20015/7
(6ss)

☆ A. Földes   ♯ Mer.MG 10121
(*Nos. 8, 24, 25*)

No. 18, E flat major, Op. 31, No. 3
... 3rd movt., Minuet   ☆ A. Rubinstein   (G.DB 9373)

No. 19, G minor, Op. 49, No. 1
W. Kempff   PV. 72185
(*No. 20*)   (♯ Pol. 18021)

H. Steurer   ♯ Ura. 7055
(*No. 4 & Polonaise*)

No. 20, G major, Op. 49, No. 2
W. Kempff   PV. 72185
(*No. 19*)   (♯ Pol. 18021)

H. Steurer   ♯ Ura. 7033
(*No. 13 & Rondos, Variations*)

No. 21, C major, Op. 53 ("*Waldstein*")
W. Kempff   ♮ PV. 72135/6
(4ss)

E. Kilenyi   ♯ Rem. 199-83
(*No. 26*)

C. Solomon   ♯ Vic.LM 1716
(*Nos. 22 & 30*)   (♭ *set WDM 1716*)

No. 22, F major, Op. 54
C. Solomon   G.C 4159
                (♯ Vic.LM 1716: ♭ *set WDM 1716*)

W. Backhaus   ♯ D.LXT 2754
(*Nos. 10 & 24*)   (♯ Lon.LL 603)

H. Steurer   ♯ Ura. 7051
(*Nos. 16 & 27*)

No. 23, F minor, Op. 57 ("*Appassionata*")
W. Gieseking (n.v.)   ♮ C.LCX 5044/6
(5ss—*Bach*)   (LVX 195/7)

W. Backhaus   ♯ D.LXT 2715
(*No. 28*)   (♯ Lon.LL 597)

W. Kempff   ♮ PV. 72123/4
(4ss)   (♯ Pol. 18021)

W. Malcuzynski   C.LX 1459/61
(5ss—*Brahms: Intermezzo, Op. 116, No. 6*)

O. Frugoni   ♯ E. & AmVox.PL 7160
(*Nos. 8 & 14*)

K. Appelbaum   ♯ West.WL 5133
(*No. 16*)

A. S. Rasmussen   (6ss)   ♮ Tono.A 166/8

E. Goldstein   ♯ MMS. 8
(*Mendelssohn*)

S. Feinberg   (6ss)   USSR. 14118/23

☆ A. Rubinstein   ♮ G.DB 9373/5
(*No. 18—Minuet*)

☆ V. Schiøler   ♯ Vic.LHMV 1031
(*Liszt: Pf. Concerto No. 1*)   (♭ *set WHMV 1031*)

☆ N. Medtner (in ♯ BB.LBC 1031: ♭ *set WBC 1031*;
   ♮ G.TH 7048/50)
A. Kitchin (♯ Mrt. 200-16, d.c.)

No. 24, F sharp major, Op. 78
K. Appelbaum   ♯ West.WL 5090
(*Nos. 9 & 31*)

W. Backhaus   ♯ D.LXT 2754
(*Nos. 10 & 22*)   (♯ Lon.LL 603)

W. Kempff   PV. 72263
(*No. 25*)

☆ A. Schnabel   ♮ G.DB 9748/9
(3ss—*Rondo a capriccio, Op. 129*)
                (in ♯ Vic.LCT 1109: ♭ *set WCT 1109*)

☆ A. Földes   ♯ Mer.MG 10121
(*Nos. 8, 17, 25*)

No. 25, G major, Op. 79
W. Kempff   PV. 72263
(*No. 24*)

☆ W. Backhaus (D.X 53098: KX 28486)
A. Földes (in ♯ Mer.MG 10121)

No. 26, E flat major, Op. 81a
F. Gulda   ♯ D.LXT 2594
(*Variations, Op. 35*)   (♯ Lon.LLP 322)
                                               (also 4ss, D.K 28449/50)

♯ = Long-playing, 33⅓ r.p.m.   ♭ = 45 r.p.m.   ♮ = Auto. couplings, 78 r.p.m.

No. 26, E flat major, Op. 81a *(continued)*
R. Serkin   ♯ AmC.ML 4432
(No. 14)
E. Kilenyi   ♯ Rem. 199-83
(No. 21)
A. Aeschbacher   (2ss)   PV. 72169

No. 27, E minor, Op. 90
W. Kempff   PV. 72243
H. Steurer   ♯ Ura. 7051
(Nos. 16 & 22)
☆ A. Schnabel   ♮ G.DB 9713/4
(4ss)   (in ♯ Vic.LCT 1109: ♭ *set WCT 1109*)

No. 28, A major, Op. 101
W. Backhaus   ♯ D.LXT 2715
(No. 23)   (♯ Lon.LL 597)

No. 29, B flat major, Op. 106 *("Hammerklavier")*
F. Gulda   ♯ D.LXT 2624
(also 10ss, D.K 28547/51)   (♯ Lon.LLP 422)
E. Petri   ♯ AmC.ML 4479
K. Appelbaum   ♯ West.WL 5150
☆ M. Horszowski (♯ EVox. 360)

No. 30, E major, Op. 109
C. Solomon   ♯ Vic.LM 1716
(Nos. 21 & 22)   (♭ *set WDM 1716*)
W. Kempff   PV. 72210
M. Horszowski   ♯ AmVox.PL 7050
(No. 32)
☆ A. Schnabel   G.DB 21337/9
(6ss)   (in ♯ Vic.LCT 1110: ♭ *set WCT 1110*)

No. 31, A flat major, Op. 110
W. Kempff   (3ss)   PV. 72244/5S
K. Appelbaum   ♯ West.WL 5090
(Nos. 9 & 24)

No. 32, C minor, Op. 111
M. Horszowski   ♯ AmVox.PL 7050
(No. 30)
☆ A. Schnabel   G.DB 21340/3
(7ss—Rondo, A major) (in ♯ Vic.LCT 1109: ♭ *WCT 1109*)
J. Páleníček   (6ss)   ♮ U.H 24157/9
☆ C. Solomon (♯ Vic.LM 1222: ♭ *set WDM 1607*)

VARIATIONS
Six, F major, Op. 34
C. Seemann   ♮ PV. 72144/5
(Bagatelles, Op. 126)

Fifteen, E flat, Op. 35 *"Eroica"*
H. Roloff   ♮ PV. 72096/7
(4ss)   (♯ Pol. 16009)

Six, on the Turkish March, Op. 76
H. Steurer   ♯ Ura. 7033
(Sonatas 13 & 20, etc.)   (♭ *UREP 15, d.c.*)

Thirty-three, on a waltz by Diabelli, Op. 120
M. Horszowski   ♯ AmVox.PL 7730

Thirty-two, C minor   (G.191)
V. Schiøler   ♮ G.DB 20163/4
(3ss—Scarlatti-Tausig : Pastorale & Capriccio)
A. Goldenweiser   (4ss)   *USSR. 14726/9*

A. 2. CHAMBER MUSIC
(3) **Equali** (G.195) 4 trombones
Brass Ens.—Shuman   in ♯ Ren.X 31

QUARTETS, pf., vln., vla., vlc.
No. 1, E flat major
No. 2, D major
No. 3, C major [1]   (G.152) 1785
A. Balsam & Pascal Trio   ♯ CHS.CHS 1215

No. 4, E flat major, Op. 16
(from the pf. & wind quintet)
A. Balsam & Pascal Trio   ♯ CHS.G 1
(Romances)   (♯ Nix.CLP 1201, *below*)

QUARTETS, STRING
COMPLETE RECORDINGS (including the Grosse Fuge)

Nos. 1 & 2	on ML 4576
Nos. 3 & 4	on ML 4577
Nos. 5 & 6	on ML 4578
No. 7 (2ss)	on ML 4579
No. 8 (2ss)	on ML 4580
Nos. 9 & 11	on ML 4581
No. 10 (2ss)	on ML 4582
Nos. 12 to 15 (2ss each)	on ML 4583/6
No. 16 & Grosse Fuge	on ML 4587

Budapest Qtt.   ♯ AmC.ML 4576/87
                  (sets SL 172/4)

C major (from Pf. Sonata, Op. 2, No. 3)[2] and No. 1	on CHS 1201
Nos. 2 & 3	on CHS 1202
Nos. 4 & 5	on CHS 1203
Nos. 6 & 11	on CHS 1204
Nos. 7 to 10 (2ss each)	on CHS 1205/8
Nos. 12 to 14 (2ss each)	on ☆ CHS 1209/11
No. 15 (2ss)	on CHS 1213
No. 16 & Grosse Fuge	on CHS 1212

Pascal Qtt.   ♯ CHS.CHS 1201/13
                (♯ Nix.CLP 1201/13)

No. 5, A major, Op. 18, No. 5
Barylli Qtt.   ♯ West.WL 5140
(No. 11)
... Andante cantabile only
Paganini Qtt. (in † ♯ Vic.LM 1197: ♭ *set WDM 1611*)

No. 7, F major, Op. 59, No. 1
Vienna Konzerthaus Qtt.   ♯ West.WL 5127
Pascal Qtt., from set (♯ Clc. 6088)

No. 8, E minor, Op. 59, No. 2
Vienna Konzerthaus Qtt.   ♯ West.WL 5098
Vegh Qtt.   ♯ DFr. 65
▽ Strub Qtt.   (8ss)   ‡ G.DB 7711/4
Pascal Qtt., from set (♯ Clc. 6117)

No. 9, C major, Op. 59, No. 3
New Italian Qtt.   ♯ D.LXT 2679
(Schubert: Quartettsatz)   (♯ Lon.LLP 321)
New Music Qtt.   ♯ BRS. 909
(Pf. Sonata No. 9, arr.)
Vienna Konzerthaus Qtt.   ♯ West.WL 5134
Pascal Qtt., from set (♯ Clc. 6085)

No. 10, E flat major, Op. 74
Vienna Konzerthaus Qtt.   ♯ West.WL 5149

No. 11, F minor, Op. 95
Barylli Qtt.   ♯ West.WL 5140
(No. 5)
☆ Griller Qtt. (♯ *Lon.LS 107*)

No. 12, E flat major, Op. 127
Vienna Konzerthaus Qtt.   ♯ West.WL 5120
Vegh Qtt.   ♯ DFr. 70
☆ Pascal Qtt. (♯ Clc. 6051)

---

[1] The Adagio is also in Pf. Sonata No. 1.
[2] Nix.CLP 1201 does not contain this, but the arr. for pf. qtt. of the Quintet, Op. 16, *above*

Quartets, String (continued)

No. 13, B flat major, Op. 130
Barylli Qtt.   ♯ **West.WL 5129**
☆ Pascal Qtt. (♯ Clc. 6058)

No. 14, C sharp minor, Op. 131
Barylli Qtt.   ♯ **West.WL 5144**
☆ Pascal Qtt., from set (♯ Clc. 6118)

No. 15, A minor, Op. 132
Erling Bloch Qtt. (10ss)   ♮ **G.DB 20143/7**
Paganini Qtt.   ♯ **Vic.LM 1179**
                                 (♭ set WDM 1577)
Vienna Konzerthaus Qtt.   ♯ **West.WL 5104**

No. 16, F major, Op. 135
Barylli Qtt.   ♯ **West.WL 5151**
(below)
Pascal Qtt., from set (♯ Clc. 6064)
... **Adagio & Scherzo only** — ARR. ORCH.
☆ N.B.C. Sym.—Toscanini
  (in ♯ Vic.LCT 1041: ♭ set WCT 65; ♭ G.7RF 222)

Grosse Fuge, B flat major, Op. 133
Barylli Qtt.   ♯ **West.WL 5151**
(above)
Pascal Qtt. (from set) (♯ Clc. 6064)

— STRING ORCH. VERSION
Stuttgart Cha.—Münchinger   ♯ **D.LXT 2663**
(Bach)   (♯ Lon.LL 526)
(also D.K 28593/4, 4ss)
Vienna Cha. Orch.—Litschauer ♯ **Van.VRS 419**
(Purcell)

———————

Quintet, C major, Op. 29 2 vlns., 2 vlas., vlc. 1801
Pascal Qtt. & W. Gerhard   ♯ **CHS.CHS 1214**
                                (♯ Nix.CLP 1214)

Quintet, E flat major, Op. 16 pf., ob., cl., hrn., bsn.
(see also above, Str. qtts. & Pf. qtt. No. 4)
French Radio Ens.   ♯ **Pat.DT 1006**

Septet, E flat major, Op. 20
cl., hrn., bsn., vln., vla., vlc., cbs. c. 1799
Berlin Phil. Cha. Ens.   ♮ **PV. 72240/2S**
(5ss)   (♯ Pol. 18030)
☆ Vienna Septet (D.K 28277/81)

Serenade, D major, Op. 8 vln., vla., vlc.
Pasquier Trio (n.v.)   ♯ **Allo.ALG 3031**
(Trio No. 2)

Serenade, D major, Op. 25 fl., vln., vla.
J. Baker, J. & L. Fuchs   ♯ **AmD.DL 9574**
(Str. Trio No. 4)

Sextet, E flat major, Op. 81b str. & 2 hrns.
... 1st movt., Allegro con brio, only
Bolshoi Theatre Qtt., Y. Shapiro &
  V. Polekh   **USSR. 019024/5**
(2ss)

Sonata, B flat major fl. & pf. (doubtful)
K. Wanausek & A. Brendel   ♯ **SPA. 28**
(Trio)
☆ J. P. Rampal & R. Veyron-Lacroix
                                ♯ **Clc. 6032**
(Bach, Dukas, Hindemith, Roussel, etc.)

Sonata, F major, Op. 17 hrn. & pf.
J. Stagliano & P. Ulanowsky   in ♯ **Bo.L 200**
(Mozart, Schubert, Schumann)
D. Shuman (trombone) & S. Raphling
(Equali)   in ♯ **Ren.X 31**

SONATAS, vln. & pf.
No. 1, D major, Op. 12, No. 1 No. 2, A major, Op. 12, No. 2
No. 3, E flat major, Op. 12,
  No. 3   No. 4, A minor, Op. 23
No. 5, F major, Op. 24   No. 6, A major, Op. 30, No. 1
No. 7, C minor, Op. 30, No. 2 No. 8, G major, Op. 30, No. 3
No. 9, A major, Op. 47   No. 10, G major, Op. 96

COMPLETE RECORDING
J. Fuchs & A. Balsam   (10ss)
                                ♯ **AmD. set DX 150**

No. 1, D major, Op. 12, No. 1
P. Kaul & N. Radisse (No. 5) ♯ **Sat.LDG 8005**
☆ J. Heifetz & E. Bay (4ss) ♮ **G.DB 9489/90**

No. 2, A major, Op. 12, No. 2
☆ J. Heifetz & E. Bay (4ss)   ♮ **G.DB 9491/2**

No. 3, E flat major, Op. 12, No. 3
Z. Francescatti & R. Casadesus ♯ **AmC.ML 4478**
(No. 4)

No. 4, A minor, Op. 23
M. Rostal & F. Osborn   ♯ **D.LXT 2752**
(No. 8)   (♯ Lon.LLP 471)
Z. Francescatti & R. Casadesus ♯ **AmC.ML 4478**
(No. 3)
J. Fournier & G. Doyen   ♯ **West.WL 5164**
(No. 6)
R. Odnoposoff & O. Herz   ♯ **Allo.ALG 3047**
(No. 8)
P. Kling & O. Schulhof   ♯ **Rem. 199-113**
(No. 5)

No. 5, F major, Op. 24 ("Spring")
N. Milstein & A. Balsam   ♯ **Vic.LM 134**
                                 (♭ set WDM 1594)
P. Kaul & N. Radisse (No. 1) ♯ **Sat.LDG 8005**
P. Kling & H. Kann (No. 4)   ♯ **Rem. 199-113**
D. Oistrakh & L. Oborin   **USSR. 18882/9**
(8ss)
☆ E. & A. Wolf   ♯ **Mer.MG 10120**
(below)

No. 6, A major, Op. 30, No. 1
J. Fournier & G. Doyen   ♯ **West.WL 5164**
(No. 4)

No. 8, G major, Op. 30, No. 3
M. Rostal & F. Osborn   ♯ **D.LXT 2752**
(No. 4)   (♯ Lon.LLP 471)
R. Odnoposoff & O. Herz   ♯ **Allo.ALG 3047**
`(No. 4)
D. Oistrakh & L. Oborin   **USSR. 017293/6**
(4ss)

No. 9, A major, Op. 47 ("Kreutzer")
M. Rostal & F. Osborn   ♯ **D.LXT 2732**
(2ss)   (♯ Lon.LL 575)
E. & A. Wolf   ♮ **Tono.X 25170/3**
(8ss)   (No. 5 on ♯ Mer.MG 10120)
Y. Menuhin & A. Baller   **JpV.SD 3042/5**
(8ss)   (set JAS 218)
J. Heifetz & B. Moiséiwitsch ♯ **Vic.LM 1193**
                                 (♭ set WDM 1612)
W. Schneiderhan & H. Berg   ♯ **Mrt. 200-21**
☆ E. Zathureczky & G. Faragó ♯ **Bne.LP 502**
M. Polyakin & A. Diakov   **USSR. 6527/30,**
                               8286/90 & 8350/1
(11ss—Schubert)

No. 10, G major, Op. 96
T. Spivakovsky & R. Firkusny ♯ **AmC.ML 4402**
(Encore pieces)

———————————————————
♯ = Long-playing, 33⅓ r.p.m.   ♭ = 45 r.p.m.   ♮ = Auto. couplings, 78 r.p.m.

SONATAS, vlc. & pf.

No. 1, F major, Op. 5, No. 1　　No. 2, G minor, Op. 5, No. 2
No. 3, A major, Op. 69　　　　No. 4, C major, Op. 102, No. 1
No. 5, D major, Op. 102, No. 2

COMPLETE RECORDING
J. Starker & A. Bogin　　　　♯ **Per.SPL 560/1**
(Nos. 1, 4, 5 on SPL 561)　　(& in set SPL 562)

No. 1, F major, Op. 5, No. 1
A. Janigro & C. Zecchi　　　♯ **West.WL 5170**
(below)
P. Tortelier & K. Engel　　　♯ **G.FALP 151**
(below)

No. 2, G minor, Op. 5, No. 2
P. Casals & R. Serkin　　　　♯ **AmC.ML 4572**
(Variations)　　　　　　　　　(& in ♯ set SL 169)
A. Janigro & C. Zecchi　　　♯ **West.WL 5170**
(above)
P. Tortelier & K. Engel　　　♯ **G. FALP 151**
(above)

No. 3, A major, Op. 69
A. Janigro & C. Zecchi　　　　**West.WL 5173**
(Variations)

TRIOS, pf., vln., vlc.

No. 2, G major, Op. 1, No. 2
E. Istomin, A. Schneider, P. Casals
　　　　　　　　　　　　　♯ **AmC.ML 4573**
　　　　　　　　　　　　　　(& in set SL 170)
Boston Trio　　　　　　　　♯ **Allo.ALG 3026**
(No. 4)

No. 4, D major, Op. 70, No. 1 ("Geister")
Boston Trio　　　　　　　　♯ **Allo.ALG 3026**
(No. 2)
Santoliquido Trio　　　　　　♮ *PV. 36033/4*
(4ss)　　　　　　　　　　　　(♯ Pol. 18044)
E. Rubbra, E. Gruenberg, W. Pleeth
(Rubbra: Trio)　　　　　　　♯ **Argo.ARS 1005**[1]

No. 5, E flat major, Op. 70, No. 2
E. Istomin, A. Schneider, P. Casals
　　　　　　　　　　　　　♯ **AmC.ML 4571**
(Trio, Op. 11)　　　　　　　　(& in set SL 170)

No. 6, B flat major, Op. 97
Trieste Trio　　　　　　　　♯ **D.LXT 2717**
(2ss)　　　　　　　　　　　　(♯ Lon.LL 599)
E. Istomin, A. Schneider, P. Casals
　　　　　　　　　　　　　♯ **AmC.ML 4574**
　　　　　　　　　　　　　　(& in set SL 170)
P. Badura-Skoda, J. Fournier, A. Janigro
　　　　　　　　　　　　　♯ **West.WL 5130**
☆ A. Jambór, V. Aitay, J. Starker
　　　　　　　　　　　　　♯ **Nix.PLP 707**
　　　　　　　　　　　　　　(♯ Clc. 6073)
(alias Carnegie Trio)

No. 7, B flat major G.154
J. Mannes, B. Gimpel, L. Silva ♯ **AmD.DL 9555**
(C. Schumann)

Trio, pf., cl., vlc., B flat major, Op. 11
M. Horszowski, R. Kell, F. Miller ♯**B.AXTL 1011**
(Mozart)　　　　　　　　　　(♯ AmD.DL 9543)
Wilkomirski Trio　　　　　　♮ **U.H 24018/20**
(6ss)

— PF., VLN., VLC. VERSION
E. Istomin, A. Schneider, P. Casals
　　　　　　　　　　　　　♯ **AmC.ML 4571**
　　　　　　　　　　　　　　(& in set SL 170)
(Pf. Trio No. 5)
A. Goldenweiser, D. Tziganov, S. Shirinsky
(6ss)　　　　　　　　　　　　**USSR. 07641/6**

Trio, pf., fl., bsn., G major (B & H 294)
A. Brendel, K. Wanausek, H. Petschek ♯**SPA. 28**
(Sonata)

TRIOS, vln., vla., vlc.

No. 1, E flat major, Op. 3
Pasquier Trio　　　　　　　♯ **Allo.ALG 3023**

No. 2, G major, Op. 9, No. 1
Bel Arte Trio (No. 3)　　　　♯ **AmD.DL 9635**
Pasquier Trio (Serenade)　　♯ **Allo.ALG 3031**

No. 3, D major, Op. 9, No. 2
Bel Arte Trio (No. 2)　　　　♯ **AmD.DL 9635**
☆ Pasquier Trio (n.v.) (No. 4) ♯ **EA.ALX 3015**
☆ Pasquier Trio (o.v.)　in † ♯ **AS. 3003LD**

No. 4, C minor, Op. 9, No. 3
Fuchs Trio (Serenade)　　　♯ **AmD.DL 9574**
☆ Pasquier Trio (No. 3)　　♯ **Allo.ALX 3015**

VARIATIONS

(12) on Ein Mädchen oder Weibchen, Op. 66
　　vlc. & pf. 1797
P. Casals & R. Serkin　　　♯ **AmC.ML 4572**
(Sonata No. 2, etc.)　　　　　(& in set SL 170)
P. Tortelier & K. Engel　　　*G.DA 5051/2*
(4ss)

(7) on Bei Männern . . . (G.158)　vlc. & pf. 1801
P. Casals & R. Serkin　　　♯ **AmC.ML 4572**
(Sonata No. 2)　　　　　　　(& in set SL 169)
A. Janigro & C. Zecchi　　　♯ **West.WL 5173**
(Sonata No. 3)

on Ich bin der Schneider Kakadu, Op. 121a
　　vln., vlc., pf.
Santoliquido Trio　　　　　　♮ **PV. 72260/1**
(Rondo, Op. 51, No. 1—A. Aeschbacher, pf.) (♯ Pol. 18044)

on Là ci darem　2 obs. & cor anglais　c. 1796
S. Sutcliffe, R. Lord, N. James　**P.R 20615**

A. 3. DANCES

CONTRETÄNZE

(2) unspec. (possibly from Deutsche, below)
Winterthur Sym.—Goehr　　♯ *MMS. 10*
(Symphony No. 8)

Unspec. — ARR. VLN. & PF. Heifetz ("Folk Dance")
☆ J. Heifetz & E. Bay　　　*G.DA 2001*
(Bach: Eng. Suite No. 6, excpt.) (in ♯ Vic.LM 1166)

(12) Deutsche Tänze G.140
French Radio—Leibowitz　　♯ **Eso.ES 512**
(Mozart, Schubert)　　　　　(♯ Cpt.MC 20003)

... Nos. 2, 8, 10, 12
☆ Vienna State Op.—Scherchen (AusT.E 1122)

... Nos. 1, 4, 6
☆ Vienna State Op.—Scherchen (AusT.E 1143)

Écossaises B & H 302　　　　pf.
A. Aeschbacher　　　　　　　*Pol. 26519*
(Für Elise)

Minuet, G major G.167　　　pf.
— ARR. VLN. & PF.
☆ M. Elman & W. Rosé　　　♭ *Vic. 49-3444*
(Drigo: Serenade)　　　　　　(also in ♭ WEPR 29)

A. 4. ORCHESTRAL

CONCERTOS, pf. & orch.

No. 1, C major, Op. 15
F. Gulda & Vienna Phil.—Böhm [1]
♯ **D.LXT 2627**
(9ss—*Bagatelles*, on D.KX 28556/60) (♯ Lon.LLP 421)
H. Roloff & Berlin Radio—Rucht
♯ **CdM.LDX 8015**
(♯ Dia.DPM 5)
E. Everett & Berlin Sym.—Balzer ♯ **Roy. 1376**
☆ W. Gieseking & Philharmonia Orch. (C.LFX 983/6;
♯ QCX 109)

No. 2, B flat major, Op. 19
W. Backhaus & Vienna Phil.—Krauss [1]
♯ **D.LX 3083**
(♯ *Lon.LS 630*)

No. 3, C minor, Op. 37
B. Moiséiwitsch & Philharmonia—Sargent
G.C 4160/3
(8ss) (♯ BB.LBC 1012: ♭ set *WBC 1012*)
L. Kraus & Vienna Sym.—Moralt
♯ **PaV.VP 220**
(♯ AmVox.PL 7270)
W. Frey & Munich Tonkünstler—Strobl
♯ **Mer.MG 10078**
G. Kuntz & Berlin Radio—Schultz ♯ **Rgt. 5026**
G. Stein & Berlin Sym. ♯ **Roy. 1304**
☆ A. Schnabel & L.P.O.—Sargent
♭ **G.DB 7377/81**
(9ss—*Rondo, C major*)
☆ C. Haskil & Winterthur Sym.—Swoboda
(♯ Sel.LPG 8316)

No. 4, G major, Op. 58
W. Gieseking & Philharmonia—Karajan [1]
♯ **C.LX 1443/6**
(8ss) (GQX 11493/6; ♯ AmC.ML 4535; ♯ *C.FC 1014*)
W. Backhaus & Vienna Phil.—Krauss [2]
♯ **D.LXT 2629**
(also, 8ss, ♮ D.AKX 28542/5: X 53107/10)(♯ Lon.LLP 417)
P. Badura-Skoda & Vienna State Op.—
Scherchen ♯ **West.WL 5143**
G. Novães & Vienna Sym.—Klemperer [1]
♯ **AmVox.PL 7090**
(♯ PaV.VP 200; EVox. 200)
F. Wührer & Austrian Sym.—Randolf
♯ **Rem. 199-72**
E. Everett & Berlin Sym. ♯ **Roy. 1305**
☆ A. Rubinstein & R.P.O.—Beecham
(♯ Vic.LCT 1032: ♭ set *WCT 48*)

No. 5, E flat major, Op. 73
E. Fischer & Philharmonia—Furtwängler
(10ss) **G.DB 21315/9**
W. Gieseking & Philharmonia—Karajan
♮ **C.LCX 5008/12S**
(9ss—last blank)
(2ss, ♯ C.CX 1010: FCX 135; ♯ AmC.ML 4623)
V. Horowitz & Vic. Sym.—Reiner
♯ **Vic.LM 1718**
(♭ set *WDM 1718*)
P. Badura-Skoda & Vienna State Op.—
Scherchen ♯ **West.WL 5114**
H. Reiter & Berlin Phil.—Schultz ♯ **Rgt. 5025**
C. de Groot & Residentie—v. Otterloo
♯ **Phi.A 00133L**
M. Huttner & Berlin Sym. ♯ **Roy. 1306**
☆ V. Schiøler & Danish Radio—Garaguly (♯ Clc. 6016)
F. Karrer & Viennese Sym.—Wöss (♯ Mrt. 200-11)

C major, Op. 56 (Triple) vln., vlc., pf., orch.
☆ J. Corigliano, L. Rose, W. Hendl, N.Y. Phil. Sym.
—Walter (♯ *C.FC 1002*)

CONCERTO, vln. & orch. D major, Op. 61
I. Haendel & Philharmonia—Kubelik [3]
(11ss) **G.C 4126/31S**
(EH 1409/14S) (♯BB.LCB 1003: ♭ set *WBC 1003*)
A. Campoli & L.S.O.—Krips [4] ♯ **D.LXT 2674**
(2ss) (♯ Lon.LL 560)
R. Ricci & L.P.O.—Boult [5] ♯ **D.LXT 2750**
(2ss) (♯ Lon.LL 562)
H. Krebbers & Residentie—v. Otterloo
♯ **Phi.A 00132L**
D. Oistrakh & USSR. Radio—Gauk
(12ss) **USSR. 019230/41**
G. Taschner & Berlin Radio—Rother
♯ **Rgt. 5029**
J. Balachowsky & Berlin Sym. ♯ **Roy. 1307**
(Unspec. excpts. in ♯ Roy. 1314)
☆ Z. Francescatti & Philadelphia—Ormandy
(♯ C.CX 1011: QCX/FCX 126: ♮ C.LNX 8058/62)

— ARR. PF. & ORCH. Beethoven
A. Balsam & Winterthur Sym.—Dahinden [1]
♯ **CHS.F 10**

Musik für die grosse Wacht-Parade (G.144) 1816
London Baroque Orch.—Haas **P.R 20614**

OVERTURES
Coriolan, Op. 62
Philharmonia—Schuechter **C.DX 1841**
(2ss) (CQX 16661: DWX 5080)
Bamberg Sym.—Keilberth **T.E 3916**
(in ♯ Cap.P 8164)
L.P.O.—v. Beinum (2ss) **D.K 23312**
(& ♯ *Lon.LD 9021*)
Sym.—Hewitt **V♯ DFr. 69**
(*Egmont Ov.*)
Residentie—v. Otterloo ♯ **Phi.A 00145L**
(½s.—*Egmont Ov.*, & *Sym. 9, s.1*)
Austrian Sym.—Singer in ♯ *Mrt. 1-16*
Rhineland Sym.—Federer ♯ **Rgt. 5035**
(*Leonore Ov. No. 2*)
☆ N.B.C. Sym.—Toscanini (♭ *G.7RF 120*)
Berlin Phil.—Kleiber (Eur.TAI 708)
Philadelphia—Ormandy (♭ *AmC.AAL 15*)

Namensfeier, Op. 115
Austrian State Sym.—Gui ♯ **MSL.MW 42**
(*Gluck, Weber, Mendelssohn*)
Berlin Sym.—Ludwig in ♯ **Roy. 1380**

Zur Weihe des Hauses, Op. 124
L.P.O.—v. Beinum ♯ *Lon. LD 9022*
(*Leonore Ov. No. 3*)
Berlin Phil.—v. Kempen **PV. 56016**
Rhineland Sym.—Federer ♯ **Rgt. 5033**
(*Smetana: Vltava*)
☆ L.P.O.—Weingartner **C.LCX 154/5**
(3ss—*Egmont, Clärchens Tod*) (GQX 11510/1)

ROMANCES, vln. & orch.
No. 1, G major, Op. 40
No. 2, F major, Op. 50
M. Rostal & Winterthur Sym.—Goehr
(*Pf. Qtt.*) ♯ **CHS.G 1**
Z. Francescatti & Col. Sym.—Morel
(*Bruch: Concerto*) ♯ **AmC.ML 4575**

[1] Cadenza by Beethoven.
[2] First cadenza by Beethoven; second by Backhaus.
[3] Cadenzas by Joachim.
[4] Cadenzas by Kreisler.
[5] First Cadenza by Kreisler; second by Ricci.

ROMANCES　(*continued*)

J. Heifetz & Vic. Sym.—Steinberg
♭ *G.7RF 167/8*
(2ss each)　　　　　　　(No. 1 only on G.DB 21471)
(♭ *Vic. 49-3611/2*: ♭ *WEPR 9*: in ♯ *LM 9014*)

L. Fuchs & Little Orch.—Scherman
♯ *B.AXL 2003*
(♯ *AmD.DL 4004*)

T. Olof (No. 1), H. Krebbers (No. 2) &
Residentie—v. Otterloo　　　♯ **Phi.A 00140L**
(*Bach: Concerto, 2 vlns.*)
(2ss each, on Phi.N 11218/9G: PhM.M 09034/5S)

J. Dumont & A. Collard (pf.) **Pat.PDT 266/7**
(No. 1 on PDT 267, No. 2 on PDT 266)

No. 2, F major, Op. 50, only
E. Telmanyi & Danish Radio—Jensen
(n.v., same no.)　　　　　　　**Tono.X 25004**

H. Lewkowicz & P. Vallribera (pf.)
SpC.RG 16178

SYMPHONIES
No. 1, C major, Op. 19
Vienna Phil.—Schuricht　　　♯ *D.LX 3084*
(2ss)　　　　　　　　　　　　　　(♯ *Lon.LS 631*)
N.B.C. Sym.—Toscanini　　　♯ **G.FALP 191**
(*Sym. No. 9*)　　(♯ Vic. set LM 6009: ♭ *set WDM 6009*)
Boston Sym.—Münch　　　　♯ **Vic.LM 1200**
(*Haydn: Sym. 103*)　　　　　　(♭ *set WDM 1622*)
Vienna State Op.—Scherchen
(*Sym. No. 9*)　　　　　in ♯ **West. set WAL 208**
Berlin Sym.—Balzer　　　　　♯ **Roy. 1302**
Sonor Sym.—Ledermann　　　♯ **Pde. 2010**
☆ B.B.C. Sym.—Toscanini (♯ Vic.LCT 1023: ♭ set WCT49)
N.Y.P.S.O.—Walter (♯ *C.FC 1005*)
Vienna Phil.—Weingartner (♯ AmC.ML 4501)
Amsterdam—Mengelberg (♭ *Cap. set KCM 8081*)

No. 2, D major, Op. 36
Vienna Phil.—Schuricht　　　♯ **D.LXT 2724**
(2ss)　　　　　　　　　　　　　　(♯ *Lon.LL 629*)
N.Y.P.S.O.—Walter　　　　　♯ **AmC.ML 4596**
(*No. 4*)
Sydney Sym.—Goossens　　　**G.ED 1206/9**
(8ss)
Homburg Sym.—Schubert　　♯ *Rgt. 5010*
Berlin Sym.—Guenther　　　♯ **Roy. 1251**
☆ L.S.O.—Weingartner (♯ AmC.ML 4502)
San Francisco—Monteux (♯ G.FALP 114)

No. 3, E flat major, Op. 55　"Eroica"
N.B.C. Sym.—Toscanini (n.v.) ♯ **G.ALP 1008**
(2ss)　　　　　　　　　　　(FALP 103: QALP 103)
Sonor Sym.—Ledermann　　　♯ **Pde. 2005**
Berlin Sym.—Friedl　　　　　♯ **Roy. 1218**
Hamburg Sym.—Schubert　　♯ *Rgt. 5007*
"Nat. Op. Orch."　　　　　　♯ *Var. 2002*
(1st movt. only in ♯ *Var. 6956* & in ♯ *Roy. 6102*)
☆ Berlin Phil.—Schuricht (♯ AmD.DL 9534)
Vienna Phil.—Weingartner (♯ AmC.ML 4503)

No. 4, B flat major, Op. 60
N.Y.P.S.O.—Walter　　　　　♯ **AmC.ML 4596**
(*No. 2*)
Berlin Phil.—Furtwängler　♯ **AmVox.PL 7210**
(2ss)
San Francisco Sym.—Monteux ♯ **Vic.LM 1714**
(*Schumann: Sym. No. 4*)　　　(♭ *set WDM 1714*)
Orch.—Hewitt　　　　　　　　♯ **DFr. 61**
(*Symphony No. 5*)
Berlin Sym.—Ludwig　　　　♯ **Roy. 1243**
Austrian Sym.—Singer　　　♯ **Rem. 199-51**
(♯ *Mrt. 200-23*)
☆ L.P.O.—Weingartner (♯ AmC.ML 4504)
Vienna Phil.—Furtwängler (♯ G.FALP 116)

No. 5, C minor, Op. 67
Vienna Sym.—Klemperer
♯ **E. & AmVox.PL 7070**
(2ss)　　　　　　　　　　　　　　(♯ PaV.VP 150)
Berlin Phil.—Jochum　(2ss)　♯ **Phi.A 00102L**
Orch.—Hewitt　　　　　　　　♯ **DFr. 61**
(*Symphony No. 4*)
Rome Sym.—Guenther (♯ Roy. 1219)
USSR. State Sym.—Gauk (USSR. 06348/55)
"Nat. Op. Orch." (♯ Roy. 2001)
(1st movt. in ♯ *Var. 6956* & in ♯ Roy. 1247)
Radio Sym. (♯ *Roy. 6030*), etc.

☆ N.B.C. Sym.—Toscanini
(in ♯ Vic.LCT 1041: ♭ set WCT 67)
Paris Cons.—Schuricht (♯ D.LXT 2513)
Boston Sym.—Koussevitzky (♯ G.FALP 182)
Vienna Phil.—v. Karajan
(♯ C.CX 1004: QCX 107: FCX 107)
L.P.O.—Weingartner (♯ AmC.ML 4505)
Sym.—Wolf (♯ *Mrt. 1-2*)
Hallé—Barbirolli (♯ BB.LBC 1018: ♭ set WBC 1018)
Amsterdam—Mengelberg (♯ T.LSK 7005)
Dresden Phil.—v. Kempen (P.OR 5073/7)

No. 6, F major, Op. 68　"Pastoral"
Vienna State Op.—Scherchen ♯ **West.WL 5108**
Pittsburgh Sym.—Steinberg　♯ **DCap.CTL 7023**
(♯ Cap.S 8159; ♯ T.LCSK 8159)
Sonor Sym.—Ledermann　　　♯ **Pde. 2011**
Berlin Sym.—Guenther　　　♯ **Roy. 1225**
☆ L.P.O.—Kleiber　　　　　♯ **D.LXT 2587**
(also ♮ ArgOd. 51006/10)　　　　(♯ Lon.LLP 33)
☆ B.B.C.—Toscanini (♯ Vic.LCT 1042: ♭ set WCT 70)
Royal Phil.—Weingartner (♯ AmC.ML 4506)
Amsterdam—Mengelberg (FT.49/52)
Vienna Sym.—Klemperer (♯ PaV.VP 100; EVox. 100)
Philadelphia—Walter (♯ C.FCX 144)
Viennese Sym.—Wöss (♯ Mrt. 200-5)
Minneapolis—Mitropoulos (♯ AmC.RL 3009)

No. 7, A major, Op. 92
Vienna State Opera—Scherchen
♯ **West.WL 5089**
(♯ Sel.LPG 8478)
Sym.—Hewitt　　　　　　　　♯ **DFr. 62**
Berlin Sym.—Balzer　　　　　♯ **Roy. 1303**
☆ Boston Sym.—Münch (♯ G.FALP 106)
Vienna Phil.—Furtwängler (♯ G.FALP 115: QALP 115;
Vic.LHMV 1008: ♭ set WHMV 1008)
Vienna Phil.—Weingartner (♯ AmC.ML 4507)
Viennese Sym.—Wöss (♯ Mrt. 200-6)

No. 8, F major, Op. 93
Berlin Sym.—Ludwig　　　　♯ **Roy. 1240**
Winterthur Sym.—Goehr　　♯ *MMS. 10*
(*Dances*)
Austrian Sym.—Busch　　　♯ **MSL.MW 39**
(*Haydn*)
Hastings Sym.—Bath　　　　♯ **Allo.ALG 3049**
(*Mozart: Sym. 31*)
Sonor Sym.—Ledermann　　　♯ **Pde. 2003**
▽ Leipzig Gewandhaus—Schmitz (Imp. 014109/11)
☆ Vienna Phil.—Weingartner (in ♯ AmC. set SL 165:
also ♯ ML 4508)

No. 9, D minor, Op. 125　"Choral"
S, A, T, B, cho., orch.
Vienna Phil.—Kleiber (4ss)　♯ **D.LXT 2725/6**
(H. Gueden, S. Wagner, A. Dermota, L. Weber,
Musikfreunde Cho.)　　　　　　(♯ Lon.LL 632/3)
N.B.C. Sym.—Toscanini　　♯ **G.FALP 190/1**
(3ss—*Sym. No. 1*) (♯ Vic. set LM 6009: ♭ set WDM 6009)
(E. Farrell, N. Merriman, J. Peerce, N. Scott, R. Shaw
Chorale)
Vienna State Op.—Scherchen
(3ss—*Sym. No. 1*)　　　♯ **West. set WAL 208**
(M. Laszlo, H. Rössl-Majdan, P. Munteanu, R. Standen,
Singakademie Cho.)

(*continued next page*)

☆ = Re-issue of a recording to be found in WERM or Supplement I.

Sym. No. 9, D minor, Op. 125 "Choral" (*continued*)

Residentie—v. Otterloo   ♯ **Phi.A 00145/6L**
(3ss—*Coriolan & Egmont Ovs.*)
(E. Spoorenberg, M. v. Isloway, F. Vroons, H. Schey, Amsterdam Toonkunst Cho.)

Leipzig Sym.—Abendroth   ♮ **U.H 24006/14**
(18ss)
(A. Schlemm, D. Eustrati, G. Lutze, K. Paul, Leipzig Radio Cho.)

Anon. Soloists & Berlin Cath. Cho. & Sym.—
Rubahn (4ss)   ♯ **Roy. 1267/8**

☆ N.Y.P.S.O.—Walter   ♯ **C.FCX 113/4**
(3ss—*Brahms: Schicksalslied*)
(I. Gonzalez, E. Nikolaidi, R. Jobin, M. Harrell & Westminster Cho.)

☆ Soloists & Vienna Phil.—Weingartner
(♯ AmC. set SL 165)

B. STAGE WORKS

EGMONT, Op. 84   Inc. music to Goethe's play
COMPLETE RECORDING
K. Nentwig (S), M. Konstantinov (speaker) & Stuttgart Pro Musica Orch.—
Reinhardt   ♯ **AmVox.PL 7640**

Overture
L.P.O.—v. Beinum   ♯ **Lon.LD 9021**
(*Coriolan*)

Sym.—Hewitt   **V♯ DFr. 69**
(*Coriolan*)

Residentie—v. Otterloo   ♯ **Phi.A 00145L**
(⅓s.—*Coriolan, & Sym. 9, s.1*)
(also *PhM.N 09027S* & Phi.N 11154G)

Austrian Sym.—Wolf   ♯ **Mrt. 1-22**
(*Smetana*)

Berlin Sym.—Ludwig   in ♯ **Roy. 1380**

    Various Orchs
(in ♯ *Var. 6933*, Var. 2021, *Var. 6949*, etc.)
☆ Boston—Koussevitzky (♭ *G.7RF 137*)
Philadelphia—Ormandy (♯ *AmC.AAL 15*)
Rome Sym.—Questa (in ♯ Roy. 1230)
Berlin Phil.—Keilberth (AusT.E 1181; in ♯Cap.P 8164)
Philharmonia—Galliera (C.M 15153)

— ARR. BAND
French Reserve—Beaufort   **V ♯ Sat.MSA 5001**
(*Bach: Toccata & Fugue*)

No. 1, Die Trommel gerühret
No. 4, Freudvoll und leidvoll
M. Maddox (S) & pf.   in ♯ **MTR.MLO 1009**

No. 7, Clärchens Tod
☆ L.P.O.—Weingartner   **C.LCX 155**
(*Weihe des Hauses, s.3*)   (GQX 11511)

FIDELIO   Opera   3 acts   1805, 2 acts 1806
COMPLETE RECORDING
Leonore ... ... H. Konetzni (S)
Marzelline ... ... I. Seefried (S)
Florestan ... ... T. Ralf (T)
Jacquino ... ... P. Klein (T)
Don Pizarro ... ... P. Schoeffler (B)
Rocco ... ... H. Alsen (Bs)
etc., Vienna State Op. Cho. & Vienna Phil.—
Böhm   ♯ **AmVox. set PL 7793**
(6ss)   (Leonore Ov. No. 3 played in Act 2)

Overture
L.P.O.—v. Beinum   **D.K 23313**
(♯ *Lon.LD 9024*)

Berlin Sym.—Ludwig   in ♯ **Roy. 1380**
☆ Vienna State Op.—Swarowsky (AusT.E 1113)

ACT I

No. 3, Ach, wär' ich schon . . .   S
E. Schwarzkopf   **C.LX 1410**
(*Carmen—Je dis que rien . . .*)   (LVX 157)
♮ E. Schumann (IRCC. 3125*)

No. 8, Ha! welch ein Augenblick   B
O. Edelmann   in ♯ **D.LXT 2672**
(*below; & Offenbach, Cornelius, etc.*)   (♯ Lon.LLP 427)
(also on D.K 28553)

No. 10, Abscheulicher! Wo eilst du hin?
Komm, O Hoffnung   S
I. Borkh   **G.DB 11544**
A. Varnay   in ♯ **Rem. 199-45**
(*Walküre, Juive, Thaïs*)
☆ L. Lehmann (in ♯ AmD.DL 9523)

No. 11, Finale . . . O welche Lust!
Wir wollen mit Vertrauen   Cho.
Berlin Municipal Op.—Rother   **G.EH 1400**
(FKX 249: GB 69)
Württemberg State Op.—Leitner   **PV. 72219**
(*Rienzi—Ihr Römer hört die Kunde*)   (♯ Pol. 18048)

ACT II

No. 13, Gott, welch' Dunkel hier!   T
In des Lebens Frühlingstagen
P. Anders   **G.DB 11543**
☆ J. Patzak   in ♯ **D.LXT 2672**
(♭ *D. 71016*; ♯ Lon.LL 427)
☆ F. Völker (Pol. 15452)
♮ J. Urlus (IRCC. 3125*)

(Die) GESCHÖPFE DES PROMETHEUS,
    Op. 43   Ballet
COMPLETE RECORDING
☆ Winterthur Sym.—Goehr (♯ Clc. 6049/50)

Overture & Nos. 1, 3, 5, 9, 14, 15, 16
L.P.O.—v. Beinum   ♯ **D.LXT 2741**
(Overture only on ♯ *Lon.LD 9024*)   (♯ Lon.LL 577)

Overture
Paris Cons.—Cluytens   **Pat.PD 144**
(MD 3)
Munich Phil.—Rieger   **PV. 36030**
(*Ruinen von Athen, Ov.*)   (♯ AmD.DL 4047)
USSR. State—K. Ivanov (USSR. 16605/6)
Varsity Sym. (in ♯ Roy. 2017 & in ♯ Roy. 6084)
☆ N.B.C. Sym.—Toscanini
(in ♯ Vic.LCT 1041: ♭ set WCT 65)
Dresden Phil.—v. Kempen (Pol. 15489)

No. 8, Marcia
☆ Dresden Phil.—v. Kempen (Pol. 15490)

LEONORE OVERTURES
(originally written for *Fidelio*)
No. 1, Op. 138
Berlin Sym.—Ludwig   in ♯ **Roy. 1380**
☆ B.B.C. Sym.—Toscanini
(in ♯ Vic.LCT 1041: in ♭ set WCT 65)

No. 2, Op. 72a
Munich Phil.—Papst   ♯ **Mer.MG 15038**
(*Brahms: Tragische Ouvertüre*)
Rhineland Sym.—Federer   ♯ **Rgt. 5035**
(*Coriolan*)
Berlin Sym.—Ludwig   in ♯ **Roy. 1380**

No. 3, Op. 72a (*see also* Fidelio, complete)
Danish Radio—Malko   ♮ **G.DB 20171/2**
(*Leonore Prohaska, Trauermarsch*)
Berlin Phil.—Keilberth   ♯ **Cap.P 8164**
(*Coriolan & Egmont Overtures*)

♯ = Long-playing, 33⅓ r.p.m.   ♭ = 45 r.p.m.   ♮ = Auto. couplings, 78 r.p.m.

28

Leonore Ov. No. 3, Op. 72a   (continued)
L.P.O.—v. Beinum   **# Lon.LD 9022**
(Zur Weihe des Hauses)
Rome Sym.—Questa   **# Roy. 1230**
(Egmont; & Mozart: Sym. No. 29)
☆ Berlin Phil.—Jochum (FT.T 101/2)
Varsity Sym. (in # Var. 2017), etc.

LEONORE PROHASKA   Inc. Music.   G.202
No. 2, Romanze   glass harmonica
B. Hoffmann   **Pol. 6002**
(Mozart & Reichardt)

No. 4, Trauermarsch [1]
Danish Radio—Malko   **G.DB 20171**
(Leonore Ov. No. 3, s.1)

(Die) RUINEN VON ATHEN, Op. 113
(Inc. Music to Kotzebue's Drama)
COMPLETE RECORDING
A. Woud (A), D. Hollestelle (B), Netherlands
Phil. Cho. & Orch.—Goehr **# Nix.CLP 1158**
                               (# CHS.CHS 1158)

Overture
Munich Phil.—Rieger   **PV. 36030**
(Prometheus Overture)   **(# AmD.DL 4047)**

No. 4, Marcia alla turca
☆ Amsterdam—Mengelberg   **T.SK 3713**
(Parsifal—Good Friday Music, s.3)

C. VOCAL

CHRISTUS AM ÖLBERGE, Op. 85
S, T, Bs, cho., orch.
COMPLETE RECORDING
M. Opawsky, R. Delorco, W. Berry, Vienna
Academy Cho. & State Op. Orch.—
Swoboda   **# Nix.CLP 1135**
(2ss)   **(# CHS.CHS 1135)**

Fantasia, C major, Op. 80   pf., cho. & orch.
Anon. soloist, cho. & Berlin Radio—
Anon.   **# Rgt. 5022**
☆ F. Wührer, Vienna Sym.—Krauss
                      (# PaV.VP 110; EVox. 110)

MASSES

D major, Op. 123   ("Missa Solennis")
S, A, T, B, cho., orch.
I. Steingruber, E. Schürhoff, E. Majkut,
O. Wiener, Academy Cho. & Vienna Sym.—
Klemperer (4ss) **# E. & AmVox. set PL 6992**
Anon. soloists, Berlin Cath. Cho. & Sym.
Orch.—Balzer (4ss)   **# Roy. 1368/9**
☆ Soloists, Kittel Cho. & Berlin Phil.—Kittel
                                 (Pol. 67477/87S)

SONGS
COLLECTION
An die ferne Geliebte, Op. 98 (Jeitteles)
Adelaide, Op. 46 (Matthisson)
Ich liebe dich   G. 235 (Herrosen)
In questa tomba oscura   G. 239 (Carpani)
(Der) Kuss, Op. 128   (Weisse)
Lied aus der Ferne   G. 242 (Reissig)
Mailied, Op. 52, No. 4 (Goethe)
(Der) Wachtelschlag   G. 237 (Metastasio-Sauter)
Wonne der Wehmut, Op. 83, No. 1 (Goethe)
A. Poell (Bs), V. Graef (pf.) **# West.WL 5124**

An die ferne Geliebte, Op. 98   Song cycle
(Jeitteles)
D. Fischer-Dieskau (B), G. Moore (pf.)
(4ss)   **♮ G.DB 9681/2**
M. Harrell (B), C. V. Bos (pf.)
(4ss)   **♭ Vic. set WDM 1591**

(Die) Ehre Gottes, Op. 48, No. 4   (Gellert)
P. Schoeffler (B), O. Schulhof (pf.)
(Schubert, etc. & Wagner)   **# MSL.MW 43**
B. Sönnerstedt (B, Swed), W. Ahlén (org.)
(Mozart: Ave verum corpus)   **Symf.R 1015**
— ARR. CHO.   Cologne Male Voice Cho. (G.EG 7487)

Es war einmal . . ., Op. 75, No. 3   (Goethe)
(Song of the flea)
M. Reizen (Bs, Russ)   **USSR. 15399**
(Moussorgsky: Song of the flea)

Ich liebe dich   G. 235   (Herrosen)
P. Schoeffler (B), O. Schulhof (pf.)
(above)   **# MSL.MW 43**
J. Vincent (S), F. de Nobel (pf.)
(Schubert, etc.)   in **# Phi.A 00610R**
E. Katulskaya (S, Russ) (USSR. 18407)

In questa tomba oscura   G. 239   (Carpani)
G. Vaghi (Bs)   **P.AB 30019**
(Tosti: Tristezza)

D. MISCELLANEOUS
FOLK-SONG ARRANGEMENT
Come fill, fill, Op. 108, No. 13   (Smyth) [2]
A. Ivanov (B, Russ)   **U.H 23835**
(Schumann: Dichterliebe, No. 7)
M. Mikhailov (Bs) (USSR. 12213), B. Gmyria (Bs)
(USSR. 16915)

Beethoven, his story and music
(Narration with orch. illustrations)
☆ F. Mack & Vox. Sym.—Goberman **# AmVox.VL 2600**

BÈGUE, Nicolas le   (c. 1630-1702)
SEE: † FRENCH ORGAN MUSIC

BELLINI, Vincenzo (1801–1835)

OPERAS
BIANCA E FERNANDO   2 acts   1826
Sorgi o padre   S
Ⓗ ☆ C. Muzio & pf. (in # Eso.ES 502*;
                           in # Cpt.MC 20009*)[3]

I CAPULETI E I MONTECCHI   4 parts   1830
Oh! quante volte   S   (Part I)
M. Carosio   **G.DB 21336**
(Manon—Adieu, notre petite table)
R. Carteri   (2ss)   **P.CB 20538**

NORMA   4 acts   1831

ACT I

Meco all' altar di Venere   T
R. Lagares   **G.DB 11354**
(Cavalleria Rusticana—Addio alla madre)

Sediziose voci (Recit.); **Casta Diva** (Cavatina) S
H. Traubel   in **# Vic.LM 123**
                               (♭ set WDM 1584)
☆ M. M. Callas   **P.R 30041**
C. Muzio & cho.   in **# AmC.ML 4404**
Ⓗ C. Boninsegna & pf.   G.VB 28*, o.n. 053050*
Lilli Lehmann   in # Ete.O-463*
B. Kiurina & cho. (Ger)   IRCC. 3114*

Ah si, fa core, abbracciami   2 Ss
Ⓗ L. Lehmann & H. Helbig (in # Ete. O-463*)

[1] ARR. by Beethoven from Pf. Sonata No. 12.
[2] Labelled A Scottish Toast or Drinking song and assumed to be this.
[3] Recorded from Edison cylinder.

NORMA (continued)

ACT II

Mira, o Norma   S, A
♯ G. Russ & V. Guerrini (HRS. 1082*)

Deh non volerli vittime   S, T, B, cho.
... Sop. part only
♯ E. Burzio (HRS. 1059*)

I PURITANI   3 acts   1835
EXCERPTS
♯ S. Kurz (S), F. de Lucia (T), U. Luppi (Bs),
    E. Gherlinzoni (T), P. Amato (B), M. Battistini (B),
    etc. (♯ Ete.ELP O-486*)

ACT I

Ah, per sempre   B
P. Silveri   **C.LX 1509**
(*Ernani—Oh de' verd'anni miei*)   (GQX 11501)
I. Petroff   in ♯ **Rem. 199-93**
♯ M. Battistini (in ♯ Ete. 451*)

A te, o cara, amor talora   T
B. Finelli, G. Sas (pf.)   in ♯ **Mon.MWL 300**
♯ A. Bonci (in ♯ GAR. 101*)

Son vergin vezzosa   S
L. Pons   **C.LX 1514**
(*Mignon—Je suis Titania*)

ACT II

Rendetemi la speme . . .
Qui la voce . . .Vien diletto   S
☆ M. Callas (2ss)   **P.R 30043**
☆ M. Carosio (♭ G.7R 137: 7RF 155)
♯ O. Boronat & pf. (G.VA 11*: o.n. 53351*)

Cinta di fiori   B
♯ E. Pinza (G.VB 70*: o.n. DB 828*)

Suoni la tromba   B, Bs
♯ T. Ruffo & De Segurola (G.VA 16*: o.n. 54360*)

ACT III

A una fonte   T
Nel mirarti   T
B. Finelli, G. Sas (pf.)   in ♯ **Mon.MWL 300**

Vieni, vieni fra queste braccia   S, T
♯ ☆ M. Galvani & F. Marconi (G.VB 4*)

Credea si misera   T
☆ B. Finelli, G. Sas (pf.)   in ♯ **Mon.MWL 300**

(LA) SONNAMBULA   3 acts   1831

ACT I

Prendi l'anel ti dono   S, T
... tenor part only
B. Finelli, G. Sas (pf.)   in ♯ **Mon.MWL 300**
♯ F. de Lucia (in ♯ CMS. 201*)

Vi ravviso   Bs
N. Rossi-Lemeni   ♮ **G.DB 9779**
(*Forza del Destino—Il Santo Nome*)
☆ R. Arié (in ♯ D.LX 3041; Lon.LPS 98)
♯ F. Chaliapin (in ♯ AudA. 0077*)
   P. Plançon (G.VB 12*: o.n. 032024*)

Son geloso del zefiro   S, T
☆ A. Galli-Curci & T. Schipa
    (in ♯ Vic.LCT 1037*; ♭ set WCT 57)
♯ M. Galvany & A. Giorgini (G.VB 26*: o.n. 054112*)

ACT III

Ah ! non credea mirarti   S
☆ C. Muzio (in ♯ AmC.ML 4404)
   L. Pagliughi (AmD. 16010)
   L. Pons (C.LFX 993)
♯ G. F. Magrini (in ♯ Ete. O-486*)

Ah ! non giunge   S
☆ L. Pons (C.LFX 993)
♯ A. Galli-Curci (G.VB 5*: o.n. DB 812*)
   L. Tetrazzini (*IRCC. 3091*)
   G. F. Magrini (in ♯ Ete. O-486*)

BENEDICT, Sir Julius (1804-1885)

(Il) Carnevale di Venezia   S
M. Robin   in ♯ *D.LX 3037*
(also D.GAF 15095)   (♯ *Lon.LPS 255*)
& many ▽ versions.

BENNET, John   (b. c. 1570)
SEE : † TRIUMPHS OF ORIANA

BENOÎT, Pierre L. L. (1834-1901)

(The) Pacification of Ghent   Opera   1876
... **Entrance of the Duke of Alba**   orch.
   ▽ Brussels Radio—Dejoncker   **T.A 10369**
   (*J. Blockx: Danse flamande, No. 5*)

SONGS
My Mother-tongue   (*Mijn Moederspraak*) (Groth)
   ▽ E. de Decker (Bs) & orch.   **C.DCB 43**
   (*M. de Mol: I know a song . . .*)

(The) Little Rose (*Heeft het Roosje milde geuren*)
   ▽ M. Greeve (M-S) & pf.   **C.DCB 14**
   (*Uyttenhove: Moederke alleen*)

My heart is full of longing   (Hiel)
F. Lepage (M-S) & pf.   **C.DCB 52**
(*A. de Boeck: Het Kerske van te lande*)
NOTE: Older recordings of these songs are now deleted

BENTZON, Niels Viggo (b. 1919)

Chamber Concerto, Op. 52
   3 pfs., 5 insts., & percussion
Copenhagen Collegium Musicum—Friisholm
(4ss)   ♮ **G.Z 7036/7**
(pfs., N. V. Bentzon, H. D. Koppel, G. Vasarhelyi)

Constellation   pf. 4 hands
N. V. Bentzon & B. Roger-Henrichson
           Mtr.CL 3002
(*Roger-Henrichson: Hieroglyphic*)

BERCHEM, Jachet van (fl. c. 1550)

O Jesu Christe   Motet
International Cho.—Maillet   **Pat.PDT 273**
(*Palestrina: Sicut cervus*)
(recorded during Mass at St. Peter's, Rome, 1951)

♯ = Long-playing, 33⅓ r.p.m.   ♭ = 45 r.p.m.   ♮ = Auto. couplings, 78 r.p.m.

BEREZOVSKY, Nicolai (b. 1900)

Suite, Op. 11　　fl., ob., cl., hrn., bsn.
New Art Quintet　　　　　　　**♯ CEd. 1003**
(Fine & Milhaud)

BERG, Alban (1885-1935)

Lyric Suite Str. Qtt. 1926
☆ [New] Pro Arte Qtt.　　　　**♯ Mtr.CL 5003/5**
(6ss)　　　　　　　　　　　　(♯ CLP 5003)

OPERAS
LULU 3 acts 1937

Lulu	I. Steingrüber (S)
Dr. Schön	O. Wiener (B)
Alwa	H. Libert (T)

etc., Vienna State Op. Cho. & Sym. Orch.—
Häfner (6ss)　　　　　**♯ AmC. set SL 121**

WOZZECK, Op. 7　3 acts　1925
COMPLETE RECORDING [1]

Marie	E. Farrell (S)
Wozzeck	M. Harrell (B)
Drum-major	F. Jagel (T)
Andres	D. Lloyd (T)

etc., New York Phil. Sym.—Mitropoulos
　　　　　　　　　　　　♯ C.FCX 157/8
(4ss)　　　　　　　　　　(♯ AmC. set SL 118)

Quartet, String, Op. 3　1910
☆ New Music Qtt. (n.n ♯ BRS. 906)

Sonata, Op. 1　pf.　1906/8
A. Schier-Tiessen　　　　　　**PV. 72140**
(Poulenc: Napoli)　　　　　　(FPV. 5032)
　☆ B. Tupas (♯ Eur.LPG 628)

SONGS
7 Early Songs; 4 Songs, Op. 2
☆ C. Rowe (S), B. Tupas (pf.) (♯ Eur.LPG 628)

(7) Early songs　1905/7
K. Harvey (S) & Zürich Radio Orch.—
Goehr　　　　　　　　　　**♯ CHS.G 12**
(below; & Hindemith)

(4) Stücke, Op. 5　　　　cl. & pf.
H. Tichman & R. Budnevich　**♯ CHS.G 12**
(Songs; & Hindemith)
　☆ S. Forrest & B. Tupas (♯ Eur.LPG 628)

(Der) Wein (Baudelaire, trs. Georg) S. & orch. 1929
C. Boerner & Janssen Sym. **♯ DCap.CCL 7515**
(Talk by A. Frankenstein)　　(♯ Cap.L 8150)

BERGER, Arthur (b. 1912)

Duo, No. 2　　　　　　　vln. & pf.
B. Earle & A. Berger　　　　　**♯ NE. 4**
(Flanagan, etc.)

Partita　pf.　1947
B. Weiser　　　　　　　　　　**♯ NE. 1**
(Flanagan, etc.)

NOTE.—Brazilian Psalm (♯ StO. 5, ♯ Argo.ARS 1003, etc.)
is by Jean Berger (b. 1909), and Legende vom Prinzen
Eugen (▽ ♯ G.DB 7652) by Theodor Berger.

BERGSMA, William Laurence (b. 1921)

Quartet, String, No. 2　1943-4
Walden Qtt.　　　　　　　　　**♯ ARS. 18**
(Shepherd: Triptych)

[1] A recording of a 1951 radio performance.

BERLIOZ, Hector (1803-1869)

BÉATRICE ET BÉNÉDICT
Opéra-comique, 2 acts　1862
Overture
Philharmonia—Kletzki　　　　**C.LX 1529**
　　　　　　　　　　　　(in ♯ C.CX 1003)
Lamoureux—Martinon　　　　**♯ Ura. 7048**
(below)
☆ Boston Sym.—Münch　in ♯ **Vic.LM 1700**
(Lalo, Ravel, etc.)　(♭ *Vic. set WDM 1700*; ♭ *G.7RF 124*)
Stadium Concerts Sym.—Smallens
　　　　　　　　　　　　♯ AmD.DL 4034
(Dvořák: Carnival Overture)
Berlin Sym.—Ludwig　　　in ♯ **Roy. 1382**

BENVENUTO CELLINI, Op. 23　Opera, 2 acts
　1838
Overture
Philharmonia—Kletzki　　♮ **C.LX 8935/6**
(3ss—Brahms: Hungarian Dances, 2 & 3) (in ♯ C.CX 1003)
Paris Cons.—Münch　　　　**♯ D.LXT 2677**
(Corsaire; & Ravel: Bolero) (♯ Lon.LLP 466, & ♯ LD 9019)
Opéra-Comique—Wolff　　in ♯ **D.LXT 2625**
(Lalo, Massenet, Saint-Saëns)　(♯ Lon.LLP 355)
Concerts Colonne—Paray　in ♯ **Pol. 545000**
Berlin Phil.—v. Kempen　　　　**PV. 36023**
　　　　　　　　　　　(in ♯ AmD.DL 4003)
Berlin Sym.—Ludwig　　　in ♯ **Roy. 1382**

(Le) Carnaval romain, Overture, Op. 9　1844
Minneapolis Sym.—Dorati　**♯ Mer.MG 50005**
(Debussy & Ravel)
Rhineland Sym.—Federer　　　**♯ Rgt. 5039**
(Roi Lear Overture)
Lamoureux—Martinon　　　in ♯ **Ura. 7043**
　　　　　　　　　　　　(♭ UREP 9)
Lamoureux—Fricsay　　　　　**PV. 36029**
(Dukas: L'Apprenti sorcier, on ♯ AmD.DL 4027)
Berlin Sym.—Ludwig　　　in ♯ **Roy. 1382**
"Nat. Op. Orch."　　　　　in ♯ **Roy. 6135**
　☆ Amsterdam—Mengelberg (Eur.TAI 718)
　Boston Sym.—Koussevitzky
　　　　　　　　(♭ G.7RF 125; ♭ Vic. 49-1178)
　Dresden Phil.—v. Kempen (Pol. 15521)

(Le) Corsaire, Overture, Op. 21　1831
Paris Cons.—Münch　　　in ♯ **D.LXT 2677**
(Benvenuto Cellini, Overture & Ravel) (in ♯ Lon. LL 466)
Philharmonia—Kletzki　　　　**C.LX 1533**
　　　　　　　　　(GQX 16654: in ♯ CX 1003)
Lamoureux—Martinon　　　in ♯ **Ura. 7048**

(La) DAMNATION DE FAUST, Op. 24　1846
INCOMPLETE RECORDING
　☆ M. Berthon, J. de Trévi, C. Panzéra, etc., Cho. &
　　Pasdeloup Orch.—Coppola (JpV. set JAS 185)

Orchestral suite
Marche hongroise; Danse des sylphes; Menuet des follets
Paris Cons.—Sebastian　　　　**♯ Ura. 7061**
(Marche funèbre & C. Franck)
　☆ Amsterdam—v. Beinum　　**♯ D.LX 3096**
(Handel & Clarke)　　　　　　(♯ Lon.LS 320)
　☆ Amsterdam—Mengelberg (♯ T.LB 6009)

Marche hongroise & Danse des Sylphes
　☆ Philharmonia—Kubelik
　　　　　　(G.S 10536: EH 1415: GB 67; BrzV. 87-5051)

Marche hongroise only
Philharmonia—Weldon　　　　**C.DX 1818**
(Mendelssohn: Athalie—War March of the Priests)
　　　　　　　　　　　　　　(DWX 5078)

(continued on next page)

DAMNATION DE FAUST : Marche hongroise (*continued*)
San Francisco—Monteux in♭ *Vic. set WDM 1618*
(*Debussy : Images, s.1*)
L.P.O.—Martinon   in ♯ *MGM.E 541*
(also in ♯ *MGM.E 145*)   (♭ *set K 112*)
Concerts Colonne—Paray   in ♯ **Pol. 545000**
   ☆ Amsterdam—Mengelberg (FT.SK 177)

ACT II
Voici des roses   B
Ⱨ M. Renaud (G.VB 20*: o.n. D 858*)

Danse des Sylphes   orch.
A. Kostelanetz Orch.   **C.DX 1845**
(*François Schubert & Rimsky-Korsakov*)
Sym.—Stokowski   in ♯ *Vic.LM 151*
(*Ibert, Sibelius, Granados*)   (♭ *set WDM 1628*)

ACT III
Menuet des follets
Brussels Radio—André   in ♯ *DT.LGM 65002*
(*Chabrier, Debussy, etc.*)   (in ♯ *T.LS 6011*)
(also on T.E 3886*)

Devant la maison   B
Ⱨ M. Renaud (G.VB 20*: o.n. D 858*)

(L') ENFANCE DU CHRIST, Op. 25
S, T, B, Bs, Bs, cho., orch.
H. Bouvier, J. Giraudeau, L. Noguéra,
H. Médus, M. Roux; R. St. Paul Cho. &
Paris Cons. Orch.—Cluytens
                    ♯ **Pat.DTX 101/2**
(4ss)   (♯ AmVox.PL 7122, o.n. 7120)

(Les) Francs-Juges, Overture, Op. 3 1828
Philharmonia—Kletzki   ♭ **C.LX 8926/7**
(3ss—*Brahms: Hungarian Dance, No. 1*) (in ♯ CX 1003)
Berlin Radio—Celibidache   ♯ **Ura. 7024**
(*Franck: Psyché*)

Grande Messe des Morts, Op. 5 1837 (*Requiem*)
   ☆ G. Jouatte (T), cho. & orch.—Fournet (♯ FCX 148/9)

Harold en Italie, Op. 16 vla. & orch. 1834
W. Primrose & Royal Phil.—Beecham
                    ♯ **C.CX 1019**
                    (♯ AmC.ML 4542)
Anon. Soloist & Berlin Sym.—Ludwig
                    ♯ **Roy. 1384**

Marche funèbre, Op. 18, No. 3 orch.
(for the last scene of Hamlet)
Paris Cons.—Sebastian   ♯ **Ura. 7061**
(*Damnation de Faust; & C. Franck*)

(Les) NUITS D'ÉTÉ, Op. 7 (Gautier) 1834
Song cycle   S & orch.
1. Villanelle   2. (Le) Spectre de la rose
3. Sur les lagunes   4. Absence
5. Au cimetière   6. (L') Ile inconnue
S. Danco & Cincinnati Sym.—T. Johnson
                    ♭ **D.AX 554/7**
(8ss) (2ss—♯ D.LXT 2605; Lon.LLP 407)

(Le) Roi Lear, Overture, Op. 4 1831
Lamoureux—Martinon   in ♯ **Ura. 7048**
Boston Sym.—Ludwig   in ♯ **Roy. 1382**
Rhineland Sym.—Federer   ♯ **Rgt. 5039**
(*Carnaval romain*)

ROMÉO ET JULIETTE, Op. 17 Dramatic Sym.
   1839
Roméo seul & Grand fête chez Capulet
Scène d'amour   Part II
   ☆ N.B.C.—Toscanini   ♯ **G.FALP 155**
(*Tchaikovsky*)

Scherzo, La reine Mab   Part IV
Bamberg Sym.—Lessing   in ♯ **Mer.MG 10080**

Symphonie fantastique, Op. 14 1831
Amsterdam—v. Beinum (n.v.) ♯ **D.LXT 2642**
                    (♯ Lon.LLP 489)
Berlin Phil.—v. Otterloo   ♯ **Phi.A 00123L**
Philadelphia—Ormandy   ♯ **AmC.ML 4467**
Berlin Sym.—Balzer   ♯ **Roy. 1325**
   ☆ San Francisco Sym.—Monteux (♯ G.FALP 118:
                    QALP 118)
Paris Cons.—Münch (C.M 15169/74)

(Les) TROYENS À CARTHAGE Opera 1859
COMPLETE RECORDING
   Didon   ...   .   A. Mandikian (S)
   Ascanius ...   . M. Rolle (S)
   Anna   ...   .   J. Collard (A)
   Aeneas ...   . J. Giraudeau (T)
   Norbal ...   . X. Depraz (Bs)
Cho. & Paris Cons. Orch.—Scherchen
                    ♯ **West. set WAL 304**
(6ss) (Ballet Music & March, on V♯ Sel.LPP 8609)

Orchestral Suite
(Overture ; Chasse royale et orage; Ballet Music ; March)
Lamoureux—Martinon   ♯ *MGM.E 127*
                    (6ss—♭ *set K 127*)
Ballet Music
Munich Phil.—Meyer   in ♯ **Mer.MG 10080**
March
Lamoureux—Martinon, also in ♯ *MGM.E 145*

Chers Tyriens   Act III
Ⱨ M. Delner (*IRCC. 200**)

Adieu, fière cité   Act V
Ⱨ F. Litvinne (*IRCC. 200**)

BERNARD DE VENTADORN   (c. 1125-1195)
SEE : † XIITH & XIIITH CENTURY MUSIC

BERNERS, Lord (1883-1950)

(The) Triumph of Neptune   Ballet Suite   1926
Royal Phil.—Beecham   ♯ **AmC.ML 4593**
(*Arnell: Punch and the child*)

BERNSTEIN, Leonard (b. 1918)

FANCY FREE   Ballet   1944
Three Dances   orch.
Philadelphia Pops.—Hilsberg   ♯ *AmC.AAL 17*
(*Walton*)

BERTANI, Lelio   (fl. 1584-1609)
SEE : † A TREASURY OF MADRIGALS

BERWALD, Franz Adolf (1796-1866)

Quartet, Strings, No. 3, E flat major 1849
   ☆ Kyndel Qtt.   ♭ **G.DB 11060S/62**

♯ = Long-playing, 33⅓ r.p.m.   ♭ = 45 r.p.m.   ♮ = Auto. couplings, 78 r.p.m.

BESARD, Jean-Baptiste (b. *c.* 1567)
SEE : † XVItH & XVIItH CENTURY SONGS

BILLINGS, William (1746-1800)

Chester: Vocal Qtt. (in *Vic. set E 100* : ♭ *set WE 100*)

(The) Dying Christian to his soul
　　(*Vital spark of heav'nly flame—Pope*)
UOS. Cho.—McConnell　　in ♯ *UOS.pte.*
(*Gritton, Warlock, etc.*)

Easter Anthem
R. Shaw Chorale　　　　in ♯ **Vic.LM 1201**
(*Bach, Schütz, etc.*)　　　　　(♭ *set WDM 1623*)

Shepherd's carol (☆ in ♯ Vic.LM 1112)

(A) Virgin Unspotted
R. Shaw Chorale　　　in Vic. set DM 1711
　　　　　　　(♭ *set WDM 1711*: ♯ *LM 1711*)

BINET, Jean (b. 1893)

Quartet, String, No. 1　1930
E. Manoliu (vln.), J. Joubert (vln.)
　L. Reisacher (vla.) & F. Moser (vlc.)
　　　　　　　　　in ♯ **D.LXT 2658**
(*Brunner & Schoeck*)　　　(in ♯ *Lon.LLP 498*)

BISHOP, Sir Henry (1786-1855)

Home, sweet home (Payne) (from the opera *Clari*, 1823)
R. Ponselle (S) & orch.　　　　　**G.VB 74**
(*Schubert: Ave Maria*) (in ♯ *Vic. LCT 10*: ♭ *set WCT 55*)
J. C. Thomas (B)　　　　　in ♯ *ISR. 10-023*
　　　　　　　　　　　　　(also ♭ *1507-45*)
Lo, here the gentle lark (after Shakespeare)
☆ L. Pons (S) & orch. (in ♯ *AmC.ML 2181*; ♭ *set A 1006*)
Pretty mocking bird (Morton)
☆ L. Pons (S) & orch. (C.LX 1462)

BIZET, Georges (1838-1875)

CLASSIFIED:　I. STAGE
　　　　　　II. ORCHESTRAL
　　　　　　III. SONGS

I. STAGE

(L') ARLÉSIENNE Inc. Music　1872
Suites 1 & 2, complete
Sym.—Stokowski　　　　　♯ **Vic.LM 1706**
(*Symphony*)　　　　　　　(♭ *set LM 1706*)
Kostelanetz Orch.　　　　♯ **AmC.ML 4409**
Vienna Radio—Schönherr　　　♯ **Vien. 1019**
French Nat. Radio—Cluytens　♯ **Pat.DTX 103**
　　　　　　　　　　　　　　(♯ QTX 103)
Bamberg Sym.—Leitner　　　　♯ **Pol. 18049**

Suite No. 1, complete
☆ Amsterdam—v. Beinum (Pol. 68183/5S)

... Nos. 1 & 3 only
Hallé—Barbirolli　　　　　♭ **G.DB 9656/7**
(*Suite No. 2—No. 4*) (*Swan Lake*, in ♯ *BLP 1004*)

Suite No. 2
... Nos. 1, 3, 4, only
Paris Opéra—Sebastian　　　♯ **Ura. 7058**
(*Faust & Thaïs*) (*Intermezzo*, on ♯ Ura. 7068)

... No. 4, Farandole, only
Hallé—Barbirolli　　　　　**G.DB 9656**
(*Suite No. 1—No. 1, s.1*) (*Swan Lake*, in ♯ *BLP 1004*)
Covent Garden—Braithwaite in ♯ **MGM.E 3000**
☆ Col. Sym.—Rodzinski (in ♭ *AmC. set A 1002*)

CARMEN　Opera　4 acts　1875
COMPLETE RECORDINGS
SET A
Carmen	...	...	...	S. Juyol (S)
Micaela	...	...		J. Micheau (S)
Don José	...	...		L. de Luca (T)
Escamillo	...	...		I. Giovanetti (B)
Zuniga	...	...		H. Medus (Bs)
El Remendado	...	...		S. Rallier (T)
El Dancaire	...	...		J. Vieuille (B)

etc., Cho. & Orch. of Opéra Comique, Paris—
　Wolff　　　　　　　　♯ **D.LXT 2615/7**
(6ss—Guiraud's recitatives used) (♯ Lon. set LLPA 6)

SET B
Carmen	...	...	...	R. Stevens (M-S)
Micaela	...	...		L. Albanese (S)
Don José	...	...		J. Peerce (T)
Escamillo	...	...		R. Merrill (B)

Shaw Chorale & Victor Sym.—Reiner
　　　　　　　　　　　♯ **Vic. set LM 6102**
(6ss—Guiraud recits. used) (34ss, ♭ *set WDM 1556*)
(ballet is *Jolie Fille de Perth—Danse bohémienne* &
　Arlésienne—Farandole)
(Highlights also on ♯ Vic.LM 1749: ♭ *WDM 1749*)

☆ S. Michel (A), M. Angelici (S), R. Jobin (T),
　　M. Dens (B), etc., Cho. & Orch. of
　　Opéra Comique—Cluytens ♯ **C.CX 1016/8**
(6ss)

"Complete Arias"
G. Toma (Bs), P. Malgarini (S), C. Elmo (M-S), G.
　Prandelli (T), La Scala Cho. & Orch.—Questa (*Ital*)
　　　　　　　　　　　　♯ **Roy. 1204**
(Highlights from above on ♯ Roy. 6067: ♭ *set 14551*, 6ss)

"Companion"　(Narration & vocal excpts. with pf.)
E. Alberts (A), M. Stagliano (S), D. Lloyd (T),
　P. Tibbets (B), B. Goldovsky (narrator) ♯ **Bo.L 100**

Highlights
K. Grayson, G. Russell, etc.　　　*MGM. 9000/1*
Anon. artists (♯ Wde. 20202 & ♯ Pde. 1001; & with
　narration, ♯ Pde.OP 101)

"Carmen Jones"　ARR. Rose
☆ Soloists, cho. & orch.—Shaw
　　　　　　　　(♯ AmD.DL 8014: ♭ *set 9-125*)

Vocal Selection
Nat. Op. soloists & orch. (in ♯ Var. 2003 & ♯ *Var. 6955*)

Orchestral Selection
Berlin Sym.—Buschkötter (Od. O-3699)
— ARR. PF. V. Horowitz (in ♯ Vic.LM 1171:♭ *set WDM 1605*)

Orchestral Suites
Suites 1 & 2, COMPLETE
N.Y. Stadium Sym.—dell'Isola ♯ *AmD.DL 4029*

No. 1, only ☆ Viennese Sym.—Singer (♯ *Mrt. 1-7, d.c.*)

Preludes, Acts I-IV
Lower Austrian Artists—Singer
(4ss)　　　　　　　　　　*AusT.M 5144/5*
Vienna Radio—Nilius　　　　*Vien.P 6043/4*
(4ss)　　　　　　　　　　(in ♯ *1010*)

(*continued on next page*)

☆ = Re-issue of a recording to be found in WERM or Supplement I.

CARMEN Opera 4 acts 1875 (*continued*)

Preludes, Acts I, II, IV
Radio Luxembourg—Pensis (♯ FestF.FLD 3)

Preludes, Acts I & IV
☆ Berlin State Op.—Ludwig (G.GB 37: FKX 159)

Preludes, Acts II & IV
Philharmonia—Schuechter (in ♯ *MGM.E 131*: ♭ *set K 131*)

Prelude, Act I
Paris Opéra—Allain (in ♯ *Rem. 149-18*)
☆ Czech Phil.—Désormière (in ♯ *Sup.LPM 36*)

ACT I

Dans l'air (*Cho. des cigarettières*)
San Francisco Op. Cho. **ML. 46**

Habanera—L'amour est un oiseau rebelle M-S
J. Tourel & Philharmonia—Robinson **C.LX1507**
(*below*) (& with Col. Sym.—Morel, in ♯ AmC.ML 4608)
E. Wysor in ♯ **Rem. 199-30**
G. Simionato **C.GQX 11503**
(*Mignon—Je connais un pauvre enfant*)
R. Stevens (from Set B) **Vic. 10-3729**
(*Flower song, J. Peerce*) (♭ 49-3729: ♭ WEPR 45)

V. Davidova (*Russ*) (*USSR. 16550*)
♮ M. Delna (HRS. 2012*)
S. Arnoldson (*G.VA 56*: o.n. 33610**)

Parle-moi de ma mère S, T
M. Tauberova & B. Blachut (*Cz*) **U.H 24219**
A. Schlemm & R. Schock (*Ger*) **G.DB 11541**
R. Papagni & R. Lagares (*Ital*) **G.DB 11352**
E. Trötschel & W. Ludwig (*Ger*)[1] **PV. 36003**
♮ G. Huguet & F. de Lucia (*Ital*) (G.VB 34*: o.n. DB 359**)

Séguedille: Près des remparts de Séville M-S
J. Tourel & Col. Sym.—Morel in ♯ AmC.ML 4608
(*Offenbach*)
R. Stevens & J. Peerce (from Set B)
♭ **Vic.WEPR 45**
(*Habanera & Chanson du Toreador*)
V. Davidova (*Russ*) (*USSR. 16549*)
♮ E. Destinn (*Ger*) (in ♯ set CEd. 7001*)

ACT II

Chanson bohème
J. Tourel & Philharmonia—Robinson **C.LX 1507**
(*Habanera*) (& with Col. Sym.—Morel in ♯ AmC.ML 4608)
☆ B. Castagna **G.DA 1951**
(*Mignon, Gavotte*)
M. Maksakova (*Russ*) **USSR. 10780/1**
♮ E. Mantelli **IRCC. 3090***
E. Destinn (*Ger*) in ♯ set CEd. 7001*

Chanson du Toreador B
P. Silveri **C.LX 1530**
(*Prince Igor—No rest, no sleep*) (GQX 11513)
☆ C. Tagliabue (*Ital*) **P.PXO 1070**
(*Otello—Credo*)
A. Hiolski (*Pol*) Muza. 1719
A. Baturin (*Russ*) USSR. 7101/2

☆ R. Merrill (from set) ♭ *Vic.WEPR 45*
♮ P. Plançon HRS. 1101*

Air de fleur—La fleur que tu m'avais jetée T
M. del Monaco (*Ital*) **G.DB 11351**
(*Cavalleria Rusticana—Addio alla Madre*)
K. Baum in ♯ **Rem. 199-63**
(*Manon Lescaut, Andrea Chenier, etc.*)
J. Peerce (from set B) **Vic. 10-3729**
(*Habanera*) (♭ 49-3729)

[1] Commences *Et tu viens de là-bas?*
[2] Recorded from Edison cylinder.

Air de fleur (*continued*)
B. Blachut (*Cz*) **U.H 24195**
(*Ballo in Maschera—Morrò ma prima, Cervinkova*)
R. Schock (*Ger*) **G.DB 11542**
(*Cavalleria Rusticana—Addio alla madre*)

☆ J. Björling in ♯ Vic.LM 104: ♭ WDM 1546
A. Miltschinoff AusT.E 1098
M. Lanza G.DB 21498
J. Melton in ♯ Vic.LM 1202: ♭ WDM 1626
L. Fehenberger (*Ger*) Pol. 68403

♮ E. Caruso (*Ital*) G.VB 57*: o.n. DB 117*
E. Caruso in ♯ Vic.LCT 1007*: ♭ set WCT 11*
F. de Lucia G.VA 13*: o.n. 52437*
J. McCormack (*Eng*) in ♯ Ete. O-469*
F. de Lucia (*Ital*) in ♯ Ete. O-464*
L. Muratore HRS. 1071*

ACT III

En vain pour éviter (Air des Cartes) S
M. Garden **G.VA 18**
(*Gretchaninov: Over the Steppe*) (▽ o.n. DA 1248)
J. Tourel & Col. Sym.—Morel
in ♯ **AmC.ML 4608**
(*above; & Offenbach*)
E. Wysor in ♯ **Rem. 199-30**
M. Maksakova (*Russ*) (*USSR. 15812*)
♮ M. Delna (HRS. 2012*)

C'est des contrebandiers (Recit.)
Je dis que rien ne m'épouvante S
E. Schwarzkopf **C.LX 1410**
(*Fidelio—Ach, wär ich schon*) (LVX 157)
M. Cebotari (*Ger*) **Pol. 68403**
(*Air de la fleur, Fehenberger*)
M. Tauberova (*Cz*) **U.H 24224**
(*Pagliacci—Prologue, Otava*)
E. Shumskaya (*Russ*) USSR. 17389/90
☆ L. Pagliughi P.R 30034
S. Danco ♭ D. 71015
♮ C. Muzio (in ♯ Eso.ES 500*; ♯ Cpt.MC 20008*)[2]

ACT IV

Les voici cho.
▽ Württemberg State Op.—Leitner (*Pol. 62861*)

C'est toi? C'est moi M-S, T (Final duet)
R. Stevens & J. Peerce in ♯ **Vic.LM 9010**
(from set B)
♮ ☆ M. Gay & G. Zenatello (*Ital*) (G.VB 43)

(La) JOLIE FILLE DE PERTH 4 acts 1867
Orchestral Suite
☆ Royal Phil.—Beecham (♮ C.GQX 8033/4)

Danse bohémienne
Kostelanetz Orch. in ♯ **AmC.ML 4409**
Covent Garden—Braithwaite in ♯ **MGM.E 3000**
(also, as "Carmen ballet", in ♯ E 3003)

Ah! Écho, viens sur l'air embaumé S (Act IV)
♮ S. Kurz (*Ital*) (G.VB 48*: o.n. 2-053077*)

(Les) PÊCHEURS DE PERLES 3 acts 1863
COMPLETE RECORDING
Leila ... ... M. Dobbs (S)
Nadir ... ... E. Seri (T)
Zurga ... ... J. Borthayre (B)
Nourabad ... ... L. Mans (Bs)
etc., Paris Phil. Cho. & Orch.—Leibowitz
(6ss) ♯ **Nix.PLP 205-1/3**
(♯ Ren. set SX 205; ♯ Clc. 6100/2)

(Les) PÊCHEURS DE PERLES (*continued*)

ACT I

Au fond du temple saint   T, B
    J. Björling & R. Merrill   **G.DB 21426**
    (*Verdi: Otello—Si, pel ciel*)   (♭ *7R 124*)
        (in ♯ *Vic.LM 7007*: ♭ *set WDM 7007*)

A cette voix . . . Je crois entendre encore   T
    A. Biasi (*Ital*)   **Trla.T 8030**
    (*De Crescenzo: Rondia al nido*)
    S. Lemeshev (*Russ*)   **USSR. 06941**
    ☆ T. Rossi   in ♯ *AmC.FL 9544*: ♭ *set F 4-41*
    ♄ E. Caruso in ♯ *Vic.LCT 1007**: ♭ *set WCT 11**
    J. McCormack (*Ital*) *G.VA 21**: o.n. *DA 502**
    L. Sobinoff (*Russ*) *G.VB 19**: o.n. *DB 896**
    E. Caruso (*Ital*) *G.VB 44**: o.n. *052066**

Me voilà seule . . .
Comme autrefois dans la nuit sombre   S
    A. Noni (*Ital*)   **G.DB 11346**
    (*Don Pasquale—So anch'io*)
    ☆ L. Pagliughi (*Ital*)   **AmD. 16010**
    ♄ O. Boronat (*Ital*)   *G.VA 11** o.n. *53353**
    G. Pareto (*Ital*)   **AF 39***

De mon amie fleur endormie   T
    ♄ E. Caruso   *G.VA 36**: o.n. *DA 114**
    F. de Lucia (*Ital*)   in ♯ *Ete.O-464**

ACT II

Love Duet—Par cet étroit sentier   S, T
    R. & B. Gigli (*Ital*)   **G.DB 11347**
    (*Elisir d'amore—Chiedi al rio*)

Ton coeur n'a pas compris   S, T
    ♄ G. Huguet & F. de Lucia (*Ital*)
        (*G.VB 34**: o.n. *DB 570**)

ACT III

L'Orage s'est calmé   B
    ☆ P. Silveri (*Ital*) (*C.GQ 7244*: *LW 54*)

II. ORCHESTRAL

Jeux d'enfants, Op. 22   orig. pf. duet
— ORCH. VERSION   Bizet & Kolpikoff
Covent Garden—Braithwaite in ♯ **MGM.E 3000**
USSR.   State   Sym.—Gauk   *USSR. 8164/7*
(4ss)

Symphony, C major   1855
    Sym.—Stokowski   ♯ **Vic.LM 1706**
    (*Arlésienne Suites*)   (♭ *set WDM 1706*)
    Utrecht Sym.—Hupperts   ♯ *MMS. 11*
    ☆ Paris Cons.—Allain (♯ *Mrt. 200-19*)

III. SONGS

Agnus Dei   (to Intermezzo from *Arlésienne*)
    W. Midgley (T), orch. & org.   **G.DB 21550**
    (*Franck: Panis Angelicus*)
    E. Hobson (S), H. Dawson (org.) **C.DX 1840**
    (*Franck: Panis Angelicus*)
    J. Wahl (T) & orch. (*Od.DK 1166*)
    ☆ J. Melton (T) & orch. (in ♯ *Vic. LM 82*: ♭ *set WDM 1365*)

Chanson d'avril, Op. 21, No. 1 (Bouilhet)
    K. Derzhinskaya (S, *Russ*)   *USSR. 10031*
    (*Sibelius: Tryst*)

Douce mer (Lamartine)   1866
    Z. Dolukhanova (A, *Russ*)   *USSR. 18473*
    (*Delibes: Bonjour, Suzon*)

Ouvre ton coeur (Bolero) (Delâtre)   1887
    ♄ G. Martinelli (T) (*G.VA 61**)

BJÖRKANDER, Nils (b. 1893)

Popular Suite   pf.
… **2. Gavotte-Caprice** ;   **3. Meditation**
    F. Kjellberg   *Symf.R 1026*

BLACHER, Boris (b. 1903)

Concertante Musik, Op. 10   orch.   1937
    ▽ Berlin Phil.—Schüler   **G.DB 4618**

Variations on a theme of Paganini, Op. 26   orch.
1948
    R.I.A.S. Sym.—Fricsay   *PV. 56001*

BLISS, Sir Arthur (b. 1891)

Concerto, piano & orch., B flat major   1939
    N. Mewton-Wood & Utrecht Sym.—Goehr
                ♯ **CHS.CHS 1167**

Pastoral : Lie strewn the white flocks   1929
    N. Evans (M-S), G. Morris (fl.), B.B.C. Cho.,
    Jacques Str. Orch.—Jacques ♮ **D.AX 565/8**
    (8ss)

BLOCH, Ernest (b. 1880)

BAAL SHEM   vln. & pf.   1923
No. 2, Nigun
    T. Magyar & W. Hielkema   ♯ *Phi.N 00125R*
    (*Ravel & Kreisler*)

Concerto grosso   str. orch. & pf.   1928
    Chicago Sym.—Kubelik   ♯ **Mer.MG 50001**
    (*Bartók*)
    ☆ Curtis Ens.—Bailly (JpV. set JAS 236)

(4) Episodes   cha. orch.   1926
    Zürich Radio—Scherman   ♯ **CHS.F 4**
    (*Copland*)

Israel Symphony   S, S, A, A, B, orch.   1916
Soloists & Vienna State Op.—Litschauer
                ♯ **Nix.VLP 423**
    [F. Helsing & H. Augstein (S), E. Hofstätter & L.
    Dorpinghaus (A), L. Heppe (B)]   (♯ *Van.VRS 423*)

(5) Jewish pieces   viola & pf.
    M. Preves & H. Brahms   ♯ *BlSoc. 1*
        (also issued as pte. rec. by Covenant Club, Illinois)

(3) Poèmes juifs   orch.   1913
    A. R. S. Orch.—Hendl   ♯ **ARS. 24**
    (*Herbert*)

Psalm 114   1912-14
    D. Giannini (S)   **IRCC. 3115**
    (*Gioconda—Suicidio!*)

Quintet, pf. & str., C major   1924
    Chigi Quintet   ♯ **D.LXT 2626**
                (♯ *Lon.LLP 382*)

Schelomo   vlc. & orch.   1915
    L. Rose & N.Y.P.S.O.—Mitropoulos
    (*Saint-Saëns*)   ♯ **AmC.ML 4425**
    T. Machula & Residentie—v. Otterloo
    (2ss)   ♯ *Phi.A 00138R*
    ☆ E. Feuermann & Philadelphia—Stokowski
        (♯ *Vic.LCT 14*: ♭ *set WCT 69*)

☆ = Re-issue of a recording to be found in WERM or Supplement I.

Sonata, Piano 1935
  R. Cumming   # ML. 7015

Voice in the Wilderness   vlc. & pf.   1936
  G. Sopkin & F. Kirsch   # BlSoc. 2

BLOW, John (1648-1708)

VENUS AND ADONIS   Opera, Prol. & 3 acts
(c. 1684)
COMPLETE RECORDING
  M. Ritchie (S), M. Field-Hyde (S), E. Cooper (S),
    G. Clinton (B), cho. & orch.—Lewis
  (2ss)   # OL.LD 34

BOCCHERINI, Luigi (1743-1805)

Concerto, D major, Op. 27 fl. & str. orch. (doubtful)
  ☆ P. Renzi & Gothic Ens. (# Clc. 6078)

Concerto, vlc. & orch., B flat major
  (A synthetic work compiled by F. Grützmacher)
  A. Janigro & Vienna State Opera—Prohaska
  (Haydn)   # West.WL 5126
  S. Sindler & Berlin Sym.—Ludwig # Roy. 1381
  (Brahms: Overtures)
  ☆ P. Casals & L.S.O.—Ronald
         (# Vic.LCT 1028: ♭ set WCT 41)

QUARTETS, String
D major, Op. 6, No. 1   1769
  La Scala Qtt.   # Ura. 7074
  (Giardini & Puccini)
  ☆ New Italian Qtt.   # D.LXT 2680
  (Haydn: Qtt. Op. 64, No. 6)   (# Lon.LL 320)

A major, Op. 33, No. 6   1781
  New Music Str. Qtt.   # BRS. 911
  (A. Scarlatti & Tartini)
  ☆ York Qtt.   # Rgt. 5051
  (Vivaldi)

Quintet, fl. & str., E flat major   1769
  R. Adeney & London Baroque Ens.
  (J. Haydn & M. Haydn)   # West.WL 5080

QUINTETS, String   2 vlns., vla., 2 vlcs.   1771
D major, Op. 12, No. 4
... Pastorale only
  Virtuosi di Roma—Fasano   # AmD.DL 9649
  (Corelli, Scarlatti, etc.)

E major, Op. 13, No. 5   ... Tempo di Minuetto only
— STR. ORCH. VERSION
  ▽ Italian Radio—Basile   P.CB 20258
  (Corelli: Suite)   (P.CB 20530, d.c.)
  ☆ Boston Prom.—Fiedler (♭ Vic. 49-1022)

— ARRANGEMENTS
  O. Frugoni (pf.)   in # AmVox.PL 7700
  (Galuppi, Chopin, etc.)
  W. Tworek (vln.)   (Pol.HA 70038)

SEXTETS
E flat major, Op. 24, No. 1 2 vlns, 2 vlas, 2 vlcs. 1776
E flat major, Op. 41 Ob., hrn., bsn., vln., vla., cbs.
  1787
Sinfonia concertante, G major   ob., hrn., bsn., str.
  London Baroque Ens.—Haas # West.WL 5077

BÖHM, Georg (1661-1733)

SEE: † CHRISTMAS ORGAN MUSIC—HEITMANN
      † LES MAÎTRES D'ORGUE DE J. S. BACH
      † ORGAN MUSIC—HEITMANN

BOËLLMANN, Léon (1862-1897)

COLLECTION
  Suite gothique, Op. 25   org.
  ... No. 3, Prière à Notre Dame — ARR. VLC. & PF.
  Menuet gothique, Op. 31   vlc. & pf. [1]
  Variations Symphoniques, Op. 23   vlc. & pf. version
  G. Schwarz & R. Gola   # Sat.LDG 8002
  (Saint-Saëns: Sonata)

Suite gothique ... No. 3 only
  H. Robinson Cleaver   in AmD. set A 880
         (# DL 5360: ♭ set 9-269)

BOIELDIEU, François (1775-1834)

OPERAS
(Le) CALIFE DE BAGDAD   1 act   1800
Overture
  L.P.O.—Martinon   in # D.LXT 2606
  (Adam & Hérold)   (# Lon.LLP 351)
  Radio Luxembourg—Pensis   # FestF.FLD 3
  (Gounod, Thomas, Offenbach, etc.)
  Rhineland Sym.—Federer   # Rgt. 5041
  (Fiedler: Lustspiel Ov.; & Weber)
  Bamberg Sym.—Lehmann   in # Pol. 16036

(La) DAME BLANCHE   3 acts   1825
Overture
  L.P.O.—Martinon   in # D.LXT 2606
  (Hérold & Adam)   (# Lon.LLP 351)
  Dresden Phil.—v. Kempen   Pol. 15526
         (o.n. ▽ 57335)

Viens, gentille Dame   T   (Act II)
  H L. Slezak (Ger) (G.VA 3*: o.n. ER 129*)

Vivre loin de ses amours (unspec.—ARR. Dumas)
  R. Soria (B) & orch.   C.DF 3388
  (Lambert: De ma Céline)

BOISMORTIER, Joseph Bodin de (1691-1765)

SEE: † # AS. 3002LD

BOITO, Arrigo (1842-1918)

MEFISTOFELE   Prologue, 4 acts, Epilogue 1868

ACT I

Dai campi, dai prati   T
  H E. Caruso (G.VA 7*: o.n. DA 550*)
Son lo spirito che nega   Bs
  G. Neri   P.AT 0268
  (Favorita—Splendon più belle ...)
  (Bohème—Vecchia zimarra, on P.AT 0269)
Se tu mi doni un' ora   T & Bs
  H G. Zenatello & A. Didur (in # Ete O-467*)

---

[1] An arrangement by the Composer of the Minuet from Suite gothique.

MEFISTOFELE (*continued*)

ACT II

Ecco il mondo　　　　　　　Bs (Sc. 2)
A. Pirogov (*Russ*)　　　　　**USSR. 14883**
(*Meyerbeer : Huguenots—Piff! Paff!*)
♄ A. Didur (in ♯ Ete. O-467*)

ACT III

L'altra notte, in fondo al mare　　S
R. Tebaldi　　　　　　　　**Fnt. 22007**
(*Aïda—O cieli azzurri*)

H. Traubel　　　　　　　in ♯ *Vic.LM 123*
(*Norma, Otello, etc.*)　　　(in ♭ set WDM 1584)

☆ C. Muzio　　　　　in ♯ **AmC.ML 4404**

♄ C. Muzio (in ♯ Eso.ES 502*; ♯ Cpt.MC 20009*) [1]

EPILOGUE

Giunto sul passo estremo　　　T
♄ E. Caruso (*G.VA 7*: o.n. DA 550**)
　D. Smirnoff (*G.VB 38*: o.n. DB 582**)

BONONCINI, Marc Antonio　(1677-1726)

SEE † ITALIAN SONGS

BONNEAU, Paul (b. 1918)

Caprice (en forme de valse)
▽ M. Mule (sax.), M. Pellas-Lenon (pf.)
　　　　　　　　　　Sel.SA 7001
(*Ibert : Histoire No. 7*)

BONPORTI, Francesco Antonio
　　　　　　　　　　(1672-1749)

Concerto, F major, Op. 10, No. 15　vln. & orch
... **Recitativo only**
Czech Phil.—Pedrotti　　　**U.H 23788**
(*Corelli : Suite for Str., excpt.*)　　(in ♯ Sup.LPM 35)
▽ A. Pelliccia & Naples Cons—Lualdi
　　　　　　　　　　G.DB 05351
(*Pergolesi : Concertino, s. 3*)

BORODIN, Alexander (1833–1887)

In the Steppes of Central Asia　orch.　1880
Paris Cons.—Cluytens　　　**Pat.PDT 280**
(2ss)　　　　(in ♯ AmVox.PL 7670; ♯ Pat.DTX 116)
R.I.A.S. Sym.—Fricsay　　　♯ *AmD.DL 4022*
(*Moussorgsky*)
Berlin Sym.—Balzer　　　　♯ **Roy. 1344**
(*R. Strauss : Don Juan*)
☆ Amsterdam—Mengelberg (FT.T 119)
"Nat. Op. Orch." (in ♯ Var. 2005)

PRINCE IGOR　Opera (*Russ*)　4 acts　1890
COMPLETE RECORDING

Prince Igor	...	...	A. Ivanov (B)
Jaroslavna	...	...	E. Smolenskaya (S)
Vladimir	...	...	S. Lemeshev (T)
Galitsky	...	...	A. Pirogov (Bs)
Konchak	...	...	M. Reizen (Bs)

etc., Bolshoi Theatre Cho. & Orch.—Melik-
Pashayev (42ss)　　　**USSR. 020673/714**
(6ss, omitting Act III, ♯ Per. set SPLP 552; ♯ CdM.LDX
8034/6)

Nos. 7, 8, 17 : Dances　　cho. & orch.
☆ Cho. & Philadelphia—Stokowski ♯ **G.FALP 105**
(*Liszt : Les Préludes*)　　　　　　(QALP 105)

ACT I

No. 2, I hate a dreary life　Bs　(*Galitsky's Song*)
B. Gmyria　　　　　　**USSR. 017501**
(*Dargomijsky : Roussalka—Miller's aria*)
☆ B. Christoff (♯ *G.BLP 1003*: ♭ 7R 150: 7RF 163)

ACT II

No. 9, Ah! let us cease these songs　M-S or A
(*Konchakovna's cavatina*)
V. Borisenko　　　　　**USSR. 17089/90**
(2ss)　　　　　　　　　　　(Muza. 1554)
E. Antonova　(*No. 12*)　　**USSR. 06449**

No. 11, Daylight is fading　　T
I. Kozlovsky　　　　　　**USSR. 06346/7**
(2ss)

No. 12, Is it thou, Vladimir
(Duet, Konchakovna & Igor) M-S or A & T
E. Antonova & I. Kozlovsky　USSR. 06422
(*No. 10*)
V. Borisenko & S. Lemeshev USSR. 017348
(*Rimsky-Korsakov : Tsar's Bride, aria, Act. IV*)

No. 13, No sleep, no rest for my afflicted soul B
G. London　　　　　　　♯ **AmC.ML 4489**
(*Demon, Don Quichotte, etc.*)
P. Silveri (*Ital*)　　　　　**C.LX 1530**
(*Carmen, Chanson du Toreador*)　　(GQX 11513)
P. Schoeffler (*Ger*)　　in ♯ **MSL.MW 44**
(*Verdi, Mozart, etc.; & Lieder*)
☆ A. Ivanov (U.H 23836)

No. 15, How goes it, Prince　Bs　(Konchak)
M. Reizen　(2ss)　　　　**USSR. 017451/2**
☆ B. Christoff (♯ *G.BLP 1003*: ♭ 7RF 164)

No. 17, Polovtsi Dances　　cho. & orch.
— ARR. ORCH. ONLY
▽ Brussels Radio—André　　　**T.E 3195/6**
(*Rimsky-K. : Antar, excpt.*)
☆ Philadelphia—Ormandy (♭ AmC.A 1519)
Rome Sym.—Questa (in ♯ Roy. 1227)
"Nat. Op. Orch." (in ♯ Var. 2005)

ACT III

No. 18, Prelude (Polovtsi March)
Bolshoi Theatre—Nebolsin　　**U.C 23920**
(2ss)
☆ Philharmonia—Dobrowen
　　　　　(in ♯ BB.LBC 1026: ♭ set WBC 1026)

QUARTETS, String
No. 1, A major　1878　... **1st movt. only**
Beethoven Qtt.　(4ss)　　　**USSR. 16514/7**

No. 2, D major　1881
Bolshoi Theatre Qtt.　　　　**USSR. 15316/25**
(10ss)
☆ Galimir Qtt.　　　　　in ♯ **Nix.PLP 505**

Quatuor B-la-F
... **3rd movt., Serenade** [2]
Glazounov Qtt.　　　　　　**USSR. 18779**
(*Mendelssohn : Trio movt*)

SONGS
Arab melody (Borodin)
M. Maksakova (S)　　　　　**USSR. 14675**
(*Glinka : O wondrous maiden*)

---

[1] Recorded from Edison cylinder.
[2] Remaining movements are by Rimsky-Korsakov, Liadov and Glazounov respectively.

SONGS (continued)

At home, some people (Nekrasov)
A. Pirogov (B)   *USSR. 14914*
(*Rimsky-Korsakov : Song*)

Song of the dark forest (Borodin)
M. Mikhailov (Bs)   *USSR. 12256*
(*Glinka : Autumn night*)
M. Reizen (Bs)   USSR. 018672
(*Beethoven : Scottish drinking song*)

To distant shores (Pushkin)
A. Baturin (B)   *USSR. 5003*
(*Glazounov : Drinking song*)
B. Gmyria (B)   USSR. 016918
(*Dargomijsky : Old corporal*)
A. Ivanov (B), A. Holeček (pf.)   U.H 23858
(*Schubert : Doppelgänger*)

SYMPHONIES

No. 1, E flat 1862/7
USSR. State Sym.—K. Ivanov *USSR. 20463/8*
(6ss)
Bavarian Sym.—Graunke   ♯ Ura. 7066
(*Dohnányi*)

No. 2, B minor 1869/76
USSR. State Sym.—K. Ivanov *USSR. 20469/74*
(6ss)
Hastings Sym.—Bath   ♯ Allo.ALG 3048
Minneapolis Sym.—Dorati   ♯ Mer.MG 50004
(*Stravinsky : Firebird*)
Rome Sym.—Questa   ♯ Roy. 1237
☆ Philharmonia—Malko   ♯ BB.LBC 1024
(*Tchaikovsky : Suite No. 3, Variations*) (♭ set WBC 1024)

Tati-tati (Variations on "*Chopsticks*")
Polka ; Requiem ; Mazurka
— ARR.   N. Tcherepnin & Janssen
Col. Sym.—Janssen   ♯ AmC.ML 4480
(*Cui, Rimsky-Korsakov, Liadov, etc.*)

BØRRESEN, Hakon (b. 1876)

(The) ROYAL GUEST   Opera 1 act 1919
(*Den kongelige Gæst*)
Prelude
Copenhagen Royal Op.—Hye-Knudsen
                                    Pol.HM 80058
▽ OLDER RECORDINGS INCLUDE:
SONG : If you have warm thanks (*G.DA 5225 & Od.D-921*)
QUARTET, Str., C minor, Scherzo (*G.DB 5282*)

BOULANGER, Lili (1893-1918)

Cortège   vln. & pf.
I. Richards & Y. Fisher   Croy.CX 2
(½s.—*Paradis : Siciliene, & Handel-Harty : Passacaglia*)

Nocturne vln. or fl. & pf. 1911
P. Fournier (vlc.) & E. Lush   G.DA 2005
(*Ravel : Pièce en forme de habanera*)
▽ F. Grinke (vln.) & I. Newton (pf.) D.M 570
(*Nováček : Perpetuum mobile*)
§ Y. Bratza (vln.) & pf. (*C. 4824, o.n. D 1574*)

BOYCE, William (1710-1779)

(8) SYMPHONIES, Op. 2 (Ed. C. Lambert)
☆ Zimbler Sinfonietta (4ss) ♯ B.AXTL 1002/3

... **Nos. 2, 3, 5, 7** (orig. scoring)
London Baroque Ens.—Haas ♯ West.WL 5159

BOZZA, Eugène (b. 1905)

Variations sur un thème libre   wind quintet
☆ New York Quintet (in ♯ Cpt.MC 20001)

BRAHMS, Johannes (1833-1897)

CLASSIFIED : *I. INSTRUMENTAL*
                    1. Orchestral 2. Chamber Music
                    3. Piano & Organ
                    4. Hungarian Dances & Waltzes

II. VOCAL
                    1. Choral   2. Partsongs
                    3. Songs   4. Volkslieder

I. INSTRUMENTAL

1. ORCHESTRAL

Akademisches Fest-Ouvertüre, Op. 80
L.P.O.—Boult   ♮ G.DB 9670/1
(3ss—*Hungarian Dances, Nos. 17 & 18*)
N.Y.P.S.O.—Walter   ♯ AmC.AAL 1
(*Hungarian Dances*)
Berlin Phil.—v. Kempen   PV. 36028
                                  (♯ AmD.DL 4048)
Bamberg Sym.—Keilberth   ♯ DT.LGM 65007
(*Meistersinger, Prelude*)   (♯ T.LB 6015)
Berlin Sym.—Ludwig (in ♯ Roy. 1381)
"Nat. Op. Orch" (in ♯ Roy. 6127)
☆ Boston Sym.—Koussevitzky
                    (♭ G.7RF 218 ; ♭ Vic. 49-0881)

CONCERTOS, pf. & orch.
No. 1, D minor, Op. 15
M. Huttner & Berlin Sym.—Rubahn ♯ Roy. 1359
☆ A. Schnabel & L.P.O.—Szell ♮ G.DB 8614/9

No. 2, B flat major, Op. 83
W. Backhaus & Vienna Phil.—Schuricht
                                    ♯ D.LXT 2723
                                  (♯ Lon.LL 628)
A. Aeschbacher & Berlin Phil.—v. Kempen
(8ss)   ♮ PV. 72177/80
                              (2ss—♯ Pol. 18024)
☆ E. Ney & Berlin Phil.—Fiedler (♯ AmD.DL 9536)
V. Horowitz & N.B.C. Sym.—Toscanini
                         (♯ Vic.LCT 1025 : ♭ set WCT 38)

Concerto, vln. & orch., D major, Op. 77
I. Stern & Royal Phil.—Beecham
                                    ♯ AmC.ML 4530
P. Rybar & West Austrian Radio—Moltkau
                                    ♯ CHS.CHS 1113
(*Cadenza by P. Rybar*)   (♯ Nix.CLP 1113)
L. Stevens & Berlin Sym.—Guenther
                                    ♯ Roy. 1252
☆ Y. Menuhin & Lucerne—Furtwängler (♯ G.FALP 122)
J. Heifetz & Boston Sym.—Koussevitzky
                         (♯ Vic.LCT 1043 : ♭ set WCT 71)
... Unspec. excerpts
F. Malachowsky & Berlin Sym. (in ♯ Roy. 1314)

Concerto, A minor, Op. 102 vln., vlc. & orch.
N. Milstein, G. Piatigorsky & Robin Hood
     Dell—Reiner   ♯ G.FALP 171
                         (♯ Vic.LM 1191 : ♭ WDM 1609)
J. Fournier, A. Janigro & Vienna State Op.—
     Scherchen   ♯ West.WL 5117
E. Prinz, W. Kunlantz & Rhineland Sym.—Federer
(♯ Rgt. 5027)
☆ D. Oistrakh, M. Sadlo & Czech Phil.—Ančerl
(Eur.TAI 738/41 ; ♯ Csm.CRLP 120 ; ♯ Syc.SR 8)

♯ = Long-playing, 33⅓ r.p.m.   ♭ = 45 r.p.m.   ♮ = Auto. couplings, 78 r.p.m.

SERENADES
No. 1, D major, Op. 11

☆ Sym. Orch.—Swoboda (‡ Nix.CLP 1087; ‡ Clc. 6094)

SYMPHONIES
No. 1, C minor, Op. 68

N.B.C.—Toscanini   **‡ G.ALP 1012**
(‡ Vic.LM 1702; & 10ss, ♭ Vic. set WDM 1702;
    ♮ G.DB 9768/72)

Amsterdam—v. Beinum   **‡ D.LXT 2675**
(n.v.)   (‡ Lon.LL 490)

Philadelphia—Ormandy   **‡ AmC.ML 4477**

Chicago Sym.—Kubelik   **‡ Mer.MG 50007**

Berlin Phil.—Keilberth   **‡ T.LSK 7008**
    (‡ Cap.P 8153)

Leipzig Radio Sym.—Abendroth ♮ **U.H 24240/5**
(11ss—*Waltz No. 15*)

Berlin Sym.—Balzer   **‡ Roy. 1289**

Robin Hood Dell—Leinsdorf **‡ BB.LBC 1004**
    (♭ set WBC 1004)

☆ L.S.O.—Weingartner (‡ AmC.ML 4510)
   Viennese Sym.—Brown (‡ Mrt. 200-7)

No. 2, D major, Op. 73

N.B.C.—Toscanini   **‡ G.ALP 1013**
    (& 8ss, ♮ G.DB 9773/6)

☆ L.P.O.—Furtwängler   **‡ D.LXT 2586**

Berlin Phil.—Jochum   **PV. 72080/2**
(6ss)   (‡ Pol. 18008; AmD.DL 9556)

Philharmonia—Kubelik   **G.DB 21466/70**
(10ss)

Leipzig Radio Sym.—Abendroth
(10ss)   ♮ **U.H 24059/63**

▽ Vienna Phil.—Böhm (‡ G.DB 7693/8)
☆ San Francisco—Monteux
    (‡ Vic.LM 1173: ♭ set WDM 1065)
   L.S.O.—Weingartner (‡ AmC.ML 4511)
   Vienna Phil.—Karajan (C.LVX 125/9)
   Austrian Sym.—Wolf (‡ Mrt. 200-8)

No. 3, F major, Op. 90

Amsterdam—Szell   **‡ D.LXT 2676**
(2ss)   (‡ Lon.LL 487)

Prague Radio—Abendroth   ♮ **U.H 23978S/82**
(9ss)

Berlin Sym.—Friedl   **‡ Roy. 1232**

Sonor Sym.—Ledermann   **‡ Pde. 2009**

☆ L.P.O.—Weingartner (‡ AmC.ML 4512)
   Boston Sym.—Koussevitzky
    (‡ G.FALP 173: QALP 173)

No. 4, E minor, Op. 98

N.B.C. Sym.—Toscanini   **‡ Vic.LM 1713**
    (♭ set WDM 1713)

N.Y.P.S.O.—Walter   **‡ AmC.ML 4472**

Berlin Sym.—Friedl   **‡ Roy. 1239**

Austrian Sym.—Wöss   **‡ Rem. 199-42**
    (‡ Mrt. 200-9)

Sonor Sym.—Ledermann   **‡ Pde. 2007**

☆ Boston Sym.—Münch (‡ G.FALP 144)
   L.S.O.—Weingartner (‡ AmC.ML 4513)
   Berlin Phil.—Sabata (P.RR 8000/5S)

Tragische Ouvertüre, Op. 81

Berlin Phil.—Lehmann   **‡ Pol. 16024**
(*Schumann : Manfred Overture*)
    (on ‡ AmD.DL 4048, d.c; 2ss, on PV. 72282)

Berlin Sym.—Ludwig   in **‡ Roy. 1381**

Munich Phil.—Rieger   **‡ Mer.MG 15038**
(*Beethoven : Leonore Ov. No. 2*)

☆ B.B.C. Sym.—Toscanini (in ♭ Vic. set WCT 49)

Variations on a theme of Haydn, Op. 56a

Philharmonia—Markevitch   ♮ **G.C 7856/7**
(4ss)   (S 10588/9)
    (*Tchaikovsky*, on ‡ BB.LBC 1010: ♭ set WBC 1010)

☆ N.Y.P.S.O.—Toscanini   **‡ Vic.LCT 1023**
    (♭ set WCT 36)

☆ Vienna Phil.—Furtwängler   **‡ G.ALP 1011**
(*Haydn: Sym. 94*)
(*Mozart: Sym. 40*, on ‡ Vic.LHMV 1010:
    ♭ set WHMV 1010)

Berlin Sym.—List   **‡ Roy. 1362**
(*Wagner: Siegfried Idyll*)

---

2. CHAMBER MUSIC

QUARTETS, String
No. 1, C minor, Op. 51, No. 1

Vegh Qtt.   **‡ D.LXT 2710**
    (‡ Lon.LL 588)

Budapest Qtt.   **‡ AmC.ML 2191**

Amadeus Qtt.   **‡ West.WL 5084**
(*Schubert*)

No. 2, A minor, Op. 51, No. 2

Hollywood Qtt.   **‡ DCap.CTL 7021**
(2ss)   (‡ Cap.P 8163; ‡ T.LCSK 8163)

Curtis Qtt.   **‡ West.WL 5152**
(*No. 3*)

No. 3, B flat major, Op. 67

Curtis Qtt.   **‡ West.WL 5152**
(*No. 2*)

QUARTETS, pf. & str.
No. 1, G minor, Op. 25

☆ R. Serkin & Members of Busch Qtt.
    (‡ C.CX 1012: FCX 106)

No. 2, A major, Op. 26

☆ R. Hillyer & Albeneri Trio (‡ Clc. 6042)

No. 3, C minor, Op. 60

☆ Horszowski, Schneider, Katims, Miller (‡ Clc. 6031)

Quintet, clar. & str., B minor, Op. 115

L. Wlach & Vienna Konzerthaus Qtt.
    ‡ West.WL 5155

R. Kell & Fine Arts Qtt.   **B.AXTL 1008**
    (‡ AmD.DL 9532)

☆ A. Gallodoro & Stuyvesant Qtt.
    ‡ Nix.CLP 1004

Quintet, pf. & str., F minor, Op. 34

Chigi Qtt.   **‡ D.LXT 2687**
    (‡ Lon.LL 501)

J. Demus & Vienna Konzerthaus Qtt.
    ‡ West.WL 5148

SONATAS, clar. & pf.
No. 1, F minor, Op. 120, No. 1

☆ R. Kell & M. Horszowski (‡ Clc. 6013)
   L. Amodio & S. Schultze (Pol. 68172/4S)

No. 2, E flat major, Op. 120, No. 2

☆ R. Kell & M. Horszowski (‡ Clc. 6013)

SONATAS, vln. & pf.
No. 1, G major, Op. 78

I. Stern & A. Zakin   **‡ AmC.ML 2193**

A. Spalding & E. Dohnányi   **‡ Rem. 199-84**
(*Hungarian Dances*)

W. Schneiderhan & F. Wührer   ♮ **PV. 72175/6**
(4ss)   (‡ Pol. 16027)

☆ = Re-issue of a recording to be found in WERM or Supplement I.

SONATAS, VLN. & PF. (*continued*)

No. 2, A major, Op. 100
W. Schneiderhan & F. Wührer   PV. 72181/2S
(3ss)
   A. Eidus & L. Mittman   # Strad.STR 611
(*Sibelius*)
   A. Spalding & E. Dohnányi   # Rem. 199-49
(*No. 3*)

No. 3, D minor, Op. 108
N. Milstein & V. Horowitz   # *G.FBLP 1026*
(# Vic.LM 106: ♭ set WDM 1551)
A. Spalding & E. Dohnányi   # Rem. 199-49
(*No. 2*)

Sonatensatz, C minor, vln. & pf. (*Allegro*)
☆ D. Oistrakh & L. Oborin (in # Csm.CRLP 105)

SONATAS, vlc. & pf.
No. 1, E minor, Op. 38
G. Cassadó & E. Schulhof   # Rem. 149-53
G. Koutzen & H. Wingreen   # CEd. 1031
(*No. 2*)
E. Bengtsson & H. D. Koppel ♮ G.DB 20148/50
(6ss)

No. 2, F major, Op. 99
G. Koutzen & H. Wingreen   # CEd. 1031
(*No. 1*)

Trio, pf., cl., vlc., A minor, Op. 114
F. Holletschek, L. Wlach, F. Kwarda
(*Horn Trio*)   # West.WL 5146
M. Horszowski, R. Kell, F. Miller
   # AmD.DL 7524
☆ E. Balogh, S. Forrest, B. Greenhouse (# Eur.LPG 622)

Trio, pf., vln., hrn., E flat major, Op. 40
F. Holletschek, W. Barylli, F. Koch
(*Clarinet Trio*)   # West.WL 5146

---

3. PIANO
COLLECTIONS
BALLADES
Op. 10, COMPLETE
No. 1, D minor   No. 3, B major
No. 2, D major   No. 4, B minor
H. Priegnitz
Op. 118, No. 3, G minor
K. Borack   # *Mer.MG 15021*

(8) CAPRICCI & INTERMEZZI, Op. 76
J. Germain   # *Clc. 6034*
(No. 7 only on Clc.C 2126)   (# *Mer.MG 15024*)

(7) FANTASIAS, Op. 116 (Capricci & Intermezzi)
(3) INTERMEZZI, Op. 117
M. Rusy   # Mer.MG 10074

(5) KLAVIERSTÜCKE, Op. 118, Nos. 1,2,4,5,6 [1]
(3) INTERMEZZI, Op. 119, Nos. 1, 2, 3
K. Borack   # *Mer.MG 15022*

RHAPSODIES
B minor, Op. 79, No. 1
G minor, Op. 79, No. 2
E flat major, Op. 119, No. 4
☆ A. Chasins   # Mer.MG 10135
(*Waltzes*)   (also on # *Clc. 6038*)

(7) FANTASIAS, Op. 116
C. Seemann   PV. 72264/5
(3½ss—*Ballade*)   (# *Pol. 16032*)

(3) INTERMEZZI, Op. 117
W. Gieseking   # AmC.ML 4540
(*Schumann*)

(6) KLAVIERSTÜCKE, Op. 118
(4 Intermezzi, Ballade & Romanze)
V. Yankoff   # Pat.DTX 108
(*Schumann: Sonata No. 2*)

BALLADES
D minor, Op. 10, No. 1 ("*Edward*")
C. Seemann   PV. 72265
(*Intermezzi, Op. 116*)

G minor, Op. 118, No. 3
J. Battista   in # MGM.E 141
(*Chopin, etc.*)   (♭ set K 141)

Capriccio, B minor, Op. 76, No. 2
G. Nováes   # AmVox.PL 7500
(*Bach, Gluck, etc.*)
F. Kramer   in # *MTR.MLP 1001*

INTERMEZZI
A minor, Op. 116, No. 2
B flat minor, Op. 117, No. 2
E. Freund   # Rem. 199-109
(*below*)
E flat major, Op. 117, No. 1
L. Kolessa   in # CHS.CHS 1108
(# Nix.CLP 1108)
B flat minor, Op. 117, No. 2
G. Nováes   in # AmVox.PL 7500
F. Karrer (*Vien.P 6063: in # 1015*)
C sharp minor, Op. 117, No. 3
L. Kolessa   in # CHS.CHS 1108
(*Variations*)   (# Nix.CLP 1108)
E flat minor, Op. 118, No. 6
W. Malcuzynski   C.LX 1461
(*Beethoven: Sonata No. 23, s.5*)
F. Kramer   in # *MTR.MLP 1001*
C major, Op. 119, No. 3
F. Karrer (*Vien. P 6063: in # 1015*)

RHAPSODIES
B minor, Op. 79, No. 1
W. Gieseking   (2ss)   C.LX 1561
G minor, Op. 79, No. 2
F. Shapiro   in # Ox.OR 105

SONATAS
No. 3, F minor, Op. 5
E. Fischer   (6ss)   G.DB 21213/5
A. Rubinstein   # Vic.LM 1189
(8ss, ♭ set WDM 1581)
E. Freund   # Rem. 199-109
(*Intermezzi*)

Variations on a theme of Schumann, Op. 9 [2]
J. Blancard   # Van.VRS 416
(*Schumann*)

Variations on a theme of Handel, Op. 24
J. Katchen   # *D.LX 3078*
(# *Lon.LS 552*)
V. Schiøler   (6ss)   ♮ G.DB 20175/7
L. Kolessa   # CHS.CHS 1108
(*Intermezzi*)   (# Nix.CLP 1108)

---

[1] For Op. 118, No. 3, see Ballades, *above*.
[2] The theme is the Albumblatt, Op. 99, No. 4.

Variations on a theme of Handel, Op. 24 (*continued*)
E. Istomin　(2ss)　　　　　　　♯ *AmC.ML 2211*
E. Kilenyi　　　　　　　　　　♯ **Rem. 199-91**
(*Schumann: Études symphoniques*)
C. Giraud-Chambeau　　　　♯ **Sat.LDG 8003**
(*Liszt: Paganini Études; & Mendelssohn*)

Variations on a theme of Paganini, Op. 35
R. Goldsand　　　　　　　♯ **CHS.CHS 1147**
(*Schumann*)　　　　　　　　　(♯ Nix.CLP 1147)
A. Földes　　　　　　　　　♯ *AmD.DL 7532*
　(Book I on PV. 72246, Book II on *PV. 36058*)

(11) Chorale-Preludes, Op. 122　org.
☆ E. White (♯ Clc. 6036)
... One, unspec.　C. Snyder (in ♯ KR. 15)

---

4. HUNGARIAN DANCES & WALTZES
COLLECTIONS　(ARR. ORCH.)
Nos. 1, 3, 5, 6, 17, 18, 19, 20, 21
Berlin Phil.—v. Kempen　　　　*PV. 36054/5*
(4ss)

No. 1, G minor　　　　**No. 3, F major**
No. 10, F major　　　　**No. 17, F sharp minor**
N.Y.P.S.O.—Walter　　　　♯ *AmC.AAL 1*
(*Akademisches Fest-Ouvertüre*)

Nos. 1 to 6
☆ Boston Pops—Fiedler (♭ *G.7BF 1023/5*; Nos. 1 & 2 on
G.B 10228; Nos. 3 & 4, ♭ *G.7BQ 1024*; Nos. 5 & 6, in
♭ *Vic.WEPR 20: 49-1449*)

No. 1, G minor　— ARR. ORCH.
Philharmonia—Kletzki　　　　**C.LX 8926**
(*Berlioz: Francs-Juges, s.1*)
　☆ Hollywood Bowl—Stokowski (♭ *Vic. 49-1293*)
　L.S.O.—Krauss (♭ *D. 71017*)
— ARR. VLN. & PF. (may be No. 5)
　I. Bezrodny & pf. (*USSR. 17425*)
　M. Zoloupova & pf. (*USSR. 10724*)

No. 2, D minor　— ARR. ORCH.
Philharmonia—Kletzki (*below*)　　**C.LX 8935**
— ARR. VLN. & PF.　L. Kogan & pf. (*USSR. 15059*)

No. 3, F major　— ARR. ORCH.
Philharmonia—Kletzki　　　　**C.LX 8935**
(*above; & Berlioz: Benvenuto Cellini Ov., s.1*)
　☆ L.S.O.—Krauss (♭ *D. 71017*)
— ARR. VLN. & PF.　D. Oistrakh & pf. (*USSR. 15059*)

No. 5, F sharp minor
No. 6, D flat major　— ARR. ORCH.
　Brussels Radio—Dejoncker (*Od. O-28297*)
　German Opera House—Schüler (*Imp. 19160*)
　Vienna Radio—Nilius (*Vien.P 6022:* in ♯ *1012*)
☆ Philharmonia—Kletzki (C.LFX 1017)
　Dresden Phil.—v. Kempen (*Pol. 26503: P.LL 3014*)

No. 5, F sharp minor
— ARR. VLN. & PF.　Joachim (trs. to G minor)
Y. Menuhin & A. Baller　　　*JpV.SF 703*
(*Nováček: Perpetuum mobile*)

D. Oistrakh & pf. (*USSR. 15058*)

No. 17, F sharp minor
No. 18, D major
— ARR. ORCH.
L.P.O.—Boult　　　　　　　　G.DB 9670
(*Akademisches Fest-Ouvertüre*)

No. 17,　— ARR. VLN. & PF.
　H. Szeryng & pf. (Orf. 4003)
　L. Kogan & pf. (*USSR. 17411*)
　M. Kozolupova & pf. (*USSR. 9295*)
　☆ I. Haendel & G. Moore
　　　　　(in ♯ BB.LBC 1013: ♭ set WBC 1013)

No. 20, E minor　— ARR. VLN. & PF.
I. Bezrodny & pf. (*USSR. 17789*)

Nos. 8, 9, 17 — ARR. VLN. & PF.
　☆ A. Spalding & A. Kookier (1s. only in ♯ Rem. 199-84)

Unspec. Dances : Jerusalem Sym.—Goehr (in ♯ Bne. 501)

WALTZES, Op. 39　　　　　pf. duet
　☆ A. Chasins & C. Keene　　♯ **Mer.MG 10135**
　(*Rhapsodies*)

— ARR. PF. SOLO
　M. Schwalb　　　　　　　♯ **Acad.ALP 302**
　(*J. Strauss*)

... Nos. 1, 2, 15　— ARR. PF. SOLO
　☆ A. Földes (in ♯ *Rem. 149-4*)

... 4 unspec.　— ARR. PF. SOLO
　B. Janis　　(in ♯ BB.LBC 1030: ♭ set WBC 1030)

... No. 2　— ARR. GUITAR　Segovia
　A. Segovia　　　　　　　in ♯ AmD.DL 9647
　(† Segovia Program)

... No. 15, A flat major
— ARR. PF. SOLO
　G. Nováes　　　　　　in ♯ AmVox.PL 7500
　V. Horowitz　　　　　　　Vic. 10-3424
　(*Moszkowski, Sousa*) (♭ *Vic.49-3424*; ♭ *G.7RF 232*, d.c.)
　F. Karrer (*Vien.P 6063:* in ♯ *1015*)
　☆ F. Ellegaard (*Pol.HA 70029*)

— ARR. VLN. & PF.
　E. Zathureczky & M. Karin　　U.H 24240
　(*Symphony No. 1, s.1*)

Liebeslieder Walzer, Op. 52
Neue Liebeslieder Walzer, Op. 65
COMPLETE RECORDING
　E. Hassler (S), H. Plümacher (A), A.
　Weikenmeier (T), F. Kelch (Bs), H. Priegnitz
　& H. Michael (pfs.)　　　　♯ **Oce.OCS 28**

Liebeslieder Walzer, Op. 52
R. Wagner Cho., E. Heckman & B. L.
Neff (pfs.)　　　　　　♯ **DCap.CTL 7028**
(*Volkslieder*) (*Eng*)　　　　　(♯ Cap.P 8176)

... Nos. 1, 3, 5, 6, 9, 10, 11, 12, 13, 17, 18
Vienna Academy Cha. Cho.—Grossman &
　pf. duet　　　　　　　in † Sel.LPG 8238

II. VOCAL

1. CHORAL (with Orchestra)
(Ein) Deutsches Requiem, Op. 45
　☆ Soloists, cho. & orch.—Shaw
　　　　　　　　　　　♯ **Vic. set LM 6004**
　(4ss)　　　　　　　　　　(♭ set WDM 1236)

Gesang der Parzen, Op. 89 (Goethe)
Nänie, Op. 82 (Schiller)
Vienna Cha. Cho. & Sym.—Swoboda
(*R. Strauss*)　　　　　　　♯ **West.WL 5081**

Rhapsodie, Op. 53 (Goethe) ("Alto Rhapsody")
　A, Male cho., orch.
M. Anderson, Shaw Chorale, Victor Sym.—
　Reiner　　　　　　　　　♯ **Vic.LM 1146**
(*Mahler*)　　　　　　　　　　(♭ set WDM 1532)
E. Höngen, Berlin Liedertafel & Berlin Phil.—
　Leitner　　　　　　　　　　PV. 72231

☆ = Re-issue of a recording to be found in WERM or Supplement I.

Schicksalslied, Op. 54 (Hölderlin)   cho. & orch.
(*Song of Destiny*)
Stanford Univ. Cho. (*Eng*) & San Francisco
Sym.—Monteux   **‡ Vic.LM 149**
(*Bach: Passacaglia & Fugue, C minor*)   (♭ *set WDM 1637*)

☆ Westminster Cho. & N.Y.P.S.O.—Walter
‡ C.FCX 114
(*Beethoven: Sym. 9, s.3*)

2. PART SONGS

Marienlied, Op. 22, No. 6: Magdalena (trad.)
unacc. cho.
R. Shaw Chorale   in **‡ Vic.LM 1201**
(*Easter songs*)   (♭ *set WDM 1623*)

Nachtwache, Op. 104 unacc. mixed cho. (Rückert)
1. Leise Töne der Brust
2. Ruh'n Sie? ruft das Horn
Copenhagen Univ. Students' Cho.—Møller
Fdn.NC 3002

3. SONGS

COLLECTIONS
Alte Liebe, Op. 72, No. 1 (Candidus)
An die Nachtigall, Op. 46, No. 4 (Hölty)
Auf dem Kirchhofe, Op. 105, No. 4 (Liliencron)
(Die) Botschaft, Op. 47, No. 1 (Daumer)
Dort in dem Weiden, Op. 97, No. 4 (Trad.)
(Der) Gang zum Liebchen, Op. 48, No. 1 (Wenzig)
Immer leiser wird mein Schlummer, Op. 105, No. 2 (Lingg)
(Der) Kranz, Op. 84, No. 2 (Schmidt)
Mädchenlied, Op. 107, No. 5 (Heyse)
Nicht mehr zu dir zu gehen, Op. 32, No. 2 (Daumer)
Salamander, Op. 107, No. 2 (Lemcke)
Sonntag, Op. 47, No. 3 (Uhland)
Von ewiger Liebe, Op. 43, No. 1 (Wenzig)
Wenn du nur zuweilen lächelst, Op. 57, No. 2 (Daumer)

A. Howland (S), P. Ulanowsky (pf.)
‡ Strad.STR 610

An eine Aeolsharfe, Op. 19, No. 5 (Mörike)
Immer leiser wird mein Schlummer, Op. 105, No. 2 (Lingg)
Mein wundes Herz verlangt, Op. 59, No. 7 (Groth)
Wiegenlied, Op. 49, No. 4 (Scherer)
Lerchengesang, Op. 70, No. 2 (Candidus)
(Der) Tod, das ist die kühle Nacht, Op. 96, No. 1 (Heine)
Vorüber, Op. 58, No. 7 (Hebbel)
Wir wandelten, Op. 96, No. 2 (Daumer)

E. Berger (S), M. Raucheisen (pf.)
(4ss)   **PV. 36047/8**

" MÄDCHENLIEDER "
Ach und du mein kühles Wasser, Op. 85, No. 3 (Kapper,
   from Serbian)
Am jüngsten Tag, Op. 95, No. 6 (Heyse, from Italian)
Auf die Nacht in der Spinnstub'n, Op. 107, No. 5 (Heyse)
Mädchenfluch, Op. 69, No. 9 (Kapper, from Serbian)
(Das) Mädchen spricht, Op. 107, No. 3 (Gruppe)
Stand das Mädchen, Op. 95, No. 1 (Kapper, from
   Serbian)

H. Mott (S), E. Lush (pf.) in **‡ Mon.MWL 301**

Von ewiger Liebe, Op. 43, No. 1 (Wenzig)
Sapphische Ode, Op. 94, No. 4 (Schmidt)
(Der) Schmied, Op. 19, No. 4 (Uhland)

☆ E. Liebenberg (A), A. Sandor (pf.) **U.F 22612**

Am Sonntag Morgen, Op. 49, No. 1 (Heyse)
(Der) Gang zum Liebchen, Op. 48, No. 1 (Wenzig)
Von ewiger Liebe, Op. 43, No. 1 (Wenzig)

☆ H. Schlusnus (B) (in ‡ AmD.DL 9622)

Am Sonntag Morgen, Op. 49, No. 1 (Heyse)
Nicht mehr zu dir zu gehen, Op. 32, No. 2 (Daumer)
I. Alexeyev (B), M. Emelianova (pf.) **U.C 24192**

Auf dem Kirchhofe, Op. 105, No. 4
(Der) Tod, das ist die kühle Nacht, Op. 96, No. 1
☆ J. Manowarda (*Pol. 26508*)

(Die) Botschaft, Op. 47, No. 1 (Daumer)
K. Ferrier (A)   in **‡ Lon.LPS 402**
(Announced but probably not issued)
☆ H. Schlusnus (in ‡ Pol. 18029; ‡ AmD.DL 9621)

(4) Ernste Gesänge, Op. 121 ("*Prediger Salomo*")
B. Sönnerstedt (B), F. Jensen (pf.)
(4ss)   ♮ **G.DB 20173/4**

H. Hotter (B), G. Moore (pf.)   ♮ **C.LX 8933/4**
(4ss)

☆ D. Ligeti (Bs), F. Berens (pf.) (‡ ML. 7025)

Feldeinsamkeit, Op. 86, No. 2
H. Hotter (B), G. Moore (pf.)   **C.LX 1403**
(*Mit vierzig Jahren*)

Geheimnis, Op. 71, No. 3 (Candidus)
(Das) Mädchen spricht, Op. 107, No. 3 (Gruppe)
E. Berger (S), M. Raucheisen (pf.)
in **‡ Ura. 7060**
(*R. Strauss, Debussy, etc.*)

(Die) Mainacht, Op. 43, No. 2 (Hölty)
▽ M. Klose (A), M. Raucheisen (pf.) **Pol. 68299**
(*Von ewiger Liebe*)

Meine Liebe ist grün, Op. 63, No. 5 (F. Schumann)
▽ K. Branzell (A)   in **‡ Rem. 149-6**
(*Mahler, Schubert, etc.*)

Mit vierzig Jahren, Op. 94, No. 1 (Rückert)
H. Hotter (B), G. Moore (pf.)   **C.LX 1403**
(*Feldeinsamkeit*)

Sapphische Ode, Op. 94, No. 4 (Schmidt)
K. Ferrier (A)   in **‡ Lon.LPS 402**
(announced but probably not issued)
N. Obukhova (MS, *Russ*) (*USSR. 17111*)

(Der) Schmied, Op. 19, No. 4 (Uhland)
Included in *Vic. set E 97*: ♭ *WE 97* (*Eng*)

Ständchen, Op. 106, No. 1 (Kugler)
☆ L. Slezak (T) (*Pol. 26506*)

Von ewiger Liebe, Op. 43, No. 1 (Wenzig)
V. de los Angeles (S), G. Moore (pf.)
(*Schumann: Der Nussbaum*)   **G.DB 21457**

Wie bist du, meine Königin, Op. 32, No. 9 (Daumer)
☆ H. Schlusnus (B) (in ‡ Pol. 18029: ‡ AmD.DL 9621)

Wiegenlied, Op. 49, No. 4 (Trad.)
M. Morley (Treb., *Eng*), J. Wills (pf.)
in **‡ D.LM 4543**
(*Schubert, Arne, Mendelssohn, etc.*)   (‡ *Lon.LPS 399*)

C. Hallgren (B) (*Swed*) (*T.A 3186*)
G. Winkler ( ) & orch. (*Dan.*) (*Tono.Z 18093*)
▽ D. Dame (T, *Eng*) (*MGM. 30265*: ♭ *KK 30265*)

— ARR. CHO.
R. Shaw Chorale (*Eng*) (in ‡ *Vic.LM 96*: ♭ *set WDM 1528*)
Bielefeld Children's Cho. (*T.A 11228*)
Wilkner Sängerknaben—Gerholdt (*Tono.K 8082*)
Berlin Mozart Cho.—Steffan (*Imp. 19115*)
F. Bender Children's Cho. (*Pol. 62890*)

— ARR. PF.
A. Földes (in ‡ *Rem. 149-4*)

— ARR. VLN. & PF.
W. Tworek & E. Vagning   **Pol.HA 70032**
(*Nováček: Perpetuum Mobile*)

---

‡ = Long-playing, 33⅓ r.p.m.   ♭ = 45 r.p.m.   ♮ = Auto. couplings, 78 r.p.m.

42

4. VOLKSLIEDER

(26) DEUTSCHE VOLKSLIEDER 4-pt. cho. [CV]
COLLECTION

(Des) Abends (CV. 20)
Abschiedslied : Ich fahr' dahin (CV. 9)
Da unten im Tale (CV. 19)
Dort in den Weiden (CV. 22)
Erlaube mir, feins Mädchen (CV. 17)
(Der) Fiedler (CV. 18)
In stiller Nacht (CV. 8)
(Der) Tote Knabe (CV. 10)
Wach auf (CV. 21)
(Die) Wollust in dem Mayen (CV. 11)
R. Wagner Cho. (*Eng*)　　　# DCap.CTL 7028
(*Liebeslieder W.*)　　　　　　　　(# Cap.P 8176)

Altes Minnelied (No. 17 of 28 Volkslieder, 1858)
— ARR. CHO. (*Love, fare thee well*)
Sale & District Cho.—Higson　　*G.B 10243*
(*Harrison : Open thy gates*)

Da unten im Tale DV. 6
E. Schwarzkopf (S), G. Moore (pf.) *C.LB 118*
(*Mozart : Der Zauberer, K 472*)　　　　(*LV 59*)

In stiller Nacht CV. 8
Copenhagen Cha. Cho.—Bertelsen　*Felix.F 51*
(*Reger : Mariä Wiegenlied*)

Finlandia Cho.—Klemetti (*Finn*) (*Od.PLD 11*)

Sandmännchen VK. 4
S. Kurz (S), J. Harrison (pf.)　　　*G.VA 2*
(*Goldmark : Königin von Saba, Lockruf*)　(o.n. *DA 753*)

Weihnachten VK. 12
J. Wilson (S), R. Baker (org.) in # AmD.DL 9554
(*Schumann, Grieg, etc.*)

(DV = 49 Deutsche Volkslieder; VK = 14 Volkskinderlieder)

BRISTOW, George F.　(1825-1898)

SEE : † AMERICAN MUSIC OF EARLY ROMANTIC PERIOD

BRITTEN, Benjamin (b. 1913)

(A) Boy was born, Op. 3 unacc. cho.　1933
... Jesu, as thou art our Saviour
Hamline Singers—Holliday　　　# NRI. 305
(*Brunswick, etc.*)

(A) Ceremony of Carols, Op. 28 Tr. cho. & hp.1942
Washington Cathedral & Cha. Choirs—
Callaway (*below*)　　　　　# WCFM. 11
Victor Female Cho.—Shaw (L. Newell, hp.)
　　　　　　　　　　　　# Vic.LM 1088
(*Poulenc : Mass, G minor*)　　(♭ set WDM 1324)

... Wolcum Yule, only
W. Schumann Cho. (in # Cap.H 9016)

Fantasy-Quartet, Op. 2 ob. & str.　1932
☆ H. Gomberg (ob.) & Galimir Trio
(*below*)　　　　　　　# Cpt.MC 20007

Hymn to St. Cecilia, Op. 27 (Auden)　1942
Washington Cathedral & Cha. Cho.—Callaway
　　　　　　　　　　　in # WCFM 11.

Hymn to the Virgin unacc. cho.　1930
Cho. of St. John's, Upper Norwood—L.
Betteridge　　　　　　　*Croy.CC 1*
(*Spicer : The Birds; & Piggott : Come my way*)

QUARTETS, String

No. 1, D major, Op. 25　1941
☆ Galimir Qtt.　　　　# Cpt.MC 20007
(*above*)

No. 2, C major, Op. 36　1945
☆ Zorian Str. Qtt.　　　　♮ G.C 7651/4
(*Purcell : Fantasia*)　　　　(TH 7051/4)

Simple Symphony, Op. 4　1934
Sydney Civic Sym. Str.—Beck　# Dia.DPM 3
(*Elgar*)

Te Deum, C major　1935
Washington Cho.—Callaway　　# WCFM. 11
(*above*)

Variations on a theme of Frank Bridge, Op. 10
Str. orch.　1937
Lausanne Cha.—Desarzens　　# CHS.F 8
(*Vaughan Williams*)

(A) Young Person's Guide to the Orchestra, Op. 34
(Variations & Fugue on a theme of Purcell)　1945
☆ Liverpool Phil.—Sargent (C.M 15182/4S)

ARRANGEMENTS

Matinées musicales, Op. 24 (after Rossini), 1941
Soirées musicales, Op. 9 (after Rossini)　1936
Covent Garden—Braithwaite　　# MGM.E 117
　　　　　　　　　　　　(♭ set K 117)
Matinées musicales only
☆ Boston Pops—Fiedler　　　# Vic.LM 1093

FOLKSONG ARRANGEMENTS

(The) Foggy Dew ; (The) Ploughboy ;
Came ye not from Newcastle
☆ P. Pears (T), B. Britten (pf.) (♭ G.7R 108)

(The) Foggy Dew
A. Schiøtz (T), H. D. Koppel (pf.)　　*G.X 8009*
(*below*)

O waly, waly (The water is wide)
K. Ferrier (A), P. Spurr (pf.)　　in *D.LX 3098*
　　　　　　　　　　　　(# Lon.LPS 538)
A. Schiøtz (T), H. D. Koppel (pf.)　*G.X 8009*
(*above*)

Sweet Polly Oliver
There's none to soothe
P. Pears (T), B. Britten (pf.)　　　*D.M 678*

BRUCH, Max (1838-1920)

CONCERTOS, vln. & orch.

No. 1, G minor, Op. 26　1868
Y. Menuhin & Boston Sym.—Münch
(6ss)　　　　　　　　G.DB 21415/7
　　(# G.FBLP 1016; Vic.LM 122 : ♭ set WDM 1547)
A. Campoli & New Sym.—Kisch ♮ D.AX 558/60
(6ss)　　　　　　　　　(D.K 23239/41)
(also on # LX 3092)
　　　　(Bach, on # D.LXT 2596; Lon.LLP 395)
J. Heifetz & L.S.O.—Sargent　# Vic.LM 9007
(*Saint-Saëns : Sonata*)　(6ss, in ♭ set WDM 9007)
Z. Francescatti & N.Y.P.S.O.—Mitropoulos
(*Beethoven : Romances*)　　# AmC.ML 4575
W. Schneiderhan & Bamberg Sym.—Leitner
(3ss)　　　　　　　　PV. 72232/3S
(Adagio only on PV. 72321)
(*Tchaikovsky : Romeo & Juliet Ov. on # Pol. 18036*)
▽ S. Borries & Prussian State—Zaun
(6ss)　　　　　　　　‡ G.DB 7672/4
☆ I. Haendel & Philharmonia—Kubelik
　　(in # BB.LBC 1013; ♭ set WBC 1013)
(continued on next page)

☆ = Re-issue of a recording to be found in WERM or Supplement I.

Concerto No. 1, G minor, Op. 26 (*continued*)
... Adagio only
H. Stanske & German Op. House—Schuricht
(☆ from set)   **Pol. 68065**
M. Gardi & Hamburg Phil.—Brückner-
Rüggeberg   **PV. 58605**
(*Svendsen : Romance*)

Kol Nidrei, Op. 47, vlc. & orch. 1881
T. de Machula & Residentie—v. Otterloo
(*Schubert : Rosamunde*)   **♯ Phi.N 00107R**
☆ P. Casals & L.S.O.—Ronald
(♯ Vic.LCT 1028: ♭ *set WCT 42*)

Serenade, Op. 75   vln. & orch.
... 4th movt. only
☆ Anon. soloist & Berlin Municipal—Meyer (Pol. 15534)

BRUCKNER, Anton (1824-1896)

(4) Kleine Orchesterstücke   *c.* 1861
... Nos. 1-3 only   ☆ Berlin Municipal—Meyer (Pol. 15538)
... No. 4, Marsch   ☆ Berlin Municipal—Meyer (Pol. 15540)

Mass, No. 2, E minor   1866
☆ Hamburg State Op.—Thurn (FT.T 161/5)

Overture, G minor   1863
Vienna Philharmonia—Adler   **♯ SPA. 25**
(*below*)
☆ Berlin Municipal—Meyer (Pol. 15539/40, *above*)

Quintet, F major   str.   1879
Koeckert Qtt. & G. Schmid (vla.) **♯ Pol. 18042**

SYMPHONIES
D minor   1869
Concert Hall Sym.—Spruit   **♯ CHS.CHS 1142**
(♯ Nix.CLP 1142)

No. 1, C minor   1866
Austrian State Sym.—Andreae **♯ MSL.MW 40**

No. 2, C minor   1873
Linz Sym.—L. G. Jochum   **♯ Ura. set 402**
(4ss)

No. 3, D minor   1873
☆ Salzburg Mozarteum Orch.—Fekete (♯ Eur.LPG 602)

No. 4, E flat major   1874   (*Romantic*)
... Scherzo only ☆ Saxon State—Böhm (G.DB 20403)

No. 6, A major   1879/81
Linz Bruckner Orch.—L. G. Jochum **♯ Ura. 7041**

No. 7, E major   1880
Vienna Phil.—Böhm   **♯ AmVox.PL 7190**
(4ss)
Berlin Phil.—Jochum   **♯ Pol. 18033/4**
(4ss)

No. 9, D minor   1884/94
Vienna Philharmonia—Adler   **♯ SPA. 24/5**
(3ss—*above*)

BRUHNS, Nikolaus (1665-1697)

SEE ALSO: † BAROQUE ORGAN MUSIC

Prelude, E minor   org.
▽ W. Bäumer   **Chr. 310B**
(*Reger : Benedictus*)

BRUMEL, Antoine (*c.* 1480-1520)

Missa de Beata Virgine
☆ M. Couraud Ens.   **♯ DFr. 11**
(▽ DFr. 51/5)

BRUNNER, Adolf (b. 1901)

SONATA, fl. & pf.   1937
A. Jaunet & W. Frey   in **♯ D.LXT 2658**
(*Binet & Schoeck*)   (♯ Lon.LLP 498)

BRUNSWICK, Mark (b. 1912)

Fragment of Sappho
Hamline Singers—Holliday   **♯ NRI. 305**
(*Ives, etc.*)

BRZEZINSKI, Franciszek (1867-194?)

Theme and Variations   pf.
M. Filar   **♯ Csm.CLPS 1005**
(*Chopin*)

BULL, John (1562-1628)

SEE ALSO: † EARLY ENGLISH KEYBOARD MUSIC

Rondo, G major   org.
R. Ellsasser   in **♯ MGM.E 3005**

BURKHARD, Willy (b. 1900)

Toccata, Op. 86 wind insts., percussion & str. orch.
Zürich Collegium Musicum—Sacher
                              ♯ D.LXT 2702
(*Müller : Symphony for Strings*)   (♯ Lon.LL 596)

BURTON, Eldin (b. 1913)

COLLECTION
Fiddlestick vln. (J. Tryon) & pf.   1946
Quintet pf. & str. qtt.   1945
Sonatina fl. (J. Wummer) & pf.   1946
Sonatina vln. (J. Tryon) & pf.   1944
E. Burton (pf.) & Contemporary Music Qtt.
                              ♯ CEd.CE 1006

BUSH, Geoffrey (b. 1919)

(A) Christmas Cantata
E. Poulter (S), E. Parkin (pf.), Wesley's Chapel
Cho.—G. Bush   **Argo.R 1005/6**
(8ss)   **& S 1001/2**

BUSONI, Ferruccio (1866-1924)

Concerto, vln. & orch., D major, Op. 35a   1898
S. Borries & Berlin Radio—Rother **♯ Ura. 7043**
(*Wolf-Ferrari*)

♯ = Long-playing, 33⅓ r.p.m.   ♭ = 45 r.p.m.   ♮ = Auto. couplings, 78 r.p.m.

44

Duettino concertante on a theme of Mozart [1]
2 pfs. 1919
  V. Vitale & P. Buonomo   *Vis.VI 4371*

Indian Diary, Book I   pf.   1915
Sonata, pf. & vln., No. 2, E minor, Op. 36a   1898
  E. Weiss & R. Burgin   **♯ Circ. 51-104**

BUSSER, (Paul) Henri (b. 1872)

(Le) Carrosse du Saint-Sacrament
... Zapatéado only
  M. Santreuil (S) & orch.—Busser   *Pac. 3787*
  (Gounod: Ave Maria)

BUTTERWORTH, George Sainton Kaye
(1885-1916)

(A) Shropshire Lad (A. E. Housman)
... No. 6, Is my team ploughing
  L. Watts (T), N. Newby (pf.)   *Argo.R 1007*
  (Ireland: The soldier)

BUXTEHUDE, Dietrich (1637-1707)

I. VOCAL
(U=Ugrino)
CANTATAS
COLLECTIONS

  Also hat Gott die Welt geliebt   (U. No. 1)
  Herr, wenn ich nur dich hab'   (U. No. 6)
  Ich sprach in meinem Herzen   (U. No. 8)
  O clemens, O mitis, O coelestis Pater   (U. No. 10)
  Schaffe in mir, Gott, ein reines Herz   (U. No. 14)
  M. Guilleaume (S), Hamburg Festival Ens.—
  Bechert   **♯ AmVox.PL 7330**

  Aperite mihi portas justitiae   (U. No. 71)
  In te, Domine, speravi   (U. No. 65)
  Jesu, dulcis memoria   (U. No. 34)
  MISSA BREVIS   (U. No. 42)
  London Choral Soc.—Bath   **♯ Allo.ALG 3035**

  Befiehl dem Engel, dass er kommt   cho. & orch.
  Erbarm' dich mein, O Herre Gott   S, B, cho. & orch.
  Fürwahr er trug unsere Krankheit   S, B, cho. & orch.
  M. Guilleaume (S), E. M. Lühr, Hamburg
  Musikfreunde Cho. & orch.—Bechert
       ♯ AmVox.PL 7430

  Ich bin die Auferstehung   (U. No. 25)
  Ich bin eine Blume zu Saron   (U. No. 26)
  Mein Herz ist bereit   (U. No. 27)
  B. Müller (Bs), Stuttgart Pro Musica Orch.—
  Grischkat, E. Hölderlin (org.)
  O Lux beata Trinitas   (U. No. 38)
  M. Guilleaume & B. Groth (S), Hamburg Bach
  Fest.—Bechert (org. cont.) **♯ AmVox.PL 7620**

Alles was ihr tut   S, A, B, cho. & orch.   1678
  A. M. Augenstein, H. Plümacher, O. von Rohr,
  Stuttgart Cho. & Swabian Sym.—Grischkat
       ♯ Ren.X 30
  (Magnificat)   (♯ Nix.PLP 230)
  W. von Lochner, Bavarian Radio Cho. &
  Orch.—Kugler   **♯ Mer.MG 10086**
  (Mozart: Church Sonatas)

Aperite mihi portas justitiae   A, T, cho.
  ☆ E. Sigfuss, A. Schiøtz & Inst. Ens—Wöldike
       (G.FKX 187)

Jesu, meine Freude   (U. No. 18)
  K. Hansel (S), G. Barritt (T), D. Baker (Bs),
  Washington Presbyterian Chu. Cho. *(Eng)*—
  Schaefer   **♯ Den.DR 2**
  (Vaughan Williams)

Magnificat   5 voices & orch. (discovered 1931)
  Stuttgart Cho. & Swabian Sym.—Grischkat
       ♯ Ren.X 30
  (above)   (♯ Nix.PLP 230)

II. INSTRUMENTAL (Organ)
(S=Spitta edn.)
ORGAN MUSIC COLLECTIONS

  Prelude, Fugue & Chaconne   (S.I-4)
  Prelude & Fugue, D major   (S.I-11)
  Chorale-Prelude: Nun bitten wir   (S.II-2-23/4)
  ☆ N. O. Raasted   **♯ *Mer.MG 15036***
  (Handel & Bach)

  Chorale-Prelude: Ach Herr, mich armen Sünder
     (S.II-2-1)
  Fugue, C major   (S.I-17)
  G. Litaize   in **♯ Sel.LPG 8234**
  († Maîtres d'Orgue)

CHORALE-PRELUDES   S.II
Ach Herr, mich armen Sünder   (Pt. 2, No. 1)
Nun bitten wir dem heil'gen Geist   (Pt. 2, No. 23)
Nun komm', der Heiden Heiland   (Pt. 2, No. 25)
Vater unser in Himmelreich   (Pt. 1, No. 9)
  F. Viderø   (n. v.)   **G.DB 10509**

Nun bitten wir dem heil'gen Geist (Pt. 2, 22 or 23)
  E. P. Biggs   in **♯ AmC.ML 4603**
  (Bach, Mattheson, etc.)

Wie schön leuchtet der Morgenstern (Pt. 1, No. 10)
  F. Heitmann   in † **♯ T.LSK 7016**
  T. Schäfer   **♯ Den.DR 2**
  (Cantata; & Vaughan Williams)

Fugue, C major   (S.I-17)
  C. Snyder   in **♯ KR. 15**
  (Karg-Elert, Dupré, etc.)

Magnificat noni toni
  H. Liedecke   **♯ Ren.X 30**
  (Choral works)   (♯ Nix.PLP 230)

Passacaglia, D minor   (S.I-1)
  F. Viderø   (n.v.)   *G.DA 5269*

Prelude & Fugue, F major   (S.I-8)
  F. Viderø   *DAG. 5270*

Toccata & Fugue, F major   (S.I-21)
  ☆ W. Supper († Nix.PLP 224-2)

BYRD, William (1543-1623)
(Roman figures refer to the volumes of the Complete edn.,
ed. Fellowes)

I. INSTRUMENTAL

(The) Carman's Whistle   (FVB. 58)
  T. Dart (hpsi.)   *D.X 540*
  († Early English Keyboard Music)

---

[1] From finale of Concerto, K 459.

Fantasia   6 viols.   (XVII)   1611
Sydney Civil Sym. Str.—Beck in **♯ Dia.DPM 4**
(*Purcell, Handel, Bach*)

Fortune (Variations)   (FVB. 65)
F. Heitmann (org.)   in † **♯ T.LSK 7010/1**

PAVANES & GALLIARDS
No. 11, Pavana Bray; Galliarda Bray   (FVB 91/2)
E. Goble (hpsi.)   **D.AX 546/7**
(† Early English Keyboard Music)

No. 19, The Earl of Salisbury   (Parthenia 6/7)
E. Goble   **D.X 540**
(† Early English Keyboard Music)

... Pavane only   ☆ A. Ehlers (in ♯ AmD.DL 8019)

Praeludium   (XVIII; No. 2)
G. Jones (org.)   **D.X 549**
(† Early English Keyboard Music)

II. VOCAL
ANTHEMS
Christ rising again   6 voices   1589   (XIII)
R. Shaw Chorale   in **♯ Vic.LM 136**
(† XVITH Cent. Music)   (in ♭ set WDM 1598)

From Virgin pure   1589   (XIII)   S & org.
(A Carowle for Christmas)
J. Wilson & R. Baker   in **♯ AmD.DL 9554**
(*Bax, Holst, etc.*)

MASSES
Five Voices
Fleet Street Cho.—Lawrence   **♯ D.LX 3060**
(n.v.)   (♯ Lon.LPS 372)

MOTETS
Ave verum corpus   (V)   4 voices
Open Score Soc.—F. Cameron **♯ Per.SPLP 535**
(† Renaissance Masterpieces)

Dies sanctificatus   (VI)   1607
O magnum mysterium   (VI)   1607
Welch Chorale   in **♯ Lyr.LL 35**
(*Gibbons, Sweelinck, etc.*)

Non nobis, Domine   Canon   (XVI)
Harvard Univ. Cho.—Russell in **♯ Fest. 70-202**
(† Pre-baroque sacred music)
Vocal Octet   in **♯ Vic.set E 101**
                          (♭ set WE 101)

SECULAR MADRIGAL
I thought that love had been a boy   (XIII)   5 voices
Renaissance Singers—Engel in **♯ AmC.ML 4517**
(† Treasury of Madrigals)

CABEZÓN, Antonio de   (1510-1566)
SEE: † HARP MUSIC

CACCINI, Giulio (1558-1618)
SEE ALSO: † ITALIAN SONGS
                 † ITALIAN ART SONGS

Amarilli   (*Nuove Musiche* No. 12, 1601)
E. Brems (M-S), S. Sørensen (hpsi.) & vlc.
(*Lotti: Pur dicesti*)   **Fdn.NC 3501**
☆ H. Spani (S)   **G.VA 60**
(*A. Scarlatti: Se Florindo è fedele*)

CAGE, John (b. 1912)

Quartet, Strings   1950
New Music Qtt.   **♯ AmC.ML 4495**
(*Piston*)

(24) Sonatas & 4 Interludes   "Prepared" pf.
1946/8
M. Ajemian   **♯ Dial. 19/20**
Older recordings included:
(3) Dances   ▽ Disc. set 877
Amores, 1 & 4 in ▽ Disc. set 675

CALDARA, Antonio (1670-1736)
SEE ALSO: † ITALIAN ART SONGS

Qui tollis peccata mundi   5 voices
▽ Male Cho.—Jacobi   **Chr. 309A**
(*Grell: Gnädig und bermherzig*)

Regina coeli laetare
☆ Berlin Cath. Cho.—Rüdel (*Chr. 611A*, o.n. ▽ *U.AP 409*)

CAMPIAN, Thomas (1567-1620)
AYRE: It fell on a summer day   1601
A. Deller (C-T), D. Dupré (lute) **G.C 4178**
(½s.—*Rosseter & Dowland*)

CAMPRA, André (1660-1744)
OPERAS
(L') EUROPE GALANTE   1697
Passepied   Hpsi. & Anon. Orch. (*Scd. 4004*)

(Les) FÊTES VÉNITIENNES   1710
Chanson du papillon
M. Laszlo (S), F. Holletschek (pf.)
(† Italian Songs)   **♯ West.WL 5119**

CANNABICH, Christian (1731-1798)
Menuetto
Stuttgart Cha. Soc.   **♯ Ren.X 40**
(*Haydn, Marais, Stamitz, etc.*) (♯ Nix.PLP 240)

CANNING, Thomas (b. 1911)

Fantasy on a hymn of Justin Morgan   str. orch.
1944
Eastman-Rochester Sym.—Hanson
(*Mennini & Foote*)   **♯ Mer.MG 40001**

CAPLET, André (1878-1925)
SEE ALSO: † HARP MUSIC

MASS, three voices   1922
... Sanctus & Benedictus only
U.O.S. Cho.—McConnell   in **♯ UOS.pte**
(*Holst, Lojero, etc.*)

Petite valse   fl. & pf.   1897
H. Barwahser & F. de Nobel **♯ Phi.A 00104L**
(½s.—*Gaubert & Schubert*)

♯ = Long-playing, 33⅓ r.p.m.   ♭ = 45 r.p.m.   ♮ = Auto. couplings, 78 r.p.m.

CARISSIMI, Giacomo (1605-1674)

JEPHTE   Oratorio   *c.* 1660
☆ Soloists, Angelicum Cho. & orch.—Gerelli
(*Marcello*)   # **Clc. 6048**

JONAS   Oratorio   S, A, T, T, B, B, cho.
COMPLETE RECORDING
   G. Vivante, L. Zinetti, G. Malipiero, M. Carlin,
   G. Ferrein, D. Caselli, Angelicum Cho. &
   orch.—Gerelli   # **AmVox.PL 7180**
   (*Vivaldi: Stabat Mater*)

Soccorretemi ch'io moro
   K. Flagstad (S), G. Moore (pf.)   *G.DA 2008*
   (*J. W. Franck: Sei nur still & Auf, auf . . .*)

Vittoria, vittoria mio core
   M. Laszlo (S), F. Holletschek (pf.)
   († Italian Songs)   # **West.WL 5119**

CARLTON, Richard (*c.* 1558-1638)

SEE: † TRIUMPHS OF ORIANA

CARPENTER, John Alden (1876-1951)

Adventures in a perambulator   1914/5   orch.
   Vienna State Op.—Swoboda # **CHS.CHS 1140**
   (1½ss—*McBride, Still, Copland*)

SONG CYCLES
Gitanjali (Tagore)
Water Colors (Giles, from the Chinese)
   A. Mock (S), S. Boyes (pf.)   # **Cmt. 1206**
   (*Loeffler: Songs*)

... When I bring you colored toys (Gitanjali: No. 1)
C. Williams (S), B. Bazala (pf.) in # *MGM.E 140*

CARR, Benjamin (1769-1831)

SEE: † AMERICAN MUSIC (INSTRUMENTAL & CHAMBER)

CARTER, Elliott (b. 1908)

Sonata, pf.   1944
   B. Webster
Sonata, vlc. & pf.   1948
   B. Greenhouse & A. Makas   # **ARS. 25**

CASALI, Giovanni Battista (1713-1792)

Ave Maria
   Lassus Vocal Qtt.—Speyer   **Chr. 326B**
   (*Asola: Christus factus est*)

CASELLA, Alfredo (1883-1947)

(11) Pezzi infantili, Op. 36   pf.
   A. Brugnolini   (4ss)   **P.PE 161/2**

CASTELNUOVO-TEDESCO, Mario (b. 1895)

Aubade
   Vocal Sextet & pf.   in # *Vic. set E 101*
                  (♭ *set WE 101*)

Concerto, guitar & orch.
   A. Segovia & New London—Sherman
                         # **C.CX 1020**
   († *Anthology*) (C.GQX 11505/7)   (♯ FCX 127: QCX 127)

Études d'ondes   pf.
— ARR. VLN. & PF.   Heifetz
   ☆ J. Heifetz & E. Bay (♭ *G.7RF 191*; *Vic. 49-1294*)

CATALANI, Alfredo (1854-1893)

OPERAS
LORELEY   3 acts   1890
Dove son   S
   ♄ ☆ C. Muzio (in ♯ *Eso.ES 500**; ♯ Cpt.MC 20008**) [1]

(La) WALLY   4 acts   1892
Ebben, ne andró lontana   S   (Act I)
   M. Vitale   **P.R 30048**
   (*Thaïs—Dis-moi qui je suis belle*)   (CB 20532)
   M. Minazzi   **P.PE 170**
   (*Bohème—Mi chiamano Mimi*)
   ☆ R. Tebaldi (in ♯ *AmD.DL 4005*)
   M. Caniglia (BrzV. 886-5002)

CATO, Diomedes (fl. XVI cent.)

SEE: † POLISH KEYBOARD MUSIC

CAVALLI, Nicolo (fl. XVIII cent.)

(Il) GIUDIZIO UNIVERSALE   Oratorio
   Soloists, Vatican Radio Cho. & Rome
   Cha. Orch.—Nucci   # **Csm.CLPS 1032**

CAVALLI, Pietro Francesco   (1602-1676)

SEE: † ITALIAN SONGS

CAVENDISH, Michael   (*c.* 1565-1628)

SEE: † TRIUMPHS OF ORIANA

ČERNOHORSKÝ, Bohuslav Matej (1684-1742)

Toccata, C major   org.
Fugue, G minor   org.
   F. Mihalek   **U.H 13130**
   (1s. each)
Toccata, C major   org.
Fugue, A minor   org.
   J. Ropek   **U.H 24029**
   (1s. each)

---

[1] Recorded from Edison cylinder.

47

CERTON, Pierre (c. 1510-1572)

SEE: † XVITH & XVIITH CENTURY SONGS

CERVETTO, Giacomo (1682-1783)

Siciliano
Stuttgart Cha. Soc.   ♯ **Ren.X 40**
(*Haydn, Cannabich, Marais, Stamitz, etc.*)
       (♯ Nix.PLP 240; ♯ Clc. 6124)

CESTI, Marc' Antonio (1618-1699)

SEE: † ITALIAN SONGS

CHABRIER, Alexis Emmanuel (1841-1894)

COLLECTION
   Bourrée fantasque (ARR. ORCH. Mottl)
   España
   Gwendoline: Overture
   Habanera
   Joyeuse Marche
   Ode à la Musique S, cho. & orch.
Concerts Colonne Orch.—Fourestier
         ♯ **Pat.DTX 117**
(L. Jourfier (S), Raymond St. Paul Cho.)
       (♯ AmVox.PL 7650)

Bourrée fantasque 1891   pf.   □
Idylle (Pièce pittoresque No. 6)   pf.
   K. Long   in ♯ **D.LK 4043**
   (½s.—*Ravel*)   (♯ Lon.LL 452)

España Rapsodie orch 1883   □
   Boston Pops—Fiedler (n.v.)   ♭ *G.7BF 1032*
   (♭ G.7BQ 1034; ♭ Vic. 49-1437 & in ♭ WEPR 1)
   Royal Phil.—Beecham   ♯ *AmC.AAL 11*
   (*Rossini: Cambiale Ov.*)   (2ss, ♭ 4-73283D)

Joyeuse Marche 1890   □
   ☆ Brussels Radio—André in ♯ *DT.LGM 65002*
   (*Debussy, Rameau, etc.*)   (in ♯ *T.LS 6011*)
   ☆ Cincinnati Sym.—Goossens (G.DB 9339)

— ARR. VLN. & PF.   Dushkin
   Z. Francescatti & A. Balsam ♯ **AmC.ML 4534**
   (*Vitali, etc.*)

Ode à la Musique (Ronsard) S, cho., orch. □
   J. Micheau, Brasseur Chorale & Paris Cons.—
   Fournet   in ♯ **D.LXT 2743**
   (*below; & Debussy*)   (♯ Lon.LL 639)

(Le) ROI MALGRÉ LUI Opera 1887
Danse slave   (orig. orch., cho., T, Bs)
Fête polonaise   (orig. orch. & cho.)
   Paris Opéra-Comique—Blareau ♯ *D.LX 3093*
   (*Messager: Les Deux Pigeons Suite*)   (♯ Lon.LS 647)

Chanson tzigane S & T (Act II)
   J. Micheau & J. Mollien   in ♯ **D.LXT 2743**
   (*above & below*)   (♯ Lon.LL 639)

Sextuor des Serves 6 S (Act II)
   J. Micheau (S) & Ens.   in ♯ **D.LXT 2743**
   (*above; & Debussy*)   (♯ Lon.LL 639)

SONGS
(L') Île heureuse (Mikael)
Villanelle des petits canards (Gérard)
   P. Bernac (B), F. Poulenc (pf.) ♯ **AmC.ML 4484**
   (*Debussy, Poulenc, Satie*)

□ See also Collections, *above*.

Suite pastorale orch. versions of pf. pieces 1897
1. Idylle   2. Danse villageoise
3. Sous bois   4. Scherzo-valse
   Covent Garden—Braithwaite ♯ **MGM.E 3000**
   (*Bizet*)

CHAMBONNIÈRES, Jacques Champion de (1602-c. 1672)

Chaconne; Rondeau, F major   hpsi.
   C. J. Chiasson   in ♯ **Lyr.LL 19**
   († French Masters . . .)

Sarabande, D minor   hpsi.
   ☆ W. Landowska
     (in ♯ Vic.LM 1217: ♭ set WDM 1181; ♭ G.7RF 254)

CHARPENTIER, Gustave (b. 1860)

LOUISE Opera 1900 4 acts
Ah! Chanson de Paris T & cho. (Act II)
   ♮ L. Slezak & cho. (*Ger*) (*G.VA 57**: o.n. 2-42730*)

Depuis le jour S (Act III)
   M. Angelici   **G.DB 11253**
   (*Bohème—Donde lieta usci*)
   M. Santreuil   **Pac. 6785**
   (*Bohème—Si, mi chiamano Mimi*)
   ☆ L. Albanese   **G.DB 21505**
   (*Manon Lescaut—In quelle trine morbide*) (♭ Vic. 49-3366)

CHAUSSON, Ernest (1855-1899)

Concert, D major, Op. 21 vln., pf. & str. qtt.
   ☆ L. Kaufman, A. Balsam & Pascal Qtt.
         ♯ **Nix.CLP 1071**

Poème de l'amour et de la mer, Op. 19 (Boucher)
   ☆ V. Osborne (S), R. Vetlesen (pf.) ♯ **ML. 7009**

Poème, Op. 25   vln. & orch.
   Y. Menuhin & L.P.O.—Boult
   (4ss)   ♮ **G.DB 9759/60**
   Z. Francescatti & Philadelphia—Ormandy
         ♯ *AmC.ML 2194*
   (*Saint-Saëns*)   (♯ *C.FC 1017*)
   K. Brandt & Berlin Sym.—Rubahn ♯ **Roy. 1339**
   (*below; & Paganini: Concerto No. 1*)

Symphony, B flat major, Op. 20
   San Francisco—Monteux   ♯ **Vic.LM 1181**
       (8ss, ♭ set WDM 1582)

Viviane, Op. 5 Sym. Poem   orch.
   Berlin Sym.—Rubahn   ♯ **Roy. 1339**
   (*Poème; & Paganini*)

CHAVEZ, Carlos (b. 1899)

Tree of Sorrow part-song
   Hamline Singers—Holliday   ♯ *NRI. 306*
   (*Harris & Křenek*)

CHEDEVILLE, Nicolas (1705-1783)

SEE: † ♯ AS. 3002LD

CHERUBINI, Maria Luigi Carlo Zenobio Salvatore (1760-1842)

ANACREON Opera 2 acts 1803
Overture
Vienna Phil.—Furtwängler	**G.DB 21493**
Austrian State Sym.—Gui	**# MSL.MW 41**
(Rossini & Verdi)	
Berlin Phil.—F. Lehmann	**# Phi.A 00115R**
(Weber, Poot, etc.)	
(also, 2ss., Phi.A 11159G: *PhM.A 09702S*)	

(Les) DEUX JOURNÉES Opera 3 acts 1800
Overture
Austrian State Sym.—Gui	**# MSL.MW 50**
(Rossini & Wolf-Ferrari)	

March, *see below*

(3) Fugues (unid.) [1] ARR. Rayment
R. Adeney (fl.) & Aeolian Str. Qtt.	**# Lyr.LL 24**
(below)	

(La) Libertà à Nice (Metastasio) 13 Duets 1793
R. McKerrow (S), H. Alexander (A), P. Hamburger (pf.)	**# Lyr.LL 33**

(4) Marches pour la Garde Nationale wind insts.
1800-24
(Bellasis 231, 232, 301; & *Deux Journées* March, ARR. Cherubini)
London Baroque Ens.—Haas	**P.R 20613**
(2ss)	

Requiem Mass, C minor 1816
Portsmouth Phil. Cho. & orch—Davison	**Ch.Soc. 9/13**
(10ss)	
[Soloists: M. Russell, V. Gulvin & D. Stairs (S); J. Farmer (A); A. Hutchings (T); W. Riley (Bs)] (# Prog. EXLP705)

Mass, C major 1816
☆ Soloists, Portsmouth Phil. Cho. & orch.—Davison
(# Lyr.LL 28; # Eur.LPG 621)

Quartet, String, No. 1, E flat major 1814
Aeolian Qtt.	**Ch.Soc. 19/21**
(6ss)	(# Lyr.LL 24)

CHOPIN, Frédéric François (1810-1849)

CLASSIFIED: I. Piano solo II. Concerted Works
III. Songs IV. Miscellaneous

I. PIANO SOLO

Andante spianato & Grande Polonaise brillante, E. flat major, Op. 22
B. Siki	♮ **P.PW 8004/5**
(3ss—Nocturne No. 9)	
☆ V. Horowitz	in # **Vic.LM 1137**

— PF. & ORCH. VERSION
J. M. Darré & Paris Cons.—Cluytens	
(4ss)	**Pat.PDT 270/1**
R. Reinhardt & Stuttgart Pro Musica	
(Variations)	**# AmVox.PL 7530**

(4) BALLADES
COMPLETE RECORDINGS
G. Doyen	**# West.WL 5169**
J. v. Karolyi	**# Pol. 16025**
E. Wild	**# CHS.CHS 1401**
C. de Groot	**# Phi.A 00129L**
(Nos. 1 & 2 also on Phi.A 11232/3G: *PhM. 09719/20S*)	

[1] From *Treatise on Counterpoint . . .*, 1835.

No. 1, G minor, Op. 23
B. Janis	in # **BB.LBC 1030**
	(♭ set WBC 1030)
C. Giraud-Chambeau	**Sat. 6002**
	(o.n. M 511)
E. Gilels	USSR. 016270/1
☆ H. Stefanska	♭ **G.7P 130**
V. Horowitz	♭ G.7RF 152; in # Vic.LM 1235
V. Schiøler	in # Mer.MG 10099
L. Bertolini	in # Csm.CLPS 1024

No. 3, A flat major, Op. 47
J. Katchen	in # **D.LX 3079**
(Scherzo No. 3, & Fantaisie)	(in # Lon.LS 554)
V. Horowitz	in # **Vic.LM 1707**
	(in ♭ set WDM 1707)
L. Oborin	**U.C 24290**
	(USSR. 16330/1)
☆ J. Demus (# Mrt. 1-18)	

No. 4, F minor, Op. 52
V. Horowitz	**G.DB 21503**
(in # Vic.LM 1707: ♭ set WDM 1707)	
☆ J. Demus (# Mrt. 1-18)	

Barcarolle, F sharp major, Op. 60
D. Lipatti	**C.LX 1437**
	(LFX 1024)
A. Cortot (n.v.)	in # **Vic.LHMV 1032**
(Étude, Nocturnes, Valses)	(♭ set WHMV 1032)
J. v. Karolyi	**PV. 56017**
(Berceuse)	(in # Pol. 18068)
E. Balogh	in # **Lyr.LL 20**
	(# Eur.LPG 616)
C. Giraud-Chambeau	**Sat. 6003**
	(o.n. M 512)
J. Smeterlin	in # **Allo.ALG 3042**
A. Uninsky	in # **Phi.A 00113L**
(Sonata No. 3, etc.)	

Berceuse, D flat major, Op. 57
M. Jonas	in # **AmC.ML 4476**
C. de Groot (n.v.)	in # **Phi.A 00106R**
E. Balogh	in # **Lyr.LL 20**
	(# Eur.LPG 616)
J. Smeterlin	in # **Allo.ALG 3042**
G. Novães	in # **AmVox.PL 7810**
J. v. Karolyi	**PV. 56017**
(Barcarolle)	(in # Pol. 18068)
A. Brugnolini	**P.PE 164**
(Mendelssohn: Variations serieuses, s.3)	
A. de Raco	**ArgOd. 66011**
(Granados: La maja y el ruisenor)	
W. Maggiar	in # **Nix.LPY 112**
☆ A. Cortot (in # Vic.LCT 1038: ♭ set WCT 60; ♭ G.7RF 238)	
L. Bertolini (in # Csm.CLPS 1024)	

Bolero, C major, Op. 19
E. Balogh	in # **Lyr.LL 20**
	(# Eur.LPG 616)

Écossaises, Op. 72, No. 3
— ARR. 4 PFS. ☆ First Pf. Qtt. (in # Vic.LM 84)

ÉTUDES
COMPLETE RECORDINGS
(Op. 10, Op. 25, & 3 Nouvelles Études)
R. Goldsand	**# CHS.CHS 1132/3**
(3ss—Variations, Op. 12; the Nouvelles Études on s.2 of 1132)	(# Nix.CLP 1132/3)
D. Saperton	**# CPf. 1201/3**
Op. 10, Nos. 2, 6, 7; Op. 25, Nos. 2, 6 & A flat, on 1201; Op. 10, Nos. 5, 11; Op. 25, Nos. 1, 3, 5, 9 on 1202 *(with the relevant Godowsky Études in each case)*; Op. 10, Nos. 1, 3, 4, 8, 9, 10, 12; Op. 25, Nos. 4, 7, 8, 10, 11, 12; D flat & F minor on 1230	

COLLECTIONS (assorted)

Op. 10: Nos. 1-8 & 12; Op. 25: Nos. 6-9 & 12
L. Effenbach   ♯ Ofo.LP 11

Op. 10: No. 12; Op. 25: Nos. 1, 2, 9
☆ R. Turner (in ♯ Cap.H 2002: ♭ set CCF 2003)

Op. 10: No. 5, G flat major; No. 8, F major
Op. 25: No. 2, F minor; No. 12, C minor
☆ L. Bertolini   ♯ Csm.CLPS 1024
(Preludes, Berceuse, etc., & Bach)

Op. 10: No. 3, E major; No. 12, C minor
Op. 25: No. 6, G sharp minor; No. 7, C sharp minor; No. 9,
        G flat major
— ARR. ORCH.
Janssen Sym. of Los Angeles   in ♯ Atst. 504

(12) ÉTUDES, Op. 10
COMPLETE RECORDING
E. Kilenyi (n.v.)   ♯ Rem. 199-57

Nos. 3, 5, 12 — ARR. 2 PFS. A. Sandford & C. Vidusso
(in ♯ Roy. 1214)

No. 2, A minor
G. Werschenska   Pol.HM 80054
(½s.—Prelude No. 20 & Nocturne No. 5)
O. Frugoni   in ♯ AmVox.PL 7700
(Bach, etc.)

No. 3, E major
A. Cortot   G.DB 21521
(Études, Op. 10, No. 4 & Op. 25, No. 2)
V. Horowitz   in ♯ Vic.LM 1707
                         (in ♭ set WDM 1707)
G. Novães   in ♯ AmVox.PL 7810
☆ E. Sauer (Qual.QMN 7015)
  O. Frugoni (Attn. 27031)
  A. Brailowsky (♭ G.7RF 220)

— ARR. 4 PFS. ☆ First Piano Qtt. (in ♯ Vic.LM 84)

— ARR. ORCH. A. Bernard Orch. (Pat.PG 594)

No. 4, C sharp minor
A. Cortot (n.v.)   G.DB 21521
(Op. 10, No. 3 & Op. 25, No. 2)
☆ H. Stefanska   CdM.GA 5035
(½s.—Mazurka No. 47 & Scherzo No. 1, s.3)
☆ M. Sheyne (in ♯ EA.ALX 7)

No. 5, G flat major
C. de Groot   in ♯ Phi.A 00106R
☆ I. J. Paderewski (in ♯ Csm.CRLP 115)
  M. Sheyne (in ♯ EA.ALX 7)
  E. Wild (in ♯ Var. 2008, etc.)

— ARR. 4 PFS. ☆ First Pf. Qtt. (in ♯ Vic.LM 84)

No. 6, E flat major
M. Jonas   in ♯ AmC.ML 4476

No. 8, F major
B. Janis   in ♯ BB.LBC 1030
                         (in ♭ set WBC 1030)
C. Giraud-Chambeau   Sat.IA 513
(No. 12)   (o.n. 4001)

No. 9, F minor
▽ W. Kedra (Muza. X1475)

No. 12, C minor
A. Semprini   G.B 10317
(Liszt: Consolation No. 3)
C. Giraud-Chambeau   Sat.IA 513
(No. 8)   (o.n. 4001)
T. Zmudzinski (Muza. 1587)
☆ J. Iturbi (G.DA 1987)
  M. Sheyne (in ♯ EA.ALX 7)
  E. Wild (in ♯ Var. 2008, ♯ Var. 6922; ♭ Roy. set 14519)

(12) ÉTUDES, Op. 25
(3) NOUVELLES ÉTUDES
COMPLETE RECORDING
G. Novães   in ♯ AmVox.PL 7560

(12) ÉTUDES, Op. 25
No. 1, A flat minor
No. 2, F minor
No. 9, G flat major
☆ M. Sheyne (in ♯ EA.ALX 7)

No. 1, A flat
C. de Groot   in ♯ Phi.A 00106R
☆ E. Wild (in ♯ Var. 2008, in ♯ Var. 6922)

No. 2, F minor
A. Cortot   G.DB 21521
(Études Op. 10, Nos. 3 & 4)
          (& in ♯ Vic.LHMV/ ♭ set WHMV 1032, d.c.)
M. Jonas   in ♯ AmC.ML 4476

No. 3, F major
J. Smeterlin   in ♯ Allo.ALG 3042

No. 5, E minor
G. Scherzer   P.E 11490
(below)
J. Smeterlin   in ♯ Allo.ALG 3042
F. Ellegaard   Pol.HM 80052
(Prelude No. 15)
♮ F. Busoni (in ♯ AudA.LA 1203*)
— ARR. 2 PFS. A. Sandford & C. Vidusso (♯ Roy. 1214)

No. 6, G sharp minor
☆ F. Ellegaard   Pol.HA 70030
(Mazurka No. 5)

No. 7 C sharp minor
C. de Groot   in ♯ Phi.A 00106R

No. 9, G flat major
G. Scherzer   P.E 11490
(above & Debussy)
☆ E. Wild (in ♯ Var. 2008, ♯ Var. 6922; in ♭ Roy. set 14519)
— ARR. 2 PFS. A. Sandford & C. Vidusso (in ♯ Roy.1214)

No. 11, A minor
☆ H. Stefanska   CdM.GA 5033
(Polonaise No. 5, s.3)

No. 12, C minor
F. Chapiro   in ♯ Ox.OR 105

_____

Fantaisie, F minor, Op. 49
J. Katchen   in ♯ D.LX 3079
(Ballade No. 3 & Scherzo No. 3)   (in ♯ Lon.LS 554)
A. Uninsky   in ♯ Phi.A 00124L
(Sonata No. 2, etc.)
G. Novães   in ♯ AmVox.PL 7810
(Impromptu No. 2, etc.)
☆ W. Malcuzynski (C.LFX 1019/20)

Fugue (played from MS. in artist's possession)
♮ N. Janotha (▽ G. 5561*)

(4) IMPROMPTUS
COMPLETE RECORDING
E. Balogh   in ♯ Lyr.LL 20
                         (♯ Eur.LPG 616)

No. 1, A flat major, Op. 29
V. Horowitz   G.DB 21425
(Valse No. 12) (in ♯ Vic.LM 1707: ♭ set WDM 1707)
M. Jonas   in ♯ AmC.ML 4476

_____

♯ = Long-playing, 33⅓ r.p.m.   ♭ = 45 r.p.m.   ♮ = Auto. couplings, 78 r.p.m.

IMPROMPTUS (*continued*)
No. 2, F sharp major, Op. 36
  G. Novães   in ♯ **AmVox.PL 7810**

No. 4, C sharp minor, Op. 66 (Fantaisie-Impromptu)
  B. Moiséiwitsch   **G.C 4184**
  (*Nocturne No. 19*)
  A. Rubinstein   ♯ **Vic.LM 1153**
  (*Nocturne No. 2, etc.*)   (♭ *WDM 1558*)
  (*Liszt: Liebestraum*, on ♭ *G. 7RF235*)
  J. Katchen   **D.AX 535**
  (*Rachmaninoff: Concerto No. 2, s.1*)
  J. Smeterlin   in ♯ **Allo.ALG 3042**
  ☆ H. Stefanska (in ♯ BB.LBC 1031,
             in ♭ *set WBC 1031*)
    V. Schiøler (in ♯ *Mer.MG 15037*)
    E. Sauer (Qual.QMN 7016)

— ARR. 4 PFS. ☆ First Piano Qtt. (in ♯ *Vic.LM 84*)

— ARR. HARP E. Vito (in ♯ *SOT. 1030*)

MAZURKAS
COLLECTIONS
Nos. 20, 21, 26, 32, 38, 40, 41
  ☆ V. Horowitz   ♯ **G.FALP 113**
  (*Schumann: Kinderszenen*)   (♭ *Vic.WEPR 31*)
  (*Nos. 26 & 38 also* ♭ *G.7RF 241*; Nos. 20 & 21, G.DB 21561:
    ♭ *7RF 242*)

Nos. 9, 14, 24, 25, 35, 44, 45, 48, 49 & 52 [1]
  W. Kapell   ♯ **Vic.LM 1715**
  (*Sonata No. 3*)   (♭ *set WDM 1715*)

Nos. 5, 20, 29, 30
  J. Smeterlin   in ♯ **Allo.ALG 3042**

No. 5, B flat, Op. 7, No. 1 (½s.)
No. 13, A minor, Op. 17, No. 4 (1s.)
No. 46, C major, Op. 68, No. 1 (½s)
  H. Stefanska   **G.C 4143**
                  (EH 1418)
  (*Nos. 5 & 46 in* ♯ BB.LBC 1031: ♭ *set WBC 1031*)

No. 2, C sharp minor, Op. 6, No. 2
  C. de Groot   in ♯ *Phi.A 00106R*

No. 5, B flat, Op. 7, No. 1
  ☆ F. Ellegaard   *Pol.HA 70030*
  (*Étude, Op. 25, No. 6*)
  F. Karrer (*Vien. P 6064*: in ♯ *1015*)

No. 7, F minor, Op. 7, No. 3
  ☆ M. Sheyne (in ♯ EA.ALX 7)

No. 17, B flat minor, Op. 24, No. 4
No. 20, D flat, Op. 30, No. 3
No. 24, C major, Op. 33, No. 3
  W. Backhaus   in ♯ *D.LX 3044*
    (D.SX 63008; in ♯ *Lon.LPS 317*)

No. 23, D major, Op. 33, No. 2
— ARR. 2 PFS. M. Rawicz & W. Landauer (*C.DB 3135*)

No. 26, C sharp minor, Op. 41, No. 1
  A. Uninsky   in ♯ *Phi.A 00113L*
  (*Sonata No. 3, etc.*)

No. 27, E minor, Op. 41, No. 2
  T. Zmudzinski   *Muza. 1587*
  (*Étude, Op. 25, No. 12*)

No. 30, G major, Op. 50, No. 1
No. 31, A flat major, Op. 50, No. 2
No. 32, C sharp minor, Op. 50, No. 3
  N. Magaloff   in ♯ *D.LX 3076*
  (*Valses & Polonaises*)   (in ♯ *Lon.LS 532*)
  (also on D.K 28587)

No. 31, A flat major, Op. 50, No. 2
  ☆ M. Sheyne (in ♯ EA.ALX 7)

No. 32, C sharp minor, Op. 50, No. 3
  S. Askenase   **PV. 72086**
  (*Sonata No. 2, s.3*)   (in ♯ *Pol. 16005*)
  M-Th. Fourneau   **C.LFX 1012**
  (*Polonaise No. 7*)
  ☆ D. Lipatti (C.LNX 2005)

No. 34, C major, Op. 56, No. 2
  W. Landowska (hpsi.)   ♯ **Vic.LM 1186**
  († Polish keyboard music)   (♭ *set WDM 1586*)

No. 41, C sharp minor, Op. 63, No. 3
  W. Malcuzynski   **C.LX 8922**
  (½s.—*Valse No. 11 & Liszt: Rapsodie espagnole, s.1*)
  R. Trouard   *Od. 188970*
  (*Valse No. 12*)
  ☆ I. J. Paderewski (in ♯ *Vic.LCT 1038*: ♭ *set WCT 60*)
    A. Földes (in ♯ *Rem. 149-4*)
    M. Sheyne (in ♯ EA.ALX 7)

No. 42, G major, Op. 67, No. 1
No. 43, G minor, Op. 67, No. 2
No. 47, G minor, Op. 68, No. 2
  ☆ M. Sheyne (in ♯ EA.ALX 7)

No. 45, A minor, Op. 67, No. 4
  P. Serebriakov   *Muza. 1590*
  (*Valse No. 7*)

No. 47, A minor, Op. 68, No. 2
  ☆ H. Stefanska   **CdM.GA 5035**
  (½s.—*Étude, Op. 10, No. 4 & Scherzo No. 1, s.3*)

No. 50, A minor, no Op. no.
  ☆ L. Oborin (in ♯ Csm.CRLP 115)

NOCTURNES
COMPLETE RECORDING, NOS. 1-19
  A. Rubinstein (n.v.)   ♯ **Vic.LM 6005**
  (4ss)   (20ss—♭ *set WDM 1570*)

COLLECTIONS
Nos. 1-10
  S. Askenase   ♯ **Pol. 16033/4**
  (4ss)

Nos. 2, 7, 8, 16, 19, 20
  M. Filar   ♯ **Csm.CLPS 1005**
  (*Brzezinski*)

No. 2, E flat major, Op. 9, No. 2
  A. Cortot (n.v.)   in ♯ **Vic.LHMV 1032**
  (*below, & Études, Valses, etc.*)   (♭ *set WHMV 1032*)
  A. Rubinstein   in ♯ **Vic.LM 1153**
  (*Debussy: La plus que lente, etc.*)   (♭ *WDM 1558*)
  ☆ R. Koczalski   **Pol. 67246** [2]
  (*Valse, Op. 18*)
  ☆ E. Silver (in ♯ Var. 2008), etc.

— ARR. 4 PFS. ☆ First Piano Qtt. (in ♯ *Vic.LM 84*)

— ARR. VLN. & PF. Sarasate
    L. McMorrow (in ♯ *AmC.GL 513*)
  ☆ D. Oistrakh (in ♯ Csm.CRLP 110)

— ARR. VLC. & PF.
  G. Cassadò & O. Schulhof (in ♯ MSL.MW 45)

No. 3, B major, Op. 9, No. 3
  G. Werschenska (2ss)   **Pol.HM 80056**

---

[1] No. 52 is in the ♭ set only.
[2] Originally 67246 contained Nocturne No. 2 and Berceuse; but now re-issued as shown.

No. 4, F major, Op. 15, No. 1
A. Cortot　　　　　　　　　　**G.DB 21447**
(*No. 7*)　　　(in ♯ Vic.LHMV 1032: ♭ set *WHMV 1032*)

No. 5, F sharp major, Op. 15, No. 2
V. Horowitz (n.v.)　　　　　♭ *G.7RF 153*
(*Liszt: Au bord d'une source*)　　(♭ *Vic. 49-0488*)
　　　　　　　　　　　　(in ♯ *Vic.LM 1235*)
C. Smith　　　　　　　　　　**C.DX 1809**
(*Valses Nos. 6 & 11*)
C. de Groot　　　　in ♯ *Phi.A 00106R*
G. Nováes　　　in ♯ **AmVox.PL 7810**
G. Werschenska　　　　**Pol.HM 80054**
(*Prelude No. 20 & Étude, Op. 10, No. 2*)
☆ M. Sheyne (in ♯ EA.ALX 7)

No. 6, G minor, Op. 15, No. 3
J. Zak　(2ss)　　　　　　　**U.H 24190**
☆ M. Sheyne (in ♯ EA.ALX 7)

No. 7, C sharp minor, Op. 27, No. 1
A. Cortot　　　　　　　　　　**G.DB 21447**
(*No. 4*)　　　(in ♯ Vic.LHMV 1032: ♭ set *WHMV 1032*)
☆W. Malcuzynski (C.LFX 1020)
　H. Stefanska (in ♯ BB.LBC 1021: ♭ set *WBC 1021*)

No. 9, B major, Op. 32, No. 1
B. Siki　　　　　　　　　　**P.SW 8004**
(*Andante spianato & Polonaise, s.1*)
K. U. Schnabel　(2ss)　　　　*Vis.VI 4383*
▽ T. Zmudzinski (*Muza. 1432*)

No. 11, G minor, Op. 37, No. 1
J. Zak　(2ss)　　　　　　　**U.H 24191**

No. 13, C minor, Op. 48, No. 1
G. Werschenska　(2ss)　　**Pol.HM 80060**

No. 14, F sharp minor, Op. 48, No. 2
A. Rubinstein　　　　　　♭ *Vic.WEPR 42*
(*Scherzo No. 3*)
J. Zak　(2ss)　　　　　　　**U.H 23856**

No. 15, F minor, Op. 55, No. 1
V. Horowitz　　　　　in ♯ **Vic.LM 1707**
　　　　　　　　　　(in ♭ set *WDM 1707*)

No. 16, E flat major, Op. 55, No. 2
— ARR. VLN. & PF.
J. Heifetz & E. Bay　　in ♯ **B.LAT 8020**
　　　　　　　　　　　　(♯ *AmD.DL 8521*)

No. 17, B major, Op. 62, No. 1
F. Chapiro　　　　　in ♯ **Ox.OR 105**

No. 19, E minor, Op. 72, No. 1
B. Moiséiwitsch　　　　　　**G.C 4184**
(*Impromptu No. 4*)
☆ V. de Pachmann (in ♯ Vic.LCT 1038: ♭ set *WCT 60*)

No. 20, C sharp minor, no Op. no.
— ARR. VLC. & PF.
E. Mainardi & F. Lehmann　　*PV. 46006*
(*Grazioli: Adagio*)

C minor, Op. posth.　1827
W. Maggiar　　　　　in ♯ *Nix.LPY 112*

POLONAISES
COMPLETE RECORDING
　A. Rubinstein (n.v.)　♯ **Vic.LM 1205 & LM 152**
(Nos. 1 to 6 on ♯ G.ALP 1028; ♯ Vic. LM 1205:
♭ set *WDM 1629*
No. 7 & Andante spianato on ♯ *LM 152*: ♭ set *WDM 1643*)

No. 1, C sharp minor, Op. 26, No. 1
W. Wolf　　　　　　　　　　**G.EH 1376**
M. Jonas　　　　in ♯ **AmC.ML 4476**
S. Askenase　　　　　　　　**PV. 72170**
(*No. 4*)

No. 2, E flat minor, Op. 26, No. 2
W. Malcuzynski　　　　　　**C.LX 1416**
(2ss)　　　　　　　　　　(*LFX 1028*)
K. U. Schnabel　(2ss)　　　*Vis.VI 4381*
S. Askenase　　　　　　　　**PV. 72146**
(*No. 3*)
— ARR. 2 PFS.　A. Sandford & C. Vidusso (in ♯ Roy. 1215)

No. 3, A major, Op. 40, No. 1　"Militaire"
N. Magaloff　　　　　in ♯ **D.LX 3076**
(*D.K 28589*)　　　　　　　(♯ *Lon.LS 532*)
O. Frugoni　　　　in ♯ **AmVox.PL 7700**
(*Bach, Schumann, etc.*)
S. Askenase　　　　　　　　**PV. 72146**
(*No. 2*)　　　　　　　　(also in ♯ *Pol. 16022*)
☆ P. Spagnolo　　　　　　*Orf. 53001*
　M. Sheyne　　　　　in ♯ EA.ALX 7
　E. Gilels　　　in ♯ Csm.CRLP 115
— ARR. ORCH.
Film Sym.—Newman (*Rna.RM 70252*)
Vienna Radio—Nilius (*Vien.L 6120*)

No. 4, C minor, Op. 40, No. 2
N. Magaloff　　　　　in ♯ **D.LX 3076**
(& *D.K 28589*)　　　　　　(♯ *Lon.LS 532*)
H. Stefanska　　　　　　　**G.C 4100**
S. Askenase　　　　　　　　**PV. 72170**
(*No. 1*)

No. 5, F sharp minor, Op. 44
H. Stefanska　　　　　**CdM.GA 5032/3**
(3ss—*Étude Op. 25, No. 11*)

No. 6, A flat major, Op. 53
V. Horowitz (n.v.)　　　　　♭ *G.7RF 134*
(2ss)　　　　(♮ ♭ *Vic. 49-0192/3*: & in ♯ *LM 1137*)
A. Uninsky　　　　　　**Phi.A 11229G**
(*Sonata No. 2, etc.* in ♯ A 00124L)　　(*PhM 09710S*)
L. Pennario　　　　in ♯ *DCap.CCL 7510*
(*Debussy & Liszt*)　　　　　(♯ *Cap.H 8156*)
J. Battista　　　　　in ♯ **MGM.E 141**
(*Schumann, Schubert, etc.*)
S. Askenase　　　　　　　　**PV. 72209**
(*No. 9*)　　　　　　　　　(♯ *Pol. 16022*)
P. Serebriakov　　　　　　*Muza. 1589*
☆ J. Lhevinne　in ♯ Vic.LCT 1038: ♭ set *WCT 60*
　V. Schiøler　　　in ♯ *Mer.MG 15037*
　J. Iturbi　　　　　♭ *Vic.WEPR 32*
　M. Sheyne　　　　in ♯ EA.ALX 7
— ARR. 2 PFS.
A. Sandford & C. Vidusso (in ♯ Roy. 1215: also ♯ *6113*)
— ARR. ORCH.　☆ A. Kostelanetz Orch. (C.M 10025)

No. 7, A flat major, Op. 61　"Polonaise-fantaisie"
M-Th. Fourneau　　　　　**C.LFX 1011/2**
(3ss—*Mazurka No. 32*)

No. 8, D minor, Op. 71, No. 1
☆ H. Stefanska (in ♯ BB.LBC 1031: ♭ set *WBC 1031*)

No. 9, B flat major, Op. 71, No. 2
S. Askenase　(*No. 6*)　　　**PV. 72209**

---

(24) PRELUDES, Op. 28
COMPLETE RECORDINGS
C. Arrau　　　　　　　♯ **AmC.ML 4420**
(Nos. 15, 23, 24 on ♭ *4-73261D*)
A. Brailowsky　　　　　♯ **G.FALP 163**
(♯ Vic.LM 1150: ♭ set *WDM 1549*)

♯ = Long-playing, 33⅓ r.p.m.　　　♭ = 45 r.p.m.　　　♮ = Auto. couplings, 78 r.p.m.

52

(24) PRELUDES, Op. 28.—COMPLETE (*continued*)

C. de Groot   # **Phi.A 00109L**
☆ A. Rubinstein   # **Vic.LM 1163**
☆ G. Novães   # **PaV.VP 120**

... Nos. 1, 3, 6, 16, 21, 22
L. Pattison   # **Cmt. 1203**
(*Bach*)

... Nos. 1, 15, 20 — ARR. 2 PFS.
A. Sandford & C. Vidusso
       (in # *Roy*. 1215; Nos. 1 & 15 only in # *Roy*. 6113)

... No. 1
   ☆ A. Földes (in # *Rem. 149-4*)

... Nos. 3, 6, 7
   ☆ M. Rosenthal (in # Vic.LCT 1038: ♭ set *WCT 60*)

... Nos. 3, 8, 16   C. Keene (in # Mer.MG 10113)

... Nos. 4 & 20   ☆ L. Bertolini (in # Csm.CLPS 1014)

... Nos. 4 & 24 — ARR. ORCH.
Sym.—Stokowski(♭ *Vic*.49-3855; No. 4 only in # LM 1238)

... Nos. 6 & 7   R. Turner
              (in # *Cap.H 2003*: ♭ set *CCF 2003*)

... No. 7, A major   ☆ M. Sheyne (in # EA.ALX 7)

—— ARR. GUITAR
A. Segovia   in # *AmD.DL 9647*
(† *Segovia Program*)

... No. 15, D flat major
F. Ellegaard (*Étude, Op. 25, No. 5*)   **Pol.HM 80052**
☆A. Cortot (*Berceuse*)   ♭ *G.7RF 238*

—— ARR. ORCH.   ☆ A. Kostelanetz Orch. (C.M 10025)

—— ARR. 4 PFS. (in # *Vic.LM 84*)

... Nos. 17-19 & 22-24
C. de Groot (from set)   **Phi.A 11240G**
                     (*PhM.A 11240S*)

... No. 18, F minor
—— ARR. 2 PFS.   A. Sandford & C. Vidusso (in # Roy. 1214)

... No. 20, C minor
G. Werschenska   **Pol.HM 80054**
(*Étude Op. 10, No. 2 & Nocturne No. 5*)

... No. 22, G minor   ☆ M. Sheyne (in # EA.ALX 7)

... No. 24, D minor
   ☆ E. Wild (in # Var. 2008; in ♭ *Roy set 14519*)

Rondo, C major, Op. 73   2 pfs.
☆ A. & H-O. Schmidt-Neuhaus (Pol. 15522)

(4) SCHERZOS
COMPLETE RECORDING
G. Schultze   **PV. 72068/9**
(1s. each)
☆ A. Rubinstein   # **G.FALP 147**

No. 1, B minor, Op. 20
L. Kentner   **C.DX 1859**
V. Horowitz   in # **Vic.LM 1707**
                     (♭ set *WDM 1707*)
☆H. Stefanska   **CdM.GA 5034/5**
(3ss—*Étude, Op. 10, No. 4 & Mazurka No. 47*)

No. 2, B flat minor, Op. 31
W. Wolf   **G.EH 1346**
☆ W. Malcuzynski (C.GQX 11452)
   A. Rubinstein (♭ *G.7RF 226*)

No. 3, C sharp minor, Op. 39
J. Katchen   in # *D.LX 3079*
(*Ballade No. 3 & Fantaisie*)   (in # *Lon.LS 554*)
W. Wolf   **G.EH 1386**
J. Smeterlin   in # **Allo.ALG 3042**
G. Novães   in # **AmVox.PL 7810**

☆ A. Rubinstein (♭ *Vic.WEPR 42*)
   M. Levitzki (in # Vic.LCT 1038: ♭ set *WCT 60*)

No. 4, E major, Op. 54
☆ C. Arrau (C.GQX 11482/3)

SONATAS
No. 1, C minor, Op. 4
R. Goldsand   # **CHS.CHS 1150**
(*Variations*)   (# Nix.CLP 1150)

No. 2, B flat minor, Op. 35
S. Askenase   **PV. 72085/6**
(3ss—*Mazurka 32*)   (# *Pol. 16005*)
E. Kilenyi   # **Rem. 199-90**
(*No. 3*)
A. Uninsky   # **Phi.A 00124L**
(*Fantasia & Polonaise*)
J. La Montaine   # **Dor.DR 332**
(*La Montaine*)
A. Rubinstein (n.v.)   # **Vic.LM 9008**
(*Debussy*)   (♭ set *WDM 9008*)
☆ V. Horowitz   # **Vic.LM 1235**
(*Chopin-Liszt Recital*)(*Schumann* in # *G.FALP 195*)
   ☆ W. Malcuzynski (♮ C.LVX 149/51; # AmC.RL 3031)
       G. Novães (# AmVox.PL 7360; EVox. 370)

No. 3, B minor, Op. 58
W. Malcuzynski   # *C.C 1005*
W. Kapell   # **Vic.LM 1715**
(*Mazurkas*)   (♭ set *WDM 1715*)
E. Kilenyi   # **Rem. 199-90**
(*above*)
S. Askenase   (4ss)   **PV. 72105/6**
R. Firkusny   # *AmC.ML 2201*
A. Uninsky   # **Phi.A 00113L**
(*Barcarolle, Valse, Mazurka*)
   ☆ G. Novães (# AmVox.PL 7360; EVox. 370)

Tarantelle, A flat major, Op. 43
E. Balogh   in # **Lyr.LL 20**
                   (# Eur.LPG 616)
W. Maggiar   in # *Nix.LPY 112*

(14) VALSES
COMPLETE RECORDINGS
L. Pennario   # **DCap.CTL 7027**
(2ss)   (# Cap.P 8172)
S. Askenase   **PV. 72072/4**
(6ss)   (FPV. 5033/5)
E. Kilenyi   # **Rem. 199-82**
R. Trouard (some are ☆)   # **Od.ODX 103**
☆ D. Lipatti   # **C.FCX 156**
(♮ C.LNX 2005/10)   (# C.QCX 156; # AmC.ML 4522)

COLLECTIONS
No. 6, D flat major, Op. 64, No. 1 ☆
No. 7, C sharp minor, Op. 64, No. 2
No. 9, A flat major, Op. 69, No. 1 ☆
No. 11, G flat major, Op. 70, No. 1 ☆
No. 12, F minor, Op. 70, No. 2
A. Cortot   in # **Vic.LHMV 1032**
(*Barcarolle, Nocturnes, etc.*)   (♭ set *WHMV 1032*)

Nos. 6, 7, 11
C. de Groot   in # *Phi.A 00106R*

Nos. 6, 7, 14   R. Turner (in # *Cap.H 2003*: ♭ set *CCF 2003*)

Nos. 1, 7, 9, 12   ☆ A. Brailowsky (♭ *Vic.WEPR 28*)

Nos. 1, 6, 7, 11 — ARR. 2 PFS.
A. Sandford & C. Vidusso
        (in # Roy. 1214; Nos. 6 & 7 in # *Roy. 6113*)

☆ = Re-issue of a recording to be found in WERM or Supplement I.

No. 1, E flat major, Op. 18
R. Trouard (2ss) (from set)   *Od. 188974*
☆ R. Koczalski   Pol. 67246 [1]
(*Nocturne No. 2*)

☆ A. Brailowsky (from set) (Vic. 12-3294; ♭ *G.7RF 157*)

— ARR. ORCH. ☆ Sym. Orch.—Stokowski (♭ *Vic. 49-3368*)

— ARR. 4 PFS.
☆ First Piano Qtt. (in ♭ *Vic.WEPR 30*: in ♯ LM 1165)

No. 2, A flat major, Op. 34, No. 1
R. Trouard   *P.PO 194*
(2ss) (from set)   (*Od. 188973*)
S. Askenase   in ♯ *Pol. 16022*

— ARR. ORCH.
☆ A. Kostelanetz Orch. (C.M 10033: ♭ *SCD 2014*)

No. 3, A minor, Op. 34, No. 2
B. Janis   in ♯ **BB.LBC 1030**
                                       (♭ set *WBC 1030*)
☆ V. Horowitz (in ♯ Vic.LM 1137; ♭ *G.7RF 231*; in
♭ *Vic.ERA 59*)
A. Previn (in ♯ *Vic.LPM 3045*: ♭ *EPB 3045*)

No. 5, A flat major, Op. 42
A. Uninsky   in ♯ **Phi.A 00113L**
(*Sonata No. 3, etc.*)
☆ E. Sauer (Qual.QMN 7016)
⌶ E. d'Albert (in ♯ AudA. LA 1203*)

No. 6, D flat major, Op. 64, No. 1
No. 7, C sharp minor, Op. 64, No. 2
No. 8, A flat major, Op. 64, No. 3
N. Magaloff   in ♯ **D.LX 3076**
(*Mazurkas & Polonaises*) (& D.K 28588) (♯ *Lon.LS 532*)

Nos. 6 & 7
E. Silver (in ♯ *Var. 2008* & in ♯ *Var. 6944*)

No. 6, D flat, Op. 64, No. 1 ("*Minute*")
C. Smith   **C.DX 1809**
(*No. 11, & Nocturne No. 5*)
G. Novães   in ♯ **AmVox.PL 7810**
S. Askenase (from set)   in ♯ *Pol. 16022*

— ARR. 4 PFS. ☆ First Piano Qtt. (♯ Vic.LM 1165)

— ARR. ORCH.
M. Skalka Orch. (*Eli. 8991*)
☆ Hollywood Sym.—Newman (*Rna.RM 70252*)

No. 7, C sharp minor, Op. 64, No. 2
M. Jonas   in ♯ **AmC.ML 4476**
G. Werschenska   **Pol.HM 80057**
(*Valse No. 9*)
S. Askenase (from set)   in ♯ *Pol. 16022*
☆ V. Horowitz   **G.DB 21425**
(*Impromptu No. 1*)   (in ♯ Vic.LM 1137)
(*Valse No. 3*, in ♭ *G.7RF 231*; ♭ *Vic.ERA 59*)
F. Karrer (*Vien.P 6064*: in ♯ *1015*)
P. Serebriakov (*Muza. 1590*)

☆ J. Lhevinne (in ♯ Vic.LCT 1038: ♭ set *WCT 60*)
O. Frugoni (Attn. 27031)
A. Brailowsky (P.RR 8061)

— ARR. 4 PFS. ☆ First Piano Qtt. (in ♯ *Vic.LM 84*)

— ARR. ORCH.
Melachrino Orch. (*G.B 10207*; in ♯ *Vic.LPM 1002*:
♭ set *EPB 1002*; BrzV. *82-5463*)
☆ A. Kostelanetz Orch. (C.M 10033)

No. 8, A flat major, Op. 64, No. 3
☆ M. Sheyne (in ♯ EA.ALX 7)

No. 9, A flat major, Op. 69, No. 1
G. Werschenska   **Pol.HM 80057**
(*Valse No. 7*)

☆ A. Brailowsky, from set (Vic. 12-3294; ♭ *G.7RF 157*)

No. 10, B minor, Op. 69, No. 2
M. Jonas   in ♯ **AmC.ML 4476**

No. 11, G flat major, Op. 70, No. 1
W. Malcuzynski   **C.LX 8922**
(¼s.—*Mazurka No. 41 & Liszt: Rapsodie espagnole, s.1*)
C. Smith   **C.DX 1809**
(*No. 6, etc.*)
F. Karrer (*Vien.P 6044*: in ♯ *1015*)
☆ E. Wild (in ♯ Var. 2008), etc.

No. 12, F minor, Op. 70, No. 2
R. Trouard   *Od. 188970*
(*Mazurka No. 41*)

No. 14, E minor, no Op. No.
S. Askenase (from set)   in ♯ *Pol. 16022*
B. Janis   in ♯ **BB.LBC 1030**
                                       (♭ set *WBC 1030*)
☆ E. Wild (in ♯ Var. 2008, & in ♯ *6922*; in♭ *Roy. set 14519*)

— ARR. 2 PFS. M. Rawicz & W. Landauer (*C.DB 3135*)

VARIATIONS on
German theme 1824
R. Goldsand   ♯ **CHS.CHS 1150**
(*Sonata, & below*)   (♯ Nix.CLP 1150)

Je vends des scapulaires, Op. 12 (Hérold)
R. Goldsand   ♯ **CHS.CHS 1133**
(*Études, Op. 25*)   (♯ Nix.CLP 1133)
R. Reinhardt   ♯ **AmVox.PL 7530**
(*Varns., Op. 2*; & *Andante spianato*)

La ci darem, Op. 2 pf., or pf. & orch.
R. Goldsand   ♯ **CHS.CHS 1150**
(*above*)   (♯ Nix.CLP 1150)
R. Reinhardt & Stuttgart Pro Musica Orch.
                             in ♯ **AmVox.PL 7530**

II. CONCERTED WORKS

CONCERTOS, pf. & orch.
No. 1, E minor, Op. 11
N. Mewton-Wood & Netherlands Phil.—
Goehr   ♯ **Nix.CLP 1153**
                                       (♯ CHS.CHS 1153)
E. Kilenyi & Austrian Sym.—Prohaska
                                   ♯ **Rem. 199-44**
C. Vidusso & Rome Sym.—Questa ♯ **Roy. 1253**
☆ A. Brailowsky & Vic. Sym.—Steinberg
                                   ♯ **G.ALP 1015**
                                       (♯ G.FALP 145: QALP 145)

No. 2, F minor, Op. 21
G. Novães & Vienna Sym.—Klemperer
                                   ♯ **AmVox.PL 7100**
                                       (♯ PaV.VP 160)
S. Askenase & Berlin Phil.—Lehmann
(5ss)   ♮ **PV. 72228/30S**
                                       (♯ Pol. 18040)
I. Nehner & Berlin Sym.—Langhans ♯ **Roy. 1340**
N. Mewton-Wood & Zürich Radio—Goehr
                                   ♯ **MMS. 4**
M. Slezarieva & F. O. K. Sym.—Smetáček
                                   ♮ **U.H 23969/72**
(7ss—*Rachmaninoff: Prelude, Op. 23, No. 1*)
☆ W. Malcuzynski & Philharmonia—Kletzki
                                       (♯ C.FCX 154: ♮ LVX 121/4)

Krakowiak (Rondo), Op. 14
☆ R. Schmid & Munich Radio—Dressel (♯ *Clc. 6076*)

---

[1] Originally 67246 contained Nocturne No. 2 and Berceuse; but now re-issued as shown.

III. SONGS

(17) POLISH SONGS, Op. 74
COMPLETE RECORDING
M. Kurenko (S), R. Hufstader (pf.) ‡ **Lyr.LL 23**
(‡ *Eur.LPG 622*)

No. 1, The Maiden's Wish (Witwicki)
Included in *Vic. set E 97*: ♭ *set WE 97* (*Eng*)

No. 8, My sweetheart (Zaleski)
G. Lavrova (*Russ*) **USSR. 18563**
(*Rossini: Song*)

No. 16, Lithuanian Song (Witwicki)
E. Bandrowska-Turska (S) **USSR. 13769**
(*Moniuszko: Song*)

IV. MISCELLANEOUS

Chopin, his story and his music
(Selections from the works, with spoken descriptions)
☆ A. Moss & Sym.—Goberman ‡ *AmVox.VL 2520*

(Les) Sylphides
— ARR. ORCH.
Covent Garden—Rignold [1] ‡ **P.PMD 1003**
(2ss) (*Tchaikovsky* on ‡ *AmD.DL 9550*) (‡ *Od.OD 1004*)
Covent Garden—Braithwaite [2] in ‡ **MGM.E 3006**
Berlin Sym.—List ‡ **Roy. 1338**
(*Delibes: Coppélia Suite*)
☆ L.P.O.—Sargent [3] (in ‡ BB.LBC 1011: ♭ *set WBC 1011*)
New York Phil. Sym.—Kurtz (C.M 15142/4)

CICONIA, Johannes (fl. *c.* 1400)
SEE: † ITALIAN MADRIGAL

CILEA, Francesco (1866-1950)

OPERAS
ADRIANA LECOUVREUR 1902
COMPLETE RECORDINGS

CASTS	SET A	SET B
Adriana		
Lecouvreur	M. Favero	C. Gavazzi (S)
Princesse de		
Bouillon	E. Nicolai	M. T. Pace (M-S)
Maurizio ...	N. Filacuridi	G. Prandelli(T)
Michonnet ...	L. Borgonovo	S. Meletti (B)

Set A
La Scala Cho. & Orch.—del Cupolo
(6ss) ‡ **Csm.CLPS 1018/20**

Set B
Italian Radio Cho. & Orch.—Simonetto
(6ss) ‡ **Sor. set 1218**

Io sono l'umile ancella S (Act I)
☆ M. Caniglia (BrzV. 886-5007)
꜀ C. Muzio (in ‡ Eso.ES 503*; ‡ Cpt.MC 20010*) [4]

Poveri fiori S (Act IV)
☆ M. Caniglia (BrzV. 886-5007)

(L') ARLESIANA 3 acts 1897
COMPLETE RECORDING

Vivetta	...	...	...	E. Tegani (S)
Rosa Mamai	...	...	G. Pederzini (M-S)
Federico	...	...	J. Oncina (T)
Metifio	...	...	O. Serpo (B)
Baldassare	...	...	A. Protti (B)

La Scala Cho. & Orch.—del Cupolo
(4ss) ‡ **Csm.CLPS 1016/7**

È la solita storia T
N. Monti **C.GQX 11453**
(*Elisir d'amore—Una furtiva lagrima*)
☆ F. Tagliavini (♭ *G.7RF 205*; in ‡ Vic.LM 1164)
G. di Stefano (♭ *G.7R 116: 7RF 119*)

Esser madre è un inferno S
☆ C. Muzio in ‡ **AmC.ML 4404**

CIMAROSA, Domenico (1749-1801)

OPERAS
(Il) MATRIMONIO SEGRETO 2 acts 1792
Overture
Florence May Fest.—Serafin **G.C 4135**
(S 10583)
L.S.O.—Kisch in ‡ **D.LX 3063**
(below) (also D.K 23201) (‡ *Lon.LPS 353*)
Bavarian Radio—Görlich in ‡ **Mer.MG 10033**
(*Donizetti, Gounod*)

Perdonate, signor mio S (Act I)
A. Noni **P.R 30050**
(*Signor Bruschino—Ah donate al caro sposo*) (CB 20525)

(Gli) ORAZII ED I CURIAZII 1794
Overture
L.S.O.—Kisch in ‡ **D.LX 3063**
(above & Gluck: Overtures) (‡ *Lon.LPS 353*)

SONATAS, pf.
No. 23, A minor　　　No. 24, C major
No. 29, C minor　　　No. 31, G major
— ARR. OB. & STR. Benjamin ("Concerto")
☆ P. Pierlot & Paris Cha.—Duvauchelle
(*Bach: Concerto, F minor*) ‡ **Lum.LD 103**

CIRRI, Giovanni Battista (1740- ?)

Concerto, A minor vlc., fl., str.
Virtuosi di Roma—Fasano ‡ **AmD.DL 9598**
(*Marcello, Albinoni, Pergolesi*)

CLARKE, Jeremiah (1659-1707)

(The) Prince of Denmark's March hpsi.
— ARR. ORGAN "*Trumpet Voluntary*"
E. P. Biggs in ‡ **AmC.ML 4603**
(*Purcell, Murrill, etc.*)
H. Robinson Cleaver in **AmD. set A 880**
(‡ *DL 5360*: ♭ *set 9-269*)

— ARR. ORCH. Wood
Amsterdam—v. Beinum in ‡ **D.LX 3096**
(*Handel*) (in ‡ *Lon.LS 620*)

— ARR. TPT. & BAND Jakeway
Salvation Army Band (*RZ.MF 358*)

CLAUDE le jeune (*c.* 1523-1600)

Psalm 42—Ainsi qu'on oit le cerf bruire
Kanawaty Vocal Ens. **Lum. 2.24.028**
(*Goudimel: Psalms 47 & 51*)

Revecy venir du printans
Renaissance Singers—Engel in ‡ **AmC.ML 4517**
(† Treasury of Madrigals)
R. Shaw Chorale in ‡ **Vic.LM 136**
(† XVIth Century Music) (in ♭ *set WDM 1598*)

---

[1] ARR. Jacob.
[2] Excerpts only.
[3] ARR. Murray & White.
[4] Recorded from Edison cylinder.

CLAUDE PETIT JEAN: *Alias* Joan de Latre
    SEE: † MADRIGALS (♯*AS. 2501LD*)

CLEMENTI, Muzio (1752-1832)

GRADUS AD PARNASSUM pf. 1817
(4) Études (unspec.)
  M. Schwalb   ♯ **Acad.ALP 303**
  (Cramer & Czerny)

SONATAS, pf.
D major, Op. 26, No. 3 1790
  G. Gorini   *P.AT 0272/3*
  (3ss—Poulenc: Nocturne)

B minor, Op. 40, No. 2
  A. Balsam   ♯ **CHS.G 11**
  (Hummel)

B flat major, Op. 47, No. 2 1781
... Rondo
  V. Horowitz   ♭ *Vic. 49-3303*
  (Scriabin)

Synthetic Sonata, B flat 2 pfs.
  ☆ A. & H-O. Schmidt-Neuhaus (Pol. 15550)

CLÉRAMBAULT, Louis Nicolas
(1676-1749)

SUITES, Organ
No. 2, G minor 1711
1. Plein jeu   2. Duo   3. Trio
4. Basse de cromorne   5. Flûtes
6. Récit de nazarde   7. Caprice sur les grands jeux
  A. Marchal   ♯ **Lum.LD 101**
  († French Organ Music)

CLIFTON, John (1781-1841)

  SEE ALSO: † AMERICAN MUSIC
          (INSTRUMENTAL & CHAMBER)

If music be the food of love
  (Twelfth Night—Shakespeare)
  L. Chelsi (T), F. Kramer (pf.)
         in ♯ **MTR.MLO 1010**

COBBOLD, William (1560-1639)

  SEE: † TRIUMPHS OF ORIANA

COPLAND, Aaron (b. 1900)

Billy the Kid Ballet 1938
Orchestral Suite ... Nos. 1 & 5 only
  ☆ N.Y.P.S.O.—Stokowski (♭ *AmC.A 1516*)

Celebration dance; Billy's demise; The open prairie again
— ARR. 2 PFS.
  A. Whittemore & J. Lowe in ♯ **Vic.LM 1705**
  (Ravel, Bax, Stravinsky, etc.)   (in ♭ *set WDM 1705*)

Concerto, clarinet & orch. 1948
  B. Goodman & Col. Sym.—Copland
  (Quartet)   ♯ **AmC.ML 4421**

Concerto, pf. & orch. 1926
  L. Smit & Rome Radio—Copland   ♯ **CHS. F4**
  (Bloch)

(An) Immorality (E. Pound) Fem. cho. & pf. 1925
  Vienna Academy Cho.—Grossmann
  (R. Thompson, Barber, etc.)   ♯ **AmVox.PL 7750**

In the beginning 1947
  San José State A cappella Cho.—Erlendson
  (Corsi, Tallis, Handl, etc.)   ♯ **ML. 7007**

Music for the Theatre 1925
  A.R.S. Orch.—Hendl   ♯ **ARS. 12**
  (Moross: Frankie & Johnnie)

Our Town Film music 1940 ... **Suite**
  Little Orch. Soc.—Scherman   ♯ *AmD.DL 7527*
  (Thomson)

Quartet, pf. & str. 1950
  New York Qtt.   ♯ **AmC.ML 4421**
  (Concerto)

(The) Red Pony Film music 1948
... Suite
  Little Orch. Soc.—Scherman   ♯ *AmD.DL 9616*
  (Thomson)

Rodeo Ballet 1942
... Hoe-down — ARR. VLN. & PF. Copland
  L. & A. Kaufman   ♯ **CHS.CHS 1140**
  (below; Carpenter, Still, etc.)

(El) Salon Mexico orch. 1936
  Columbia Sym.—Bernstein   ♯ *AmC.ML 2203*
  (Milhaud)

... Themes from, — ARR. PF. & ORCH. J. Green
  "Fantasia Mexicana"
  L. Hambro & Orch.—Marrow in ♯ *MGM.E 539*

Sextet str. qtt., clar. & pf. 1937 [1]
  Juilliard Qtt., D. Oppenheim, L. Hambro
         ♯ **AmC.ML 4492**
  (Kohs: Concerto)

Sonata, vln. & pf. 1943
  ☆ J. Fuchs & L. Smit (♯ *D.AXT 233048*)

Ukulele Serenade vln. & pf. 1926
  L. & A. Kaufman   in ♯ **CHS.CHS 1140**
  (above)

FOLKSONG ARRANGEMENTS
(5) Old American Songs
1. The boatmen's dance (Minstrel Song, 1843)
2. Long time ago (Ballad)
3. The dodger (Campaign Song)
4. Simple gifts (Shaker Song)
5. I bought me a cat (Children's Song)
  W. Warfield (B), A. Copland (pf.)
         ♯ *AmC.ML 2206*
  (Dougherty: 5 Sea Shanties)

CORELLI, Arcangelo (1653-1713)

(12) CONCERTI GROSSI, Op. 6
COMPLETE RECORDING
  Corelli Tri-Centenary—Eckertsen
         ♯ **AmVox. set PL 7893**
  (6ss) (D. Guilet & E. Bachmann, vlns; F. Miller, vlc.)

No. 1, D major
  Bavarian State—F. Lehmann   **PV. 4410**

---

[1] A version of his *Short Symphony* (No. 2), 1933.

No. 3, C minor
Homburg Sym.—F. Schubert   # *Rgt. 5015*
(*Vivaldi*)

No. 8, G minor (*"Christmas Concerto"*)
Virtuosi di Roma—Fasano   # **AmD.DL 9649**
(*Scarlatti, Vivaldi, etc.*)
Vienna Sym.—Heiller [1]   # **Per.SPLP 540**
(*Sonata; & Vivaldi*)   (# *Clc. 6093*)
☆ Vienna Cha.—Heiller [1] (# *Clc. 6069*)

"Concerto", F major   ob. & str.
— ARR. Barbirolli from Vln. Sonatas, Op. 5
P. Pierlot, Paris Phil.—Leibowitz # **Oce.OCS 29**
(*Gluck & Haydn*)

SONATAS, Op. 5 vln. & cont.
Nos. 3, 6, 10, 12
☆ R. Brink & D. Pinkham (hpsi.) (# **EA.ALX 109**)

No. 7, D minor
☆ J. Starker & M. Meyer (pf.)
(# **Per.SPLP 540**; # **Clc. 6093**)

No. 9, A major
... 2nd movt., Giga   — ARR. HARP
A. Sacchi   in # *NRI. 403*
(*Debussy, Loeillet, Zabel, etc.*)

D major (unspec.) (additional to previous entry)
▽ A. Spalding & A. Kooiker (pf.)   # **Rem. 199-23**
(*Bach & Tartini*)

"Suite for Strings" ARR. Arbós
☆ Italian Radio—Tansini (P.CB 20528)

... Sarabande & Badinerie only
Czech Phil.—Pedrotti   **U.H 23788**
(*Bonporti: Vln. Concerto—Recitativo*) (in # **Sup.LPM 35**)

... Giga & Badinerie only
☆ Berlin Phil. Cha.—Benda (P.RR 8173)

CORNELIUS, Peter (1824-1874)

(Der) BARBIER VON BAGDAD (*Ger*) Opera
2 acts   1858
Overture, D major
☆ Dresden Phil.—v. Kempen (Pol. 15495)

Salaam Aleikum! Bs & cho.   Act II
(*Heil diesem Hause . . .*)
O. Edelmann   in # **D.LXT 2672**
(*Wagner, Beethoven, etc.*) (D.K 28553) (# **Lon.LLP 427**)
H. H. Nissen & W. Strienz   in # **Ura. 7026**

SONGS
COLLECTION
Hirschlein ging im Wald spazieren (Kuh)
Im Lenz (Heyse)
Komm, wir wandeln zusammen, Op. 4, No. 2 (Cornelius)
Möchte im Walde mit Dir gehen, Op. 4, No. 3 (Cornelius)
Morgenwind (Heyse)
T. Lemnitz (S), M. Raucheisen (pf.) # **Ura. 7013**
(*Schubert, Wolf*)

In der Mondnacht (Heyse)
M. Klose (A), M. Raucheisen (pf.) in # **Ura. 7053**
(*Jensen, Grieg, Pfitzner, etc.*)

(Ein) Ton, Op. 3, No. 3 (Cornelius)
Wiegenlied, Op. 1, No. 3 (Cornelius)
L. Lehmann (S)   in † # **Pembroke set**

Weihnachtslieder, Op. 8
I. Seefried (S), E. Werba (pf.)   **PV. 72252**

[1] Probably the same recording.

CORNET, Pieter (*c.* 1560-1626)

SEE: † OLD NETHERLANDS MASTERS

CORSI, Giuseppe (fl. XVIIth cent.)

Adoramus Te, Christe Motet
San José State A cappella Cho.—Erlendson
                                   # **ML. 7007**
(*Copland, Tallis, Handl, etc.*)

COSTELEY, Guillaume (1531-1606)

Allez, mes premières amours
Renaissance Singers—Engel in # **AmC.ML 4517**
(† *Treasury of Madrigals*)

Allons, gay, gay, gay bergères
R. Shaw Chorale   in **Vic. set DM 1711**
(♭ *set WDM 1711*: # **LM 1711**)

Mignonne, allons voir . . .
Bristol Univ. Fr. Circle—Barham
                           in # **Per.SPLP 535**
(† *Renaissance Masterpieces*)

O que je suis troublé
Kanawaty Vocal Ens.   *Lum. 2.24.029*
(*Goudimel*)

COUPERIN, François (1668-1733)

CLASSIFIED : I (a) Harpsichord   I (b) Organ
             II. Chamber Music   III. Vocal Music

I (A) HARPSICHORD

Ordre XIV, omitting *La Julliet*
E. Harich-Schneider   # *Ura. 5003*
(*Pantomime*)

Ordre XXIV COMPLETE
E. Harich-Schneider   # *Ura. 5001*

COLLECTIONS
Allemande (IX)
(La) Julliet (XIV)
(La) Létiville (XVI)
Musette de Choisi (XV)
    G. Leonhardt   **Phi.A 11214G**
                                   (*PhM.A 09716S*)

Le Dodo . . . ; Le Tic-toc-choc
Les Fauvettes plaintives; La Muse-plantine
L'Arléquine; Les Ombres errantes
Les Barricades mystérieuses; Les Folies françaises
La Passacaille
    ☆ M. Meyer (pf.)   # *DFr. 16*

Les Brinborions (XXIV)   La Fauvettes plaintives (XIV)
La Fine Madelon (XX)   La Linotte éfarouchée (XIV)
La Lutine (III)   La Musette de Choisi (XV)
Musette de Taverni (XV)   Les Ombres errantes (XXV)
La Sezile (XX)   Le Tic-toc-choc ou les Mail-
Les Tours de passe-passe   lotins (XVIII)
    (XXII)   Le Trophée (XXII)
La Visionnaire (XXV)

— ARR. R. Strauss as Divertimento, *q.v.*
Berlin Radio Orch.—Rother   # **Ura. 7042**
(*Strauss: Taillefer*)

Air dans le goût polonais (XX)
W. Landowska (hpsi)   **♯ Vic.LM 1186**
(† Polish keyboard music)   (♭ set *WDM 1586*)

(L') Arléquine (XXIII)
(Les) Barricades mystérieuses (VI)
☆ W. Landowska (in ♯ Vic.LM 1217; ♭ *G.7RF 216*;
   ♭ *Vic. set WDM 1181*)

(Le) Carillon de Cythère (XIV)
C. Solomon (pf.)   **G.C 4119**
(*Beethoven: Sonata No. 8, s.5*)
(*Bach: WTC. No. 28 on* ♭ *G.7P 123*)

(Les) Fastes de la Grande et Ancienne
    Ménestrandise (XI)
☆ S. Marlowe   in **♯ MGM.E 538**
(*Rameau*)

(Les) Graces naturéles (XI)
L. Selbiger   **C.LD 3**
(*below*)

(Les) Moissonneurs (VI)
K. Rapf   in **♯ Van.BG 510**
(in *Notenbuch für A. M. Bach, q.v., s.v.* J. S. Bach)

(La) Pantomime (XXVI)
E. Harich-Schneider   **♯ Ura. 5003**
(*Ordre XIV*)

(Le) Rossignol en amour (XIV)
L. Selbiger   **C.LD 3**
(*above*)

Soeur Monique (XVIII)
F. Ellegaard (pf.)   **Pol.HA 70035**
(*Daquin: Le Coucou*)

(Le) Tic-toc-choc (XVIII)
☆ S. Marlowe (*above*)   in **♯ MGM.E 538**

— ARR. HARP   O. Erdeli (*USSR. 20996*)

(Les) Vendangeuses (V)
☆ A. Ehlers (in **♯ AmD.DL 8019**)

I (B) ORGAN
MESSE POUR LES CONVENTS
Premier couplet du Kyrie
5ᵉ couplet du Gloria
Récit de cromorne en taille
G. Litaize   **♯ Sel.LPG 8234**
(† Maîtres d'orgue)

MESSE POUR LES PAROISSES
COMPLETE
W. Austin   **♯ A 440.12-5**

II. CHAMBER MUSIC
(Les) GOÛTS RÉUNIS
No. 6, B flat   fl. & orch.
☆ J. P. Rampal & Str. Orch.—Oubradous
    ♯ Clc. 6021
(*below*)   (♭ *Tono.A 175/6*)

No. 13, G major
☆ F. Oubradous (bsn.), G. Marchesini (vlc.)
(*above*)   **♯ Clc. 6021**

(Les) NATIONS : No. 3, L'Impériale
SONATA : L'Apothéose de Lully
☆ Hewitt Cha. Orch. (♯ DFr. 3)

SONATA : La Sultane
... Overture & Allegro only   — ARR. Milhaud
N.Y.P.S.O.—Mitropoulos   **♯ AmC.AAL 16**
(*Travis*)

III. VOCAL MUSIC
Faisons du temps un doux usage (Vaudeville)
☆ Pro Musica Cho. Soc.—Calder (in **♯ CID. 33007**)

[1] Or might be Op. 20, No. 1.

COUPERIN, Louis (1626-1661)
SEE ALSO : † FRENCH ORGAN MUSIC

CHACONNES
D minor (55)
☆ A. Ehlers (in **♯ AmD.DL 8019**)

COWELL, Henry Dixon (b. 1897)

PIANO MUSIC COLLECTION
   Tides of Manaunan; Exultation;
   The harp of life; Lilt of the reel;
   Advertisement; Antimony; Aeolian Harp;
   Sinister Resonance; Anger Dance; Banshee;
   Fabric; What's there? Amiable conversation;
   Fairy Answer; Jig; The Snows of Fujiyama;
   The Voice of Lir; Dynamic Motion;
   Trumpet of Angus Og; Tiger
H. D. Cowell   **♯ Circ. 51-101**

Symphony No. 5   1948
A.R.S. Orch.—Dixon   **♯ ARS. 2**

CRAMER, Johann Baptist (1771-1858)

ÉCOLE DE VÉLOCITÉ
(13) Études (unspec.)   pf.
M. Schwalb   **♯ Acad.ALP 303**
(*Czerny & Clementi*)

CRANFORD, William   (fl. XVIIth Century)
SEE: † CATCHES & GLEES

CREQUILLON, Thomas   (d. *c.* 1557)
SEE: † XVIth & XVIIth CENTURY SONGS

CRESTON, Paul (b. 1906)

Here is my footstool, Op. 11 (Tagore)
☆ De Paur Infantry Cho.   in **♯ AmC.ML 4144**

CROCE, Giovanni (*c.* 1557-1609)

O vos omnes
Tenebrae factae sunt   4 voices
▽ Male Cho.—Jakobi   **Chr. 308A**
(*Bells of Bochum Priory*)

CUI, César Antonovitch (1835-1918)

Cantabile, Op. 36, No. 2   vlc. & pf.
J. Pacey & F. Kramer   in **♯ MTR.MLP 1003**

Miniature March, Op. 39, No. 5 [1] pf. — ARR. ORCH.
Bolshoi Theatre—Fayer   **USSR. 6359**
(*Liadov: Musical Box*)

Orientale, Op. 50, No. 9   vln. & pf.
M. Erdenko & pf.   **USSR. 14171**
(*Vieuxtemps: Nightingale*)

Orientale, Op. 50, No. 9 (*continued*)

— ARR. VLC. & PF.
　☆ G. Piatigorsky & R. Berkowitz
　　　　　　　　　　in ♯ *AmC.RL 3015*
　(*Rimsky, etc., & Shostakovitch*)
　J. Pacey & F. Kramer　　in ♯ *MTR.MLP 1003*

SONGS
Bolero
　N. Kazantseva　　　　　　　　*USSR. 18160*
　(*Auber: Village Song*)

(The) Burnt Letter (Pushkin)
　V. Kilchevsky　　　　　　　　*USSR. 15257*
　(*Statue & Thou and You*)

Parting　(Mickiewicz)
　N. Shpiller (S)　　　　　　　*USSR. 19999*
　(*Glinka: The Lark*)

The Statue of Czarskoë Selo, Op. 57, No. 17
　　(Pushkin)
　V. Kilchevsky　　　　　　　　*USSR. 15256*
　(½s.—*Thou and You, & The Burnt Letter*)
　T. Pyle (B, *Eng*), R. Viola (pf.) in *Vic. set E 101*
　(*Wolf*)　　　　　　　　　　(♭ *set WE 101*)

Thou and You (Pushkin)
　V. Kilchevsky　　　　　　　　*USSR. 15256*
　(½s.—*Statue & Burnt Letter*)

Tati-tati: Paraphrases on *Chopsticks* pf. duet
Theme, 24 variations & finale [2]
Valses
　— ARR. ORCH. N. Tcherepnin & Janssen
　Col. Sym.—Janssen　　　♯ *AmC.ML 4480*
　(*Borodin, Liszt, Rimsky, etc.*)

CZERNY, Carl (1791-1857)

(6) Études (unspec.)　　pf.
　M. Schwalb　　　　　　　♯ *Acad.ALP 303*
　(*Clementi & Cramer*)

DAHL, Ingolf (b. 1912)

Concertino a tre　cl., vln., vlc.　1947
　M. Lurie, E. Shapiro, V. Gottlieb
　(*Schuman: Str. Qtt.*)　　　♯ *AmC.ML 4493*

Variations on a Swedish folk tune　unacc. fl.
　D. Anthony　　　　　　　　♯ *Cmt. 1205*
　(*Piston: Sonata*)

DAMASE, Jean-Michel (b. 1927)

(La) CROQUEUSE DE DIAMANTS Ballet 1949
(Les) Bicyclettes; Nocturne; Toccata;
(La) Valse à cinq temps
　J-M. Damase (pf.)　　　　　*D.GAF 15102*

DANDRIEU, Jean François (1681-1738)

SEE: † FRENCH MASTERS . . .

DANZI, Franz (1763-1826)

Quintet, Op. 67, No. 1　wind insts.
　New Art Wind Quintet ♯ *CEd. set CE 20*
　(*Mozart, Stamitz, Reicha*)　　　　　　**0**

---

[2] Jointly with Liadov & Rimsky-Korsakov

DAQUIN, Louis Claude (1694-1772)

SEE ALSO: † FRENCH MASTERS . . .
　　　　　　† FRENCH ORGAN MUSIC

(Le) Coucou　hpsi.
　F. Ellegaard (pf.)　　　　　*Pol.HA 70035*
　(*Couperin: Soeur Monique*)

— ARR. HARP　O. Erdeli (*USSR. 18953*)

Noël No. 10, G major, Grand jeu et duo
　☆ F. Germani　　　　　　♭ *G.7BF 1044*
　(*Mulet: Toccata, F sharp minor*)

DARGOMIJSKY, Alexander (1813-1869)

OPERAS
ROUSSALKA　4 acts　1856
COMPLETE RECORDING
　Soloists, Bolshoi Theatre Cho. & Orch.—
　　Nebolsin (38ss)　　　*USSR. 020231/68*

Overture
　Bolshoi Theatre—Nebolsin (from set)
　　　　　　　　　　　　　U.H 23907

Ah, you young girls (Miller's Aria, Act I)　Bs
　M. Reizen　　　　　　　　*USSR. 017699*
　(*Tchaikovsky: Pique-Dame, aria*)

　B. Gmyria　　　　　　　　*USSR. 017500*
　(*Borodin: Prince Igor, Galitsky's Song*)

Princess's aria (Act II)　A
　E. Antonova　　　　　　　　*USSR. 9005*
　(*Serov: Rogneda—Rogneda's song*)

Some unknown power　(Act III)　T
　⌶ L. Sobinoff (G.VB 45*: o.n. DB 893*)

What does this mean?　　Bs & T
　(*Mad Scene & Death of Miller, Act III*)
　A. Pirogov, S. Streltsov　　*USSR. 9670/3*
　M. Reizen, G. Nelepp　　*USSR. 017799/800*

Princess's aria　(Act III)　A
　E. Antonova　(2ss)　　　　*USSR. 9002/3*

SONGS
Blue eyes (Tumansky)
　A. Ivanov (B)　　　　　　　*USSR. 18484*
　(*Lileta*)

Darling girl　(Anon.)
　V. Davidova (S)　　　　　　*USSR. 17881*
　(*Varlamoff: Snow-storm*)

Darling girl　(Anon.)
I love him still　(Zhadovsky)
　J. Tourel (M-S), G. Reeves (pf.)
　　　　　　　　　　in ♯ *AmC.ML 2198*

Deep in my memory　(Davidov)
　M. Mikhailov (Bs)　　　　　*USSR. 12216*
　(*below*)

(The) Drunken Miller　(Pushkin)
　M. Mikhailov (Bs)　　　　　*USSR. 12217*
　(½s.—*Titular Councillor & Deep in my memory*)

Fair maidens　Duet　(Pushkin)
　G. Sakharova, Z. Dolukhanova　*USSR. 17782*
　(*Tchaikovsky: In the garden...*)

SONGS (continued)

How often I hear (Zhadovsky)
S. Preobrazhenskaya (S)   *USSR. 19563*
(*Russian Folk Song*)

It's all the same to me (Miller)
M. Maksakova (S)   *USSR. 15807*
(*You will soon forget me; & Tchaikovsky: Song*)

Lileta (Delvig)
A. Ivanov (B)   *USSR. 18485*
(*Blue eyes*)

Lonely and sad (Lermontov)
I. Kozlovsky (T)   *USSR. 20454*
(*Tchaikovsky: Behind the window . . .*)

Lost in your embraces (Kurotchkin)
A. Ivanov (B)   *USSR. 17014*
(½s.—*My dear, my darling, & Glinka: Nightingale*)

My dear, my darling (Davidov)
A. Ivanov (B)   *USSR. 17014*
(½s.—*Lost in your embraces, & Glinka: Nightingale*)

(The) Old Corporal (Kurotchkin)
B. Gmyria (B)   *USSR. 016917*
(*Borodin: To distant shores*)
M. Reizen (Bs), A. Makharov (pf.)
(2ss)   *USSR. 21215/6*

Oriental Ballad (Pushkin)
P. Nortsov (S)   *USSR. 4580*
(*Rimsky-Korsakov: 2 songs*)

(The) Titular Councillor (Pushkin)
M. Mikhailov (Bs)   *USSR. 12217*
(½s.—*Drunken Miller & Deep in my memory*)

Vanka-tanka Duet
G. Vinogradov (T), A. Ivanov (B)
(*Vilbois: Seafarers*)   *USSR. 12747*

(The) Worm (Kurotchkin)
B. Gmyria (Bs)   *USSR. 19455*
(*Moussorgsky: Song of the flea*)

You will soon forget me (Zhadovsky)
M. Maksakova (S)   *USSR. 15806*
(½s.—*Tchaikovsky: Song; & It's all the same to me*)

DAVIES, William (1859-1907)

SEE: † WELSH RECORDED MUSIC SOCIETY

DEBUSSY, Achille Claude (1862-1918)

CLASSIFIED: I. Instrumental
    A. Piano B. Chamber Music
      C. Orchestral

II. Vocal
    A. Cantatas B. Dramatic Works
    C. Songs & Part Songs

I. INSTRUMENTAL
A. PIANO
COLLECTIONS

Arabesques 1 & 2
Preludes: I, 5: Les Collines d'Anacapri
    I, 8: La Fille aux cheveux de lin
    II, 3: La Puerta del vino
Images: II, 3: Poissons d'or
    La Plus que lente
H. Henkemans   *‡ Phi.A 00600R*
(for 78 r.p.m. issues, see individual titles)

COLLECTIONS (continued)

Arabesques 1 & 2
ESTAMPES
(La) Plus que lente
Rêverie
M. Pressler   *‡ MGM.E 178*

Arabesques 1 & 2
Preludes: I, 2: Voiles
    I, 8: La Fille aux cheveux de lin
    I, 9: La Sérénade interrompue
    I, 12: Minstrels
Children's Corner: 3, Serenade for the doll
    6, Golliwogg's Cake-walk
☆ G. Casadesus   *‡ Sti. 45*

---

(2) Arabesques 1888
W. Gieseking (n.v.)   *C.LX 1556*
H. Henkemans   *Phi.A 11217G*
    (*PhM.A 09715S*)

A. Sandford (in ‡ Roy. 1215, in ♯ Roy. 6100, & in
    ♭ Roy. set 14587)
☆ J. Iturbi (in ‡ Vic.LM 1167:♭ set WDM 1604)

— ARR. HARP   Renié
A. Sacchi   in ‡ NRI. 403
(*Haydn, Handel, Corelli, etc.*)

CHILDREN'S CORNER SUITE 1908
W. Gieseking (n.v.)   ♮ C.LC 4000/2
(6ss)   (‡ AmC.ML 4539)
C. Seemann   PV. 72271
A. Sandford   ‡ Roy. 1246
(*Prokofiev: Peter & the Wolf*)   (& ‡ Roy. 6109, 2ss)

... No. 3, Serenade for the doll
☆ V. Horowitz   G.DB 6971
    (in ‡ Vic.LM 1171: in ♭ set WDM 1605)

... No. 5, The little shepherd
G. Scherzer   P.E 11495
(*No. 6 & Preludes*)

... No. 6, Golliwogg's Cake-walk
G. Scherzer   P.E 11495
(*above*)
C. Keene (in ‡ Mer.MG 10113)
☆ O. Levant (♭ AmC.A 1537)

— — ARR. ORCH.   ▽ New Mayfair—Goehr
    (G.B 9508 : AA 610)

Danse (Tarantelle styrienne) 1890
— ARR. ORCH.   Ravel
☆ Brussels Radio—André in ‡ DT.LGM 65002
(*Chabrier, Rameau, etc.*)   (‡ T.LS 6016)

En blanc et noir 2 pfs. 1915
V. Vronsky & V. Babin   ‡ AmC.ML 4470
(*Stravinsky: Petrouchka excpts.*)

(6) Épigraphes antiques pf. duet 1915
C. Norwood & E. Hancock   ‡ Lyr.LL 21
(*below*)   (‡ Eur.LPG 630)
G. Gorini & S. Lorenzi   Dur.SA 142/3
(4ss)   (*Ravel: Ma Mère l'oye, in ‡ Csm.CLPS 1026*)

ESTAMPES 1903
COMPLETE: See Collections, ante
No. 2, Soirée dans Grenade
☆ G. Leroux   U.H 24180
(*Grétry: Rosière Républicaine Suite, s.1*)

No. 3, Jardins sous la pluie
A. Sandford
(in ‡ Roy. 1215, in ‡ Roy. 6100, & in ♭ Roy. set 14587)

---

‡ = Long-playing, 33⅓ r.p.m.   ♭ = 45 r.p.m.   ♮ = Auto. couplings, 78 r.p.m.

(12) Études　1915
　M. Haas　　　　　　　　　　　PV. 72206/8
　(6ss)　　　　　　(♯ Pol. 18046; AmD.DL 9599)
　C. Rosen　　　　　　　　　　　♯ REB. 6

... No. 11 only
　G. Gorini　　　　　　　　　　P.AB 30023
　(Malipiero: Risonanze)

IMAGES
Set I (1905)　1. Reflets dans l'eau
　　　　　　　2. Hommage à Rameau
　　　　　　　3. Mouvement
Set II (1907)　1. Cloches à travers les feuilles
　　　　　　　2. Et la lune descend . . .
　　　　　　　3. Poissons d'or

COMPLETE RECORDING
　☆ W. Gieseking　(2ss)　　　　♯ C.FC 1015

SET I
No. 1, Reflets dans l'eau
　A. Uninsky　　　　　　　　Phi.A 11210G
　(Prokofiev: Toccata)　　　　　　(PhM. 09708S)
　M. Panzéra　　　　　　in ♯ Mer.MG 10097
　(Songs; & Fauré)
　F. Chapiro　　　　　　　in ♯ Ox.OR 105
　☆ G. Leroux　　　　　　　　U.H 24178
　(Méhul: Jeune Henri, Overture, s.1)

No. 2, Hommage à Rameau
　G. Copeland　　　　　　in ♯ MGM.E 151

SET II
No. 3, Poissons d'or
　A. Rubinstein (n.v.)　　　in ♯ Vic.LM 9008
　(Chopin, etc.)　　　　　　(♭ set WDM 9008)
　H. Henkemans　　　　　　Phi.A 11216G
　(Prelude I-4)　　　　　　　(PhM. 09714S)

_____

Masques　1904
　A. Rubinstein　　　　　in ♯ Vic.LM 9008
　(Chopin, etc.)　　　　　　(♭ set WDM 9008)

Nocturne, D flat major　1890
　☆ W. Gieseking (C.GQ 7250)

Petite Suite　pf. duet　1889
　C. Norwood & E. Hancock　　　♯ Lyr.LL 21
　　　　　　　　　　　　(♯ Eur.LPG 630)
　E. Bartlett & R. Robertson　　♯ MGM.E 161
　(Ravel)

— ARR. ORCH.　H. Busser
　Robin Hood Dell—Reiner　　♯ Vic.LM 1724
　(Mendelssohn & Ravel)　　　(♭ set WDM 1724)
　Berlin Radio—Celibidache　　♯ Ura. 5006
　(Roussel)

... No. 4, Ballet
　V. Vitale & P. Buonomo　　　Vis.VI 4370
　(Milhaud: Scaramouche, s.3)

(La) Plus que lente, Valse　1910
　☆ A. Rubinstein　　　　in ♯ Vic.LM 1153
　(Liszt, etc.)
　　　(♭ Vic.WEPR 41: ♭ set WDM 1558; ♭ G.7RF 248)
　H. Henkemans　　　　　　Phi.A 11211G
　(Preludes I-3 & 8)　　　　　(PhM. 09712S)

— ARR. VLN. & PF.　Roques
　I. Kawaciuk & F. Vrána　　　U.H 23994
　(Provaznik: Indian Song)
　☆ J. Heifetz & E. Bay (in ♯ Vic.LM 1166)

POUR LE PIANO, Suite　1901
No. 1, Prelude
　G. Scherzer　　　　　　　　P.E 11490
　(Chopin: Études, Op. 25, Nos. 2 & 9)
　☆ G. Copeland (in ♭ MGM. set K 59)

No. 3, Toccata
　☆ E. Joyce (in ♯ AmD.DL 9528)

PRELUDES, Books I & II　1910-13
COMPLETE RECORDING
　H. Henkemans　　♯ Phi.A 00142L & A 00148L
　　Bk. I—1 & 2 also on Phi.A 11215G: PhM.A 09713S
　　Bk. I—4 also on Phi.A 11216G: PhM.A 09714S
　　Bk. I—3 & 8 also on Phi.A 11211G: PhM.A 09712S
　　Bk. I—9 & 12 & Bk. II—3 also on Phi.A 11177G:
　　　PhM. 09711S

Book I, Nos. 2, 10; Book II, Nos. 2, 6
　☆ G. Copeland (in ♭ MGM. set K 59)

BOOK I
COMPLETE
　W. Gieseking (n.v.)　　　　♯ AmC.ML 4537
　E. Kilenyi　　　　　　　　♯ Rem. 199-50
　☆ A. Cortot　　　　　　　　♯ G.BLP 1006
　(Schumann:　Kinderszenen　on　♯ Vic.LHMV　1009:
　♭ set WHMV 1009)

No. 8, La Fille aux cheveux de lin
　A. Rubinstein　　　　　in ♯ Vic.LM 9008
　(Chopin, etc.)　　　　　　(♭ set WDM 9008)
　C. Keene　　　　　　in ♯ Mer.MG 10113
　(Clair de lune, etc. & Chopin, Liszt, etc.)
　A. Sandford (in ♯ Roy. 1215: in ♯ Roy. 6100: & in
　♭ Roy. set 14587)

— ARR. VLN. & PF.　Hartmann
　Y. Menuhin & G. Moore　　　G.DA 2023
　(Handel: Te Deum—No.　17)
　☆ J. Heifetz & E. Bay (♯ G.7RF 172; ♭ Vic. 49-3312)

— ARR. HARMONICA & PF.　L. Adler & G. Moore (C.DB 3119)

No. 9, La Sérénade interrompue
　K. U. Schnabel　　　　　　Vis.VI 4382
　(No. 11)

No. 10, La Cathédrale engloutie
　W. Malcuzynski　　　　　　C.LB 119
　A. Rubinstein (n.v.)　　　in ♯ Vic.LM 9008
　(Chopin)　　　　　　　　(♭ set WDM 9008)
　M. Panzéra　　　　　　in ♯ Mer.MG 10097
　(Songs; & Fauré)

— ARR. ORCH.
　Janssen Sym. of Los Angeles　in ♯ Atst. 504

No. 11, La Danse de Puck
　K. U. Schnabel　　　　　　Vis.VI 4382
　(No. 9)

No. 12, Minstrels
　M. Panzéra　　　　　　in ♯ Mer.MG 10097
　(Songs: & Fauré)

— ARR. VLN. & PF. Hartmann
　☆ Z. Francescatti & M. Lanner (♭ AmC.A 1533)

BOOK II
COMPLETE
　W. Gieseking (n.v.)　　　　C.LC 4011/6
　(12ss)　　　　　　　　　(♯ AmC.ML 4538)

No. 3, La Puerta del vino
　C. Arrau　　　　　　　　　C.LX 1550
　(Granados: Goyescas, No. 4)　　(GQX 11504)

☆ = Re-issue of a recording to be found in WERM or Supplement I.

No. 7, La Terrasse des audiences . . .
No. 8, Ondine
A. Rubinstein   in # **Vic.LM 9008**
(*Chopin, etc.*)   (♭ *set WDM 9008*)

No. 12, Feux d'artifice
G. Scherzer   **P.E 11495**
(*Children's Corner, Nos. 5 & 6*)

Rêverie 1890
A. Sandford (in # *Roy. 1215*: in # *6100*: in ♭ *set 14587*)
E. Silver (in # *Var. 2008*: in # *6944*)

☆ J. Iturbi
  (in # *Vic.LM 1167*: ♭ *set WDM 1604*: ♭ *WEPR 33*)

Suite bergamasque 1890
W. Gieseking (n.v.)   ♮ **C.LX 8898/9**
(4ss)   (LFX 1025/6: ♮ LCX 5002/3: GQX 8035/6)
(*Children's Corner Suite on* # *AmC.ML 4539*)

. . . No. 3, Clair de lune
L. Pennario   in # *DCap.CCL 7510*
                              (# *Cap.H 8156*)
W. Gieseking (from set)   **C.LDX 13**
(*Sinding: Rustle of Spring*)
O. Frugoni   in # *AmVox.PL 7700*
(*Scuderi, Bartók, etc.*)
E. Farnadi   **C.LVX 188**
(*Liszt: Spanish Rhapsody, s.3*)
C. Keene (in # *Mer.MG 10113*)
A. Sandford (in # *Roy. 1215*: in # *6100*)
E. Silver (in # *Var. 2008*; in # *Roy. 6944*: in ♭ *set 14587*)
☆ J. Iturbi
  (in # *Vic.LM 1167*: in ♭ *set WDM 1604*: ♭ *WEPR 32*)
G. Copeland (in ♭ *MGM. set K 59*)
O. Levant (♭ *AmC.A 1537*)

—— —— ARR. HARP E. de Vito (in # *SOT. 1030*)

—— —— ARR. ORCH.
☆ Sym. Orch.—Stokowski
      (♭ *Vic.WEPR 47*: # *Vic.LM 1154*)
G. Melachrino Orch.—(in # *Vic.LPM 1002*: in ♭ *set EPB 1002*; G.S 10575*)
Col. Sym.—Rodzinski (in ♭ *AmC. set A 1002*)
Metropole—v. d. Linden (PhM.P *01009S*; also *D.C 16176* & Phi.A *1122*)
Col. Orch. (in # *AmC.GL 510*), etc.

I (B) CHAMBER MUSIC

Quartet, String, G minor, Op. 10 1893
Stuyvesant Qtt.   # **Phil. 104**
(*Ravel*)
Hirsch Qtt.   in # **Argo.ARS 1002**
(*Arensky & Rawsthorne*)
☆ Paganini Qtt.   # *G.FBLP 1024*
(2ss)

SONATAS

No. 1, D minor, vlc. & pf.
Cumberland Forest Festival (# pte. recording)

No. 2, flute, viola & harp 1916
J. P. Rampal, P. Pasquier, O. Ledentu
(*Lesur: Sextet*)   # *Sel.LP 8312*

No. 3, G minor, vln. & pf. 1917
R. Odnoposoff & L. Hambro # **Allo.ALG 3025**
(*Villa-Lobos*)
C. Ferras & P. Barbizet   ♮ **D.GAB 15097/8**
(3ss—*Ravel: Pavane pour une infante . . .*)
☆ J. Heifetz & E. Bay   # **Vic.LM 1184**
(*Respighi: Sonata*)   (# *G.FALP 165*)
(3ss.—*La plus que lente*, in ♭ *Vic.set WDM 1515*)
☆ Z. Francescatti & R. Casadesus # *C.FCX 125*
(*Franck: Sonata*)

I (C) ORCHESTRAL

(La) Boîte à joujoux Ballet 1913
. . . **Ronde** — ARR. PF.
G. Copeland   in # *MGM.E 151*

(2) Danses harp & str. 1904
A. Stockton & Ens.—Slatkin
            in # *DCap.CCL 7509*
(*Ravel: Intro. & Allegro*)   (# *Cap.L 8154*)
P. Berghout & Amsterdam Cha. Music Soc.—
      v. Beinum   # *D.LX 3097*
(*Ravel: Intro. & Allegro*)   (# *Lon.LS 621*)

. . . **Danse sacrée only** — ARR. PF.
☆ G. Copeland (in ♭ *MGM. set K 59*)

Fantaisie pf. & orch. 1889
F. Pelleg & Netherlands Phil.—Goehr
(*Fauré*)   # **CHS.G 9**

IMAGES (Set III) 1906-12
1. Gigues   2. Ibéria   3. Rondes de Printemps
COMPLETE RECORDING
San Francisco—Monteux (n.v.) # **G.FALP 174**
(# *Vic.LM 1197*: 9ss—*Damnation of Faust, Marche* in
 ♭ *set WDM 1618*)
(Nos. 1 & 3 on ♭ *WEPR 12*)

No. 2, Ibéria
Philadelphia—Ormandy   # **AmC.ML 4434**
(*below*)
☆ Brussels Radio—André
            (# *DT.LGX 66001*: # *T.LSK 7015*)

Jeux (Poème dansé) 1913
☆ Augusteo (St. Cecilia) Sym.—de Sabata
(*Respighi*)   # *G.FALP 178*

(La) Mer 1905
N.Y.P.S.O.—Mitropoulos   # **AmC.ML 4434**
(*above*)
N.B.C.—Toscanini   **G.DB 21453/5**
(6ss)   (♭ *Vic. set WDM 1583*)
(*Mendelssohn: M.S.N.D. excpts.* in # *Vic.LM 1221*)
Suisse Romande—Ansermet (n.v.) # *D.LXT 2632*
(*Ravel: Ma Mère l'oye*)   (# *Lon.LLP 388*)
            (also, 6ss—*D.K 28466/8*)
☆ Czech Phil—Désormière (# *Sup.LPM 14*)
Brussels Radio—André (♭ *Cap. set KCM 8010*)

(3) Nocturnes 1893-9
Suisse Romande—Ansermet (Anon. cho.)
            # *D.LXT 2637*
(*Ravel: Rapsodie espagnole*)   (# *Lon.LL 530*)
Philharmonia—Galliera (2ss)   # *C.S 1002*
(with Glyndebourne Chorus)   (No. 2 on DX 1780)
(No. 1, Nuages, is ☆)
Sym. Orch.—Stokowski (with Shaw Chorale)
            # **Vic.LM 1154**
(*Clair de lune & Prélude . . .* in # only) (♭ *set WDM 1560*)
(No. 2 on ♭ *Vic.WEPR 47*)
Minneapolis Sym.—Dorati   # **Mer.MG 50005**
(*Berlioz & Ravel*)

No. 1, Nuages
☆ Czech Phil—Désormière (# *Sup.LPM 14*)

No. 2, Fêtes
☆ Czech Phil—Désormière (# *Sup.LPM 20*)
Col. Sym.—Rodzinski (in ♭ *AmC. set A 1003*)
—— ARR. 2 PFS. Gearhart
V. Morley & L. Gearhart (in # *AmC.ML 2197*)

Prélude à l'après-midi d'un faune 1894
Suisse Romande—Ansermet in # *D.LX 3072*
(*Ravel, Prokofiev, Stravinsky*)   (in # *Lon.LS 503*)
Aarhus Municipal—Jensen   **Tono.X 25178**

= Long-playing, 33⅓ r.p.m.   ♭ = 45 r.p.m.   ♮ = Auto. couplings, 78 r.p.m.

Prélude à l'après-midi d'un faune (*continued*)

Danish Radio—Malko   **G.DB 10503**
(*Saint-Saëns, in # BB.LBC 1019:* ♭ *set WBC 1019*)

Austrian Sym.—Moreau   **# Rem. 149-51**
(*Franck: Variations*)

Berlin Sym.—List   **# Roy. 1313**
(*Ravel: Bolero*)

"Nat. Op. Orch."   **# Roy. 6126**
(*Mendelssohn: M.N.D. Overture*)

☆ Sym. Orch.—Stokowski   **G.DB 21279**
                  (in # Vic.LM 1154)

▽ Boston Sym.—Koussevitzky (Vic. 18-0042)

— ARR. PF. Copeland   ☆ G.Copeland (in ♭ MGM. set K 59)

Rhapsody, clarinet & orch.   1910
R. Kell & J. Rosen (pf.)   **# AmD.DL 9570**
(*Hindemith & Stravinsky*)

II. VOCAL
(A) CANTATAS

(La) Demoiselle Élue   2 S, cho., orch.   1887
J. Micheau, J. Collard (M-S), E. Brasseur
Chorale & Paris Cons. Orch.—Fournet
                  # D.LXT 2743
(*Chabrier*)   (# Lon. LL 639)

L'ENFANT PRODIGUE (Guimand) 1884
Azaël! Pourquoi m'as-tu quittée? (Air de Lia)
E. Wysor (A)   in **# Rem. 199-30**

(B) DRAMATIC WORKS
PELLÉAS ET MÉLISANDE Opera in French
5 acts 1902
COMPLETE RECORDINGS
Set A

Pelléas	...	...	...	P. Mollet (B)
Golaud	...	...	...	H. Rehfuss (B)
Arkël	...	...	...	A. Vessières (Bs)
Mélisande	...	...	...	S. Danco (S)
Geneviève	...	...	...	H. Bouvier (M-S)
Yniold	...	...	...	F. Wend (S)
A Shepherd ⎫			
A Doctor ⎬	...	...	...	D. Olsen (B)

Suisse Romande Orch.—Ansermet
                 # D.LXT 2711/4
(8ss)   (# Lon. set LLA 11)

Set B ☆

Mélisande	...	...	I. Joachim (S)
Pelléas	...	...	J. Jansen (T)
Golaud	...	...	H. B. Etcheverry (B)

etc., Cho. & Sym. Orch.—Désormière
(6ss)   **# Vic. set LCT 6103**
                    (♭ set WCT 61)

Mes longs cheveux   S, T, B   (Act III)
... Mélisande's part only
☆ Mary Garden & Debussy (pf.) (IRCC. 3048* & in
                   # AudA. LA 1203*)

(C) SONGS & PART SONGS
COLLECTIONS

Beau Soir (Bourget) 1878
(L') Échelonnement des haies (Verlaine) 1891
(Le) PROMENOIR DES DEUX AMANTS
                 (Lhermitte) 1910
P. Bernac (B), F. Poulenc (pf.) **# AmC.ML 4484**
(*Chabrier, Poulenc, Satie*)

Romance (Bourget)
(La) Grotte (Chansons de France—Lhermitte)
(Le) Faune; Colloque sentimentale (Fêtes Galantes—
         Verlaine)
C. Panzéra (B), M. Panzéra (pf.)
(*Pf. pieces; & Fauré*)   **# Mer.MG 10097**

Apparition (Mallarmé)
Clair de lune (Verlaine)
Pantomime (Verlaine)
Pierrot   (de Banville)   all 1882/4
E. Berger (S), M. Raucheisen (pf.) in **# Ura. 7060**
(*Handel, Schubert, etc.*)

---

(3) Chansons de Bilitis   (Loüys)   1898
J. Tourel (M-S), G. Reeves (pf.)
(*Ravel*)   **# AmC.ML 2184**

(3) Chansons de Charles d'Orléans   S, A, T, B
Carrillo Vocal Qtt.   (? Span)   **Orf. 22001**
☆ Pro Musica Cho. Soc.—Calder (in # CID. 33007)
    Couraud Ens.   (V# DFr. 21)

ARIETTES OUBLIÉES   (Verlaine)   1888-1903
No. 1, C'est l'extase langoureuse
No. 2, Il pleure dans mon coeur
J. Tourel (M-S), E. I. Kahn (pf.)   **C.LB 125**
(1s. each)

No. 2, 3, 5
☆ M. Garden (S), & Debussy (pf.) (IRCC. 3048* & in
            # AudA. LA 1203*

No. 2, Il pleure dans mon coeur
— ARR. VLN. & PF.   Hartmann
B. Urban & V. Urban   **# CEd. 1005**
(*Milhaud, Ibert, Ravel*)
☆ J. Heifetz (in # Vic.LM 1166)

(3) Ballades de François Villon   1910
... Nos. 2 & 3   ☆ C. Panzéra (B) & orch. (JpV.NF 4169)

Beau Soir   (Bourget)
C. Williams (S), B. Bazala (pf.) in **# MGM.E 140**
(*Debussy, Koechlin, Respighi, etc.*)

FÊTES GALANTES   (Verlaine)   1904
SERIES I: No. 3, Clair de lune
▽ M. Garden (S) (G.DA 1098; Vic. 1439)

SERIES II: COMPLETE
☆ J. Bathori (S) (JpC.SW 274)

(5) POÈMES DE CHARLES BAUDELAIRE
    1887-9
No. 3, Le Jet d'eau only
☆ C. Croiza (M-S) (JpC.SW 278)

Noël des enfants qui n'ont plus de maisons
(*Debussy*)
J. Wilson (S), G. Trovillo (pf.) in **# AmD.DL9554**
(*Ravel, Respighi, etc.*)

DEFOSSEZ, René (b. 1905)

Concerto, vln. & orch.   1951
F. Petronio & Belgian Nat.—Defossez
                # D.LX 133011

DELAGE, Maurice (b. 1879)

(3) CHANTS DE LA JUNGLE
      (Kipling, trs. Fabulet-d'Humières)
... Berceuse phoque

(4) POÈMES HINDOUES
1. Madras: Une belle . . . (Bhartrihari)
2. Lahore: Un sapin isolé . . . (after Heine)
3. Benares: Naissance du Bouddha   (Delage)
4. Jaipore: Si vous pensez . . . (Bhartrihari)
   M. Angelici (S) & Inst. Ens.—Cluytens
                G.DA 5054/5
                   (♭ G.7RF 113/4)
(4ss—UNESCO recording)
(with *Guarnieri* in # G.FBLP 1014)

☆ = Re-issue of a recording to be found in WERM or Supplement I.

DELDEN, Lex van (b. 1919)

Partita piccola unacc. wordless cho.
1. Prélude 2. Cloches 3. Barcarolle
4. Dance 5. Postlude

Netherlands Cha. Cho.—de Nobel
     ♯ Phi.N 00127R

(Sweelinck, Voormolens, Dresden)

DELIBES, Clément Philibert Léo
(1836-1891)

I. STAGE WORKS

COPPÉLIA Ballet 2 acts 1870

Nos. 6, 7, 17
 Covent Garden—Irving   **G.C 4105**
 (& in ♯ BB.LBC 1011: ♭ set WBC 1011) (EH 1419: ♭ 7P 124)

Nos. 1a, 1b, 5, 14, 6
 Paris Opéra—Blot (*Sylvia*) **♯ G.FALP 101**

Nos. 3 & 9a
 French Radio—G. Derveaux **Pac. 4872**

Nos. 6, 7, 9b, 11, 19a, 19b
 Grand Prix Orch.—Desmond (*Sylvia*) in ♯ **Rgt. 5048**

Nos. 6, 20a, 9b, 11, 7
 Vienna Radio—Schönherr (*Sylvia*) **♯ Vien. 1020**

No. 3
 Lower Austrian Artists—Schönherr *Aus T.M 5147*
 (*Naïla Valse*) (& in ♯ *Rem. 149-39*)

Nos. 1b & 7
 Lower Austrian Artists—Schönherr *Aus T.M 5148*
    (& in ♯ *Rem. 149-39*)

Unspec. excerpts
 Berlin Sym.—List   **♯ Roy. 1338**
 (*Chopin: Les Sylphides*)
 Covent Garden—Braithwaite in ♯ **MGM.E 3006**

LAKMÉ Opera 3 acts 1883
COMPLETE RECORDINGS
Set A
 Lakmé ... ... M. Robin (S)
 Gérald ... ... L. de Luca (T)
 Nilakantha ... ... J. Borthayre (B)
 Frédéric ... ... J. Jansen (B)
 Mallika ... ... A. Disney (A)
 Ellen ... ... C. Collart (S)
 Mistress Bentson ... ... J. Perriat (M-S)
 Rose ... ... S. Lemaître (S)
 Hadji ... ... P. Germain (T)
 Domben ... ... E. Chastenet (T)
 Marchand Chinois ... C. Rouquetty (T)
Paris Opéra-Comique Cho. & orch.—Sebastian
     ♯ D.LXT 2738/40
(6ss)   (♯ Lon. set LLA 12)

Set B
 Lakmé ... ... A. Neouvlas (S)
 Gérald ... ... C. Vezzani (T)
 Frédéric ... ... L. Musy (B)
 Nilakantha ... ... A. Pernet (Bs)
Paris Opéra Cho. & Orch.—Busser ♯ **CEd. 5002**
(Announced, but never issued)

COLLECTION
 No. 8, Pourquoi dans les grands bois
 No. 20, Où va la jeune hindoue?
 No. 24, Dans la forêt près de nous
 ☆ L. Pons (in ♯ *AmD.DL 4024*)

No. 6, Fantaisie aux divins mensonges T (Act I)
 S. Lemeshev (*Russ*) **USSR. 16284/5**
 (2ss)

No. 16, Ballet Music
 Covent Garden—Braithwaite in ♯ **MGM.E 3003**
 (*Rossini, Verdi, Ponchielli*)

No. 18, Lakmé, ton doux regard se voile Bs
 B. Gmyria (*Russ*) **USSR. 16536**
 (*Faust—Veau d'or*)

No. 20, Où va la jeune Hindoue . . .
 Là-bas dans le forêt S (Bell song)
 G. Gasparyan (2ss) **USSR. 019912/3**
 N. Kazantseva (*Russ*) (*USSR. 12797/8*)
 M. Zvezdina (*Russ*) (*USSR. 17642/3*)
 ☆ L. Pons (♭ Vic. 17-0183 & ♭ AmC.A 1510)

 ♮ S. Kurz (*Ger*) (G.VB 2*: o.n. DB 684*)

Air de Gérald (unspec.)
 ♮ E. Clement (HRS. 1116*)

Naïla Valse (Pas des Fleurs) 1867
Lower Austrian Artists—Schönherr
     Aus T.M 5147
(*Coppélia, Mazurka*) (& in ♯ *Rem. 149-39*, & *149-45*, d.c.)
A. Bernard Str. Orch. (*Od. 282479*)
Rome Sym.—Questa (in ♯ *Roy. 1227*)

SYLVIA Ballet 3 acts 1876
Orchestral Suite
 Covent Garden—Rignold ♮ **P.PW 8000/1**
 (4ss) (Od. O-3696/7; ♯ AmD.DL 9549)
 Paris Opéra—Fourestier **♯ G.FALP 101**
 (*Coppélia*) (♯ QALP 101)
 Grand Prix Orch.—Desmond in ♯ **Rgt. 5048**
 Munich Phil.—Lehmann **PV. 56006/7S**
 (3ss) (in ♯ Pol. 18007)
 Covent Garden—Braithwaite in ♯ **MGM.E 3006**
 Vienna Radio—Schönherr **♯ Vien. 1020**
 (*Coppélia*)
 ☆ Paris Cons.—Désormière (♮ D.GAG 2349/51)

Nos. 4 & 5 Austrian Sym.—Schönherr (in ♯ *Rem. 149-45*)
No. 4 — VOCAL ARR. ☆ L. Pons (♭ AmC.A 1534)

II. OTHER WORKS

SONGS

Bonjour, Suzon (A. de Musset)
 Z. Dolukhanova (A, *Russ*) **USSR. 18472**
 (*Bizet: Song*)

Eglogue (Hugo)
Que l'heure est donc brève (Sylvestre)
 C. Williams (S), B. Bazala (pf.) in ♯ *MGM.E 140*
 (*Respighi, Malipiero, Carpenter, etc.*)

(Les) Filles de Cadiz (A. de Musset)
 E. Bandrowska-Turska (S, *Pol*) USSR. 13784
 (*Roczycki: Caton, valse*)
 ☆ J. MacDonald (S) & orch. ♭ **G.7BF 1021**
 (*Pestalozza: Ciribiribin*)
 M. Truman (S) (in ♯ *Vic.LM 145*: ♭ set WDM 1616)

DELIUS, Frederick (1862-1934)

COLLECTION OF ORCHESTRAL PIECES
 Caprice & Elegy (E. Aller, vlc.)
 Irmelin: Prelude
 Hassan: Intermezzo & Serenade
 On hearing the first cuckoo in Spring
 Summer night on the river
 Concert Arts Orch.—Slatkin ♯ **DCap.CTL 7029**
    (♯ Cap.P 8182)

Eventyr Ballade 1917
 Royal Phil.—Beecham (4ss) ♮ **C.LX 8931/2**

♯ = Long-playing, 33⅓ r.p.m. ♭ = 45 r.p.m. ♮ = Auto. couplings, 78 r.p.m.

KOANGA   Opera   1895/7
Closing Scene
  Cho. & Royal Phil.—Beecham   **C.LX 1502**

North Country Sketches   1913/14
  Royal Phil.—Beecham   **C.LX 1399/401**
  (6ss)

(A) Song before Sunrise   1918   (1½ss)
Summer Evening   (2 half sides)
Summer night on the river   1912   (1½ss)
  Royal Phil.—Beecham   (4ss)   ♮ **G.DB 9757/8**

DELMAR, Desider

Hungarian Sketches
  Frankenland Sym.—Kloss   ♯ **Lyr.LL 29**
  (La Violette, Laszlo & Schoop)

DELVINCOURT, Claude (b. 1888)

Prélude chorégraphique   orch.
  ▽ Pierné Concerts—Désormière   (AA. 26)

Sonata, vln. & pf.   1922
  M. Crut & J.-C. Englebert   ♯ **Sel.LPG 8241**
  (Honegger: Sonata)

SONGS
(L')Enlèvement en mer
  C. Panzéra (B), M. Panzéra (pf.)
                              in ♯ **Mer.MG 10098**
  (Ravel, Aubert, Poulenc, etc.)

DIAMOND, David (b. 1915)

Rounds   str. orch.   1944
  ARS. Orch.—Hendl   ♯ **ARS.7**
  (Swanson)

DIMITRESCU, Ion

Peasant Dance
  Rumanian Sym.—Silvestri   **U.E 26127**
  (Enesco: Rumanian Rhapsody, s.1)

Quartet, String   (? excerpt only)
  Rumanian Radio Qtt.   **U.D 26133**

DITTERSDORF, Karl Ditters von
                    (1739-1799)

Symphony, A minor
  Frankenland State Sym.—Kloss   ♯ **Lyr.LL 26**
  (Hohenzollern)

DOBIÁŠ, Václav (b. 1909)

Czechoslovak Polka   A Peace Cantata
  Czech Singers & Children's Cho., Czech Phil.
  —Ančerl   (6ss)   ♮ **U.H 23819/21**

DOHNÁNYI, Ernö (b. 1877)

Quartet, str., No. 2, D flat major, Op. 15
  Stradivari Qtt.   ♯ **Strad.STR. 614**
  (below)

(4) RHAPSODIES, Op. 11   pf.
  M. Schwalb   ♯ **Acad.ALP 301**
  (Weiner)
  E. Dohnányi   ♯ **Rem. 199-43**
  (Schumann)

No. 3, C major
  ☆ E. Joyce   in ♯ **AmD.DL 9528**
  — ARR. 2 PFS.   M. Rawicz & W. Landauer (C.DX 1836)

Serenade, C major, Op. 10   vln., vla., vlc.
  Stradivari Trio   ♯ **Strad.STR 614**
  (above)

Sonata, vlc. & pf., B flat minor, Op. 8
  J. Scholz & M. Schwalb   ♯ **Acad.ALP 305**
  (Bach-Kodály)

Suite, F sharp minor, Op. 19
  ☆ L.S.O.—Sargent   ♯ **C.S 1001**

Symphonic Minutes, Op. 36
  Bavarian Sym.—Graunke   ♯ **Ura. 7066**
  (Borodin)

Variations on a Nursery Song, Op. 25   pf. & orch.
  F. Jacquinot & Philharmonia—Fistoulari
  (R. Strauss: Burleske)   ♯ **MGM.E 3004**

(The) Veil of Pierrette   Ballet   1910
... **No. 5, Wedding Waltz**
  Bavarian Sym.—Graunke   **PV. 56008**
  (Gioconda—Dance of the Hours)
  ☆ Berlin State Op.—Abendroth (P.DPW 52)

DOIN, Gaston   (b. 1879)

SONGS
(L')Enfant dort   (de Musset)
(Les) Plus doux instants   (de Musset)
(L')Occident   (Lamartine)
(Le) Spectre de la rose   (Gauthier)
  M. Santreuil (S), I. Tull Trio   **Pac. 3777/8**
  (1s. each)

DOMENICO, Gian   (d. 1570)
  SEE: † ♯ AS. 2502

DONATO, Baldassare   (1548-1603)
  SEE: † ITALIAN MADRIGALS (FAIT)

DONIZETTI, Gaetano (1797-1848)

I. NON-OPERATIC MUSIC

Sinfonia Concertante, B flat major
  Bavarian Radio—Altmann   ♯ **Mer.MG 10033**
  (Cimarosa, Gounod)

☆ = Re-issue of a recording to be found in WERM or Supplement I.

II. OPERAS

DON PASQUALE   3 acts   1843
COMPLETE RECORDINGS

Set W
Soloists, Vienna Cha. Cho. & State Op. Orch.
—Quadri (4ss)   # **West. set WAL 206**

Set U
Soloists, La Scala Cho. & Orch.—Parodi
(4ss)   # **Ura. set 228**

Casts of Sets W & U

	Set W	Set U
Norina ...	L. Aimaro (S)	D. la Gatta (S)
Ernesto ...	J. Oncina (T)	A. Lazzari (T)
Dr. Malatesta ...	S. Colombo (B)	A. Poli (B)
Don Pasquale ...	M. Luise (Bs)	F. Corena (Bs)
Notary ...	J. Schmiedinger (B)	G. del Signore (T)

"COMPLETE ARIAS"
A. Tuccari (S), C. Valletti (T), G. Conti (B),
L. Neroni (Bs), Rome Op. House Cho. &
Orch.—Questa   # **Roy. 1205**
("Highlights" from above on # *Roy. 6069*)

Overture
Hallé—Barbirolli   *G.DA 2004*
La Scala—Parodi   ♭ *Ura.UREP 2*
(*Verdi*) (from set)
Berlin Municipal Op.—Rother in # **Ura. 7057**

☆ New Sym.—Erede (# *Lon.LD 9010*)
Dresden Phil.—v. Kempen (Pol. 15482)

ACT I
Bella siccome un angelo   B
♮ G. de Luca (in # *GAR. 100**)

Sogno soave e casto   T
♮ A. Bonci (in # *GAR. 101**)

Quel guardo il cavaliere
So anch'io la virtù magica   S
A. Noni   *G.DB 11346*
(*Pêcheurs de Perles—Comme autrefois*)
☆ M. Carosio (♭ *G.7R 137: 7RF 155*)

♮ G. Pareto (AF. 39*)

Pronto io . . . Vado, corro   S & B
M. Tauberova & Z. Otava (*Cz*)   **U.H 24194**
♮ L. Bori & G. de Luca (AF. 46*)

ACT II
Povero Ernesto!
Cercherò lontana terra   T
G. Prandelli (includes Prelude) in # **D.LXT 2688**
(*Ponchielli, Gounod, Rossini, etc.*)   (# *Lon.LL 534*)
C. Valletti   **P.BB 25290**
(*Com' è gentil*)
♮ A. Bonci (in # *GAR. 101**)

E se fia   T
B. Finelli, G. Sas (pf.) in # **Mon.MWL 300**

ACT III
Cheti, cheti (Duetto comico) B & Bs
♮ G. de Luca & F. Corradetti (in # *GAR. 100**)

Com' è gentil   T
C. Valletti   **P.BB 25290**
(*Povero Ernesto*)
♮ E. Caruso & pf. (G.VB 55*: o.n. DB 159*)

Tornami a dir   S & T
♮ M. Galvany & A. Giorgini (G.VB 26*: o.n. 054111*)

DON SÉBASTIEN   5 acts (*French*)   1843
Seul sur la terre   T (Act II)
B. Finelli (*Ital*), G. Sas (pf.) in # **Mon.MWL 300**

O Lisbonne, O ma patrie   B (Act III)
♮ M. Battistini (*Ital*) (in # *Ete.O-462**)

(L')ELISIR D'AMORE   2 acts   1832
COMPLETE RECORDING

Adina	...	...	...	... A. Noni (S)
Nemorino	...	...	...	C. Valletti (T)
Belcore	...	...	...	...A. Poli (B)
Dulcamara	...	...	S. Bruscantini (Bs)

Italian Radio Cho. & Orch.—Gavazzeni
(6ss)   # **Sor. set 1235**

ABRIDGED RECORDING

Adina	...	...	...	I. A. Tellini (S)
Nemorino	...	...	...	C. Solari (T)
Dulcamara	...	...	...	E. Faticanti (Bs)

☆ La Scala Cho. & Orch.—Molajoli
                # **AmC.ML 4408**

ACT I
Quanto è bella!   T
☆ B. Gigli & Cho. (♭ *G.7R 127: 7RQ 114*)
F. Tagliavini
        (♭ *G.7RF 204*; *Vic. 49-1413*, d.c.; in # *LM 1164*)

Chiedi al rio   S & T
R. & B. Gigli   **G.DB 11347**
(*Pêcheurs de Perles—Par cet étroit sentier*)

Udite, udite o rustici   Bs & cho.
♮ A. Didur (HRS. 1080*)

Adina, credimi   T
☆ T. Schipa (*Vic. 425-7002*: ♭ *453-7002*)

ACT II
Una furtiva lagrima   T
C. Valletti   **P.R 30045**
(*Werther—Pourquoi me réveiller*)   (BB 25289)
G. Prandelli   in # **D.LXT 2688**
(*Ponchielli, Rossini, etc.*)   (# *Lon.LL 534*)
W. Midgley   **G.DB 21501**
(*Africaine—O Paradis*)
N. Monti   **C.GQX 11453**
(*Arlesiana—Lamento*)
P. Munteanu   **Pol. 68468**
(*Barbiere—Ecco ridente . . .*)
M. Alexandrovitch (*Russ*) (USSR. 016128)
☆ F. Tagliavini (♭ *G.7RF 204*; *Vic. 49-0334* d.c.;
        in # *LM 1164*, & in # *LM 1202*: ♭ *set WDM 1626*)
M. Lanza (♭ *G.7RF 142*; *Vic. 49-3203* d.c.)

♮ E. Caruso & pf. (G.VB 44*: also VB 16*: o.n. 052073*)
E. Caruso & pf. (G.VA 12*: o.n. 52065*)
E. Caruso & orch. (in # *Vic.LCT 1007*: ♭ *set WCT 11*)
J. McCormack (in # *Vic.LCT 1036**: ♭ *set WCT 53**)

(La) FAVORITA   4 acts   1840

ACT I
Una vergine, un angel di Dio (Romanza) T
B. Finelli (T), G. Sas (pf.) in # **Mon.MWL 300**
♮ A. Bonci (in # *GAR. 101**)

Su crudeli e chi v'arresta?
♮ A. Meitschik (*IRCC. 3090**)

Non sai tu   T & Bs
♮ R. d'Alessio & E. Pinza (*G.VA 70**)

ACT II
Vien, Leonora   B
I. Petroff   in # **Rem. 199-93**

♮ M. Battistini (in # *Ete. O-462**)
T. Ruffo (IRCC. 3110*)

= Long-playing, 33⅓ r.p.m.   ♭ = 45 r.p.m.   ♮ = Auto. couplings, 78 r.p.m.

<table>
<tr><td>

(La) FAVORITA (continued)

ACT III

Fia dunque vero . . . O mio Fernando M-S or A
　☆ M. Anderson　　　　in ♯ **Roy. 1278**
　　　　　　　　　(in ♯ Roy. 6020: in ♭ set 14516)
　Ⅱ M. Delna (Fr) (CRS. 60*)
　　E. Mantelli (HRS. 1098*)

ACT IV

Splendon più belle in ciel　　　　Bs
　G. Neri　　　　　　　　　　**P.AT 0268**
　(Mefistofele—Son lo spirito)

Spirto gentil (Romanza)　　　T
　Ⅱ J. McCormack (in ♯ Ete. O-469*)
　　A. Bonci (in ♯ GAR. 101*)

(La) FILLE DU RÉGIMENT　2 acts　1840
Overture
　Berlin Municipal Op.—Rother　in ♯ **Ura. 7057**

ACT I

Quel destin, quel favor　　　T
　B. Finelli, G. Sas (pf.)　　in ♯ **Mon.MWL 300**

Il faut partir　　　　　　S
　G. Arnaldi (Ital)　　　　**P.PE 175**
　(Nozze di Figaro—Deh! vieni, non tardar)
　☆ L. Pagliughi (Ital) (AmD. 16009)

ACT II

Entr'acte—Tyrolienne　　　orch.
　— ARR. SOP. & ORCH.
　☆ E. Berger (Pol. 26501)

Excerpts, Acts I & II (unid.)
　Ⅱ M. Sembrich, E. van Cauteren, T. Salignac & C. Gilibert
　　(IRCC. 170*)

LINDA DI CHAMOUNIX　3 acts　1842
O luce di quest'anima　S　(Act I)
　☆ L. Pons　　　　　　　**C.LX 1418**
　(Rigoletto—Tutte le feste)
　G. Gasparyan (Russ) (USSR. 19902)

LUCIA DI LAMMERMOOR　3 acts　1835
"HIGHLIGHTS"
　　Cruda, funesta smania　Act I
　　Regnava nel silenzio　Act I
　　Egli s'avanza!
　　Sulla tomba . . . Verranno a te　Act I
　　Chi mi frena in tal momento?　Act II
　　Il dolce suono
　　Alfin son tua
　　Tombe degl'avi miei　Act III
　　Di chi mai, di chi piangete?　Act III
　P. Munsel (S), J. Peerce (T), R. Merrill (B),
　E. Pinza (Bs)　　　　♯ **Vic.LM 1710**
　　　　　　　　　(♭ set WDM 1710)

"Complete Arias"
　L. Rossi (S), A. Mercangeli (S), C. Valletti (T),
　La Scala Cho. & Orch.—Questa ♯ **Roy. 1211**
　("Highlights" from above on ♯ Roy. 6070: ♭ set 14552, 6ss)

Vocal Selection
　Nat. Op. Soloists & orch. (in ♯ Var. 2003 & in ♯ 6960)

Selection — ARR. HARP　V. Dulova (USSR. 17846/7)

ACT I

Sulla tomba . . . Verranno a te　S & T
　Ⅱ A. de Angelis & F. de Lucia (in ♯ CMS. 201*)

Cruda, funesta smania　　　B
　G. Malaspina　　　　　**P.AT 0275**
　(Menotti: Amelia goes to the Ball, aria)
　Ⅱ M. Battistini (in ♯ Ete. O-462*)
　　A. Magini-Coletti (HRS. 1111*)

</td><td>

ACT II

Spargi d'amaro pianto　　　　S
　☆ L. Pons (♭ Vic. 17-019)
　　L. Pagliughi (AmD. 16008)

ACT III

Dalle stanze, ove Lucia　　Bs & cho.　.
　Ⅱ E. Pinza & cho. (G.VB 70*: o.n. DB 699*)

Tombe degl'avi miei
Tu che a Dio　　　　　T & Bs
　☆ F. Tagliavini & I. Tajo (♭ G.7RF 206; ♮♭ Vic. 49-1411/2:
　　　　　　　　　　　　in ♯ LM 1169)

Tombe degl'avi, only
　G. Prandelli　　　　in ♯ **D.LXT 2688**
　(Ponchielli, Gounod, etc.)　　(in ♯ Lon.LL 534)
　J. McCormack (in ♯ Vic.LCT 1036*: in ♭ set WCT 53*)
　Ⅱ A. Bonci (in ♯ GAR. 101*)

Giusto Cielo! rispondete　　Bs & cho.
　☆ B. Gigli, E. Pinza & cho.
　　　　　　　(in ♯ Vic.LCT 1037: in ♭ set WCT 57)

Tu che a Dio　　　　　T & Bs
　☆ B. Gigli & E. Pinza (in ♯ Vic.LCT 1037: in ♭ set WCT 57)

. . . Tenor part only
　Ⅱ A. Bonci (in ♯ GAR. 101*)
　　G. Anselmi (IRCC. 3126*)

LUCREZIA BORGIA Prologue & 2 acts 1833
Di pescatore ignobile　　T (Prologue)
　B. Finelli, G. Sas (pf.)　　in ♯ **Mon.MWL 300**

Vieni la mia vendetta　Bs　(Act I)
　Ⅱ F. Chaliapin (G.VB 72*)

DOWLAND, John (1563-1626)

AYRES: COLLECTION
Fine knacks for ladies　II
I saw my lady weep　II
If floods of tears　II
Say, Love, if ever thou didst find　III
Sweet, stay a while　(Donne)　IV
Toss not my soul　II
Weep you no more, sad fountains　III
When Phoebus first did Daphne love　III
Woeful heart　III
　J. Langstaff (B), H. Chessid (hpsi.)
　　　　　　　　　　　♯ **Nix.PLP 227**
　(Purcell)　　　　　　　　(♯ Ren.X 27)

Flow, my tears　II
I saw my lady weep　II
Fantasia　(lute)
　H. Cuenod (T), H. Leeb (lute)　♯ **West.WL 5085**
　(† 16th & 17th Century Songs)

Sorrow, sorrow, stay　II
　A. Deller (C-T), D. Dupré (lute)　　**G.C 4178**
　(Campian & Rosseter)

Faburden to the Old 100th
　Royal Festival Cho.—Boult　in **G.DB 21273**
　(Purcell)
　R.S.C.M. Choirs　　　　in **C.DX 1780**
　(Stanford)
　Margaret Dodd Singers　in ♯ **NRI. 2007**
　(† American Music: Bay Psalm Book)

Galliard (unspec.) — ARR. GUITAR
　☆ A. Segovia (in ♯ AmD.DL 5257)

SEE ALSO Farnaby, infra

</td></tr>
</table>

☆ = Re-issue of a recording to be found in WERM or Supplement I.

DRESDEN, Sem (b. 1881)

Daer was a wuf   unacc. cho.
Netherlands Cha. Cho.—de Nobel
                                    ♯ **Phi.N 00127R**
(Sweelinck, van Delden, Voormolen)

DRIFFIL, W. Ralph

Toccata   organ
F. Asma   **Phi.N 12040G**
(Krizhanovsky: Largo)   *(PhM.N 12040S)*
(& with Bach, Handel, Mendelssohn, in ♯ *Phi.A 00147L)*

DUFAY, Guillaume (*c.* 1400-1474)

Alma redemptoris mater
F. Peeters (org.)   in ♯ **Ren.X 39**
(† Old Netherlands Masters)

Magnificat octavi toni
Radcliffe Choral Soc.—Russell in ♯ **Fest. 70-202**
(† Pre-baroque Sacred Music)

DUKAS, Paul (1865-1935)

(L')Apprenti sorcier   (Scherzo after Goethe)
    orch. 1897
Lamoureux—Fricsay   **PV. 36027**
(Berlioz: Carnaval Romain on ♯ *AmD.DL 4027)*
Brussels Radio—André   in ♯ **D.LGM 65004**
(Grétry: Céphale et Procris, Suite)   *(♯ T.LS 6016 d.c.)*
                                    (also FT.T 175/6)
☆ N.B.C. Sym.—Toscanini   ♯ **G.FALP 130**
(Smetana & Saint-Saëns)   *(♯ QALP 130)*
USSR. State—Gauk   **USSR. 20156/9**
(4ss)

Fanfare pour précéder La Péri   1912
(La) Péri   Ballet, 1 act   1910/12
☆ Concerts Colonne—Paray   ♯ **Pol. 545000**
(Berlioz)

(La) Plainte, au loin, du faune   pf.   1920
— ARR. FL. & PF.   Samazeuilh
☆ J. P. Rampal & R. Veyron-Lacroix ♯ **Clc.6032**
(Bach, Beethoven, Roussel, Honegger, etc.)

DUPARC, Marie Eugène Henri Fouques
(1848-1933)

(L')Invitation au voyage   (Baudelaire)   1870/1
☆ C. Croiza (M-S) (JpC.SW 277)

DUPRÉ, Marcel (b. 1886)

ORGAN MUSIC
Antiphon No. 2, Op. 18, No. 3
    ▽ E. P. Biggs (in AmC. set M 802: ♯ ML 4195)

Berceuse   ▽ M. Dupré (G.D 1722)

(Le) Chemin de la Croix, Op. 29   1932
C. Watters   (4ss)   ♯ **CEd. 1009**

CHORALE PRELUDES
Nos. 8, 19, 41, 64, 74, 67
    ▽ M. Dupré (Lum. 3.26.013: o.n. 32010)

Intermezzo
C. Snyder   in ♯ **KR. 15**
(Duruflé: Sicilienne; Purvis: In Babilone; & Buxtehude, etc.)

Prelude & Fugue, G minor, Op. 7, No. 3
    ▽ V. Fox (in Vic. set M 1177)

Symphonie-Passion, Op. 23   1925
C. Watters   (2ss)   ♯ **CEd. 1020**

Variations sur un Noël, Op. 20
C. Crozier   in ♯ **Ken. 2553**
(† French Organ Music)
    ▽ E. P. Biggs (Vic. 11-9329)

DURANTE, Francesco (1684-1755)

Vergin, tutto amor
B. Neely (treble), G. Moore (pf.)   **G.B 10096**
(Marcello: Quella fiamma)

DUSSEK (or DUSIK), Jan Ladislav
(1761-1812)

Sonata, F sharp minor, Op. 61   pf.
"Élégie harmonique"
O. Vondrovic   (4ss)   ♮ **U.H 13119/20**

DVARIONAS, B.

Concerto, vla. & orch.
… 2nd movt. only
A. Livont & USSR. State—Dvarionas
                            USSR. 16991/3
*(3ss—Karosas: Suite, vln. & pf.—Allegro, A. Livont &
O. Shtelberg)*

DVOŘÁK, Antonin (1841-1904)

CLASSIFIED :   I. Orchestral   II. Dances
              III. Instrumental & Chamber Music
              IV. Operas   V. Choral
              VI. Songs

I. ORCHESTRAL
CONCERTOS
G minor, Op. 33, pf. & orch.
F. Maxian & Czech Phil.—Talich
(10ss)   ♮ **U.H 24137/41**
F. Wührer & Vienna Sym.—Moralt
                            ♯ **AmVox.PL 7630**
                                    (♯ EVox. 420)

A minor, Op. 53, vln. & orch.
N. Milstein & Minneapolis—Dorati
                            ♯ **G.FALP 158**
            (♯ Vic.LM 1147: ♭ set WDM 1537)
☆ G. Kulenkampff & Berlin Phil.—Jochum
                                    (♯ T.LSK 7004)

♯ = Long-playing, 33⅓ r.p.m.   ♭ = 45 r.p.m.   ♮ = Auto. couplings, 78 r.p.m.

68

CONCERTOS (*continued*)

B minor, Op. 104, vlc. & orch.
Z. Nelsova & L.S.O.—Krips   ♯ D.LXT 2727
(♭ Lon.LL 537)
G. Cassadò & Austrian Sym.—Wöss
♯ Rem. 199-38
(also with Vienna Artists' Orch. on ♯ Etu. 702)
A. Wurtz & Berlin Radio—Schultz ♯ Rgt. 5045
☆ P. Casals & Czech Phil.—Szell
♯ Vic.LCT 1026
(♭ set WCT 39)
S. Seidler & Berlin Sym.—Balzer ♯ Roy. 1262
(Unspec. excerpts in ♯ Roy. 1315)

(The) Golden Spinning Wheel, Op. 109
☆ Czech Phil.—Talich   ♯ Sup.LPV 6
(*Little Dove*)   (♯ Ura. 7073, d.c.)
(*Tchaikovsky: Sym. 4, s.3 on ♯ LPM 9*)

(10) Legends, Op. 59
... Nos. 1, 2, 3, 4, 7, 8
Berlin Radio—Lehmann   ♯ Ura. 7010
(*below*)

... No. 10, B flat major
☆ Philharmonia—Kubelik (G.DB 4317)

(The) Little Dove, Op. 110
Berlin Radio—Lehmann   ♯ Ura. 7010
(*Legends*)
☆ Czech Phil.—Talich   ♯ Sup.LPV 6
(*above*)

(The) Noonday Witch, Op. 108
Czech Phil.—Talich (4ss)   ♮ U.H 23734/5
(*Othello Overture on ♯ Sup.LPM 22*)
(*Golden Spinning Wheel, & Waltzes on ♯ Ura. 7073*)

Notturno, B major, Op. 40 Str. orch.
OVERTURES
Amid Nature, Op. 91
Carnival, Op. 92
Othello, Op. 93
Vienna Sym.—Swoboda   ♯ CHS.CHS 1141

Carnival, Op. 92
Stadium Concerts Sym.—Smallens
♯ *AmD.DL 4034*
(*Berlioz: Beatrice & Benedict Ov.*)
☆ Czech Phil.—Talich   in ♯ *Sup.LPM 15*
(*Slavonic Dances & Waltz*)
☆ Czech Phil.—Kubelik (G.DB 4307)

Othello, Op. 93
☆ Czech Phil.—Talich (♯ Sup.LPM 22)

Scherzo capriccioso, Op. 66
☆ Philharmonia—Kubelik (G.DB 4316/7)
Vienna Sym.—Swoboda (♯ Sel.LPG 8332)

Serenade, E major, Op. 22
Prague Soloists Orch.—Talich ♮ U.H 23810/3
(8ss)   (♯ Sup.LPM 32)

SLAVONIC RHAPSODIES, Op. 45
No. 2, G minor
Bamberg Sym.—Lehmann   PV. 72227
(2ss)
(*Rhapsody No. 3 on ♯ AmD.DL 4016; ♯ Pol. 16037*)

No. 3, A flat major
Bamberg Sym.—Leitner (2ss)   PV. 72258
(*above in ♯ AmD.DL 4016; ♯ Pol. 16037*)

Suite, D major, Op. 39 ("*Czech*")
Winterthur Sym.—Swoboda ♯CHS.CHS 1157
(*Ott. No. 6*)   (also ▽ 2ss, CHS.CHS 1069)

Symphonic Variations, Op. 78
Czech Phil.—Šejna (6ss)   ♮ U.H 24248/50

SYMPHONIES
E flat major 1873
☆ Vienna Sym.—Swoboda (♯ Sel.LPG 8332)

D minor 1874
Vienna State Opera Orch.—Swoboda
♯ CHS.F 11

No. 2, D minor, Op. 70 1885
Czech Phil.—Šejna (10ss)   ♮ U.H 23814/8
Berlin Phil.—Schrader   ♯ Ura. 7015

No. 3, F major, Op. 76 1875
Netherlands Phil.—Goehr   ♯ CHS.G 2
Czech Phil.—Šejna (10ss)   ♮ U.H 24182/6

No. 4, G major, Op. 88 1889
Amsterdam—Szell   ♯ D.LXT 2461
(also, 10ss, D.K 23281/5)   (♯ Lon.LL 488)
Czech Phil.—Talich (n.v.)   ♮ U.H 24142/6
(10ss)
Berlin Sym.—Rubahn   ♯ Roy. 1317
☆ Philharmonia—Kubelik (♯ Vic.LHMV 1014:
♭ set WHMV 1014)
N.Y.P.S.O.—Walter (♯ C.FCX 143: C.GQX 11465/8)

No. 5, E minor, Op. 95 ("*From the New World*")
New Sym.—Jorda   ♯ D.LXT 2608
(♯ Lon.LLP 432)
Chicago Sym.—Kubelik   ♯ G.ALP 1018
(♯ Mer.MG 50002)
Cleveland—G. Szell   ♯ AmC.ML 4541
Vienna State Philharmonia—Horenstein
♯ AmVox.PL 7590
Berlin Sym.—List (2ss)   ♯ Roy. 1257
(2nd movt. only in ♯ Roy. 6114)
☆ Sym.—Stokowski (♯ G.FALP 104)
Danish Radio—Malko
(♯ BB.LBC 1005: ♭ set WCB 1005; G.EH 1378/82)
Berlin Phil.—v. Karajan (P.RR 8018/23)
▽ Viennese Sym.—Singer (♯ Mrt. 200-14)

... **Largo (2nd movt.) only   (abridged)**
Berlin State—Gaebel (*Imp. 19361*)

— — ARR. VOICE
E. Sack (S, *Ger*) (T.E 3905)
I. Hübener (S, *Ger*) (Od.O-28322)

— — ARR. VLN. & PF. Kreisler
Y. Menuhin & A. Baller   JpV.SD 3046
(*Ravel: Pièce en forme de habanera*)

II. SLAVONIC DANCES
COMPLETE RECORDING, Nos. 1-16, Opp. 46 & 72
☆ Czech Phil.—Talich (4ss)   ♯ Ura. set 604
(Op. 46 only, also ♯ Ura. 7076; Op. 72 only, ♯ Ura. 7079;
Nos. 1, 5, 10 on ♭ UREP 21 & Nos. 2, 8, 15 on
♭ UREP 22)
(5ss, with Carnival & Waltz, in ♯ Sup.LPM 15/17)

Nos. 1 to 8
Austrian Sym.—Singer   ♯ Rem. 199-106

Nos. 1 to 4
Munich Phil.—Rieger (2ss)   PV. 72066
(*Borodin on ♯ AmD.DL 9546*)   (FPV. 5026)

No. 1, C major, Op. 46, No. 1
☆ Cleveland Sym.—Szell (*No. 3*) C.LX 1411
L.P.O.—Martinon   in ♯ *MGM.E 541*
(*Liszt, Berlioz, etc.*)   (♭ set K 112)

☆ = Re-issue of a recording to be found in WERM or Supplement I.

No. 2, E minor, Op. 46, No. 2
— ARR. VLN. & PF. Kreisler [1]
Y. Menuhin & A. Baller   JpV.SD 3038
(*Tartini: Devil's Trill, s.3*)

M. Kozolupova & pf. (*USSR. 9294*)

No. 3, D major, Op. 46, No. 3
☆ Cleveland—Szell   C.LX 1411
(*No. 1*)

No. 6, A flat major, Op. 46, No. 6 (Orch. "No. 3")
☆ Amsterdam—v. Beinum (D.AX 354)

No. 8, G minor, Op. 46, No. 8
☆ Cleveland—Szell (*No. 15*)   C.LX 1537

— ARR. VLN. & PF.
H. Szeryng & pf.   Orf. 4002
(*Tchaikovsky & Rimsky-Korsakov*)

No. 10, E minor, Op. 72, No. 2
☆ Philadelphia—Ormandy (♭ *AmC.A 1519*)

— ARR. VLN. & PF. Kreisler ("No. 2")
☆ I. Stern & A. Zakin (♭ *AmC.A 1517*)

No. 15, C major, Op. 72, No. 7
☆ Cleveland Sym.—Szell   C.LX 1537
(*No. 8*)

III. INSTRUMENTAL & CHAMBER MUSIC

A. INSTRUMENTAL

(8) HUMORESQUES, Op. 101 pf
No. 7, G flat major
A. Tatum   in ‡ *AmC.GL 101*
                                (♭ *set G 4-12*)

— ARR. ORCH.
Lusson-St. Croix Phil.—Monteverdi (in ‡ *McG. 3303*)
Stradivari Orch. (*D.F 44138*)

— ARR. VLN. & ORCH. Waxman
▽ I. Stern & Sym.—Waxman   in ‡ *AmC.ML 2103*

— ARR. VLN. & PF.
W. Tworek & E. Vagning   Pol.HM 80059
(*Falla: Vida Breve—Danza No. 1*)
L. Kaufman & P. Ulanowsky (in ‡ *DCap.CCL 7513*;
                                ‡ *Cap.L 8165*)
☆ F. Kreisler (in ‡ *Vic.LCT 1049*: ♭ *set WCT 80*)
V. Prihoda (*Pol. 48379*; *P.LL 3003*)

— ARR. VOICE
E. Sack (S, *Ger*) (*T.E 3905*)

Variations, A flat major, Op. 36   pf.
J. Páleníček (4ss)   ♮ U.H 24260/1

(8) WALTZES, Op. 54   pf.
Nos. 1-4 — ARR. ORCH. Dvořák
Prague Soloists Orch.—Talich   U.H 23977
(1s. each)   (also in ‡ *Ura. 7073*)
(No. 4 on U.H 23962 with *Fibich: Fall of Arcona Ov., s.1*)
(No. 1 only in ‡ *Sup.LPM 15*)

B. CHAMBER MUSIC

QUARTETS, String
No. 2, D minor, Op. 34
Czechoslovak Qtt. (8ss)   ♮ U.H 24147/50

No. 3, E flat major, Op. 51
Boskovsky Qtt.   ‡ D.LXT 2601
(also, 8ss, D.K 28455/8: K 23254/7)   (‡ Lon.LLP 387)

No. 6, F major, Op. 96 ("*American*")
Koeckert Qtt.   PV. 72083/4
(4ss)   (2ss, ‡ *Pol. 16001*)
(*Smetana: Qtt.* on ‡ *AmD.DL 9637*)

Hungarian Qtt.   ‡ CHS.CHS 1157
(*Suite*)
Stradivari Qtt.   ‡ Strad.STR 613
(*Smetana*)

... Lento only
Paganini Qtt. (in † ‡ Vic.LM 1192: ♭ *set WDM 1611*)

No. 8, G major, Op. 106
Ondříček Qtt. (10ss)   ♮ U.H 23779/83

Quintet, 2 vlns., 2 vlas., vlc., E flat major, Op. 97
Budapest Qtt. & M. Katims   ‡ *AmC.ML 2173*

Serenade, D minor, Op. 44 1878
London Baroque Ens.—Haas   P.R 20604/6
(6ss)   (‡ *PMB 1001*; ‡ *AmD.DL 7533*)

TRIOS, pf., vln., vlc.
No. 3, F minor, Op. 65
A. Balsam, L. Kaufman, M. Cervera
                             ‡ CHS.CHS 1117
Czech Trio (10ss)   ♮ U.H 24030/4

No. 4, E minor, Op. 90 ("*Dumky*")
Czech Trio (8ss)   ♮ U.H 24151/4
Budapest Trio (6ss)   ♮ Tono.X 25180/2

IV. OPERAS

ARMIDA, Op. 115 4 acts 1904
Overture
Prague Nat. Theatre—Vogel   U.H 23960
                             (in ‡ *Sup.LPM 36*)

DIMITRI, Op. 64 4 acts 1882
Overture
Prague Nat. Theatre—Vogel   U.H 23961
                             (in ‡ *Sup.LPM 36*)

(The) JACOBIN, Op. 84 3 acts 1889
"Highlights"
Soloists, Cho. & Orch. of Prague Nat. Theatre
—Vogel (10ss)   ♮ U.H 24234/8

We are foreigners, we have wandered S & B
E. Trötschel & H. Günter (*Ger*)
Oh God, how hopeless (Terinka's Song) (Act II)
E. Trötschel (*Ger*)   PV. 72239
(1s. each)   (in ‡ *Pol. 18057*)

RUSALKA, Op. 114 3 acts 1901
COMPLETE RECORDING (in *German*)
Rusalka ... ... E. Trötschel (S)
The Prince ... ... H. Schindler (T)
The Water Spirit ... ... G. Frick (Bs)
etc., Dresden State Op. Cho. & Saxon State
Orch.—Keilberth   ‡ Ura. set 219
(6ss)

ABRIDGED RECORDING (in *Czech*)
☆ Czech Nat. Theatre Company   ‡ Syc.SR 4

O moon in the deep sky S (Act I)
J. Hammond   G.DB 21451
(*Tchaikovsky: Pique Dame, No. 20*)
H E. Destinn (*Ger*) (G.VB 24*: o.n. 2-043016*)
E. Destinn (*Ger*) (in ‡ set CEd. 7001*)

---

[1] This is No. 1 of Kreisler's arrs. trs. to G minor. The recordings listed may equally well be Kreisler's No. 2, i.e. No. 10,
Op. 72, No. 2. They have not been heard.

V. CHORAL

STABAT MATER, Op. 58   Oratorio
S, A, T, B, cho. & orch.
D. Tikalova, M. Krasova, B. Blachut, K. Kalas,
Czech Singers, Czech Phil.—Talich
                                    ♮ **U.H 24065/76**
(24ss)   (♯ *Sup.LPM 24/6*, 6ss)

VI. SONGS

(10) BIBLICAL SONGS, Op. 99
Nos. 1 & 7   *C.DB 2977*
Nos. 3, 4, 9   *C.DX 1800*
J. Watson (A), G. Moore (pf.)   (4ss)

No. 4, The Lord is my Shepherd
No. 9, I will lift up mine eyes
F. Jagel (T), A. B. Miller (org.) in *AmD. set A 883*
                                    (♯ *DL 5363*: ♮ *set 9-272*)

Echoes from Moravia, Op. 32   S, A, pf.
M. Fuchs, M. Klose (*Ger*), M. Raucheisen
(*omitting one duet*)   ♯ *Ura. 5002*

(7) GYPSY SONGS, Op. 55   (Heyduk)
V. Bedner (B), A. Holeček (pf.) ♮ **U.H 24232/3**
(4ss)

... **No. 4, Songs my mother taught me**
V. Krylova   *USSR. 18196*
(*Smetana: Brandenburgers, aria*)

— — ARR. VLN. & PF.
▽ W. Tworek (*D.C 16020*)
☆ E. B. Nielsen (*G.DA 5267*)

— — ARR. VLC. & PF.
☆ P. Casals (in ♯ Vic.LCT 1050: ♮ *WCT 72*)

(A) Lullaby   (Trad.)
G. Lavrova   (*Russ*)   *USSR. 15278*
(*Moniuszko: Swallow*)

When thy sweet glances, Op. 83, No. 7
(Pfleger-Moravsky)
A. Yakovenko (*Russ*)   *USSR. 19242*
(*Pergolesi: Se tu m'ami*)

EASDALE, Brian (b. 1909)

(The) RED SHOES (Music from the film)   1949
☆ Philharmonia—Mathieson (*C.M 15179/80*)

EAST, Michael (c. 1580-1648)

SEE: † TRIUMPHS OF ORIANA

ECCARD, Johann (1553-1611)

Vom Himmel hoch   5 voices
Barmen Singers   *Chr. 324A*
(‡s.—*Bach: Ch.-Prel.*; & *Praetorius*)

ECCLES, Henry (1652-1742)

Sonata, G minor vln. & cont. (ARR. Salmon)
G. Knudsen & E. Garcia (pf.)   ♯ *ML. 5002*
(*Reger, Knudsen, Gjerstrøm*)

EDMUNDSON, Garth
SEE: † AMERICAN CHURCH MUSIC

EGGE, Klaus (b. 1906)

Concerto No. 2, pf. & orch.   1944
R. Riefling & Oslo Phil.—Fjeldstad
(5ss—*below*)   ♮ **Nera.SK 15545/7**

Fantasy in Halling style, Op. 12   pf.   1939
R. Riefling   (*above*)   **Nera.SK 15545**

EGK, Werner (b. 1910)

ABRAXAS   Ballet   1947
Orchestral Suite
☆ Berlin R.I.A.S. Sym.—Fricsay (*FPV. 5022*)

Französische Suite (after Rameau)   1950
Leipzig Gewandhaus—Egk
Geigenmusik   vln. & orch.   1936
E. Bischoff & Berlin Radio—Egk   ♯ **Ura. 7022**

(Die) ZAUBERGEIGE   Opera   1934
Overture
☆ Berlin State Op.—Swarowsky (*Pol. 26516*)

EINEM, Gottfried von (b. 1918)

Capriccio for Orchestra, Op. 2
R.I.A.S. Sym.—Fricsay   *PV. 36038*

ELGAR, Sir Edward (1857-1934)

Cockaigne, Overture, Op. 40
Hallé—Barbirolli   (4ss)   ♮ **G.DB 9633/4**

Concerto, vln. & orch., B minor, Op. 61
☆ J. Heifetz & L.S.O.—Sargent   ♯ **G.ALP 1014**

Introduction & Allegro, Op. 47   str. orch.
New Sym.—Collins   in ♯ **D.LXT 2699**
(*Serenade*; & *Vaughan Williams*)   (♯ *Lon.LL 583*)
Sydney Civic Sym.—Beck   ♯ **Dia.DPM 3**
(*Britten: Simple Symphony*)

POMP & CIRCUMSTANCE MARCHES, Op. 39
No. 1, D major
Royal Festival Hall Orch. & Cho.—Sargent
(2ss)   **G.DA 1981**
                          (in ♯ BB.LBC 1028: ♮ *set WBC 1028*)
Royale Concert Orch. (in ♯ *Roy. 1233*)
☆ Boston Prom.—Fiedler (♮ *G.7BF 1030*)

— ARR. ORGAN   V. Fox   (♯ *AmC.AAL 20*)

Salut d'amour, Op. 12
W. Krüger Orch. (*Imp. 19109*)

— ARR. VLN. & PF.   ☆ V. Prihoda (*Pol. 48379*)

— ARR. VOICE   Z. Gabor (S, *Hung*) (*Qual.QB 2001*)

Serenade, E minor, Op. 20   str. orch.
New Sym.—Collins   in ♯ **D.LXT 2699**
(*Intro. & Allegro*; & *Vaughan Williams*)   (♯ *Lon.LL 583*)
Concert Hall Sym.—Goehr   ♯ **Nix.CLP 1154**
(*Enigma Variations*)   (♯ *CHS.CHS 1154*)

☆ = Re-issue of a recording to be found in WERM or Supplement I.

Sonata, E minor, Op. 82   vln. & pf.
J. Tryon & J. La Montaine   **♯ CEd. 1019**
(*R. Strauss: Sonata*)

Variations on an original theme, Op. 36 ("*Enigma*")
Concert Hall Sym.—Goehr   **♯ CHS.CHS 1154**
(*Serenade*)   (♯ Nix.CLP 1154)

ENESCO, Georges (b. 1881)

Cantabile & Presto   fl. & pf.
S. Caratelli & P. Miguel   **♯ NRI. 402**
(*Karg-Elert, Platti*)

Dixtuor, D major, Op. 14 10 wind insts.
French Nat. Orch. Ens.—Enesco **♯ Rem. 199-107**
(*Kodaly: Sonata*)

Octet, C major, Op. 7 str. 1905
Ensemble—Enesco   **♯ Rem. 199-52**

RUMANIAN RHAPSODIES, Op. 11 orch.
No. 1, A major
Sym.—Enesco   **♯ Rem. 149-47**
(*Liszt: Les Préludes*)
L.P.O.—Martinon   in **♯ MGM.E 541**
(*Dvořák, Liszt, etc.*)   (♭ set K 112)
Rumanian Sym.—Silvestri   ♮ **U.E 26127/8**
(*3ss—Dimitrescu: Peasant Dance*)
Los Angeles Phil.—Wallenstein ♯**AmD.DL 4012**
(*Smetana*)
  ☆ Chicago Sym.—Stock (in ♯ AmC.RL 3002)
  Sym.—Stokowski (♭ G.7RF 234: ♭ Vic. 49-0127)

No. 2, D major
Concerts Colonne—Enesco   **♯ Rem. 149-52**
(*Smetana*)

Sonata, No. 3, A minor, Op. 25 vln. & pf.
(*In the popular Rumanian style*)
G. Enesco & C. Chailley-Richez ♯ **Rem. 149-42**

ERKEL, Ferenc (1810-1893)

HUNYADI LÁSZLÓ Opera 4 acts 1844
Overture
USSR. State Sym.—Shomodi *USSR. 18828/31*
(4ss)

FALCONIERI, Andrea (c. 1590-1656)

  SEE: † ITALIAN SONGS
       † ITALIAN MADRIGALS (FAIT)
       † ITALIAN ART SONGS

FALLA, Manuel de (1876-1946)

(El) AMOR BRUJO Ballet M-S & orch 1915
COMPLETE RECORDING (omitting Nos. 3, 6, 16)
  ☆ A. M. Iriarte & Paris Cons.—Argenta
                   ♯ C.C 1004
(C.M 15176/8)   (♯ FC 1010)

Orchestral Suite
  ☆ Czech Phil.—Meylan (♯ Sup.LPM 20)

No. 7, Danza ritual del fuego
Boston Prom.—Fiedler   in ♯ **Vic. LM 162**
  (♭ 49-0526: & in ♭ set WDM 1639: ♭ WEPR 25)
D'Artega Orch. (in ♯ Var. 6929; in ♭ Roy. set 14511)

— ARR. PF. Falla
C. de Groot   **Phi.A 11202G**
(*below*)   (*PhM.A 09705S*)
(*below & Albeniz*, in ♯ Phi.A 00131R)
  ☆ O. Levant (♭ AmC.A 1537)

No. 7, Danza ritual del fuego
No. 11, Danza del terror
— ARR. PF.
  ☆ A. Rubinstein (♭ G.7RF 178)
J. Iturbi (in ♯ Vic.LM 1167: ♭ set WDM 1604:♭ WEPR 33)

Danza (unspec.—probably No. 7)
— ARR. PF.
G. Copeland   in ♯ **MGM.E 151**

No. 14, Pantomima
— ARR. VLN. & PF. Kochanski
  ☆ J. Heifetz & E. Bay (in ♯ Vic.LM 1166)

(7) CANCIONES POPULARES ESPAÑOLAS
(Blas de Laserna) 1914
1. El paño moruno 2. Seguidilla murciana
3. Asturiana   4. Jota
5. Nana   6. Canción   7. Polo
V. de los Angeles (S), G. Moore (pf.)
                ♮ **G.DB 9731/2**
(4ss)   (in ♯ Vic.LM 131:♭ set WDM 1635)
G. Souzay (B), J. Bonneau (pf.) ♯ **D.LX 3077**
(*Ravel: Histoires naturelles*) (♯ Lon.LS 536)
L. de Ibarrondo (M-S), M. Sandoval (pf.)
(*Sandoval: 7 Songs*)   **♯ AmC.ML 2189**
A. M. Iriarte (M-S), R. Machado (pf.)
(*Nin & Vives*)   **♯ Pat.DT 1007**

… **Nos. 1, 3, 4, 6, 7** — ARR. VLC. & PF. Maréchal
B. Michelin & T. Janopoulo   **C.LFX 990/1**
(4ss)   (♮ ArgC. 500240/1)

… **Nos. 1 & 6** — ARR. PF. Halffter
C. de Groot   **♯ Phi.A 00131R**
(*above & below*; & *Albeniz*)
      (also Phi.A 11204G: PhM. 09707S)

… **Nos. 1 & 4** — ARR. VLN. & PF.
H. Szeryng & pf.   **Orf. 4001**
(*Albeniz: Malagueña*)

… **No. 4, Jota**
  ☆ T. Schipa (T) (in ♯ Vic.LPT 3008: ♭ EPBT 3008;
                      JpV.NF 4161)

Concerto, hpsi., fl., ob., cl., vln., vlc. 1923/6
  ☆ R. Kirkpatrick, S. Baron, M. Miller, H.
    Freeman, A. Schneider, B. Greenhouse
(*Stravinsky*)   **♯ Clc. 6030**

Fantasia Betica pf. or hpsi. 1919
F. Pelleg (hpsi.)   **♯ CHS.G 16**
(*Kodály*)

Homenaje, pour le tombeau de Debussy guitar
A. Segovia   in ♯ **B.AXTL 1010**
(† Segovia Concert)   (♯AmD.DL 9638)
R. de la Torre   in ♯ **Phil. 106**
(† Guitar Recital)

Noches en los jardines de España pf. & orch.
1909/15
C. Curzon & New Sym.—Jorda ♯ **D.LXT 2621**
(*below*) (n.v.)   (♯ Lon.LLP 445)
          (also, 6ss, D.K 28599/601)
M. Huttner & Berlin Sym.—Balzer ♯ **Roy. 1275**
(*Mozart: Serenade, K 525*)
  ☆ A. Rubinstein & St. Louis Sym.—
    Golschmann   **♯ G.FALP 112**
(*Mozart: Pf. Concerto, K 488*)

♯ = Long-playing, 33⅓ r.p.m.   ♭ = 45 r.p.m.   ♮ = Auto. couplings, 78 r.p.m.

(4) Pièces espagnoles pf. 1907-8
... **No. 1, Aragonesa (Jota)** — ARR. GUITAR
L. Maravilla   in ♯ **Sel.LPG 8495**
(† Tañidos)

... **No. 2, Cubana; No. 4, Andaluza**
J. Bolet   in ♯ **Bo.B 300**
(Albeniz, Granados, Lecuona)

(El) SOMBRERO DE TRES PICOS Ballet 1919
COMPLETE RECORDING (including Interludes, Sop.)
S. Danco & Suisse Romande—Ansermet
♯ **D.LXT 2716**
(♯ Lon.LL 598)

A. P. de Prulière & Opéra-Comique—Martinon
(2ss)   ♯ **Ura. 7034**
(Three Dances on ♭ UREP 11)

Scenes & Dances from Part I
☆ L.S.O.—Jorda   ♯ **D.LXT 2621**
(Noches ..., above)   (♯ Lon.LLP 445)

... **No. 2, Danza del molinera**
Rosario & Antonio (castanets) & orch.
C.DX 1817
(below)   (CQX 16656: DWX 5074: M 15185)

3 Dances from Part II
☆ Paris Cons.—Cluytens (Pat.MDT 12/13)

... **No. 2, Danza del molinero** (Farruca)
Rosario & Antonio   **C.DX 1817**
(above)

L. Maravilla (guitar) (Od. 184848 & † TAÑIDOS)

(La) VIDA BREVE Opera 2 acts 1913
Danza No. 1
Rosario & Antonio (castanets) & orch. **C.DX 1846**
☆ M.G.M. Orch.—Marrow (in ♯ MGM.E 539)

— ARR. PF. Samazeuilh
C. de Groot   ♯ **Phi.A 00131R**
(above; & Albeniz) (also in Phi.A 11202G: PhM. 09705S)

— ARR. VLN. & PF. Kreisler
J. Martzy & J. Antonietti   **PV. 36015**
(½s.—Milhaud: Ipanema; & Ravel)
W. Tworek & E. Vagning   **Pol.HM 30059**
(Dvořák: Humoresque)
☆ G. & J. Neveu (♭ G.7RF 132)

FARMER, John (fl. 1600)
SEE: † TRIUMPHS OF ORIANA

FARNABY, Giles (c. 1560-1600)
SEE ALSO: † EARLY ENGLISH KEYBOARD MUSIC
COLLECTION
CANZONETS 4 voices 1598
Among the daffadillies
Ay me, poor heart!
Construe my meaning
(The) Curtain drawn
I saw my love lie sleeping
Lady, the silly flea
My lady's coloured cheeks
Simkin said that Sis was fair
Sometime she would, and sometime not
Oriana Singers—Hobbs

VIRGINALS PIECES
Galiarda (FVB 269 or 195)
His humour (FVB 196)
Mal Sims (FVB 281)
(A) Maske (FVB 198, 199, or 209)
Pavan: Lachrymae (Dowland, arr. Farnaby)
Woody Cock (FVB 141)
B. Winogron   ♯ **EMS. 5**

FARRAND, Noel

Allegro assai
B. Earle (vln.) or A. Loft (vla.) & pf.   ♯ **NE. 4**
(Berger, Flanagan, R. Smith)

FARRANT, Richard (d. 1581)
SEE: † RENAISSANCE MASTERPIECES

FAURÉ, Gabriel (1845-1924)

CLASSIFIED: I. Piano   II. Instrumental
      III. Chamber Music   IV. Orchestral
      V. Stage Works   VI. Vocal

I. PIANO

COLLECTION
Dolly, Op. 56 (with G. Casadesus)
Nocturne No. 7, Op. 74
Barcarolle No. 5, Op. 66
Impromptu No. 5, Op. 102
R. Casadesus   ♯ **AmC.ML 2205**

BARCAROLLES
No. 2, G major, Op. 41   in ♯ **Mer.MG 10097**
M. Panzéra
(Songs & Debussy)

No. 5, F sharp minor, Op. 66
B. Léonet (2ss)   **G.SL 177**

IMPROMPTUS
No. 2, F minor, Op. 31
☆ E. Joyce (in ♯ AmD.DL 9528)

No. 3, A flat major, Op. 34
A. Iturbi   ♭ **Vic. 49-3309**
(Infante)

NOCTURNES
No. 1, E flat major, Op. 33, No. 1
No. 2, B major, Op. 33, No. 2
No. 3, A flat major, Op. 33, No. 3
No. 4, E flat major, Op. 36
No. 6, D flat major, Op. 63
No. 7, C sharp minor, Op. 74
E. Boynet   ♯ **AmVox.PL 7520**

No. 1, E flat minor, Op. 33, No. 1
B. Léonet (2ss)   **G.SK 118**

Romance sans paroles, A flat, Op. 17, No. 3
☆ F. Ellegaard (Pol.HA 70029)

Thème et variations, C sharp minor, Op. 73
T. v. d. Pas   ♯ **Phi.N 00126R**
(Pijper, Voormolen, Orthel)

II. INSTRUMENTAL

Berceuse, Op. 16 vln. & pf.
C. Ferras & P. Barbizet   **D.GAG 15099**
(Massenet: Thaïs—Meditation)

— ARR. VLC. & PF.
J. Serres & A. Leyvastre in V♯ **Sat.MSA 5003**

Élégie, C minor, Op. 24   vlc. & pf.
P. Fournier & E. Lush   **G.DB 21333**
J. Serres & A. Leyvastre in V♯ **Sat.MSA 5003**
(continued on next page)

☆ = Re-issue of a recording to be found in WERM or Supplement I.

Êlégie, C minor, Op. 24 (*continued*)

— VLC. & ORCH. VERSION
B. Michelin & Haarlem Sym.—Hupperts
(*Lalo*)   ♯ CHS.CHS 1162

Papillon, Op. 77   vlc. & pf.
J. Serres & A. Leyvastre in V♯ *Sat.MSA 5003*

III. CHAMBER MUSIC

QUARTETS, pf. & str.
No. 1, C minor, Op. 15
G. Casadesus & Guilet Trio   ♯ Polym. 1007
(*Sonata*)
☆ A. Rubinstein & Members of Paganini Qtt.
                              (♯ *G.FBLP 1010*)

QUARTET, String, E major, Op. 121
Guilet Qtt. (*Sonata*)   ♯ Polym. 1008

QUINTETS, pf. & str.
No. 2, C minor, Op. 115
☆ R. Lev & Pascal Qtt.   ♯ Nix.CLP 1093

SONATAS, vln. & pf.
No. 1, A major, Op. 13
J. Fournier & G. Doyen   ♯ West.WL 5156
(*No. 2*)
M. Chauveton & B. Smith   ♯ Allo.ALG 3032
(*Lalo: Sonata*)

No. 2, E minor, Op. 108
J. Fournier & G. Doyen   ♯ West.WL 5156
(*No. 1*)
D. Guilet & G. Casadesus   ♯ Polym. 1008
(*above*)
R. Posselt & J. Rezits   ♯ Fest. 70-203
(*Martinu & Haydn*)

SONATAS, vlc. & pf.
No. 2, G minor, Op. 117
D. Soyer & L. Mittman   ♯ Polym. 1007
(*Quartet*)

IV. ORCHESTRAL

Ballade, F sharp major, Op. 19 pf. & orch.
M. Long & Paris Cons.—Cluytens ♮ C.LX 8953/4
(4ss)   (♯ FCX 169)

Masques et Bergamasques, Op. 112
Netherlands Phil.—Goehr   ♯ CHS.G 9
(*Debussy*)

Pavane, Op. 50   (& cho. *ad lib.*)
London Cha. Orch. & Cho.—Bernard G.C 4197

V. STAGE WORKS

PELLÉAS ET MÉLISANDE, Op. 80
(Inc. Music, ORCH. by Koechlin)

No. 2, Fileuses — ARR. VLC. & PF.
J. Serres & A. Leyvastre in V♯ *Sat.MSA 5003*

SHYLOCK, Op. 57
... Nocturne — ARR. 2 PFS. Gearhart
V. Morley & L. Gearhart in ♯ *AmC.ML 2197*

VI. VOCAL

REQUIEM, Op. 48 S, B, cho., orch., org.
M. Angelici, L. Noguéra, St. Eustache Singers
& Orch.—Cluytens; M. Duruflé, org.
                              ♯ C.FCX 108
N. Sautereau, B. Demigny, Paris Phil. Cho. &
orch.—Leibowitz   ♯ Oce.OCS 26
☆ S. Dupont, M. Didier, Lyons Cho. & Orch.—
Bourmauck (♯ AmC.ML 4529)
Soloists, Disciples of Massenet, Montreal Fest. Orch.—
Pelletier (♯ CanVic.LCT 7003)

SONGS
COLLECTIONS

Adieu, Op. 21, No. 3 (Grandmougin)
Chanson du pêcheur, Op. 4, No. 1 (Gautier)
(L')HORIZON CHIMÉRIQUE, Op. 118 (de Mirmont)
Lydia, Op. 4, No. 2 (Leconte de Lisle)
C. Panzéra (B), M. Panzéra (pf.)
(*Barcarolle; & Debussy*)   ♯ Mer.MG 10097

(L')Automne, Op. 18, No. 3 (Silvestre)
Mandoline, Op. 58, No. 1 (Verlaine)
Soir, Op. 83, No. 2 (Samain)
I. Kolassi (M-S), J. Bonneau (pf.)
                              in ♯ D.LX 3080
(*Ravel, Aubert, etc.*)   (♯ Lon.LS 568)

(La) BONNE CHANSON, Op. 61 Song Cycle
(Verlaine)
☆ C. Panzéra (B), M. Panzéra-Baillot (pf.) (JpV.ND 787/9)

Après un rêve
— ARR. VLN. & PF. Casals
G. Knudsen & E. Garcia   ♯ ML. 5003
(*Halvorsen, Tveit, Knudsen, etc.*)   (also ML. 42)

— ARR. VLC & PF. ☆ R. Krotschak (in ♯ Eur.LPG 631)

(L')Automne, Op. 18, No. 3 (Silvestre)
☆ J. McCormack (T) (G.VA 72)

(Les) Berceaux, Op. 23, No. 1 (Sully Prud'homme)
A. Mestral (B), I. Aïtoff (pf.) PhM.A 77501S
(*Schumann: Beiden Grenadiere*)
J. Chalud-ben-Baruch & orch.   Sat. 1001
(*Schubert: Der Doppelgänger*)

Clair de lune, Op. 46, No. 2 (Verlaine)
A. Mestral (B), I. Aïtoff (pf.) PhM.A 77500S
(*Schubert: Erlkönig*)

Noël, Op. 43, No. 1 (Wilder)
J. Wilson (S), G. Trovillo (pf.) in ♯ AmD.DL 9554
(*Debussy, Ravel, etc.*)

FEKETE, Zoltan (b. 1909)

CAUCASUS, Op. 10 Ballet 1948
Suite
Vienna State Opera—Fekete ♯ Csm.CLPS 1011
(*Schubert: Schneewittchen*)
(*Tchaikovsky: Tempest*, on ♯ Eur.LPG 606)

NOTE.—For Suites ARR. Fekete, *see* Handel & Schubert

FESTA, Costanzo (1490-1545)

SEE: † ITALIAN MADRIGAL

FIBICH, Zdeněk (1850-1900)

In the Twilight, Op. 39   orch.
☆ Czech Phil.—Šejna   ♯ Sup.LPM 13
(*Novák*)

OPERAS

(The) FALL OF ARCONA, Op. 55
Prologue & 3 acts. 1900
Overture
Prague Nat. Theatre—Vogel   ♮ U.H 23962/3
(*Dvořák: Waltz, Op. 54, No. 4*)

♯ = Long-playing, 33⅓ r.p.m.   ♭ = 45 r.p.m.   ♮ = Auto. couplings, 78 r.p.m.

HEDY, Op. 43   4 acts   1896
Ballet Music
    ☆ Prague Nat. Theatre—Škvór # *Sup.LPM 23*
    (*Schubert: Rosamunde*)

Moods, Impressions & Reminiscences
Selection   — ARR. ORCH.   J. Ridký
F.O.K. Sym.—Ridký (4ss)   ♮ **U.H 23939/40**

Poem, Op. 41, No. 4   pf.   — ARR. ORCH.
R. Crean Orch. (in # *D.LF 1082*; *Lon.LPB 424*)
Stradivari Orch. (*D.FF 44139*)

Spring, Op. 13 (*Vesna*)   orch.
Czech Phil.—Klima (4ss)   ♮ **U.H 24251/2**

Symphony No. 2, E flat major, Op. 38
Czech Phil.—Šejna (10ss)   ♮ **U.H 23964/8**

FICKENSCHER, Arthur (b. 1871)

From the Seventh Realm   pf. & str. qtt.
A. Fickenscher & Anon. Qtt.   # *ML. 5004*

Willow Wood
    (4 Sonnets from D. G. Rossetti's *House of Life*)
C. Porter (M-S), vla., bsn. & pf. # **ML. 7020**

FINE, Irving (b. 1914)

Partita   fl., ob., cl., hrn., bsn.
New Art Quintet   # **CEd. 1003**
(*Milhaud*)

FIORAVANTI, Valentino (1764-1837)

(Le) CANTATRICI VILLANE Opera 2 acts 1799
COMPLETE RECORDING
  Rosa   ...   .   A. Noni (S)
  Agata   ...   .   E. Orell (S)
  Giannetta ...   . F. Cadoni (M-S)
  Don Bucefalo ...   ...   S. Bruscantini (Bs)
  Don Marco... ...   ... F. Balabrese (B)
  Carlino   ...   .   A. Lazzari (T)
  etc., Naples Op. Cho. & orch.—Rossi
                                # **Sor. 50102**

FISCHER, Johann Caspar Ferdinand
(c. 1660-1746)

MUSICALISCHER PARNASSUS   hpsi.
Suite No. 2, Melpomene . . . Passepied
  ☆ A. Ehlers (in # *AmD.DL 8019*)

FLANAGAN, William (b. 1923)

Chaconne   vln. & pf.   (or vla. & pf.)
B. Earle or A. Loft & pf.   in # **NE. 4**
(*Berger, Smith, etc.*)

Sonata, piano   1950
B. Weiser   # **NE. 1**
(*Sessions, Berger, etc.*)

FLOTOW, Friedrich von (1812-1883)

OPERAS
ALESSANDRO STRADELLA 3 acts 1844 (*Ger*)
Overture   ☆ Berlin State Op.—Ludwig (Pol. 15485)

Horch, Liebchen   T   (Act I)
  ☰ L. Slezak (IRCC. 3098* & in # *Ete. 461**)

Seid meiner Wonne stiller Zeugen   S   (Act II)
  ☆ F. Jokl (in # *Ete.ELP 461*)

Tief in den Abruzzen   ☰ H. Jadlowker (in # *Ete. 461**)

Wie freundlich strahlt der Tag T & Cho. (Finale, Act III)
  ... Hymnus: Jungfrau Maria
  ☆ J. Schmidt (*P.DP 311*)

MARTHA   4 acts   1847   (*Ger*)
COMPLETE RECORDING
  Martha   ...   .   E. Berger (S)
  Nancy   ...   ... E. Tegethoff (M-S)
  Lionel   ...   .   P. Anders (T)
  Lord Tristram   ...   ...   E. Fuchs (B)
  Plunket   ...   .   J. Greindl (Bs)
  etc., Berlin Municipal Op. Cho. & Radio Orch.
    —Rother (6ss)   # **Ura. set 217**

"Highlights"
  Anon. Soloists, Berlin Op. Cho. & Orch. # **Roy. 1355**

Vocal Selections
  T. Richter(S), A. Western(M-S), H. Kraus (T), G. Frei (Bs),
  German Opera House Cho. & Orch.—Diez T.E 3912
                            (AusT.E 1182)

Overture
Rhineland Sym.—Federer   # *Rgt. 5056*
(*Adam*)
  ☆ Boston Prom.—Fiedler (G.C 4156)
  Dresden Phil.—v. Kempen (Pol. 15324)

Die letzte Rose   S   (Act II)
M. Guilleaume   **T.E 3923**
(*Mignon—Connais-tu le pays?*)
A. M. Alberghetti (*Eng*)   **AmC. 73264D**
(*Verdi*) (GQX 11513)   (# *3/♭ 4-73264D*)
  ☆ E. Berger (*Pol. 26501*)
  ☰ E. de Cisneros   (HRS. 1115*)

Ach, so fromm   T   (Act III)
Mag der Himmel euch vergeben   quintet & cho.
W. Ludwig, L. Wissmann, H. Plümacher,
G. Grefe, G. Neidlinger, Württemberg State
Op. Cho.   **Pol. 62878**

Ach, so fromm only
C. Valletti (*Ital*)   **P.AT 0243**
(*Barbiere—Si il mio nome . . .*)
  C. Ravazza (*Ital*) (*G.B 10202*)
  M. Alexandrovitch (*Russ*) (*USSR. 16540*)
  ☆ (*Ital*) F. Tagliavini (in # Vic.LM 1164; ♭ *G.7RF 207*)
  E. Caruso (in # Vic.LCT 1039: ♭ *set WCT 62*)
  ☰ A. Dippel (IRCC. 3112*)

FOERSTER, Joseph Bohuslav (1859-1951)

Czech Dance
Film Sym.—Strníště   **U.H 23992**
(*Novák: Devil's Polka*)

FOOTE, Arthur William (1853-1937)

(A) Night Piece   fl. & str.   1918
J. Baker & Cha. Orch.—Saidenberg
(*Griffes*)   # *AmD.DL 4013*

☆ = Re-issue of a recording to be found in WERM or Supplement I.

Suite, E major, Op. 63   str. orch.   1907/8
A.R.S. Orch.—Hendl   # *ARS. 22*
(*Griffes*)

Eastman-Rochester Sym.—Hanson
(*Mennini & Canning*)   # **Mer.MG 40001**

FORTNER, Wolfgang (b. 1907)

SONG: **Geh unter, schöne Sonne**   (Hölderlin)
G. Baum (B), F. Leitner (pf.)   **Pol. 15555**
(*Oboussier*)   (▽ o.n. 57093)

Symphony
... **Finale**
R.I.A.S. Sym.—Fricsay   **Pol. 68418**

FRANÇAIX, Jean (b. 1912)

Concertino   pf. & orch.   1932
☆ J. Françaix & Berlin Phil.—Borchard
(*Serenade*)   # *T.LS 6003*

Quintet, Wind insts.   1948
New Art Wind Quintet   # **CEd. 2001**
(*Nielsen*)

Sérénade for 12 instruments
☆ Hamburg Cha. Orch.—Schmidt-Isserstedt
(*Concertino*)   # *T.LS 6003*

Trio, C major, vln., vla., vlc.
☆ Pasquier Trio (FPV. 5030)

FRANCESCHINI, Gaetano   (fl. XVIII Cent.)

SEE: † AMERICAN MUSIC: INST. & CHAMBER

FRANCK, César Auguste (1822-1890)

CLASSIFIED: I (A) Piano & Organ
              (B) Chamber Music
              (c) Orchestral
           II. Songs

I (A) PIANO & ORGAN
(for Organ unless otherwise stated)

ORGAN MUSIC COLLECTIONS
(6) PIÈCES: 1. Fantaisie, Op. 16
            2. Grande pièce symphonique, Op. 17
            3. Prélude, Fugue et Variation, Op. 18
            4. Pastorale, Op. 19
            5. Prière, Op. 20
            6. Final, Op. 21   (1014)
(3) PIÈCES: 1. Fantaisie, A major
            2. Cantabile, B major
            3. Pièce héroïque
       Andantino, G minor   (1015)
       (L')Organiste, Vols. I & II   (1016/7)
C. Watters   # **CEd. 1014/7**
(Part of a projected recording of all the organ works)

       Grande pièce symphonique, Op. 17
       Prélude, Fugue et Variation, Op. 18
       Cantabile, B major
       Pièce héroïque
A. Marchal   # **Lum. 3 LD 100**

(3) CHORALS   1890
Prélude, Fugue et Variation, Op. 18
R. Noehren   (4ss)   # **Aphe.AP 4/5**

(3) CHORALS
Prière, Op. 20
C. Watters [1]   # **CEd. 1007**

Cantabile, B major   (3 pieces, No. 2)
C. Snyder   in # **KR. 15**
(*Brahms, Karg-Elert, etc.*)

Choral No. 3, A minor
☆F. Germani   # *G.DLP 1002*
(*Bach: Prelude & Fugue, E minor*)

Final, B flat major, Op. 21
F. Jackson   **Ebor.E 504**
(York Minster organ)   (pte. issue)

Grande pièce symphonique, Op. 17
E. Nies-Berger   # **CHS.CHS 1145**
(*Liszt: Variations*)   (# Nix.CLP 1145)

Prélude, Aria et Final   pf.   1886/7
Prélude, Chorale et Fugue   pf.   1884
J. Demus   # **West. WL 5163**

Prélude, Chorale et Fugue   pf.   1884
☆ W. Malcuzynski (C.GQX 11454/5: M 15166/7;
                                    # AmC.RL 3031)

I (B) CHAMBER MUSIC

Quartet, D major, strings   1889
WQXR Qtt.   # **Polym. 1010**
... **Scherzo** — ARR. BRASS QTT.
Foden's Champion Qtt. (*Pax.PR 578*)

Sonata, A major, vln. & pf.   1886
I. Stern & A. Zakin   # *AmC.ML 2204*
☆ Z. Francescatti & R. Casadesus # **C.FCX 125**
(*Debussy*)

I (C) ORCHESTRAL

(Le) Chasseur maudit
Royal Phil.—Beecham   ♮ **C.LX 8813/4**
(4ss)   (GQX 11489/90)
(*Rimsky-Korsakov: Golden Cockerel* on # AmC.ML 4454)

Psyché   Sym. Poem
... **Nos. 1, 2, 4 only**
Linz Bruckner Sym.—L. G. Jochum # **Ura. 7024**
(*Berlioz: Francs-Juges*)
☆ Chicago Sym.—Defauw (G.DB 21344/5)

Redemption Sym. Poem S, cho. & orch 1871/2
... **No. 5, Morceau symphonique**
Paris Cons.—Sebastian   # **Ura. 7061**
(*Berlioz*)

Symphony, D minor   1888
Vienna Phil.—Furtwängler [2] # *AmVox.PL 7230*
Paris Phil.—Désormière   ♮ **U.H 24021/5**
(10ss)   (# Dia.DPM 6; # CdM.LDX 8027)
☆ Paris Cons.—Münch   # **D.LXT 2692**
(1½ss—*Variations symphoniques*)   (# Lon.LL 464)
Residentie—v. Otterloo   # **Phi.A 00144L**
☆ San Francisco—Monteux   **G.DB 21442/6**
              (# G.ALP 1019: FALP/QALP 123)
Robin Hood Dell—Leinsdorf   # **BB.LBC 1001**
                                   (b set WBC 1001)
Berlin Sym.—Balzer   # **Roy. 1288**

---

[1] It is not clear whether this disc is part of the set of complete works or will eventually be superseded by it. It will be observed to overlap.
[2] Actual concert performance, 1945.

Symphony, D minor (*continued*)

Austrian Sym.—Wolf   # **Rem. 199-36**
                                    (# Ply. 12-4; # Mrt. 200-4)

Sonor Sym.—Ledermann   # **Pde. 2012**

☆ Amsterdam—Mengelberg (♮ FT.T 142/6; # T.LSK 7001)
   Philharmonia—Galliera (C.M 15156/60)
   Minneapolis—Mitropoulos (# AmC.RL 3006)

... 2nd movt., Allegretto, only
☆Col. Sym.—Rodzinski (in ♭ AmC. set A 1003)

Variations symphoniques pf. & orch 1885
W. Gieseking & Philharmonia—v. Karajan
(4ss)   ♮ **C.LX 8937/8**
                                    (♮ C.LCX 5000/1)
(*Mozart: Concerto, K488 on* # AmC.ML 4536)

A. Brailowsky & Vic. Sym.—Morel
                                    # **G.FALP 172**
(*Liszt: Totentanz*)   (# Vic.LM 1195)
(3ss—*Rachmaninoff: Prelude, Op. 32, No. 5*,
                            in ♭ Vic. set WDM 1572)

M. Huttner & Berlin Sym.   # **Roy. 1320**
(*Liszt: Pf. Concerto, No. 1*)

F. Valenzi & Austrian Sym.—Moreau
(*Debussy*)   # **Rem. 149-51**

☆E. Joyce & Paris Cons.—Münch # **D.LXT 2692**
(*Symphony, D minor*)   (# Lon.LL 464)

☆M. Lympany & Philharmonia—Süsskind
                                  # **G.CLP 1002**
(*Schumann*)   (# Vic.LHMV 1013: ♭ set WHMV 1013)

☆ G. Anda & Amsterdam—v. Beinum (# AmD.DL 9542)

II. SONGS

Panis Angelicus 1872
W. Midgley (T)   **G.DB 21550**
(*Bizet: Agnus Dei*)

E. Hobson (S), H. Dawson (org.)   **C.DX 1840**
(*Bizet: Agnus Dei*)

J. Wahl (T) (*Od.DK 1166*)
☆ C. Lynch (T) & org. (in # AmC.RL 3016)
   J. McCormack (T) (in # Vic.LCT 1121: ♭ set WCT 1121)
   R. Crooks (T) & orch. (♭ Vic. 17-0189)
   J. Melton (T) & orch. (in # Vic.LM 82: ♭ set WDM 1365)

— ARR. CHO.
Canterbury Cho. (in # MGM.E 102: ♭ set K 102)

— ARR. ORCH.
Boston Pops—Fiedler   ♭ **G.7BF 1035**
(J. Langendoen, vlc. solo)   (♭ Vic. 49-1447)
(*Schubert: Ave Maria*)

FRANCK, Johann Wolfgang
(*c.* 1641-*c.* 1700)

Auf, auf zu Gottes Lob
Sei nur still (Elmenhorst)
(from *Geistliche Lieder*, 1691)

K. Flagstad (S), G. Moore (pf.) **G.DA 2008**
(*Carissimi: Soccorretemi ch'io morro*)

FRANZ, Robert (1815-1892)

SONGS

Dies und das, Op. 30, No. 5   (From the Scottish)
Für Musik, Op. 10, No. 1   (Geibel)
Gute Nacht, Op. 5, No. 7   (Eichendorff)
Ständchen, Op. 17, No. 2   (Osterwald)
Weisst du noch, Op. 42, No. 4   (Roquette)

L. Lehmann (S)   in † # **Pembroke set**

FRESCOBALDI, Girolamo (1583-1643)

SEE ALSO: † LES MAÎTRES D'ORGUE DE J. S. BACH

(5) Gagliarde hpsi.
... No. 2 only   ☆ A. Ehlers (in # AmD.DL 8019)

Pastorale gentile
E. Zathureczky (vln.) & M. Karin (pf.)
(*Zsolt: Dragonflies*)   **U.H 24264**

Toccata per l'elevazione   — ARR. ORCH.
Vatican Radio Cha.—Nucci   ♭ **Csm.CW 4530**
(*Gounod: Marche Pontificale*)   (in # CLPS 1050)

FRIEDELL, Harold   (b. 1905)

SEE: † AMERICAN CHURCH MUSIC

FRIEDRICH II (der Grosse) (1712-1786)

Concerto No. 3, C major   fl. & str. orch.
C. Wanausek & Vienna Phil.—Adler   # **SPA. 23**
(*Quantz*)

... Allegro & Grave only
▽ F. Enke, & E. Bodky (hpsi.) (Od. matrix Qu. 529;
   illustration to Forstner's book)

SONATAS, flute & continuo
No. 48, E minor
G. Scheck, F. Neumeyer (hpsi.), A. Wenzinger
(gamba) (2ss)   **PV. 4406**

No. ?, C minor   (*c.* 1747)
J.-P. Rampal, R. Veyron-Lacroix (hpsi.) †**AS.168**
                                  (& # 3002 LD)

FROBERGER, Johann Jakob (1616-1667)

SEE ALSO: † LES MAÎTRES D'ORGUE DE J. S. BACH

Suite No. 30, A minor
Variations on Die Mayerin
E. Harich-Schneider (hpsi.)   **PV. 3404**
(announced but perhaps not issued)

FURTWÄNGLER, Wilhelm (b. 1886)

Concerto, pf. & orch., B minor
... Symphonic dialogue No. 2, only
▽ E. Fischer & Berlin Phil.—Furtwängler
(3ss)   **G.DB 4696/7S**

Symphony No. 2, E minor
Berlin Phil.—Furtwängler   ♮ **PV. 72159/64**
(12ss)   (# Pol. 18017/8)

FUX, Johann Joseph (1660-1741)

COLLECTION OF KEYBOARD WORKS
Aria passeggiata   (organ)
Arpeggio & Fuga   (organ)
Chaconne, D major   (hpsi.)
Sonata No. 6, G minor   (piano)
Suite No. 3, G minor   (piano)
Suite No. 4, A major   (hpsi.)

K. Rapf   # **SPA. 27**

───
☆ = Re-issue of a recording to be found in WERM or Supplement I.

GADE, Niels Vilhelm (1817-1890)

(The) Children's Christmas Eve, Op. 36
 pf. & voice (*ad lib.*)
... No. 2, Christmas song   (H. C. Andersen)   1859
(*Child Jesus lay in the manger*)
  O. Werner (B), J. Øian (pf.)   *Od.ND 7046*
(*Adam: Minuit, Chrétiens*)
  ☆A. Schiøtz (T), M. Wöldike (org.) [1] *G.X 7254*
(*Berggren: Christmas Song*)
  Copenhagen Youth Acad. Cho.—Asmussen
                                    Felix.F 45
(*Praetorius: Es ist ein Rös entsprungen*)

(The) ERLKING'S DAUGHTER, Op. 30
 (*Elverskud*) Ballad Soli, cho., orch.
... No. 2, Olaf's Song: When through the meadows
  H. Street (T), K. Olsson (pf.)   **Tono.A 182**
(*Knud Lavard*)

(A) FOLK LEGEND Ballet 1853
 (*3 acts: 1 & 3 by Gade, 2 by Hartmann*)
... Polonaise & Wedding Waltz
 ☆ Copenhagen Royal Op. Orch. (*Od.DK 1102*)

SONGS
Gird yourself, you hero from Golgotha   (Ewald)
  F. Andersson (Bs), H. Jensen (org.) *Felix.F 55*
(*Trad.: Siberian tune*)

Knud Lavard (Hauch)
  H. Street (T), K. Olsson (pf.)   **Tono.A 182**
(*Erlking's Daughter, No. 2*)

GALLIARD, Johann Ernst (*c.* 1687-1749)

(6) Sonatas, bsn. or vlc. & cont.
No. 1, A minor; No. 3, F major
 ☆ H. Busch (vlc.), E. Weiss-Mann (♯ *Ome. & CID. 33008*)

GALLOIS-MONTBRUN, Raymond

SEE: MONTBRUN, R. G., *infra*

GALLON, Noël (b. 1891)

Chanson du vieux
  C. Panzéra (B), M. Panzéra (pf.)
                      in ♯ **Mer.MG 10098**
(*Ravel, Milhaud, Tremois, etc.*)

Quintet   hp., 2 vlns., vla., vlc.
... 1st & 2nd movts. only
 ▽ P. Jamet Quintet (*AA. 20*)

Recitative & Allegro   Bsn. & pf.
 ▽ F. Oubradous & N. Gallon (*OL. 9*)

GALUPPI, Baldassare (1706-1785)

SONATA, D major, Op. 1, No. 4   hpsi.
... Adagio only
  O. Frugoni (pf.)   in ♯ **AmVox.PL 7700**
(*Chopin, Bach, etc.*)

GASTOLDI, Giovanni Giacomo
                (*c.* 1566-1622)

Fahren wir froh im Nacken
  Trapp Family Cho.—Wasner
                   in ♯ **CHS.CHS 1101**

GAUBERT, Philippe (1879-1941)

Sonata, No. 1, A major, fl. & pf.   1918
  H. Barwahser & F. de Nobel   ♯ **Phi.A 00104L**
(♯s.—*Caplet & Schubert*)

GEHOT, Joseph   (b. 1756)

SEE: † AMERICAN MUSIC: INST. & CHAMBER

GEMINIANI, Francesco (1687-1762)

Sonata, B flat major   vln. unacc.
  F. Ostrovsky   ♯ **CEd. 1029**
(*Stravinsky & Ostrovsky*)

GERSHWIN, George (1898-1937)

PIANO MUSIC COLLECTIONS
  L. Hambro   ♯ **Wald. 200**
  ♯ G. Gershwin   ♯ *AudA. 0073*
  First Pf. Qtt.   ♯ *Vic.LM 125*
(*Excerpts also on* ♭ *Vic.WEPR 8*) (♭ set *WDM 1574*)

(An) American in Paris   orch.   1928
  N.B.C. Sym.—Toscanini   ♯ **Vic.LM 9020**
(*Prokofiev: Classical Sym.*)   (♭ set *WDM 1657*)
  Kingsway Sym.—Camarata   ♯ **B.LAT 8014**
(*Rhapsody in Blue*)   (♯ *AmD.DL 8519*)
  M.G.M. Orch.—J. Green   *MGM. 425/6*
(4ss) (*MGM. 9030/1: 5080/1*) (in ♯ *MGM.E 93*: ♭ *K 93*)
  Kostelanetz Orch.   ♯ **AmC.ML 4455**
(*Rhapsody in Blue*)   (♮ set *MM 1020*: ♭ set *A 1020*)
  P. Whiteman Orch.   ♯ *Cap.H 301*
(♯ *FCap.LDC 04*)   (♭ set *EBF 301*)
(*Rhapsody in Blue* on ♯ Cap.P 303; ♯ *T.LCA 303*)
  Vienna Sym.—Dixon   ♯ *PaV.VPO 3000*
(*Rhapsody in Blue*)   (♯ *AmVox.VL 3130*)
  ☆G. Gershwin (pf.) & Vic. Sym.—Shilkret
                              ♯ *Vic.LPT 29*
(*Rhapsody in Blue*)   (♭ set *WPT 38*)

— ARR. 2 PFS. Gearhart
  V. Morley & L. Gearhart (in ♯ *AmC.ML 2197*)

— ARR. 4 PFS
  First Piano Qtt. (in ♯ *Vic.LM 125*: ♭ set *WDM 1574*:
                                  ♭ *WEPR 8*)

Concerto, F major   pf. & orch.   1925
 ☆ O. Levant & N.Y.P.S.O.—Kostelanetz (♯ *C.FCX 118*)

(A) Cuban Overture   orch.   1932
  A. Kostelanetz Orch.   ♯ **AmC.ML 4481**
(*Porgy, etc.*)

---

[1] Apparently a re-issue with d.c.   Originally *X 7254* was listed as having the same coupling as *X 6611*, but this was probably an error.

PORGY AND BESS Opera 3 acts 1935

COMPLETE RECORDING
　C. Williams, I. Matthews, L. Winters, cho. &
　　orch.—Engel　(6ss)　　♯ **AmC. set SL 162**

ABRIDGED RECORDING
　☆ A. Brown, T. Duncan, N. Y. Cast (♯ AmD.DL 8042;
　　♯ B.LAT 8021)

Orchestral Selection
　A. Kostelanetz Orch.　　　♯ **AmC.ML 4481**
　(*Cuban Overture, etc.*)

Vocal Selection
　Royale Operetta Singers & Orch. in ♯ **Roy. 1242**
　　　　　　　(♯ *Roy. 6095*, 2ss: ♭ *set 14588*, 6ss)

Bess, you is my woman now
I got plenty o' nuttin'
Summertime
　R. Stevens (M-S), R. Merrill (B) & cho. (♭ *Vic.WEPR 34*)

I got plenty o' nuttin'
It ain't necessarily so
Lullaby　— ARR. 4 PFS.
　First Piano Qtt. (in ♯ *Vic.LM 125*: in ♭ *set WDM 1574*)

Summertime　　　　　　　　　A
　☆ R. Stevens (from set) (Vic. 12-3160)
　G. Rowes (in ♭ *AmC. set A 1003*)

Where's my Bess　　　　　　　B
　☆ R. Merrill (from set) (Vic. 12-3160)

(3) Preludes　　　　　　　pf.
... **No. 1, B flat major**
　☆ A. Földes (in ♯ *Rem. 149-4*)

... **No. 2** — ARR. SAX. & PF.　Rascher
　S. Rascher & D. Tudor　in ♯ **CHS.CHS 1156**

Rhapsody in Blue pf. & orch.　1924
　L. Pennario & P. Whiteman's Orch. ♯ *Cap.H 302*
　(♯ *FCap.LDC 04*)　　　　　　(♭ *EBF 302*)
　(*American in Paris* on ♯ Cap.P 303; ♯ T.LCA 303)
　H. Rothmüller & R.B.T. Orch.—Kudritzi
　　　　　　　　　　　　　　Pol. 57387
　V. Rivkin & Vienna Sym.—Dixon
　　　　　　　　　　　♯ *PaV.VPO 3000*
　(*American in Paris*)　　　　(♯ *AmVox.VL 3130*)
　A. Sandford & Kingsway Sym.—Camarata
　(*American in Paris*)　　　　　♯ **B.LAT 8014**
　(4ss, ♮ D.AK 24082/3)　　　　(♯ AmD.DL 8519)

　H. Kiessling & Orch.—Edelhagen (Phi.P 44104G)
　☆ E. Wild & Orch.—Whiteman (♯ *Crl. 58063*)
　G. Gershwin & P. Whiteman's Orch (♯ *Vic.LPT 29*:
　　　　　　　　　　　　　　　　♭ *set WPT 38*)
　A. Templeton & Kostelanetz Orch. (♯ AmC.ML 4455)

— ARR. 4 PFS.
　First Pf. Qtt. (in ♯ *Vic.LM 125*:♭ *set WDM 1574*:
　　　　　　　　　　　　　　　　♭ *WEPR 8*)

Variations on "I got rhythm"　pf. & orch.
　☆ O. Levant & M. Gould Orch. (C.M 10037: GFX 184)

GERVAISE, Claude (fl. 1550)

　SEE ALSO: † FRENCH MASTERS . . .

DANCERIES
　(some are only *published* by Gervaise)
— ARR. FL., OB., CL., HRN., BSN.　Désormière

Basse danse	Bransle de Bourgogne
Gaillarde	Allemande
Tourdion	Bransle de Champagne

　R. Cortet, L. Gromer, Vacellier, Raumont,
　　Grandmaison　　　　　　**D.GAG 15113**
　(2ss)

GESUALDO, Don Carlo (*c.* 1560-1615)

　SEE ALSO: † ITALIAN MADRIGALS
　　　　　　† A TREASURY OF MADRIGALS

MADRIGALS
COLLECTION
Felice Primavera—Danzan le Ninfe
Io pur respiro
Io tacerò
Meraviglia d'amore—Et ardo e vivo
Merce i grido piangendo
Moro lasso
　Randolph Singers—Randolph ♯ **West.WL 5171**
　(*Monteverdi*)

GIARDINI, Felice de (1716-1796)

Sonata-Trio, E flat major
　La Scala Trio　　　　　　　♯ **Ura. 7074**
　(*Puccini & Boccherini*)

GIBBONS, Ellis (1570-*c.* 1650)

　SEE: † TRIUMPHS OF ORIANA

GIBBONS, Orlando (1583-1625)

I. VOCAL

ANTHEMS
Almighty and everlasting God　4 voices
O God, the King of Glory　5 voices & org.
O Lord, increase my faith　4 voices
Psalm 145: The eyes of all　4 voices & org.
This is the record of John　T, cho., str., orch.
　Purcell Performing Soc.—J. R. King
　　　　　　　　　　　　♯ **Allo.ALG 3038**
　(*below; & Locke & Philips*)

Hosanna to the Son of David　6 voices
　Welch Chorale　　　　in ♯ **Lyr.LL 35**
　(*Sweelinck, Weelkes, etc.*)

O Lord, increase my faith　4 voices
　Wesley's Chapel Cho.—Cleall　*Argo.R 1001*
　(*C. K. Scott: The Lord is my Shepherd*)

MADRIGALS　5 voices　1612
(The) Silver Swan
What is our life?　(Raleigh)
　Renaissance Singers—Engel in ♯ **AmC.ML 4517**
　(† A Treasury of Madrigals)

(The) Silver Swan
　Trapp Family Cho.—Wasner
　　　　　　　　　in ♯ **CHS.CHS 1101**

SERVICES
Magnificat　(ARR. Royle Shore)
　Cho. of St. John's, Upper Norwood—
　　L. Betteridge (org.)　　　　**Croy.CX 1**
　(*Bairstow: Save us, O Lord*)

Magnificat & Nunc dimittis (unspec.)
　Open Score Soc.—F. Cameron ♯ **Per.SPLP 535**
　(† Renaissance Masterpieces)
　Purcell Performing Soc.　　in ♯ **Allo.ALG 3038**
　(*above*)

☆ = Re-issue of a recording to be found in WERM or Supplement I.

II. INSTRUMENTAL

(A) Fancy in A Re   (Glyn. IV-6)
G. Jones (org.)   **D.X 549**
(† Early English Keyboard Music)

(2) Fantasies   Str. Qtt.
New Music Qtt.   ♯ **BRS. 913**
(*Locke & Purcell*)

Fantasy   (Glyn V-16)
E. Goble (hpsi.)   **D.AX 547**
(† Early English Keyboard Music)

(The) Lord of Salisbury—his Pavan & Galliard
(Parthenia 18 & 19)
E. Goble (virginals)   **D.X 550**
(† Early English Keyboard Music)

Prelude   (Glyn IV-14)
E. Goble (virginals)   **D.X 551**
(† Early English Keyboard Music)

GILSON, Paul (1865-1942)

(La) Mer   Sym. Poem, recitation & orch.   1890
Belgian Nat. Orch.—L. Weemaels
           ♯ *D.LX 133010*
(slightly abridged—no recitation)

... Sailors' Dance only
▽ Brussels Radio—Dejoncker   *T.A 10368*

Mother   Song in *Flemish* (Lambrechts)
F. Lepage (M-S) & orch.   *C.DCB 50*
(*Mortelmans: Song*)

GINASTERA, A. E. (b. 1916)

SONGS
Chacarera; Triste
J. Tourel (S), G. Reeves (pf.) in ♯ *AmC.ML 2198*

GIORDANI, Tommaso (c. 1733-1806)

     SEE ALSO: † ITALIAN SONGS
                † ITALIAN ART SONGS

Caro mio ben[2]
R. Schock & orch.   **G.DA 5515**
(*Handel: Serse, Largo*)
    F. Brückner (T) (*Tpo. 3848*)
    ℍ A. Bonci (HRS. 1113*)

GIORDANO, Umberto (1867-1948)

OPERAS
ANDREA CHÉNIER   4 acts   1896
COMPLETE RECORDING
   Andrea Chénier   ...   ...   G. Sarri (T)
   Gerard   ...   .   A. M. Serra (B)
   Maddalena ...   .   F. Sacchi (S)
   Contessa   ...   ...   L. de Lelio (M-S)
  etc., Rome Opera Cho. & Orch.—Paoletti
  (6ss)   ♯ **Ura. set 218**

EXCERPTS
M. Seinemeyer (S), A. Roselle (S), T. Pattiera (T),
   G. Zenatello (T), G. Lauri-Volpi (T), A.
   Piccaver (T), F. Corradetti (B) ♯ Ete. O-484
(some are * & some ☆)

ACT I
Un dì all'azzurro spazio   T
   F. Ferrari   in ♯ **D.LXT 2688**
   (*Rossini, Gounod, etc.*)   (in ♯ **Lon.LL 534**)
   M. Lanza   **G.DB 21486**
   (Act IV—*Come un bel dì*)
   V. Campagnano   **P.PE 176**
   (*Aïda—Celesta Aïda*)
   K. Baum   **Hma. 15005**
   (*Trovatore—Ah, si ben mio & Di quella pira*)
             (also in ♯ Rem. 199-63)
   ℍ E. Johnson (IRCC. 3089*)

ACT II
Ora soave   S & T
   ℍ A. Oltrabella & B. de Muro (*G.VA 52*: o.n. DA. 495**)

ACT III
Nemico della patria   B
   ☆ A. Reali (P.PXO 1071)

La Mamma morta   S
   ☆ R. Tebaldi (in ♯ *AmD.DL 4005*)
   C. Muzio (in ♯ *AmC.ML 4404*)
   ℍ C. Muzio (in ♯ Eso.ES 508*: ♯ Cpt.MC 20010*) [1]

Si, fui soldato   T
   ℍ E. Johnson (IRCC. 3089*)

ACT IV
Come un bel dì di maggio   T
   M. Lanza   **G.DB 21486**
   (*Un dì all'azzurro spazio*)
   K. Baum   in ♯ **Rem. 199-63**
   (*Aïda, Tosca, etc.*)
   M. del Monaco   *G.DA 11333*
   (*Werther—Pourquoi me réveiller*)
   ☆ A. Piccaver (*Ger*) (Pol. 67540; ♯ Ete. O-484)

Vicino a te ... La nostra morte   S & T
   ☆ M. Seinemeyer & T. Pattiera (*Ger*) (in ♯ Ete. O-484)
   ℍ A. Oltrabella & B. de Muro (*G.VA 52*: o.n. DA 495**)
   C. Boninsegna & C. Bolis (*G.VB 4*: o.n. DB 492**)

FEDORA   3 acts   1898
COMPLETE RECORDINGS

	Set A	Set B
Fedora	M. Caniglia (S)	V. Calma (S)
Olga	C. Piccini (S)	O. Rovero (S)
Loris	G. Prandelli (T)	R. Pellizzoni (T)
De Siriex ...	S. Colombo (B)	A. Gilardoni (B)

Set A
Italian Radio Cho. & Orch.—Rossi
(4ss)   ♯ **Sor. set 1222**

Set B
La Scala Cho. & Orch.—Quadri
(4ss)   ♯ **Csm.CLPS 1021/2**

O grandi occhi   S   (Act I)
   E. Nicolai   **P.R 30049**
   (*Samson et Dalila—Amour viens aider*)   (CB 20512)

Son gente risoluta   S   (Act I)
   ▽ ℍ M. Jeritza (*G.DA 579*; Vic. 990**)

Amor ti vieta   T   (Act II)
   R. Lagares   *G.DA 11336*
   (*Cavalleria Rusticana—Siciliana*)
   ℍ E. Caruso (also on *G.VA 53**)

---

[1] Recorded from Edison cylinder.   [2] Also attributed to Giuseppe Giordani (c. 1744-1798)

MADAME SANS-GÊNE 3 acts (*Ital*) 1915
Che me non facchio　　　　　　　　　S
　H C. Muzio (in # Eso.ES 502*; # Cpt.MC 20009*) [1]

MESE MARIANO 1 act 1910
COMPLETE RECORDING
　　Carmela　...　...　...　V. Calma (S)
　　La Contessa　...　...　R. Villiani (S)
　　Mother Superior　...　V. Palombini (M-S)
　　Suor Pazienza　...　...　M. E. Casals (S)
　La Scala Cho. & Orch.—Rivoli
　　　　　　　　　　　　# Csm.CLPS 1023

SIBERIA 3 acts 1903
Mattinata　　　　　　　　　B
　H T. Ruffo (HRS. 1085*)

GIULIANI, Mauro (1780-*c.* 1840)

SEE: † SEGOVIA CONCERT

GJERSTRØM, Gunnar (b. 1891)

(The) Myth — ARR. VLN. & PF.　Knudsen
　G. Knudsen & E. Garcia　　　# *ML. 5002*
　(*Reger, Eccles, etc.*)

GLAZOUNOV,
　Alexander Konstantinovitch (1865-1936)

Album Leaf
　T. Dokshitsev (hrn.) & Radio Sym.—Samosud
　(2ss)　　　　　　　　　　*USSR. 20992/3*

Bauernfräulein Ballet
...**Unspec. Excerpts**
　USSR. Radio Sym.—Orlov　♮ *U.H 23905/6*
　(3ss—*Raymonda, Adagio*)

Christmas Singers (from *Jour de fête*) str. qtt.
　Dancers, etc. & Radio Artists Str. Qtt.
　(*Rimsky-Korsakov & Liadov*)　# Circ. 51-103
　☆ Galimir Qtt.　　　　in # Nix.PLP 505

Concerto, Saxophone & Orch. 1936
　M. Abato & Orch.—Pickering　　# **Phil. 103**
　(*Ibert*)

Concerto, A minor, Op. 82 vln. & orch. 1904
　D. Oistrakh & USSR State Sym.—Kondrashin
　(6ss)　　　　　　　　　♮ *U.H 23871/3*
　(*Moussorgsky: Intermezzo,* in # *Sup.LPM 7*)
　(*Kabalevsky: Vlc. concerto* in # *Van.VRS 6005*)
　M. Polyakin & USSR State Sym.—Orlov
　(6ss)　　　　　　　　　*USSR. 09893/8*
　H. Girdach & Berlin Radio Sym.—Schultz
　　　　　　　　　　　　# *Rgt. 5021*

Lyrical Poem, Op. 12　　orch.
　Bolshoi Theatre—Samosud　♮ *U.C 23932/3*
　(4ss)

(5) Novelettes, Op. 15　　str. qtt.
... **No. 2, Orientale & No. 5, All'ungherese**
　Glazounov Qtt.　　　　　*USSR. 14896/9*

QUARTETS, String
No. 5, D minor, Op. 70
　Glazounov Qtt.　(10ss)　　*USSR. 6555/64*

RAYMONDA, Op. 57 Ballet
... **Valse fantasque** ("*Grande valse*")
　☆ Philharmonia—Malko　　# *G.FBLP 1004*
　(¼s.—*Seasons, excpts*; & *Tchaikovsky*)

... **Adagio**
　Bolshoi Theatre—Fayer　　　U.H 23905
　(*above*)

(Les) RUSES D'AMOUR, Op. 61 Ballet 1899
Intro. & Allegretto—**Allegro** (Act I)
　Philharmonia—Malko　　　　G.C 7874
　(*Seasons, s.1*)

Scènes de ballet, Op. 52
... **1. Préambule ; 6. Danse Orientale ; 7. Waltz**
　USSR. Radio Sym.—Gauk　*USSR. 20990/1 &*
　(4ss)　　　　　　　　　　　　*20998/9*

(The) SEASONS, Op. 67 Ballet
　French Nat. Sym.—Désormière
　　　　　　　　　　　　# DCap.CTL 7018
　　　　　　　(# Cap.P 8157; # T.LCSK 8157)

... **Orch. Suite: Nos. 1, 2, 3, 4, 5, 9, 13**
　Philharmonia—Malko　　♮ G.C 7874/5
　(3ss—*Ruses d'amour, Op. 61, excpts.*)
　(¼s.—*Raymonda excpt. & Tchaikovsky: Capriccio italien*
　　　　　　　　　　　on # *G.FBLP 1004*)

... **Nos. 2, 3, 4, 15**
　Sym.—Glazounov　　　　*USSR. 16210/1*
　(2ss—probably ☆ of Columbia recording)

Sérénade espagnole, Op. 20, No. 2 vlc. & pf.
　S. Knushevitsky & pf.　　*USSR. 18969*
　(*Schumann*)
　☆ R. Krotschak (in # Eur.LPG 631)

Slavonic Festival, Op. 26　　orch.
　USSR. Radio Sym.—Kovalev　*USSR. 20413/6*
　(4ss)

SONGS
In my blood the fire of desire burns (Pushkin)
　Z. Dolukhanova (A)　　　*USSR. 18967*
　(*Rubinstein: Night*)

Why are the voices silent (*Drinking Song*) (Pushkin)
　A. Baturin (B)　　　　　*USSR. 4934*
　(*Borodin: To distant shores*)

SYMPHONIES
No. 4, E flat major, Op. 48
　Leningrad Phil.—Mravinsky　♮ U.H 23908/11
　(8ss)

No. 5, B flat major, Op. 55
　USSR. Radio—N. Golovanov　USSR.018396/403
　(8ss)
　☆ Czech Phil.—Ivanov　　# *Sup.LPM 18*

VALSES DE CONCERT
No. 1, D major, Op. 47
　Melachrino Orch.　　　　G.C 4098
　(*Lecuona: Danza Lucumi*)　　(EH 1422)
　USSR. Radio—N. Golovanov　*USSR. 12593/5*
　(3ss—*Liadov: Song of Sorrow*)

Valse (unspec.)　　　　pf.
　P. Serebriakov　　　　　*USSR. 16399*
　(*Tchaikovsky: The Months, No. 8*)

GLIER, Reinhold Moritzovitch (b. 1875)

Ballet Suite, No. 1
... **Friends' Dance & Gypsy Dance**
　☆Bolshoi Theatre—Fayer in # Csm.CRLP 108/9

---

[1] Recorded from Edison cylinder.

81

Concerto for voice & orch.
☆N. Kazantseva (S), USSR. Radio Sym.—
  Golovanov   ♮ *U.C 23944/6*
  (5ss—*Tchaikovsky: Casse Noisette, March*)

(The) Copper Horseman Ballet
  (or better: *The Bronze Horseman*)
  ☆ Bolshoi Theatre—Glier (♮ *U.C 24287/8*)

Festival Overture [1] (ORCH. Rogal-Levitsky)
  Bolshoi Theatre—Nebolsin   **USSR. 03728**
  (*Ippolitoff-Ivanoff: Voroshilov March*)

Octet, D major, Op. 5 strings 1900
  ... 4th movt., Allegro assai, only
  D. Tziganov (vln.) & Ens.   **USSR. 021069/70**
  (2ss)

(The) RED POPPY, Op. 70 Ballet 1927
No. 14, Sailors' Dance (*Yablochko*)
  Bolshoi Theatre—Fayer   **USSR. 5797**
  (*Ossetinian: Lezginka*)

  ☆ Philharmonia—Malko (♭ *G.7BF 1019*: *7P 128*;
           in ♯ *BB.LBC 1026*: ♭ *set WBC 1026*)
  Col. Sym.—Rodzinski (in ♭ *AmC. set A 1003*)
  Carnegie Pops—O'Connell (in ♭ *AmC. set A 1001*)

— ARR. 4 PFS.
  ☆ First Pf. Qtt. (in ♯ Vic.LM 1165)

Romance, C minor, Op. 3 vln. & pf.
  G. Barinova (2ss)   **USSR. 12954/5**
  R. Vlasov & V. Vladimirova   **U.H 24039**
  (*van Goens: Scherzo*)

  ☆I. Bezrodny & V. Yampolsky **USSR. 17788**
  (*Brahms: Hungarian Dance, No. 20*)

SHAH SENEM Opera 4 acts 1927 or 1934
Festival March; Iranian Dance
  USSR. Radio Sym.—Orlov   **U.H 23904**

SONG: Oh, how great is my sorrow
  V. Borisenko (M-S) & orch.   **Muza.X 1556**
  (*Tchaikovsky: The wild stars*)

SYMPHONY: No. 3, B minor, Op. 42
  (*Ilya Mourometz*)
  Moscow Phil.—Glier   ♯ *CEd. 3002*

GLINKA, Michael Ivanovitch (1803-1857)

Festival Polonaise, F major orch.
  USSR. Radio—Gauk (2ss) *USSR. 18564/5*

Jota Aragonesa orch. (*Caprice brillant*)
  USSR. State—Samosud   **U.H 23874**

OPERAS & STAGE WORKS
(A) LIFE FOR THE TZAR 4 acts & epilogue 1836
  (or *Ivan Sussanin*)
COMPLETE RECORDING (with some cuts)
  Ivan Sussanin ...   ... M. Mikhailov (Bs)
  Antonida... ...   ... N. Shpiller (S)
  Vanya ...   ...   E. Antononova (M-S)
  Sobinin ...   ...   G. Nelepp (T)
  etc., Bolshoi Theatre Cho. & Orch.—
  Melik-Pashayev (44ss) **USSR. 020813/56**
                        (6ss, in ♯ Van.VRS 6010/2)

Ballet Music
  ☆Bolshoi Theatre—Samosud ♯ Csm.CRLP 111
  (*Prince Igor Dances*)

Antonida's Romance; & Act IV, COMPLETE
  Bolshoi Theatre Co.—Samosud
                      ♯ Csm.CRLP 117
  (*Boris, Selection*) (Parts are ☆)

No. 2, On the river's further side   S
  (*Antonida's Cavatina & Rondo*)
  E. Shumskaya (2ss)   **USSR. 019967/8**

No. 4, Joyful reunion   Bs, S, T
  M. Reizen, E. Shumskaya, G. Nelepp
                              USSR. 19973/4

Nos. 5-7, Dances
  ... Mazurka
  ☆ N.Y. Phil. Sym.—Kurtz (♭ *AmC.A 1509*)

  ... Waltz
  Bolshoi Theatre—Melik-Pashayev
  (2ss)   **USSR. 20891/2**

Nos. 19-21 (Act IV, Sc. 2, COMPLETE)
  M. Reizen & Cho. (6ss)   **USSR. 018041/6**

No. 20 b/c, Sussanin's Aria   Bs
  A. Ognivtsev (2ss)   **USSR. 19112/3**
  B. Gmyria (2ss)   **USSR. 17413/4**
  ⌘ F. Chaliapin (in ♯ *AudA. 0077**)

— CHORAL VERSION
  Don Cossacks—Jaroff   in ♯ **AmC.ML 4473**
  (*Gretchaninoff, Folksongs, etc.*)

RUSLAN AND LUDMILLA Opera 5 acts 1842
Overture; Fairy Dance;
Oriental Dances; Wizard's March
  L.S.O.—Fistoulari   ♯ *MGM.E 105*
                              (♭ set K 105)
Overture
  Philharmonia—Kletzki   **C.LX 8951**
  (*Moussorgsky: Night on the Bare Mountain, s.1*)
  Vienna Radio—Nilius   *Vien.P 6021*
  (2ss)   (in ♯ *1012*)
  Bamberg Sym.—Lehmann   **PV. 72235**
  (*Tchaikovsky: Romeo & Juliet, s.1*)
  ☆Bolshoi Theatre—Samosud   **U.H 24281**
  (2ss)

ACT I
No. 2, Ludmilla's Cavatina: Soon I must leave thee
  I. Maslennikova (S) & cho. **USSR. 018434/5**
  (2ss)

ACT II
No. 7, Farlaf's Rondo: The happy day is gone Bs
  M. Reizen   **USSR. 15685**
  (*Serov: Judith, Holofernes' War Song*)
  B. Gmyria   **USSR. 019978**
  (*Tchaikovsky: Iolanthe, aria*)

ACT III
No. 11, Persian Song — ARR. VLN. & PF.
  ☆ D. Oistrakh (in ♯ Csm.CRLP 105)

No. 12, Gorislava's Cavatina: O my Ratmir! S
  N. Pokrovskaya (2ss)   **USSR. 16242/3**

ACT IV
No. 17, Far from my beloved (Ludmilla's aria) S
  I. Maslennikova (2ss)   *USSR. 18359a/60a*

No. 19, Dances (Oriental Dances)
  Philharmonia—Malko   **G.C 4196**

PRINCE KHOLMSKY 1840
  Inc. music to tragedy by Kukolnik
Overture
  USSR. State Sym.—A. Gauk *USSR. 16778/9*
  (2ss)

[1] Perhaps *Solemn Overture for the 20th Anniversary of the October Revolution*, Op. 72.

Quartet, Strings, F major   1830
... **Finale (Rondo), only**
  Bolshoi Theatre Qtt.   (2ss)   *USSR. 18746/7*

SONGS

Autumn Night (Rimsky-Korsakov)
  M. Mikhailov (Bs)   *USSR. 12255*
  (Borodin: Song of the dark forest)

  M. Reizen (Bs)   *USSR. 9666*
  (When you asked me)

(The) Blue waves are still (Kukolnik)
  N. Shpiller (S)   *USSR. 18375*
  (Rimsky-Korsakov: Hebrew song)

(The) Conqueror   (Zhukovsky)
  S. Lemeshev (T)   *USSR. 17265*
  (Night)

Do not tempt me (Elegy)   (Boratinsky)
  ▽ E. Katulskaya (S), S. Lemeshev (T)
  (2ss)   *USSR. 15971/2*

Elegy   (Yakovlev)
  ▽ A. Kaktins (B) (¶ *G.EK 61*)

Even a single moment
  E. Katulskaya (S)   *USSR. 18588*
  (In a magic dream)

(The) Forest murmurs
  S. Lemeshev (T)   *USSR. 017303*
  (Rachmaninoff: O cease thy singing)

Had I but known
  K. Derzhinskaya (S)   *USSR. 10030*
  (Gurilev: Coachman's song)

I had just recognised you   (Delvig)
  S. Shaposhnikov ( ), E. Lebedev (pf.)
  (Why do you weep?)   *USSR. 21238*

In a magic dream
  E. Katulskaya (S)   *USSR. 18587*
  (Even a single moment)

(The) Lark   (Kukolnik)
  N. Shpiller (S)   *USSR. 20000*
  (Cui: Parting)

— ARR. PF.   Balakirev: L. Oborin (*USSR. 16798/9*)

Night   (Delvig)
  S. Lemeshev (T)   *USSR. 17266*
  (Conqueror)

Nightingale   (Zabell)
  And. Ivanov (B)   *USSR. 17013*
  (Dargomijsky: 2 songs)

O wondrous maiden   (Kukolnik)
  M. Maksakova (S)   *USSR. 14678*
  (Borodin: Arab melody)

Venetian Night (Kozlov) — ARR. CHO. Balakirev
  State Cho.—Sveshnikov   *USSR. 18203*
  (Alabiev: In the Dance)

When you asked, darling (Elegy)
  M. Reizen (Bs)   *USSR. 9665*
  (Autumn night)

Why do you weep?   (Delvig)
  S. Shaposhnikov ( ), E. Lebedev (pf.)
  (I had just recognised you)   *USSR. 19704*

You swore you loved me   (Rimsky-Korsakov)
  M. Maksakova (S)   *USSR. 16203*
  (Bulakhov: Song)

Variations on The Nightingale (Alabiev) pf.
  I. Mikhnovsky   (2ss)   *USSR. 16377/8*

Variations on a theme of Mozart   harp
  S. Erdeli   (2ss)   *USSR. 02118/9*

GLUCK, Christoph Willibald von
(1714-1787)

I. INSTRUMENTAL

Ballet Suite   — ARR.   Mottl
  German Phil. Prague—Keilberth   ♯ **Ura. 7018**
  (Prologo)

Ballet (unspec. ?   Orphée 29/30)   — ARR. GUITAR
  A. Segovia   ♯ **AmD.DL 9647**
  († Segovia Program)

Concerto, G major, fl. & orch.
  J.-P. Rampal & Paris Phil.—Leibowitz
  (Corelli & Haydn)   ♯ **Oce.OCS 29**
  W. Urfer & Winterthur Sym.—Dahinden
  (Haydn)   ♯ **CHS.F 7**

II. OPERAS

ALCESTE   3 acts   1776
COMPLETE RECORDING

Alceste	...	...	E. Semser (S)
Admète	...	...	E. Seri (T)
Evandre	...	...	J. Mollien (T)
High Priest }			
Hercule }	...	...	J. Hoffman (B)
Oracle }			
Thanatos }	...	...	L. Mans (Bs)

  Cho. & Paris Phil.—Leibowitz
  (6ss)   ♯ **Oce. set OCL 304**

Overture
  L.S.O.—Kisch   ♯ *D.LX 3063*
  (below; & Cimarosa)   (♯ *Lon.LPS 353*)
  (also, 2ss, D.K 23231)
  Prague German Phil.—Keilberth   ♯ **Ura. 7028**
  (below & Spohr)
  ☆ Berlin Phil.—Furtwängler (FT.T 122)

Divinités du Styx
  ☆S. Danco   **D.KX 28313**
  (Dido & Aeneas—Dido's lament)
  ☆ E. Wysor (in ♯ *Rem. 149-2*)

IPHIGÉNIE EN AULIDE   1774
Overture   (concert ending by Wagner)
  L.S.O.—Kisch *(above)*   ♯ *D.LX 3063*
  (also, 2ss, D.K 23246)   (♯ *Lon.LPS 353*)
  Berlin Phil.—Abendroth   ♯ **Ura. 7028**
  (above & Spohr)
  Austrian State Sym.—Gui   ♯ **MSL.MW 42**
  (Beethoven, Weber, Mendelssohn)
  ▽Suisse Romande—Blech   **D.K 28382/3** [1]
  (3ss—*Mozart: Contretänze, K 609*)
  ☆ Berlin Municipal—Ludwig (Pol. 15531)

No. 28, Ballet . . . Gavotte
  — ARR. 4 PFS.   ☆ First Piano Qtt. (in ♯ Vic.LM 1165)

(L') IVROGNE CORRIGÉ   2 acts   1760
COMPLETE RECORDING (ed. Leibowitz & Gradwohl)

Mathurin	...	...	J.-C. Benoît (T)
Lucas	...	...	B. Demigny (T)
Colette	...	...	C. Collard (S)
Mathurine	...	...	F. Betti (S)

  etc.; Paris Phil.—Leibowitz   ♯ **Nix.PLP 238**
                                  (♯ Ren.X 38)

---

[1] Original information gave this as 2ss only on K 28382.

ORPHÉE ET EURIDICE   3 acts   1762 & 1774
COMPLETE RECORDING (in *Italian*) [1]
Orfeo ... ...   M. Klose (A)
Eurydice ... ...   E. Berger (S)
L'Amor ... ...   R. Streich (S)
etc.; Berlin Municipal Op. Cho. & Orch—
Rother (6ss)   # Ura. set 223

ACT II

No. 28, Danse des Furies
☆ Dresden Phil.—v. Kempen (Pol. 15493; P.RR 8149)

No. 29, 30, Dance of the Blessed Spirits
☆N.B.C.—Toscanini   G.DB 21497
(*Smetana: Vltava, s.3*)
(♭ *G.7RF 196*; ♭ Vic. 49-3301 d.c. & in ♭ *set WDM 1505*)
☆ Dresden Phil.—v. Kempen (Pol. 15488)

— ARR. PF.
G. Novães   in # AmVox.PL 7500
(*Brahms, Bach, Purcell, etc.*)

No. 30, Mélodie
— ARR. VLC. & PF.   Grünfeld
E. Mainardi & M. Raucheisen   *Pol. 26521*
(*Paradies: Siciliense*)

No. 33, Quel nouveau ciel   A
R. Stevens (*Ital*)   in # Vic.LM 9010
(*Carmen, Figaro, etc.*)   (♭ *set WDM 9010*)
E. Nicolai (M-S, *Ital*)   P.CB 20531
(*Werther—Air de la lettre*)
☆ L. Sidney (*Ger*) (Vien. 5004; Eur.TGB 150)

ACT III

No. 43, J'ai perdu mon Eurydice   A
M. Klose (*Ital*)   in # Ura. 7017
(*Handel, etc.*)
R. Stevens (*Ital*)   in # Vic.LM 9010
(*above*)   (♭ *set WDM 9010*)
E. Wysor (*Ital*)   in # Rem. 199-30
M. Mödl (*Ger*)   T.E 3897
(*Don Carlos—O don fatale*)
☆ L. Sidney (*Ger*) (Eur.TGB 150; Vien. 5004)
H M. Delna (*CRS. 60**)

PARIDE ED ELENA   5 acts   (*Italian*)   1770
O del mio dolce ardor   ☆ J. Palmer (*Csm.C 30*)
Spiagge amate   ☆ C. Muzio (S) & pf. (in # Eso.ES 508*;
Cpt.MC 20010*) [2]

(Il) PROLOGO   S, A, orch.   1767
— ARR. AS *Frühlingsfeier* [3]
Berlin Boys Cho. & Orch.—Steffen
(*Ballet Suite*)   # Ura. 7018

GODARD, Benjamin (1849-1895)

Concerto, vln. & orch., No. 1, Op. 35
... Canzonetta   ☆ D. Oistrakh & pf. (in # Csm.CRLP 105)

OPERAS, etc.
JOCELYN   4 acts   1888
Cachés dans cet asile   (Berceuse)   T
G. Fields (S, *Eng*) (*D.F 9828*: in # *LF 1080*)
I. Hübner (S, *Ger*) (*Od.O-28322*)
☆ N. Eddy (B, *Eng*) (♭ *AmC.A 1535*)
T. Rossi (in # *AmC.FL 9544*: ♭ *set F 4-41*)
H J. McCormack (in # Vic.LCT 1036*: in ♭ *set WCT 53**:
in # *Vic.LCT 1121**: in ♭ *set WCT 1121**)

— ARR. VLN. & PF.
W. Tworek & E. Vagning   *Pol.HA 70031*
(*Gossec: Gavotte*)

[1] Nos. 17, 31, 46, 48, 49, 51, are omitted.
[2] Recorded from Edison cylinder.
[3] New *Ger* words (Klopstock) to a pièce d'occasion.

— ARR. VLC. & PF.
A. Navarra & J. Dussot   C.LFX 1010
(*Werther—Intermezzo*)
☆ R. Krotschak (T.E 19501)

— ARR. ORCH.
Metropole—v. d. Linden (*PhM.P 01006S*)
Berlin State Orch.—Gaebel (*Imp. 19361*)

— ARR. ORG.   V. Fox (in # *AmC.AAL 18*)

(La) VIVANDIÈRE   3 acts   1895
Viens avec nous, petit   S
Je viens encore une fois   S
S. Michel   *Pat.PD 145*

SONG: Chanson du berger   (Florian)
N. Kazantseva   *USSR. 17479*
(*Neapolitan song*)

GODOWSKY, Leopold (1870-1938)

Alt Wien—ARR. 2 PFS.
Sisters J. Madeleine & F. Therese in # **Conl.SF 1**
(also ♮ & ♭)

STUDIES on Chopin's Études   pf.   1904
... On Chopin's Op. 10, Nos. 2, 6, 7; Op. 25, Nos. 2, 6 & A flat
(on 1201)
... On Chopin's Op. 10, Nos. 5, 11; Op. 25, Nos. 1, 3, 5, 9
(on 1202)
D. Saperton   CPf. 1201/2
(*Chopin: Études & J. Strauss: transcriptions*)

GOEB, Roger (b. 1917)

Quintet, trombone & strings
D. Shuman & Radio Artists Qtt.
(*Starer & Raphling*)   # Circ. 51-102

Prairie Songs   woodwind quintet   1947
Five-Wind Ens.   # ARS. 10
(*Swanson & Weber*)

GOETZ, Hermann (1840-1876)

(Der) WIDERSPENSTIGEN ZÄHMUNG
Opera   4 acts   1874
COMPLETE RECORDING
Katherine ... ...   M. Teschemacher (S)
Bianca ... ...   E. Trötschel (S)
Petruchio... ...   M. Ahlersmeyer (B)
Baptista ... ...   S. Nilsson (Bs)
Lucentio ... ...   P. Mirov (T)
Hortensio ... ...   G. Frick (Bs)
Dresden State Op. Cho. & Orch.—Elmendorff
(6ss)   # Ura. set 221
... Die Kraft versagt   (Act IV)   ▽ F. Beckmann (A)
(*G.DA 4480*)

GOLDMARK, Karl (1830-1915)

OPERAS
(Die) KÖNIGIN VON SABA, Op. 27 4 acts 1875
Excerpts
W. Hesch (Bs), E. Elizza (S), L. Slezak (T),
S. Kurz (S), E. Bland (S), F. Wiedemann (B)
Ete.O-473*

Am Fusse des Libanon T (Act I)
Ᵽ L. Slezak (in ♯ Ete. O-473* & in ♯ *Ete. 452*)
A. Dippel (IRCC. 3112*)

Magische Töne T (Act II)
Ᵽ L. Slezak (in ♯ Ete. O-473* & in ♯ *Ete. 452*)

Ballet Music (Act III)
☆ Boston Prom.—Fiedler (♭ *Vic.* 49-0329: in ♯ LM 9005)

Wohin lenk' ich die müden Schritte T
Ᵽ L. Slezak (in ♯ Ete. O-473*: in ♯ *Ete. 452*)

(Ein) WINTERMÄRCHEN 4 acts 1908
Schmücket euch mit Rosen S (Act II)
Ᵽ A. V. Neshdanova (*Russ*) (G.VB 37*: o.n. 023052*)

Symphony—Die ländliche Hochzeit, Op. 36
(*Rustic Wedding Symphony*)
Vienna State Op.—Swoboda ♯ CHS.CHS 1138

GOMBERT, Nicolas (*c.* 1505-*c.* 1570)

SEE: † Courtly Music of XVIth Century

GOMES, Antonio Carlos (1836-1896)

OPERAS

(Il) GUARANY 4 acts 1870
Overture — ARR. PF.
Muraro (*BrzOd.* 13152)

SALVATOR ROSA 4 acts 1874
Overture
Italian Radio—Mignone P.CB 20525

(Lo) SCHIAVO 4 acts 1889
Prelude, Act IV
Italian Radio—Mignone P.CB 20527

Aubade
Sym. Orch.—Migliori *BrzOd.X 3334*

Alba dorata del natio mio suol, Act III
Oh com' è splendido e bello il sol, Act IV
M. Minazzi P.PE 172

SONG: Quem sabe (Bittencourt Sampaio)
C. Maristany (S) & Str. Qtt. *BrzOd. 3273*

GOMEZ CRESPO, J.

SEE: † Spanish Guitar Music

GOSSEC, François Joseph (1734-1829)

OPERAS

(La) FÊTE DE VILLAGE 1778
Gavotte Hpsi. & Anon. Orch. (*Scd. 4003*)

ROSINE 1786
Gavotte — ARR. VLN. & PF. Burmester
W. Tworek & E. Vagning (*Pol.HA 70031*)

GOTTSCHALK, Louis M. (1829-1869)

SEE ALSO: † American Music, Vol. I
† American Music of Early Romantic
Period

Cakewalk Ballet Suite
(ARR. H. Kay from Gottschalk's music)
N.Y.P.S.O.—Mitropoulos ♯ AmC.ML 4616
(*Gould: Fall River Legend, Suite*)

GOUDIMEL, Claude (c. 1505-c. 1572)

PSALMS
No. 47, Or sus ! tous humains . . .
No. 51, Miséricorde au pauvre vicieux
Kanawaty Vocal Ens. *Lum. 2.24.028*
(*Claude le jeune: Psalm 42*)

No. 68, Que Dieu se montre . . .
M. Dodd Singers in ♯ *NRI. 2007*
(† *American Music—Bay Psalm Book*)

No. 137, Estans assis aux rives aquatiques
No. 149, Chantons à Dieu
Kanawaty Vocal Ens. *Lum. 2.24.029*
(*Costeley: O que je suis troublé*)

GOUNOD, Charles François (1818-1893)

I. INSTRUMENTAL

Marche funèbre d'une marionnette
☆ Boston Pops—Fiedler (♭ *G.7BF 1022*; ♭ *Vic.WEPR 27*)

Marche pontificale
Vatican Radio Orch. (*Gluck*) *Csm.C 30*
(*Frescobaldi: Toccata* on ♭ *Csm.CW 4530*;
also in ♯ CLPS 1050)

Symphony, B minor 9 wind insts.
Winterthur Sym.—Desarzens ♯ CHS.F 2
(*Liszt*)
Bavarian Radio—Strobl ♯ Mer.MG 10033
(*Cimarosa, Donizetti*)

II. CHURCH MUSIC

GALLIA, "Lamentation" 1871
Jérusalem
Canterbury Cho. (*Eng*) in ♯ *MGM.E 102*
(♭ set K 102)

MESSE À STE. CÉCILE 1868
... Sanctus only
Canterbury Cho. in ♯ *MGM.E 102*
(♭ set K 102)

MORS ET VITA Oratorio 1885
Judex orch. & cho.
— ARR. BS SOLO
K. Borg *Felix.Ø 65*
(*Schubert: Litany*)

III. OPERAS

FAUST 5 acts 1859
Complete Recordings
Set D

Marguerite	...	...	...E. Steber (S)
Faust	...	...	E. Conley (T)
Méphistophélès	...	...	...C. Siepi (Bs)
Valentine	...	...	F. Guarrera (B)

Metropolitan Cho. & Orch.—Cleva
♯ AmC. set SL 112

(6ss) (omitting Ballet Music)

(*continued on next page*)

☆ = Re-issue of a recording to be found in WERM or Supplement I.

FAUST (continued)

Set B

Marguerite	... ...	Géori-Boué (S)
Faust	... ...	... G. Noré (T)
Méphistophélès	... ...	... R. Rico (Bs)
Valentine	... ...	... R. Bourdin (B)

☆Cho. & Royal Phil.—Beecham
(6ss) **# Vic. set LCT 6100**
(♭ set WCT 52)
("Highlights" on # Vic.LCT 1100: ♭ set WCT 1100)

Vocal Excerpts
(Love duet, Jewel Song, Méphistophélès' Serenade, Trio & Finale)
R. Peters, J. Peerce, E. Pinza in **# Vic.LM 7016**
(Tonight we sing, film music) (♭ set WDM 7016)

Highlights
Anon. Artists (# Wde. 20203; Pde. 1002; & with Narration, # Pde.OP 102)
☆ N.Y. City Op. Cho. (in ♭ MGM. set K 80)

Orch. Selection
MGM. Orch.—Stothart (MGM. 9006)

Prelude
☆ Dresden Phil.—v. Kempen (Pol. 15520)
Paris Opera—Fourestier (in # BB.LBC 1016: ♭ set WBC 1016)

ACT I

Salut ! ô mon dernier matin ! T
I. Zidek **U.H 24226**
(Barbiere—La calunnia)

Mais ce Dieu T & Bs
J. Spataru & R. Arié in **# D.LXT 2688**
(Donizetti, Rossini, etc.) (in # Lon.LL 534)
♯ A. Giorgini & E. Pinza (Ital) (G.VA 70*)

ACT II

(La) Kermesse cho.
San Francisco Op. Cho. **ML. 48**

Avant de quitter ces lieux B
T. Baylé **Phi.N 11179G**
(Contes d'Hoffmann—Scintille, diamant) (PhM.N 09011S)
Alex. Ivanov (Russ) (USSR. 13270/1)
I. P. Alexeyev (Russ) (U.C 23859)

(Le) Veau d'or Bs
E. Pinza in **# Vic.LM 157**
(Figaro, Kiss me Kate, etc.) (in ♭ set WDM 1655)
J. Greindl (Ger) **Pol. 62887**
(Serenade)
B. Gmyria (Russ) (USSR. 16535)
☆ M. Székely (Hung.) (Qual.QKM 5012)
M. Bohnen (Ger) (in # Ete. 460)
♯ A. Didur (Ital) (in # Ete. O-467*)
R. Blass (IRCC. 3110*)

Valse — ARR. ORCH.
Munich Phil.—Lehmann **PV. 46003**
(Tchaikovsky: Serenade—Waltz)
(originally on PV. 72014, with Ballet s.3)
☆ Boston Prom.—Fiedler (♭ Vic.WEPR 5: in # LM 9005: ♭ 49-1444)

ACT III

Faites-lui mes aveux M-S
V. Borisenko (Russ) **USSR. 17350**
(Rimsky-Korsakov: May Night, duet)

Salut ! Demeure chaste et pure T
J. Björling (n.v.) **# Vic.LM 105**
(Pagliacci, Bohème, etc.) (♭ set WDM 1546)
(& in # Vic.LM 1202: ♭ set WDM 1626)
I. Kozlovsky (Russ) (USSR. 9174/5)
S. Lemeshev (Russ) (USSR. 17971/2)
♯ L. Muratore (HRS. 1071*)

Il était un roi de Thulé S
Air des bijoux: Ah ! je ris . . . S
C. Carroll in **# Rem. 149-41**
(Roméo, Bohème, Turandot, etc.)
☆ V. de los Angeles (♭ G.7RF 118)
R. Tebaldi (# Lon.LD 9017)

Air des bijoux only
G. Zhukovskaya (Russ) (USSR. 9784/5)
♯ E. Destinn (Ger) (in # set CEd. 7001*)

Seigneur Dieu ! Que vois-je ? S, A, T, Bs
E. Shumskaya, N. Ostroumova, I. Kozlovsky, A. Pirogov
(USSR. 21201/4)

Il était temps Bs
M. Reizen (Russ) (USSR. 9918)

Il se fait tard S, T, Bs
☆ Géori-Boué, G. Noré & R. Rico, from set
(in # Vic.LM 1162)
♯ F. Scheff, T. Salignac, M. Journet (IRCC. 170*)
... Duet only: E. Shumskaya & V. Kilichevsky
(USSR. 15539/40)

ACT IV

Versez vos chagrins M-S
I. Kozlovsky (T, Russ) (USSR. 020121)

Seigneur, daignez permettre . . . S, Bs, cho.
♯ M. Michaelova & F. Chaliapin (G.VB 1*: o.n. DB 618*)

Choeur des Soldats
Grand Cho. (Ital) **P.PO 192**
(Trovatore—Gypsy Chorus) (perhaps ☆ of R 138)

Vous qui faites l'endormie (Serenade) Bs
E. Pinza in **# Vic.LM 157**
(Figaro, Very warm for May, etc.) (♭ set WDM 1655)
J. Greindl (Ger) **Pol. 62887**
(Veau d'or)
H. Reinmar (Ger) **Od. O-28111**
(Moussorgsky: Song of the flea)
☆ M. Bohnen (Ger) (in # Ete. 460)
♯ F. Chaliapin (Russ) (in # AudA. 0077*)
P. Plançon & pf. (G.VA 6*: o.n. 2-2663*)

Par ici ! M-S & cho.
Écoute-moi bien B
♯ Barbieri, M. Battistini & Cho. (Ital)
(G.VB 69*: o.n. 054454/5*)
T. Ruffo (Ital) (HRS. 1085*)

ACT V

Ballet Music—Nuit de Walpurgis
Covent Garden—Rignold ♮ **P.PW 8002/3**
(4ss) (Od. O-3700/1)
(Schumann: Carnaval on # AmD.DL 9548)
Philharmonia—Irving (4ss) ♮ **G.C 7932/3**
Covent Garden—Braithwaite in #**MGM.E 3003**
Munich Phil.—Lehmann **PV. 72103/4S**
(3ss) (in # Pol. 18007)
(originally PV. 72104 was double-sided, Valse, Act II on reverse)
Metropolitan Op.—Cleva **# AmC.ML 4515**
(Aïda—Prel. & Ballet) (omitting No. 3) (♭ A 1544)
Paris Opéra—Sebastian **# Ura. 7058**
(Thaïs & Arlésienne) (♭ UREP 12)
☆ Paris Opéra—Fourestier (in # BB.LBC 1016: ♭ set WBC 1016)
... Excerpts only
▽ Chicago Phil.—Weber (in # Mer.MG 20014; Clc. 6040)

Alerte ! Alerte ! S, T, Bs
☆ F. Heldy, F. Ansseau, M. Journet **G.VB 71**
(Hamlet—Doute de la lumière)

= Long-playing, 33⅓ r.p.m.   ♭ = 45 r.p.m.   ♮ = Auto. couplings, 78 r.p.m.

MIREILLE   4 acts (orig. 5)   1864
Overture
Radio Luxemburg Sym.—Pensis ♯ **FestF.FLD 3**
(*Thomas, Offenbach, Adam, etc.*)

O légère hirondelle   S   (Act I)
Ⅱ M. Galvany (*Ital*) (*G.VA 4**: o.n. *DA 494**)

Anges du Paradis   T   (Act III)
Ⅱ E. Scaremberg (HRS. 1027*)

(La) REINE DE SABA   4 acts   1862
Plus grand dans son obscurité   S (Act III)
E. Wysor (A)   in ♯ **Rem. 199-30**

ROMÉO ET JULIETTE   5 acts   1867
Voyons, nourrice ... (Scene, Juliet & Nurse, Act I)
Je veux vivre dans ce rêve   (Valse)   S
I. Maslennikova & A. Ostroumova
                USSR. 020120
(*Faust—Versez vos chagrins*) (*Russ*)

... Valse only
C. Carroll   in ♯ *Rem. 149-41*
(*Bohème, Turandot, Ballo, etc.*)

Ah ! lève-toi, soleil   T   (Act II)
Ⅱ D. Smirnoff (*Russ*) (G.VB 38*: o.n. DB 595*)
L. Muratore (HRS. 1092*)

Salut, tombeau (Act V)   ... T part only
Ⅱ P. Franz (AF. 43)

IV. SONGS

Ave Maria (Meditation on Bach: Prelude, WTC. 1)
M. Guilleaume (S), org. & orch.   *Pol. 48644*
(*Handel: Serse—Largo*)
T. Lemnitz (S) & orch.   *T.A 11153*
(*Schubert: Ave Maria*)   (in ♯ *LB 6022*)
M. Santreuil (S), Mme. Bergez-Cazalon (pf.)
(*Busser: Zapatéado*)   *Pac. 3787*
P. Schoeffler (B), G. Cassadò (vlc.) & pf.
        in ♯ **MSL.MW 45**
M. Angelici (S), L. Laskine (hp.) & str. orch.
              G.DA 5056
(*J. B. Faure: Santa Maria*)   (♭ *G.7RF 110*)
    J. Candel (S), cho. & orch. (in *PhM.A 02900S*:
                 Phi.A 17901G)
    F. Ferrari (T) (*P.R 3531*)
    I. Nyberg (Child S) (*D.F 44179*)
☆ J. Melton (T) & orch. (in ♯ *Vic.LM 82*:♭ *set WDM 1365*)
    L. Pons (S) & orch. (in ♯ *AmC.ML 2181*: ♭ *set A 1006*)
    M. Lanza (T) (♭ *G.7RF 144*)
    C. Kullman (T) (C.DCX 104)
    R. Tauber (*Od. O-4672*), etc.

— ARR. CHO.
Wiltener Sängerknaben—Gerholdt   *Tono.K 8083*
(*Reger: Mariä Wiegenlied*)

— ARR. VLN. & PF.
B. Saenger & H. Rothmüller (*Od.O-28276*)
T. Magyar (Phi.N 11227G & in ♯ *Phi.N 00605R*)

— ARR. VLN. & ORG.
C. Cavalcabe & W. Marti (Antro.AK 10001)

Heureux sera le jour (after Ronsard)
Venise (de Musset)
C. Mauranne (B), L. Bienvenu (pf.) *Pat.PD 156*

Noël (Barbier)
Noël des Bergers (Abbé Maris)
J. Wilson (S), R. Baker (org.) in ♯ **AmD.DL 9554**
(*Massenet, Fauré, etc.*)

There is a green hill far away (Mrs. Alexander)
K. Joyce (A), H. Dawson (org.)   *P.R 3577*
(*Elijah—O Rest in the Lord*)

GRADWOHL, Pierre   (b. 1905)

Divertissement champêtre   Ballet suite
Paris Cons. Students'—Gradwohl ♯ **Ren.X 41**
(*Auric: Suites*)

GRAINGER, Percy A. (b. 1882)

COLLECTION
Country Gardens	Early one morning
Handel in the Strand 1912	Irish tune from County Derry
Mock Morris 1911	Molly on the shore 1918
Shepherd's Hey	

P. Grainger (pf.) & Sym.—Stokowski
            ♯ **Vic.LM 1238**
            (♭ set *WDM 1663*)

Handel in the Strand
☆Boyd Neel Orch.   **Lon. 12017**
(*Vaughan Williams: Fantasia*)   (♭ *40357*)

Irish Tune from County Derry
Mock Morris
Sydney Civic Sym. Str.—Beck in ♯ **Dia.DPM 1**

Irish Tune from County Derry
Molly on the shore
☆ Carnegie Pops—O'Connell (in ♭ *AmC. set A 1001*)

GRAM, Peder   (b. 1881)

Poème lyrique, Op. 9   orch.   *c.* 1912
Danish Radio—Tuxen   **Pol.HM 80050**

GRANADOS, Enrique (1867-1916)

(12) DANZAS ESPAÑOLAS, Op. 37   pf.   1893
No. 4, G major, Villanesca
— ARR. ORCH.
Madrid Iberica Orch.—Lago   *Od. 184916*
(*Albeniz: Cádiz*)

No. 5, E minor, Andaluza or Playera
G. Copeland (n.v.)   in ♯ *MGM.E 87*
             (♮ *set 87*: ♭ *K 87*)
J. Bolet   in ♯ **Bo.B 300**
(*Albeniz, Falla, Lecuona*)

☆ J. Iturbi (♭ *G.7R 111*)
A. Földes (in ♯ *Rem. 149-4*)

— ARR. VLN. & PF.   Kreisler
Y. Menuhin & A. Baller   **JpV.SD 3049**
(*Kreisler: Caprice viennois*)   (in set JAS 230)

— ARR. VLC. & PF.
G. Cassadò & O. Schulhof   in ♯ **MSL.MW 45**
                 (Hma. 14002)

— ARR. GUITAR
R. de la Torre   in ♯ **Phil. 106**
(† Guitar recital)
☆ A. Iglesia (*P.D 890*)

No. 6, D major, Rondalla Aragonesa (Jota)
☆ A. Földes (in ♯ *Rem. 149-4*)

No. 10, G major (Allegretto) (Danza triste)
☆ J. Iturbi (♭ *G.7R 111*)

☆ = Re-issue of a recording to be found in WERM or Supplement I.

GOYESCAS pf. 1912

COMPLETE RECORDING of Book I
    F. Valenzi   # Etu. 701

No. 4, Quejas o la Maja y el Ruiseñor
    C. Arrau   C.LX 1550
    (1½ss—*Debussy: Prel. Bk. II, No. 3*)   (GQX 11504)
    A. de Raco   ArgOd. 66011
    (*Chopin: Berceuse*)
    G. Cases   ArgOd. 66010
    (*Albeniz: Mallorca*)

— ARR. CASTANETS & PF.
    Rosario & Antonio (2ss)   *C.C 10151*

GOYESCAS Opera 3 scenes 1916

Intermezzo
    Philharmonia—Weldon   C.DX 1801
    (*Meyerbeer: Prophète—March*)   (DWX 5075)
    ☆ Sym.—Stokowski (in # Vic.LM 151:♭ 49-0882)

— ARR. VLC. & PF. Cassadò
    G. Piatigorsky & R. Berkowitz   ♭ G.7RF 229
    (*Saint-Saëns: Le cygne*)
                  (in # Vic.LM 1187:♭ set WDM 1578)
    ☆ B. Michelin & T. Janopoulo (ArgC. 266576)
    P. Casals (in # Vic.LCT 1050:♭ set WCT 72)

Prelude, Scene 3   orch.
La Maja y el Ruiseñor   S
    ☆ V. de los Angeles (♭ G.7RF 150: 7R 149)

Madrigal   vlc. & pf.
    J. Serres & A. Leyvastre in V# Sat.MSA 5004
    (*Nin*)

(10) TONADILLAS AL ESTILO ANTIGUO
No. 2, 5, 6
    ☆ V. de los Angeles (S), G. Moore (pf.)
        (in # Vic.LM 131:♭ set WDM 1635;
                    ♭ G.7RF 103 & 156)

No. 1, La Maja de Goya
— ARR. GUITAR
    R. de la Torre   in # Phil. 106
    († Guitar Recital)

No. 2, El Majo discreto
    J. Tourel (M-S), G. Reeves (pf)
               in # AmC.ML 2198

GRAZIOLI, Giovanni Battista
(*c.* 1750-*c.* 1820)

Sonata, No. 5, G major   hpsi.
… Adagio only   — ARR. VLC. & PF.
    E. Mainardi & F. Lehmann   *PV. 46006*
    (*Chopin: Nocturne No. 20*)

GREAVES, Thomas (fl. *c.* 1600)
SEE: † A TREASURY OF MADRIGALS

GREGORIAN CHANT
(Selected items only)

COLLECTIONS
    Speyer Seminary Cho.—Soissong **Chr. 311/22C**
    (24ss)
    En-Calcat Benedictines   **SM. 51/60**
    (20ss, including one of bells and one containing—*C. Jacob: Improvisation on Salve Festa Dies*)
    Col. Radio Cho.—Bruning   *AmC. 2005F*
    ☆ Gethsemani Monks (♮ AmC. set MM 1021)

Rorate coeli desuper
Resonet in laudibus
    Welch Chorale   in # Lyr.LL 35
    (*Victoria, Palestrina, etc.*)

GRETCHANINOFF, Alexander (b. 1864)

LITURGY, No. 2, Op. 29
… **No. 8, Creed**
    ☆ St. Eustache Singers—Martin (*Fr*) (Pac. 6479)

SONGS
COLLECTION (unspec.—"*Augmented Litany*")
    Don Cossack Cho.—Jaroff in #AmC.ML 4473

Cradle Song, Op. 1, No. 5 (Lermontov)
    J. Tourel (M-S), G. Reeves (pf.)
               in # AmC.ML 2198
    N. Kazantseva (S)   USSR. 17284
    (*Little Bird*)

Little Bird (Polonsky)
    N. Kazantseva (S)   USSR. 17285
    (*Cradle song*)

Over the Steppe, Op. 5, No. 1 (Pleshcheev)
    M. Garden (S), J. Dansereau (pf.)   *G.VA 18*
    (*Carmen—En vain pour éviter*)   (▽ o.n. DA 1248)
    J. Tourel (M-S), G. Reeves (pf.)
               in # AmC.ML 2198

GRÉTRY, André Ernest Modeste
(1741-1813)

OPERAS
CÉPHALE ET PROCRIS 3 acts 1773
Ballet Suite—ARR. Mottl
    ☆Brussels Radio—André in # DT.LGM 65004
    (*Dukas: L'apprenti sorcier*)   (in # T.LS 6011)

RICHARD COEUR DE LION 3 Acts 1784
La danse n'est pas ce que j'aime T (Act I)
    E. Katulskaya (S, *Russ*)   USSR. 15847
    (*Figaro—Deh, vieni . . .*)

(La) ROSIÈRE RÉPUBLICAINE 1 act 1793
Ballet Suite — ARR. Meyrowitz
    Paris Phil.—Désormière   ♮ U.H 24180/1
    (3ss—*Debussy: Soirée dans Grenade*)
    (*Massenet on # CdM.LDX 8028*)

GRIEG, Edvard Hagerup (1843-1907)

CLASSIFIED: I. Piano   II. Chamber Music
          III. Orchestral   IV. Dramatic
          V. Choral   VI. Songs

I. PIANO

COLLECTIONS
LYRIC PIECES
    Op. 12: 1. Arietta; 4. Dance of the Elves; 5. Folk song; 6. Norse
    Op. 43: 1. Butterfly; 2. Lonely Wanderer; 4. Little Bird
    Op. 47: 1. Valse Impromptu; 4. Halling; 7. Elegy
    Op. 57: 6. Longing for Home
    Op. 65: 6. Wedding Day at Troldhaugen
    Op. 68: 4. Evening in the mountains; 6. At the cradle
    Op. 71: 3. Puck
MOODS, Op. 73: 6. Mountaineer's Song; 7. Homage to Chopin
    G. Johannesen   # AmVox.PL 7380
    Brooklet, Op. 62, No. 4
    Lonely Wanderer, Op. 43, No. 2
    Summer's Eve, Op. 71, No. 2
    To Spring, Op. 43, No. 6
    ☆E. Joyce   in # AmD.DL 9538

= Long-playing, 33⅓ r.p.m.   ♭ = 45 r.p.m.   ♮ = Auto. couplings, 78 r.p.m.

88

Lonely Wanderer, Op. 43, No. 2
To Spring, Op. 43, No. 6
Wedding Day at Troldhaugen, Op. 65, No. 6
☆W. Gieseking   C.LFX 1016
                                    (♭ AmC.A 1542)

Album Leaf, A major, Op. 28, No. 3
— ARR. VLN. & PF. Hartmann ☆ M. Elman (♭ Vic.WEPR 29)
— ARR. ORCH. Hall Concert Orch. (in # Var. 6924)

Erotik, Op. 43, No. 5
— ARR. ORCH. H. Busch Salon (Pol. 47843)

Norwegian Peasant Dances, Op. 72 (Slåtter)
A. Földes (6ss)   ♮ Tono.A 183/5
                              (# Mer.MG 10136)

... Nos. 2 & 14 only
R. Riefling   Nera.SK 15517
(Concerto, s.1)

Scherzo-Impromptu, Op. 73, No. 2
— ARR. VLN. & PF.
I. Haendel & G. Moore   G.B 10135
(Ravel: Pièce en forme de habanera)

To Spring, Op. 43, No. 6
C. de Groot   Phi.N 11158G
(½s.—Sinding: Rustle of Spring; & Liszt) (PhM.N 9000S)
☆V. Schiøler   in # Mer.MG 10099
(Chopin, Liszt, Mendelssohn, etc.)
Ħ E. Grieg (in # AudA.LA 1203*)

Wedding day at Troldhaugen, Op. 65, No. 6
M. Flipse   Phi.N 11235G
(Liszt: Liebestraum)   (PhM. 09047S)

— ARR. ORCH.
Bavarian Sym.—Graunke   PV. 56013
(Sigurd Jorsalfar—Homage March)   (# AmD.DL 4023)

II. CHAMBER MUSIC
SONATAS, vln. & pf.
No. 1, F major, Op. 8
No. 3, C minor, Op. 45
J. Fuchs & F. Sheridan   # B.AXTL 1017
                              (# AmD.DL 9571)

III. ORCHESTRAL
Concerto, A minor, pf. & orch., Op. 16
W. Gieseking & Philharmonia—v. Karajan
                              C.LX 1503/6
(7ss—Sinding: Rustle of Spring)
(2ss, # C.C 1003: QC 1008: FC 1008; AmC.ML 4431)
C. Curzon & L.S.O.—Fistoulari # D.LXT 2657
                              (# Lon.LLP 512)
R. Riefling & Oslo Phil.—Grüner-Hegge
                      ♮ Nera.SK 15517/20
(7ss—Norwegian Peasant Dances)
G. Stein & Berlin Sym.—Rubahn # Roy. 1264

☆ V. Schiøler & Danish Radio—Tuxen (# Clc. 6035)
D. Lipatti & Philharmonia—Galliera (# AmC.ML 4525)
F. Karrer & Viennese Sym.—Wöss (# Mrt. 200-10)

... 1st movt., condensed
A. Semprini & Melachrino Orch. (G.B 10295)

(2) Elegiac Melodies, Op. 34 str. orch.
1. Heart's wounds   2. Spring (from Songs, Op. 33)
Residentie—v. Otterloo   Phi.N 11187G
                              (PhM.N 09028S)

... No. 2, Spring H. Krüger Orch. (Imp. 19126)

¹ Originally part of Suite No. 2.

From Holberg's time, Op. 40   str. orch.
Eastman-Rochester Sym.—Hanson
(Hanson: Concerto)   # AmC.ML 4403
Cha. Orch.—Byrns   # DCap.CTL 7022
(Arensky: Variations)   (# Cap.P 8158)
(2ss, # T.LCB 6029)

Lyric Suite, Op. 54
... No. 3, Nocturne Hall Concert Orch. (in # Var. 6924)

(4) Norwegian Dances, Op. 35
Philharmonia—Fistoulari   # MGM.E 3001
(Peer Gynt Suite 1)
Danish State Radio—Tuxen   ♮ Tono.Y 30010/1
(4ss) (Symphonic Dances on # Mer.MG 10132)

... No. 2, A minor
Royale Concert Orch. (in # Roy. 1233 & in # 6026)
"Nat. Op. Orch." (in # Var. 2007)
H. Spitalny Orch. (in # Roy. 6920: ♭ set 14518)

(4) Symphonic Dances, Op. 64
Danish State Radio—Jensen ♮ Tono.Y 30007/9
(6ss) (Norwegian Dances on # Mer.MG 10132)
☆ Dresden Phil.—v. Kempen (Pol. 15491/2)

... No. 1, G major
Philharmonia—Dobrowen   G.C 4142
                              (ZN 599: ♭ 7BF 1047)

IV. DRAMATIC WORKS
PEER GYNT
INCIDENTAL MUSIC, Op. 23
Digest of the Play (in French) with music
Actors, J. Micheau (S) & Lamoureux—Fournet
                              # Pat.DTX 111

Solveig's Sunshine Song, Act I
P. Munsel (S, Eng)   in # Vic.LM 66
                   (▽ Vic. set DM 1157: ♭ WDM 1157)
Z. Gabor (Hung) (Qual.QB 2001)
☆ E. Berger (Ger) (Pol. 26502)

— ARR. VLN. & CHA. ORCH.
F. Akos & Berlin Municipal Op. Ens. (T.A 11187)

ORCHESTRAL SUITES
No. 1, Op. 46; No. 2, Op. 55;
Prelude; Bridal Procession;
The three Huldres (with diction);
Dance of the Mountain King's Daughter ¹;
Solveig's Cradle Song (all from Op. 23)
Oslo Phil.—Grüner-Hegge   Nera.SK 15521/6
[Solveig's Songs sung by E. Prytz (S)]

No. 1, Op. 46; No. 2, Op. 55;
Dance of the Mountain King's Daughter
(from Op. 23)¹
Boston Pops—Fiedler   # Vic. LM 7002
                              (8ss, ♭ set WDM 7002)

Nos. 1 & 2 complete
Residentie—v. Otterloo   # Phi.N 00101L
[Solveig's Song sung by E. Spoorenberg] (N 11137/40G)
Vienna Radio—Schönherr   # Vien. 1018
Berlin Sym.—Balzer (# Roy. 1300)

Suite No. 1
☆L.P.O.—Cameron (4ss)   ♮ D.AX 421/2
                              (K 23222/3)
Bamberg Sym.—Leitner (3ss)   PV. 56014/5S
Philharmonia—Fistoulari   # MGM.E 3001
(Norwegian Dances)
Jerusalem Sym.—Goehr   # Bne. 501
(Brahms)

(continued on next page)

PEER GYNT
Suite No. 1 (*continued*)

Austrian Sym.—Brown   ♯ **Rem. 199-68**
(*Golden Cockerel*)   (♯ Mrt. 200-22)
  "Nat. Op. Orch." (in ♯ Var. 2007)
  Hall Concert Orch. (in ♯ Var. 6924)
  Sym. Orch (in ♯ Roy. 6062: ♭ set 14540, 5ss)
☆ Dresden Phil.—v. Kempen (*Pol.LL 3015/6*)
  Hallé—Barbirolli (G.DB 4310/1; ♯ BB.LBC 1017:
                                   ♭ set WBC 1017)
  Philadelphia—Ormandy (♭ AmC.A 1536)

... Nos. 1, 3, 4, only
☆ Chicago Sym.—H. Weber (in ♯ Clc. 6041)

Suite No. 2, Op. 55

L.S.O.—Irving (4ss)   ♮ **G.C 7902/3**
                                   (♯ BB.LBC 1017: ♭ set WBC 1017)
Varsity Sym. (in ♯ Var. 2030)
☆ Dresden Phil.—v. Kempen (Pol. 15500/1)

SIGURD JORSALFAR
Suite, Op. 56

Cincinnati Sym.—Johnson   ♮ **D.AX 552/3**
(4ss)   (♯ LXT 2630; Lon.LLP 406)

... No. 3, Homage March, only
Bavarian Sym.—Graunke   **PV. 56013**
(*Wedding Day at Troldhaugen*)   (♯ AmD.DL 4023)
Berlin Sym.—Ludwig   in ♯ **Roy. 1217**

V. CHORAL

(The) **Great White Host, Op. 30, No. 10** (Brorson)
  B & male cho.
H. Nørgaard (Bs) & Male Cho.—Asmussen
(*Grieg: Ave Maris Stella*)   **Felix.F 46**

(The) **Son of God has set me free, Op. 74, No. 2**
  (Björnson)
St. Olaf Cho.—Christiansen   in ♯ **StO. 3**
(*Bach, Palestrina, Milhaud, etc.*) (*Eng*)

VI. SONGS
COLLECTIONS
  Dereinst, Gedanke mein, Op. 48, No. 2 (Geibel)
  Greetings to you, ladies, Op. 49, No. 3 (Drachmann)
  Gruss, Op. 48, No. 1 (Heine)
  (A) Hope, Op. 26, No. 1 (Paulsen)
  Verse for an Album, Op. 25, No. 3 (Ibsen)
  With a primrose, Op. 26, No. 4 (Paulsen)
  Zur Rosenzeit, Op. 48, No. 5 (Goethe)
B. Sönnerstedt (B), F. Jensen (pf.) G.DB 10506/7

  Mother's Sorrow, Op. 15, No. 4 (Richardt)
  (A) Swan, Op. 25, No. 2 (Ibsen)
  Thanks for thy counsel, Op. 21, No. 4 (Björnson)
  With a water-lily, Op. 25, No. 4 (Ibsen)
T. Niemala (S), P. Koskimies (pf.) ♯ WCFM. 5
(*Kilpinen, Sibelius*)

  Eros, Op. 70, No. 1 (Benzon) ☆
  From Monte Pincio, Op. 39, No. 1 (Björnson)
  Return to Rundarne Op. 33, No. 9 (Vinje)
  Spring, Op. 33, No. 2 (Vinje)
  (A) Swan, Op. 25, No. 2 (Ibsen) ☆
  (The) Youth, Op. 33, No. 1 (Vinje)
K. Flagstad & Orch.   ♯ **Vic.LM 99**
                                   (♭ set WDM 1533)
(for European individual issues, *see below*)

  Among the roses, Op. 39, No. 4 (Jansen)
  Autumn storm, Op. 18, No. 4 (Richardt)
  Christmas Lullaby (Langsted)
  Eros, Op. 70, No. 1 (Benzon)
  (Der) Jäger (Schulze—orig. Ger) pub. 1908
M. Klose (A, *Ger*), M. Raucheisen (pf.)
                                   in ♯ **Ura. 7053**
(*Cornelius, Strauss, Jensen, Pfitzner*)

Along the river, Op. 33, No. 5 (Vinje)
A. Yakovenko (*Russ*)   **USSR. 18974**
(*I wandered . . .*)

Ave Maris Stella
Copenhagen Acad. Cho.—Asmussen *Felix.F 46*
(*The Great White Host*)

Christmas Lullaby (Langsted)
(*Julens Vuggesång*)
Christmas Snow, Op. 49, No. 5 (Drachmann)
(*Julsne*)
J. Wilson (S, *Ger*), G. Trovillo (pf.)
                                   in ♯ **AmD.DL 9554**
(*Humperdinck, Gounod, etc.*)

(The) Discreet Nightingale, Op. 48, No. 4
(*Vogelweide*)
G. Catley (S, *Eng*), W. Parry (pf.) **G.B 10340**
(*Lehmann: Whene'er a snowflake*)

(A) Dream, Op. 43, No. 6 (Bodenstedt)
A. Ohlson (T), S. Ehrling (pf.)   **Od.SD 5646**
(*Järnefelt: Sunday*)
☆ R. Crooks (T, *Eng*), F. Schauwecker (pf.)
(*Schubert: Ständchen*)   **G.DA 1952**
☆ R. Tauber (T) (in ♯ AmD.DL 9547)

Eros, Op. 70, No. 1 (Benzon)
☆ R. Tauber (T) & Orch. (in ♯ AmD.DL 9547)

I love thee, Op. 5, No. 3 (H. C. Andersen)
J. Vincent (S), F. de Nobel (pf.) Phi.A 11242G
(½s.—*Mendelssohn & Schubert*)
                        (PhM.A 11242S: in ♯ Phi.A 00610R)
  E. Pinza (Bs, *Eng*) (Vic. 10-3281: in ♭ Vic. set WDM 1524)
  H. E. Groh (T, *Ger*) (♯ D.LM 4549: & D.F 43283)
  E. Smolenskaya (*Russ*) (USSR. 16875)
☆ M. Lanza (T, *Eng*)
          (in ♯ Vic.LM 1188: in ♭ set WDM 1606)
  J. Peerce (T, *Eng*) (in ♯ Vic.LM 78)

I wandered one lovely Summer's eve, Op. 26, No. 2
(*Paulsen*)
A. Yakovenko (*Russ*)   **USSR. 18975**
(*Along the river*)

Mother's Sorrow, Op. 15, No. 4 (Richardt)
▽ K. Flagstad (S) & orch. (*G.X 3068*)

Now the evening is light and long, Op. 49, No. 4
(*Drachmann*)
V. Davidova (*Russ*)   **USSR. 14764**
(*Spring rain*)

Return to Rundarne, Op. 33, No. 9 (Vinje)
K. Flagstad (S) & orch.   **G.DA 1992**
(*below*)
☆ O. Frantzen (B) (*Od.D-6978*)

Spring, Op. 33, No. 2 (Vinje)
K. Flagstad (S) & orch. (2ss)   **G.DA 1904**
E. Berge (S), cho. & orch.   **Felix.Ø 63**
(*Backer-Grøndahl: At eventide*)

— ARR. VOCAL TRIO (in Vic. set E 100: ♭ WE 100)

Spring rain, Op. 49, No. 6 (Drachmann)
V. Davidova (*Russ*)   **USSR. 14765**
(*above*)

Thanks for thy counsel, Op. 21, No. 4 (Björnson)
E. Smolenskaya (*Russ*)   **USSR. 16876**
(*I love thee*)

When I die, Op. 59, No. 1 (Paulsen)
A. Yakovenko (*Russ*)   **USSR. 18674**
(*With a water-lily*)

With a primrose, Op. 26, No. 4 (Paulsen)
☆ O. Frantzen (B) (*Od.D-6978*)

With a water-lily, Op. 25, No. 4 (Ibsen)
A. Yakovenko (*Russ*)   **USSR. 18673**
(*above*)

♯ = Long-playing, 33⅓ r.p.m.   ♭ = 45 r.p.m.   ♮ = Auto. couplings, 78 r.p.m.

90

(The) Youth, Op. 33, No. 1   (Vinje)
K. Flagstad (S) & orch.   *G.DA 1992*
(above)

VII. MISCELLANEOUS
Grieg, his story & his music
☆D. Perry (narrator) & orch. *AmVox.VL 2560*

GRIFFES, Charles Tomlinson (1884-1920)

Poem fl. & orch. 1918
J. Baker & Cha. Orch.—Saidenberg
(Foote)   ♯ *AmD.DL 4013*
C. Wanausek & A. R. S. Orch.—Hendl ♯*ARS. 22*
(Foote)

(4) Roman Sketches, Op. 7 pf. 1915/6
  1. The White Peacock
  2. The Fountain of Acqua Paola
  3. Nightfall
  4. Clouds
L. Hambro   ♯ **Wald.W 100**
(Sonata)

No. 1, The White Peacock
— ARR. ORCH.   Griffes
☆ N.Y. Phil. Sym.—Stokowski (♭ *AmC.A 1516*)

(2) Sketches on Indian Themes str. qtt.
… No. 2 only
☆ Coolidge Qtt. (Jp V.SD 3067 in set JAS 236)

Sonata, piano 1920
J. Behrend   ♯ **Allo.ALG 3024**
(† American Music)
L. Hambro   ♯ **Wald.W 100**
(above)

GRIGNY, Nicolas de (1671-1703)

SEE: † FRENCH MASTERS . . .
    † FRENCH ORGAN MUSIC
    † LES MAÎTRES D'ORGUE DE J. S. BACH

GRISON, J.

Toccata   organ
F. Asma   **Phi.N 11168G**
(Rheinberger) (also in *PhM.N 09002S* & ♯ *Phi.N 00118L*)

GROFÉ, Ferdy (b. 1892)

Death Valley Suite
Sym. orch.—Grofé (2ss)   ♯ *Cap.H 271*
(also with *Grand Canyon*, ♯ Cap.P 272)   (♭ set *EBF 271*)

(The) Grand Canyon, Suite orch. 1931
Capitol Sym.—Grofé   ♯ *DCap.LC 6536*
    (♯ *Cap.L 270:* ♭ set *ECF 270*)
(also with *Death Valley* on ♯ Cap.P 272)
… On the Trail
☆ N.B.C. Sym.—Toscanini (from set) (♭ *Vic.WEPR 15*)

GROSSMANN, Sasha (b. 1907)

(8) RUSSIAN DANCES
No. 6, E flat major; No. 7, F major
F.O.K. Sym.—Smetáček   **U.H 23986/7**
(Nos. 1 to 5 also recorded, ▽ U.F 22764/5 & F 23001)

GRUEN, John (b. 1927)

SONGS
Chansons de Geishas   (from the Japanese)
Hälfte des Lebens   (Hölderlin)
(Die) Sirenen   (Kafka)
(4) Songs   (E. E. Cummings)
(4) Stundenbuch-Lieder   (Rilke)
  G. Bannister (S), J. Gruen (pf.)   ♯ **Elek. 1**

GUARNIERI, Camargo (b. 1907)

Quartet, Strings, No. 2
Pascal Qtt.   ♯ *G.FBLP 1014*
(Delage: Songs)

Sonatina, fl. & pf. 1947
S. Caratelli & G. Manley   ♯ **NRI. 406**
(Milhaud, Hindemith, Ibert, etc.)

GUERRERO, Francisco (1527-1599)

Villanesca 4 voices
Comillas Schola Cantorum   *SpC.R 18029*
(J. I. Prieto: Adios)

GUILMANT, Alexandre (1837-1911)

Variations on an ancient Polish Noël org.
G. Thalben-Ball   *G.B 10148*
(Thalben-Ball: Elegy)

▽ Older recordings include:
Canzona   W. Alcock (*G.B 2466*)
Grand choeur, D minor, Op. 18, No. 1   G. D. Cunningham
              (*C.DB 1143*)
Grand choeur, E flat major, Op. 40   E. Martin (*G.C 271**)
Sonata No. 1 . . . Pastorale   H. Ley (*G.C 1537*)
Sonata No. 4, D minor   S. Roper (*G.C 1446*)

GURIDI, Jesús (b. 1886)

SONGS: Canciones castellanas
Jota; No quiero tus avellanas
☆ V. de los Angeles (S), G. Moore (pf.) (♭ *G.7RF 215*;
      in ♯ *Vic.LM 131:* ♭ set *WDM 1635*)

HAHN, Reynaldo (1875-1947)

CIBOULETTE Operetta 1923
ABRIDGED RECORDING
  Ciboulette   …   …   …   Géori-Boué (S)
  Antonin   …   …   …   R. Amade (T)
  Duparquet   …   …   …   R. Bourdin (B)
  Roger   …   …   …   …G. Rey (Bs)
etc., R.St.Paul Cho. & Paris Cons. Orch.—
Cariven   ♯ **Pat.DTX 115**

Nous avons fait un beau voyage
MALVINA Operetta 1935
Duo du vieux chêne
Géori-Boué (S), R. Bourdin (B)   *Sat.D 604*

SONGS
COLLECTION
(7) Chansons grises   (Verlaine)
D'une prison   (Verlaine)
Offrande   (Verlaine)
Si mes vers avaient des ailes   (Hugo)
  L. Chelsi (B) & pf.   ♯ **MTR.MLO 1008**

(L')Heure exquise   (Verlaine)
H E. Calvé (HRS. 1046*)
  V. Maurel (B) (*IRCC. 3100**)

☆ = Re-issue of a recording to be found in WERM or Supplement I.

HAIEFF, Alexei (b. 1914)

Concerto, pf. & orch. 1952
L. Smit & A.R.S. Orch.—Hendl   ♯ **ARS. 9**
(Ward)

HALÉVY, Jacques François Fromental Elias (1799-1862)

(La) JUIVE Opera 5 acts 1835
EXCERPTS
J. Mardones (Bs), C. David (S), A. Scampini (T),
J. Mann (T), A. Didur (Bs), L. Slezak (T),
W. Hesch (Bs) (2ss)   ♯ **Ete.O-475***

Si la rigueur et la vengeance Bs (Act I)
E. List   in ♯ **Rem. 199-73**
(Schubert, Thomas, etc.)

Unspec. Aria (Act I)
Ⓗ L. Slezak *(Ger)* (in ♯ *Ete. 461**)

Il va venir S (Act II)
A. Varnay   in ♯ **Rem. 199-45**
(Thaïs, Aïda, Simone Boccanegra, etc.)

Vous qui du Dieu vivant (Malédiction) Bs (Act III)
Ⓗ A. Didur (in ♯ Ete.O-475* & in ♯ O-467*)

Rachel, quand du Seigneur T (Act IV)
☆ J. Schmidt (in ♯ *T.LS 6007*)
J. Peerce (in ♯ Vic.LM 1169)
Ⓗ E. Caruso (in ♯ Vic.LCT 1007*: in ♭ *set WCT 11**)

HALFFTER ESCRICHE, Ernesto (b. 1905)

SEE: † HARP MUSIC

HALVORSEN, Johan (1864-1935)

Entry of the Boyars orch
Oslo Phil.—Fjeldstad   **Nera.SK 15508**
(Hansen: Valdres March)
☆ Boston Pops—Fiedler (♭ *G.7RF 1022*)
Carnegie Pops—O'Connell
        (in ♯ AmC.ML 4118: ♭ *set A 1013*)

Norwegian Rhapsody No. 1, A major
Oslo Phil.—Fjeldstad (4ss) ♮ **Nera.SK 15503/4**

SONGS
Curls (Krag) (Krøllane) [1]
(The) Dance at Uvår (Krag) [1]
Ingemann-Stad (B) & orch.   **G.AL 2879**

Suite ancienne, Op. 31   orch.
Oslo Phil.—Fjeldstad (6ss) ♮ **Nera.SK 15500/2**

Veslemoy's Song (Mosaic No. 4) vln. & pf.
G. Knudsen & E. Garcia   ♯ **ML. 5003**
(Knudsen, Tveit, Haydn, etc.)

HAMMERSCHMIDT, Andreas (1612-1675)

SEE: † ITALIAN MADRIGALS
      † ANCIENT MUSIC OF THE CHURCH

---

[1] From *Skaergårdsviser.*
[2] Recorded from Edison cylinder.

HANDEL, George Frederick (1685-1759)

CLASSIFIED: I. VOCAL (A) Operas (B) Oratorios
                          (C) Other
            II. INSTRUMENTAL (A) Harpsichord
                             (B) Chamber Music
                             (C) Orchestral

I. VOCAL
(A) OPERAS

ACIS AND GALATEA S, T, T, B, Cho., Orch.
        1732
M. Ritchie, W. Herbert, R. Lewis, T. Anthony,
Handel Soc. Cho. & Orch.—Goehr
(6ss)   ♯ **HDL. 2**

ALCESTE 1749
Orch. Suite — ARR. Fekete: *See* Suites, II(c), *below*

ATALANTA 1736
Care selve   S
B. Gigli (T) & orch.   **G.DA 1918**
(Carnevale: Ave Maria)
(Bononcini: Per la gloria, on ▽ DA 1956)
Y. Ciannella & R. Viola (pf.) in **Vic. set E 100**
        (♭ set WE 100)

(II) FLORIDANTE 1721
Alma mia
☆ E. Pinza (Bs) & pf. (in ♯ Vic.LCT 1031: ♭ *set WCT 47*)

GIULIO CESARE IN EGITTO 1724
Dall' ondoso periglio . . .
Aure, deh, per pietà B (Act III)
H. Hotter   **C.LX 1538**

RINALDO 1711
Lascia ch'io pianga
Ⓗ C. Muzio (in ♯ Eso.ES 500*; ♯ Cpt.MC 20008*) [2]

RODRIGO 1707
Overture . . . Passacaille
— ARR. VLN. & PF. Harty
I. Richards & Y. Fisher   **Croy.CX 2**
(Paradies & Boulanger)

SEMELE 1743
Where'er you walk   T
☆ R. Lewis (D.X 10283)

O sleep ! why dost thou leave me ? S
E. Berger (S), M. Raucheisen (pf.) in ♯ **Ura. 7060**
(Schubert, Mozart, etc.)

SERSE 1738
Ombra mai fu ("*Largo*") T
R. Schock (T)   **G.DA 5515**
(Giordani: Caro mio ben)
M. Guilleaume (S)   **Pol. 48644**
(Gounod: Ave Maria)
M. Klose (A)   in ♯ **Ura. 7017**
(Monteverdi, etc.)
R. Merrill (B), Y. Menuhin (vln.) & pf.
        in ♯ **Vic.LM 1703**
        (♭ set WDM 1703)
F. Brückner (T) *(Tpo. 3848)*
☆ K. Ferrier (A) (D.X 10283)
R. Tauber (T) *(Od.O-4672)*
E. Caruso (T) (in ♯ Vic.LCT 2: ♭ *set WCT 7*)

ARRANGEMENTS
ORCH. ☆ Boston Prom.—Fiedler (♭ *G.7P 119: 7BF 1050*)

ORGAN V. Fox (in ♯ *AmC.AAL 20*)
        H. R. Cleaver (in *AmD.* set A 880: ♯ *DL 5360*:
                ♭ set 9-269)
☆ F. Asma (Pol. 57397)

SERSE—Ombra mai fu, ARRANGEMENTS (*continued*)

VLN. & CHA. ORCH.
  F. Akos & Berlin Municipal Op. Ens. (*T.A 11159*)

VLN.
  B. Saenger & H. Rothmüller (pf.) (*Od.O-28276*)
  ☆ V. Prihoda (*P.LL 3001*)

VLC. V. d'Orio & M. Leftcroft (pf.) (*Imp. 19217*)

(B) ORATORIOS, ETC.

ALEXANDER'S FEAST Ode 1736
L. Scheunemann (S), L. Chabay (T), K.
Falkner (Bs), Cornell Univ. Cho. & Handel
Soc. Orch.—Hull   **♯ HDL. set 13**
(4ss)

**(L') ALLEGRO, IL PENSIEROSO, ED IL
MODERATO** 1740
No. 5, Haste thee, nymph
Kirkintilloch Junior Cho.—MacPherson (*P.R 3474*)

No. 19, Let me wander, not unseen ("*Siciliana*")
— ARR. CHO.
Trapp Family Cho.—Wasner
    in ♯ **CHS.CHS 1101**

ATHALIA 1733
Alleluia   Cho.
— ARR. ORCH. Fekete *See*: Jephtha, suite

ISRAEL IN EGYPT 1737
S, S, A, T, B, B, Cho., Orch.
COMPLETE RECORDINGS
E. Morison, M. Kalmus, M. Thomas, R. Lewis,
D. Lee, S. Riley, Handel Soc. Cho. & orch.
—Goehr (4ss)   **♯ HDL. set 1**
J. Welting, I. Bialas, E. Munzig, W. Horst,
G. Räker, H. Rungenhagen, Berlin Radio
Cho. & Sym.—Koch **♯ CdM.LDX 8032/3**
(4ss—*Ger*)   (♯ Van.BG 521/2)

JEPHTHA 1751
Orchestral Suite — ARR. Fekete: *See* Suites, II(c), *below*

JOSHUA 1747
No. 53, Shall I in Mamre's fertile plains Bs
H. Hotter (*Ger*)   **C.LX 1516**
(*Samson—No. 81*)

No. 61, Oh ! had I Jubal's lyre   S
H Lilli Lehmann (*Ger*) (in ♯ Ete.O-463*)

JUDAS MACCABAEUS 1746
COMPLETE RECORDING
P. Moffet (S), B. Jensen (A), W. Olvis (T),
M. Sorensen (T), M. Hayes (Bs), Utah Univ.
Cho. & Utah Sym.—Abravanel
    ♯ HDL. set 12
(6ss)   (♯ Clc. 6120/2)

No. 22, Disdainful of danger   cho.
— ARR. ORCH. Fekete *See*: Jephtha, suite

MESSIAH 1742
COMPLETE RECORDINGS
A. Kupper (S), R. Anday (A), L. Fehenberger
(T), J. Greindl (Bs), Salzburg Cath. Cho. &
Festival Orch.—Messner (*Ger*)
(6ss)   **♯ Rem. set 199-69**
☆ E. Suddaby (S), M. Thomas (A), H. Nash (T), T.
Anthony (Bs), Cho. & Royal Phil.—Beecham
(8ss—♯ Vic. set LCT 6401: ♭ set WCT 34; Nos. 13
& 44 also ♭ 49-0819)

OMITTING Nos. 7, 34-36, 48-49, 52-55
L. Marshall (S), M. Palmateer (A), J. Vickers
(T), J. Milligan (Bs), Toronto Mendelssohn
Cho. & Orch.—MacMillan; hpsi. & org.
(6ss)   **♯ Bea.LPS 001**

Abridged ☆ Augustana Cho. (♯ *Bib.KL 214*: ♭ *set X 0306*)

PART I

No. 2, Comfort ye, my people
No. 3, Every valley   T
  ☆ H. Nash (♭ *G.7P 112*)

No. 4, And the glory of the Lord cho.
Munich Phil. Cho.—Lamy (*Ger*) **PV. 46001**
(*No. 44*)

PART II

No. 44, Hallelujah !   cho.
Royal Festival Cho.—Sargent **G.DB 21274**
(*No. 57*)
Munich Phil. Cho.—Lamy (*Ger*) **PV. 46001**
(*No. 4*)
Canterbury Cho.—Marrow, & org.
    in ♯ *MGM.E 20*
Radio Kids Bible Club, Little Evelyn & Children's Cho.
    (in ♯ *ISR.501*)
  ☆ Shaw Chorale & org. (♭ *Vic.WEPR 44*)
  St. Hedwig Cath. Berlin.—Forster (*Ger*)
    (in ♯ *T.LB 6022*)

PART III

No. 45, I know that my redeemer liveth S
E. Steber   **♯ AmC.ML 4521**
(*Creation, Elijah, & Bach*)

No. 57, Amen   cho.
Royal Festival Cho. & Orch.—Sargent
(*No. 44*)   **G.DB 21274**

ODE ON ST. CECILIA'S DAY S, T, cho., orch.
1739
L. Hoffmann, W. Ludwig, R. Lamy Cho.,
Berlin Radio Sym.—Rother (*Ger*) [1]
    ♯ Ura. 7023

PASSION ACCORDING TO ST. JOHN 1704
K. Harvey (S), G. Pfenninger (A), E. Häfliger
(T), D. Olsen (Bs), Zürich Bach Cho. &
Winterthur Sym.—Henking (*Ger*)
(4ss)   **♯ HDL. set 16**

SAMSON 1743
No. 81, How willing my paternal love Bs
H. Hotter (*Ger*)   **C.LX 1516**
(*Joshua, No. 53*)

SOLOMON 1748
No. 40, Beneath the vine
— ARR. ORCH. Fekete *See*: Jephtha, suite

(The) TRIUMPH OF TIME & TRUTH 1757
Orch. Suites ARR. Fekete *See*: section II(c), *below*
Sharp thorns despising
— ARR. OB. & PF. Rothwell ("*Rondo*")
E. Rothwell & W. Parry   **G.B 10237**
(*Nicholas: Melody*)

(C) OTHER VOCAL WORKS

ANTHEMS—Coronation 1727
Let thy hand be strengthened
Danish State Radio Cho. & Orch.—Wöldike
(*Utrecht Te Deum*)   **♯ HSLP. 2046**

---

[1] Omits Minuet in Overture, & Nos. 2 (recit.), 11 (Aria), 12 (recit.); cuts are made in Nos. 9, 10 & 13.

Zadok the Priest
Royal Festival Cho. & Orch.—Sargent
G.DA 1980

CANTATAS
Apollo e Dafne S, B, orch. (B & H 16) 1707-8
K. Harvey, D. Olsen & Zürich Radio Orch.—
Goehr ♯ HDL. 14
(♯ Clc. 6123)

Armida abbandonata (B & H 13)
Agrippina condotta a morire (B & H 14) 1707-8
A. Giebel (S), Stuttgart Ton-studio Orch.—
Lamy; & hpsi.
Pensieri notturni di Filli (B & H 17) 1707-8
A. Giebel, A. Mann (recorder), H. Elsner (hpsi.),
& vlc. ♯ Oce.OCS 30

Dalla guerra amorosa Bs & cont. (B & H 8) 1707-8
H. O. Hudemann, F. Neumeyer (hpsi.), A.
Wenzinger (vlc.) PV. 7404

Look down, harmonious Saint ("In praise of Harmony")
V. Bak (S, Ger) & Orch.—Graunke
♯ Mer.MG 10085
(Mozart: Arias & Regina Coeli)

Unid. . . . Dank sei dir, Herr ("Arioso")
☆ H. Schlusnus (Pol. 67467)

TE DEUM, D major (Utrecht)
S, S, A, A, T, B, cho. & orch. 1713
R. Guldbaek, V. Garde, E. Brems, D. Schou,
O. Walbom, V. Holbøll, E. Nørby, Danish
State Radio Cho. & Orch.—Wöldike
(Anthem) ♯ HSLP. 2046

TE DEUM, D major (Dettingen)
S, A, T, B, Cho., Orch. 1743
K. Hansel, R. Koerner, G. Barritt, H. Rank,
Presbyterian Cho. & Nat. Gallery Orch.—
Bales ♯ WCFM. 6

... **No. 17, Vouchsafe, O Lord** (Dignare, Domine)
— — ARR. VLN. & PF. Flesch ("Prayer")
Y. Menuhin & G. Moore G.DA 2023
(Debussy: Fille aux cheveux de lin)
T. Magyar & W. Hielkema Phi.N 11230G
(Rimsky-Korsakov) (PhM. 09045S)

II. INSTRUMENTAL
(A) HARPSICHORD
AYLESFORD PIECES [1]
Allegretto grazioso ; Gavotte
— ARR. GUITAR Segovia
A. Segovia in ♯ B.AXTL 1010
(† Segovia Concert) (♯ AmD.DL 9638)

Sarabande ; Minuet — ARR. Segovia
A. Segovia in ♯ AmD.DL 9647
(† Segovia Program)

(6) FUGUES
No. 4, D major ; No. 5, A minor c. 1720
F. Pelleg ♯ HDL. 5
(Suites)

(3) LESSONS [2]
No. 1, B flat major (Prelude, Air & Variations)
No. 2, G minor (Minuet)
F. Pelleg ♯ HDL. 6
(below)

No. 3a, G major (Chaconne & 30 Variations)
F. Pelleg ♯ HDL. 7
(below)

SUITES [3]
COLLECTION
No. 1, A major ; No. 2, F major ; No. 3, D minor
F. Pelleg ♯ HDL. 4

No. 4, E minor ; No. 5, E major ; No. 6, F sharp minor
F. Pelleg (Fugues) ♯ HDL. 5

No. 7, G minor ; No. 8, F minor
F. Pelleg (Lessons) ♯ HDL. 6

No. 9, G minor ; No. 10, D minor
No. 11, D minor; No. 12, E minor
F. Pelleg (Lesson) ♯ HDL. 7

OTHER RECORDINGS
No. 3, D minor
H. Schnauffer ♯ Mer.MG 15033
(Bach: Concerto)

No. 5, E major
W. Gieseking (pf.) C.LX 1532

... **Air & Variations** "Harmonious Blacksmith"
S. Sørensen (Fdn.NC 1001)
☆ W. Landowska (in ♯ Vic.LM 1217: ♭ set WDM 1181;
♭ G.7RF 254)

— — ARR. HARP
A. Sacchi in ♯ NRI. 403
(Debussy, Haydn, Corelli, etc.)

No. 6, F sharp minor
... **Gavotte** — ARR. VLN. & PF.
M. Elman & W. Rosé in ♭ Vic. set WDM 1590
(Sonatas)

No. 7, G minor
... **Passacaille**
☆ A. Ehlers (in ♯ AmD.DL 8019)

— — ARR. VLN. & VLA. Halvorsen
L. & R. Persinger ♯ Strad.STR 608
(Turina, Villa-Lobos, Hindemith)

No. 8, F minor ... 1st & 2nd movts.
— — ARR. ORG. Guilmant ("Prelude & Fugue")
P. Alsfelt in ♯ Mer.MG 15036
(Buxtehude & Bach)

No. 11, D minor ... Sarabande only
S. Sørensen (above) Fdn.NC 1001

(B) CHAMBER MUSIC
(2) Arias 2 hrns., obs. & bsns.
Gavotte & March tpt., obs., bsns. & side drum
London Baroque Ens.—Haas P.R 20617
(2ss)

SONATAS, Op. 1 c. 1724
FLUTE & CONTINUO

No. 1, E minor	No. 2, G minor
No. 4, A minor	No. 5, G major
No. 7, C major	No. 9, B minor
No. 11, F major	

J. Baker (fl.), S. Marlowe (hpsi.)
(4ss) ♯ AmD. set DX 116

---

[1] "8 pieces for hpsi. in library of Marquis of Aylesford."
[2] In the *Handel Gesellschaft* edition, Nos. 1 & 2 are called Suite No. 1 of Book II; and No. 3a is called Suite No. 2 of Book II.
[3] Numbered according to the B & H edition. In the *Handel Gesellschaft* edition, Nos. 9, 10, 11 & 12 are called Book II, Nos. 6, 3, 4 & 5 respectively.

No. 9, B minor ... Andante only
— — ARR. VLC. & PF. Hubay (*"Larghetto"*)
M. Wellerson & I. Rossican **Phi.N 12042G**
(½s.—*Popper & Paganini*)   (*PhM. 12042S*)

OBOE & CONTINUO
No. 8, C minor
P. Pierlot & I. Nef (hpsi.)   **♯ DO.LD 6**
(*Concerto*)

VIOLIN & CONTINUO
No. 3, A major   No. 13, D major
No. 10, G minor   No. 14, A major
No. 12, F major   No. 15, E major
A. Campoli & G. Malcolm (hpsi.)
                                      ♯ D.LXT 2751
(2ss)   (♯ *Lon.LL 652*)

No. 3, A major   — ARR. SAX. & PF.
S. Rascher & D. Tudor   in ♯ **CHS.CHS 1156**

No. 10, G minor   ("No. 2")
I. B. Meinert, W. Gerwig (lute), J. Koch
(gamba)   **PV. 7408**

No. 12, F major
M. Michailow & E. Milzkott (hpsi.)
                                   ♯ CdM.LD 8019
(*Concerto Grosso, Op. 6, No. 12*)

No. 13, D major ; No. 14, A major
No. 15, E major
M. Elman & W. Rosé (pf.)   ♯ **Vic.LM 1183**
(9ss—*Hpsi. Suite 6, Gavotte,* in ♭ *set WDM 1590*)

No. 13, D major
G. de Vito & G. Malcolm (hpsi.)
(4ss)   ♮ **G.DB 9696/7**

TRIOS (SONATAS), 2 violins & continuo
Op. 2, No. 4, B flat major
Op. 2, No. 8, G minor
Op. 2, No. 9, E major   1733
Op. 5, No. 3, E minor   1738
W. & M. Schweyda (vlns.), J. Behr (pf.)
                              ♯ Ura. 7046

―――――――――

(C) ORCHESTRAL
(6) CONCERTI GROSSI, Op. 3 (B & H. 1-6) 1729
COMPLETE RECORDING
Vienna State Op. Orch.—Prohaska
                          ♯ Van.BG 505/6
(3ss—*Concerto, C major*) (♯ *Nix.BLP 305-1/2*)

No. 5, D minor
Berlin Cha.—Lange   ♮ **U.H. 23958/9**
(3ss—*Bach: W.T.C.—Prelude & Fugue, A minor*)

(12) CONCERTI GROSSI, Op. 6
2 vlns., vlc., str. orch. (B & H. 12-23) 1739
No. 1, G major ; No. 2, F major ; No. 3, E minor
O. Büchner, F. Berger, H. Melzer, Bamberg
Sym.—F. Lehmann & hpsi.   **PV. 7405/7**
(2ss each)

No. 1; No. 3 ; No. 5, D major; No. 12, B minor
Homburg Sym.—P. Schubert   ♯ **Rgt. 5017/9**

Nos. 1, 3, 5
Berlin Str. Orch.—Ludwig   ♯ **Roy. 1373**
(2ss)

No. 5, D major
Boyd Neel Orch.[1]   ♯ **D.LX 3055**
(*No. 6*)   (♯ *Lon.LPS 396*)
Philharmonia—Markevitch   ♮ **G.C 7852/3**
(4ss) (G.EH 2007/8: DB 4308/9)

[1] n.v. (with T. Dart, hpsi.).

No. 6, G minor
Boyd Neel Orch.[1]   ♯ **D.LX 3055**
(*No. 5*)   (♯ *Lon.LPS 396*)

No. 7, B flat major
No. 8, C minor
Boyd Neel Orch.[1]   ♯ **D.LX 3081**
(1 side each)   (♯ *Lon.LS 543*)

No. 7, B flat major
— ARR. STR. QTT. & SYM. ORCH.   Schoenberg
Janssen Sym. Orch.   ♯ **AmC.ML 4406**
(*Mozart*)

No. 9, F major
No. 10, D minor
Boyd Neel Orch.[1]   ♯ **D.LX 3099**
                             (♯ *Lon.LS 585*)

No. 12, B minor
Berlin Radio Cha.—Haarth   ♯ **CdM.LD 8019**
(*Sonata*)

―――――――――

Concerto, C major   (Alexander's Feast) 1736
2 vlns., 2 obs., str. (B & H. 7)
Vienna State Opera—Prohaska ♯ **Van.BG 506**
(*Concerti Grossi, Op. 3, s.3*) (♯ *Nix.BLP 305-2*)

— ARR. 2 VLCS. & ORCH.   Ronchini
Janssen Sym. Orch.   ♯ **DCap.CTL 7013**
(*below, & Haydn*)   (♯ *Cap.P 8137*)

CONCERTOS a due cori
B flat major   2 obs., 3 bsns., str. (B & H. 27)
F major   2 obs., 2 hrns., 2 bsns. (B & H. 28)
Copenhagen Collegium Musicum—Friisholm
                            ♯ **HS.HSL 1049**

CONCERTOS, Oboe & Orch.
No. 1, B flat major   (B & H. 8)
No. 2, B flat major   (B & H. 9)
No. 3, G minor   (B & H. 10)
P. Pierlot & orch.—A. Lewis   **V♯ DO.LD 5/6**
(3ss—*Sonata*)

No. 1, B flat major   (B & H. 8)
B. Gassmann & Janssen Sym. ♯ **DCap.CTL 7013**
(*above & Haydn*)   (♯ *Cap.P 8137*)

No. 3, G minor   (B & H. 10)
"No. 4", E flat major (ed. Stein, from Upsala;
pub. 1935)
H. Kamesch & Vienna State Opera—Kuyler
(*below*)   ♯ **Oce.OCS 25**

No. 3, G minor
J. Tancibudek & Sydney Civic—Beck
(*Bach, Byrd, Purcell*)   ♯ **Dia.LPM 4**

(6) CONCERTOS, Organ & Orch., Op. 4
(B & H. 1-6) 1738
W. Kraft & Stuttgart Pro Musica Orch.—
R. Reinhardt   ♯ **AmVox. set PL 7132**
(4ss)   (♯ *EVox. 451/2*)

No. 2, B flat major, Op. 4, No. 2
... Finale
A. M. Henderson (solo)   **D.K 2446**
(*Liszt: Legend of St. Elizabeth, No. 3*)

(6) CONCERTOS, Organ & Orch., Op. 7
(B & H. 7-12) 1740
W. Kraft & Stuttgart Pro Musica Orch.—R.
Reinhardt (4ss) ♯ **E. & AmVox. set PL 7202**

No. 11, G minor, Op. 7, No. 5
... 2nd movt., Basso ostinato, only
F. Asma (solo)   in ♯ **Phi.N 00147L**
(*Bach, Mendelssohn, etc.*)

(4) CONCERTOS, Organ & Orch. (B & H. 13-16)

No. 13, F major   No. 14, A major
No. 15, D minor   No. 16, F major
 E. Hölderlin & Stuttgart Pro Musica Orch.—
  R. Reinhardt (4ss) **♯ AmVox. set PL 7802**

Nos. 13, 14 & 15
 F. Pelleg (hpsi.) & Zürich Radio—Goehr
            ♯ HDL. 3

Nos. 13 & 14
 G. Leonhardt & Vienna State Opera—Kuyler
 (*above*)   **♯ Oce.OCS 25**

MUSIC FOR THE ROYAL FIREWORKS 1749
 (B & H. "Concerto" 26)
 ☆ Berlin Municipal—Meyer (Pol. 15515/7)

Suite — ARR. Harty
 Amsterdam—v. Beinum **♯ D.LX 3096**
 (*Berlioz & Clarke*)   (♯ *Lon.LS 620*)

 ☆ L.P.O.—Harty (♯ AmC.RL 3019)

(The) WATER MUSIC (B & H. "Concerto" 25)
 1715
COMPLETE RECORDING
 (original version, ed. Chrysander)
 Berlin Phil.—F. Lehmann ♮ **PV. 7401/3**
 (6ss)   (2ss—♯ AmD.DL 9594)
 Cha. Orch.—Hewitt (2ss) **♯ DFr. 74**

Suite — ARR. Harty
 Philharmonia—Karajan ♮ **C.LX 8945/6**
 (4ss)
 Boston Sym.—Münch **♯ Vic.LM 7009**
 (*Mozart & Schumann*) (♭ *set WDM 7009*)
 Pro Arte—Marrow **♯ MGM.E 132**
 (1½ss—*Bach: Suite 3, Air*) (♭ *set K 132*)
 ☆ L.P.O.—Harty (♯ AmC.RL 3019)

... No. 3, Hornpipe — ARR. 4 PFS.
 ☆ First Piano Qtt. (in ♯ Vic.LM 1165)

MISCELLANEOUS SUITES
"Alceste" Suite [1] — ARR. Fekete
"Festival" Suite [1] — ARR. Fekete
 Vienna Sym.—Fekete **♯ Csm.CLPS 1012**
 (1 side each)   (♯ *Eur.LPG 603*)

(The) Great Elopement — ARR. Beecham
SUITE NO. 1
... No. 6, Quarrel; No. 9, Minuet; No. 10, Hornpipe
SUITE NO. 2
... No. 1, March; No. 2, The Exquisites; No. 5, Serenade
 Royal Phil.—Beecham (4ss) [2] **G.DB 21396/7**
 (*Mozart, in* ♯ Vic. LHMV 1030: ♭ *set WHMV 1030*)

Jephtha Suite — ARR. Fekete
 1. Jephtha, Overture 2. Solomon, No. 40
 3. Judas Maccabaeus, No. 22 4. Athalia, Cho.
 ☆ Salzburg Mozarteum—Fekete (♯ Eur.LPG 605, d.c.)

"Triumph of Time and Truth" Suite [1]
 — ARR. Fekete
 ☆Vienna Sym.—Fekete (2ss) **♯ Lyr.LL 25**
 (o.n. ♯ Per.SPLP 525) (♯ *Eur.LPG 614*)

HANDL, Jacob (1550-1591)

Ascendit deus
 San José State A Cappella Cho.—Erlendsen
          ♯ ML. 7007
 (*Corsi, Copland, Villa-Lobos, etc.*)

Ecce quomodo moritur justus
 Vienna Academy Cha. Cho.—F. Grossmann
        in † ♯ **Sel.LPG 8238**
 Netherlands Cha. Cho.—de Nobel
          Phi.N 12027G
 (½s.—*Lassus & Lotti*) (*PhM.N 09024S*)

Hodie Christus natus est
 Vienna Academy Cha. Cho. in † ♯ **Sel.LPG 8238**
 (*above*)

Resonet in laudibus
 Welch Chorale   in ♯ **Lyr.LL 35**
 (*Gregorians, Victoria, etc.*)

HANFF, Johann Nicolaus (1630-1706)

 SEE: † ORGAN MUSIC — HEITMANN

HANSON, Howard (b. 1896)

Centennial Ode Speaker, B, Cho., Orch. 1950
 L. Treash, D. Meyers, Eastman School Cho.,
 Eastman-Rochester Sym.—Hanson **♯ Roch. 1**

Concerto, pf. & orch., G major, Op. 36 1948
 R. Firkusny & Eastman-Rochester Sym.—
  Hanson (*Grieg*)   **♯ AmC.ML 4403**

Drum Taps (W. Whitman) cho. & orch. 1935
 Eastman Cho. & Eastman-Rochester Sym.—
  Hanson   **♯ Mer.MG 40000**
 (*R. Thompson*)

SYMPHONIES
No. 2, Op. 30 "Romantic" 1930
 ☆ Eastman-Rochester Sym.—Hanson (JpV.SD 3018/21)

No. 4, Op. 34 "Requiem" 1943
 A.R.S. Orch.—Dixon   **♯ ARS. 6**

HARRIS, Roy (b. 1898)

Quintet, pf. & str. 1937
 Cumberland Forest Festival (♯ Pte. recording)

Symphony No. 3 orch. 1938
 A.R.S. Sym.—Hendl   **♯ ARS. 28**
 (*Schuman*)

HARRIS, Russell (b. 1914)

Tarye no longer partsong
 Hamline Singers—Holliday **♯ NRI. 306**
 (*Chavez & Křenek*)

HARRISON, Lou (b. 1917)

(The) Only jealousy of Emer
 (Performance of W. B. Yeats' verse play with music by
  L. Harrison)
 Ens.—Harrison   **♯ Eso. 506**

Suite for violoncello & harp 1949
 S. Barab & L. Lawrence
Suite No. 2, Str. qtt. 1948
 New Music Str. Qtt. **♯ AmC.ML 4491**
 (*Thomson*)

---

[1] It has not been possible to ascertain the exact contents of these suites. The *Alceste* suite is stated by M. Fekete also to contain extracts from *Solomon* and *Deborah*, and the *Triumph of Time & Truth* suite extracts from *Jephtha* and *Deborah*.
[2] In G.B., ♮ G.DB 9672/3 only.

HARTMANN, Johan Peter Emilius
(1805-1900)

(The) Golden Horns, Op. 11
☆ A. Poulsen (Diction) & Copenhagen Radio Orch.—
Tuxen (Pol.HM 80034/5)

Now in thought I am folding my hands (Langsted)
M. Aabjørn (T), H. Jensen (org.) *Felix.F 52*
(Hoffmann: When Jesus ended the day)

HARTMANN, Karl Amadeus (b. 1905)

Symphony No. 4, Str. Orch. 1950
Brussels Radio—André ♯ *DT.LGM 65001*
(♯ *Cap.L 8146*; ♯ *T.LS 6021*)

... Finale : Adagio appassionato
R.I.A.S. Sym.—Fricsay Pol. 68147
(2ss)

HARTY, Sir Hamilton (1879-1941)

FOLK-SONG ARRANGEMENT
My Lagan Love (MacCathmhaoil)
R. Hayward (B) & orch. in ♯ *D.LF 1086*

HASSE, Johann Adolph (1699-1783)

SEE : †AS 167 & ♯ 3002LD

HASSLER, Hans Leo (1564-1612)

SEE : †ITALIAN MADRIGALS

HAUER, Johann Matthias (b. 1893)

Hölderlin Lieder
P. Batic (A), R. Leukauf (pf.) ♯ NRI. 405
(Křenek & Kodály)

HAYDN, Franz Josef (1732-1809)

CLASSIFIED : I. VOCAL
II. INSTRUMENTAL
A. Piano   B. Chamber Music
C. Orchestral   D. Miscellaneous

I. VOCAL

Arianna a Nasso, Op. 65 Cantata 1789
J. Tourel (M-S), R. Kirkpatrick (pf.)[1]
(Songs) ♯ HSLP. 2051

ARIAS   S

Ein' Magd, ein' Dienerin (Cantilena pro Adventu)
Son pietoso (Aria di Lindora) 1780-90
Chi vive amante (Aria di Erissena) 1787
Berenice che fai ? (Scena di Berenice) 1795
Solo e pensoso ("Russian aria") 1798
G. Hopf & Vienna Sym.—v. Zallinger
♯ HSLP. 2045
(♯ Nix.HLP 2045)

[1] XVIIIth Century-type piano.

MASSES

No. 1, F major, Missa brevis a due soprani c. 1750
(Novello 11)

No. 5, B flat major, S. Joannis de Deo c. 1775
(Novello 8)
Vienna Academy Cha. Cho. & Sym. Cha. Orch.
—Gillesberger ♯ Lyr.LL 30
(H. Heusser & A. Berger, sops., in No. 1)

No. 2, E flat major, in honorem B.V. Mariae
S, A, T, B, cho., orch. (Novello 12) 1766
E. Roon, H. Rössl-Majdan, W. Kmentt, W.
Berry, Academy Cho. & Vienna Sym.—
Grossmann ♯ AmVox.PL 7020
(B. Seidlhofer, organ)

No. 6, C major, "Mariazeller" 1782
(Novello 15)
☆G. Rathauskeller (S), A. Janacek (A), etc.
Vienna Academy Cho. & Vienna Sym.
Orch.—Gillesberger ♯ Nix.HLP 2011

No. 8, B flat major, Sti. Bernardi de Offida 1796
(Novello 1)
Copenhagen Boys & Men's Cho. & Royal
Opera Orch.—Wöldike ♯ HSLP. 2048

No. 9, D minor, "Nelson" 1798 (Novello 3)
E. J. Connor (S), N. B. Ludwig (A), T. R.
McNutt (T), R. E. Grooters (Bs), Bryn
Mawr & Haverford Chos. & orch.—W. H.
Reese ♯ HC. pte.
☆L. della Casa (S), E. Höngen (A), etc.,
Vienna Academy Cho. & Sym. Orch.—
J. Sternberg ♯ Nix.HLP 2004

No. 10, B flat major, "Theresia" 1796
(Novello 16)
☆Soloists, Vienna State Opera Cho. & Vienna
Sym.—Krauss ♯ EVox. 210
(♯ PaV.VP 210)

No. 12, B flat major, "Harmonie" 1802
(Novello 6)
I. Katschinka (S), M. Kenney (A), H. Löffler
(T), K. Engen (Bs), Vienna Soc. Cho. &
orch.—Larsen ♯ Nix.PLP 541
(♯ Per.SPLP 541)

OPERAS

(L')ISOLA DISABITATA 1779
Overture (G.A. No. 13)
Winterthur Sym.—Goehr ♯ *MMS. 6*
(Symphony 96)

PHILEMON UND BAUCIS 1 act 1773
(for Marionettes)
COMPLETE RECORDING
S. Naidis (S), E. Roon (S), E. Majkut (T),
W. Kmentt (T), Vienna State Opera Cho. &
Sym. Orch.—v. Zallinger ♯ AmVox.PL 7660

(Lo) SPEZIALE 3 acts 1768
(The Apothecary)
ABRIDGED RECORDING in English
Soloists, cho. & orch.—Kramer
♯ MTR.MLO 1007

ORATORIOS

(The) CREATION (*Die Schöpfung*) 1798
COMPLETE RECORDING in German
☆T. Eipperle (S), J. Patzak (T), G. Hann (Bs),
Vienna State Op. Cho. & Vienna Phil.—
Krauss ♯ Nix.HLP 2005-1/3
(6ss) (♯ Era.LDE 3005/6, 4ss)

No. 9, With verdure clad S
E. Steber ♯ AmC.ML 4521
(Bach: Cantata excpts; & Messiah, Elijah)

(The) SEASONS (*Die Jahreszeiten*) 1801
COMPLETE RECORDING in *German*
E. Trötschel (S), W. Ludwig (T), J. Greindl (Bs),
St. Hedwig's Cath. Cho., R.I.A.S. Cha. Cho.,
& R.I.A.S. Sym. Orch.—Fricsay
(8ss)   ♯ *Pol.* 18025/8
(Choruses Nos. 31 & 33 also on *PV.* 36063)

(Die) SIEBEN WORTE B & orch. 1784
— ARR. STR. QTT. (Op. 51) 1787
Schneider Qtt.   ♯ HS.HSQ 39

— ARR. SOLOISTS, CHO. & ORCH. 1797
H. Güden (S), C. Ölschläger (A), J. Patzak (T),
H. Braun (B) & Salzburg Cath. Cho. &
Orch.—Messner (4ss)   ♯ *Rem.* set 199-66

STABAT MATER S, A, T, B, cho. 1773
A. Felbermeyer, S. Wagner, W. Kmentt,
O. Wiener, Vienna Academy Cha. Cho. &
Vienna Sym.—Gillesberger ♯ EVox. 331/2
(4ss)   (♯ AmVox. set PL 7412)

SONGS
COLLECTIONS

> Fidelity (Mrs. Hunter) 1794
> (The) Mermaid's Song (Mrs. Hunter) 1794
> My mother bids me bind my hair (Mrs. Hunter) 1794
> (The) Sailor's Song (Mrs. Hunter) 1798
> She never told her love (Shakespeare) 1798
> (The) Spirit Song (Mrs. Hunter)
> J. Tourel (M-S), R. Kirkpatrick (pf.) [1]
> (*Arianna*)   ♯ HSLP. 2051

> (Das) Leben ist ein Traum (Gleim)
> (The) Mermaid's Song (Mrs. Hunter)
> My mother bids me . . . (Mrs. Hunter)
> She never told her love (Shakespeare)
> (The) Spirit Song (Mrs. Hunter)
> T. Niemela (S), P. Koskimies (pf.) ♯ WCFM. 10
> (*Schubert*)

II. INSTRUMENTAL
A. PIANO

(10) Deutsche Tänze, "Ballo Tedesco"
... Five only
☆ W. Landowska (hpsi.) (in ♭ *Vic.* set WCT 43)

SONATAS [2]
COLLECTIONS

No. 1, C major	No. 6 (26), G major
No. 2, B flat major	No. 7 (27), C major
No. 3, C major	No. 8 (28), G major
No. 4, D major	No. 9 (29), F major
No. 5 (25), A major	No. 10, C major

S. Marlowe (hpsi.)   ♯ HS. set 3037
(4ss)   (♯ Nix.HLP 3037-1/2)

No. 13 (17), E major
No. 19 (22), D major 1767
No. 31 (24), E major 1776
No. 32 (36), B minor 1776
S. Stravinsky   ♯ Allo.ALG 3040

No. 2, B flat major
F. Neumeyer (clavichord)   PV. 3405

No. 3, C major ... Minuet only
☆ A. Ehlers (hpsi.) (in ♯ AmD.DL 8019)

No. 19 (22), D major (Old Peters No. 9)
... Adagio — ARR. VLC. & PF.
P. Casals & E. Istomin
(in ♯ AmC. set SL 167, "inscription" disc)

No. 20 (32), C minor 1771
☆V. Pleasants   ♯ *Nix.HLPY 3013*
(*No. 50*)

No. 23 (13), F major 1773
R. Trouard   Od. 123916/7
(3ss—Bach: Cantata 29, Sinfonia) (in ♯ Od.OD 1002)
R. Wallenborn   ♯ HSLP. 3035
(*No. 32*)
G. Anda   T.E 3918/9
(3ss—Mozart: Sonata No. 17, s.3)

No. 24, D major 1773
No. 30 (35), A major 1776
R. Wallenborn   ♯ HSLP. 3036

No. 32 (36), B minor 1776
R. Wallenborn (*No. 23*)   ♯ HSLP. 3035

No. 36 (6), C sharp minor 1780
... Minuet only
☆ W. Landowska (hpsi.) (in ♭ *Vic.* set WCT 43)

No. 37 (7), D major 1780
A. d'Arco [3] (2ss)   Pat.PDT 269

No. 40 (16), G major 1784
— ARR. VLN., VLA., VLC. (Op. 53, No. 1)
Paris String Trio   ♯ OL.LD 38
(*Divertimenti*)

No. 44 (4), G minor 1789
No. 45 (26), E flat major 1766
V. Pleasants   ♯ HSLP. 3033
                                (♯ *Nix.HLPY 3033*)

No. 46 (38), A flat major c. 1770
No. 49 (3), E flat major, Op. 66 1790
V. Pleasants   ♯ HSLP. 3034
                                (♯ *Nix.HLPY 3034*)

No. 50 (23), C major 1793/4
☆V. Pleasants   ♯ *Nix.HLPY 3013*
(*No. 20*)

---

(6) Variations, C major 1790
— ARR. HARP Salzédo
A. Sacchi   in ♯ NRI. 403
(*Zabel: Légende; Debussy, etc.*)

Variations, F minor, Op. 83
(Andante con variazioni) 1793
A. Baller (2ss)   JpV.SD 3036

Miscellaneous : Flötenuhrstücke
... Nos. 2, 6, 7, 11, 13, 15, 17, 18 — ARR. ORG.
G. Jones   G.C 4177
(2ss) (Steinkirchen org.)   (EH 1375)

... Nos. 19, 21, 22, 27, 30 — ARR. FL. & PF. Vesper
(labelled *5 Stücke für das Laufwerk*)
F. Vesper & M. van Luin (2ss)   C.DC 571

B. CHAMBER MUSIC

Cassation, C major lute, vln., gamba
SEE infra: Qtt. Op. 1, No. 6

Divertimento, E flat major hrn. vln., vlc
(Larsen E♭7) 1767
F. Koch, W. Schneiderhan, N. Hübner
                                ♯ HSLP. 1044
(*Notturni*)   (♯ Nix.HLP 1044)

DIVERTIMENTI

A major; D major; G major vln., vla., vlc.
SEE: TRIOS, baryton, vln., vlc.

D major viola d'amore, vla. descant, gamba
SEE: TRIOS, baryton, vln., vlc.

---

[1] XVIIIth Century-type piano.
[2] In order of GA. The nos. in brackets are those of the Augener edition.
[3] Labelled "No. 6."

QUARTETS, String

Op. 1, COMPLETE RECORDING   pub. 1764
No. 0, E flat major [1]; No. 1, B flat major
No. 2, E flat major; No. 3, D major;
No. 4, G major; No. 6, C major
Schneider Qtt.   **♯ HS.HSQ 1/3**
(6ss)   (set HSQ-A)

C major, Op. 1, No. 6
— ARR. LUTE, VLN. & GAMBA   "Cassation"
W. Gerwig, I. Brix-Meinert, J. Koch   **PV. 4405**
(2ss)

F major, Op. 3, No. 5   c. 1769
Kalki Qtt.   **♯ T.LS 6019**
(Qtt. Op. 64, No. 5)
☆Griller Qtt.   **♯ D.LX 3087**
(Mozart: Qtt. No. 6, K 159)   (♯ Lon.LS 656)
☆Amadeus Qtt. (in ♯ Sel.LPG 8338)

... **2nd movt., Andante cantabile (Serenade)** only
Paganini Qtt.   in † ♯ **Vic.LM 1192**
                                 (in ♭ set WDM 1611)
Sydney Civic Str. Orch.—Beck (♯ Dia.DPM 1)
▽ Zernick Qtt. (Imp. 19079)

Op. 17, COMPLETE RECORDING   1771
No. 1, E major; No. 4, C minor (HSQ 13; Nix.HLP 13)
No. 2, F major; No. 3, E flat major (HSQ 14; Nix.HLP 14)
No. 5, G major; No. 6, D major (HSQ 15; Nix.HLP 15)
Schneider Qtt.   (6ss)   **♯ HS.set HSQ-E**

E flat major, Op. 33, No. 2 ... **Minuet**
— ARR. VLN. & PF. Burmester
G. Knudsen & E. Garcia   in ♯ **ML. 5003**
(Fauré, Tveitt, Prokofiev, etc.)   (also ML. 41)

C major, Op. 33, No. 3   1781
☆ Pro Arte Qtt. (G.DB 20401/2)

D minor, Op. 42   1785
Schneider Qtt.   **♯ HS.HSQ 37**
(Qtt. Op. 77, No. 1) (♯ Nix.HLP 37)   (in set HSQ-M)

Op. 50, COMPLETE RECORDING   1784
No. 1, B flat major; No. 2, C major
No. 3, E flat major; No. 4, F sharp minor
No. 5, F major; No. 6, D major
Schneider Qtt.   **♯ HS.HSQ 22/4**
(6ss) (♯ Nix.HLP 22/4)   (set HSQ-H)

D major, Op. 64, No. 5
Kalki Qtt.   **♯ T.LS 6019**
(Qtt. Op. 3, No. 5)
☆Hungarian Qtt.   **♯ G.FALP 131**
(Mozart)

E flat major, Op. 64, No. 6   pub. 1790
St. George Qtt.   (4ss)   **Argo.S 1006/7**
☆New Italian Qtt.   **♯ D.LXT 2680**
(Boccherini: Qtt. Op. 6, No. 1)   (♯ Lon.LL 320)

F major, Op. 74, No. 2   1793
☆Baroque Qtt.   **♯ Nix.PLP 503**
(Mozart: Qtt. K 421)

D minor, Op. 76, No. 2   1797/8
C major, Op. 76, No. 3   "Emperor"
☆Galimir Qtt.   **♯ Nix.PLP 504**
(1 side each)

C major, Op. 76, No. 3
Koeckert Qtt.   (4ss)   **♮ PV. 72202/3**
                                       (♯ Pol. 16026)
☆ Amadeus Qtt. (G.EH 1387/9: GB 59/61)

... **2nd movt., Theme & Variations** — ARR. STR. ORCH.
Berlin Municipal—Otto   **T.E 3911**

D major, Op. 76, No. 5
☆ Vienna Konzerthaus Qtt. (♯ Sel.LPG 8338)

G major, Op. 77, No. 1   1799
Schneider Qtt.   **♯ HS.HSQ 37**
(Op. 42) (♯ Nix.HLP 37)   (in set HSQ-M)
Heifetz Qtt.   **♯ EMS. 301**
(below)

— ARR. FL. & PF.   A. E. Müller
J. Baker & S. Arnold   **♯ Ox.OR 106**
(Mozart)
☆R. le Roy & P. Loyonnet   **♯ Nix.CLP 1082**
(Pergolesi)

F major, Op. 77, No. 2
Schneider Qtt.   **♯ HS.HSQ 38**
(Op. 103) (♯ Nix.HLP 38)   (in set HSQ-M)
Heifetz Qtt.   **♯ EMS. 301**
(above)

B flat major, Op. 103   1803
Schneider Qtt.   **♯ HS.HSQ 38**
(Opp. 42 & 77) (♯ Nix.HLP 38)   (in set HSQ-M)
☆ Amadeus Qtt. (♯ Sel.LPG 8338)
NOTE: See also Die Sieben Worte (Sec. I)

———— END OF STR. QTTS. ————

SONATAS, vln. & vla.
No. 1, C major ... **3rd movt., Tempo di minuetto**
— ARR. VLC. & PF.   Piatti
P. Casals & Blas Net (in ♭ Vic. set WCT 42)

No. 5, D major—ARR. VLN. & VLC.   Op. 93, No. 3
R. Posselt & S. Mayes   **♯ Fest. 70-203**
(½s.—Martinů & Fauré)

TRIOS, Baryton, vln. & vlc.
As SYNTHETIC DIVERTIMENTO, D MAJOR
No. 56, D major, 1st movt.
No. 36, D major, 2nd movt.
No. 34, D major, 2nd movt.
No. 35, A major, 1st movt.
No. 36, D major, 1st movt.
Adagio (unid.)
No. 78, D major, 3rd movt.
Stuttgart Cha. Soc.[2]   **♯ Ren.X 40**
(Milandre, Cervetto, Cannabich, etc.)
                          (♯ Nix.PLP 240; Clc. 6124)

No. 74, D major
— ARR. VLN., VLA., VLC.   (Op. 32, No. 1)
☆Pasquier Trio   in † ♯ **AS. 3003LD**

No. 108, A major   (Op. 21, No. 6)
No. 114, D major   (Op. 21, No. 4)
No. 124, G major   (Op. 21, No. 5)
— ARR. VLN., VLA. & VLC.   "Divertimenti"
Paris String Trio   **♯ OL.LD 38**
(Pf. Sonata 40, ARR.)

TRIOS, pf., vln. or fl., vlc.
No. 17 (29), F major, Op. 68   1790/1
No. 16 (30), D major, Op. 63   1790
No. 15 (31), G major, Op. 62   1790
R. Veyron-Lacroix, J.-P. Rampal (fl.), J.
Huchot   **♯ OL.LD 35**

No. 25 (1), G major, Op. 73, No. 2   c. 1795
... **Rondo all'ongarese** only   ("Gypsy Rondo")
— ARR. ORCH.   Stradivari Orch. (D.F 44139)

No. 29 (5), E flat major, Op. 75, No. 3
☆J. Février, J. Fournier, P. Fournier
                                 in † ♯ **AS. 3003LD**

[1] This work was Op. 1, No. 1 in the first edition, but was replaced in later editions by No. 5, B flat major (omitted from this recording).
[2] Viola d'amore, descant viola, gamba.

G major, Op. 53, No. 1 *SEE:* Sonata, pf., No. 40

TRIOS, 2 fls. & vlc. ("London Trios")
1. C major 2. G major
3. G major 4. G major
  ☆ P. Kaplan, L. Schaefer, S. Mayes (♯ *CID. 33006*)

C. ORCHESTRAL

CONCERTOS, clavier & orch.
F major (Larsen F1) before 1771
  M. Roesgen-Champion (pf.) & Paris Cons.—
    Goldschmidt ♯ **Clc. 6068**
(*C.P.E. Bach: Concerto*) (♯ *Per.SPLP 556*)

G major, "No. 2" (Larsen G1) *c.* 1772
  ☆ E. Heiller & Collegium Musicum, Vienna—A. Heiller
    (♯ Nix.HLP 1014)

D major, Op. 37 (Larsen D2) (later Op. 21)
  ☆ W. Landowska (hpsi.) & orch.—Bigot
    (♯ *Vic.LCT 1029:* ♭ *set WCT 43*)

CONCERTO, clavier, vln. & orch.
F major (Larsen F3) 1765
  L. Salter (hpsi.), J. Pougnet & London Baroque
  —K. Haas [1] **P.R 20594/6**
(*5ss—Minuets*) (♯ *AmD.DL 9561*)

CONCERTO, fl. & orch.
D major (really by L. Hoffmann) (Larsen VII-6)
  G. Scheck & Scheck-Wenzinger Ens.
  (*Telemann: Overture*) ♯ **Ura. 7031**

CONCERTOS, horn & orch.
No. 1, D major 1762 (Larsen VII-5)
  ☆ F. Koch & Vienna Sym.—Heiller (♯ *Era.LDE 2002*)

No. 2, D major 1770 (doubtful)
  Alfred Brain & Janssen Sym. ♯ **DCap.CTL 7013**
(*Handel*) (♯ *Cap.P 8137*)

CONCERTOS, organ & orch.
No. 1, C major 1756 (Larsen Clav. C1)
No. 2, C major *c.* 1760 (Larsen Clav. C2)
  A. Heiller & Vienna Sym.—Gillesberger
    ♯ **HSLP. 1043**
    (♯ Nix.HLP 1043)

Concerto, tpt. & orch., E flat major 1796
  ☆ H. Wobitsch & Vienna State Op.—Heiller
    (♯ *Era.LDE 2002*)

CONCERTOS, vln. & orch.
A major ("Melk") *c.* 1765
  ☆ E. Bertschinger & Vienna Collegium—Heiller
    (announced as ♯ Nix.HLP 1017 but not issued)

C major, "No. 1" 1765
  ☆S. Goldberg & Philharmonia—Süsskind
(*Bach*) ♯ **Od.ODX 104**

G major, "No. 2" *c.* 1768
  ☆ E. Bertschinger & Collegium Musicum—A. Heiller
    (♯ Nix.HLP 1014)

CONCERTOS, vlc. & orch.
D major (Pohl e.5) pub. 1772
  A. Tusa & Winterthur Sym.—Dahinden
(*Divertimento; & Gluck*) ♯ **CHS.F 7**

D major, "Op. 101" 1783
  P. Fournier & Philharmonia—Kubelik
    G.DB 21448/50
(6ss—cadenzas by Fournier)
  E. Mainardi & Berlin Phil.—Lehmann
    ♮ **PV. 72127/8**
(4ss) (♯ *Pol. 16023*)

  A. Janigro & Vienna State Opera—Prohaska
(*Boccherini*) ♯ **West.WL 5126**
  M. Gendron & Vienna State Opera—Sternberg
(*Saint-Saëns*) ♯ **Oce.OCS 23**
  W. Reichardt & Stuttgart Pro Musica—R.
    Reinhardt [2] ♯ **E. & AmVox.PL 7390**
(*Sinfonia Concertante*)
  G. Cassadò & Austrian Sym.—Wolf
(*Mozart*) ♯ **Rem. 199-79**

(12) Deutsche Tänze (Larsen T7) 1792
  ☆Vienna State Op.—Gillesberger
(*below*) ♯ **Nix.HLP 1022**

Divertimento, D major fl. & str. (ed. Scherchen)
  W. Urfer & Winterthur Sym.—Dahinden
(*above; & Gluck*) ♯ **CHS.F 7**

MARCHES
B flat major 1794 (Slow March)
C major 1783 (for *Armida*)
E flat major 1783
E flat major 1794
  London Baroque Ens.—Haas ♯ **West.WL 5080**
(*Divertimento; & Boccherini, M. Haydn*)

(12) Minuets 1792 (Larsen T6)
  ☆Vienna State Op.—Gillesberger
(*above*) ♯ **Nix.HLP 1022**

...No. 9, C major; No. 11, E flat major
  London Baroque Ens.—Haas **P.R 20596**
(*Clavier Concerto, F major, s.5*) (♯ *AmD.DL 9561*)

NOTTURNI 1790
No. 1, C major No. 2, F major
No. 4, F major No. 7, C major
  ▽ ☆Vienna Cha.—Litschauer ♯ **Nix.HLP 1023**

No. 3, G major No. 5, C major
No. 6, G major
  Vienna Cha.—Litschauer ♯ **HSLP. 1044**
(*Divertimento*) (♯ Nix.HLP 1044)

No. 1, C major (Pohl No. 7)
  London Baroque Ens.—Haas ♯ **West.WL 5080**
(*Marches, Boccherini, M. Haydn*)

Sinfonia Concertante, B flat major, Op. 84 1792
  ob., bsn., vln., vlc. & orch.
  W. Wolsing, C. Bloch, L. Hansen, A. Medici &
    Danish Radio Orch.—Busch **G.C 4122/4**
(*5ss—Mozart: Contre Tänze, K 609, Nos. 1, 2, 4*)
    (♮ DB 20134/6)
  F. Milde, H. Gehring, R. Barchet, S. Barchet &
    Stuttgart Pro Musica—R. Reinhardt
('*Cello Concerto*) ♯**E. & AmVox.PL 7390**
  Soloists & Munich Phil.—Rieger
(*Sym. 85*) ♯ **Mer.MG 10116**

SYMPHONIES [3]
No. 1, D major 1759
  ☆Vienna Sym.—Sternberg **P.R 20616**
(*Nos. 13 & 28 on* ♯ *P.PMA 1001; Od.ODX 108*)

No. 6, D major "Le Matin" 1761
  Bamberg Sym.—Weisbach ♯ **Mer.MG 10079**
(*No. 13*)
  ☆Vienna Cha.—Litschauer ♯ **Nix.HLP 1047**
(*Mozart: Cl. Concerto*)

No. 7, C major "Le Midi" 1761
  Austrian Sym.—Randolph ♯ **Rem. 199-71**
(*Mozart: Sym. 33*)

---

[1] Cadenzas by L. Salter.
[2] Played in the (original) André edition. Most or all other recordings are in the Gevaert re-scoring.
[3] In order of GA. The nos. in brackets are those of the old B & H edition.

No. 12, E major　1763
Vienna State Academy Cho.—Loibner
(Nos. 23, 29, 30)　　　　　　# **Lyr.LL 36**

No. 13, D major　1763
Bamberg Sym.—Weisbach　# **Mer.MG 10079**
(No. 6)
☆Vienna Sym.—Sternberg　# **P.PMA 1001**
(Nos. 1 & 28)　　　　　　(# Od.ODX 108)

No. 19, D major　*c.* 1764
Bamberg Sym.—Weisbach　# **Mer.MG 10077**
(Mozart)

No. 22, E flat major　"The Philosopher"　1764
London Baroque Ens.—Haas　♮ **P.SW 8122/3**
(4ss)　　　　　　　　(# AmD.DL 9561)

No. 23, G major　1764
Vienna State Academy Cha.—Loibner
(Nos. 12, 29, 30)　　　　　# **Lyr.LL 36**

No. 28, A major　1765
☆Vienna Sym.—Sternberg　# **P.PMA 1001**
(¼s.—Nos. 1 & 13)　　　　(# Od.ODX 108)

No. 29, E major　1765
No. 30, C major　"Alleluia"　1765
Vienna State Academy Cha.—Loibner
(Nos. 12 & 23)　　　　　　# **Lyr.LL 36**

No. 39, G minor　*c.* 1769
☆Vienna Sym.—Sternberg　♮ **P.SW 8145/6**
(4ss)

No. 43, E flat major　"Mercury"　before 1772
☆Danish Radio—Wöldike　# **Nix.HLP 1041**
(No. 50)

No. 45 (18), F sharp minor　"Farewell"　1772
Stuttgart Cha.—Münchinger　# **D.LXT 2669**
(Wagner: Siegfried Idyll)　　　(# Lon.LL 525)
(D.K 28590/2, 6ss)
Munich Phil.—Melichar　# *Mer.MG 15028*
(2ss)
Paris Cons.—Goldschmidt　# **Pat.DTX 105**
(No. 85)　　　　　　　　(QTX 105)
Stuttgart Pro Musica—Seegelken
(No. 96)　　　　　　　# **AmVox.PL 7310**

No. 46, B major　1772
Concert Hall Sym.—Goehr　# **CHS.G 14**
(Wondratscheck)

No. 47, G major　1772
☆Vienna Cha.—Litschauer　**P.R 20600/2**
(6ss)　　　　　　　　(Od.O-9180/2)
(No. 84 on # P.PMA 1002; Od.ODX 110)

No. 48 (25), C major　"Maria Theresia"　1772
☆ Vienna State Op.—Scherchen (AusT.E 1131/3)

No. 49, F minor　"Passione"　1768
London Mozart Players—H. Blech
　　　　　　　　　　# **D.LXT 2573**
(Mozart: Divertimento, K 131)　(# Lon.LL 586)
London Haydn Orch.—Newstone
　　　　　　　　　　# **Nix.NLP 902**
(No. 73)　　　　　　　(# HSLP. 1052)

No. 50, C major　1773
☆Danish Radio—Wöldike　# **Nix.HLP 1041**
(No. 43)

No. 54, G major　1774
Vienna State Academy Cha.—Swarowsky
(No. 70; & Mozart)　　　　# **Lyr.LL 32**

No. 55 (21), E flat major "Schoolmaster"　1774
☆ Vienna Sym.—Scherchen (# Sel.LPG 8330)

No. 61, D major　1776
Danish Radio Cha. Orch.—Wöldike
(Mozart: Concerto)　　　　# **HS.HSL 1047**

No. 70, D major　1779
Vienna State Academy Cha.—Swarowsky
(No. 54; & Mozart)　　　　# **Lyr.LL 32**

No. 73, D major　"The Hunt"　1781
London Haydn Orch.—Newstone
　　　　　　　　　　# **Nix.NLP 902**
(No. 49)　　　　　　　(# HSLP. 1052)

No. 80, D minor　*c.* 1782
☆ Vienna Sym.—Scherchen (# Sel.LPG 8320)

No. 84, E flat major　1786
☆Vienna Collegium Musicum—Heiller
　　　　　　　　　　P.R 20607/9
(6ss) (No. 47 on # P.PMA 1002; Od.ODX 110)

No. 85 (15), B flat major　"The Queen"　1786
Paris Cons.—Goldschmidt　# **Pat.DTX 105**
(No. 45)　　　　　　　(QTX 105)
Munich Phil.—Rieger　　# **Mer.MG 10116**
(Sinfonia Concertante)

No. 86 (10), D major　1786
Salzburg Mozarteum—Fekete
　　　　　　　　　　# **Mer.MG 10071**
(No. 88) (Sym. C major on # Eur.LPG 604; Sat.LDG 8004)

No. 88 (13), G major　*c.* 1786
Berlin Phil.—Furtwängler　♮ **PV. 72157/8**
(4ss)　　　(# Pol. 18016; # AmD.DX 119, 1s.)
Salzburg Mozarteum—Fekete # **Mer.MG 10071**
(No. 86)
☆Danish Radio—Busch　　# **Vic.LHMV 1019**
(Mozart)　　　　　　(♮ set WHMV 1019)
☆ Salzburg Festival—P. Walter
　　　　　　(# Mrt. 1-19; also # Rem. 199-89)

No. 92 (16), G major　"Oxford"　1788
Residentie—v. Otterloo　(2ss)　# *Phi.A 00100R*
Munich Phil.—Rieger　(2ss)　# *Mer.MG 15040*
Vienna State Op.—Scherchen　# **West.WL 5137**
(No. 94)
Berlin Sym.—Seegers　(2ss)　　# **Roy. 1327**
☆Cleveland Sym.—Szell　　# **C.CX 1028**
(No. 101)

No. 93 (5), D major　1791
Austrian Sym.—Singer　　# **Rem. 199-110**
(Schubert: Sym. No. 3)
☆ Royal Phil.—Beecham (C.GQX 11472/4)

No. 94 (6), G major　"Surprise"　1791
Royal Phil.—Beecham (6ss)　**C.LX 1499/1501**
(No. 103 on # AmC.ML 4453)
Vienna Phil.—Furtwängler　　**G.DB 21506/8**
(Brahms: Variations on # G.ALP 1011)
(Mozart: Serenade, K 525 in # Vic.LHMV 1018:
　　　　　　　　　　♮ set WHMV 1018)
Amsterdam—v. Beinum　　# **D.LXT 2686**
(Mozart: Symphony No. 33)　　(# Lon.LL 491)
Paris Cons.—Cluytens (6ss)　**Pat.MDT 9/11**
Vienna State Op.—Scherchen # **West.WL 5137**
(No. 92)
☆Berlin Phil.—Lehmann　　# *Pol. 16012*
(No. 101 on # AmD.DL 9617)
Sonor Sym.—Ledermann (# Pde. 2008)
Rome Sym.—Questa (# Roy. 1223)
Nat. Opera Orch. (# Roy. 6099)

No. 95 (9), C minor　1791
☆ Vienna Sym.—Scherchen (# Sel.LPG 8319)

☆ = Re-issue of a recording to be found in WERM or Supplement I.

No. 96 (14), **D major** "Miracle" 1791
Stuttgart Pro Musica—R. Reinhardt
(*No. 45*)   ♯ **AmVox.PL 7310**
Vienna State Op.—Scherchen ♯ **West.WL 5111**
(*No. 98*)
Winterthur Sym.—Goehr   ♯ **MMS. 6**
(*Isola Disabitata, Ov.*)

No. 97 (7), **C major** 1792
Homburg Sym.—P. Schubert   ♯ **Rgt. 5014**

No. 98 (8), **B flat major** 1792
Vienna State Op.—Scherchen
(*No. 96*)   ♯ **West.WL 5111**
Munich Phil.—Rieger   (2ss) ♯ *Mer.MG 15039*

No. 99 (3), **E flat major** 1794
Vienna State Op.—Scherchen ♯ **West.WL 5102**
(*No. 101*)

No. 100, G major "Military" 1794
Copenhagen Royal Op.—Malko   G.C 4187/9
(6ss)   (♮ G.DB 20153/5)
☆L.P.O.—v. Beinum   ♯ **D.LXT 2683**
(*No. 104*)   (♯ Lon.LL 339)
Salzburg Festival—Weidlich   ♯ *Rem. 149-43*
(& with *No. 88*, ♯ Rem. 199-89)   (♯ *Mrt. 1-20*)
    Berlin Sym.—Seegers (♯ Roy. 1328)
   ☆ Vienna Sym.—Scherchen (♯ Sel.LPG 8319)

No. 101 (14), **D major** "Clock" 1794
Vienna State Op.—Scherchen ♯ **West.WL 5102**
(*No. 99*)
R.I.A.S. Sym.—Fricsay   ♮ **PV. 72110/1**
(4ss)   (♯ *Pol. 16013*)
(*No. 94* on ♯ AmD.DL 9617)
☆Philadelphia—Ormandy   ♯ **C.CX 1028**
(*No. 92*)
☆N.B.C. Sym.—Toscanini   ♯ **G.FALP 124**
(*Mozart: Sym. No. 35*)
Austrian State Sym.—Busch   ♯ **MSL.MW 39**
(*Beethoven*) (*4th movt. only on Hma. 15000*)
Berlin Sym.—Balzer   ♯ **Roy. 1356**

No. 102 (12), **B flat major** 1795
Paris Cons.—Goldschmidt   ♯ *Pat.DT 1004*
(2ss)
Munich Phil.—Reinwald   ♯ **Mer.MG 10084**
(*No. 103*)

No. 103 (1), **E flat major** "Drum Roll" 1795
Royal Phil.—Beecham   ♯ **AmC.ML 4453**
(*No. 94*)
Boston Sym.—Münch   ♯ **Vic.LM 1200**
(*Beethoven: Sym. 1*)   (♭ set WDM 1621)
Bamberg Sym.—Heger   ♯ **Mer.MG 10084**
(*No. 102*)
Berlin Sym.—Seegers   ♯ **Roy. 1329**
   ☆ Vienna Sym.—Scherchen (♯ Sel.LPG 8320)

No. 104 (2), **D major** "London" 1795
Austrian Sym.—Annovazzi   ♯ **Rem. 199-56**
(*Mozart*)
☆L.P.O.—Krips   ♯ **D.LXT 2683**
(*No. 100*) (also on D.X 53091/3)   (♯ Lon.LL 339)
   ☆ Vienna Sym.—Scherchen (♯ Sel.LPG 8330)
    Paris Cons.—Cluytens (Pat.MDT 5/7)

C major (ed. Fekete) [1]
☆Salzburg Mozarteum—Fekete
                     ♯ **Sat.LDG 8004**
(*Sym. No. 86*)   (also ♯ Eur.LPG 604, d.c.)

"Toy" Symphony, C major [2]
Philharmonia—Weldon   **C.DX 1784**
     (GQX 11509: SVX 36: DWX 5070: DDX 28)
Paris Radio—Leibowitz   in ♯ **Oce.OCS 29**
(*Corelli & Gluck*)
   ☆ Boston Sym.—Koussevitzky
           (♭ G.7RF 176; Vic.WEPR 7)

[1] One of the 78 Symphonies attributed to Haydn by A. Sandberger (MS., Boston).
[2] Now attributed to Leopold Mozart.

D. MISCELLANEOUS

Andante & Minuet — ARR. GUITAR
   ☆ A. Segovia (in ♯ *AmD.DL 5257*)

Andantino quasi minuetto (unid.)
— ARR. GUITAR
   T. Usher   *Deci.C 1644*
   (*Sor: Andantino*)

HAYDN, Johann Michael (1737-1806)

Divertimento, C major vln., vlc., cbs.
   J. Pougnet, J. Whitehead, J. E. Merritt
                   ♯ **West.WL 5080**
   (*Boccherini & J. Haydn*)

Symphony, G major 1783
— ARR. & attrib. Mozart "No. 37"
ZAÏRE Inc. music to Voltaire's play
... **Turkish Suite**
   ☆Vienna Sym.—Swoboda   ♯ **Sel.LPG 8323**

HEISE, Peter Arnold (1830-1879)

SLEEPING BEAUTY (*Tornerose*) Cantata 1874
(The) Prince's Romance (*Kongesønnens Romance*)
   H. Street (T), K. Olsson (pf.)   *Tono.K 8089*
   (*Forest loneliness*)

SONGS
ARNE Song cycle (Bjørnson)
... **(The) Eagle rises on mighty wings**
   (*Ørnen løfter med staerke Slag*)
   E. Nørby (Bs), G. Nørby (pf.)   *Tono.K 8073*
   (*Lange-Muller: A strip of misty heath*)

Barren is the land (*Gold er den Jord*) (Hostrup)
   E. Sjøberg (T), E. Vagning (pf.)   *Pol.X 51403*
   (*Rung: Where the Nile waters ...*)

Forest loneliness (*Skoveensomhed*) (Aarestrup)
   H. Street (T), K. Olsson (pf.)   *Tono.K 8089*
   (*Sleeping Beauty—Prince's Romance*)

Little Karen (Plough)
   (*Husker du I Høst?; Do you remember harvest-time?*)
   J. Wahl (B) & orch.   *Od.DK 1165*
   (*Gyldmark: Behind the red gate*)

(A) Mountaineer (Ibsen) (*Bergmanden*)
(A) Summer night (Winther) (*En Sommernat*)
   B. Löwenfalk (B), L. Christiansen (pf.) **G.Z 348**

HENRIQUES, Fini Valdemar (1867-1940)

Cradle Song, Op. 3 (*Vuggevise*) (Andersen)
— ARR. VLN. & PF.
   A. Brugman & B. Linderud (*Tono.K 8088*)

(The) LITTLE MERMAID 1910
Ballet after H. C. Andersen (*Den lille Havfrue*)
Orchestral suite
Copenhagen Royal Op.—Hye-Knudsen
(4ss)   **Pol. Z 60146/7**

Romance, D major vln. & pf.
   ☆ M. Skalka & V. Borggaard (*Eli. 9055*)

HERBERIGS, Robert (b. 1886)

(Les) Joyeuses Commères de Windsor
　　Sym. poem after Shakespeare
(Le) Chant de Hiawatha
　　Sym. poem after Longfellow
… Kabibonoka only
　　Belgian Nat.—L. Weemaels　　♯ *D.LX 133019*

HERBERT, Victor (1859-1924)
(His Musical Comedies & Songs are not entered)

American Fantasy
Irish Rhapsody　orch.　pub. 1910
Pan-Americana　orch.　1924
　　Philadelphia Pops—Ormandy
　　　　　　　　　　　　　♯ *AmC.AAL 21*
　　　　　　　　　　　　　(♭ *set A 1030*)

Concerto, vlc. & orch., Op. 30, No. 2　1894
　　B. Greenhouse & A.R.S. Orch.—Schönherr
　　(*Bloch*)　　　　　　　　　　♯ *ARS. 24*

HÉROLD, Louis Joseph Ferdinand
(1791-1833)

OPERAS
(Le) PRÉ AUX CLERCS　3 acts　1832
Jours de mon enfance　S　(Act II)
　H H. Francillon-Kaufmann (*IRCC. 3103**)

ZAMPA　3 acts　1831
Overture
　　L.P.O.—Martinon　　　in ♯ *D.LXT 2606*
　　(*Adam & Boieldieu*)　　(♯ *Lon.LLP 351 & LD 9011*)
　　　　　　　　　　　　　　(also, 2ss, D.K 23208)
　　Boston Pops—Fiedler (n.v.)　♭ *Vic.WEPR 23*
　　(*Zigeunerbaron Ov.*) (probably o.v. on G.DB 4315:
　　　　　　　　　　　　　　　　　FKX 145)
　　Rhineland Sym.—Federer　　♯ *Rgt. 5038*
　　(*Weber & Thomas*)
　　Dresden Phil.—v. Kempen　　**Pol. 15535**
　　　　　　　　　　　　　　　(o.n. ▽ 57351)
　　Berlin Sym.—Balzer　　in ♯ *Roy. 1383*

HEWITT, James (1770-1827)
　SEE: † AMERICAN MUSIC (INST. & CHAMBER)

HIDALGO, Juan (fl. XVIIth Cent.)
　SEE: † SPANISH CHORAL MUSIC

HILL, Alfred (b. 1869)

Blue evening　▽ C. Amodio Quintet (*C.DO 2928*)

Minuet　A. Shaw Ens. (*C.DO 3091*)

SONGS & PART SONGS
And everyone will love me
God be in my head
　　H. de Tarczynska (S)　　　*C.DO 3325*

Caprice; In spite of all
　　H. de Tarczynska (S)　　　*C.DO 3330*

Maori lullaby　A. Rixon Singers (*P.A 7701*)

There is a river　A. Rixon Singers (*P.A 7707*)

HILTON, John, senior (d. c. 1608)
　SEE: † TRIUMPHS OF ORIANA

HILTON, John, junior (1599-1657)
　SEE: † CATCHES AND GLEES

HINDEMITH, Paul (b. 1895)

Concerto, vla. & orch. "Der Schwanendreher" 1935
　　G. Breitenbach & Vienna Sym.—Haefner
　　(*below*)　　　　　　　　♯ **AmVox.PL 7460**
　　Anon. soloist & Berlin Sym.—List ♯ **Roy. 1311**
　　(*Smetana: My Country, No. 2*)

Hérodiade　Ballet　1944
("A recitation for Chamber orchestra after a poem by
　Mallarmé")
　　Vienna Sym.—Haefner　　♯ **AmVox.PL 7460**
　　(*above*)

Kammermusik No. 1, Op. 24, No. 1　Cha. orch.
　1922
　　Little Orch. Soc.—Scherman　♯ **B.AXL 2005**
　　(*Stravinsky: Suites*)　　　(‡ *AmD.DL 7529*)

Kammermusik No. 2, Op. 24, No. 2
　fl., ob., cl., hrn., bsn.　1922
　　French Wind Quintet　　　♯ **OL.LD 21**
　　(*Sonata, below*)

Kammermusik No. 4, Op. 36, No. 3　vln. & orch.
　1925
　　P. Rybar & Winterthur Sym.—Swoboda
　　(*below*)　　　　　　　　♯ **West.WL 5074**

Morning Music　brass insts.　1932
　(*Plöner Musiktag—No. 1*)
　　Brass Ens.—Shuman　　　♯ **Circ.L 51-100**
　　(*below*)

Philharmonic Dances　orch.　1937
　(or: *Symphonische Tänze*)
　　R.I.A.S. Sym.—Fricsay　　　**PV. 72078/9**
　　(4ss)　　　(‡ *Pol. 16011; AmD.DL 7520*)

(8) Pieces for Str. Qtt., Op. 44, No. 3
　　Radio Artists Qtt.　　　♯ **Circ.L 51-100**
　　(*above & below*)

QUARTETS, String
No. 3, C major, Op. 22　1922
　　Hollywood Qtt.　　　　♯ **DCap.CTL 7016**
　　(*Prokofiev*)　　　　　　(‡ *Cap.P 8151*)
　　Fine Arts Qtt.　　　　♯ **Mer.MG 10105**
　　(*Ravel*)

No. 4, D major, Op. 32　1924
　　☆Guilet Qtt.　　　　　♯ **CHS.CHS 1086**

SONATAS
Bassoon & piano　1938
　　B. Garfield & T. Lettvin　　♯ **EMS. 4**
　　(*below*)

Clarinet & piano　1939
　　R. Kell & J. Rosen　　　♯ **AmD.DL 9570**
　　(*Debussy & Stravinsky*)

Flute & piano　1936
　　S. Caratelli & G. Manley　　♯ **NRI. 406**
　　(*Guarnieri, Milhaud, Ibert, etc.*)
　　☆J.-P. Rampal & R. Veyron-Lacroix
　　　　　　　　　　　　　　♯ **Clc. 6032**
　　(*Bach, Dukas, Honegger, Roussel, etc.*)

☆ = Re-issue of a recording to be found in WERM or Supplement I.

SONATAS (continued)

Oboe & piano 1938
P. Pierlot & A. d'Arco   # OL.LD 21
(Kammermusik)

Organ, No. 1 1937
F. Heitmann   in † # T.LSK 7010/1

Piano solo, Nos. 1 & 2 1936
L. H. Behrendt   # SPA. 33[1]

Piano 4-hands 1938
Two Pianos 1942
K. & M. Kohn   # Cmt. 1203

Trombone & piano 1940
D. Shuman & V. Rivkin   # Circ.L 51-100
(above & below)
R. Smith & T. Lettvin   # EMS. 4
(above & below)

Trumpet & piano 1939
A. Wilson & T. Lettvin   # EMS. 4
(above)

Violin & piano, No. 3, E major 1935
R. Posselt & A. Sly   in # Acad.ALP 304
(Prokofiev, etc.)

Viola & piano, F major, Op. 11, No. 4 1922
F. Tursi & J. Echaniz   # CHS.G 12
(Berg)

Violoncello & piano, Op. 11, No. 3
C. Stern & P. O'Niel   # SPA. 8
(R. Strauss)

Symphony, Mathis der Maler 1934
☆N.B.C. Sym.—Cantelli   ♮ G.DB 9765/7
(6ss)   (# BLP 1010)
☆ Berlin Phil.—Hindemith (# T.LB 6002; FT,T 124/6)

Theme and four variations pf. & orch.
(The four temperaments)
F. Holletschek & Vienna Sym.—Swoboda
(above)   # West.WL 5074
☆L. Foss & Zimbler Sinfonietta   # B.AXL 2001

Trauermusik vla. & str. 1936
R. Persinger & Cha. Ens.   # Strad.STR 608
(Turina, Villa-Lobos, Handel)

— ARR. TBN. & STR. QTT.
D. Shuman & Radio Artists Qtt.
(above)   # Circ.L 51-100

HØFFDING, Finn (b. 1899)

Dialogues, Op. 10 ob. & cl.
W. Wolsing & P. A. Erichsen   G.DB 5274

It is perfectly true, Op. 37 Fantasy, orch. 1947
(after H. C. Andersen)
▽ Tivoli—Jensen (Tono.X 25090)

(The) Violet dot (Kristensen) male cho. 1940
▽ Students' Cho.—Hye-Knudsen (G.X 6689)

HOHENZOLLERN,
Prince Louis Ferdinand von (1772-1806)

Rondo No. 2, pf. & orch.
O. A. Graef & Frankenland State Sym.—Kloss
(Dittersdorf)   # Lyr.LL 26

[1] Announced but apparently not issued.

HOLMBOE, Vagn (b. 1909)

Quartet, String, No. 1, Op. 46
E. Bloch Qtt. (6ss)   ♮ G.DB 20137/9

HOLMES, John (fl. 1601)
SEE: † TRIUMPHS OF ORIANA

HOLST, Gustav Theodore (1874-1934)

Christmas Song (Personent hodie) (ARR. Holst)
J. Wilson (S), G. Trovillo (pf.) in # AmD.DL 9554
(Brahms, Schumann, etc.)
UOS Cho.—McConnell   in # UOS.pte.
(Lojero: Piffero di Natale; Billings, etc.)

Lullay, my liking, Op. 34b (Anon.) 1916
Randolph Singers   in # West.WL 5100
Columbia Choristers—Engel in # AmC.ML 2199

Midwinter (C. Rossetti)
Columbia Choristers—Engel in # AmC.ML 2199

(The) Planets, Op. 32 1915
☆ B.B.C. Sym.—Boult (# Vic.LHMV 1002:
♭ set WHMV 1002)

HOMANN,
SEE: † AMERICAN MUSIC OF EARLY ROMANTIC PERIOD

HONEGGER, Arthur (b. 1892)

Concertino, piano & orch. 1924
F. Jacquinot & Philharmonia—Fistoulari
MGM.E 122
(Milhaud; Concerto)   (♭ set K 122)

Danse de la chèvre fl. unacc.
☆J. P. Rampal   # Clc. 6032
(Bach, Dukas, Beethoven, Hindemith, etc.)

Monopartita orch. 1951
(for the 600th anniversary of entry of Canton Zürich into
the Swiss Confederation)
French Nat. Radio—Sacher   # Pat.DT 1009
(below)

(7) Pièces brèves pf. 1920
L. Thyrion   in # Phi.N 00601R
(Satie, Auric, Poulenc)

(Le) ROI DAVID Opera-Psalm 1923 version
Narrator, S, A, B, org. & orch.
J. Hervé, J. Micheau, J. Collard, P. Mullet,
M. Duruflé, cho. & French Nat. Radio—
Honegger   # West. set WAL 204
(4ss)

Sonata No. 1, vln. & pf. 1916-18
M. Crut & J. C. Englebert   # Sel.LPG 8241
(Delvincourt: Sonata)

Sonata, vla. & pf. 1920
K. Boon & C. de Groot   # Phi.A 00613R
(Milhaud: Sonata)
M. Mann & D. Newlin (2ss)   PV. 72249

SONG: Murcie en fleurs (Aguet) 1940
C. Panzéra (B), M. Panzéra (pf.)
         in # **Mer.MG 10098**
(*Milhaud, Ravel, Aubert, etc.*)

Suite archaïque orch. 1950-1
1. Ouverture   2. Pantomime
3. Ritournelle et Sérénade   4. Processional
    French Nat. Radio—Sacher   # *Pat.DT 1009*
    (*above*)

HORNEMAN, Christian Frederik Emil
(1841-1906)

ALADDIN Opera, 4 acts 1888
Overture 1866
  ▽Danish Radio—Tuxen   **Pol.HM 57187**

GURRE Inc. music to Drachmann's drama 1902
Orchestral Suite
  ▽Danish Radio—Tuxen   **Pol.HM 80047/8**

Other ▽ recordings include:
Our home (from University Cantata, 1906) (*G.X 6900*)

NOTE:
From the green tree's lofty top
      (in *G.Z 227, AL 1366, Pol.X 51307, etc.*)
King of Kings (*G.X 6899, DA 5213, Pol. 43315, etc.*)
are by J. O. E. Horneman (1809-1870)

HOVHANESS, Alan (b. 1911)

COLLECTION
Achtamar   pf.
Concerto   pf. & cha. orch.
Shatakh   vln. & pf.
Tzaikerk   vln., fl. & orch.
  ☆ M. Ajemian, etc. (# Mtr.CLP 505)

HOWE, Mary (b. 1882)

Interlude fl. & pf.
(3) Pieces after Emily Dickinson str. qtt.
Suite str. qtt. & pf.
   Catholic Univ. of America Ens.   # **WCFM. 9**

SONGS & CHORUSES: COLLECTION
   SONGS:
     Ma douleur   (Baudelaire)
     Fragment   (C. Lee)
     O Proserpina
       (Shakespeare—Winter's Tale, Act. IV, Sc. 3)
     Mein Herz   (M. Schaffy)
     When I died in Berners Street   (Wylie)
   K. Hansel (S), T. Schaffer (pf.)

     Lullaby for a Forester's child   (Frost)
     (The) Rag Picker   (F. Shaw)
     Innisfree   (Yeats)
     To the unknown soldier   (N. G. Lely, from the Greek)
   H. Ronk (T), T. Schaffer (pf.)

   CHORUSES
     Williamsburg Sunday   (K. G. Chaplin)
     (The) Horseman   (W. de la Mare)
     Music when soft voices die   (Shelley)
     Chain Gang song   (trad.)
     Cavaliers   (Masefield)
     Song of Ruth   (Old Testament, Ruth I)
   Howard Univ. Cho.—Lawson   # **WCFM. 13**

▽ Older issues include:
   Str. Qtt. ... Allegro inevitabile
     Coolidge Qtt. (Vic. 11-8126 in set M 891)
   Stars   Nat. Sym., U.S.A.—Kindler (Vic. 11-8608)

HUBAY, Jenö (1855-1937)

Hejre Kati **Op. 32**   M. Skalka Orch. (*Eli. 8988*)

(The) VIOLIN MAKER OF CREMONA Opera 1 act 1894
Intermezzo   G. Garay (vln.) & pf.   (*Qual.QKM 5002*)

(The) Zephyr **Op. 30, No. 5**   vln. & pf.
  ☆ D. Oistrakh & S. Topilin (in # Csm.CRLP 105)

HÜE, Georges (1858-1948)

SONG: À des oiseaux   (Adenis)
  ▽L. Pons (S) & orch.   **C.LX 1539**
   (⅓s.—*Rachmaninoff: How fair this spot; & Martini: Plaisir
   d'amour*) (in AmC. set MM 942: # *ML 2138*)

HUMFREY, Pelham (1647-1674)

As freezing fountains
My lytell prety one
   L. Watts (T), N. Newby (pf.)   *Argo.R 1008*
   (*Anon: Have you seen but a white lily grow*)

(A) **Hymne to God the Father**   (Donne)
   A. Deller (C-T), G. Jones (org.)   **G.C 4144**
   (*Purcell: Evening Hymn*)

HUMMEL, Jan Nepomuk (1778-1837)

Concerto, A minor, Op. 85, pf. & orch.
   A. Balsam & Winterthur Sym.—Ackermann
   (*Clementi*)   # **CHS.G 11**

Écossaise, C major   pf.   (unid.)
— ARR. ORCH.   Anon. orch. (*Scd. 2006*)

Rondo, E flat, Op. 11   ("Rondo favori")   pf
   G. Werschenska   **Pol.HM 80053**
   (*Mozart: Rondo, K 485*)

HUMPERDINCK, Engelbert (1854-1921)

Maurische Rhapsodie 1898
   Leipzig Gewandhaus—Abendroth   # **Ura. 7020**

OPERAS
HÄNSEL UND GRETEL 3 acts 1893
COMPLETE RECORDING

Hänsel	M. L. Schilp (M-S)
Gretel	... E. Berger (S)
Father	H. H. Nissen (Bs)
Mother	... E. Waldenau (S)
Hexe	M. Arndt-Ober (A)
Sandman	H. Erdmann (M-S)

   etc., Berlin Mozart Boys' Cho., Berlin Radio
   Sym.—Rother   (4ss)   # **Ura. set 212**

Orchestral Suite
   Vienna Radio—Nilius   **Vien.L 6068**
                     (in # *1009*)
  ☆C.B.S.—Barlow   # **AmC.RL 3010**
   (*Schubert: Sym. 2*)
  ☆ Berlin State—F. Walter (G.FKX 246)

Prelude   ☆ Sym.—Stokowski (♭ Vic. 49-1376)

Abendsegen, Act I — ARR. CHO.
   Trapp Family (*Eng*) (in # CHS.CHS 1101)

☆ = Re-issue of a recording to be found in WERM or Supplement I.

HÄNSEL UND GRETEL (*continued*)
Dream Pantomime, Act II
Vic. Sym.—Reiner   ♭ *Vic. 49-3442*
Philharmonia—Weldon   **C.DX 1811**
              (♭ *SCD 2013*)
☆ L.P.O.—Collins (♯ *Lon.LD 9025*)

(Die) KÖNIGSKINDER   3 acts   1910
Introduction, Act III
☆ Dresden Phil.—Seidler (Pol. 15508)

SONGS
Am Rhein   (Wildenroth)
    ☆ H. Schlusnus (B) (in ♯ *AmD.DL 9623*)

(Der) Stern von Bethlehem   (H. Humperdinck)
    J. Wilson (S), G. Trovillo (pf.) in ♯ **AmD.DL 9554**
    (*Gounod, Massenet, etc.*)

HUNT, Thomas (fl. 1600)
    SEE: † TRIUMPHS OF ORIANA

HURLSTONE, William Y. (1876-1906)

(The) Derby Ram   (Trad.; ARR. Hurlstone)
Wilt thou be my dearie ?   (Burns)
    F. Smith (B), M. Carr (pf.)   **Croy.CX 3**
    (*Stanford & Parry*)

HUYBRECHTS, Albert (1899-1938)

Sicilienne   (Hommage à G. Fauré)   pf.
    P. de Clerck   **C.BF 5008**
    (*J. Stehmann: Matins*)

IBERT, Jacques (b. 1890)

Capriccio   orch.   1938
Divertissement   orch.   1930
Suite élisabethaine   S, cho., orch.   1942
    ☆ E. Loose, Academy Cho. & Vienna Sym.—Swoboda
              (♯ *Sel.LPG 8489*)

Concerto da camera   sax. & 11 insts.   1934
    M. Abato & orch.—Shulman   ♯ **Phil. 103**
    (*Glazounov*)

Escales   Suite, orch.   1922
    Sym.—Stokowski   ♯ *Vic.LM 151*
    (*Berlioz, Sibelius,Granados*)
         (*Berlioz* only in ♭ set *WDM 1628*)
    ☆ N.Y.P.S.O.—Rodzinski   ♯ *C.FC 1003*
    (*Milhaud: Suite francaise*)

(10) HISTOIRES   pf.
No. 7, Bajo la mesa   — ARR. SAX & PF.
    ▽ M. Mule & M. Pellas-Lenon   *Sel.SA 7001*
    (*P. Bonneau: Caprice en forme de valse*)

(Le) JARDINIER DE SAMOS   1924
    Inc. music to Vildrac's comedy
Prelude, Act II
    B. Urban (vln.), M. Hubert (vlc.)   ♯ **CEd. 1005**
    (*Ravel, Milhaud, Debussy*)

(3) Pièces brèves   fl., ob., cl., hrn., bsn.
    Paris Wind Quintet   (2ss)   **D.GAF 15112**
    ☆ New York Quintet (in ♯ *Cpt.MC 20001*)

Pièce pour flûte seule   pub. 1936
    S. Caratelli   ♯ **NRI. 406**
    (*Guarnieri, etc.*)

INFANTE, Manuel (b. 1883)

Canto flamenco   pf.
    (from *Pochades andalouses*)
    L. Podolsky   in ♯ *Cmt. 1204*
    (*Liszt, Méhul, etc.*)

Guadalquivir   pf.
    A. Iturbi   ♭ *Vic. 49-3309*
    (*Fauré*)

Tientos   pf.
    G. Copeland   in ♯ *MGM.E 87*
              (♮ set 87: ♭ *K 87*)

INGEGNERI, Marc' Antonio (c. 1545-1592)

O bone Jesu   3 voices
    Harvard Univ. Cho.—Russell in ♯ *Fest. 70-202*
    († Pre-baroque sacred music)

Tenebrae factae sunt
    ☆ Milan Madrigalists—Fait
             in ♯ *Csm.CLPS 1027*
    († Italian Madrigals)

IPPOLITOFF-IVANOFF, Michael Michaelovitch (1859-1935)

ASSYA, Op. 30   Opera   1899
In cellar cool   (Fischer's song, incorp. in the opera)
    M. Mikhailov (Bs)   *USSR. 12212*
    (*Beethoven: Scottish toast*)

Bless the Lord, O my soul   cho.
    ☆ De Paur Infantry Cho. (in ♯ *AmC.ML 4144*)

Caucasian Sketches, Op. 10   1894
    Paris Cons.—Désormière   in ♯ *D.LXT 2610*
    (*Tchaikovsky: Sleeping Beauty*)   (♯ *Lon.LLP 440*)
    Philharmonia—Schuechter   ♯ *MGM.E 137*
    ☆ Philharmonia—Malko (in ♯ *BB.LBC 1019*:
                    ♭ set *WBC 1019*)
    Austrian Sym.—Wöss (♯ *Mrt. 1-4* & ♯ *Rem. 199-88*, d.c.)

... No. 4, Procession of the Sardar only
    Philharmonia—Weldon   **C.DX 1792**
    (*Thaïs, Meditation*)

Voroshilov March, Op. 67
    Bolshoi Theatre—Nebolsin   **USSR. 03727**
    (*Glier: Festival Overture*)

IRELAND, John (b. 1879)

April   pf.   1924
    J. Ireland   **G.DB 9651**
    (*Mai-Dun, s.1*)

Decorations   pf.   1913
London Pieces   pf.   1917-20
Sonata, E minor   pf.   1920
    E. Parkin   ♯ **Argo.ARS 1004**

Mai-Dun   Sym. rhapsody   orch.   1921
    Hallé—Barbirolli   ♮ **G.DB 9651/2**
    (3ss—*April*)

SONGS
Sea Fever   (Masefield)
    F. Harvey (B), with orch.   **G.B 10233**
    (*Moussorgsky: Song of the flea*)

(The) Soldier   (Brooke)
    L. Watts (T), N. Newby (pf.)   *Argo.R 1007*
    (*Butterworth: Is my team ploughing*)

♯ = Long-playing, 33⅓ r.p.m.   ♭ = 45 r.p.m.   ♮ = Auto. couplings, 78 r.p.m.

106

ISAAC, Heinrich (c. 1450-1517)

Christus is opgestanden
T'meiskin was jonck
Innsbruck, ich muss dich lassen
Dutch Vocal Qtt.—Raugel   † # AS. 2501LD

Innsbruck . . . (Herr Gott, lass dich erbarmen)
F. Peeters   in # Ren.X 39
(† Old Netherland Masters)

Proprium missae in Dominica Laetare
Aachen Cath. Cho.—Rehmann   PV. 5403

Vergangen ist mir Glück und Heil
Harvard & Radcliffe Choirs   in # Acad. 308
(† Courtly Music)

IVES, Charles Edward (b. 1874)

(A) Set of pieces pf. & orch. 1912-15
S. Anderson & Vienna State Op.—Sternberg
(Milhaud)   # Oce.OCS 31

(The) Sixty-seventh Psalm
Hamline Singers—Holliday   # NRI. 305
(Křenek, etc.)

SONATAS
Piano, No. 1 1902-10
W. Masselos   # AmC.ML 4490

Violin & pf.
No. 1 1903-8
No. 3 1907-10
J. Field & L. Mittman   # Lyr.LL 17

IVES, Simon (1600-1662)
SEE : † Catches and Glees

JACOB le Polonais (fl. XVIth Cent.)
SEE : † Polish Keyboard Music

JACOBI, Frederick (b. 1891)

Concerto, vln. & orch. (A. Gertler, vln.) 1937
Concertino, pf. & str. orch. (I. Jacobi, pf.) 1935
Dance ; Nocturne in Nineveh (F. Stoefs, fl.) 1922-8
Belgian Nat. Radio Orch.—André   # SPA. 7

JACOPO DA BOLOGNA (fl. XIVth Cent.)
SEE : † Italian Madrigal

JACOTIN (Jacques Godebrye) (c. 1445-1528)
SEE : † Courtly Music of the XVIth Century

JÄRNEFELT, Armas (b. 1869)

Berceuse, G minor orch.
Praeludium orch.
▽Covent Garden—Braithwaite   G.B 10136
                                (TG 101 : EG 7726)
☆ Sym.—Järnefelt (Od.PLD 19)

... Berceuse only   B. Saenger (vln.) & orch. (Od.O-28365)

Sunday (Leino) Song
A. Ohlson (T), S. Ehrling (pf.)   (Swed)
(Grieg: A dream)   Od.SD 5646

JANÁČEK, Leoš (1854-1928)

KATYA KABANOVA Opera, 3 acts 1921
Highlights
E. Zachardova, S. Spurna, J. Válka, A. Pelc,
E. Šíma, cho., Brno Radio Sym.—Bakala
(6ss)   ♮ U.H 24215/7

Sinfonietta orch. 1926
Leipzig Radio—V. Neumann   # Ura. 7030
(Rossini - Respighi: Rossiniana)

☆Czech Phil.—Bakala   # Sup.LPM 21

Slavonic Mass 1926
Soloists, Mixed Cho., Brno Radio Sym.—
Bakala (Fr. Michalek—org.) ♮ U.H 23791/6
(12ss)   (# Sup.LPM 39/40, 3ss; # Ura. 7072)

Sonata, 1-x-1905 pf.
J. Páleniček   ♮ U.H 24211/2
(4ss) (Slavonic Mass, s.1 on # Sup.LPM 39)

▽Z. Jilek (2ss)   Esta.F 5197

Youth Suite, 6 wind insts. 1924
Berlin Radio Ens.—M. Lange # CdM.LDX 8017
(Mozart: Musikalischer Spass)

JANNEQUIN, Clément (c. 1500-c. 1560)

CHANSONS
Collection of 14
☆ M. Couraud Ens. (# DFr. 12)

Au joly bois
Harvard & Radcliffe Choirs   in # Acad. 308
(† Courtly Music)

Au joly jeu
☆ Pro Musica Cho.—Calder (in # CID. 33007)

(La) plus belle de la ville
Bristol Univ. Fr. Circle—Banham
                              in # Per.SPLP 535
(† Renaissance Masterpieces)

MASS, La Bataille
... Benedictus; Osanna
Monaco Cath. Cho.—H. Carol
                              in † # SM. 33-01

JAUBERT, Maurice (1900-1940)

(L')Eau vive Song cycle (Giono)
... (Le) Marmitier only
J. Jansen (B), L. Laskine (hp.) D.GAF 15107
(½s.—Thiriet: Visiteurs du soir)

JENNINGS, Arthur B.
SEE : † American Church Music

☆ = Re-issue of a recording to be found in WERM or Supplement I.

JENSEN, Adolf (1837-1879)

SONGS
O lass dich halten, gold'ne Stunde, Op. 35, No. 3 (Roquette)
(Der) Schmied, Op. 24, No. 6 (Uhland)
Über Nacht
    M. Klose (A), M. Raucheisen (pf.)
                     in ♯ **Ura. 7053**

JERSILD, Jørgen (b. 1913)

Alice in Wonderland (F. Geill) Inc. music
Actors, Danish Radio Madrigal Cho. & orch.—
    Wöldike (*Dan*) (6ss)   ♮ **G.Z 7041/3**

JOHNSON, Edward (fl. 1600)

SEE: † Triumphs of Oriana

JOHNSON, Hunter (b. 1906)

LETTER TO THE WORLD Ballet 1940, rev. 1948
Suite Cha. orch. 1952
    Concert Hall Cha. Orch.—Hull
    (J. Kirkpatrick—pf.)   ♯ **CHS.CHS 1151**
    (*Vaughan Williams*)   (♯ **Nix.CLP 1151**)

JOHNSON, Robert (c. 1583-1633)

SEE: † Early English Keyboard Music

JOIO, Norman dello (b. 1913)

(A) Psalm of David (the 51st Psalm, *Latin*)
Crane Cho. & N.Y. State Univ. Teachers'
College Orch.—Hosmer   ♯ **CHS.CHS 1118**

Symphony, The Triumph of St. Joan
Louisville Sym.—Whitney   ♯ **AmC.ML 4615**
(*Villa-Lobos*)

JONES, Robert (d. c. 1617)

SEE: † Triumphs of Oriana

JONGEN, Joseph (1873–1953)

Berceuse pf.
Petite Suite, Op. 75 pf. 1924
… **No. 2, Conte plaisant** only
    S. Cambier (1s. each)   **C.DCB 58**

Soleil à midi pf. 1908
    P. de Clerck (2ss)   **C.BF 5007**

SUITES orch.
No. 3, dans le style ancien, Op. 93 1930
    Belgian Nat.—Quinet   ♯ **D.LX 133012**

JONGEN, Léon (b. 1885)

Malaisie orch. suite 1935
1. Bali   2. Bourouboudour   3. Manilla—La Feria
    Belgian Nat.—L. Jongen   ♯ **D.LX 133009**

JOSQUIN des Prés (c. 1445-1521)

Canzona
    F. Peeters (org.)   in ♯ **Ren.X 39**
    († Old Netherlands Masters)

CHANSONS
COLLECTION of 13
    ☆ M. Couraud Ens. (♯ *DFr. 7*)

Coeurs désolez
    ☆ Pro Musica—Calder (in ♯ *CID. 33007*)

Mille regretz
    Harvard & Radcliffe Choirs   in ♯ **Acad. 308**
    († Courtly Music)

Scaramella
    Dutch Vocal Qtt.—Raugel   † ♯ *AS. 2501LD*

MOTETS
Ave Maria
    Nonesuch Singers—Smith   in ♯ **Per.SPLP 535**
    († Renaissance Masterpieces)
    ☆Dessoff Cho.—Boepple   ♯ **Nix.CLP 47**
    (*Lassus*)

… **Ave vera virginitas** (sung to Veni, creator Spiritus)
    Harvard Univ. Cho.—Russell in ♯ *Fest. 70-202*
    († Pre-baroque sacred music)

Ave verum corpus
    Nonesuch Singers—R. D. Smith
                 in ♯ **Per.SPLP 535**
    (†Renaissance Masterpieces)

De profundis
    ☆Dessoff Cho.—Boepple   ♯ **Nix.CLP 47**
    (*Lassus*)

JOSTEN, Werner (b. 1888)

ENDYMION Ballet suite 1933
    Vienna Philharmonia—Haefner   ♯ **SPA. 16**
    (*Antheil*)

KABALEVSKY, Dmitri (b. 1904)

COLAS BREUGNON, Op. 24 Opera, 3 acts 1938
Overture ☆ N.B.C. Sym.—Toscanini (♭ *G.7RF 128*)

(The) COMEDIANS, Op. 26 orch. suite
(omits nos. 5 & 10)
    USSR. State Sym.—Yuriev   **U.C 23847/8**

… Nos. 2, 3, 4 Sym.—Straszynski (2ss)   *Muza. 1586*

… No. 2 Variety Theatre—Vlach (*U.C 24199*)

Concerto No. 2, G minor pf. & orch. 1948
    G. Ginsberg, USSR. State—Anosov
    (6ss)   ♮ **U.H 23912/4**

♯ = Long-playing, 33⅓ r.p.m.   ♭ = 45 r.p.m.   ♮ = Auto. couplings, 78 r.p.m.

108

Concerto, vln. & orch., C major, Op. 48 1948
　☆D. Oistrakh & USSR. Sym.—Kabalevsky
　　　　　　　　　　　　　# Van.VRS 6002
　(Khrennikov)　(♮ *U.C 23941/3*; also on # *Csm.CLPS 123*)

... **Andante cantabile** only
　I. Bezrodni & Sym. Orch.—Straszynski
　　　　　　　　　　　　　Muza. 1553

Quartet, Strings, No. 2, G minor, Op. 44
　Beethoven Qtt. (8ss)　　USSR. 015424/31

SONGS & PART SONGS
Before the monument (Lebedev-Kumach)
　A. Pirogov (B)　　　　*USSR. 14775*
　(Mokroŭsov: The Falcons are coming)

Our country (Prishelets)
　Railwaymen's Children's Ens.　*USSR. 18925*
　(Levina: We pass by the Kremlin)

Pioneers' Songs (Vysotskaya)
... **Our leader**
... **The Pioneer patrol**
　Children's Cho. & orch.—Roitman
　　　　　　　　　　　　　USSR. 21015
　(½s. each—*Levina: Pioneers' Camp song*)

(The) TARAS FAMILY Opera *c.* 1951
Taras' aria, Sc.7　　　B
　A. Pirogov (2ss)　　*USSR. 19207/8*

KALINNIKOV, Basil Sergeivitch
　　　　　　　　　(1866-1901)

(The) Crane
　Railwaymen's Children's Cho.—Dunayevsky (*USSR.6371*)

Symphony No. 1, G minor
　USSR. State Radio—Rakhlin　# West.WL 5136

KALLSTENIUS, Edvin (b. 1881)

Scherzo fugato, Op. 4 (1907, orch. 1923)
　Stockholm Radio—Hellman　　*Cup. 4116*

KAPR, Jan (b. 1914)

In Soviet Land Cantata
　Prague Radio Cho., Czech Phil.—Ančerl
　(5ss—*Serenade*)　　　　♮ U.H 23983/5

Serenade orch.
　Film Sym.—Strníště　　　U.H 23983
　(In Soviet Land, s.I)

KARG-ELERT, Sigfrid (1877-1933)

Landscape in the mist, Op. 96, No. 2 org.
　C. Snyder　　　　　in # KR. 15
　(Schumann, Dupré, etc.)

Sonata appassionata, F sharp minor, Op. 140
　fl. unacc.
　S. Caratelli　　　　# NRI. 402
　(Enesco, Platti)

Soul of the lake, Op. 96, No. 1 org.
　R. Ellsasser　　　in # MGM.E 3005

KAUFMAN, Armin (b. 1902)

Music for trumpet & string orch. 1948
　H. Wobitsch & Vienna Cha. Orch.—Litschauer
　(Milhaud)　　　　　　# SPA. 12

KERCKHOVEN, Abraham van der (1627-1673)

SEE : † OLD NETHERLANDS MASTERS

KHACHATURIAN, Aram (b. 1903)

Concerto, D flat major pf. & orch. 1936
　M. Huttner & Berlin Sym.—Rubahn # Roy.1276
　☆ O. Levant & N.Y.P.S.O.—Mitropoulos (# *C.FCX 136*)

Concerto, D major vln. & orch. 1940
　☆ D. Oistrakh & USSR. State—Gauk
　　　　　　(# *Csm.CRLPX 001*; ♮ *U.H 24098/103*)

Concerto, vlc. & orch.
　S. Knushevitsky & USSR. State—Gauk
　　　　　　　　　　　♮ U.H 23922/6
　(10ss)　　　　　　　(# *Sup.LPV 43*)

Dance, B flat major, Op. 1 vln. & pf.
　☆ D. Oistrakh & pf. (in # Csm.CRLP 105)

GAYANEH Ballet
Suites 1 & 2
　☆ N.Y.P.S.O.—Kurtz (# C.FCX 153)

Suite No. 1
　Berlin Sym.—Hermann　　# Roy. 1294
　(Rimsky-Korsakov: Capriccio espagnol) (& in # *Roy. 6129*)
... Nos. 1 & 2 ☆ N.Y.P.S.O.—Kurtz (♮ *AmC.A 1509*)
... Nos. 1, 3, 5 ☆ Philharmonia—Malko
　　　　　　(G.S 10593: FKX 159: ♮ *7P 103*)
... **Nos. 1 & 2** — ARR. VLN. & PF.
　L. Kogan & pf.　　　*USSR. 15901/2*

... **No. 1, Sabre Dance**
　Aarhus Municipal—Jensen　　*Tono.L 28044*
　(Bartered Bride—Dance of the Comedians)
　　　　　　　　　　(in # *Mer.MG 15045*)
　Rhineland Sym.—Federer　　in # Rgt. 5049
　Variety Theatre—Vlach (*U.C 24199*)
　☆ Chicago Sym.—Rodzinski (♮ *Vic. 49-0137*)

— — ARR. PF. Swarsenski
　C. de Groot　　　　*PhM.A 11245S*
　(Bartók: Allegro barbaro)

— — ARR. 2 PFS. M. Rawicz & W. Landauer (*C.DB 3030*)

— — ARR. 4 PFS.
　First Piano Qtt.　　　*Vic. 10-3416*
　(Anderson)　　　　　(♮ *49-3416*)

Lezghinka (from Dance Suite No. 5) 1933
　☆Bolshoi Theatre—Nebolsin
　　　　　　　　in # Csm.CRLP 108/9

MASQUERADE Inc. music to Lermontov's play
... Waltz & Mazurka Ens.—Yuriev　*USSR. 13814/6*
... Waltz — ARR. 2 PFS. M. Rawicz & W. Landauer
　　　　　　　　　　　　(*C.DB 3030*)

Song Poem vln. & pf. 1929
　☆ D. Oistrakh (in # *Csm.CRLP 110*; *U.C 24112*)

SONGS & PART SONGS
(The) Baltic Sea (Rodionov)
　A. Pirogov (B)　　　　*USSR. 11714*
　(Bely: Ballad of Captain Gastello)

☆ = Re-issue of a recording to be found in WERM or Supplement I.

SONGS & PARTSONGS (*continued*)
Drinking Song (Trad.)
Kanali Erg (Grashi)
   Z. Dolukhanova (A, *Armenian*) *USSR. 19860/1*

O Garden, my beloved
   M. Alexandrovich (T)   *USSR. 16118*
   (*Kompaneyets: Cradle Song*)

Story of Grandfather Frost
   Anon. Artists   # *Csm.CRLPX 003*

What children dream of (Gradov)
   Children's Cho.—Chmyrev (*USSR. 19564*)

Symphony No. 2 1943
   ☆USSR. State—Gauk (14ss)   ♮ **U.H 23890/6**

Toccata, E flat minor   pf.
   V. Warlev   **Tono.A 174**
   (½s.—*Prokofiev & Schubert*)
   F. Kramer   in # *MTR.MLP 1001*
   B. Böttner   **T.E 3921**
   (*Rachmaninoff: Prelude, Op. 3, No. 2*)

KHRENNIKOV, Tikhon (b. 1913)

(The) CAVALIER WITH THE GOLDEN STAR
   film
   ... On the Kuban steppe; On the steppe road
   Piatnitsky People's Cho.   *USSR. 20279/80*

DON QUIXOTE Inc. music
Antonia's song
   V. Krasnovitskaya   *USSR. 21091*
   (*Zhukovsky: Film music excpt.*)

MUCH ADO ABOUT NOTHING Inc. music
Song of the drunkard
   B. Gmyria (B)   *USSR. 16916*
   (*Beethoven: "Scottish Drinking Song"*)

Orch. Suite
   USSR. Sym.—Stassevitch   # **Van.VRS 6002**
   (*Kabalevsky*)

SONGS
Ballad
   M. Alexandrovich (T)   *USSR. 16357*
   (*Nightingale and rose*)

(The) Nightingale and the rose
   M. Alexandrovich (T)   *USSR. 16356*
   (*Ballad*)

Students' Song (Kovalenkov)
   V. Nechayev (T)   *USSR. 16239*
   (*Blanter: Moscow Waltz*)

(The) Train goes ever more quickly (Svetlov)
   G. Vinogradov (T)   *USSR. 15872*
   (*Ferkelman: Along the steep bank*)

Winter road (Pushkin)
   G. Vinodradov (T)   *CdM.PM 737*
   (*Sorokin: At the frontier*)

KIENZL, Wilhelm (1857-1941)

OPERAS
(Der) EVANGELIMANN, Op. 45   2 acts 1895
O schöne Jugendtage, Act II   A
   R. Siewert   **G.EH 1429**
   (*Samson et Dalila, aria*)

Selig sind, die Verfolgung leiden, Act II   T
   ☆ W. Ludwig (Pol. 15477)

(Die) KUHREIGEN, Op. 85   3 acts 1911
Zu Strassburg auf der Schanz, Act I   T
   ☆ W. Ludwig (Pol. 15477)

KILPINEN, Yrjö (b. 1892)

SONGS
(6) Fjeldlieder Tunturilauluja
(5) Lieder der Liebe I, Op. 61 (Morgenstern)
   T. Niemela (S), P. Koskimies (pf.)
   (*Grieg, Sibelius*)   # **WCFM. 5**

In the evening (Leino)
   (or: *Evening Song: Iltalaulu*)
   — ARR. ORCH.
   ☆Odeon Orch.—Cronvall   *Od.PLD 15*
   (*Sibelius: Waltz*)

KIRBYE, George (*c.* 1565-1634)

   SEE : † TRIUMPHS OF ORIANA

KNUDSEN, Gunnar (b. 1907)

Norwegian Rhapsody   vln. & pf. 1942 (MS.)
   G. Knudsen & E. Garcia   # **ML.5002**
   (*Reger, Eccles, etc.*)

Reflections (ed. Garcia)[1]
   G. Knudsen & E. Garcia   # *ML. 5003*
   (*Prokofiev, Tveitt, Fauré, etc.*)

KODÁLY, Zoltán (b. 1882)

I. INSTRUMENTAL

Dances from Galanta   orch. 1933
   L.P.O.—Cameron   ♮ **G.C 7896/7**
   (4ss)   (in # BB.LBC 1011: ♭ *set WBC 1011*)
   Berlin Radio—L. G. Jochum   # **Ura. 7014**
   (*below*)
   ☆Berlin Phil.—de Sabata   # **AmD.DL 9518**
            (P.RR 8006/7)

Quartet, String, No. 2, D major, Op. 10 1916-7
   Walden Qtt.   # **Lyr.LL 22**
   (*Szymanowski: Qtt.*)
   Hungarian Qtt.   # **CHS.G 16**
   (*Falla*)

Sonata, vlc. unacc., Op. 8 1915
   ☆J. Starker   # **Nix.PLP 510**

Sonata, vlc. & pf., Op. 4 1909-10
   F. Danyi & R. Wille   # **CdM.LDX 8007**
   (*Psalmus Hungaricus*)
   R. Matuschka & O. Schulhof   # **Rem. 199-107**
   (*Enesco: Dixtuor*)

II. VOCAL

OPERAS
HARY JÁNOS 1926
Suite
   Austrian Sym.—Halasz   # *Rem. 149-44*
   ☆Bavarian State—Solti   # **AmD.DL 9518**

---

[1] Diction; it is not clear whether a monologue or a discussion, with or without musical illustrations. It has not been possible to hear the disc.

OPERAS (continued)

(The) SPINNING ROOM OF THE SZEKELYS
(Székely Fonó) 1 act 1932
... **Song (unspec.)**
☆E. Rösler (T) (Qual.QKM 5015)

PARTSONG: Whitsunday
☆ Children's Cho.—Csorda (Qual.QNM 7028)

Psalmus Hungaricus, Op. 13 T, cho., orch. 1923
H. Krebs, Berlin Radio Cho. & Orch.—
Rother (Ger) ♯ **Ura. 7014**
(Dances) (Vlc. Sonata on ♯ CdM.LDX 8007)

SONGS
Farewell to the Carnival, Op. 6, No. 7.; The Forest
D. Ligeti (Bs), F. Berens (pf.) **ML. 10-4/3**

Sappho's love-song; At night; The Forest
Op. 9, Nos. 2, 3, 5
P. Batic (A), R. Leukauf (pf.) ♯ **NRI. 405**
(Křenek & Hauer)

HUNGARIAN FOLKSONGS

I call loudly	Carriage, cart
I should go off	The Bad Wife
A tiny apple fell	Song of Doberdo
Hussar's song	Wherever I pass
Woman, woman, get out of bed	A long time ago

L. Chabay (T), T. Kozma (pf.) ♯ **BRS. 914**
(Bartók)

KOECHLIN, Charles (1867-1950)

Si tu le veux (de Marsan)
A. Dassary (T), J. Simonot (pf.) **Pat.PG 527**
(Lanjean: Comment l'appellerons-nous?)
C. Williams (S), B. Bazala (pf.) in ♯ **MGM.E 140**
(Delibes, Respighi, Malipiero, etc)

KOHS, Ellis B. (b. 1916)

Concerto, viola & str. nonet 1940-9
F. Molnar & Str. Nonet ♯ **AmC.ML 4492**
(Copland: Sextet)
☆ F. Molnar & Str. Ens. (♯ ML. 7004)

KOPPEL, Herman David (b. 1908)

Ternio, Op. 53b vlc. & pf.
E. B. Bengtsson & H. D. Koppel
(4ss) ♮ **G.DA 20100/1**

KORNGOLD, Erich Wolfgang (b. 1897)

COLLECTION
MUCH ADO ABOUT NOTHING, Op. 11 Inc. music 1919
... Overture; Mädchen im Brautgemach;
Holzapfel und Schlehwein;
Garden scene; Masquerade
Austrian State Sym.—Korngold
(part also on Hma. 15002)

(Die) TOTE STADT, Op. 12 Opera 1920
... Glück, das mir verblieb S & T
H. Zadek & A. Dermota (also on Hma. 14004)

SONATA No. 1, D minor ... Passacaglia 1908
SONATA No. 2, C minor ... Largo 1910
Fairy Tales, Op. 3 ... The Princess & the pea; Epilogue 1910
IMPROVISATIONS on: Kathrin (1936); Tote Stadt (1920);
Violanta (1915)
E. W. Korngold (pf.) ♯ **MSL.MW 46**

KOUTZEN, Boris (b. 1901)

Quartet, Strings, No. 2 1944
B. Koutzen, B. Robbins, C. Cooley, H.
Shapiro ♯ **SPAM. 1**
(Shepherd)

KREISLER, Fritz (b. 1875)

I. ORIGINAL WORKS
A. INSTRUMENTAL
(vln. & pf. unless otherwise stated)

COLLECTION
Caprice viennois, Op. 2
Liebesfreud
Liebeslied
(The) Old Refrain (Brandl, ARR. Kreisler)
Schön Rosmarin
Tambourin chinois, Op. 3
G. Alès (vln.) & orch.—Dupré ♯ **DCap.LC 6537**
(♯ Cap.L 273: ♭ set KCF 273)

Caprice viennois, Op. 2
T. Spivakovsky & A. Balsam in ♯ **AmC.ML 4402**
(Beethoven, Sarasate, etc.)
Y. Menuhin & A. Baller (pf.) **JpV.SD 3049**
(Granados: Danza No. 5) (in set JAS 230)
J. Pougnet & orch.—Torch **P.E 11497**
(Praeludium & Allegro)
T. Magyar & W. Hielkema **Phi.N 11226G**
(Tambourin chinois) (PhM. 09044S & in ♯ Phi.N 00605R)
L. Stevens (in ♯ Roy. 1245: in ♯ 6110: ♭ set 14577)
☆ Z. Francescatti & A. Balsam (C.LFX 1015)
F. Kreisler & Vic. Sym.—O'Connell
(in ♯ Vic.LCT 1049: ♭ set WCT 63)
— ARR. 2 PFS.
A. Whittemore & J. Lowe in ♯ Vic.LM 1305:
♭ set WDM 1565)

(La) Gitana
Z. Francescatti & A. Balsam **C.LX 1422**
(Recit. & Scherzo - Caprice)
J. Pougnet & S. Torch Orch. **P.R 3556**
(below)
L. Stevens (in ♯ Roy. 1245: in ♯ 6110: in ♭ set 14577)
☆ F. Kreisler & Vic. Sym —O'Connell
(in ♯ Vic.LCT 1049: ♭ set WCT 63)
— ARR 2 PFS.
A. Whittemore & J. Lowe
(in ♯ Vic.LM 130: in ♭ set WDM 1585)

Liebesfreud; Liebesleid
E. Nielsen & L. Christiansen **G.DA 5266**
T. Magyar & W. Hielkema **Phi.N 11228G**
(PhM. 09042S & in ♯ Phi.N 00605R)
L. Stevens (in ♯ Roy. 1245: ♯ 6110: ♭ set 14577)
Liebesfreud only
J. Pougnet & S. Torch Orch. (above) **P.R 3556**
☆ F. Kreisler & Vic. Sym.—O'Connell
(in ♯ Vic.LCT 1049: in ♭ set WCT 63)
— ARR. SAX. ▽ M. Mule (Sel.SA 7002)
— ARR. 2 PFS.
A. Whittemore & J. Lowe
(in ♯ Vic.LM 130: ♭ set WDM 1585)
Sisters J. Madeleine & F. Therese (in ♯ Conl.SF 1: also ♮ & ♭)
Liebesleid only
K. Gordon & H. Greenslade (Rondino) **P.R 3447**
M. Michailow & E. Milzkott **T.A 10944**
(The Old Refrain)
— ARR. 2 PFS.
A. Whittemore & J. Lowe
(in ♯ Vic.LM 130: ♭ set WDM 1585)
— ARR. 4 PFS. First Piano Qtt. (in ♯ Vic.LM 1165)
— ARR. ORCH. ☆ A. Kostelanetz Orch. (C.M 10036)

☆ = Re-issue of a recording to be found in WERM or Supplement I.

ORIGINAL WORKS (*continued*)

Recitative & Scherzo-Caprice, Op. 6 vln. unacc.
☆ Z. Francescatti   **C.LX 1422**
(*La Gitana*)

Rondino on a theme of Beethoven
K. Gordon & H. Greenslade   **P.R 3447**
(*Liebesleid*)
L. Stevens (in ♯ Roy. 1245: in ♯ *6110*: ♭ *set 14577*)

Schön Rosmarin
☆ F. Kreisler & Vic. Sym.—O'Connell
(in ♯ Vic.LCT 1049: in ♭ *set WCT 63*)

Tambourin chinois, Op. 3
T. Magyar & W. Heilkema   **Phi.N 11226G**
(*Caprice viennois*) (*PhM. 09044S* & in ♯ *Phi.N 00605R*)
I. Kawaciuk & F. Vrána   **U.H 23993**
(*Paganini: Variations on Rossini's Mosé*)
A. Brugman & B. Lindervel (*Tono.K 8087*)
L. Stevens (in ♯ Roy. 1245: in ♯ *6110*: ♭ *set 14577*)
☆ F. Kreisler & Vic. Sym.—O'Connell
(in ♯ Vic.LCT 1049: ♭ *set WCT 63*)
Z. Francescatti & A. Balsam (C.LFX 1015)

— ARR. 2 PFS.
A. Whittemore & J. Lowe
(in ♯ *Vic.LM 130*: ♭ *set WDM 1585*)

— ARR. ORCH.   ☆ A. Kostelanetz Orch. (C.M 10036)

B. VOCAL

(The) KING STEPS OUT Film music
Stars in my eyes   S
☆ G. Moore (in ♯ AmD.DL 9593)

— ARR. 2 PFS.
A. Whittemore & J. Lowe
(in ♯ *Vic.LM 130*: ♭ *set WDM 1585*)

SISSY operetta
Liebesleid ; Caprice viennois — VOCAL ARR.
☆ R. Tauber (in ♯ AmD.DL 9547)

II. COMPOSITIONS "in the style of" others

Allegretto (Porpora)
Grave (W. F. Bach)
Minuet (Porpora)
Praeludium & Allegro (Pugnani)
ARR. OF **Londonderry Air**
Z. Francescatti & A. Balsam ♯ AmC.ML 4534
(*Poulenc, Chabrier, Villa-Lobos, etc.*)
(*Allegretto only on* ♭ *AmC.A 1533*)

Praeludium & Allegro (Pugnani)
J. Pougnet & S. Torch Orch.   **P.E 11497**
(*Caprice viennois*)
T. Magyar & W. Hielkema   ♯ **Phi.N 00125R**
(*Ravel & Bloch*)
☆ I. Haendel & G. Moore (♭ *G.7P 121*)

... **Praeludium only** — ARR. SAX. & PF.
S. Rascher & D. Tudor   in ♯ **CHS.CHS 1156**

(La) Précieuse (L. Couperin)
— ARR. SAX.   ▽ M. Mule (*Sel.SA 7002*)

Sicilienne et Rigaudon (Francoeur)
T. Magyar & W. Hielkema   **Phi.N 11194G**
(*Paradies: Sicilienne*)   (*PhM. 09013S*)

Variations on a theme of Corelli (Tartini)
T. Magyar & W. Hielkema   **Phi.N 11157G**
(*Ravel: Pièce en forme de habanéra*)   (*PhM.N 09009S*)
☆ D. Oistrakh (in ♯ Csm.CRLP 110)

III. ARRANGEMENTS

Londonderry Air
☆ F. Kreisler & F. Rupp
(in ♯ Vic.LCT 1049: ♭ *set WCT 80*)

(The) Old refrain   (Brandl)
M. Michailow & E. Milzkott   **T.A 10944**
(*Liebesleid*)
Marek Weber & Orch. (in ♯ *AmC.GL 514*)

KŘENEK, Ernst (b. 1900)

CHORAL WORKS
Lamentations of Jeremiah, Op. 93
(The) Seasons, Op. 35
Hamline Singers—Holliday   ♯ **NRI. 306**
(*Chavez & Russell Harris*)

PARTSONGS
Schifferliedchen
Zur Erntezeit
Hamline Singers—Holliday   ♯ **NRI. 305**
(*Morales, etc.*)

(5) Piano Pieces, Op. 39 1925 (⅓s.)
(8) Piano Pieces 1946 (½s.)
Sonata No. 3, Op. 92, No. 4 pf. 1943
E. Křenek   ♯ **SPA. 4**

Sonata No. 4   pf.
B. Abramowitsch   ♯ **ML. 7014**

Sonata   vla. & pf.
M. Mann & Yaltah Menuhin   **PV. 36005**

SONGS: Fiedellieder, Op. 64
P. Batic (A), R. Leukauf (pf.) ♯ **NRI. 405**
(*Kodály & Hauer*)

Symphonic Elegy   str. orch.
(In memoriam Anton von Webern)
N.Y.P.S.O.—Mitropoulos   ♯ **AmC.ML 4524**
(*Schoenberg*)

KREUTZER, Conradin (1780-1849)

OPERA AND STAGE
(Das) NACHTLAGER IN GRANADA
opera 2 acts 1834
Overture ☆ Dresden Phil.—v. Kempen (*Pol. 15496*)
Galop: Düsseldorf Police Orch. (*Pal. 1317*)

(Der) VERSCHWENDER Inc. music 1833
Hobellied ☆ L. Slezak (*Pol. 48552*)

Septet, E flat major, Op. 62
Cl., hrn., bsn., vln., vla., vlc., cbs.
Vienna Septet   ♯ **D.LXT 2628**
(also D.KX 28538/41)   (♯ Lon.LLP 420)

KRIZHANOVSKY, Ivan Ivanovitch
(1867-1924)

Dies Irae   org.
... **Largo only**
F. Asma   **Phi.N 12040G**
(*Driffil: Toccata*)   (*PhM.N 12040G*)
(*Bach, Handel, Mendelssohn, etc.* in ♯ Phi.N 00147L)

♯ = Long-playing, 33⅓ r.p.m.   ♭ = 45 r.p.m.   ♮ = Auto. couplings, 78 r.p.m.

KROMMER-KRAMÁŘ, František
(1789-1831)

Harmonie, Op. 71
J. Schejbal & E. Linhart (obs.), V. Riha &
A. Rybin (cls.), E. Kaucky & M. Stefek (hrns.),
K. Bidlo & K. Vacek (bsns) & L. Rioonka
(c-bsn.) (6ss)   ♮ **U.H 13121/3**

KUCHAŘ, Jan Chrysostomos
(1751-1829)
(Kucharz, Johann Baptist)

FANTASIAS   organ
D minor
F. Michalek (2ss)   **U.H 13131**

G minor
M. Šlechta (2ss)   **U.H 13132**

KUHLAU, Friedrich Daniel Rudolph
(1786-1832)

(The) ELVES' HILL, Op. 100 1828
(*Elverhøj*: Inc. music to Heiberg's play)
No. 2, I walked in the grove one summer evening S
No. 3, I leaned my head against the fairy hill S
E. Gottschalch   *Pol.HA 70040*

KUNC, Jan (b. 1883)

Frühe Blätter, Op. 20   pf.
(5) Waltzes   pf.
M. Lorkovic   ♯ *Phi.N 00117R*
(*Tajcevic: 7 Balkan dances & Papandopoulo: Contredanse*)
(Blätter 2, 6 & 7, also on Phi.N 11184G;
Waltzes also on Phi.N 11185G)

LALO, Victor Antoine Édouard (1823-1892)

Concerto, vln. & orch., F major, Op. 20 1872
M. Solovieff & Vienna State Op.—Swoboda
(*Schubert*)   ♯ **CHS.CHS 1143**

Concerto, vlc. & orch., D minor 1876
B. Michelin & Haarlem Sym.—T. Verheij
(*Fauré*)   ♯ **CHS.CHS 1162**
T. de Machula & Residentie—v. Otterloo
♯ *Phi.N 00602R*
S. Seidler & Berlin Sym.—Rubahn ♯ **Roy. 1279**
(Unspec. excerpts in ♯ Roy. 1315)

NAMOUNA Ballet 1882
Orchestral Suites 1 & 2, Complete
Paris Cons.—Sebastian   ♯ **Ura. 7068**
(1¾ss—*Bizet: L'Arlésienne, Intermezzo*)

(Le) ROI D'YS Opera, 3 acts 1888
Overture
Opéra-Comique—Wolff   in ♯ **D.LXT 2625**
(*Berlioz, Massenet, Saint-Saëns*)   (♯ Lon.LLP 355)
Boston Sym.—Münch   ♯ **Vic.LM 1700**
(*Berlioz, Ravel, etc.*)   (in ♭ set WDM 1700)

Vainement, ma bien aimée—Aubade T (Act III)
☆ T. Rossi (in ♯ *AmC.FL 9544*: ♭ set F 4-41)

Sonata, vln. & pf., D major, Op. 12
M. Chauveton & B. Smith   ♯ **Allo.ALG 3032**
(*Fauré*)

Symphonie espagnole, Op. 21 vln. & orch. 1873
J. Heifetz & Vic. Orch.—Sternberg
♯ *G.FBLP 1019*
(♯ Vic.LM 127: ♭ set WDM 1603)
Anon. soloist & Berlin Sym.—Balzer (♯ Roy. 1287)

☆ Z. Francescatti & Sym.—Cluytens (ArgC, 500236/9)
Y. Menuhin & Colonne—Fournet (♯ G.FALP 107)
D. Oistrakh & USSR. State—Kondrashin
(♮ U.H 24094/7; USSR. 015565/72)

LA MONTAINE, John (b. 1920)

PIANO MUSIC
(A) Child's Picture Book
Sonata
Toccata
J. La Montaine   ♯ **Dor.DR 332**
(*Chopin: Sonata No. 2*)

LANDINO, Francesco (c. 1325-1397)
SEE: † ITALIAN MADRIGAL

LANDOWSKA, Wanda (b. 1881)
SEE: † POLISH KEYBOARD MUSIC

LANGE-MÜLLER, Peter Erasmus
(1850-1926)

RENAISSANCE, Op. 59 1901
(Inc. music to Drachmann's play)
Giulio's Nocturne   Declam. & orch.
☆ A. Poulsen & Copenhagen Radio—Tuxen
(Pol. HM 80035)

SONGS
(A) Strip of misty heath (Lange)
(*En Rand af diset Hede*)
E. Nørby (Bs), G. Nørby (pf.)   *Tono.K 8073*
(*Heise: Arne, Song*)

Summer lightning, Op. 10, No. 6 (Lange-Müller)
(*Kornmodsglansen*)
Y.M.C.A. Men's Cho.—G. Jensen   *G.X 8045*
(*Paulsen: When the firths shine blue*)

LANGLAIS, Jean (b. 1907)
SEE: † FRENCH ORGAN MUSIC

LANNER, Joseph Franz Karl (1801-1843)

WALTZES
Hofballtänze, Op. 161
Krönungswalzer, Op. 133
Lebenspulse, Op. 172
Mitternachtswalzer, Op. 8
Viennese Waltz (unid.)
Schneider String Ens.   ♯ *AmC.ML 2179*
(*Strauss*)

(continued on next page)

☆ = Re-issue of a recording to be found in WERM or Supplement I.

WALTZES (continued)

(Die) Kosenden, Op. 128
Hofballtänze, Op. 161
"Alt Wien"
Berlin Radio—Dobrindt   in ♯ Ura. set 215
(Nedbal: Polenblut, s.3)

Hofball-Tänze, Op. 161   (Court Ball Waltzes)
Bavarian Sym.—Nick   PV. 56009
(below)
Vienna Radio
(Vien.P 6038; Am.Vien.V 4006: in ♯ VNLP 1003)
Orch.—Schönherr (BrzOd. 8401 & Imp. 19179)
Orch.—Kolesa (in ♯ Phi.P 10100R)

(Die) Romantiker, Op. 167
Vienna Radio—Schönherr   Vien.P 6058
(Die Werber)

(Die) Schönbrunner, Op. 200
Bavarian Sym.—Nick   PV. 56009
(above)
Vienna State Op.—Schönherr   Pol. 48525
(J. Strauss: Freut euch des Lebens)
M. Schönherr Orch. (Imp. 19179 & BrzOd. 8401)
Vienna Radio—Schönherr
(Vien.P 6037: in ♯ 1003; in ♯ AmVien.VNLP 1008)

(Die) Werber, Op. 103
Vienna Radio—Schönherr   Vien.P 6058
(Die Romantiker)

LAPARRA, Raoul (1876-1943)

Murciana   pf.
G. Copeland   in ♯ MGM.E 151

LARSSON, Lars-Erik (b. 1908)

Pastoral Suite, Op. 19   orch.   1938
Stockholm Radio—Westerberg   ♯ D.LX 3086
(Wirén: Serenade)

LASERNA, Blas de (1751-1816)
SEE: † SPANISH CHORAL MUSIC

LASSUS, Orlande de (c. 1530-1594)

CHANSONS
COLLECTION of 15
☆ M. Couraud Ens. (♯ DFr. 8)

Ich waiss mir ein Meidlein
Harvard & Radcliffe Choirs   in ♯ Acad. 308
(† Courtly Music)

Matona, mia cara   ("Sérénade de Lansquenet")
Trapp Family Cho.—Wasner
in ♯ CHS.CHS 1101
☆ Vienna Academy Cha. Cho. (in ♯ Sel.LPG 8238)

Ne vous soit étrange
Renaissance Singers—Engel in ♯ AmC.ML 4517
(† Treasury of Madrigals)

Ola ! o che bon eccho !   8 voices   1581
R. Shaw Chorale   in † ♯ Vic.LM 136
(† XVIth Century Music)   (in ♭ set WDM 1598)
Glasgow Orpheus—Roberton (Eng) G.B 10196
(Roberton: White waves)

Qui s'y frotte, s'y pique
☆ Pro Musica Cho.—Calder (in ♯ CID. 33007)

MASSES
Octavi toni   "Puisque j'ai perdu"
Aachen Cath. Boys' Cho.—Rehmann
(3ss)   PV. 5401/2S

... Sanctus, Benedictus, Agnus Dei
Lassus Vocal Qtt., Speyer   Chr. 327A
(Jubilate Deo)

MOTETS, HYMNS, etc.
Auditui meo dabis gaudium   2 voices
Ipsa te cogat pietas   2 voices
Non avertas faciem tuam a me   2 voices
Spiritus tuus
Harvard Univ. Cho.—Russell in ♯ Fest. 70-202
(† Pre-baroque Sacred Music)

Adoramus te, Christe
Netherlands Cha. Cho.—de Nobel
Phi.N 12027G
(½s.—Handel & Lotti)   (PhM.N 090245S)

Jubilate Deo
Lassus Vocal Qtt., Speyer   Chr. 327A
(Mass, Octavi toni, excerpts)

Nos qui sumus in hoc mundo
Monaco Cath. Cho.—H. Carol in † ♯ SM. 33-01

De Lamentatione Hieremiae prophetae
... Lamentations 1 & 2 for Holy Saturday
☆Dessoff Cho.—Boepple   ♯ Nix.CLP 47
(Josquin)

LASZLO, Alexander (b. 1895)

Improvisations on "Oh Susannah ! "   orch.
Frankenland Sym.—Kloss   ♯ Lyr.LL 29
(La Violette, Delmar & Schoop)

LATRE, Joan de (d. c. 1589)
SEE: † MADRIGALS (♯ AS. 2501 LD)

LAWES, Henry (1595-1662)
SEE: † CATCHES AND GLEES

LEAUMONT, Chevalier Marie Robert de
(fl. XVIIIth Cent.)
SEE: † AMERICAN MUSIC (INST. & CHAMBER)

LECLAIR, Jean-Marie (1697-1764)

SONATA, Op. 9, No. 3, D major vln. or fl. & cont.
... Sarabande & Tambourin
— ARR. SAX. & PF.   Bumcke
S. Rascher & D. Tudor   in ♯ CHS.CHS 1156

LECOCQ, Charles (1832-1918)

(La) FILLE DE MME. ANGOT   Operetta, 3 acts
1872
ABRIDGED RECORDING (with Fr narration)
☆L. Dachary (S), S. Michel (M-S), J. Peyron (T),
M. Dens (B), cho. & Lamoureux Orch.—
Gressier   ♯ Pat.DTX 110
(♯ AmVox.PL 20000)

♯ = Long-playing, 33⅓ r.p.m.   ♭ = 45 r.p.m.   ♮ = Auto. couplings, 78 r.p.m.

Orchestral Suite (ARR. Mohaupt)
▽N.Y.P.S.O.—Kurtz **AmC. set X 305**
(4ss) (♯ ML 4083)

GIROFLÉ-GIROFLA Operetta 1874
ABRIDGED RECORDING in *German*
E. Senff-Thies, I. Borsow, K. Prantsch-
Kaufmann, etc. & Berlin Radio—Lachner
  ♯ Ura. 7054

SONGS
(La) Chanson d'amour (Le) Ruisseau
Cueillette Lilas blancs
W. Clément (B) & pf. **G.SK 119/120**

LECUONA, Ernesto (b. 1896)
SEE: † TAÑIDOS
  There are many other recordings of popular dances by this composer (*e.g.* ♯ Vic.LM 162: ♭ *WP 276*, etc.)

LEGLEY, Victor (b. 1915)

Suite pour orchestre 1944
1. Prélude 2. Sarabande
3. Menuet 4. Pavane 5. Gigue
Belgian Nat.—Quinet **♯ D.LX 133014**

LEGRENZI, Giovanni (*c.* 1625-1690)
SEE: † ITALIAN SONGS

LEGUERNEY, Jacques (b. 1906)

(7) POÈMES DE FR. MAYNARD
1. Les Plaintes d'Orphée
2. Épigramme à un mauvais payeur
3. À Chloris
4. Secret amour
5. Compliments à une duègne
6. Dans la forêt
G. Souzay (B), J. Bonneau (pf.) **D.AF 21369/70**

(La) Solitude (de Viau)
P. Bernac (B), J. Bonneau (pf.) **PhM.A 77502S**

LEHAR, Franz (1870-1948)

I. NON-OPERATIC
Gold und Silber Walzer, Op. 75
Hallé—Barbirolli (2ss) **G.DB 21520**
  Vienna Light Orch. (*Nix.BY 9021*)
  M. Lanner Orch. (*G.EG 7760*)
  H. Bund Orch. (*AusT.P 7175*)
  Vienna Radio—Schönherr (*Vien.P 6041*: in ♯ *1005*;
    AmVien.V 3001: in ♯ *VNLP 1003*)
  Viennese Sym. Orch. (*CGD.PV 1563*)
  F. Mihalovic Orch. (*T.A 11192*)
  M. Marrow Orch. (in ♯ *MGM.E 94*)
  Royale Concert Orch. (in ♯ *Roy. 1249*)
  Anon. Orch. (in ♯ *Var. 6938*)
  S. Romberg Orch. (in ♯ *Vic.LM 9019*), etc.
  ▽ Vienna Radio Orch. (in ♯ *Rem. 149-3*)
  ☆ Zürich Tonhalle—Lehar (♯ *Lon.LD 9003*)
    Berlin State Opera—Beutler (*Pol. 57418*)

Jetzt geht's los March
  Vienna Radio—Schönherr (*Vien.A 6056*: in ♯ *1005*)

Nachledil Marsch
  Vienna Radio—Schönherr
  (*Vien.A 6033*: in ♯ *1005*; *AmVien.V 4005*: in ♯ *VNLP 1062*)

SONG: Dir sing' ich mein Lied (P. Herz)
☆H. E. Groh (T) & orch. **Od.O-28213**
(*Stolz: Auf der Heide . . .*)

II. OPERETTAS
(Die) BLAUE MAZUR 1920
Polenlied T ☆ M. Lichtegg (in ♯ Lon.LLP 52)

EVA 1911
Prelude
  Vienna Radio—Schönherr **Vien.L 6107**
  (*Das Fürstenkind—Resignation*)
    (in ♯ *1005*: in ♯ *AmVien.VNLP 1006*)

Walzerintermezzo
Zwanzinette
  Vienna Radio—Schönherr **Vien.P 6069**

Wär es auch nichts als ein Augenblick S
  H. Horthy (*Hung*) (*Qual.QB 2061*)

— ORCH. VERSION (Eva Waltz)
☆Zürich Tonhalle—Lehar **D.K 23234**
(*Graf von Luxemburg—Waltz-Intermezzo*) (& K 23307)

FRASQUITA 1922
Vocal Selections in *French*
☆ C. Supervia (3ss—re-issued on IRCC. *3127* & *3128*;
  o.n. *U.AP 1020* & ▽ *U.EP 1024*)

Hab' ein blaues Himmelbett T
  K. Jautz (*Imp. 19173*)
☆ M. Lichtegg (in ♯ Lon.LLP 52)

FRIEDERIKE 1928
O Mädchen, mein Mädchen T
Sah ein Knab' ein Röslein steh'n T
  ▽F. Völker **Pol. 21811**
  ☆ R. Tauber (*Od.O-4667*)

O Mädchen . . . only
  J. Udwardy (*Hung*) (*Qual.QB 2073*)
  ☆ P. Anders (AusT.E 1174)

Warum hast du mich wachgeküsst ? S
  I. Tamás (*Hung*) (*Qual.QB 2011*)

(Das) FÜRSTENKIND 1909
Alt und Jung S & T
  ▽ G. Alpar & H. E. Groh (*Od.O-25179*)

Resignation
  Vienna Radio—Schönherr **Vien.L 6107**
  (*Eva, Prelude*) (in ♯ *1005*; in ♯ *AmVien. 1006*)

GIUDITTA 1934
Freunde, das Leben ist lebenswert T
  K. Friedrich in ♯ **D.LX 3068**
  (*below*) (D.K 23229: 28554) (♯ *Lon.LS 428*)

Intermezzo, Act II
  Rhineland Sym.—Federer in ♯ **Rgt. 5049**

Meine Lippen, sie küssen so heiss S
  H. Gueden in ♯ **D.LX 3071**
  (*Kalman: Gräfin Mariza, etc.*) (♯ *Lon.LS 477*)
  (D.K 28585)
  I. Tamás (*Hung*) (Qual.QMN 7030)

Schön wie die blaue Sommernacht S, T
  H. Gueden & K. Friedrich in ♯ **D.LX 3068**
  (*Land des Lächelns, etc.*) (♯ *Lon.LS 428*)
  (D.K 23237: 28565)

Schönste der Frauen
  K. Friedrich in ♯ **D.LX 3068**
  (*above*) (D.K 23229: 28554) (♯ *Lon.LS 428*)

☆ = Re-issue of a recording to be found in WERM or Supplement I.

OPERETTAS (*continued*)

(Der) GÖTTERGATTE 1904
Overture
Vienna Radio—Schönherr   *Vien.P 6123*

Was ich längst erträumte   T
K. Friedrich   in ‡ *D.LX 3068*
(*Rastelbinder—Wenn zwei sich lieben*) (‡ *Lon.LS 428*)
(D.K 23238: K 28555)

(Der) GRAF VON LUXEMBURG 1909
Waltz-Intermezzo
☆Zürich Tonhalle—Lehar   D.K 23234
(*Eva—Waltz*)   (K 23307)
Viennese Sym. Orch. (CGD.PV 1564)
A. Bernard Str. Orch. (*Od. 282481*)

Bist du's, lachendes Glück   S, T
☆ L. della Casa & H. Roswänge (D.GAH 15055)

Mädel klein, Mädel fein   T
☆ M. Lichtegg (in ‡ Lon.LLP 51; D.K 23306)

(Das) LAND DES LÄCHELNS 1923
Vocal Selection
T. Eipperle (S), P. Anders (T), A. Rothenberger
(S), W. Hofmann (T) & orch.—Marszalek
PV. 58607
(‡ *Pol. 45020*)

Immer nur lächeln
Von Apfelblüten einen Kranz
Dein ist mein Ganzes Herz
Beim Tee en deux   (duet)
J. de Bourges (S), M. Dens (B) (*Fr*)
Pat.PDT 277 & PD 159

Unspec. Excerpts
Anon. soloists & Dresden State Op. Cho. &
Orch.—Rubahn   ‡ **Roy. 1263**
(*Lustige Witwe*)   (& ‡ *Roy. 6123*, 2ss)

Overture
Berlin State—Marszalek   Pol. 57412
Austrian Sym.—Schönherr   ‡ *Rem. 149-40*
(*below*)
Rhineland Sym.—Federer   in ‡ Rgt. 5049

Dein ist mein Ganzes Herz   T
Ich trete ins Zimmer ... Immer nur lächeln
☆ F. Volker (*Pol. 48498*)
H. E. Groh (*Od.O-28418*)

Dein ist mein Ganzes Herz   T
J. Löhe   T.A 11348
(*Paganini—Gern hab' ich die Frau'n geküsst*)
L. Melchior (*Eng.*) (in ‡ *MGM.E 109*; & *MGM. 3003*)

Ich möcht einmal   S
H. Gueden   in ‡ *D.LX 3071*
(*Gräfin Dubarry, etc.*)   (‡ *Lon.LPS 477*)
(& D.K 23228: K 28567)

Von Apfelblüten einen Kranz   T
☆ P. Anders (AusT.E 1174)

Wer hat die Liebe uns ins Herz gesenkt   S, T
H. Gueden & K. Friedrich   in ‡ *D.LX 3068*
(*Giuditta, etc.*)   (‡ *Lon.LS 428*)
(& D.K 23237: K 28565)

(Die) LUSTIGE WITWE 1905
COMPLETE RECORDING in *English*
D. Kirsten (S), G. Warner (S), R. Rounseville
(T), cho. & orch.—Engel   ‡ **AmC.ML 4666**
(originally announced as ‡ AmC. set SL 171)
(♮ set C 320: ♭ *set B 320*)

ABRIDGED RECORDING in *French*
D. Duval, J. Jansen, C. Devos, etc., St. Paul
Cho. & Lamoureux Orch.—Gressier
‡ **Pat.DTX 113**

ABRIDGED RECORDING in *English*
☆R. Stevens (M-S), D. Morgen (T)
(8ss)   ♭ *AmC. set A 849*

Vocal Selection
E. Trötschel, V. Bak, W. Ludwig, W. Hofmann,
Munich Op. Cho. & Phil.—Nick
(2ss)   PV. **58601**
(‡ *Pol. 45020*; ‡ *AmD.DL 4001*)

Excerpts
F. Lamas, T. Erwin, cho. & orch.—Blackton (*Eng*)
(8ss)   *MGM. 532/5*
(Film version)   (‡ *MGM.E 157*: ♭ *set K 157*)   (‡ *D 107*)
Dresden State Op. Soloists, Cho. & Orch.—Rubahn
‡ **Roy. 1263**
(*Land des Lächelns*)   (‡ *Roy. 6115*, 2ss)
G. MacRae & L. Norman (*Eng*)   ‡ *Cap.L 335*
(♮ *set DDN*: ♭ *set KDF 335*)
M. Merkes, P. Merval, etc.   (*Fr*)   *Od. 282556*

Orchestral Selections
Melachrino Orch.   G.C 4193
(2ss)   (♭ *7P 134*)
Vienna Radio—Sandauer (*Phi.N 41119G*: *PhM. 43900S*)

Overture
Rhineland Sym.—Federer   in ‡ *Lon.LD 9003*)
☆ Zürich Tonhalle—Lehar (‡ *Lon.LD 9003*)

Dann geh' ich in's Maxim   T   ☆ M. Lichtegg (in ‡ Lon.LLP 52)

Viljalied; Valse
E. Farrell (S), C. Fredericks (B, *Eng*)   in ‡ Vic.LK 1004
Géori-Boué (*Fr*) (*Sat.D 601 & 602*)

Viljalied   S
L. Dobay (*Hung*) (*Qual.QB 2060*)
☆ J. MacDonald (*Eng*) (*G.DA 1939*)

Waltz — ORCH. VERSION   (Ball-sirenenwalzer, etc.)
Viennola Orch.—Eisle (*Vien.A 4904/5*, 2ss)
Vienna Radio—Schönherr
(*Vien.P 6017*; *AmVien.V 3003*: in ‡ *VNLP 1003*)
Viennese Sym. Orch. (CGD.PV 1564)
A. Bernard Str. Orch. (*Od. 282457*; *P.DPF 42*)
☆ S. Romberg Orch.
(in ‡ *Vic.LM 91* & ‡ *LM 9019*: ♭ *WDM 9019*)

MARISKA
Lied und Czardas   H. E. Groh (T) (*Od.O-26369*)
— ARR. ORCH.   Orch.—Kolesa (in ‡ *Phi.P 10100R*)

PAGANINI 1925
Vocal Selections
H. Gueden (S)   in ‡ *D.LX 3071*
(*Kalman*)   (‡ *Lon.LS 477*)
(D.K 28586)
☆ E. Schwarzkopf (S), R. Glawitsch, etc. (AusT.E 1172)

Orchestral Selection
☆ Berlin State Op.—Marszalek (Pol. 57442)

Gern hab' ich die Frau'n geküsst   T
J. Löhe   T.A 11348
(*Land des Lächelns—Dein ist mein ganzes Herz*)
☆ M. Lichtegg (in ‡ Lon.LLP 52)

Liebe, du Himmel auf Erden   S
☆ H. Gueden (D.M 38113)

Niemand liebt dich so wie ich   S, T
▽M. Slezak & H. E. Groh   P.DPW 54
(*Heuberger: Das Opernball—Im Chambre ...*)
(*Od.O-26162*, d.c.)
☆ L. Claus & W. Ludwig (Pol. 57417)

‡ = Long-playing, 33⅓ r.p.m.   ♭ = 45 r.p.m.   ♮ = Auto. couplings, 78 r.p.m.

116

(Der) RASTELBINDER 1902
Wenn zwei sich lieben　　　T
K. Friedrich　　　in ‡ *D.LX 3068*
(*Göttergatte, etc.*)　　　(‡ *Lon.LS 428*)
　　　(D.K 23238: K 28555)

☆ C. Vanconti-Tauber & R. Tauber
　　　(Od.O-9174: P.BX 612)

WIENER FRAUEN 1902
Overture
Austrian Sym.—Schönherr　　‡ *Rem. 149-40*
(*above*)

WO DIE LERCHE SINGT 1918
Palotas
Walzerintermezzo
Vienna Radio—Schönherr　　*Vien.P 6070*
(1s. each)　　　(in ‡ *1005*)

(Der) ZAREWITSCH 1911
Vocal Selection　☆ C. Spletter (S), etc. (Imp. 014118)
Orchestral Selection
▽ Berlin State Op.—Melichar (Pol. 15388: 57443)
Einer wird kommen S　☆ H. Gueden (*D.M 38113*)
Warum hat jeder Frühling S, T　(*Napoletana*)
... Tenor solo only
　H. Rosenberg (*Imp. 19025*)
　☆ M. Lichtegg (in ‡ Lon.LLP 52)
Wolgalied　　　T
　F. Brückner　　　*Tpo. 3634*
　(*Land des Lächelns*)
　P. Anders　　　*G.FKX 224*
　(*Kalman: Zirkusprinzessin, excpt.*)　(EH 1359)
　N. Gedda (*Swed*) (Od. SD 6079)
　E. Rösler (*Hung*) (*Qual.QB 2072*)
　T. Udwardy (*Hung*) (Qual.QMN 7032)
　F. Völker (Pol. 57414)
　E. Laider (*Dan*) & cho. (*Pol.X 51424*)
　M. Lichtegg (in ‡ Lon.LLP 52)

ZIGEUNERLIEBE 1910
COMPLETE RECORDING
R. Seegers (S), I. Mentzel (S), H. E. Groh (T),
A. Appelt (T), C. H. Karell (B), Radio Berlin
Cho. & Orch.—Dobrindt　　**Ura. set 205**
(4ss)

Overture Sym. Orch. (Qual.QMN 7029)
Es liegt in blauen Fernen
　H V. Schwarz & R. Tauber (in ‡ *Ete. 459*)
Ich bin ein Zigeunerkind ☆ M. Lichtegg (in ‡ Lon.LLP 52)
Und nenn' mein Lieb' dich ☆ R. Tauber (in ‡ AmD.DL 9597)
— ORCH. VERSION　☆ A. Kostelanetz Orch. (C.M 10035)
Wer einst ein Mädel **H** V. Schwarz (in ‡ *Ete. 459*)
Zörika, kehre zurück　☆ M. Lichtegg (in ‡ Lon.LLP 52)

LEISRING, Volkmar (fl. 1611-1665)
　SEE: † XVITH CENTURY MUSIC

LENTON, John (*c.* 1656-1719)
　SEE: † CATCHES AND GLEES

LEONCAVALLO, Ruggiero (1858-1919)

I. SONGS

Mattinata　(*Aubade*)
J. Peerce (T)　　　in ‡ *Roy. 1278*
　　　(& in ‡ *Roy. 6020* & ♭ *set 14540*)
☆ J. Björling (T)　　　♭ *G.7R 106*
　R. Tauber (T, *Ger*)　　in ‡ AmD.DL 9547
　J. Schmidt (T), o.v.　　in ‡ *T.LB 6007*
H E. Caruso (T), R. Leoncavallo (pf.)
　　　*G.VA 32** & VA 53**, o.n. DA 546**
　R. Tauber (T)　　　*IRCC. 3101**
　F. de Lucia (T)　　　HRS. 1073**

[1] Recorded from Edison cylinder.

II. OPERAS

(La) BOHÈME 4 acts 1897
Testa adorata　　　T
　M. del Monaco　　　*G.DA 11332*
　(*Manon Lescaut—Donna non vidi mai*)
　H ☆ E. Caruso (in ‡ Vic.LCT 1034**: ♭ *set WCT 35*)

(I) PAGLIACCI Prol. & 2 acts 1892
COMPLETE RECORDINGS

	Set F	Set G
Nedda ...	L. Aimaro (S)	G. Gavazzi (S)
Canio ...	R. Tucker (T)	C. Bergonzi (T)
Tonio ...	G. Valdengo (B)	C. Tagliabue (B)
Beppe ...	T. Hayward (T)	S. di Tommaso (T)
Silvio ...	C. Harvuot (B)	M. Rossi (B)

Set F, with Metropolitan Op. Cho. & orch.—
Cleva (4ss)　　　‡ **AmC. set SL 113**

Set G, with Radio Italiana Cho. & orch.—
Simonetto　　　‡ **Sor. set 1227**
(4ss) (3ss—*Cavalleria Rusticana* in set 1238)

"Highlights"
A. la Pollo (S), G. Sarri (T), B. Donati (T),
I. Petroff (B), Florence May Festival—
Ghiglia　　　‡ **Rem. 199-40**
L. Albanese, J. Peerce, L. Warren, R. Merrill
　　　‡ **Vic.LM 1160**
(*Cavalleria Rusticana*)　　　(♭ *set WDM 1565*)
Anon. soloists & Berlin Op. Cho. (‡ Roy. 1351 & 1323)
Anon. artists (‡ Wde. 20209; also ‡ *Pde. 1004*,
　　　& with Narration, ‡ Pde.OP 109)

Prologue: Si può, Signori !　　　B
I. Petroff　　　in ‡ *Rem. 199-93*
M. Dens (*Fr*)　(2ss)　　　*Pat.PD 163*
P. Lisitsian (*Russ*—2ss)　　USSR. 12514/5
A. Hiolski (*Pol*—2ss)　　　Muza. 1558
☆ T. Gobbi　　♭ *G.7RQ 212*: ♭ *7RF 212*
　A. Reali　　　P.PXO 1071
　L. Warren　　　in ‡ Vic.LM 1168
　R. Merrill
　　　in ‡ *Vic.LM 115* & in ♭ *set WDM 1542*
　Z. Otava (*Czech*)　　　U.H 24224
　H. Schlusnus (*Ger*)　　　Pol. 67188
H M. Battistini　　　in ‡ Ete.O-462**

ACT I

Un grande spettacolo　　　T & cho.
　H A. Alvarez (HRS. 1078**)

Andiam !　(*Coro delle Campane: Glockenchor*)
Württemberg St. Op.—Leitner　*Pol. 62879*
(*Trovatore—Gypsy cho.*) (*Ger*)　(‡ 18048)

Qual fiamma . . . Stridono lassù　S
　(*Nedda's Bird song*)
C. Carroll　　　in ‡ *Rem. 149-41*
　(*Don Giovanni, Figaro, etc.*)
E. Trötschel (*Ger*)　　　*PV. 36043*
　(*Lortzing: Waffenschmied—Wir armen*)
　H C. Muzio (in ‡ Eso.ES 502**; ‡ Cpt. MC 20009**) [1]
　E. Destinn (*Ger*) (in ‡ set CEd. 7001**)

Nedda ! Silvio ! . . . No, più non m'ami　S, B
　H C. Muzio & M. Laurenti
　　　(in ‡ Eso.ES 502**; ‡ Cpt.MC 20009**) [1]

Recitar ! . . . Vesti la giubba　　T
M. del Monaco　　　*G.DB 21452*
　(*Otello—Niun mi tema*)　(*below,* on G.DB 11344)
　(*Aïda,* on ♭ Vic. 49-3676)
☆ R. Tucker　　　*C.LX 1545*
　(*Rigoletto—Parmi veder*)
J. Björling (n.v.)　　in ‡ *Vic.LM 105*
　(*Faust, Africaine, etc.*)　(♭ *set WDM 1546*)

(*continued on next page*)

Recitar! . . . Vesti la giubba (*continued*)

F. Vroons   **Phi.N 11174G**
(*Tosca—Recondita, & Rigoletto*)   (*PhM.A 9010S*)
(*Oberon & Cavalleria R.* in ♯ Phi.N 00119L)

L. Melchior (n.v.)   in ♯ *MGM.E 109*
        (♭ *set K 109:* ▽ *30264, also MGM. 9063*)

K. Baum   in ♯ **Rem. 199-63**
(*Gioconda, Carmen, etc.*)

L. Melchior & L.S.O.—Barbirolli **AF.AGSB 2**
(*Africaine—O Paradis!*) (*Ger*)

J. Peerce   in ♯ Roy. 1278: ♭ *set 14540*

▽ F. Völker (*Ger*)   Pol. 67159

☆ M. Lanza   ♭ *G.7RQ 144:* ♭ *7RF 144*
J. Peerce   in ♯ Vic.LM 1169

♂ E. Caruso & pf.   *G.VA 30*,* o.n. *DA 546**
    E. Caruso in ♯ Vic.LM 1202*: ♭ *set WDM 1626**
    & in ♯ Vic.LCT 1007*: ♭ *set WCT 11*:* ♭ *ERAT 1**
    F. Ansseau (*Fr*)   AF. 38

Intermezzo   orch.
Berlin State—L. Ludwig   **G.DB 11502**
(*Cavalleria Rusticana—Intermezzo*)

Philharmonia—Schuechter   in ♯ *MGM.E 131*
(*Intermezzi*)   (♭ *set K 131*)

Hilversum Radio—v. Kempen   **Phi.N 12011G**
(*Cav. Rusticana—Intermezzo*) (*PhM.N 09008S* & in
                                       ♯ Phi.N 00119L)

☆ Berlin Municipal—Haarth (Pol. 15502)

ACT II

O Colombina—Serenata   T part only
I. Kozlovsky (*Russ*)   **USSR. 10720**
(*Trio*)

No, Pagliaccio non son   T
M. del Monaco   **G.DB 11344**
(*Vesti la giubba*)

L. Melchior   in ♯ *MGM.E 109*
        (in ♭ *set K 109:* ▽ *30264: also MGM. 9063*)

♂ F. Ansseau (AF. 38)

ZAZÀ   5 acts   1900
Ed ora io mi domando   T   (Act II)
M. Alexandrovich (*Russ*)   **USSR. 17578**
(*Bohème—Marcel's aria*)

Mamma ! io non l'ho avuta mai . . .
Dir che ci sono al mondo S (Act III)
    ♂ C. Melis (IRCC. 3113*)

Zazà, piccola zingara B (Act IV)
P. Lisitsian (*Russ*)   **USSR. 16264**
(*Verdi: Trovatore, aria*)

————————————

LÉONIN, Magister (*c.* 1183)
    SEE: † XIITH & XIIITH CENTURY MUSIC

————————————

LESUR, Daniel (b. 1908)

Sextet fl., ob., vln., vla., vlc., hpsi. 1943-8
Alma Musica Sextet   ♯ *Sel.LP 8312*
(*Debussy: Sonata No. 2*)

————————————

LIADOV, Anatol Constantinovich
(1855-1914)

(The) Enchanted Lake, Op. 62 orch.
F.O.K. Sym.—Smetáček   **U.H 24254**

Glorifications (from *Jour de fête*) str. qtt.
Dancers, etc. & Radio Artists' Str. Qtt.
                                       ♯ **Circ. 51-103**
(*Rimsky-Korsakov & Glazounov*)
☆Galimir Qtt.   in ♯ **Nix.PLP 505**

Kikimora, Op. 63   orch.
F.O.K. Sym.—Smetáček   **U.H 24253**
French Nat.—Dobrowen   **G.DB 11254**
                                        (♭ *7RF 219*)

(The) Musical Box, Op. 32   pf.
— ARR. HARP
O. Erdeli   **USSR. 18952**
(*Daquin: Le Coucou*)

— ARR. ORCH.
Bolshoi Theatre—Fayer   **USSR. 6360**
(*Cui: Miniature march*)
Boston Pops—Fiedler   ♭ *Vic. 49-1428*
                                    (& in ♭ *WEPR 26*)
Columbia Orch. (in ♯ *AmC.GL 513*)

Polonaise, C major, Op. 49   orch.
USSR. State Sym.—K. Ivanov **USSR. 16818/9**
(2ss)

PRELUDES, piano
B minor, Op. 11
☆ J. Flier (in ♯ Csm.CRLP 115)

B flat minor, Op. 31, No. 2
D flat major, Op. 57, No. 1
F minor, Op. 57, No. 2
V. Sofronitsky (2ss)   **USSR. 17186 & 8**

(8) Russian Folk Dances (or Songs), Op. 58 orch.
Youth Sym.—Kondrashin   ♭ **U.H 23877/8**
(*Nyazi: Rast,* on ♯ *Sup.LPM 34*)
... Nos. 6 & 7
☆ Carnegie Pops—O'Connell (in ♭ *AmC. set A 1001*)
... No. 6 ☆ Carnegie Pops—O'Connell (♭ *AmC.A 1532*)

"Tati-tati" Paraphrases on *Chopsticks*, pf. duet
Theme, 24 variations & finale [1]
Valse; Gigue; Galop; Cortège
— ARR. & ORCH. N. Tcherepnin & Janssen
Col. Sym.—Janssen   ♯ **AmC.ML 4480**
(*Liszt, Cui, Rimsky-Korsakov*)

FOLK SONG ARR.: Lullaby
State Boys' Cho.—Sveshnikov   **USSR. 16020**
(*Blagoobrazov: On the Dnieper*)

————————————

LIAPOUNOV, Sergius Mikhailovich
(1859-1924)

(12) Études d'exécution transcendante, Op. 11 pf.
L. Kentner (18ss)   **C.LX 1428/36**

————————————

LICHFILD, Henry (fl. XVI-XVIIth Cent.)
    SEE: † A TREASURY OF MADRIGALS

————————————

LIPATTI, Dinu (1917-1950)

Sonatina for left hand   pf.
B. Siki (2ss)   **P.E 11503**

————————————

LISLEY, John (fl. *c.* 1600)
    SEE: † TRIUMPHS OF ORIANA

————————————————————————————————

[1] Jointly with Cui, Rimsky-Korsakov & Borodin.

LISZT, Franz (1811-1886)

CLASSIFICATION:
A. INSTRUMENTAL   I. Orchestral
              II. Piano & Orch.
              III. Piano Solo
                    1. Studies
                    2. Various Original
                    3. Dance Forms
                    4. On National Themes
                    5. Transcriptions
              IV. Piano 4-hands
              V. 2 Pianos
              VI. Organ
B. VOCAL   IX. Sacred Choral
              XI. Songs with piano

A. INSTRUMENTAL
I. ORCHESTRAL

(A) Faust Symphony G.14 (with T & cho.)
Anon. soloist & cho., Berlin Sym. Orch.—Balzer
(3ss—*Festklänge*)   **♯ Roy. 1385/6**

Festklänge G.7 (Sym. Poem No. 7)
Berlin Sym.—Balzer   **♯ Roy. 1386**
(*Faust Symphony*)

Héroïde funèbre G.8
Munich Phil.—Mennerich   **♯ Mer.MG 10115**
(*Schumann*)

Mazeppa G.6 (Sym. Poem No. 6)
Berlin Sym.—Balzer   **♯ Roy. 1388**
(*Mephisto-Waltz & Tasso*)

Mephisto-Waltz G.16 (2)
Bavarian Radio—Görlich   in **♯ Mer.MG 10080**
Rhineland Sym.—Federer   **♯ Rgt. 5043**
(*Mozart & Wagner*)
Berlin Sym.—Balzer   **♯ Roy. 1388**
(*Mazeppa & Tasso*)

(Les) Préludes G.3 (Sym. Poem No. 3)
Berlin Phil.—Ludwig (2ss)   **PV. 72143**
(*Tchaikovsky: Capriccio Italien*, on ♯ AmD.DL 7530)
Brussels Radio—André (2ss)   **TV.VSK 9017**
(*Rosenkavalier Waltzes* in ♯ Cap.L 8173)
Residentie—v. Otterloo   **♯ Phi.A 00114L**
(*Concerto No. 1*)   (also, 4ss, Phi.A 11152/3G)
Leipzig Gewandhaus—Konwitschny
               ♮ **U.H 23950/2**
(5ss—*Pastorale*)   (*Hungarian Fantasia* on ♯ Sup.LPM 19)
USSR Radio Sym.—Rakhlin **USSR. 018460/4**
(5ss—*Schumann - Liszt: Widmung*)
Homburg Sym.—Schubert (2ss)   **♯ Rgt. 5009**
Austrian Sym.—Singer   **♯ Rem. 149-47**
(*Enesco*)   (& ♯ Mrt. 1-16, d.c.)
☆ Paris Cons.—Lindenberg   ♯ Od.ODX 101
   Sym.—Stokowski   ♯ G.FALP 105
   Berlin Phil.—v. Kempen   P.RR 8065/6

Tasso G.2 (Sym. Poem No. 2)
Winterthur Sym.—Desarzens   **♯ CHS.F 2**
(*Gounod*)
Berlin Sym.—Balzer   **♯ Roy. 1388**
(*Mephisto-Waltz & Mazeppa*)
☆ Budapest Phil.—Ferencsik (Qual.QMN 7035/6)

A. II. PIANO & ORCHESTRA
CONCERTOS
No. 1, E flat major G.44
S. Cherkassky & Philharmonia—Fistoulari
(4ss)   ♮ **G.DB 9763/4**

V. Schiøler & Danish State Radio—Dobrowen
(5ss—*Valse Impromptu*)   ♮ **G.DB 20165/7**
(*Beethoven: Sonata No. 23* on ♯ Vic.LHMV 1031)
E. Farnadi & Vienna State Op.—Scherchen
(*below*)   **♯ West.WL 5168**
C. de Groot & Hilversum Radio—v. Otterloo
               ♯ Phi.A 00114L
(*Les Préludes*)   (also, 4ss, Phi.A 11182/3G)
M. Huttner & Berlin Sym.—Balzer **♯ Roy. 1320**
(*Franck: Variations symphoniques*)
☆A. Rubinstein & Dallas Sym.—Dorati
(4ss)   **G.DB 21205/6**

— ARR. PF. & BAND
R. Beaufort & French Reserve—C. Beaufort
            V♯ Sat.MSA 5002

No. 2, A major G.45
R. Casadesus & Cleveland—Szell
            ♯ AmC.ML 4588
(*Weber: Konzertstück*)
E. Farnadi & Vienna State Op.—Scherchen
(*above*)   **♯ West.WL 5168**
M. Huttner & Berlin Sym.—Balzer ♯ **Roy. 1383**
(*Hérold & Beethoven*)

Hungarian Fantasia G.43
R. Trouard & French Radio—Cloëz
            Od. 123933/4
(4ss) (Od.O-9178/9) (*with Les Préludes*, on ♯ Od.ODX 101)
E. Kilenyi & orch.—Prohaska   **♯ Rem. 199-61**
(*Mozart*)
I. Antal & Prague Radio—Šejna ♮ **U.H 23832/3**
(4ss)   (*Les Préludes* on ♯ Sup.LPM 19)

Totentanz G.46
A. Brailowsky & Vic. Sym.—Reiner
            ♯ G.FALP 172
(*Franck: Variations symphoniques*)
         (♯ Vic.LM 1195; ♭ set WDM 1615)
F. Jacquinot & Philharmonia—Fistoulari
            ♯ MGM.E 182
(*Rimsky-Korsakov: Concerto*)

A. III. PIANO SOLO
1. STUDIES

(12) Études d'exécution transcendante G.52
No. 5, Feux follets
C. Giraud-Chambeau   **Sat. 6001**
(*Liebestraum*)

(6) Études d'exécution transcendante d'après Paganini G.53

COMPLETE RECORDING
☆R. Goldsand   **♯ CHS.CHS 1149**
(*Rachmaninoff*)

No. 2, E flat major, "Octave"
No. 6, A minor, "Theme & variations"
   (Paganini Caprices 17 & 24)
C. Giraud-Chambeau   **♯ Sat.LDG 8003**
(*Mendelssohn & Brahms: Variations*)

No. 3, A flat minor, "La Campanella"
   (Paganini, Concerto . . . Ronde)
No. 4, E major, "Arpeggio"
   (Paganini Caprice 1)
No. 5, E major, "La Chasse"
   (Paganini Caprice 9)
A. Uninsky   **♯ Phi.A 00136R**
(*Spanish Rhapsody*)
(Nos. 3 & 4 also on Phi.A 11212G: *PhM. 09709S*)
          (continued on next page)

☆ = Re-issue of a recording to be found in WERM or Supplement I.

Paganini Études G. 53 *(continued)*
No. 3, A flat major
  C. Horsley   **G.C 4169**
  (Étude de Concert, No. 3)
  L. Hernádi   **Qual.KNM 7100**
  (Hungarian Rhapsody No. 15)
  S. Barere   in ‡ **Rem. 199-35**
  J. Battista   in ‡ *MGM.E 141*
  (Beethoven, Brahms, etc.)

No. 5, E major
  ☆ J. M. Darré (JpV.SD 3068)

(3) Études de Concert G.57
  (Caprices poétiques)
No. 2, F minor *(La leggierezza)*
  S. Barere   in ‡ **Rem. 199-35**
No. 3, D flat major *(Un sospiro)*
  C. Horsley   **G.C 4169**
  (Paganini Étude No. 3)
  E. Wild   in ‡ **Strad.STR 607**

(2) Concert Studies G.58
  J. v. Karolyi   **PV. 72200**
  (Consolation No. 3 & Liebestraum)
  C. Keene   in ‡ **Mer.MG 10113**

No. 1, Waldesrauschen
  C. de Groot   **Phi.N 11158G**
  (Sinding: Rustle of Spring & Grieg: To Spring)
                                  (PhM.N 9000S)
  ☆ R. Trouard (Od.O-9175)

No. 2, Gnomenreigen *(Ronde des Lutins)*
  C. Horsley   **G.C 4132**
  (Chopin—Liszt: Chant Polonais, No. 5)
  E. Farnadi   **C.LVX 170**
  (Liebestraum No. 3)
  E. Wild   in ‡ **Strad.STR 607**
  S. Rachmaninoff   in ‡ **Csm.CRLP 115**
  F. Karrer   *Vien.P 6065*
  (Consolation No. 3)   *(in ‡ 1015)*
  ▽ S. Barere (in ‡ Rem. 199-17)
  ☆ E. von Sauer (Qual.QMN 7037)

A. III. 2. *VARIOUS ORIGINAL WORKS*
Am Grabe Richard Wagners G.114 1883
  L. Kentner   **C.DX 1822**
  (En rêve)

ANNÉES DE PÈLERINAGE
FIRST YEAR, SWITZERLAND G.73
No. 3, Pastorale
  G. Axelrod   **U.H 23852**
  (Hungarian Rhapsody No. 2, s.1)
  (Les Préludes, s.1, on U.H 23950)

No. 4, Au bord d'une source
  V. Horowitz   ♭ *G.7RF 153*
  (Chopin: Nocturne No. 5)   *(♭ Vic. 49-0488)*
                          (& in ‡ Vic. LM 1235)
  C. Giraud-Chambeau   **Sat. 6004**
  (Hungarian Rhapsody No. 11)   *(o.n. M 510)*
  ☆ R. Trouard (Od.O-9175)

No. 9, Les Cloches de Genève
  G. Ginsburg (2ss)   **USSR. 15946/7**

SECOND YEAR, ITALY G.74
COMPLETE RECORDING
  ☆E. Balogh   ‡ **Eur.LPG 629**

No. 2, Il Pensieroso
No. 3, Canzonetta di Salvator Rosa
  K. U. Schnabel   *Vis.VI 4380*
  (1s. each)

No. 4, Sonetto del Petrarca No. 47
No. 5, Sonetto del Petrarca No. 104
No. 6, Sonetto del Petrarca No. 123
  W. Kempff   ‡ **D.LXT 2670**
  (Schumann: Arabesque & Papillons)   *(‡ Lon.LL 515)*

No. 5, Sonetto del Petrarca No. 104
  V. Horowitz   ♭ *G.7RF 174*
  (Valse oubliée No. 1) (in ‡ Vic.LM 100: ♭ set WDM 1534)
  T. v. d. Pas   ‡ **Phi.A 00137L**
  (½s.—Sonata)
  S. Barere (n.v.)   in ‡ **Rem. 199-35**

THIRD YEAR G.76
No. 4, Les Jeux d'eaux à la Villa d'Este
  ☆ J. Iturbi (♭ G.7RF 177; in ‡ Vic.LM 1167:
                           ♭ set WDM 1604)
No. 7, Sursum corda
  ☆ B. Bartók (Qual.QMN 7001)

—— *END OF ANNÉES DE PÈLERINAGE* ——

Ballade No. 2, B minor G.84
Berceuse, D flat major G.87
  E. Wild   in ‡ **Strad.STR 607**

(6) CONSOLATIONS G.85
COMPLETE RECORDING
  G. Manley   ‡ **NRI. set 501**
  (R. Strauss: Enoch Arden)

No. 3, D flat major only
  G. Sandor   ‡ **AmC.ML 2209**
  (Spanish Rhapsody)
  J. v. Karolyi   **PV. 72200**
  (½s.—Liebestraum & Studies)
  A. Semprini   **G.B 10317**
  (Chopin: Étude, Op. 10, No. 12)
  F. Karrer   *Vien.P 6065*
  (Gnomenreigen)   *(& in ‡ 1015)*

En rêve (Nocturne) G.120   1885
  L. Kentner   **C.DX 1822**
  (Am Grabe Richard Wagners)

HARMONIES POÉTIQUES ET RELIGIEUSES
  G.86
No. 7, Funérailles
  V. Horowitz (n.v.)   ♭ *G.7RF 173*
               (in ♭ Vic. set WDM 1534: ‡ LM 100)
  S. Barere   **‡ Rem. 199-85**
  (Sonata)
  J. Bolet   in ‡ **Bo.B 301**
  (Beethoven, St.-Saëns, etc.)
  G. Axelrod   ♮ **U.H 23854/5**
  (3ss—A. Rubinstein: Melody)

(La) Lugubre Gondola G.112
  J.-M. Damase (2ss)   **D.GAF 15101**

SONATA, B minor G.91
  A. Uninsky   ‡ **Phi.A 00137L**
  (1½s.—Sonetto 104)
  S. Barere   ‡ **Rem. 199-85**
  (Funérailles)
  L. Kentner (6ss)   **C.DX 1760/2**
  A. Földes (4ss)   ♮ **PV. 72137/8**
                          (‡ AmD.DL 7528)
  E. Bernathova (6ss)   ♮ **U.H 24228/30**

Variations on a theme of Bach G.93
  (Weinen, Klagen, Sorgen, Zagen)
  I. Kabos   ‡ **BRS. 910**
  (Weihnachtsbaum)
  L. Podolsky   in ‡ **Cmt. 1204**
  (Méhul, Szymanowski, etc.)

---

‡ = Long-playing, 33⅓ r.p.m.   ♭ = 45 r.p.m.   ♮ = Auto. couplings, 78 r.p.m.

Variations on a theme of Bach (*continued*)
—ORGAN VERSION G.463
E. Nies-Berger   ♯ **CHS.CHS 1145**
(*Franck*)   (♯ Nix.CLP 1145)

Weihnachtsbaum G.99 (12 pieces)
A. Brendel   ♯ **SPA. 26**

... Nos. 1 to 7 only
I. Kabos   ♯ **BRS. 910**
(*Variations*)

A. III. 3. *DANCE FORMS*
Csárdás macabre G.137 1881-2
L. Kentner   **C.DX 1813**
(2ss)   (CQX 16655)

(2) POLONAISES G.136
No. 2, E major
E. Wild   in ♯ **Strad.STR 607**

VALSES
Valse impromptu, A flat major G.126
V. Schiøler   **G.DB 20165**
(*Liszt: Concerto No. 1, s.1*)

Valse oubliée, No. 1 G.128-3
A. Rubinstein   ♯ **Vic.LM 1153**
(*above, Debussy, etc.*) (♭ set WDM 1558: & ♭ WEPR 41)
V. Horowitz   ♭ **G.7RF 174**
(*Sonetto del Petrarca 104*)
    (in ♯ Vic.LM 100: ♭ set WDM 1534)
S. Barere   in ♯ **Rem. 199-35**

A. III.
4. *PF. WORKS ON NATIONAL THEMES*
HUNGARIAN RHAPSODIES G.157
    (ORCH. VERSION, G. 34)
No. 2, C sharp minor
A. Brailowsky (n.v.)   ♭ **G.7RF 121**
    (♭ Vic. 49-0262)

E. Wild   in ♯ **Strad.STR 607**
G. Axelrod   ♮ **U.H 23852/3**
(3ss—*Pastorale*)
☆ A. Brailowsky (o.v.) (P.RR 8039)

♭ F. Busoni (in ♯ AudA.LA 1023*)

— ORCH. VERSION (No. 4)
USSR. State Radio—Rakhlin *USSR. 19543/6*
(4ss)
Bavarian Sym.—Nick   **PV. 56005**
(*No. 12*)   (FPV. 5029; ♯ AmD.DL 4000)
L.P.O.—Martinon   in ♯ **MGM.E 541**
    (♭ set K 112)
▽ Chicago Sym.—H. Weber
    (in ♯ Mer.MG 20013; Clc. 6041)
☆ Boston Prom.—Fiedler (♭ Vic. 49-0308; ♭ G.7BF 1011)
Col. Sym.—Rodzinski
    (in ♭ AmC. set A 1002: ♯ AAL 2, d.c.)

No. 6, D flat major
V. Horowitz (2ss) (n.v.)   ♭ **G.7R 142**
    (♭ G.7RF 151; ♮ ♭ Vic. 49-0486/7: ♭ WEPR 10)
(*Au bord d'une source & Chopin, in ♯ Vic.LM 1235*)
B. Janis   in ♯ **BB.LBC 1030**
    (♭ set WBC 1030)
E. Gilels (2ss)   *USSR. 17053/4*
    (U.C 24283)

No. 8, F sharp minor
G. Fedorova (2ss)   **USSR. 021067/8**

No. 10, E major
G. Ginsburg (2ss)   *USSR. 12916/7*

No. 11, A minor
C. Giraud-Chambeau   **Sat. 6004**
(*Au bord d'une source*)   (o.n. M 510)

No. 12, C sharp minor
☆ A. Sienkiewicz (Qual.QMN 7034)

— ORCH. VERSION (No. 2)
Bavarian Sym.—Nick   **PV. 56005**
(*No. 2*)   (FPV. 5029; ♯ AmD.DL 4000)

No. 14, F minor — ORCH. VERSION (No. 1)
Hungarian Radio—Polgár *Qual.QKM 5004/5*
(3ss—"*The Cranes fly high*," unid.)

No. 15, A minor (*Rakóczy March*)
L. Hernádi   **Qual.KNM 7100**
(*Paganini Étude No. 3*)

— ARR. Horowitz
☆ V. Horowitz
    (♭ G.7RF 175; in ♯ Vic.LM 100: ♭ set WDM 1534)

Spanish Rhapsody G.168
W. Malcuzynski   ♮ **C.LX 8922/3**
(3ss—*Chopin: Mazurka 41 & Valse 11*)
G. Sandor   ♯ **AmC.ML 2209**
(*Mephisto Waltz*)
M. Schwalb   ♯ **Acad.ALP 307**
(*Ravel: Valses nobles et sentimentales*)
E. Farnadi   **C.LVX 187/8**
(3ss—*Debussy: Clair de lune*)
A. Uninsky   ♯ **Phi.A 00136R**
(*Paganini Études*)

— ARR. PF. & ORCH. Busoni
G. Bachauer & New London—Sherman
(4ss)   ♮ **G.C 7854/5**
(♭ Vic. set WDM 1696)   (G.ZN 600/1)
(*Mozart: Pf. Concerto, K 537 on ♯ Vic.LM 9000*)
G. Ginsburg & USSR. Radio Sym.—
  Shereshevsky (6ss)   *USSR. 20479/84*

A. III.
5. *PF. TRANSCRIPTIONS & PARTITIONS*
ARCADELT: Ave Maria G.96-2
W. Rummel   **Pol. 67936**
(*Liebestraum*)

CHOPIN: (6) Chants Polonais G. 265
No. 1, The Maiden's wish, Op. 74, No. 1
C. Keene   in ♯ **Mer.MG 10113**
(*Studies; Rachmaninoff, Chopin, etc.*)

No. 5, My Joys, Op. 74, No. 12
C. Horsley   **G.C 4132**
(*Gnomenreigen*)
☆ C. Arrau (C.GQX 11483)

GOUNOD: Valse from Faust G.142
▽ S. Barere (in ♯ Rem. 199-17)
☆ E. Joyce (in ♯ AmD.DL 9528)

LISZT: (3) LIEBESTRÄUME G.326
No. 3, A flat major
A. Rubinstein (*Chopin*)   ♭ **G.7RF 235**
(*Mendelssohn, etc. in ♯ Vic.LM 1153:* ♭ set WDM 1558)
L. Pennario   in ♯ **DCap.CCL 7510**
(*Chopin & Debussy*)   (♯ Cap.H 8156)
J. v. Karolyi   **PV. 72200**
(½s.—*Consolations No. 3 & Studies*)
E. Farnadi   **C.LVX 170**
(*Gnomenreigen*)

(continued on next page)

☆ = Re-issue of a recording to be found in WERM or Supplement I.

Liebesträume: No. 3, A flat major (continued)

B. Janis   in ♯ BB.LBC 1030
                                      (♭ set WBC 1030)
M. Flipse   Phi.N 11235G
(Grieg: Wedding Day)   (PhM.N 09047S)
☆V. Schiøler   in ♯ Mer.MG 10099
(Chopin, Grieg, etc.)
C. Giraud-Chambeau   Sat. 6001
(Feux follets)
J. Battista   in ♯ MGM.E 141
(Beethoven, Brahms, etc.)
▽ S. Barere [1]   in ♯ Rem. 199-17
(above; & Chopin)
☆ J. Iturbi
(in ♯ Vic.LM 1167: ♭ set WDM 1604: ♭ WEPR 32)

— ARR. VLC. & PF.   Navarra
A. Navarra & J. Dussot   C.LFX 1009
(Tannhäuser—Star of Eve)

Mephisto-Waltz No. 1   G.286
G. Sandor   ♯ AmC.ML 2209
(Consolation)

MENDELSSOHN: Wedding March   G.195
(ARR. Horowitz)
☆V. Horowitz   ♯ G.FBLP 1015
(Mendelssohn: Variations)   (& ♭ Vic. WEPR 10)

MOZART: Reminiscences of Don Giovanni
G.203
S. Barere (n.v.)   in ♯ Rem. 199-35

ROSSINI: Soirées Musicales   G.209
No. 9, La Danza   — ARR. 4 PFS.
☆ First Piano Qtt. (in ♯ Vic.LM 1165)

SCHUBERT
LIEDER:
   Auf dem Wasser zu singen   G.343-2
   Der Erlkönig   G.343-4
   Die Forelle   G.394
   Gretchen am Spinnrade   G.343-8
   Liebesbotschaft   G.345-10
   Der Lindenbaum   G.346-7
Soirées de Vienne: No. 6, A major   G.212
   E. Petri   ♯ AmC.ML 4436
   (Schubert - Tausig: Andantino varié)

SCHUMANN: Widmung   ("Liebeslied")   G.351
   M. Grünberg   USSR. 018465
   (Les Préludes, s.5)
   M. Pressler   ♯ MGM.E 119
   (Schumann: Arabeske, Carnaval, etc.)

VERDI: Rigoletto, Paraphrase de Concert   G.219
   G. Ginsburg   (2ss)   USSR. 20994/5

WAGNER: Spinning Chorus   G.225
   G. Werschenska   (2ss)   Pol.HM 80061

Tannhäuser March   G.230-1
   ▽ V. Sapellnikov (Voc.A 0268*)

A. IV. PIANO 4-HANDS

Variations on Chopsticks   G.364
— ARR. & ORCH.   N. Tcherepnin
Col. Sym.—Janssen   ♯ AmC.ML 4480
(Borodin, Cui, Rimsky-Korsakov)

A. VI. ORGAN

Prelude & Fugue on the name of B.A.C.H.   G.448
R. Noehren   in ♯ Aphe.AP 2
(Reger & Vierne)   (& 78 r.p.m., Aphe.AP 3)

See also: A. III (2), Variations on a theme of Bach

B. VOCAL
IX. SACRED CHORAL WORKS
(The) LEGEND OF ST. ELISABETH   G.495
No. 3, Crusaders' March   orch.
— ARR. ORGAN
A. M. Henderson   D.K 2446
(Handel: Org. Concerto, B flat—Finale)

B. XI. SONGS (with piano)
Es muss ein Wunderbares sein   (Redwitz)   G.633
J. Vincent (S), F. de Nobel (pf.)
(Wagner, Beethoven, etc.)   in ♯ Phi.A 00610R
A. Sved (B) & orch. (Hung)   Qual.MN 1001
(below)
☆ R. Tauber (in ♯ AmD.DL 9547)

Freudvoll und leidvoll   (Goethe)   G.599
Z. Gaidai (Russ)   USSR. 14491
(Wieder möcht ich dir begegnen)

Kennst du das Land   (Goethe)   G.594
M. Ritchie (S), G. Malcolm (pf.)   G.C 4168
(2ss)

O Lieb! so lang du lieben kannst (Freiligrath) G.617
C. Hallgren (B, Swed) (T.A 3186)
⊞ L. Slezak (T) (in ♯ Ete. 453*)

Oh, quand je dors   (Hugo)   G.601
P. Schoeffler (B), O. Schulhof (pf.)
                                 in ♯ MSL.MW 44
(Schubert, Loewe, etc. & Arias)
A. Sved (B) & orch.   Qual.MN 1001
(above)

Wieder möcht ich dir begegnen (Cornelius) G.641
Z. Gaidai (Russ)   USSR.14492
(Freudvoll und leidvoll)

LITOLFF, Henry Charles (1818-1891)
Concerto symphonique, Op. 102   pf. & orch.
… Scherzo
W. Atwell & Neophonic Sym.—Mantovani
                                     D.F 9864

LOCATELLI, Pietro (1693-1764)
Concerto grosso, E flat major, Op. 4, No. 10
(ed. Marinuzzi)
Vienna Cha. Orch.—Litschauer ♯ Van.VRS 418
(Respighi)

(12) CONCERTOS, vln. & orch., Op. 3
No. 12, D major ... Capriccio only
▽C. v. Neste (Stravinsky)   G.DB 4702

— — ARR. VLN. & PF.   "Le Labyrinthe"
H. Szeryng & M. Berthelier   T.E 3887
(Wieniawski: Scherzo-Tarantelle)

LOCKE, Matthew (1630-1677)
ANTHEMS
Lord, let me know mine end
O give thanks unto the Lord
Sing unto the Lord a new song
Purcell Performing Soc.—J. R. King
(Gibbons & Philips)   ♯ Allo.ALG 3038

---

[1] The entry for this disc under Mephisto-Waltz No. 1 at WERM p. 794 is incorrect; the contents must have been changed
   after the disc was first announced.

Suite (Consort) No. 6　str. qtt. (orig. viols)
New Music Qtt.　　　　　　　　**♯ BRS. 913**
(*Gibbons & Purcell*)

LOEFFLER, Charles Martin (1861-1935)

SONGS: UNSPECIFIED

A. Mock (S), S. Boyes (pf.)　　　　**♯ Cmt. 1206**
(*Carpenter*)

LÖHNER, Johann (1645-1705)

O Ewigkeit
K. Flagstad (S), G. Moore (pf.)　　**G.DB 21490**
(*Bach: Komm, süsser Tod*)

LOEILLET, Jean-Baptiste (1680-1730)

Lesson No. 1, E minor . . . Courante　hpsi.
Suite No. 1, G minor . . . Gigue
　☆ A. Ehlers (in ♯ AmD.DL 8019)

SONATAS
F major, fl. & cont., Op. 1, No. 1 [1]
G minor, 2 fls. (or vlns.) & cont.
G minor, fl., ob. & cont., Op. 2, No. 4 [1]
　☆ P. Kaplan, L. Schaefer, J. Holmes, E. Bodky (hpsi.)
　　& vlc. (♯ Ome. & CID.LX 33009)

B flat major, Op. 3, No. 2　recorder & hpsi.
D. Barnett & N. Salas　　　**C.DOX 1004**
(2ss)

"Sonata", C major　— ARR. OB. & PF. Rothwell
(Four movements from the Flute Sonatas, Op. 3)
1. 1st movt. of No. 1　　2. 2nd movt. of No. 10
3. 1st movt. of No. 4　　4. 2nd movt. of No. 1
E. Rothwell & W. Parry　　　**G.B 10291**
　　　　　　　　　　　　　　(*JK 2795*)

Trio-Sonata, B minor　　fl., vlc., hpsi.
M. Wittgenstein, M. Hubert, S. Marlowe
(*Telemann*)　　　　　　**♯ West.WL 5076**

Toccata (unspec.)　— ARR. HP.　Grandjany
A. Sacchi　　　　　　in ♯ *NRI. 403*
(*Handel, Haydn, Debussy, etc.*)

LOEWE, Johann Karl Gottfried
(1796-1869)

LIEDER UND BALLADEN
COLLECTION
(Des) Glockentürmers Töchterlein, Op. 112a　(Rückert)
Hochzeitslied, Op. 20, No. 1　(Goethe)
Kleiner Haushalt, Op. 71　(Rückert)
Odins Meeresritt, Op. 118　(Schreiber)
Süsses Begräbnis, Op. 62, No. 4　(Rückert)
　W. Warfield (B), O. Herz (pf.) ♯ AmC.ML 4545
(† *Ancient Music of the Church*)

Archibald Douglas, Op. 128　(Fontane)
J. Greindl (Bs), H. Klust (pf.)　　**PV. 72102**
(2ss)　　　　　　　　　　　(in ♯ *Pol. 16010*)

Edward, Op. 1, No. 1　(Herder)
(Der) Nöck, Op. 129, No. 2　(Kopisch)
　☆J. Greindl (Bs), H. Klust (pf.)
　　　　　　　　　　　　♯ AmD.DL 9610
(*below*)　　　　　　　　　(in ♯ *Pol. 16010*)

[1] Op. nos. quoted by French reviewers.

Meeresleuchten, Op. 145, No. 1　(Siebel)
Odins Meeresritt, Op. 118　(Schreiber)
　☆G. Hann (Bs), F. Leitner (pf.)
　(*Schumann, & above*)　　**♯ AmD.DL 9610**

(Das) Erkennen, Op. 65, No. 2　(Vogl)
　☆H. Schlusnus (B)　　　　**Pol. 67212**
　(*Der Schatzgräber*)

(Der) Nöck, Op. 129, No. 2　(Kopisch)
　W. Strienz (Bs) & orch.　　in ♯ **Ura. 7026**
　(*Arias & Lieder*)

Prinz Eugen, der edle Ritter, Op. 92 (Freiligrath)
P. Schoeffler (B), O. Schulhof (pf.)
　　　　　　　　　　　in ♯ **MSL.MW 44**
　(*Schubert, Liszt, etc.*)

(Der) Schatzgräber, Op. 59, No. 3　(Goethe)
　☆H. Schlusnus (B)　　　　**Pol. 67212**
　(now with *Das Erkennen*)

Tom der Reimer, Op. 135　(Rückert)
P. Schoeffler (B), O. Schulhof (pf.)
　　　　　　　　　　　in ♯ **MSL.MW 43**
　(*Schubert, etc. & Wagner*)
　☆ L. Slezak (T)　　　　　**Pol. 15447**
　　H. Schlusnus (B)　　in ♯ **AmD.DL 9623**
　　F. Völker (T)　　　　　**Pol. 15462**

(Die) Uhr, Op. 123, No. 3　(Seidl)
　☆ H. Schlusnus　　　in ♯ **AmD.DL 9623**
　　F. Völker　　　　　　　**Pol. 15462**

LOPATNIKOFF, Nikolai Lvovitch
(b. 1903)

Divertimento, Op. 34　orch.
La Jolla (Cal.) Festival—Sokoloff ♯ **CHS.G 4**
(*Rozsa*)

Sonata No. 2, Op. 32　vln. & pf.
J. Fuchs & A. Balsam　　　**♯ AmD.DL 9541**
(*Piston*)

LORTZING, Gustav Albert (1801-1851)

OPERAS
UNDINE　4 acts　1845
Vater, Mutter, Schwestern, Brüder　T　(Act III)
　☆ F. Völker (*Pol. 26509*)

(Der) WAFFENSCHMIED　3 acts　1846
Wir armen, armen Mädchen　S　(Act II)
　E. Trötschel　　　　　　**PV. 36043**
　(*Pagliacci—Qual fiamma*)

(Der) WILDSCHÜTZ　3 acts　1842
Overture
　Dresden Phil.—v. Kempen　　**Pol. 15430**
　　　　　　　　　　　　　(o.n. ▽ 57127)

ZAR UND ZIMMERMANN　3 acts　1837
Overture
　☆ Dresden Phil.—v. Kempen (Pol. 15494)

Lebe wohl, mein flandrisch' Mädchen　T　(Act II)
　☆ F. Völker (*Pol. 26509*)

Holzschuhtanz　(Clog Dance, Act III)　orch.
　Berlin State—Steeger　　　**Pol. 26514**
　(*Smetana: Bartered Bride—Furiant*)

LOTTI, Antonio (c. 1667-1740)

SEE ALSO: † ITALIAN ART SONGS

Crucifixus
Netherlands Cha. Cho.   **Phi.N 12027G**
(*below*)
  ☆ St. Eustache Singers—Martin (*Pac. 6479*)

Pur dicesti (Aria from *Arminio*, 1714)
E. Brems (M-S), S. Sørensen (hpsi.) & vlc.
(*Caccini: Amarilli*)   **Fdn.NC 3501**

Vere languores nostros
Netherlands Cha. Cho.—de Nobel
         Phi.N 12027G
(*Lassus & Handl*)   (*PhM.N 09024S*)

LÜBECK, Vincent (1654-1740)

CANTATAS
Gott, wie dein Name   cho., orch.
Hilf deinem Volk, Herr Jesu Christ
  S, A, T, B, cho., orch.
A. M. Augenstein, H. Plümacher, W.
Hohmann, O. von Rohr, Stuttgart Cho. &
Swabian Sym.—Grischkat   **♯ Ren.X 32**
(*below*)   (♯ Nix.PLP 232)

PRELUDES & FUGUES   org.
C minor; E major
E. Hölderlin   **♯ Ren.X 32**
(*above*)   (♯ Nix.PLP 232)

LUENING, Otto (b. 1900)

Prelude on a hymn-tune by Billings
(2) Symphonic Interludes   orch.   1935
A.R.S. Orch.—Dixon   **♯ ARS. 8**
(*Thomson*)

Suite for Soprano & Flute
  ▽ E. Luening & O. Luening (*NMQR. 1513*)

LULLY, Jean-Baptiste (1632-1687)

OPERA ARIA COLLECTION
AMADIS DE GAULE   1684
  Amour, que veux-tu ?
ATYS   1676
  Atys est trop heureux
  Espoir si cher
CADMUS ET HERMIONE   1673
  Amants, aimez vos chaines
  Belle Hermione, hélas, hélas
  Vous êtes le charme
(La) NAISSANCE DE VÉNUS   1665
  Rochers, vous êtes sourds
PERSÉE   1682
  Hymen, o doux
PHAÉTON   1683
  Dieu, qui vous declarez
PSYCHÉ   1678
  Admirons le jus de la treille
  Que vos âmes s'émeuvent
THÉSÉE   1675
  Trop heureux qui moissonne
C. Rowe (S), A. Linville (Bs), A. Duvernoy
(hpsi.)   **♯ Lyr.LL 16**

(La) NOCE DE VILLAGE   Ballet   1663
Air pour Mme. la Dauphine (Pavane)
Hpsi. & anon. orch. (*Scd. 4001*)

LUMBYE, Hans Christian (1810-1874)
(Condensed list only)

I. WORKS IN DANCE FORMS

GALOPS, etc.
Champagne
Tivoli—T. Lumbye   **Tono.X 25175**
(in ♯ Mer.MG 10130)   (also on *L 28039*)
  H. Bund Orch. (*Imp. 19098* & *19002*, d.c.)
  ☆ Concert—Waldimir (*D.C 16212*)
— ARR. 2 PFS.   M. Rawicz & W. Landauer (*C.DD 559*)

Indian War Dance
Railway (*Jernbane*)
  ☆Copenhagen Royal Op.—Høeberg
         Pol.X 51186

Railway (*Jernbane*)
Tivoli—T. Lumbye   **Tono.L 28038**
      (in ♯ Mer.MG 10130)

MARCHES
King Christian IX
King Frederik VII
Tivoli—T. Lumbye   **Tono.L 28037**
      (in ♯ Mer.MG 10130)

POLKAS
Amager
Tivoli—T. Lumbye   **Tono.X 25175**
(in ♯ Mer.MG 10130)   (also on *L 28038*)

Columbine (P-M)
Tivoli—T. Lumbye   **Tono.L 28039**
      (in ♯ Mer.MG 10130)

WALTZES
Amelie; Sophie
Tivoli—T. Lumbye   **Tono.X 25174**
      (in ♯ Mer.MG 10130)

Queen Louise
Tivoli—T. Lumbye   **Tono.X 25175**
      (in ♯ Mer.MG 10130)

II. OTHER WORKS

Dream Pictures   orch.   1846
  ☆ Danish Radio—Grøndahl (*G.ZN 565*)

McBRIDE, Robert Guryn (b. 1911)

Aria & Toccata in Swing   vln. & pf.   1946
L. & A. Kaufmann   **♯ CHS.CHS 1140**
(*Still, Copland & Carpenter*)

MACDOWELL, Edward (1861-1908)

Concerto No. 2, D minor, Op. 23 pf. & orch. 1890
A. Jenner & Vienna State Op.—Swoboda
(*Woodland Sketches*)   **♯ CHS.CHS 1137**

Suite No. 2, "Indian", Op. 48   orch. 1897
A.R.S. Orch.—Dixon   **♯ ARS. 3**

WOODLAND SKETCHES, Op. 51   pf.   1896
No. 1, To a wild rose
No. 2, Will o' the wisp
No. 4, In Autumn
No. 5, From an Indian lodge
No. 6, To a water lily
No. 9, By a meadow brook
No. 10, Told at sunset
A. Balsam   (*above*)   **♯ CHS.CHS 1137**

♯ = Long-playing, 33⅓ r.p.m.   ♭ = 45 r.p.m.   ♮ = Auto. couplings, 78 r.p.m.

124

WOODLAND SKETCHES (*continued*)

No. 1, To a wild rose
No. 2, Will o' the wisp
No. 3, At an old trysting place
No. 4, In Autumn

    P. Spagnolo   **P.PE 159**
    (*Prokofiev: March & Suggestion diabolique*)

... No. 1 — ARR. 2 PFS.
Sisters J. Madeleine & F. Therese   in ♯ Conl.SF 1
                                        (also ♮ & ♭)

—— ARR. ORCH. Columbia Orch. (in ♯ *AmC.GL 512*)

MAHLER, Gustav (1860-1911)

(Das) **Klagende Lied** S, A, T, orch. 1880, rev. 1898
    I. Steingruber, S. Wagner, E. Majkut, Vienna
    Cha. Cho. & Vienna State Op.—Fekete
    (2ss)   ♯ **Mer.MG 10102**
                                    (♯ Eur.LPG 608)

(Das) **Lied von der Erde** A, T, orch. 1908
    K. Ferrier, J. Patzak, Vienna Phil.—Walter
                                    ♯ **D.LXT 2721/2**
    (3ss—*Rückert Songs*)   (♯ Lon.LL 625/6)

    ☆E. Cavelti, A. Dermota & Vienna Sym.—
    Klemperer   ♯ **EVox. 130**
                                    (♯ PaV.VP 130)

SONGS
Kindertotenlieder (Rückert) 1902
    K. Ferrier (A) & Vienna Phil.—B. Walter
                                    ♮ **C.LX 8939/41**
    (6ss)   (2ss, in ♯ *AmC.ML 2187*; ♯ *C.C 1009*)

    L. Lail (M-S) & Berlin Radio—Kleinert
    (*below*)   ♯ **Ura. 7016**

    M. Anderson (A) & San Francisco Sym.—
    Monteux   ♯ **Vic.LM 1146**
    (*Brahms*)   (6ss, in ♭ *set WDM 1531*)

    V. Rosza (S) & Vienna State Opera—Fekete
                                    ♯ **Mer.MG 10103**
    (*below*)   (♯ Eur.LPG 611)

    H. Schey (B) & Residentie—v. Otterloo
    (2ss)   ♯ **Phi.A 00103R**

(Des) **KNABEN WUNDERHORN**
    2 Volumes, 1892-4

Das irdische Leben
Lob des hohen Verstands
Rheinlegendchen
Wer hat dies Liedlein erdacht
Der Schildwache Nachtlied
Verlorene Müh'
Trost im Unglück
Wo die schönen Trompeten blasen
Des Antonius von Padua Fischpredigt
Lied des Verfolgten im Turm
Urlicht (see also Symphony No. 2)

    ☆L. Sydney (A), A. Poell (B), Vienna State Op.
    Orch.—Prohaska   ♯ **Nix.VLP 412-1/2**
    (*Lieder aus letzter Zeit*)   (♯ CID.VAT 33010/1)
    (Poell sings the 2nd, 5th, 7th & 10th songs)

Wer hat dies Liedlein erdacht; Rheinlegendchen
    A. Felbermeyer (S), A. Poell (B), V. Graef (pf.)
    (*below*)   in ♯ **Van.VRS 424**

Es sungen drei Engel
Included in ♯ VRS 421, *below*

Das irdische Leben
    ▽K. Branzell (A)   in ♯ **Rem. 149-6**
    (*Schubert, Wolf, etc.*)

Rheinlegendchen
    ☆ H. Schlusnus (B) & orch. (in ♯ *Ete. 471*)

---

(14) **LIEDER UND GESÄNGE AUS DER
    JUGENDZEIT** 1885-92
    (Vols. II & III have words from *Des Knaben Wunderhorn*)
    VOL. I. 1. Frühlingsmorgen (Leander)
            2. Erinnerung (Leander)
            3. Hans und Grete (Volkslied)
            4. Serenade aus Don Juan (T. de Molina)
            5. Phantasie aus Don Juan (T. de Molina)
    VOL. II. 1. Um schlimme Kinder artig zu machen
            2. Ich ging mit Lust . . .
            3. Aus ! Aus !
            4. Starke Einbildungskraft
    VOL. III. 1. Zu Strasburg auf der Schanz'
            2. Ablösung im Sommer
            3. Scheiden und Meiden
            4. Nicht Wiedersehen
            5. Selbstgefühl

COMPLETE RECORDINGS
    A. Felbermeyer (S), A. Poell (B), V. Graef (pf.)
    (*above*)   ♯ **Van.VRS 424**
    I. Steingruber (S), H. Häfner (pf.) ♯ **SPA. 20**
    (*Symphony No. 3, s.1*)

... VOL. I, Nos. 1, 2, 3; VOL. II, Nos. 2, 4;
        VOL. III, Nos. 2, 3, 4
    ☆D. Halban (S), B. Walter (pf.)
                                in ♯ **AmC. set SL 171**
    (*Symphony No. 5, s.1*)

... VOL. I, Nos. 1 & 3; VOL. II, No. 2; VOL. III,
    No. 3; *and* Es sungen drei Engel (from
    Knaben Wunderhorn Songs, Vol. I)
    A. Felbermeyer (S), A. Poell (B) & Vienna
    State Op. Orch.—Prohaska ♯ **Van.VRS 421**
    (*Lieder von Rückert*)

(7) **LIEDER AUS LETZTER ZEIT** 1902
A. (5) *LIEDER VON RÜCKERT*
1. Ich atmet' einen linden Duft
2. Liebst du von Schönheit
3. Blicke mir nicht
4. Ich bin der Welt abhanden gekommen
5. Um Mitternacht
    A. Felbermeyer (S), A. Poell (B) & Vienna State
    Op. Orch.—Prohaska   ♯ **Van.VRS 421**
    (*above*)
    I. Steingruber (S) & Vienna State Op. Orch.—
    Fekete   ♯ **Mer.MG 10103**
    (*above*)   (♯ Eur.LPG 611)

... Nos. 1, 4, 5 only
    K. Ferrier (A) & Vienna Phil.—Walter
                                ♯ **D.LXT 2722**
    (*Das Lied von der Erde, s.3*)   (♯ Lon.LL 626)

... No. 4 only ☆ Mme. Ch. Cahier (in ♯ *Ete. 471*)

B. (2) *LIEDER FROM DES KNABEN
        WUNDERHORN*
6. Revelge (Reveillé)
7. Der Tambourgesell
    A. Poell (B), Vienna State Op. Orch.—Prohaska
                                ♯ **Nix.VLP 412-1/2**
    (*above*)   (♯ CID.VAT 33010/1)

... No. 7 only
    ☆ H. Schlusnus (B) & orch. (in ♯ *Ete. 471*)

LIEDER EINES FAHRENDEN GESELLEN
    (Mahler) 1883
    J. Metternich (B) & Berlin Radio Orch.—
    Ludwig (*above*)   ♯ **Ura. 7016**
    ☆B. Thebom (M-S) & orch.—Boult
                                ♯ **Vic.LM 1203**
    (*Wolf: Songs*)   (♭ set WDM 1627)

SYMPHONIES
No. 1, D major ("Titan") 1888
    ☆ Minneapolis Sym.—Mitropoulos (C.LOX 752/7)

☆ = Re-issue of a recording to be found in WERM or Supplement I.

SYMPHONIES (continued)

No. 2, C minor ("Resurrection") S, A, cho., orch.
1894
I. Steingruber, H. Rössl-Majdan, Academy &
Musikfreunde Chos., Vienna Sym.—Klemperer
(4ss) ♯ **AmVox.PL 7080**
(♯ EVox. 382)

... **Urlicht** (4th movt.) only
☆ Mme. Ch. Cahier (in ♯ *Ete. 471*)

(See also: Lieder, Knaben Wunderhorn)

No. 3, D minor A, cho., orch. 1896
H. Rössl-Majdan, Vienna State Op. Cho. &
Vienna Philharmonia—Adler ♯ **SPA. 20/2**
(5ss—*Lieder aus der Jugendzeit*)

No. 4, G major S & orch. 1900
M. Ritchie & Amsterdam—v. Beinum
♯ **D.LXT 2718**
(♯ Lon.LL 618)

I. Camphausen & Berlin Sym.—Balzer
♯ **Roy. 1308**

☆ D. Halban & N.Y.P.S.O.—Walter ♯ **C.CX 1034**

No. 5, C sharp minor 1902
Vienna State Op.—Scherchen
♯ **West. set WAL 207**
(3ss—*Symphony No. 10*)
☆N.Y.P.S.O.—Walter ♯ **AmC.set SL 171**
(3ss—*Songs*)

No. 8, E major S, S, A, A, T, B, Bs, 3 chos., orch.
1907
E. M. Matheis, D. Ilitsch, R. Anday, G.
Milinkovic, E. Majkut, G. Oeggl, H. Wiener,
Wiener Sängerknaben, Kammerchor &
Singakademie Cho. & Vienna Sym.—
Scherchen ♯ **AmC. set SL 164**
(4ss—*Actual performance*, 1951)
St. Stephen's Cath. & Vienna State Op. Chos.
& Vienna Phil.—Alwin (4ss) ♯ **CEd. 3001**
(*Announced, but never released*)

No. 9, D minor 1909
Vienna Sym.—Horenstein ♯ **AmVox.PL 7602**
(4ss)

No. 10, F sharp major
(unfinished: completed by Křenek)
... **1st movt., Adagio,** only
Vienna State Op.—Scherchen
♯ **West. set WAL 207**
(*Symphony No. 5, s.1*)

... **1st. movt., Adagio, & 3rd movt., Purgatorio,** only
Zürich Tonhalle—Franz Schmidt
♯ **RH.pte. issue**

MALEINGRAU, Paul de (b. 1887)
SEE: † FRENCH ORGAN MUSIC

MALIPIERO, Gian Francesco (b. 1882)

FILOMELA E L'INFATUATO Opera, 1928
(orig. *Ger*)
Se tu m'ami (Rolli)
C. Williams (S), B. Bazala (pf.) in ♯ *MGM.E 140*
(*Carpenter, Dougherty, Delibes, etc.*)

Poemi asolani pf. 1916
H. Schnabel ♯ **SPA. 15**
(*Weber*)

Risonanze pf. pub. 1920
G. Gorini **P.AB 30023**
(*Debussy: Étude*)

MANFREDINI, Francesco (b. 1688-d. ?)

Sinfonia da chiesa, con una pastorale, Op. 2, No. 12
2 vlns. & orch. 1709
... **1st movt., Pastorale** only
L. Kaufman, A. Fietz & str. orch.—Dahinden
(*Torelli, etc.*) ♯ **CHS.F 17**

MARAIS, Marin (1656-1728)

Aria (unid.)
H. Kirschner (descant viola), F. Beyer (viola
d'amore), W. Biller (gamba)
in ♯ **Nix.PLP 240**
(in ♯ Ren.X 40; ♯ Clc. 6124)

(5) French Dances [1] gamba & hpsi.
(Bourrée, Passepied, Sarabande, Minuet, Gavotte)
E. Lake & D. Erhart (2ss) **Argo.S 1004**

MARCELLO, Alessandro (1684-1750)

CONCERTO, D minor, oboe & str. orch.
R. Reversy & Suisse Romande—Ansermet [2]
♯ **D.LX 3100**
(*Vivaldi: Bassoon Concerto*) (♯ Lon.LS 591)
☆ L. Goossens & Philharmonia—Süsskind
(C.GQX 11446/7)
P. Renzi & Gothic Ens. (♯ Clc. 6078)

MARCELLO, Benedetto (1686-1739)

Aria, A minor Str. (ed. Bonelli) [3]
Virtuosi di Roma—Fasano ♯ **AmD.DL 9598**
(*Albinoni, Cirri, Pergolesi*)

Quella fiamma che m'accende Cantata
B. Neely (Tr.), G. Moore (pf.) **G.B 10096**
(*Durante: Vergin tutt' amor*)
M. Laszlo (S), F. Holletschek (pf.)
♯ **West.WL 5119**
(† *Italian Songs*)

(50) PSALMS 1724-7
No. 1—Beato l'uomo
☆Soloists, Angelicum Cho. & Orch.—Gerelli
(*Carissimi*) ♯ **Clc. 6048**

No. 19—I cieli narrano ... Excerpt
— ARR. ORGAN
E. P. Biggs in ♯ **AmC.ML 4603**
(*Buxtehude, Bach, etc.*)
R. Ellsasser in ♯ **MGM.E 3005**

MARCHAND, Louis (1669-1732)
SEE: † FRENCH ORGAN MUSIC

MARENZIO, Luca (1553-1599)
SEE: † ITALIAN MADRIGALS
† ♯ *AS. 2502LD*

MARINI, Biagio (1597-1663)
SEE: † ♯ *AS. 2502LD*

---

[1] Edition privately prepared from manuscript. It is doubtful if this disc was ever on sale.
[2] Ed. Bonelli, C minor.
[3] From an unspec. concerto.

MARSCHNER, Heinrich August (1795-1861)

HANS HEILING Opera, Intro. & 3 acts 1833
Overture
☆ Berlin State—Ludwig (Pol. 15523)

An jenem Tag B (Act I)
♄ J. Luria (IRCC. 3096*)

MARSON, George (d. 1632)
SEE: † TRIUMPHS OF ORIANA

MARTIN, Frank (b. 1890)

Petite Symphonie concertante
hp., hpsi., pf., str. 1945
P. Jamet, G. Vaucher-Clerc, D. Rossiaud &
Suisse Romande—Ansermet ♯ D.LXT 2631
(Stravinsky)   (♯ Lon.LLP 390)

MARTINI IL TEDESCO (J.P.A. Schwarzendorf) (1741-1816)

Plaisir d'amour (Florian) Song
☆L. Pons (S) & orch.   C.LX 1539
(Hue: À des oiseaux & Rachmaninoff: How fair this spot)
K. Reimann (T)   Od.O-28362
☆ R. Tauber   in ♯ AmD.DL 9547
♄ E. Calvé   AF. 42*

MARTINŮ, Bohuslav (b. 1891)

CONCERTOS
Double str. orch., pf. & timpani 1941
Philharmonia—Kubelik   ♮ G.C 7911/3
(S. Crook, pf.) (6ss)

Str. qtt. & orch. 1932
Vienna Konzerthaus Qtt. & Vienna Sym.—
Swoboda   ♯ West.WL 5079
(Partita & Serenade)

Duo, vln. & vlc. 1928
R. Posselt & S. Mayes   ♯ Fest. 70-203
(Haydn & Fauré)

Partita (Suite No. 1) str. orch. 1932
Winterthur Sym.—Swoboda ♯ West.WL 5079
(Concerto & Serenade)

(Les) Ritournelles (6 pf. pieces, 1932)
▽C. Rosen   in ♯ EMS. 2
(Sonata, Études, Polkas)

Serenade cha. orch. 1930
Winterthur Sym.—Swoboda ♯ West.WL 5079
(Concerto & Partita)

Sonata, 2 vlns. & pf. 1932
Sonatina, 2 vlns. & pf. 1931
M. & W. Schweyda & J. Behr   ♯ Ura. 5004

Toccata e Canzone cha. orch. 1946
Concert Hall Sym.—Swoboda   ♯ CHS.F 16
(Roussel)

MARX, Joseph (b. 1882)

Old Vienna Serenades (unid.)   orch.
Vienna Sym.—Moralt   ♯ Abbey. 3
(Siegel: Between two worlds)

Prelude, E flat minor   pf.
G. Scherzer   P.R 3437
(Prokofiev: Prelude, Op. 12, No. 7)

MASCAGNI, Pietro (1863-1945)

OPERAS

(L')AMICO FRITZ 3 acts 1891
Son pochi fiori   S (Act I)
♄ C. Muzio (IRCC. 3083*)

Suzel, buon dì (Cherry Duet) T, S (Act II)
♄ B. Gigli & N. Baldisseri (G.VB 46*: o.n. 2-054107/8*)

Intermezzo, Act III   orch.
Philharmonia—Schuechter   in ♯ MGM.E 131
(Intermezzi)   (♭ set K 131)

Ed anche Beppe amò . . . O Amore T (Act III)
. . . O Amore only
♄ F. de Lucia (in ♯ Ete. O-464* & in ♯ CMS. 201*)

CAVALLERIA RUSTICANA 1 act 1890
COMPLETE RECORDINGS
Set E

Santuzza	... ...	G. Simionato (M-S)
Lola	... ...	F. Cadoni (M-S)
Turiddu	... ...	A. Braschi (T)
Alfio	... ...	C. Tagliabue (B)
Lucia	... ...	L. Pellegrino (A)

etc., Turin Radio Cho. & Orch.—Basile
                              ♯ Sor. set 1233
(4ss) (3ss—Pagliacci in ♯ set 1238)

Set F V. Petrova (S), E. Ruhl (T), I. Petroff (B),
etc. & Florence May Festival Cho. & Orch.—
Ghiglia   ♯ Rem. 199-74
Set A
☆ L. B. Rasa, B. Gigli, G. Bechi, G. Simionato, M.
Marucci, La Scala—Mascagni
                 (♯ G.FALP 108/9: QALP 108/9)

HIGHLIGHTS
Z. Milanov, J. Björling, R. Merrill
                              ♯ Vic.LM 1160
(Pagliacci)   (mostly ☆)   (♭ set WDM 1565)
Soloists & Berlin Op. Cho. & Orch (♯ Roy. 1350)

Orchestral Selection
Salzberg Fest. Orch.—P. Walter (♯ Rem. 149-24)
☆ Berlin State Op.—Melichar (Pol. 15386: 57421)

Siciliana   T
A. Braschi   P.AT 0278
(Addio alla madre) (from Set E)
R. Lagares   G.DA 11336
(Fedora—Amor ti vieta)
♄ E. Caruso   ♭ Vic.ERAT 1*
                    & G.VA 30*: o.n. DA 545*
J. McCormack (Eng)   in ♯ Ete.O-469*
E. Clément (Fr)   HRS. 1116*

Gli aranci olezzano   cho.
Württemberg State Op.—Leitner(Ger) PV.56004
(below)   (♯ Pol. 18048)
☆ La Scala Cho. (Pol. 15554)

Regina Coeli . . . Inneggiamo, il Signor S & cho.
Württemberg State Op.—Leitner(Ger) PV.56004
(above)   (♯ Pol. 18048)

☆ = Re-issue of a recording to be found in WERM or Supplement I.

CAVALLERIA RUSTICANA (continued)

Voi lo sapete   S
  G. Brouwenstijn   **Phi.N 11169G**
  (Tosca—Vissi d'arte)   (PhM.A 09004S)
  (Oberon & Pagliacci, in ‡ Phi.N 00119L)
  A. Varnay   in ‡ **Rem. 199-53**
  (Ballo, Manon Lescaut, etc.)
  E. Nicolai   **P.CB 20511**
  (Don Carlos—O don fatale)
  ☆ M. Caniglia   BrzV. 886-5002
  ⌐ C. Boninsegna   in ‡ Ete.O-468*
                      & G.VB 11*: o.n. 053172*
  R. Ponselle   in ‡ Gol. 1201*
  E. Destinn (Ger)   in ‡ set CEd. 7001*

Tu qui Santuzza . . . No, No, Turiddu   S, T
  ⌐ C. Boninsegna & J. Gravina (HRS. 1117*)

Intermezzo
  Philharmonia—Weldon   **C.DX 1807**
  (Tchaikovsky: Sleeping Beauty—Waltz)   (DWX 5073)
  Berlin State—L. Ludwig   **G.DB 11502**
  (Pagliacci—Intermezzo)
  Hilversum Radio—v. Kempen   **Phi.N 12011G**
  (Pagliacci—Intermezzo)
                  (PhM.N 09008S; & in ‡ Phi.N 00119L)
  Philharmonia—Schuechter   in ‡ **MGM.E 131**
  (Intermezzi)   (♭ set K 131)
  Boston Pops—Fiedler   in ♭ **Vic.WEPR 20**
  (From "Highlights" set)
  ☆ Berlin Municipal—Haarth (Pol. 15528)
   etc.

— VOCAL ARR.   (Ave Maria)
  J. Melton (in ‡ Vic.LM 82: ♭ set WDM 1365)

Brindisi—Viva il vino   T, [M-S] & cho.
  A. Braschi, F. Cadoni (M-S) & cho.
                                   P.RO 30005
  (2ss)   (from Set E)   (AT 0279)
  ▽ F. Völker (Ger)   Pol. 90059
  ☆ P. Anders (Ger)   AusT.E 1170
  ⌐ E. Caruso & pf.   G.VA 33*: o.n. DA 545*

Addio alla madre . . . Mamma, quel vino   T
  M. del Monaco   **G.DB 11351**
  (Carmen—Flower song)
  A. Braschi   **P.AT 0278**
  (Siciliana)   (from Set E)
  R. Lagares   **G.DB 11354**
  (Norma—Meco all' altar)
  R. Schock (Ger)   **G.DB 11542**
  (Carmen—Flower song)
  ☆M. Lanza   **G.DB 21523**
  (L'Africaine—O Paradis)   (♭ 7R 146)
  (in ‡ Vic.LM 7015: ♮ set DM 7015; ♭ ERA 51)
  ☆R. Tucker   **C.LX 1508**
  (Aïda—Celeste Aïda)
  ☆ J. Björling in ‡ Vic. LM 105: ♭ set WDM 1546
  J. Schmidt (Ger)   in ‡ Ete. 460
  ⌐ E. Caruso in ‡ Vic.LCT 1039*: ♭ set WCT 62*

ISABEAU   3 parts   1911
Questo mio bianco manto   S   (Part I)
Venne una vecchierella   S   (Part III)
  ⌐ C. Boninsegna (HRS. 1086*)

LODOLETTA   3 acts   1917
Flammen, perdonami, Act III   S
  M. Minazzi   **P.FP 751**
  (Rondine—Chi il bel sogno di Doretta)

MASON, Daniel Gregory (b. 1873)

Chanticleer, Op. 27   Festival Overture, orch. 1926
  A.R.S.Orch.—Dixon   ‡ **ARS. 20**
  (Powell)

MASSENET, Jules Émile Frédéric
(1842-1912)

I. OPERATIC & STAGE WORKS

(Le) CID   4 acts   1885
Ballet Music, Act II
  1. Castillane   2. Andalouse   3. Aragonaise
  4. Aubade   5. Catalane   6. Madrilène
  7. Navarraise
  L.S.O.—Irving   ‡ **D.LXT 2746**
  (Meyerbeer: Patineurs, Ballet)   (‡ Lon.LL 651)
  Paris Phil.—Désormière   ♮ **U.H 24026/8**
  (6ss)   (Grétry & Méhul in ‡ CdM.LDX 8028)
  Netherlands Phil.—Spruit   ‡ **Nix.CLP 1155**
  (Rimsky-Korsakov)   (‡ CHS.CHS 1155)

O Souverain ! O Juge ! O Père (Prière)   T
  ☆J. Schmidt (Ger)   **P.DP 311**
  (Flotow: Alessandro Stradella, aria)
  ⌐ E. Caruso
      (in ‡ Vic.LCT 1034*: set ♭ WCT 35* & G.DB 123*)

DON CÉSAR DE BAZAN   3 acts   1872
Sevillana: Je sais . . .   S   (Act III)
  G. Gasparyan   **USSR. 19903**
  (Donizetti: Linda di Chamounix—O luce . . .)
  V. Barsova (Russ)   **USSR. 9958**
  (Manon—aria)

DON QUICHOTTE   5 acts   1910
Mort de Don Quichotte   Bs, B, S   (Act V)
  G. London (singing Don & Sancho) & R.
    Nadell   ‡ **AmC.ML 4489**
  (Paladilhe: Patrie, excpt.; & Prince Igor, etc.)

ESCLARMONDE   4 acts   1889
Regardez-les, ces yeux   S   (Act III)
  ⌐ M. Kousnezoff (HRS. 1050*)

HÉRODIADE   4 acts   1881
Prophète bien aimé   S   (Act I)
  Géori-Boué   **Sat.C 703**
  (Thaïs—Dis-moi que je suis belle)

Il est doux, il est bon   S   (Act I)
  A. Varnay   in ‡ **Rem. 199-53**
  (Fliegende Holländer, Oberon, etc.)
  ☆ N. Vallin   in ‡ **AmD.DL 9566**
  ⌐ C. Muzio (Ital)
          in ‡ Eso.ES 500*; Cpt.MC 20008* [1]
  A. Adiny   IRCC. 3014*

Quand nos jours s'éteindront   T part only
  ⌐ F. Tamagno   G.VA 62*

MANON   4 acts   1884
COMPLETE RECORDING
  Manon Lescaut   ...   ...   J. Micheau (S)
  Chevalier des Grieux ...   L. de Luca (T)
  Lescaut   ...   ...   R. Bourdin (B)
  Comte des Grieux ...   J. Giovanetti (Bs)
  etc., cho. & orch of Opéra-Comique, Paris—
    Wolff   ‡ **D.LXT 2618/20**
  (6ss—with narration)   (‡ Lon. set LLPA 7)

COLLECTION OF ARIAS   S
  Je suis encore tout étourdie
  Voyons, Manon, plus de chimères
  Adieu, notre petite table
  Obéissons quand leur voix . . .   (Gavotte)
  ☆ N. Vallin (in ‡ AmD.DL 9566)

ACT I

J'ai marqué l'heure du départ . . .   S, T
  I. Maslennikova, S. Lemeshev (Russ)
  (2ss)   **USSR. 016282/3**
  ⌐ M. Carré & L. Beyle (HRS. 1102*)

---

[1] Recorded from an Edison cylinder.

MANON (*continued*)

ACT II

J'écris à mon père . . . On l'appelle Manon   S, T
  H M. Carré & L. Beyle (HRS. 1102*)

Adieu, notre petite table   S
  M. Carosio (*Ital*)   **G.DB 21336**
  (*Bellini: Capuleti—Oh! quanti volte*)
  M. Minazzi (*Ital*)   **P.RO 30004**
  (*Puccini: Rondine, aria*)   (*FB 752*)
  ☆ V. de los Angeles (♭ *G.7RF 158*)

En fermant les yeux   T
  W. Midgley (*Eng*)   **G.DB 21358**
  (*Ah! fuyez douce image*)
  ☆D. Georgevic   **D.K 23211**
  (*Traviata—De miei bollenti spiriti*)
  G. Mattera (*Ital*)   **P.AT 0289**
  (*Rigoletto—Donna è mobile*)
  S. Lemeshev (*Russ*)   **USSR. 17970**
  (*Meyerbeer: Africaine—O Paradis*)

  H J. McCormack (*Ital*)   G.VA 21*: o.n. DA 297*
  E. Caruso & pf. (*Ital*)   G.VA 58*: o.n. 52345*
       also   G.VA 32*: o.n. DA 125*
  L. Sobinoff (*Russ*)   G.VB 19*: o.n. DB 894*
  L. Slezak   in ♯ Ete. 461*

ACT III

Obéissons quand leur voix appelle (*Gavotte*) S
  H G. Farrar   G.VA 13*: o.n. DA 510*
  C. Muzio   HRS. 1068*
  G. Vix   HRS. 1055*

Je suis seul . . . Ah! fuyez, douce image   T
  W. Midgley (*Eng*)   **G.DB 21358**
  (*En fermant les yeux*)
  S. Lemeshev (*Russ*)   **USSR. 18416/7**
  ☆ B. Gigli (*Ital*)   BrzV. 886-5003
  A. Piccaver (*Ger*)   Pol. 35068
  H E. Scaremberg   HRS. 1027*
  L. Slezak   in ♯ Ete. 461*

(Le) ROI DE LAHORE   5 acts   1877
Promesse de mon avenir   B   (Act IV)
  G. Taddei (*Ital*)   **P.R 30047**
  (*Africaine—Adamastor . . .*)   (BB 25296)

THAÏS   3 acts   1894
COMPLETE RECORDING
  Thaïs   ... ...   Géori-Boué (S)
  Nicias   ... ...   J. Giraudeau (T)
  Athanaël   ... ...   R. Bourdin (B)
  Palémon   ... ...   M. Roux (Bs)
  Myrtale   ... ...   O. Riquier (S)
  etc., Paris Op. Cho. & Orch.—Sebastian
  (6ss)   **♯ Ura. set 227**

Ballet Suite
  Paris Opéra—Sebastian   **♯ Ura. set 7058**
  (*Faust & Arlésienne*)

ACT I

Que te fait si sévère   S
  H M. Edvina (*G.VA 48*: o.n. DA 447**)

ACT II

Ah! je suis seule . . . Dis-moi que je suis belle   S
  (*Air du miroir*)
  J. Hammond (2ss)   **G.DA 1997**
  Géori-Boué   **Sat.C 703**
  (*Hérodiade—Prophète bien aimé*)
  A. Varnay   in ♯ **Rem. 199-45**
  (*Aïda, Simone Boccanegra, Trovatore, etc.*)
  M. Santreuil   **Pac. 6786**
  (*Madama Butterfly—Un bel di*)
  M. Vitale (*Ital*)   **P.R 30048**
  (*La Wally—Ebben . . .*)   (CB 20532)

Méditation (Intermezzo)   orch.
  Philharmonia—Weldon   **C.DX 1792**
  (*Ippolitoff-Ivanoff: Caucasian Sketch No. 4*)
  ☆ Boston Prom.—Fiedler (♭ *G.7P 119: 7BF 1050*)

— ARR. VLN. & PF.
  Z. Francescatti & A. Balsam   ♯ **AmC.ML 4534**
  (*Kreisler, Chabrier, Villa-Lobos, etc.*)   (♭ *A 1533*)
  L. Kaufman & P. Ulanowsky
         ♯ **DCap.CCL 7513**
  (*Dvořák, Schubert, Rimsky, etc.*)   (♯ *Cap.L 8165*)
  C. Ferras & R. Barbizet   **D.GAG 15099**
  (*Fauré: Berceuse*)
  T. Magyar & W. Hielkema   **Phi.N 11227G**
  (*Gounod: Ave Maria*)   (*PhM. 09043S* & ♯ *Phi.N 00605R*)
  ☆ M. Elman   ♭ *Vic.WEPR 29*;   ¶ *Phi.N 00605R*
  F. Kreisler in ♯ *Vic.LCT 1049*: ♭ *set WCT 80*

— ARR. VLN. & ORG.
  C. Cavalcabo & W. Marti (*Antro.AK 10001*), etc.

L'amour est une vertu rare   S
  H M. Edvina (*G.VA 48*: o.n. DA 447**)

WERTHER   4 acts   1892
COLLECTION OF ARIAS
Werther ! Qui m'aurait dit . . .
Va ! laisse-les couler
Ah, mon courage m'abandonne
  ☆ N. Vallin (in ♯ *AmD.DL 9566*)

Prelude   orch.
  Opéra-Comique—Wolff   in ♯ **D.LXT 2625**
  (*Berlioz, Lalo & Saint-Saëns*)   (♯ *Lon.LLP 355*)

ACT I

O nature (Invocation)   T
  I. Kozlovsky (*Russ*)   (2ss)   **USSR. 9158/9**

Intermezzo   vlc. & orch.
— ARR. VLC. & PF.   "*Clair de lune*"
  A. Navarra & J. Dussot   **C.LFX 1010**
  (*Godard: Jocelyn, Berceuse*)

Il faut nous séparer   T, S
  I. Kozlovsky & N. Rozhdestvenskaya
         USSR. 9166
  (*Death of Werther*)   (*Russ*)

ACT III

Werther ! qui m'aurait dit   S or M-S
  S. Michel   (2ss)   **Pat.PD 164**
  G. Simionato (*Ital*)   **C.GQX 11499**
  (*below*)
  E. Nicolai (*Ital*)   **P.CB 20531**
  (*Gluck: Orphée, No. 33*)
  ☆ G. Swarthout (♯ *Vic.LM 1156*: ♭ *set WDM 1562*)

Va ! laisse-les couler (*Air des larmes*)   S or M-S
  G. Simionato (*Ital*)   **C.GQX 11499**
  (*above*)
  M. Maksakova (*Russ*)   **USSR. 15813**
  (*Carmen—Air des cartes*)

Pourquoi me réveiller   T
  M. del Monaco (*Ital*)   **G.DA 11333**
  (*Andrea Chénier—Come un bel dì . . .*)
  C. Valletti (*Ital*)   **P.R 30045**
  (*Elisir d'Amore—Una furtiva . . .*)   (BB 25289)
  I. Kozlovsky (*Russ*)   **USSR. 9161**
  (*Aria, Act II, unspec.*)
  ☆ B. Gigli (*Ital*)   BrzV. 886-5003
  H G. Martinelli (*Ital*)   G.VA 61*
  F. de Lucia (*Ital*)   in ♯ Ete.O-464*

ACT IV

Mort de Werther, T part only
  I. Kozlovsky (*Russ*)   **USSR. 9167**
  (*Duet, Act I*)

☆ = Re-issue of a recording to be found in WERM or Supplement I.

II. 1. ORCHESTRAL

Phèdre, Overture　1873
　Opéra-Comique—Wolff　　in ‡ **D.LXT 2625**
　　(*Berlioz, Lalo, Saint-Saëns*)　(‡ Lon.LLP 355 & *LD 9020*)
　Rhineland Sym.—Federer　　‡ **Rgt. 5050**
　　(*Suppé & Rossini*)

Scènes napolitaines (Orch. Suite No. 5)　1876
　... Danse
　Vienna Radio—Nilius　　**Vien.L 6092**
　　(*Moniuszko: Halka—Mazurka*)　　(in ‡ *1009*)

Scènes pittoresques　(Orch. Suite No. 4)　1874
　1. Marche　　　　　2. Air de ballet
　3. Angelus　　　　 4. Fête bohème
　Berlin Radio—L. Ludwig　　‡ **Ura. 7039**
　　(*Saint-Saëns*)
　☆ Lamoureux—Tomasi (Pat.MDT 18/19: PE 11001/2)

II. 2. SONGS

Élégie (Gallet) with vlc. obbligato
　P. Schoeffler (B), G. Cassadò & pf.
　　　　　　　　in ‡ **MSL.MW 45**
　　(also, with *R. Strauss: Morgen, Hma. 14003*)
　R. Stevens (M-S), M. Elman (vln.) & pf.
　　　　　　　　in ‡ **Vic.LM 1703**
　　　　　　　　(♭ set *WDM 1703*)
　☆ R. Crooks (T) & orch. (♭ *Vic. 17-0189*)
　Ħ F. Kaschowska (S) (*IRCC. 3120**)
　E. Caruso (T), M. Elman (vln.) (in ‡ Vic.LCT 2**:
　　　　　　　　　　♭ set *WCT 7**)
　— ARR. ORCH.　Mantovani Orch. (*D.F 9440*)

Noël des fleurs (Schneider)　1912
　J. Wilson (S), G. Trovillo (pf.)
　　　　　　　　in ‡ **AmD.DL 9554**
　　(*Fauré, Debussy, etc.*)

MATTHESON, Johann (1681-1764)

Aria, E minor　(unspec.)
　— ARR. ORGAN
　E. P. Biggs　　in ‡ **AmC.ML 4603**
　　(*Schubert, R. Strauss, etc.*)

Sonata, E minor　　vln. & cont.
　☆ L. Kaufmann & A. Geoffroy-Dechaume (hpsi.)
　　　　　　　　(in ‡ *Eur.LPG 627*)

MAUDUIT, Jacques (1557-1625)

　SEE : † MONACO CATHEDRAL

MEDTNER, Nicolai Raslovitch (1879-1951)

Lyric Fragment, Op. 23, No. 1　　pf.
　L. Podolsky　　in ‡ **Cmt. 1204**
　　(*Reger, Scriabin, etc.*)

SONGS
Einsamkeit, Op. 18, No. 3　(Goethe)
Elfliedchen, Op. 6, No. 3　(Goethe)
Im Vorübergehen, Op. 6, No. 4　(Goethe)
Meeresstille - Glückliche Fahrt　(Goethe)
(The) Muse, Op. 29, No. 1　(Pushkin)
Praeludium, Op. 46, No. 1　(Goethe)
(Die) Quelle　(Chamisso)
(The) Rose, Op. 29, No. 6　(Pushkin)
Selbstbetrug, Op. 15, No. 2　(Goethe)
So tanzet　(Goethe)
Waltz, Op. 37, No. 4　(Pushkin)
When roses fade, Op. 36, No. 3　(Pushkin)
Winternacht　(Eichendorff)
　E. Schwarzkopf (S), N. Medtner (pf.)
　(8ss)　　　　　　**C.LX 1423/6**
　　(*The Pushkin songs are sung in English, the others in German*)

MÉHUL, Etienne Henri (1763-1817)

(Le) JEUNE HENRI　Opera, 2 acts　1797
Ouverture de chasse
　Paris Phil.—Désormière　　‡ **CdM.LDX 8028**
　　(⅓s.—*Grétry; & Massenet: Le Cid*)
　　(3ss—*Debussy: Reflets dans l'eau*, on ♮ U.H 24178/9)

Sonata, A major, Op. 1, No. 3　　pf.
　L. Podolsky　　in ‡ **Cmt. 1204**
　　(*Szymanowski, Medtner, etc.*)

MENDELSSOHN, Alfréd

(The) Downfall of Doftanea
　Rumanian Radio Sym.—Silvestri ♮ *U.D 26124/6*
　　(6ss)

MENDELSSOHN-BARTHOLDY, Felix von (1809-1847)

CLASSIFIED :
　　1. Piano & Organ　　　2. Chamber Music
　　3. Orchestral　　　　　4. Stage Music
　　5. Songs & Partsongs　6. Choral
　　7. Miscellaneous

1. PIANO & ORGAN
(for pf. solo unless otherwise stated)

(3) CAPRICES, Op. 33
No. 3, B flat minor
　D. Winand-Mendelssohn　　**PV. 72098**
　　(*Rondo capriccioso*)

ÉTUDES, Op. 104, Book 2
No. 2, F major
　A. d'Arco　　**Pat.PDT 274**
　　(*Schubert: Impromptu, Op. 90, No. 2*)

Prelude & Fugue, C minor, Op. 37, No. 1　org.
　J. Eggington　　‡ **OL.LD 58**
　　(*below*)

Rondo capriccioso, E major, Op. 14
　(with Andante)
　C. Arrau　(2ss)　　**C.LX 1515**
　F. Ellegaard　(2ss)　　**Pol.HM 80055**
　D. Winand-Mendelssohn　　**PV. 72098**
　　(*Caprice, Op. 33, No. 3*)
　J. Bolet　　in ‡ **Bo.B 301**
　　(*below*)
　☆V. Schiøler　　in ‡ **Mer.MG 10099**
　　(*Grieg, Liszt, Scriabin, etc.*)
　— ARR. ORCH.　Nilius
　Vienna Radio—Nilius　　**Vien.L 6091**
　　(*Sibelius: Valse Triste*)　　(in ‡ *1009*)

(6) SONATAS, OP. 65　　org.
COLLECTION
No. 1, F minor
No. 3, A major
No. 6, D minor
　J. Eggington　　‡ **OL.LD 58**
　　(1⅓ss—*Prelude & Fugue*) (originally announced as LD 43)

No. 2, C minor
　F. Asma　(2ss)　　**Phi.N 11167G**
　　(*Rheinberger, Grison & Bach* in ‡ Phi.A 00118L)
　　(also, 2ss, *PhM.N 09023S*)

No. 3, A major
　F. Jackson　　**Ebor.E 504**
　　(York Minster organ)　　(pte. issue)

---

‡ = Long-playing, 33⅓ r.p.m.　　♭ = 45 r.p.m.　　♮ = Auto. couplings, 78 r.p.m.

130

ORGAN SONATAS (*continued*)

No. 6, D minor
A. Schweitzer   **♯ AmC.ML 4602**
(*Bach*)   (& in set SL 172)

... 1st movt. (Variations on *Vater unser*)
F. Asma (2ss)   **Phi.N 12041G**
(alsoi n ♯ Phi.N 00147L)   (*PhM.N 12041S*)

SONGS WITHOUT WORDS
COLLECTIONS
> No. 1, E major, Op. 19, No. 1
> No. 12, F sharp minor, Op. 30, No. 6
> No. 27, E minor, Op. 62, No. 3
> No. 34, C major, Op. 67, No. 4
> No. 45, C major, Op. 102, No. 3
> No. 46, G minor, Op. 102, No. 4

A. Ferber   **♯ D.LM 4544**
(*Schumann: Kinderszenen*)   (♯ *Lon.LPS 453*)

> No. 12, F sharp minor, Op. 30, No. 6
> No. 29, A minor, Op. 62, No. 5
> (*Venetian Gondola songs 2 & 3*)
> No. 25, G major, Op. 62, No. 1 (*Spring Song*)
> No. 34, C major, Op. 67, No. 4 (*Spinning Song*)

G. Puchelt   **G.EH 1425**

> No. 25, G major, Op. 62, No. 1
> No. 35, B major, Op. 67, No. 5

E. Goldstein   in **♯ MMS.8**
(*Beethoven*)

> No. 14, C minor, Op. 38, No. 2
> No. 23, A minor, Op. 53, No. 5
> No. 30, A minor, Op. 67, No. 1

—— ARR. ORCH.   Anon. orch. (Scd. 5002, 5004, 5010)

No. 1, E major, Op. 19, No. 1
— ARR. VLN. & PF.   Heifetz
☆ J. Heifetz & E. Bay (in ♯ Vic.LM 1166: ♭ *ERA 71*)

No. 3, A major, Op. 19, No. 3 (*Hunting song*)
J. Bolet   in **♯ Bo.B 301**
(*above; & Liszt, Beethoven, etc.*)

No. 6, G minor, Op. 19, No. 6
(*Venetian Gondola Song No. 1*)
— ARR. GUITAR   Segovia
A. Segovia   in **♯ B.AXTL 1005**
(† *Segovia Recital*)   (♯ *AmD.DL 9633*)

No. 30, A major, Op. 62, No. 6 (*Spring Song*)
☆ V. Horowitz (in ♯ Vic.LM 1171: ♭ *set WDM 1605*)

— ARR. 2 PFS.
Sisters J. Madeleine & F. Therese
    in **♯ Conl.SF 1**

— ARR. ORCH.
Paris Opéra—Cloëz   *Od. 188972*
(*Mozart: Rondo alla turca*)
Col. Orch (in ♯ *AmC.GL 510*)
etc.

No. 34, C major, Op. 67, No. 4
A. Rubinstein   ♭ *G.7RF 159*
(*Rachmaninoff: Prelude, Op. 3, No. 2*)
(*Schubert, etc.* in ♯ Vic.LM 1153: ♭ *set WDM 1558*:
    ♭ *WEPR 41*)
S. Rachmaninoff (in ♯ Csm.CRLP 115)

— ARR. VLC. & PF.
G. Cassadò & O. Schulhof   in **♯ MSL.MW 45**

No. 40, D major, Op. 85, No. 4
☆ V. Horowitz (in ♯ Vic.LM 1171: ♭ *set WDM 1605*)

(17) Variations sérieuses, D minor, Op. 54
A. Cortot (4ss) (n.v.)   ♭ *G.DA 7042/3*
F. Pelleg   **♯ CHS.CHS 1127**
(*Concerto*)

C. Giraud-Chambeau   **♯ Sel.LDG 8003**
(*Liszt: Paganini Études, & Brahms*)

D. Winand-Mendelssohn (2ss)   *PV. 36008*
A. Brugnolini   *P.PE 163/4*
(3ss—*Chopin: Berceuse*)

☆V. Horowitz   **♯ G.FBLP 1015**
(*Liszt*)

2. CHAMBER MUSIC

Octet, E flat major, Op. 20   4 vlns, 2 vlas, 2 vlcs.
... Scherzo   — ARR. ORCH.   Mendelssohn
☆Winterthur Sym.—Busch   in **♯ Nix.CLP 61**
(*Schubert*)   (♯ Clc. 6056)

QUARTETS, pf. & str.
No. 2, F minor, Op. 2
☆A. Balsam & Guilet Trio   **♯ CHS.CHS 1095**
(*below*)

QUARTETS, String
No. 1, E flat major, Op. 12
... 2nd movt., Canzonetta, only
Paganini Qtt. (in † ♯ Vic.LM 1192: ♭ *set WDM 1611*)

SONATA, F minor, Op. 4, vln. & pf.
D. Guilet & A. Balsam   **♯ CHS.CHS 1095**
(*Quartet*)

SONATA, No. 1, B flat major, Op. 45, vlc. & pf.
N. & J. Graudan   **♯ AmVox.PL 6980**
(*Symphony No. 4*)

Song without words, D major, Op. 109   vlc. & pf.
☆ P. Casals & Blas-Net
    (in ♯ Vic.LCT 1050: ♭ *set WCT 72*)

TRIOS, pf., vln., vlc.
No. 1, D minor, Op. 49
☆A. Rubinstein, J. Heifetz, G. Piatigorsky
    ♯ G.ALP 1009
(*Ravel: Trio*)   (♯ FALP 111)

... 3rd movt., Scherzo   — ARR. VLN. & PF. Heifetz
☆ J. Heifetz & E. Bay (in ♯ Vic.LM 1166)

3. ORCHESTRAL

Calm Sea and Prosperous Voyage, Overture, Op. 27
Berlin Phil.—Lehmann   **PV. 72171**
(2ss)   (in ♯ *AmD.DL 4015*)
Vienna Sym.—Moltkau   **♯E. & AmVox.PL 7440**
(*below*)   (o.n. ♯ *EVox. 290*)
Austrian Sym.—Paulmüller   **♯ Rem. 199-86**
(*Schubert: Sym. 5*)

Capriccio brillant, B minor, Op. 22   pf. & orch.
F. Pelleg & Winterthur Sym.—Goehr
(*Paganini*)   **♯ CHS.G 13**

CONCERTOS, pf. & orch.
No. 1, G minor, Op. 25
F. Pelleg & Winterthur Sym.—Goehr
(*Variations*)   **♯ CHS.CHS 1127**
H. Roloff & Bamberg Sym.—Lehmann
(3ss)   **PV. 72217/8S**
    (♯ Pol. 18073; ♯ *AmD.DL 9652*)
O. Frugoni & Vienna Sym.—Moralt
(*Symphony No. 4*)   **♯ PaV.VP 290**
(*Overtures, on* ♯ E. & AmVox.PL 7440; o.n. ♯ *EVox. 290*)
A. Sandford & Rome Sym.—Guenther
    ♯ Roy. 1221
(*MSND, excpts.*)

☆ M. Lympany & Philharmonia—Kubelik
    (G.EH 1383/4; ♯ Vic.LHMV 1025; ♭ *set WHMV 1025*)

☆ = Re-issue of a recording to be found in WERM or Supplement I.

CONCERTOS, pf. & orch. (*continued*)

No. 2, D minor, Op. 40
H. Roloff & Bamberg Sym.—Lehmann
♮ **PV. 72269/70**
(4ss)   (♯ Pol. 18073; ♯ AmD.DL 9652)
☆A. Balsam & Sym.—Gimpel   ♯ **Ren.X 28**
(*Symphony No. 1*)

Concerto, A flat major, 2 pfs. & orch. 1824
O. Frugoni, A. Taddei & Vienna Sym.—Moralt
♯ **EVox. 190**
(now ♯ E. & AmVox.PL 7400; PaV.VP 190)

Concerto, D minor, vln. & str. orch. 1822
Y. Menuhin & Vic. Str. Orch.   ♯ **Vic.LM 1720**
(*below*)   (♮ set WDM 1720)

Concerto, E minor, Op. 64, vln. & orch.
Y. Menuhin & Berlin Phil.—Furtwängler
♯ **Vic.LM 1720**
(*above*)   (♮ set WDM 1720)
T. Varga & Berlin Phil.—Lehmann
♮ **PV. 72125/6**
(4ss)   (♯ Pol. 16015)
D. Oistrakh & Sym.—Kondrashin
USSR. 017327/33
(7ss—*Auf Flügeln des Gesanges*)
L. Kaufman & Netherlands Phil.—Ackermann
♯ **MMS. 7**
F. Malaschowsky & Berlin Sym.   ♯ **Roy. 1286**
(excpts. also, ♯ Roy. 1314)
☆I. Stern & Philadelphia—Ormandy
C.LX 1445/7
(LZX 268/70: ♮ LNX 8039/41)
☆ J. Heifetz & Royal Phil.—Beecham
(♯ G.FALP 136: QALP 136)
W. Schneiderhan & Viennese Sym.—Scherman
(♯ Mrt. 1-14)

Fair Melusina, Overture, Op. 32
Vienna Sym.—Moltkau   ♯ E. & **AmVox.PL 7440**
(*above*)   (o. n. ♯ EVox. 290)
Vienna State Op.—Prohaska   ♯ **Van.VRS 425**
(*Symphony 5*)
Austrian State Sym.—Gui   ♯ **MSL.MW 42**
(*Gluck, Beethoven, Weber*)

(The) Hebrides, Overture, Op. 26
Royal Phil.—Beecham   ♯ *AmC.AAL 7*
(*Ruy Blas*)   (2ss—♮ 4-73281D)
Philharmonia—Schuechter   **C.DX 1835**
(CQX 16658)
Berlin Phil.—Lehmann   *PV. 36012*
(in ♯ AmD.DL 4015)
Boston Prom.—Fiedler (n.v.)   ♯ *Vic.LM 164*
(*Rimsky-Korsakov, Tchaikovsky*)   (♮ set WDM 1647)
Austrian Sym.—Gui   ♯ **MSL.MW 49**
(*Symphony No. 5*)
"Nat. Op. Orch."   in ♯ Var. 6937 & ♯ Var. 2021
☆ Vienna Phil.—Furtwängler   ♮ G.7RF 102
Hallé—Barbirolli   ♮ G.7R 120
Berlin State—Ludwig   in ♯ BB.LBC 1028:
♮ set WBC 1028
Vienna State Op.—Swarowsky   AusT.E 1114

Rondo brillant, E flat major, Op. 29 pf. & orch.
M. Lympany & L.S.O.—H. Menges G.C 4191
(2ss)   (in ♯ Vic.LHMV 1025: ♮ set WHMV 1025)

Ruy Blas, Overture, Op. 95
Royal Phil.—Beecham   ♯ *AmC.AAL 7*
(*Hebrides*)   (2ss—♮ 4-73282D)
Austrian Sym.—Singer   ♯ *Mrt. 1-16*
(*Beethoven, Liszt*)
Vienna Radio—Nilius   **Vien.L 6031**
☆ San Francisco Sym.—Monteux (♮ G.7RF 123)

Scherzo (unspec.) Vienna Radio—Nilius (*Vien.P 6095*)

SYMPHONIES

No. 1, C minor, Op. 11   1824
☆Stuttgart Phil.—v. Hoogstraten   ♯ **Ren.X 28**
(*Pf. Concerto No. 2*)   (and not 2ss, as before)

No. 3, A minor, Op. 50 "Scottish"   1842
Vienna Sym.—Klemperer
♯ **E. & AmVox.PL 7080**
(o.n. ♯ EVox. 320)
Dresden State Op.—Kempe   ♮ **U.H 23953/7**
(10ss) (3ss—*MSND Overture* in ♯ Sup.LPM 11/12)
Berlin Sym.—Balzer   ♯ **Roy. 1330**
☆ Minneapolis Sym.—Mitropoulos (♯ AmC.RL 3017)

No. 4, A major, Op. 90 "Italian"   1833
Minneapolis Sym.—Dorati   ♯ **Mer.MG 50010**
(*Mozart*)
Munich Phil.—Rieger   **PV. 72107/8**
(4ss)   (2ss—♯ AmD.DL 7508; ♯ Pol. 16019)
Vienna Sym.—Klemperer   ♯ **AmVox.PL 6980**
(*Cello Sonata No. 1*)
(*Pf. Concerto No. 1*, on ♯ PaV.VP 290)
(*Schubert: Symphony No. 4* on ♯ E. & AmVox.PL 7860)
Cleveland Sym.—Szell (n.v.)   ♯ **AmC.ML 4498**
(*MSND Music*)
Berlin Sym.—Balzer   ♯ **Roy. 1331**
Winterthur Sym.—Dahinden   ♯ *MMS. 3*
☆ Boston Sym.—Koussevitzky
(♯ G.FBLP 1003: QBLP 1003)
Czech Phil.—Pedrotti (♯ Sup.LPM 10)

No. 5, D major, Op. 107 "Reformation"   1830
Austrian Sym.—Gui   ♯ **MSL.MW 49**
(*Hebrides Overture*)
Vienna State Op.—Prohaska   ♯ **Van.VRS 425**
(*Melusine Overture*)

---

4. STAGE MUSIC.

ATHALIE, Op. 74   Inc. music for Racine's play
1834-5
War March of the Priests
Philharmonia—Weldon   **C.DX 1818**
(*Berlioz: Damnation of Faust—Marche hongroise*)
(DWX 5078)
☆ Boston Prom.—Fiedler (♮ Vic. 49-0292)
— ARR. ORGAN
V. Fox   in ♯ **AmC.ML 4401**
(♮ set A 1008)
H. Robinson Cleaver   in ♯ *AmD. set A 880*
(♯ DL 5360: ♮ set 9-269)

(A) MIDSUMMER NIGHT'S DREAM
Inc. Music
Overture & Nos. 1, 5, 7, 9, 12
☆N.B.C. Sym.—Toscanini (with S & cho.)
(*Debussy*)   ♯ **Vic.LM 1221**
(*Scherzo only*, with *Kabalevsky*,
in ♮ G.7RF 128; Vic. 49-3156)
(*Scherzo* also in ♮ Vic. sets WDM 1167 & WDM 1368)

Overture & Nos. 1, 5, 7, 9
Robin Hood Dell—Reiner   ♯ **Vic.LM 1724**
(*Debussy & Ravel*)   (♮ set WDM 1724)
(Nos. 1, 5 & 7 also ♮ Vic.WEPR 38)
N.Y.P.S.O.—Szell   ♯ **AmC.ML 4498**
(*Symphony No. 4*)

Overture & Nos. 1, 7, 9
Austrian Sym.—H. A. Brown   ♯ **Rem. 199-67**
(*Rosenkavalier Waltzes*)

Overture & Nos. 1 & 9
Berlin Sym.—Guenther   ♯ **Roy. 1221**
(*Pf. Concerto No. 1*)   (& in ♯ Roy. 6040)

Nos. 1, 7, 9
☆Berlin Phil.—Fricsay   ♯ *AmD.DL 4025*

♯ = Long-playing, 33⅓ r.p.m.   ♮ = 45 r.p.m.   ♮ = Auto. couplings, 78 r.p.m.

Overture
　☆Berlin Phil.—Fricsay　　　　# *AmD.DL 4006*
　(Weber)

　"Nat. Op. Orch."　　　　# *Roy. 6126*
　(Debussy: L'Après-Midi . . .)
　☆ Vienna State Op.—Scherchen (# *Sup.LPM 12*)

No. 1, Scherzo
　☆ Col. Sym.—Rodzinski (in ♭ *AmC. set A 1002*)

— ARR. PF.　Schiøler
　☆V. Schiøler　　　　in # *Mer.MG 10099*
　(Chopin, Liszt, Scriabin, etc.)

No. 9, Wedding March
　Italian Radio—Basile　　　　P.CB 20530
　(Boccherini: Minuet)

　"Nat. Op. Orch." (in # *Var. 6937*), etc.

— ARR. ORGAN　V. Fox (in # *AmC.AAL 18*), etc.

---

5. SONGS & PARTSONGS
A. SONGS & DUETS

Collection

Auf Flügeln des Gesanges, Op. 34, No. 2 (Heine)
(Die) Liebende schreibt, Op. 86, No. 3 (Goethe)
(Der) Mond, Op. 86, No. 5 (Geibel)
Neue Liebe, Op. 19a, No. 4 (Heine)
Schilflied, Op. 71, No. 4 (Lenau)
　V. Graef (S), L. Pommers (pf.)
　　　　　　　# CHS.CHS 1159
　(First Walpurgis Night)

Collection of 12 Duets

Op. 63 : 1. Ich wollt' mein Lieb' ergösse sich (Heine)
　　　　2. Abschiedslied der Zugvögel (Fallersleben)
　　　　3. Gruss (Eichendorff)
　　　　4. Herbstlied (Klingemann)
　　　　5. O sah ich auf der Heide dort
　　　　　　(O wert thou in the cauld blast—after Burns)
　　　　6. Maiglöckchen und die Blümelein (Fallersleben)
Op. 77 : 1. Sonntagsmorgen (Uhland)
　　　　2. Das Ährenfeld (Fallersleben)
　　　　3. Lied aus Ruy Blas (after Hugo)
Volkslieder : Wie kann ich froh und lustig sein ? (Kaufmann)
　　　　　Abendlied (Heine)
　　　　　Wasserfahrt (Heine)
　J. Carlton (S), M. Tobias (A), P. Ulanowsky (pf.)
　　　　　　　# MGM.E 118
　　　　　　　(♭ set K 118)

Abschiedslied der Zugvögel, Op. 63, No. 2
　(Fallersleben)
　A. Tomaschek (S), A. Schneewein (A) *(Vienna. 1014)*

Auf Flügeln des Gesanges, Op. 34, No. 2 (Heine)
　J. Moor (S), H. W. Haeusslein (pf.)　*Eli. 9035*
　(Bei der Wiege)

　J. Vincent (S), F. de Nobel (pf.) *Phi.A 11242G*
　(½s.—*Grieg & Schubert*)
　　　　　(*PhM.A 11242S* & in # *Phi.A 00610R*)

　M. Morley (Treb., *Eng*), M. Wills (pf.)
　　　　　　　in # *D.LM 4543*
　(Arne, Brahms, Schubert, Nevin, etc.)　(# *Lon.LPS 399*)

— ARR. VLN. & ORCH.　Anderson
　☆N. Milstein & Vic. Orch.—Fiedler
　　　　　　　♭ *G.7RF 183*
　(Poldini: Poupée valsante)　　　(♭ *Vic. 49-1280*)

— ARR. VLN. & PF.　Achron
　☆ J. Heifetz & E. Bay (in # *Vic.LM 1166*)
　　I. Haendel & G. Moore
　　　　　　(in # *BB.LBC 1013*: ♭ *set LBC 1013*)

Bei der Wiege, Op. 47, No. 6 (Klingemann)
　J. Moor (S), H. W. Haeusslein (pf.)　*Eli. 9035*
　(Auf Flügeln . . .)

(Der) Mond, Op. 86, No. 5 (Geibel)
Venetianisches Gondellied, Op. 57, No. 5 (Moore)
　L. Lehmann (S)　　　　in † # Pembroke set

(Das) Hohe Lied　(♯ E. Destinn (S) in ♯ set CEd. 7001*)
　　　is by Arnold Mendelssohn (1855-1933)

5. B. PARTSONG

Abschied vom Walde, Op. 59, No. 3 (Eichendorff)
　Berlin Displaced Persons' Cho.—Wirth-Willons
　　　　　　　G.EG 7650
　(Wehowski: Die Ausgewiesenen)

---

6. CHORAL & SACRED WORKS
ELIJAH
Abridged Recording
　(Nos. 1, 3, 4, 8, 10-13, 14, 16, 19 (pt), 20, 21,
　　26, 30, 31, 33, 38)
　☆ Augustana Handel Cho. (# Bib.TA 208: ♭ set X 0302)

No. 4, If with all your hearts　　T
　I. Lindholm (*Swed*)　　　*Symf.B 5603*
　(below)

No. 21, Hear ye, Israel　　S
　E. Steber　　　　# AmC.ML 4521
　(Bach: Cantata excpts.; & Creation, Messiah)

No. 28, Lift thy eyes (*Engeltrio*)
　☆ Mormon Tabernacle Cho.—Cornwall (C.LHX 10)

No. 29, He watching over Israel　　cho.
　☆ Shaw Chorale & org. (♭ *Vic.WEPR 44*)

No. 31, O rest in the Lord　　A
　K. Joyce　　　　*P.R 3577*
　(Gounod: There is a green hill)

No. 39, Then shall the righteous . . .　T
　F. Jagel & A. B. Miller (org.) in *AmD.set A 883*
　　　　　　(# *DL 5363*: ♭ *set 9-272*)

FESTIVAL HYMN
No. 2, Hark the herald angels sing　　cho.
　Randolph Singers　　　in # West.WL 5200
　Haven of Rest Vocal Qtt.　　in # ISR.HR 129
　etc.

— SOLO ARR.
　M. Anderson (A) (in # *Vic.LM 7008*: ♭ *set WDM 7008*)

— ARR. MUSIC BOXES
　Bornand Coll. (in # Nix.VLP 428: Van.VRS 428)

(The) First Walpurgis Night, Op. 60 (Goethe)
　A. Woud (A), L. Larsen (T), D. Hollestelle (B),
　Netherlands　Phil.　Cho.　(*Ger*)　&　Orch—
　　Ackermann　　　　# CHS.CHS 1159
　(Songs)

Hear my prayer . . . O for the wings of a dove
　(Psalm 55)　S, cho., orch., org.
　☆ E. Lough & Temple Chu. Cho. (♭ *G.7P 111*)

SAINT PAUL, Op. 36　Oratorio
No. 20, I praise Thee, O Lord　Bs [& cho.]
　I. Lindholm (T, *Swed*)　　　*Symf.B 5603*
　(above)

---

7. MISCELLANEOUS

Mendelssohn, his story and his music
　(Narration with musical illustrations)
　D. Perry (narrator), etc.　　# *AmVox.VL 2530*

☆ = Re-issue of a recording to be found in WERM or Supplement I.

MENGELBERG, Kurt Rudolf (b. 1892)

Magnificat   A & orch.
A. Woud & Amsterdam—E. Jochum
Phi.A 11241G

Salve Regina   S & orch.
▽J. Vincent & Amsterdam—W. Mengelberg
T.SK 3084/5

MENNINI, Louis (b. 1920)

Arioso   str. orch.   1947
Eastman-Rochester Sym.—Hanson
♯ Mer.MG 40001
(Canning & Foote)

MENOTTI, Gian-Carlo (b. 1911)

Concerto, F major   pf. & orch.   1952
Y. Boukoff & Paris Cons.—Cluytens
♯ G.FALP 176

OPERAS
AMAHL AND THE NIGHT VISITORS
Television Opera   24 Dec. 1951
ABRIDGED RECORDING
Amahl   ...   ...   C. Allen (Tr)
Mother   ...   ...   R. Kuhlmann (M-S)
King Melchior   ...   ...   D. Aiken (B)
King Balthasar   ...   ...   L. Lishner (Bs)
King Caspar   ...   ...   A. McKinley (T)
Original Cast & Orch.—Schippers
♯ Vic.LM 1701
(♭ set WDM 1701)

AMELIA GOES TO THE BALL   1 act   1937
Dearest Amelia   B   *(Amelia cara)*
G. Malaspina *(Ital)*   **P.AT 0275**
(Lucia di Lammermoor—Cruda, funesta . . .)

(The) CONSUL   3 acts   1950
Magda's Aria: To this we've come   S, M-S, A, B
I. Borkh *(Ger)* & anon. trio   **G.DB 11537**
(2ss)

(The) MEDIUM   2 acts   1947
COMPLETE RECORDING of the film version
(from the sound-track, incl. *c.* 30 minutes music not in the
former "complete" recording from stage version;
omitting overture)
A. M. Alberghetti (S), B. Dame (S), B. Kibler
(S), M. Powers (A), D. Morgan (B), Rome
Radio Orch.—Schippers   **♯ Mer. set MGL 7**
(4ss)

MERBECKE, John (*c.* 1523-1585)

SEE: † MUSIC OF THE LITURGY

MESSAGER, André Charles Prosper
(1853-1923)

(Les) DEUX PIGEONS   Ballet   1886
Orchestral Suite
Paris Opéra-Comique—Blareau   **♯ D.LX 3093**
(Chabrier)   (♯ Lon.LS 647)
Paris Opéra—Fourestier   **♯ Pat.DTX 106**
(below)

ISOLINE   3 acts   1888
Orchestral Suite
Paris Opéra—Fourestier   **♯ Pat.DTX 106**
(above)

MONSIEUR BEAUCAIRE   3 acts   1919
(Orig. *Eng*)
ABRIDGED RECORDING   ARR.   Hiégel
M. Angelici & L. Berthon (S), R. Lenoty (T),
M. Dens (B), etc., cho. & Lamoureux Orch.
—Gressier   **♯ Pat.DTX 103**
(2ss)   (♯ AmVox.PL 20300)

Overture   ☆ Lamoureux—Cariven (*BrzPat.FC 003*)

La Rose rouge   M. Merkès (*Od. 282557*)

Duo de la rose   Géori-Boué & R. Bourdin (*Sat.D 601*)

VÉRONIQUE   3 acts   1898
Overture   ☆ Lamoureux Orch.—Cariven (*BrzPat.FC 003*)

De ci, de là   S & B
Géori-Boué & R. Bourdin   **Sat.D 603**
(Terrasse: Au temps des croisades, valse)

Si j'avais vos ailes !   (unid.) ⊞ A. Ackté (*IRCC. 3104**)

MESSIAEN,   Olivier   Eugène   Prosper
Charles (b. 1908)

(L')ASCENSION   (4 Meditations)   org.   1934
... No. 3, Transports de joie; No. 4, Prière du Christ
C. Watters   **♯ CEd. 1004**
(below; & Schoenberg)

(Le) Banquet céleste   org.   1928
C. Crozier   **♯ Ken. 2553**
(below; & † French Organ Music)
C. Watters   **♯ CEd. 1004**
(above; & Schoenberg)

(4) Études de Rhythme   pf.   1949
Île de feux, I & II; Neumes rythmiques;
Mode de valeurs et d'intensités
O. Messiaen   **C.LFX 998/9**
(4ss)   (UNESCO recording)

(La) Nativité du Seigneur   org.   1935
(9 Meditations)
R. Noehren   **♯ Allo.ALG 3030**
(Grace Episcopal Chu. org.,   Sandusky, O.)
E. White   **♯ Mer.MG 10069**
(Memorial Hall org., Methuen, Mass.)

... No. 2, Les Bergers
C. Crozier   **♯ Ken. 2553**
(above; & † French Organ Music)

MEYERBEER, Giacomo (1791-1864)

OPERAS
(L')AFRICAINE   5 acts   1865
"Highlights"
⊞ F. Litvinne (S), H. Lazaro (T), G. Dubois (T),
R. Blanchart (B), G. de Luca (B), E. Badini
(Bs), R. Stracciari (B), A. Talexis (S)
(Fr & Ital)   (2ss)   **♯ Ete.O-485***

ACT II
Sur mes genoux   S
⊞ C. Muzio *(Ital)* (in ♯ Eso.ES 500*; ♯ Cpt.MC 20008*)[1]

Fille des rois . . . Quand l'amour m'entraîne   B
⊞ M. Battistini *(Ital)* (*AF.AGSB 4**)

---
[1] Recorded from Edison cylinder.

(L')AFRICAINE (*continued*)

ACT III

Adamastor, roi des vagues   B
G. Taddei (*Ital*)   **P.R 30047**
(*Roi de Lahore—Promesse . . .*)   (BB 25296)

ACT IV

O Paradis !   T
W. Midgley (*Ital*)   **G.DB 21501**
(*Elisir d'amore—Una furtiva*)

J. Björling (*Ital*) (n.v.)   in ♯ *Vic.LM 106*
(*Pagliacci, Cavalleria, Faust, etc.*)   (♭ set WDM 1546)

S. Lemeshev (*Russ*)   USSR. 17973
R. Schock (? *Ger*) in ♯ Roy. 1213 & 1256

☆ F. Tagliavini (*Ital*)♭ G.7RF 205; in ♯ Vic.LM 1164
M. Lanza (*Ital*)   G.DB 21523: ♭ 7R 146
J. Peerce (*Ital*)   ♭ *Vic.WEPR 36*
L. Melchior (*Ger*)   AF.AGSB 2

Ħ G. Anselmi (*Ital*)   IRCC. 3126*
E. Caruso (*Ital*) in ♯ Vic.LCT 1007*; ♭ set WCT 11

L'avoir tant adorée   B
Ħ M. Battistini (*Ital*) (AF.AGSB 4*)

(L')ÉTOILE DU NORD   3 acts   1854
La, la, la, air chéri   S   (Act III)
Ħ L. Tetrazzini (G.VB 15* : o.n. DB 542*)

(Les) HUGUENOTS   5 acts   1836
Excerpts
ĦL. Slezak (T), J. Mardones (Bs), S. Kurz (S),
    F. Hempel (S), H. Jadlowker (T), P.
    Knüpfer (Bs), B. Kemp (S), R. Mayr (Bs)
    etc.   ♯ **Ete.O-458***
(*2ss—Fr, Ital, Ger*)

ACT I

Plus blanche que la blanche ermine   T
Ħ P. Franz (AF. 43*)

Piff, paff, piff, paff   Bs
A. Pirogov (*Russ*)   **USSR. 14882**
(now with *Mefistofele*)
Ħ P. Plançon (HRS. 1101*)

ACT II

O beau pays de la Touraine   S
D. Pantofel-Nechetskaya (*Russ*)
(2ss)   **USSR. 15792/3**
Ħ L. Tetrazzini (*Ital*) (G.VB 41* : o.n. DB 535*)

ACT IV

Gloire au Grand Dieu vengeur   Ens.
(*Bénédiction des poignards*)
Ħ J. Delmas (Bs) (HRS. 1049*)

O ciel ! où courez-vous   S & T
☆M. Teschemacher & M. Wittrisch (*Ger*)
(2ss)   **G.DB 21511**
Ħ A. de Angelis & F. de Lucia (*Ital*)
                (in ♯ Ete.O-464* & CMS. 201*)

(Le) PARDON DE PLOËRMEL   3 acts   1859
Ombre légère (Shadow Song) S (Act II)
E. Spoorenberg   **Phi.N 11172G**
(*Contes d'Hoffmann—Doll song*)   (*PhM.N 09006S*)
N. Kazantseva (*Russ*)   **USSR. 13521/2**
Ħ S. Kurz (in ♯ Ete.O-485*)

Ah ! mon remords te venge B (Act III)
Ħ G. de Luca (G.VB 6* : o.n. Vic. 6443*;
          & (*Ital*) in ♯ Ete.O-485* & ♯ GAR. 100*)

(Le) PROPHÈTE   5 acts   1849
Excerpts
Ħ L. Slezak (T), K. Branzell (A), J. Manceau
    (A), R. Berger (T) (2ss)   ♯ **Ete.O-476***
(Some are electric recordings, e.g. re-issues of Pol. 66690
    & 561026)   (*Ger, Fr*)

ACT II

Pour Bertha . . . (*Pastorale*)   T
Ħ L. Slezak (*Ger*) (in ♯ Ete.O-476* & in ♯ *Ete. 452*)

Ah ! mon fils   A
Ħ M. Duchêne (*IRCC. 3106*)
E. de Cisneros (HRS. 1115*)

ACT III

Prelude: Quadrille (Skating scene) orch.
Used in *Les Patineurs* ballet, ARR. Lambert, see *below*,
Miscellaneous

ACT IV

Marche du couronnement   orch.
Philharmonia—Weldon   **C.DX 1801**
(*Granados: Goyescas, Intermezzo*)   (DWX 5075)
Vienna Radio—Schönherr   *Vien.P 6121*
(*Bartered Bride, Dance of Comedians*)

Roi du ciel (Hymne triomphale) T & cho.
Ħ L. Slezak (*Ger*) (in ♯ Ete.O-476* & in ♯ *Ete. 452*)

ACT V

O prêtres de Baal   A
☆ E. Wysor (in ♯ *Rem. 149-2*)

ROBERT LE DIABLE   5 acts   1831
Va ! dit-elle   S   (Act I)
Quand je quittai la Normandie S (Act III)
Ħ E. Destinn (IRCC. 3097* & in ♯ set CEd. 7001*)
Ah ! L'honnête homme . . . Le bonheur . . . T & Bs (Act III)
Ħ E. Clément & M. Journet (G.VB 30* : o.n. 2-034015/6*)
Valse infernale (Act III)   Ħ J. Nivette (Bs) (HRS. 1083*)
Robert, toi que j'aime   S   (Act IV)
Ħ Lilli Lehmann (*Ger*) (in ♯ Ete. O-463*)

MISCELLANEOUS

(Les) Patineurs   Ballet
(from various operas, ARR. C. Lambert)
L.S.O.—Irving   ♯ **D.LXT 2746**
(*Massenet: Le Cid—Ballet Music*)   (♯ Lon.LL 651)
☆ (excpts.) Sadlers Wells—Lambert (♭ G.7P 102)

MIASKOVSKY, Nicolai (1881-1950)

Concerto, D minor, Op. 44 vln. & orch. 1938
☆D. Oistrakh & USSR. Sym.—Gauk
                              ♯ **Per.SPLP 539**
(*Prokofiev: Concerto*)   (10ss, ♮ U.H 23885/9)

QUARTETS, Strings
No. 11 . . . Finale, Allegro non troppo, only
Beethoven Qtt.   **USSR. 019482**
(*Symphony No. 27, s.9*)

No. 13 . . . 1st & 4th movts. only
Beethoven Qtt.   (4ss)   *USSR. 18980/3*

SYMPHONIES
No. 21, F sharp minor, Op. 51 1940
☆USSR. State Sym.—Rakhlin ♯ **Csm.CRLP 107**
(*Tchaikovsky: Marche slave*)

No. 27, C minor, Op. 85 1949–50
USSR. State Radio—Gauk
                              USSR. 019483/91
(*9ss—Quartet No. 11, Finale*)

MICHEELSEN, Hans Friedrich   (b. 1902)
SEE : † ORGAN MUSIC—HEITMANN

☆ = Re-issue of a recording to be found in WERM or Supplement I.

MICHNA, Adam (1600-1676)

MASS No. 1 (in honour of St. Wenceslas)
Soloists, Brno Radio Cho. & Cha. Orch.—Bakala
(8ss)   ♮ **U.H 13124/7**
(Fr. Michalek—org.)

MIGNONE, Francisco (b. 1897)

Fantasia brasileira (unspec.) pf. & orch.
C. Vidusso & Italian Radio—Mignone
                                    P.AT 0240/1

MILAN, Luis (c. 1500-1565)

SEE : † HARP MUSIC
      † SEGOVIA CONCERT
      † SEGOVIA PROGRAM

MILANDRE (fl. 1755-1782)

Andante; Minuetto
H. Kirschner (descant viola), F. Beyer (viola
d'amore), W. Siller (gamba) in ♯ **Nix.PLP 240**
                    (in ♯ Ren.X 40; ♯ Clc. 6124)

MILHAUD, Darius (b. 1892)

Classified : 1. Piano   2. Chamber Music
             3. Orchestral   4. Theatre, Film, etc.
             5. Songs   6. Cantatas

1. PIANO

Album d'Emma Bovary 1934
M. Chapiro   ♯ **Sel.LPG 8439**
(Soirées de Petrograd)

(Le) Muse ménagère pf., later orch. 1944
Vienna Philharmonia—Haefner   ♯ **SPA. 12**
(Kaufman)

SAUDADES DO BRAZIL pf. 1920-1
COMPLETE RECORDING
Z. Skolovski   ♯ **AmC.ML 4523**
(Concerto No. 4)

... 5 Unspec. dances
J. Germain   ♯ **Clc. 6071**
(½s.—Cheminée & Création)

No. 5, Ipanema — ARR. VLN. & PF.
J. Martzy & J. Antonietti   **PV. 36015**
(½s.—Falla & Ravel)

No. 7, Corcovado — ARR. VLN. & PF.
☆ J. Heifetz & E. Bay (in ♯ Vic.LM 1166; ♭ G.7RF 250)

Scaramouche 2 pfs. 1937
V. Vitale & P. Buonomo   **Vis.VI 4369/70**
(3ss—Debussy: Petite Suite, Ballet)

... Brasileira — ARR. 4 PFS.
☆ First Pf. Qtt. (in ♯ Vic.LM 1165)

2. CHAMBER MUSIC

(La) Cheminée du roi René fl., ob., cl., hrn., bsn.
1939-41
French Wind Quintet   ♯ **OL.LD 20**
(below)

Paris Wind Quintet   ♮ **D.GAF 15114/5**
☆Conservatoire Quintet—Oubradous
                                  ♯ **Clc. 6071**
(½s.—Saudades & Création)

Élégie vlc. & pf. 1945
E. B. Bengtsson & H. D. Koppel **G.DB 20163**
(Stravinsky: Suite italienne, s.I)

(2) Esquisses fl., ob., cl., hrn., bsn.
1. Madrigal.   2 Pastorale
New Art Quintet   ♯ **CEd. 1003**
(Berezkovsky & Fine)
☆ New York Quintet (in ♯ Cpt. 20001)

Pastorale ob., cl., bsn. 1936
— ARR. ORGAN   ☆ E. P. Biggs (JpC.Z 121)

SONATAS, Violin & pf.
No. 1 1911
R. Soetens & S. Roche   ♯ **Sel.LPG 8232**
(Trio)

No. 2 1917 (pour M. André Gide)
R. G. Montbrun & K. Yasukawa **JpV.SD 3076/7**
(4ss)   (set JAS 276)
B. & V. Urban   ♯ **CEd. 1005**
(Ravel, Debussy, Ibert)

SONATA, Vla. & pf., No. 2 1944
K. Boon & C. de Groot   ♯ **Phi.A 00613R**
(Honegger: Sonata)

Sonatine, fl. & pf. 1922
S. Caratelli & G. Manley   ♯ **NRI. 406**
(Guarnieri, Ibert, Hindemith, Shaposhnikov)

Suite d'après Corrette ob., cl., bsn. 1937
P. Pierlot, J. Lancelot, P. Hongne ♯ **OL.LD 20**
(above)

Trio, vln., vla., vlc. 1947
☆Pasquier Trio   ♯ **Sel.LPG 8239**

3. ORCHESTRAL

CONCERTOS, piano & orch.
No. 1 1934
F. Jacquinot & Philharmonia—Fistoulari
                                  ♯ **MGM.E 122**
(Honegger: Concertino)   (♭ set K 122)

No. 4 1948
☆Z. Skolovski & French Nat. Radio Orch.—
Milhaud   ♯ **AmC.ML 4523**
(Saudades)

Fantaisie pastorale pf. & orch. 1938
S. Anderson & Vienna State Op.—Sternberg
(Ives)   ♯ **Oce.OCS 31**

(5) Études pf. & orch. 1920
(3) Rag-caprices orch. 1927
Serenade orch. 1920-1
☆ P. Badura-Skoda & Vienna Sym.—Swoboda
                                  (♯ Sel.LPG 8328)

Suite française band or orch. 1945
☆N.Y.P.S.O.—Milhaud   ♯ **C.FC 1003**
(Ibert: Escales)

4. THEATRE & FILM

(La) Création du monde Ballet nègre 19 insts. 1923
Members Col. Sym.—Bernstein ♯ **AmC.ML 2203**
(Copland)
Chamber Ens.—Oubradous   ♯ **Clc. 6071**
(Cheminée & Saudades)

♯ = Long-playing, 33⅓ r.p.m.   ♭ = 45 r.p.m.   ♮ = Auto. couplings, 78 r.p.m.

MAXIMILIEN Opera 3 acts 1932
Orchestral Suite
☆ Vienna Sym.—Swoboda (‡ Sel.LPG 8328)

(Le) VOYAGEUR SANS BAGAGE 1936
    (Inc. Music for Anouilh's play)
... **Petite Suite** vln., cl. & pf. 1937
J. Parennin, U. Delecluse, A. Haas-Hamburger
                                         ‡ Clc. 6099
    (Poulenc)   (‡ Per.SPL 563)

5. SONGS & PARTSONGS

(6) Chants populaires hébraïques (Trad.) 1925
... **No. 4, Berceuse**
C. Panzéra (B), M. Panzéra (pf.)
                         in ‡ Mer.MG 10098
(Ravel, Aubert, Ropartz, etc.)

(3) Pieces (unspec.)   cho.
Fleet Street Cho.—Lawrence
                         in ‡ Argo.ARS 1003[1]
(Rubbra & J. Berger)

(3) Poèmes de Jean Cocteau 1913
☆ J. Bathori (S), D. Milhaud (pf.) (JpC.SW 276)

(3) Poèmes juifs 1916
☆ J. Bathori (S), D. Milhaud (pf.) (JpC.SW 275)

(Les) Soirées de Pétrograd (Chalupt) 1919
    I. L'Ancien régime (6 songs)
    II. La Révolution (6 songs)
J.-C. Benoit (B), J. Stip (pf.)   ‡ Sel.LPG 8439
(Album d'Emma Bovary)

6. CANTATA

Cantate de la paix (Claudel) 8-pt. cho. unacc. 1937
St. Olaf Cho. *(Eng)*—O. C. Christiansen
                         in ‡ StO. 3
(Grieg, Bach, Hokanson, etc.)

MILLÖCKER, Karl (1842-1899)

(Der) BETTELSTUDENT 3 acts 1882
ABRIDGED RECORDING
☆ I. Eisinger, J. Patzak, etc. (Pol. 57426/9)

Vocal Selections
D. Lindgren, A. Ohlson, etc. *(Swed)* (Od.D-6078)
☆ C. Spletter, H. Tolksdorf, etc. (Imp. 014122)

Ach ich hab sie ja nur ...
H. Reinmar (B)   *Od.O-28138*
(Zigeunerbaron, No. 3)
☆ G. Hann (Pol. 57440)

Ich hab' kein Geld   T
P. Grundén *(Swed)* *(G.X 7725)*
☆ M. Lichtegg (in ‡ Lon.LLP 55)

Ich knüpfte manche zarte Bande   T
▽ F. Völker   *Pol. 10284*
(Suppé: Boccaccio, aria—J. Patzak)

P. Grundén *(Swed)* *(G.X 7725)*
☆ M. Lichtegg (in ‡ Lon.LLP 51)

Waltz on themes from Bettelstudent: "Laura"
A. Lutter Orch. *(Od.O-28256)*

GASPARONE 3 acts 1884
Vocal Selection
☆ C. Spletter, F. Klarwein, etc. (Imp. 014124)

Dunkelrote Rosen bring' ich, schöne Frau   T
    W. Strienz (Bs) *(D.F 43343)*
☆ W. Ludwig (Pol. 57422)

Komm, mia bella S   ☆ J. Patzak (T) *(Pol. 48500)*

GRÄFIN DUBARRY 1879 (rev. Mackeben)
Vocal Selection S. Barabas (S), A. Fügel (T) & cho. PV. 49001

Orchestral Selection Orch.—Mackeben   *PV. 49002*

Ich schenk' mein Herz   S
    H. Güden   in ‡ *D.LX 3071*
    (Lehar: Land des Lächelns, excpt. on D.K 23228)
    (& D.K 28567)   (‡ *Lon.LPS 477*)
    E. Mayerhofer   in ‡ *D.LM 4548*
                                    (‡ *Lon.LPS 41*)
    E. Sack (in ‡ *T.LB 6001*: also ‡ *T.LB 6020*)

Rasch wie der Blitz Polka-schnell
    Vienna Radio—Schönherr   *Vien.P 6085*
    (J. Strauss: Vom Donaustrand)

MILTON, John, senior (*c.* 1563-1647)
    SEE: † TRIUMPHS OF ORIANA

MINKUS, Louis (1827-?)

BALLETS (M. Petipa)
DON QUIXOTE Prol. & 4 acts 1869
BAYADERKA (La Bayadère) 4 acts 1877
Unspecified Excerpts
    Bolshoi Theatre Orch.—Anon.
                         in ‡ Csm.CRLP 108/9

MOLLER, John Christopher (*c.* 1750-1803)
    SEE: † AMERICAN MUSIC: INST. & CHAMBER

MOMPOU, Federico (b. 1893)

(6) Cancós i Danza   pf.
... **No. 1 only**
G. Copeland (pf.)   in ‡ *MGM.E 151*

... **No. 6 only**
P. Spagnolo   *P.PE 157*
(½s.—*Prelude No. 5; Sinding & Scott*)

Con magia
Planys
G. Copeland (pf.)   in ‡ *MGM.E 87*
                                 (♮ set 87: ♭ K 87)

(4) Impressiones Íntimes   pf.
G. Soriano (2ss)   SpC.RG 16177

Prelude No. 5   pf.
P. Spagnolo   *P.PE 157*
(½s.—*Canco i danza No. 6; Sinding & Scott*)

MONIOT d'ARRAS (fl. XIIIth Cent.)
    SEE: † XIITH & XIIITH CENTURY MUSIC

---

[1] Announced but not issued.

MONIUSZKO, Stanislav (1819-1872)

OPERAS
HALKA 4 acts 1854
Duet, unspec., Act I   S & B
  A. Bolechowska & J. S. Adamczewski
  (2ss)   **Muza.X 1628**

Mazurka Act I
  Vienna Radio—Nilius   **Vien.L 6092**
  (*Massenet: Scènes napolitaines, excpt.*)   (in ♯ *1013*)

I wish I were a lark (Halka's aria, Act II) S
  Z. Gaidai (*Russ*) (2ss)   **USSR. 12529/30**

(The) Wind whistles T (Act IV)
  B. Poprotsky (2ss)   **USSR. 20960/1**
  P. Belinnik (*Russ*)   **USSR. 20003/4**

Recit. & John's Aria (unspec.)
  (perhaps: *How oft have I thought*)
  A. Hiolski   **Muza. 1717**
  (*Joteyko: Sigismund August, aria*)

(The) HAUNTED CASTLE (*Strazny Dwór*)
  4 acts 1865
Sword-bearer's Aria   B
  A. Hiolski   **Muza.X 1557**
  (*Verbum Nobile, aria*)

Welcome of the sword-bearer   B
  A. Hiolski   **Muza. 1718**
  (*Verbum Nobile—Stanislav's aria*)

JAWNUTA (*Cyganie*)
Mazurka
  Sym. orch.—Straszynski   **Muza. 1550**
  (2ss)

VERBUM NOBILE 1 act 1861
Martin's Monologue   B
  A. Hiolski   **Muza.X 1557**
  (*Haunted Castle—aria*)

Susan's Elegy   S
  M. Drewniak   **Muza.X 1629**
  (*Evening song*)

Duet of Susan & Stanislaus S & B
  A. Bolechowska & A. Hiolski   **Muza. 1769**
  (2ss)

Stanislav's aria   Bs
  A. Hiolski   **Muza. 1718**
  (*Haunted Castle—Welcome of sword-bearer*)

SONGS
Evening Song (Syrokomla) (*Piesn wieczorna*)
  M. Drewniak (S) & orch.   **Muza.X 1629**
  (*Verbum Nobile—aria*)
  Z. Dolukhanova (A)   **USSR. 18850**
  (*Tchaikovsky: The fires in the rooms . . .*)

(The) Swallow
  G. Lavrova (*Russ*)   **USSR. 15277**
  (*Dvořák: Lullaby*)

MONTBRUN, Raymond Gallois (b. 1918)

Lorsque tu dors 3 songs (Marrat)
  ▽ J. Jansen (B) & orch. (*AA. 9*)

Symphonie concertante, E major vln. & orch.
  R. G. Montbrun & Tokyo Sym.—Ueda
               JpV.SD 3069/72
  (8ss)   (set JAS 244)

MONTE, Philippe de (1521-1603)
SEE : † OLD NETHERLANDS MASTERS

MONTEVERDI, Claudio (1567-1643)

MADRIGALS
COLLECTION
Io mi son giovinetta (IV)
Non più guerra, pietate (IV)
O rossignol (III)
Si ch'io vorrei morire (IV)
Sovra tenere herbette (III)
A un giro sol (IV)
Ohimè—Se tanto amate (IV)
  Randolph Singers—Randolph
  (*Gesualdo*)   **♯ West.WL 5171**

(II) BALLO (delle Ninfe d'Istro) 5 voices (VIII)
  (*Volgendo il ciel*)
  Scuola Veneziana Ens.—Ephrikian
  (*below*)   **♯ Per.SPL 551**

Ecco mormorar l'onde (II)
  Milan Madrigalists—Fait   **♯ Csm.CLPS 1027**
  († Italian Madrigals)

Lagrime d'amante al sepolcro dell' amata (VI) 1609
  ☆ Couraud Ens. (♯ DFr. 20)

LAMENTO DI ARIANNA 5 voices   (VI) 1614
  Milan Madrigalists—Fait   **♯ Csm.CLPS 1027**
  (*Ecco mormorar*)
  ☆ Couraud Ens. (♯ DFr. 20)

... **No. 1, Lasciatemi morire**, only
  Trapp Family Cho.   **Orf. 1002**
  (*Morley: Now is the month of maying*)
  R. Shaw Chorale   **♯ Vic.LM 136**
  († XVIth Century Music)   (in ♭ set WDM 1598)

Mentre vaga angioletta 2 T (VIII)
  Scuola Veneziana Ens.—Ephrikian
  (*below*)   **♯ Per.SPL 551**

Non più guerra, pietate (IV) 1615
  Renaissance Singers—Engel **♯ AmC.ML 4517**
  († Treasury of Madrigals)

Partenza amorosa ("Se pur destino") (VII)
  M. Laszlo (S), F. Holletschek (pf.)
             in **♯ West.WL 5119**
  († Italian Songs)

Tempro la cetra (VII)
  ☆M. Meili & Basle Ens.—Wenzinger
             in **♯ Nix.CLP 1085**

OPERAS
ARIANNA 8 scenes 1608
Lasciatemi morire   A
  M. Klose & orch [1]   in **♯ Ura. 7017**
  (*Schubert, etc.*)
  M. Laszlo (S), F. Holletschek (pf.)
             in **♯ West.WL 5119**
  (in † Italian Songs)
  ☆ E. Pinza (Bs) & pf. (in ♯ Vic.LCT 1031: ♭ set WCT 47)

**(II) COMBATTIMENTO DI TANCREDI E
  CLORINDA** (Tasso) (VIII) 1624
  R. Giancola (S), M. Amadini (A), G. Ferrein
  (Bs) & Scuola Veneziana Orch.—Ephrikian
  (*above*)   **♯ Per.SPL 551**
  G. Rapisardi (S), L. Ribacchi (M-S), M.
  Carlin (T), La Scala Cha. Ens.—Sanzogno
  (*Albinoni*)   **♯ Csm.CLPS 1014**
  D. Abel (S), H. Cuénod (T), D. Olsen (B),
  Zürich Radio Orch.—Goehr   **♯ CHS.F 5**
  (*below*)

---

[1] ARR. Orff.

OPERAS (continued)

(L')INCORONAZIONE DI POPPEA 3 acts
1642
Oblivion soave   A
☆ E. Pinza (Bs) & pf. (in # Vic.LCT 1031: ♭ set WCT 47)

ORFEO 5 acts 1607
Ritornelli, Sinfonie & Toccata
☆ Czech Phil.—Pedrotti (in # Sup.LPM 35)

(Il) RITORNO D'ULISSE IN PATRIA
3 acts 1641
Iro's aria: O dolor, o martir   (Act III)
☆M. Meili (T)   in # Nix.CLP 1085

TIRSI E CLORI Ballet 1615 (VII)
COMPLETE RECORDING
☆E. Scherz-Meister (S), M. Meili (T), cho. &
Inst. Ens.—Wenzinger   in # Nix.CLP 1085

SACRED WORKS
Beatus vir 6 voices (XV)
Laudate Dominum 5 voices (XV)
Ut queant laxis 2 voices (XV)
R. Giancola (S), L. Piovesan (S), M. Amadini
(A), E. Cristinelli (T), M. Cortis (B), G.
Ferrein (Bs) & Scuola Veneziana Orch.—
Ephrikian [1]   # Per.SPLP 536
(# Nix.PLP 536; # Clc. 6092)

Laudate Dominum Bs & cont. (XVI)
W. Warfield (B), A. Tietjen (org.)
† in # AmC.ML 4545
(in † Ancient Music of the Church)

VESPERS OF THE BLESSED VIRGIN 1610
(XIV)
Domine ad adjuvandum 4 voices & insts.
Nigra sum S & str.
Ave, maris stella 8 voices & insts.
Magnificat 8 voices & insts.
Venice Schola Cantorum & Cha. Ens.—
Ephrikian   # Per.SPL 558

Sonata sopra Sancta Maria S & insts.
D. Abel & Zürich Radio Orch.—Goehr
(above)   # CHS.F 5

MOORE, Douglas (b. 1893)

Quintet, Clarinet & strings 1946
D. Oppenheim & New Music Qtt.
(Riegger)   # AmC.ML 4494

Symphony No. 2, A major 1946
A.R.S.O.—Dixon (Thompson)   # ARS. 45

MORALES, Cristobal (c. 1500-1553)

Lamentabatur Jacob
Hamline Singers—Holliday   # NRI. 305
(A. Scarlatti, etc.)

Peccantem me
Monaco Cath. Cho.—H. Carol in † # SM. 33-01

MORENO TORROBA, Federico (b. 1891)

SEE ALSO : † SPANISH GUITAR MUSIC
† SEGOVIA RECITAL
† SEGOVIA PROGRAM

Con un beso; Solterón
P. Gallego Orch.   SpC.R 18232

Fandango castellano [2] guitar
▽ V. Gomez (in AmD. set A 60: # DL 8017)

Fandanguillo [2] guitar
G. Guiletti (Imp. 19127)

LUISA FERNANDA Zarzuela
M. Perez (S), M. Gonzalez (S), F. Naya (T),
G. Mar (B), E. Camara (T), cho. & orch.
—Roig   # Sor. 70002
☆ A. Ottein, E. Vendrell, M. Redondo, etc.
(ArgOd. 196564/7)

(La) MESONERA DE TORDESILLAS
Pavane
Madrid Iberica Orch.—Lago   Od. 184917
(Toutullo: Le Baturrica)

MORLEY, Thomas (1557-c. 1603)

(Roman figures refer to the Vols. of The English Madrigal
School)

Agnus Dei
R. Shaw Chorale   in # Vic.LM 136
(† XVIth Century Music)   (in ♭ set WDM 1598)

Arise, awake XXXII
Madrigal Guild—Washington   # ML. 7002
(in † Triumphs of Oriana)

Hard by a crystal fountain XXXII
Madrigal Guild—Washington   # ML. 7000
(in † Triumphs of Oriana)

It was a lover (Shakespeare) Ayre
H. Cuenod (T), H. Leeb (lute) # West.WL 5085
(† XVIth & XVIIth Century Songs)

Now is the month of maying Ballett, 5 vv. IV
Trapp Family Cho.   Orf. 1002
(Monteverdi: Lasciatemi morire)

Victor Ens. (in Vic. set E 97: ♭ WE 97)

MOSZKOWSKI, Moritz (1854-1925)

En automne, Op. 36, No. 4   pf.
J. Bolet   in # Bo.B 301
(Mendelssohn, Liszt, etc.)

Étude, F major   pf.
V. Horowitz   Vic. 10-3424
(Brahms; Sousa)   (♭ 49-3424 & in ♭ ERA 59)
(Brahms, Schumann, on ♭ G.7RF 232)

Guitare, Op. 45, No. 2   pf.
— ARR. VLN. & PF.
Y. Sitkovetsky & pf.   USSR. 17550
(Paganini: Moto perpetuo)

Serenata, Op. 15, No. 1   pf.
— ARR. VLN. & PF.
W. Tworek & E. Vagning   Pol.HA 70038
(Boccherini: Minuet)

— ARR. GUITAR L. Almeida (in # Crl. 56049)

— ARR. ORCH. Col. Orch. (in # AmC.GL 512)

SPANISH DANCES pf. 4 hands, ARR. ORCH.
Book I, Op. 12, No. 5 W. Kaiser Orch. (Imp. 19262)

Valse, E major, Op. 34, No. 1   pf.
— ARR. HARP
E. Vito   in # SOT. 1030

---

[1] Contains in error, 3 excerpts from Vivaldi: Dixit. This should have been corrected in later pressings.
[2] Probably the same; from Suite castellana.

MOUSSORGSKY, Modest Petrovitch
(1839-1881)

1. INSTRUMENTAL & ORCHESTRAL

By the water (unid., ARR. Horowitz)
☆ V. Horowitz (pf.) (in ♯ Vic.LM 1171: ♭ set WDM 1605)

Intermezzo orch. 1867 (orig. pf. 1861)
USSR. State Sym.—Orlov **U.H 23919**
(2ss) *(Glazounov, in ♯ Sup.LPM 7)*

Night on the Bare Mountain
(ed. Rimsky-Korsakov)
Philharmonia—Malko ♮ **G.C 7914/5**
(3ss—*Khovanshchina, Entr'acte, Act IV*) (GB 71/2)

Philharmonia—Kletzki ♮ **C.LX 8951/2**
(3ss—*Russlan & Ludmilla, Ov.*)

R.I.A.S. Sym.—Fricsay **PV. 36042**
(2ss) *(Borodin: In the Steppes of . . .* on ♯ *AmD.DL 4022)*

USSR. State Radio—Golovanov
♯ **Van.VRS 6000**
(Rimsky-Korsakov)

Paris Cons.—Cluytens ♯ **Pat.DTX 116**
(Borodin & Rimsky-Korsakov) (♯ AmVox.PL 7670)

Berlin Phil.—L. Ludwig ♯ **Ura. 7035**
(below & Rimsky-Korsakov) (♭ UREP 6)

Brussels Radio—André ♯ **Cap.H 8169**
(Saint-Saëns: Danse macabre)

☆ Philadelphia—Stokowski (♭ Vic. 49-0722)

Pictures from an Exhibition pf. 1874
J. Katchen ♯ **D.LK 4046**
(♯ Lon.LLP 330)

E. Goldstein ♯ **CHS.CHS 1410**

S. Biro ♯ **Rem. 199-75**

☆ V. Horowitz (♯ G.FALP 146)

— ARR. ORCH. Ravel
Chicago Sym.—Kubelik ♯ **G.BLP 1002**
(♯ Mer.MG 50000)

Amsterdam—Dorati ♯ **Phi.A 00607R**

N.B.C. Sym.—Cantelli ♯ **Vic.LM 1719**
(Tchaikovsky: Romeo & Juliet) (♭ set WDM 1719)

Berlin Sym. (♯ Roy. 1283)

☆ French Nat. Radio—Kletzki (♯ C.LNX 8030/3)
Berlin State Op.—Melichar (Pol. 15448/51S)

Scherzo, B flat major orch. 1858
Moscow Radio—Gauk [1] **U.H 24273**
(Mozart: Pf. Concerto, A major, K 488, s.1)

Scherzo, C sharp minor pf. 1858
M. Yudina (2ss) **USSR. 18594/5**

2. OPERAS

BORIS GODOUNOV Prol. & 4 acts 1874
COMPLETE RECORDINGS

Set A [2]

Boris
Vaarlam } ... ... B. Christoff (Bs)
Pimen
Marina
Feodor } ... ... E. Zareska (M-S)
Dmitri ... ... N. Gedda (T)
Prince Shuisky, etc. ... A. Bielecki (T)

etc., Paris Russian Cho. & Nat. Radio Orch.
Dobrowen (8ss) ♯ **G.ALP 1044/7**
(♯ FALP 184/7)
(♯ Vic. set LHMV 6400: 26ss, ♭ set WHMV 6400)

Set B [3]

Boris ... ... A. Pirogov (Bs)
Feodor ... ... B. Zlatogorova (M-S)
Xenia ... ... E. Kruglikova (S)
Prince Shuisky ... ... N. Khanaiev (T)
Pimen ... ... M. Mikhailov (Bs)
Gregory ... ... G. Nelepp (T)
Vaarlam ... ... Yakuschenko (Bs)

etc., Bolshoi Theatre Cho. & orch.—Golovanov
(44ss) **USSR. 019056/93**
(omitting some numbers)
(6ss, in ♯ CdM.LDX 8047/9; ♯ Per. set SPL 554;
also in ♯ Csm.CRLP 124/6)
(abridged, also ♯ Per.SPL 565)

"Highlights"
M. Reizen & soloists, cho. & orch. of Marinsky
Theatre—Kabalevsky ♯ **Csm.CRLP 117**
(Glinka) (See below for USSR. issues of this recording)

Abridged recording (in *Ital*)
☆ E. Pinza (Bs) & Met. Op.—Cooper (♯ JpC.WL 5004)

PROLOGUE, Scene II
Coronation Scene
M. Reizen, N. Khanaiev & cho. **USSR. 18452/5**
(4ss)

... **solo part only** Bs
B. Gmyria **USSR. 19100**
(Tchaikovsky: Mazeppa, Three Treasures)

E. Pinza in ♯ **Vic.LM 7016**
(Tonight we sing, Film music) (♭ set WDM 7016)

ACT I, Scene 1
Still one more page (Pimen's monologue) Bs
☆ B. Christoff ▽ G.DA 1938: ♭ 7RF 213

ACT II, Scene 2
In the town of Kazan (Vaarlam's song) Bs
B. Gmyria **USSR. 18748**
(Sadko, Song of the Viking guest)

G. Frei (*Ger*) in ♯ Roy. 1213
☆ B. Christoff ♯ G.BLP 1003: ♭ 7RF 166
L. Neroni (*Ital*) P.PXO 1069

ACT II
COMPLETE RECORDING
M. Reizen (Bs) & Marinsky Theatre Ens.
(8ss) **USSR. 017644/51**

I have attained power (Monologue) Bs
B. Gmyria (2ss) **USSR. 18764/5**
A. Majak (*Pol*) (2ss) **Muza. 1722**

ACT III, Scene 2
Polonaise
Berlin Phil.—L. Ludwig ♯ **Ura. 7035**
(above, below, & Rimsky-Korsakov)

ACT IV, Scene 1
I am dying (Death of Boris)
M. Reizen, soloists & cho. **USSR. 18550/3**
(4ss)

J. Greindl (*Ger*) **PV. 36039**

E. Pinza in ♯ **Vic.LM 7016**
(Tonight we sing, Film music) (♭ set WDM 7016)

G. Frei (*Ger*) in ♯ Roy. 1213

☆ R. Arié ♭ D. 71007 & in ♯ D.LX 3041:
♯ Lon.LPS 98

B. Christoff [4] ♭ G.7RF 166, 1s. only &
♭ 7RF 105: & in ♯ BLP 1003
(Farewell only on ♭ G.7R 114)

H A. Didur (*Ital*) in ♯ Ete.O-467*

---

[1] So labelled, but may well be ☆ of Golovanov recording.
[2] With minor cuts: the revised Rimsky-Korsakov 1908 version is used.
[3] With minor cuts: the Rimsky-Korsakov version is used, except that the Cathedral scene is restored from the orig. version
and the last two scenes are reversed, as in the original.
[4] The complete scene occupies 3ss on 78 r.p.m. (G.DB 6935 & DB 21097) and 45 r.p.m.; G.DB 21097: ♭ 7RF 166 commences
Hark! 'tis the funeral bell.

OPERAS (*continued*)

KHOVANSHCHINA 3 acts 1886
Prelude
  ☆USSR. Radio Sym.—Golovanov *U.C 23921*

ACT II
Mysterious powers ! (*Martha's Divination*)
  A. Rudenko (2ss) *USSR. 19908/9*

ACT IV
Dances of the Persian Slaves
  Philharmonia—Dobrowen *G.S 10587*
  Berlin Phil.—L. Ludwig ♯ *Ura. 7035*
  (*above, below, & Rimsky-Korsakov*)

Entr'acte
  Philharmonia—Malko *G.C 7914*
  (*Night on the Bare Mountain, s.1*) (GB 72)
  Berlin Phil.—L. Ludwig ♯ *Ura. 7035*
  (*above & Rimsky-Korsakov*)

ACT V
Dositheus' Aria Bs
  ☆ B. Christoff (♭ *G.7R 136: 7RF 165*)

Final Scene
  S. Preobrazhenskaya, I. Nechayev, M. Reizen
  (2ss) *USSR. 16443/4*

SOROCHINTSY FAIR 3 acts 1911-23
Gopak orch. (Act. III)
  ☆ Philharmonia—Malko (♭ *G.7P 128: 7BF 1019*)

Why, my sad heart *SEE below*, Songs

---

3. SONGS
COLLECTION
Yeremoushka's Cradle Song (Nekrassov)
Hopak (Shevchenko, trs. Mey)
The Little Star (Grekov)
To the Dnieper (Shevchenko, trs. Mey)
The Orphan (Moussorgsky)
Gathering mushrooms (Mey)
The He-Goat (Moussorgsky)
Ballade (Golenishchev-Kutuzov)
Savishna (Moussorgsky)
Songs & Dances of Death (Golenishchev-Kutuzov)
SOROCHINTSY FAIR: Why, my sad heart
  ☆V. Rosing (T), M. Foggin (pf.)
    ♯ *AmD.DL 9577*

(The) Banks of the Don (Koltsov)
Hopak (Shevchenko, trs. Mey)
  J. Tourel (M-S), G. Reeves (pf.)
    in ♯ *AmC.ML 2198*

(The) Grave (after Pleshcheev) 1859
  (*Sadly rustled the leaves*)
  B. Christoff (Bs), G. Moore (pf.) *G.DB 21383*
  (*Trad.: Siberian Prisoner's Song*)

(The) Little Star (Grekov)
  N. Rossi-Lemeni (Bs), G. Favaretto (pf.)
    P.AB 30013
  (*Songs & Dances of Death, No. 1*)

Softly the spirit flew up to heaven (Tolstoy)
  B. Christoff (Bs), G. Moore (pf.) *G.DB 21484*
  (*below*)

Song of the flea (Goethe, trs. Strugovshchikov)
  B. Christoff (Bs) & orch. [1] *G.DB 21305*
  (*Arr. Koenemann: Song of the Volga Boatmen*)
    (♭ *G.7RF 214: 7R 143*)
  M. Reizen (Bs) *USSR. 14910*
  (*Beethoven: Song of the flea*)

[1] Orch. Rimsky-Korsakov.
[2] See also *Motets, Collections*, below.

B. Gmyria (Bs) *USSR. 19456*
(*Dargomijsky: The Worm*)
F. Harvey (B, *Eng*) & orch. *G.B 10233*
(*Ireland: Sea Fever*)

H. Reinmar (B, *Ger*) & orch. (*Od.O-28111*)
E. List (Bs, *Ger*), O. Schulhof (pf.) (in ♯ Rem. 199-73)
E. Koreh (Bs, *Hung*) (*Qual.QB 2045*)

SONGS & DANCES OF DEATH: Cycle
  (Golenishchev-Kutusov)
... No. 1, Trepak
  N. Rossi-Lemeni (Bs), G. Favaretto (pf.)
    P.AB 30013
  (*The little star*)

... No. 4, Field-Marshal Death
  B. Christoff (Bs), G. Moore (pf.) *G.DB 21484*
  (*above*)
  G. Nelepp (T) (2ss) *USSR. 15040/1*

Tell me why (Anon.) 1858
  S. Preobrazhenskaya (M-S) *USSR. 18631*
  (*Tchaikovsky: O if you knew*)

You drunken sot ! (Moussorgsky)
  ☆ L. Neroni (Bs, *Ital*), M. Ortuso (guitar) (*P.PXO 1069*)

MOUTON, Jean (1475-1523)

Ave Maria Motet
  ☆ Pro Musica—Calder (♯ *CID. 33007*)

MOYZES, Alexander (b. 1906)

Down the River Vah, Op. 26 Suite, orch.
  Slovak Phil.—Rajter ♮ *U.H 24166/8*

MOZART, Wolfgang Amadeus
(1756-1791)

CLASSIFIED : I. VOCAL MUSIC
    A. Church Music   B. Opera
    C. Arias & Songs
  II. INSTRUMENTAL MUSIC
    A. Piano   B. Chamber Music
    C. Divertimenti & Serenades
    D. Orchestral

I. VOCAL MUSIC
A. CHURCH MUSIC & MASONIC WORKS

Adoramus te, Christe K 327 (by Gasparini) [2]
  Cho.—Wilhousky in ♯ *DCap.LC 6576*
    (♯ *Cap.L 9015*)

Ave verum corpus K 618 Cho. [2]
  R.I.A.S. Boys' Cho.—Arndt *D.M 33013*
  (*Vespers—Laudate Dominum*)
  Cho.—Deniau (org. acc.) *Sat.M 1002*
  (*Bach: Lobe den Herrn*)
  Canterbury Cho. in ♯ *MGM.E 102*
    (♭ set K 102)

  ▽ St. Michael's Chu. Cho.—Kromolicki
    (*Chr. 611A*; o.n. ▽ *U.AP 409*)

  ☆ St. Hedwig's Cath. Cho. (Vic. 38-4174: ♭ *53-4174*)
  R. Shaw Chorale (♭ *Vic.WEPR 44*)

— ARR. SOLO B. Sönnerstedt (B, *Swed*) & org. (*Symf.R 1015*)

CHORUSES (Masonic)
COLLECTION (unspec. but probably contains:)
Ihr unsere neuen Leiter   K 484
Lasst uns mit geschlung'nen Händen   K 623a
Zerfliesset heut', geliebte Brüder   K. 483
Indiana Univ. Cho.—Hoffmann   **# MR. 101**

Dixit Dominus & Magnificat, C major K 193 1774
Salzburg   Mozarteum   Cho.   &   Orch.—H.
Schneider   **# Lyr.LL 18**
(*Mass No. 8*)   (# Eur.LPG 609)

Exsultate, jubilate K 165 S & orch.
C. Lorand & orch.—Fekete   **# Mer.MG 10081**
(*Schubert*)   (# Eur.LPG 612)
B. Troxell & orch.—Bales   in **# WCFM. 8**
(*Zaïde excpt. & Horn Concerto*) (Cadenza by R. Strauss)
E. Berger & M. Raucheisen (pf.) in **# Ura. 7060**
(*Brahms, R. Strauss, etc.*)
H E. Schumann (RR.1*; o.n. Pol. 65688/9*)

MASSES
No. 8, F major, K 192 1774
L. Leitner (S), B. Franz (A), H. Grabner (T),
E. J. Lassner (Bs), Mozarteum Cho. & orch.
—H. Schneider   **# Lyr.LL 18**
(*Dixit*)   (# Eur.LPG 609)

No. 9, D major K 194 1774
No. 10, C major K 220 1775
G. Rathauscher (S), E. Hofstätter (A), L.
Heppe (B), W. Berry (Bs), Academy Cho. &
Vienna Sym.—Grossmann **# AmVox.PL 7060**
                                 (# Clc. 6074)

No. 10, C major, only
L. Dutoit (S), E. Hofstätter (A), K. Equiluz (T),
L. Heppe (B), Vienna Academy Cho. &
Paris Collegium Musicum—Grossmann
(*Choral Works*)   **# Sel.LPG 8331**

No. 16, C major K 317 ("Coronation")
☆ Soloists & Festival Cho. & orch.—Gillesberger
                                 (# Era.LDE 2003)

No. 18, C minor K 427
☆Soloists, Vienna Acad. Cho. & Sym. Orch.—
v. Zallinger (4ss)   **# Nix.HLP 2006-1/2**

... Et incarnatus est   S
A. Permin & org. (2ss)   **Tono.A 180**

No. 19, D minor K 626 (*Requiem*)
Y. Ciannella (S), D. Okerson (A), W. Carringer
(T), R. Keast (B), R. Shaw Chorale & Vic.
Sym.—Shaw   **# Vic.LM 1712**
                                 (♭ set WDM 1712)
H. Güden (S), R. Anday (A), J. Patzak (T), J.
Greindl (Bs), Salzburg Cath. Cho. &
Mozarteum Orch.—Messner
(4ss)   **# Rem. set 199-96**

MOTETS & OFFERTORIES
COLLECTIONS
Misericordias Domini   K 222
Sancta Maria, mater Dei   K 273
Lacrimosa   K 93c
Offertorium   K 117   ... Jubilate
Offertorium   K 342 (new K.Anh. 240b)
... Benedicite angel i[1]
Alma Dei Creatoris   K 277 (new K 272a)
Regina coeli   K 276
Soloists, cho. & orch.—Raugel † **# AS. 2504LD**
(M. Duruflé, organ)

Ave, verum corpus K 618
Adoramus te, Christe K 327 (by Gasparini)
Venite, populi K 260 (Double cho. & cont.)
Vienna Academy Cha. Cho.—Grossmann
                                 # Sel.LPG 8331
(unacc.) (*Choruses & Mass No. 10*)
(also on **V# *Sel.LPP 8606*)
(Ave verum & Venite also in † **# Sel.LPG 8238**)

Regina Coeli, B flat major K 127 S, cho., orch. 1772
V. Bak, Munich Cha. Cho. & Orch.—Graunke
                                 # Mer.MG 10085
(*Arias, & Handel*)

Vesperae de Dominica, C major K 321
S, A, T, B, cho., orch.
☆Soloists & Reinhart & Winterthur Chos. &
orch.—Reinhart   **# Nix.CLP 1083**
                                 (# Clc. 6063)

Vesperae Solennes de Confessore, C major K 339
... **No. 5, Laudate Dominum**
K. Munk & Copenhagen Boys' Cho.
(2ss)   **Felix.F 62**
R.I.A.S. Boys' Cho.—Arndt   **D.M 33013**
(*Ave verum*)
☆ A. Schlemm & St. Hedwig's Cath.
                        (Vic. 38-4174: ♭ 53-4174)

I. B. OPERAS & STAGE WORKS

BASTIEN UND BASTIENNE K 50 1 act 1768
COMPLETE RECORDING
☆Soloists & Ton-Studio Orch.—R. Reinhardt
(2ss only)   **# Nix.PLP 542**
                        (# Per.SPLP 542; # Clc. 6089)
(Overture only in # Per.SPL 559)

(La) CLEMENZA DI TITO K 621 2 acts 1791
COMPLETE RECORDING

Titus	... ...	A. Weikenmeier (T)
Vitellia	...	K. Nentwig (S)
Sextus	...	... H. Plümacher (A)
Annius	...	M. Mangold (M-S)
Servilia	...	F. Sailer (S)
Publius	...	B. Müller (Bs)

Swabian Cho. Soc. & Stuttgart Ton-Studio
Orch.—Lund   **# Nix.PLP 550-1/3**
(5ss—*Petits Riens*)   (# Per. set SPLP 550)

Overture
Berlin Phil.—Lehmann   **PV. 36060**
(*Idomeneo Overture*)   (in # AmD.DL 4035)
Stuttgart Ton-Studio—Lund in **# Per.SPL 559**
(from set)

No. 10, Vengo! aspettate! S, T, B
K. Hansel, J. Collins, J. Yard & pf.
                               in **# Den.DR 1**

No. 23, Non più di fiori   A
☆ E. Wysor (in *Rem. 149-2*)

COSI FAN TUTTE K 588 2 Acts 1790
COMPLETE RECORDINGS
Set B[2]

Fiordiligi	... ...	E. Hassler (S)
Dorabella	...	H. Plümacher (M-S)
Despina	...	K. Nentwig (S)
Ferrando	...	A. Weikenmeier (T)
Guglielmo	...	K. Hoppe (B)
Don Alfonso	...	F. Kelch (Bs)

Stuttgart Ton-Studio Cho. & Orch.—Dünnwald
(6ss)   **# Nix.PLP 555-1/3**
                (# Rem. set 199-117 & # Per. set SPLP 555)

Set C (in *English*)

Fiordiligi	...	E. Steber (S)
Dorabella	...	B. Thebom (M-S)
Despina	...	R. Peters (S)
Ferrando	...	R. Tucker (T)
Guglielmo	...	F. Guarrera (B)
Don Alfonso	...	L. Alvary (Bs)

Met. Op. Cho. & Orch.—Stiedry
(6ss)   **# AmC. set SL 122**

---

[1] Perhaps by Leopold Mozart.
[2] Omitting Nos. 7, 24, 28; and making cuts in **Nos.** 13, 18, 29, 31.

COSI FAN TUTTE (*continued*)

Overture
L.S.O.—Krips   in ♯ **D.LXT 2684**
(*below*)   (in ♯ Lon.LL 356)
Berlin Phil.—Lehmann   *PV. 36060*
(*Entführung Overture*)   (in ♯ AmD.DL 4035)
Rhineland Sym.—Federer   ♯ *Rgt. 5040*
(*Gazza Ladra & Entführung Ovs.*)
Stuttgart Ton-Studio—Dünnwald
(from set)   in ♯ **Per.SPL 559**

ACT I
No. 12, In uomini, in soldati   S
A. Noni (*No. 19*)   *G.DA 1986*

No. 14, Come scoglio   S
 ♮ G. Ritter-Ciampi (*IRCC. 3084**)

No. 17, Un' aura amorosa   T
C. Holland   in ♯ *Pat.DT 1008*
(*Don Giovanni No. 11, & Arias*)
H. Roswaenge (*Ger*)   in ♯ **Ura. 7027**

ACT II
No. 19, Una donna a quindici anni   S
A. Noni (*No. 12*)   *G.DA 1986*

No. 26, Donne mie, la fate a tanti   B
F. Corena   in ♯ *D.LX 3095*
(*Figaro, Don Giovanni, Zauberflöte*)   (♯ Lon.LS 671)

DON GIOVANNI K 527   1787
COMPLETE RECORDINGS
Set A

Donna Anna	... ...	I. Souez (S)
Donna Elvira	...	L. Helletsgrüber (S)
Zerlina	... ...	A. Mildmay (S)
Don Ottavio	...	K. von Pataky (T)
Don Giovanni	...	J. Brownlee (B)
Leporello	...	S. Baccaloni (Bs)

☆Glyndebourne Cho. & Orch.—Busch
                                 ♯ **Vic. set LCT 6102**
(6ss)   (♭ *set WCT 59*)

Set B
☆ Grob-Prandl, Konetzni, Heusser, Handt, Stabile,
   Pernerstorfer, Poell, etc., Vienna State Op.—
   Swarowsky (♯ Era.LDE 3002/4, 6ss)

Selected Arias: Nos. 4, 6, 7, 10, 11, 12, 13, 17, 18, 19, 22, 23
(from complete recording)   (☆ ♯ Nix.HLP 2031)

Overture
L.S.O.—Krips   in ♯ **D.LXT 2684**
(*above & below*)   (in ♯ Lon.LL 356; & LD 9001)
Berlin Phil.—Lehmann   *PV. 72237*
(*Zauberflöte Overture*)   (in ♯ AmD.DL 4035)
Berlin Sym.—Weisenhutter (in ♯ Roy. 1203: ♭ set 14591)
Anon. orch (in ♯ Roy. 6058: & ♯ Var. 2009)

ACT I
No. 4, Madamina, il catalogo   Bs
F. Corena   in ♯ *D.LX 3095*
(*Cosi, Figaro, Zauberflöte*)   (♯ Lon.LS 671)
E. Pinza (n.v.)   in ♯ *Vic.LM 107*
(*No. 12, etc.*)   (♭ set WDM 1555)
(*Don Carlos aria, in* ♭ *Vic.WEPR 37*)
☆P. Schoeffler   in ♯ **D.LXT 2685**
(*Nozze di Figaro No. 9, etc.*)   (♯ Lon.LLP 457)
B. Gmyria (*Russ*)   *USSR. 16420/1*

No. 7, Là ci darem la mano
☆E. Rethberg & E. Pinza   *G.DA 1950*
(*Nozze di Figaro, No. 2*) (in ♯ Vic.LCT 1031: ♭ set WCT 46)
R. Streich & H. Wocke (? *Ger*)(in ♯ Roy. 1203:♭ set 14591)

No. 10, Don Ottavio, son morta S & T
Or sai chi l'onore   S
☆L. Welitsch & A. de Paolis   *C.LB 124*
                                         (*LW 61*)
... Aria only, Or sai ...
 ♮ Lilli Lehmann   in ♯ Ete.O-463*
F. Leider (*Ger*)   in ♯ Ete.O-477*

No. 11, Dalla sua pace   T
J. Peerce   ♭ *Vic. 49-3302*
(*No. 22*)   (in ♯ LM 1169)
C. Holland   ♯ *Pat.DT 1008*
(*Cosi No. 17, & Arias*)
☆A. Dermota   in ♯ **D.LXT 2685**
(*below*)   (♯ Lon.LLP 457)
☆ R. Tauber   Od.O-9177
P. Anders (*Ger*)   in ♯ *T.LS 6005*

No. 12, Finch'han del vino   B
E. Pinza (n.v.)   in ♯ *Vic.LM 107*
(*No. 17, etc.*)   (♭ set WDM 1555)
☆ S. O. Sandberg (*Ger*)   P.BX 609
 ♮ F. d'Andrade   in ♯ Ete.O-479*

No. 13, Batti, batti, o bel Masetto S
C. Carroll   in ♯ *Rem. 149-41*
(*Figaro, Faust, etc.*)
   M. Truman in ♯ Vic.LM 145: ♭ set WDM 1616
   R. Streich (? *Ger*) in ♯ Roy. 1203: ♭ set 14591
 ♮ S. Kurz   AF. 47*

ACT II
No. 17, Deh, vieni alla finestra   B
E. Pinza (n.v.)   in ♯ *Vic.LM 107*
(*Figaro, No. 3, etc.*)   (♭ set WDM 1555)
   H. Wocke (? *Ger*)   in ♯ Roy. 1203: ♭ set 14591
☆ S. O. Sandberg (*Ger*)   P.BX 609
 ♮ G. Baklanoff   G.VA 51*: o.n. DA 464*
M. Renaud (*Fr*)   in ♯ Ete.O-479*

No. 19, Vedrai carino   S
R. Streich   in ♯ Roy. 1203: ♭ set 14591

No. 21, Ah, pietà, signori miei   Bs
F. Corena   in ♯ *D.LX 3095*
(*Cosi, Figaro, Zauberflöte*)   (♯ Lon.LS 671)

No. 22, Il mio tesoro   T
J. Peerce   ♭ *Vic. 49-3302*
(*No. 11*)   (♯ Vic.LM 1169)
☆A. Dermota   in ♯ **D.LXT 2685**
                                         (♯ Lon.LLP 457)
   R. Schock (? *Ger*) in ♯ Roy. 1203: ♭ set 14591
                                     & in ♯ 1256
☆ P. Anders   in ♯ *T.LS 6005*
 ♮ F. de Lucia   G.VA 65*
☆ J. McCormack   in ♯ Vic.LM 1202*:
                                 ♭ set WDM 1626*

No. 25, Crudele ! . . . Non mi dir   S
☆L. Welitsch   *C.LB 121*
                                         (*LW 57*)

(Die) ENTFÜHRUNG AUS DEM SERAIL K 384
  (*Il Seraglio*)   3 acts   1782
EXCERPTS from complete recording
Nos. 1, 4, 15, 6, 10, 11, 8, 12, 18, 19
☆W. Lipp & E. Loose (S), W. Ludwig (T),
   P. Klein (T), etc., Vienna State Op. Cho.
   & Vienna Phil.—Krips   ♯ **D.LXT 2635**
(2ss)   (♯ Lon.LLP 458)

☆ = Re-issue of a recording to be found in WERM or Supplement I.

ENTFÜHRUNG AUS DEM SERAIL (continued)

Overture

L.S.O.—Krips   in # D.LXT 2684
(above & below)   (in # Lon.LL 356)

Berlin Phil.—Lehmann   PV. 36050
(Cosi Overture)   (in # AmD.DL 4036)

Vienna State Op.—Swarowsky   AusT.E 1118
(Fliegende Holländer Ov. s.3)

Rhineland Sym.—Federer   # Rgt. 5040
(Cosi & Gazza Ladra Overtures)

Berlin Sym.—Guthan (in # Roy. 1209)
Vienna Radio—Nilius (Vien.P 6084: in # LP 1010;
    # AmVien.VNLP 1005)
Anon. orch. (in # Roy. 6048 & # Var. 2007)

ACT I

No. 1, Hier soll ich dich denn sehen   T
☆ P. Anders   in # T.LS 6005

ℍ L. Slezak   in # Ete.O-479*

No. 2, Wer ein Liebchen hat gefunden   Bs
G. Frei   in # Roy. 1209

No. 4, Konstanze ! . . . O wie ängstlich   T
☆ W. Ludwig   Pol. 68469
(No. 15)

☆ R. Tauber   Od.O-9177

ℍ L. Slezak   in # Ete.O-479*

No. 6, Ach, ich liebte   S
ℍ Lilli Lehmann   in # Ete.O-463*

ACT II

No. 8, Durch Zärtlichkeit und Schmeicheln   S
ℍ E. Schumann   RR. 4*

No. 10, Welcher Kummer . . . Traurigkeit   S
W. Lipp   PV. 36044

No. 11, Martern aller Arten   S
W. Lipp   PV. 36051

M. Cebotari   in # Ura. 7036
(Figaro, Salome, Butterfly)

ℍ Lilli Lehmann   in # Ete.O-463*
F. Hempel (Ital)   G.VB 22*: o.n. DB 331*

No. 12, Welche Wonne   S
ℍ E. Schumann   RR. 4*

No. 15, Wenn der Freude Tränen fliessen   T
W. Ludwig (No. 4)   Pol. 68469

No. 16, Ach Belmonte, Ach mein Leben   2 S, 2 T
☆ W. Lipp, E. Loose, W. Ludwig, P. Klein
    from set (D.K 23267)

ACT III

No. 18, Im Mohrenland gefangen war   T
☆ P. Anders   in # T.LS 6005

No. 19, Ha ! Wie will ich triumphieren   Bs
ℍ W. Hesch   in # Ete.O-479*

IDOMENEO, RE DI CRETA   K 366   1781
COMPLETE RECORDING including Ballet K 367
☆Soloists, Vienna Sym. Orch. & Cho.—
    v. Zallinger (8ss)   # Nix.HLP 2020-1/4

COLLECTED EXCERPTS
Set C   Overture &
No. 1, Quando avrai fine omai (Recit)
    Padre, germani, addio ! (Aria) S
No. 6, Vedrommi intorno (Aria)   T
No. 11, Se il padre perdei (Aria)   S
No. 12, Fuor del mar (Aria)   T
No. 14, March   Orch.
No. 15, Placido è il mar   Cho.
No. 17, Qual nuovo terrore !   Cho.
No. 18, Corriamo, fuggiamo   Cho.
No. 19, Zeffiretti lusinghieri (Aria)   S
No. 21, Andrò ramingo e solo   Qtt.
No. 24, O voto tremendo   Cho.
No. 26, Accogli, o re del mar   2 T

S. Jurinac & D. McNeil (S), R. Lewis & A.
    Young (T), Glyndebourne Fest. Cho. &
    Orch.—F. Busch   # Vic.LHMV 1021
(Nos. 19 & 21 also on G.DB 21525) (♭ set WHMV 1021)
(Nos. 14, 15 & 24 on G.DB 21526; No. 1 on G.DB 21527)

Set D   Overture & Choruses:
No. 3, Godiam la pace
No. 8, March (orch. only)
No. 9, Notturno s'onori !
No. 15, Placido è il mar
No. 25, March (orch. only)
No. 32, Scenda Amor
Vienna State Op. Cho. & Sym.—v. Zallinger
    # HSLP. 2042
(Ballet Music) (☆ from Complete Recording)

Overture
Philharmonia—Kubelik (2ss)   G.DB 21465
Berlin Phil.—Lehmann   PV. 36060
(Clemenza, Overture)   (in # AmD.DL 4036)
☆ Dresden Phil.—v. Kempen (Pol. 15506; P.RR 8122;
    & with Gluck: Orphée, Dance, on Pol. 15493)
Vienna Sym.—v. Zallinger, from set (in # Per.SPL 559)

No. 11, Se il padre perdei   S
H. Gueden   in # D.LX 3067
(Figaro: No. 27 on D.K 23292)   (# Lon.LPS 485)
(Aria, Non temer amato ben on D.K 28570)

Ballet Music   K 367
Stuttgart Pro Musica—Seegelken
    # PaV.VP 240
(Les Petits Riens)   (# AmVox.PL 7250)
☆Vienna Sym.—v. Zallinger   # HSLP. 2042
(above)

(Le) NOZZE DI FIGARO   K 492   4 acts   1786
COMPLETE RECORDINGS
Set B[1]

Susanna	...	...	I. Seefried (S)
La Contessa	...	E. Schwarzkopf (S)
Cherubino	...	...	S. Jurinac (S)
Marcellina	...	E. Höngen (A)
Figaro	...	...	E. Kunz (B)
Il Conte	...	...	G. London (B)
Bartolo	...	...	M. Rus (Bs)

Vienna State Op. Cho. & Vienna Phil.—v.
    Karajan (6ss)   # C.CX 1007/9
(32 ss, C.LWX 410/25)   (# AmC. set SL 114)

Set C[2]

Susanna	...	...	A. Noni (S)
La Contessa	...	G. Gatti (S)
Cherubino	...	J. Gardino (S)
Marcellina	...	M. T. Pace (M-S)
Figaro	...	...	I. Tajo (B)
Il Conte	...	S. Bruscantini (B)
Bartolo	...	F. Corena (Bs)

Radio Italiana Cho. & Orch.—Previtali
(6ss)   # Sor. set 1219

Set A[3]

Susanna	...	...	A. Mildmay (S)
La Contessa	...	A. Rautavaara (S)
Cherubino	...	L. Helletsgrüber (S)
Figaro	...	W. Domgraf-Fassbänder (B)
Il Conte	...	...	R. Henderson (B)

☆Glyndebourne Cho. & Orch.—Busch
(4ss)   # Vic. set LCT 6001
    (♭ set WCT 54)

---

[1] Omits all recitatives.
[2] Omits No. 17; includes recitatives; hpsi. is used.
[3] Omits Nos. 8 & 23; includes some recitatives; pf. is used. All sets omit Nos. 24 & 25.

144

NOZZE DI FIGARO (*continued*)

"COMPLETE ARIAS"

G. P. Zabia (S), C. Elmo (M-S), L. Neroni (Bs),
G. Gatti (S), G. Tomei (Bs), Brasini (B), &
La Scala Cho. & Orch.—Questa ♯ **Roy. 1210**
("Highlights" from above on ♯ *Roy. 6073*: ♭ *set 14591*)

Highlights
Anon. Artists in ♯ Var. 2003: ♯ Var. 6955; ♯ Wde. 20208;
Pde. 1008; & with narration, ♯ Pde.OP 112.

Overture

☆L.S.O.—Krips   in ♯ **D.LXT 2684**
(*above & below*)   (in ♯ Lon.LL 356)

Philharmonia—Kubelik   **G.DB 21548**
(*Schauspieldirektor Overture*)

Boston Sym.—Münch   ♯ ***Vic.LM 7009***
(*Handel & Schumann*)   (♭ *set WDM 7009*)

Berlin Phil.—Lehmann   *Pol. 62891*
(*Schauspieldirektor Overture*)   (♯ *AmD.DL 4036*)

Austrian Sym.—Heger   ♯ **Rem. 199-70**
(*Pf. Concerto, K 491*)

Vienna Radio—Nilius   **Vien.L 6119**
(*Schauspieldirektor Overture*)

Anon. orch (in ♯ *Var. 6936*)

☆ Vienna Phil.—Karajan (o.v.) (C.LVX 86)
Dresden Phil.—v. Kempen (Pol. 15506)

ACT I

No. 2, Se a casa madama   S & B
☆ E. Rethberg & E. Pinza
    (G.DA 1950; in ♯ Vic.LCT 1031: ♭ *set WCT 46*)

No. 3, Se vuol ballare   B
E. Pinza (n.v.)   in ♯ ***Vic. LM 107***
(*No. 9, etc.*)   (♭ *set WDM 1555*)

F. Corena   in ♯ ***D.LX 3095***
(*Cosi, Don Giovanni, Zauberflöte*)   (♯ *Lon.LS 671*)

☆ H. Rehkemper (*Ger*) (*Pol. 26510*)

No. 4, La vendetta   Bs
F. Corena   in ♯ ***D.LX 3095***
(*above & below*)   (♯ *Lon.LS 671*)

No. 6, Non so più   (*Je ne sais quelle ardeur*)   S
R. Stevens   in ♯ **Vic.LM 9010**
(*below*)   (♭ *set WDM 9010*)

E. Wysor   in ♯ **Rem. 199-30**

☆ M. Angelici (*Fr*) (♭ *G.7RF 108*)

No. 9, Non più andrai   B
F. Corena   in ♯ ***D.LX 3095***
(*above*)   (♯ *Lon.LS 671*)

J. Greindl   *PV. 36026*
(*No. 26*)   (& in Ger on *PV. 36025*)

E. Pinza (n.v.)   in ♯ ***Vic.LM 107***
(*Zauberflöte No. 10, etc.*)   (in ♭ *set WDM 1555*)

☆P. Schoeffler   in ♯**D.LXT 2685**
(*Don Giovanni, No. 8 on D.K 23305*)   (♯ *Lon.LLP 457*)

☆ E. Pinza (o.v.)   in ♯ Vic.LCT 1031:♭ *set WCT 46*
H. Rehkemper (*Ger*)   *Pol. 26510*

◨ M. Battistini   in ♯ Ete.O-462*
J. Mardones   HRS. 1057*
M. Sammarco   in ♯ Ete.O-479*

ACT II

No. 10, Porgi amor   S
M. Reining   in ♯ **D.LXT 2685**
(*below & Zauberflöte*   (in ♯ Lon.LLP 457)

☆ V. de los Angeles   ♭ *G.7RF 158*
L. Lehmann   in ♯ AmD.DL 9524
E. Rethberg in ♯ Vic. LCT 1031: ♭ *set WCT 46*

◨ E. Destinn (*Ger*)   in ♯ set CEd. 7001*

No. 11, Voi che sapete   S
(*Mon coeur soupire*)
H. Gueden   in ♯ *D.LX 3067*
(*No. 27, on D.K 28575*)   (♯ *Lon.LPS 485*)

R. Stevens   in ♯ **Vic.LM 9010**
(*above & Carmen, etc.*)   (♭ *set WDM 9010*)

☆L. della Casa   in ♯ **D.LXT 2685**
        (♯ Lon.LLP 457)

☆ M. Angelici (*Fr*)   ♭ *G.7RF 108*

◨ N. Melba   in ♯ Vic.LCT 1039*: ♭ set WCT 62*

No. 12, Venite, inginocchiatevi   S
(*Komm' näher . . .*)
E. Trötschel   *PV. 36011*
(*No. 27*)   (& in Ger on *PV. 36010*)

ACT III

No. 16, Crudel, perchè finora   S & B
☆ E. Rethberg & E. Pinza
     (in ♯ Vic.LCT 1031: ♭ *set WCT 46*)

No. 17, Hai già vinta . . .   (Recit)
Vedro mentr'io sospiro   (Aria)   B
☆ S. O. Sandberg (*Ger*) (P.BX 609)

No. 19, E Susanna non vien   (Recit)
Dove sono   (Aria)   S
E. Schwarzkopf (from set)   **C.LX 1575**

☆M. Reining   in ♯**D.LXT 2685**
(*Don Giovanni, Zauberflöte*)   (♯ Lon.LLP 457)

. . . Dove sono only
☆ E. Rethberg (in ♯ Vic.LCT 1031: ♭ *set WCT 46*)

No. 20, Sull'aria ! . . . che soave zeffiretto   2 S
◨ N. Larsen-Todsen & H. Matsson (*Swed*)
     (IRCC. 3122*)

ACT IV

No. 26, Tutte è disposto . . .
Aprite un po'   Bs
F. Corena   in ♯ ***D.LX 3095***
(*Don Giovanni, Zauberflöte, etc.*)   (*Lon.LS 671*)

E. Pinza   in ♯ ***Vic.LM 157***
(*Faust, etc.*)   (♭ *set WDM 1655*)

J. Greindl   *PV. 36026*
(*No. 9*)   (& on Ger on *PV. 36025*)

No. 27, Giunse alfin il momento   (Recit.)
Deh vieni, non tardar   (Aria)   S
H. Gueden   ♯ *D.LX 3067*
(*No. 11, on D.K 28575*)   (♯ *Lon.LPS 485*)
(*Idomeneo—Se il padre on K 23292*)

E. Trötschel   *PV. 36011*
(*No. 12*)   (& in Ger on *PV. 36010*)

R. Tebaldi   **Fnt. 22008**
(*Traviata—Addio del passato*)

G. Arnaldi   **P.PE 175**
(*Fille du Régiment—Il faut partir*)

C. Carroll   in ♯ **Rem. 149-41**
(*Faust, Romeo, Bohème, etc.*)

M. Cebotari (*Ger*)   in ♯ **Ura. 7036**
(*Entführung, Butterfly & Salome*)

M. Guilleaume (*Ger*)   **T.E 3927**
(*Zauberflöte, No. 17*)

C. Rubio   **SpC.RG 16174**
(*Purcell: Dido & Aeneas, aria*)

E. Katulskaya (*Russ*)   **USSR. 15846**
(*Grétry: Richard Coeur-de-lion, aria*)

☆ L. Lehmann (*Ger*)   in ♯ AmD.DL 9523

◨ S. Kurz   AF. 47*

☆=Re-issue of a recording to be found in WERM or Supplement I.

(Les) PETITS RIENS K 299b Ballet 1778
Stuttgart Pro Musica—R. Reinhardt
PaV.VP 240
(Idomeneo Ballet) (# AmVox.PL 7250)

Stuttgart Ton-Studio—Lund # Nix.PLP 550-1
(Clemenza di Tito) (in # Per. set SPLP 550)
(Overtures, in # Per. SPL 559)

☆Paris Cons.—Goldschmidt † # AS. 3001LD
(Divertimento, K 131)

... No. 9, Gavotte : *See* Minuets & Gavotte, Sec. II. D. 2,
infra

(Il) RE PASTORE K 208 2 acts 1775
COMPLETE RECORDING
Aminta ... ... A. Giebel (S)
Elisa ... ... K. Nentwig (S)
Tomiri ... ...H. Plümacher (A)
Agenore ... ... W. Hohmann (T)
Alessandro ... ... A. Weikenmeier (T)

Stuttgart Ton-Studio Cho. & Orch.—Lund
(4ss) # Per. set SPL 553
(Overture only in # Per. SPL 559) (# Nix.PLP 553-1/2)

No. 10, L'amerò, sarò costante S
☆ E. Schwarzkopf, F. Sedlak (vln.) & Vienna Phil.—
J. Krips (C.LFX 1018)
E. Berger (*Ger*), O. Shumsky (vln.) & G. Schick (pf.)
(G.DB 21495)
G. Ritter-Ciampi (in # Ete.O-479)

(Der) SCHAUSPIELDIREKTOR K 486 1786
(Impresario)
Overture
L.S.O.—Krips in # D.LXT 2684
(above & below) (in # Lon.LL 356)
Philharmonia—Kubelik G.DB 21548
(Nozze di Figaro Overture)
Berlin Phil.—Lehmann *Pol. 62891*
(Nozze di Figaro Overture) (in # AmD.DL 4036)
Vienna Radio—Nilius **Vien.L 6119**
(Figaro Overture)

THAMOS, KÖNIG IN ÄGYPTIEN K 345 1780
(Incidental Music to play by T. P. v. Gebler)
COMPLETE RECORDING
1. Schon weichet dir, Sonne Cho.
2, 3, 4, 5, Entr'actes Orch.
6. Gottheit, Gottheit, über alle Cho.
7a. Entr'acte
7b. Ihr Kinder des Staubes Bs & Cho.
G. Neidlinger & Stuttgart Pro Musica Cho. &
Orch.—R. Reinhardt # AmVox.PL 7350

... 5 Entr'actes
☆ Austrian Sym.—Günther (# Mrt. 1-5 & # Rem. 199-59,
d.c.)
(A recording by Vienna Artists' Sym.—Fekete was
listed (# Etu. 705), but in a letter to *Saturday Review*,
M. Fekete stated that he had never in his life conducted this music.)

ZAÏDE K 344 (new K 336b) 1780
COMPLETE RECORDING
Zaïde ... ... M. Dobbs (S)
Gomatz ... ... H. Cuénod (T)
Soliman ... ... J. Peyron (T)
Osmin ... ... J. Riley (T)
Allazim ... ... B. Demigny (Bs)

& Paris Phil.—Leibowitz
(4ss) # Polym. & WCFM. 901/2

No. 3, Ruhe sanft, mein holdes Leben S
B. Troxell in # WCFM. 8

No. 8, O selige Wonne S, T, B
K. Hansel, J. Collins, J. Yard & pf.
in # Den.DR 1

(Die) ZAUBERFLÖTE K 620 1791
COMPLETE RECORDINGS
Set B
Pamina ... ... I. Seefried (S)
Königin der Nacht ... W. Lipp (S)
Tamino ... ... A. Dermota (T)
Papageno ... ... E. Kunz (B)
Sarastro ... ... L. Weber (Bs)
Papagena ... ... E. Loose (S)
Monostatos... ... ... P. Klein (T)

Musikfreunde Cho. & Vienna Phil.—v. Karajan
(6ss) # C.CX 1013/5
(FCX/QCX 150/2; # AmC. set SL 115)
(37ss on C.LWX 426/44—LWX 434 is single-sided)

Set A
Pamina ... ... T. Lemnitz (S)
Königin der Nacht... ... E. Berger (S)
Tamino ... ...H. Roswaenge (T)
Papageno ... ... G. Hüsch (B)
Sarastro ... ... W. Strienz (Bs)

☆Cho. & Berlin Phil.—Beecham
Vic. set LCT 6101
(6ss) (♭ set WCT 56)

Orchestral Selection: Royale Concert Orch. (in # Roy. 1336)

Overture
L.S.O.—Krips in # D.LXT 2684
(& D.K 23311) (# Lon.LL 356 & # LD 9001)
Bamberg Sym.—Keilberth T.E 3914
Berlin Phil.—Lehmann PV. 72237
(Don Giovanni Overture) (in # AmD.DL 4035)
Rhineland Sym.—Federer # Rgt. 5043
(Liszt: Mephisto-Waltz, & Wagner)
☆ B.B.C.—Toscanini
(♭ G.7RF 140; ♭ Vic.WEPR 14 & 49-1423)
French Nat. Sym.—Lindenberg (P.E 11496)
Berlin Sym.—Wiesenhutter (in # Roy. 1203)
Various orchs.
(in # Var. 2009 & 6947, # Roy. 6048 & 6058, etc.)

ACT I

No. 2, Der Vogelfänger bin ich ja B
K. Schmitt-Walter T.A 11188
(No. 20)

No. 3, Dies Bildnis ist bezaubernd schön T
☆A. Dermota (n.v.) in # D.LXT 2685
(in # Lon.LLP 457)
☆ P. Anders (in # T.LS 6005)

No. 4, Zum Leiden bin ich auserkoren S
W. Lipp (from set B) C.LVX 153
(No. 14)
☆ H. Schymberg T.SK 19034
E. Reichelt Pol. 15478
⊞ F. Hempel (*Ital*) G.VB 21*: o.n. DB 331*
M. Ivogün in # Ete.O-479*

No. 7, Bei Männern S & B
T. Schmidt & P. Schmidtman (T) (in # Roy. 1203)

ACT II

No. 10, O Isis und Osiris Bs
E. Pinza (*Ital*, n.v.) in # Vic.LM 107
(No. 15, etc.) (♭ set WDM 1555)
P. Schoeffler in # MSL.MW 44
(Borodin, Offenbach, etc. & Lieder)
L. Weber (from Set B) C.LVX 159
(No. 15)
▽G. Hann Pol. 68296
(No. 15)

No. 14, Der Hölle Rache S
W. Lipp (from Set B) C.LVX 153
(No. 4)
☆ E. Reichelt Pol. 15478
H. Schymberg T.SK 19034
⊞ M. Ivogün in # Ete.O-479*
F. Hempel (*Ital*) G.VB 21*: o.n. DB 365*
A. V. Nezhdanova (*Russ*) G.VB 37*: o.n. 023101*

= Long-playing, 33⅓ r.p.m. ♭ = 45 r.p.m. ♮ = Auto. couplings, 78 r.p.m.

(Die) ZAUBERFLÖTE *(continued)*

No. 15, In diesen heil'gen Hallen   Bs
F. Corena   in ♯ *D.LX 3095*
(above)   (♯ *Lon.LS 671*)
E. Pinza *(Ital)*   in ♯ *Vic.LM 107*
(Don Giovanni, No. 4, etc.)   (♭ *WDM 1555*)
W. Strienz   in ♯ **Ura. 7026**
L. Weber (from Set B)   **C.LVX 159**
(No. 10)
▽G. Hann   *(No. 10)*   **Pol. 68296**
G. Frei   in ♯ Roy. 1203
н P. Knüpfer   AF. 40*

No. 17, Ach ich fühl's   S
M. Guilleaume   **T.E 3927**
(Nozze di Figaro, No. 19)
☆L. della Casa   in ♯ *D.LXT 2685*
(Figaro, Don Giovanni, etc.)   (in ♯ *Lon.LLP 457*)
☆ L. Lehmann   in ♯ AmD.DL 9523
н E. Destinn   in ♯ CEd. set 7001*

No. 20, Ein Mädchen oder Weibchen   B
K. Schmitt-Walter   *T.A 11188*
(No. 2)

I. C. ARIAS & SONGS

1. ARIAS

COLLECTION   S

Ah, lo previdi   K 272
Ch'io mi scordi di te . . . Non temer amato bene   K 505 [1]
Bella mia fiamma . . . Resta, o cara   K 528
Nehmt meinen Dank, ihr holden Gönner   K 383
    K. Nentwig & Stuttgart Pro Musica Orch.—
    Reinhardt *(below)*   ♯ **AmVox.PL 7370**

Ombra felice . . . Io ti lascio   K 255   A
    R. Michaelis & Pro Musica—Reinhardt
(above)   ♯ **AmVox.PL 7370**

Ma, che vi fece, o stelle
. . . Sperai vicino il lido   K 368   S
Mia speranza adorata
. . . Ah, non sai, quel pena sia   K 416   S
    V. Bak & orch.—Graunke   ♯ **Mer.MG 10085**
(Regina Coeli; & Handel)

Männer suchen stets zu naschen   K 433   Bs
    ("Warnung")
    E. Berger (S), G. Schick (pf.) in ♯ *Vic.LM 133*
(Songs, & Schubert)   (♭ *set WDM 1589*)
    I. Seefried (S), G. Moore (pf.)   **C.LX 1543**
(⅓s.—Songs)
    ☆E. Schwarzkopf (S), G. Moore (pf.) *C.LD 2*
(Der Zauberer)

Mandina amabile   K 480   S, T, B
    (for F. Bianchi's La villanella rapita)
    K. Hansel, J. Collins, J. Yard & pf. in ♯Den.DR 1

Mia speranza adorata . . . Ah, non sai . . . K 416 S
    T. Stich-Randall & Naples Scarlatti Orch.—
    Paumgartner   ♯ **Csm.CLPS 1035**
(March, K 335; & A. Scarlatti)

Misero ! o sogno ! . . . Aura, che intorno K 431 T
Per pietà, non ricercate   K 420   T
    C. Holland & Paris Cons.—Goldschmidt
                    ♯ *Pat.DT 1008*
(Così, No. 17 & Don Giovanni, No. 11)

Nehmt meinen Dank, ihr holden Gönner K 383 S
Per pietà, bell' idol mio   K 78   S
    ☆M. Stader & H. Erisman (pf.)   **G.C 4182**

Non più, tutto ascoltai . . .
Non temer amato ben [2]   K 490   1786   S
    H. Gueden   in ♯ *D.LX 3067*
(Idomeneo, No. 11, on D.K 28570)   (♯ *Lon.LPS 485*)

---

2. SONGS

COLLECTIONS

    (Das) Veilchen   (Goethe)   K 476   ø
    (Das) Lied der Trennung   (Schmidt)   K 519
    Abendempfindung   (Campe)   K. 523   ø
    Sehnsucht nach dem Frühlinge   (Overbeck)   K 596
    Als Luise die Briefe . . .   (Baumberg)
      (Unglückliche Liebe)   K 520
    (Die) Verschweigung   (Weisse)   K 518   ø
    (Der) Zauberer   (Weisse)   K 472
    An Chloë   (Jacobi)   K 524
    Dans un bois solitaire   (de la Motte)   K 308
    E. Margano (S), J. v. Wering (18th Cent. pf.)
                       ♯ *Phi.N 00611R*
    (Those marked ø also in Phi.N 12043G; *PhM.N 12043S*)

    (Das) Kinderspiel   (Overbeck)   K 598
    (Der) Zauberer   (Weisse)   K 472
    (Die) Zufriedenheit   (Miller)   K 349
    I. Seefried (S), G. Moore (pf.)   **C.LX 1543**
    (⅓s. each—*Aria, Männer suchen . . .*)

    Abendempfindung   (Campe)   K 523 (1 side)
    Sehnsucht nach dem Frühlinge (Overbeck) K 596 (⅓s.)
    (Das) Veilchen   (Goethe)   K 476 (⅓s.)
    I. Seefried (S), G. Moore (pf.)   **C.LX 1549**

    Abendempfindung   (Campe)   K 523
    Dans un bois solitaire   (de la Motte)   K 308
    (Das) Veilchen   (Goethe)   K 476
    (Der) Zauberer   (Weisse)   K 472
    E. Berger (S), G. Schick (pf.)   in ♯ *Vic.LM 133*
(Aria, above; & Schubert)   (♭ *set WDM 1589*)

Als Luise die Briefe . . .   (Baumberg)   K 520
    I. Seefried (S), G. Moore (pf.)   *C.LB 114*
(Traumbild)

An Chloë   (Jacobi)   K 524
    I. Seefried (S), G. Moore (pf.)   *C.LB 116*
(Ridente la calma)
    Z. Dolukhanova (A, *Russ*) (USSR. 18663)

Gesellenreise   K 468
O heiliges Band   K 148
    Members Indiana Univ. Cho.—Hoffmann
                       ♯ **MR. 101**

Ridente la calma   K 152 (new K 210a)
    (Der Sylphe des Friedens)
    I. Seefried (S), G. Moore (pf.)   *C.LB 116*
(An Chloë)
    Z. Dolukhanova (A), B. Kozel (pf.)
                      USSR. 019579
(Rimsky-Korsakov: Song)

(Das) Traumbild   (Hölty)   K 530
    I. Seefried (S), G. Moore (pf.)   *C.LB 114*
(Als Luise . . .)

(Das) Veilchen   (Goethe)   K 476
    н L. Slezak (T) (in ♯ Ete. 453*)

(Der) Zauberer   (Weisse)   K 472
    E. Schwarzkopf (S), G. Moore (pf.) *C.LB 118*
(Brahms: Da unten im Tale)   (LW 59)
(Männer suchen stets . . . on LD 2)

Wiegenlied   (Gotter)   K 350
    ("Schlafe mein Prinzchen")
    (NOT by Mozart but by B. Flies)
    G. Winkler *(Dan)* (Tono.Z 18093)

(continued on next page)

---

[1] With R. Reinhardt, pf. obbligato.
[2] For *Idomeneo.*

Wiegenlied (*continued*)

— ARR. CHORUS
F. Bender Children's Cho.   *Pol. 62890*
(*Brahms: Wiegenlied*)
Bielefeld Children's Cho.—Oberschelp
     T.A 11228

(*Brahms: Wiegenlied*)
Wiltener Sängerknaben—Gerholdt *Tono.K 8032*
(*Brahms: Wiegenlied*)
etc., etc.

---

3. MISCELLANEOUS

(6) NOTTURNI
3 voices & 2 cl. & basset-hrn., or 3 b-hs.
Due pupille amabile (Anon.) K 439
Ecco, quel fiero istante (Metastasio) K 436
Luci care, luci belle (Anon.) K 346, New K 439a
Mi lagnerò tacendo (Metastasio) K 437
Più non si trovano (Metastasio) K 549
Se lontan, ben mio, tu sei (Metastasio) K 438
— ARR. 3 VOICES & PF.   Paumgartner
K. Hansel (S), J. Collins (B), J. Yard (B), W.
Reese (pf.)   in ‡ **Den.DR 1**

CHORUSES a capella
D'Bäurin hat d'Katz verlor'n (K.Anh. 188)
Liebes Mädchen, hör' mir zu[1] (K 441c) T, T, B
Grazie agl' inganni tuoi (Metastasio) K 532 S, T, B
Vienna Academy Cha. Cho. Members
     ‡ **Sel.LPG 8331**
(*Motets & Mass No. 10*)

TRIOS   S, T, B
(Das) Bandel (Mozart) K 441
Caro bell' idol mio (Anon.) K 562 Canon, unacc.
Grazie agl' inganni tuoi (Metastasio) K 532
K. Hansel (S), J. Collins (B), J. Yard (B),
W. Reese (pf.)   in ‡ *Den.DR 1*

(Das) Bandel K 441
Vienna Boys' Cho.—Lacovitch ‡ *Phi.A 00606R*
(*Schubert & J. Strauss*)

SPURIOUS
(Das) Alphabet K.Anh. 294d (by C. F. Par)
Vocal Trio & pf.   in *Vic. set E 100*
(*Arne, Schumann, etc.*)   (♭ *set WE 100*)

II. INSTRUMENTAL MUSIC

A. PIANO MUSIC
1. PIANO SOLO
(& Glass Harmonica Solo)

Adagio, B minor K 540
L. Kraus   ‡ *E. & AmVox.PL 7300*
(⅓s.—*Concerto, K 537*)   (‡ PaV. 170)
P. Badura-Skoda[2]   in ‡ **West.WL 5153/4**

Adagio, C major K 356 (new K 617a)
Glass Harmonica
B. Hoffmann   *Pol. 6002*
(*Beethoven & Reichardt*)

Allegro & Andante, F major K 533
P. Badura-Skoda[2]   in ‡ **West.WL 5153/4**

FANTASIAS
C major K 394 (Prelude & Fugue)
L. Epstein[3]   in ‡ **SPA. 6**
P. Badura-Skoda[2]   in ‡ **West.WL 5153/4**
R. Kirkpatrick   ‡ *BRS. 912*
(*Sonata, K 570 & Suite*)

C minor K 396 (Adagio)
G. Maier   in ‡ *Ban.BC 1001*

D minor K 397
C. Seemann   **PV. 72205**
(*Minuet, K 355 & Rondo, K 485*)
L. Dumont   ‡ **CHS.CHS 1115**
(*Sonatas*)   (‡ Nix.CLP 1115)
G. Maier   in ‡ *Ban.BC 1002*
☆ W. Landowska (pf.) (in ♭ *Vic. set WCT 44*)

Gigue, G major K 574
G. Maier   in ‡ *Ban.BC 1001*

Minuet, D major K 355 (New K 594a)
L. Epstein[3]   in ‡ **SPA. 6**
C. Seemann   **PV. 72205**
(⅓s.—*Rondo, K 485 & Fantasia, K 397*)
G. Maier   in ‡ *Ban.BC 1001*
☆ W. Landowska (hpsi.) (in ‡ Vic.LM 1217; ♭ *G.7RF 184*)

RONDOS
D major K 485
L. Epstein[3]   in ‡ **SPA. 6**
G. Werschenska   **Pol.HM 80053**
(*Hummel: Rondo, E flat*)
C. Seemann   **PV. 72205**
(⅓s.—*Minuet, K 355 & Fantasia, K 397*)
☆ W. Landowska (hpsi.) (in ‡ Vic.LM 1217; ♭ *G.7RF 184*)

F major K 494
P. Badura-Skoda[2]   in ‡ **West.WL 5153/4**

A minor K 511
G. Neuhaus   **USSR. 015202/3**

SONATAS
No. 3, B flat major K 281
No. 5, G major K 283
No. 15, C major K 545
No. 16, B flat major K 570
J. Blancard   ‡ **D.LXT 2666**
(2ss)   (‡ Lon.LL 529)

No. 4, E flat major K 282
G. Maier   in ‡ *Ban.BC 1002*

No. 8, A minor K 310
☆ D. Lipatti (C.LFX 1005/6: ♮ GQX 8031/2)

No. 10, C major K 330
C. Seemann (2ss)   **PV. 72201**
L. Cifarelli   **P.PE 165/6**
(*Davico: 3 Children's pieces*)
F. Chapiro   in ‡ **Ox. 105**
(*Scarlatti, Debussy, etc.*)
A. Balsam   ‡ **CHS.CHS 1116**
(*Concerto, K 415*)   (‡ Clc. 6060)
L. Dumont   ‡ **CHS.CHS 1115**
(*No. 17 & Fantasia*)   (‡ Nix.CLP 1115)
Lazare-Lévy   ‡ **Sel.LPG 8518**
(*No. 11*)
G. Maier   in ‡ *Ban.BC 1001*
... **Andante** only (excpts. — ARR. ORCH.) Anon. orch.(*Scd.5003*)

No. 11, A major K 331
L. Kreutzer   *JpC.P 40/1*
Lazare-Lévy   ‡ **Sel.LPG 8518**
(*No. 10*)
... **3rd movt., Rondo alla turca,** only
☆ W. Landowska (hpsi.) (♭ *G.7RF 184:* ‡ *Vic.LM 1217*)
A. Ehlers (hpsi.) (in ‡ AmD.DL 8019)
V. Horowitz (in ‡ Vic.LM 1171: ♭ *set WDM 1605*)

---

[1] Labelled *Gestörtes Ständchen* but presumably this.
[2] Each item is recorded twice; on 5153 a piano of 1785 is used, on 5154 a modern piano.
[3] On a reproduction of Mozart's own piano.

No. 11, A major . . . Rondo alla turca (*continued*)
— — ARR. 4 PFS.
  First Pf. Qtt. (in ♯ Vic.LM 1227: ♭ set *WDM 1624*)

— — ARR. ORCH.
  Paris Opéra—Cloëz   *Od. 188972*
  (*Mendelssohn: "Spring Song"*)
  Vienna Radio—Nilius (in ♯ *Vien. 1013*)

No. 12, F major   K 332
  L. Kraus   ♯ **AmVox.PL 7040**
  (*No. 17*)

No. 13, B flat major   K 333
  ☆L. Kraus   ♯ **AmD.DL 8523**
  (*Duo, vln. & vla.*)

No. 14, C minor   K 457
  . . . Finale only: M. Yudina (USSR. 014990)

No. 15, C major   K 545
  . . . 1st movt., Allegro, only
  G. Maier   in ♯ *Ban.BC 1002*

No. 16, B flat   K 570
  C. Arrau (6ss)   C.LX 1551/3
  L. Epstein [3]   in ♯ SPA. 6
  R. Kirkpatrick   ♯ **BRS. 912**
  (*Suite, Fantasia*)

— ARR. PF. & VLN.
  ☆ L. Mittman & O. Shumsky (in ♯ EA.ALX 112)

No. 17, D major   K 576
  G. Anda   T.E 3917/8
  (*3ss—Haydn: Sonata, F major*)
  L. Dumont   ♯ **CHS.CHS 1115**
  (*No. 10, & Fantasia*)   (♯ Nix.CLP 1115)
  L. Kraus (*No. 12*)   ♯ **AmVox.PL 7040**
  W. Schatzkamer   ♯ *Vic.LM 156*
  (*Scriabin*)
  (*3ss—Scarlatti: Sonatas, in* ♭ *set WDM 1650*)

Suite, C major   K 399 (new K 385 i)
  R. Kirkpatrick   ♯ **BRS. 912**
  (*Sonata, K 570 & Fantasia*)

VARIATIONS on [4]
Ah, vous dirai-je, maman   K 265
  G. Maier   in ♯ *Ban.BC 1002*

— ARR. 4 PFS.
  First Pf. Qtt. (in ♯ Vic.LM 1227: ♭ set *WDM 1624*)

Je suis Lindor   K 354
  A. Balsam   ♯ **CHS.CHS 1405**
  (*Concerto, K 451*)   (♯ Clc. 6061; Nix.CLP 1405)

Salve tu, Domine   (Paisiello)   K 398
  L. Epstein [3]   in ♯ SPA. 6

Unser dummer Pöbel meint   K 455
  C. Seemann (2ss)   PV. 72114
  (*Concerto, K 503, in* ♯ *AmD.DL 9568*)

II. (A) 2. PIANO DUET & 2 PIANOS
(inc. Mechanical Organ)

Fantasia, F minor   K 608 (orig. mech. org.)
— ARR. ORGAN
  F. Germani (4ss)   ♮ **G.C 7922/3**

— ARR. ORCH.
  ▽ Vienna Sym.—Fekete (not Wöss) (in ♯ Rem. 199-2)
    Vienna Artists—Fekete (♯ Etu. 705) [5]

Fugue, C minor   K 426   2 pfs.
  ☆G. & J. Dichler   U.H 23973
  (*Tchaikovsky: Mozartiana, s.1*)

SONATAS, pf. duet
F major   K 497;   C major   K 521
  P. Badura-Skoda & J. Demus   ♯ **West.WL 5082**

"Sonata for mechanical organ, C major"
  SEE *infra*, II, D.4, Sonatas

II. B. CHAMBER MUSIC

(4) ADAGIOS   K 404a   Str. trio
Nos. 1-4   COMPLETE
  Pasquier Trio (n.v.)   V♯ *DFr. 4/5*

No. 1, D minor; No. 2, G minor
  Janssen Sym. Orch.   ♯ **AmC.ML 4406**
  (*Bach: Fugues, & Handel*)

DUOS, vln. & vla.
No. 1, G major   K 423
  ☆S. Goldberg & F. Riddle   ♯ **AmD.DL 8523**
  (*Pf. Sonata, K 333*)

QUARTETS, Flute & str.
No. 1, D major   K 285   No. 2, G major   K 285a☆
No. 3, C major   K 285b☆   No. 4, A major   K 298
COMPLETE RECORDING
  J.-P. Rampal & Pasquier Trio   ♯ **BàM.LD 03**

No. 1, D major   K 285
  ☆H. Rečnicek & str. trio   ♯ **Sel.LPG 8336**
  (⅔s.—*Oboe Qtt. & Divertimento*)

QUARTET, Oboe & strings, F major   K 370
  H. Gomberg & Galimir Trio ♯ **AmD.DL 9618**
  (*Telemann*)
  M. Tabuteau, I. Stern, W. Primrose, P. Tortelier
                                       ♯ **AmC.ML 4566**
  (*Divertimento, K 251*)   (& in set SL 170)
  ☆ H. Kamesch & str. trio (♯ Sel.LPG 8336)

— ARR. HARMONICA & STR.
  L. Adler & Winterthur Trio ♯ **CHS.CHS 1161**
  (*Purcell, Vivaldi, etc.*)

QUARTETS, 2 vlns., vla., vlc.
No. 6, B flat major   K 159
  Griller Qtt.   ♯ **D.LX 3087**
  (*Haydn: Qtt., Op. 3, No. 5*)   (♯ Lon.LS 656)

No. 8, F major   K 168
  Griller Qtt.   ♯ **D.LXT 2728**
  (*No. 17*)   (♯ Lon.LL 658)

The 6 "Haydn" Quartets (Nos. 14-19)
COMPLETE RECORDING
  Roth Qtt. (6ss)   ♯ **Mer.MG 10108/10**
                                          (set MGL 8)

No. 14, G major   K 387
  ☆Amadeus Qtt.   ♯ *G.DLP 1003*

No. 15, D minor   K 421
  ☆Hungarian Qtt.   ♯ *G.FALP 131*
  (*Haydn: Qtt., Op. 64, No. 5*)
                        (also now ♮ G.DB 9106/8, auto only in G.B.)
  ☆Baroque Qtt.   ♯ *Nix.PLP 503*
  (*Haydn: Qtt., Op. 74, No. 2*)

. . . 3rd movt., Menuetto, only
  Paganini Qtt.   † ♯ *Vic.LM 1192*
                                          (♭ set *WDM 1611*)

No. 16, E flat major   K 428
  Amadeus Qtt.   ♯ **West.WL 5099**
  (*No. 17*)

---

[3] On a reproduction of Mozart's own piano.
[4] In order of K numbers.
[5] In a letter to *Saturday Review*, M. Fekete stated he had never recorded with this orch. or for this company.

STRING QUARTETS (*continued*)

No. 17, B flat major K 458 "Hunt"
Griller Qtt.   ♯ **D.LXT 2728**
(*No. 8*)   (♯ Lon.LL 658)
Amadeus Qtt.   ♯ **West.WL 5099**
(*No. 16*)

☆ Loewenguth Qtt. (♯ *Pol. 16004*)

No. 18, A major K 464
Amadeus Qtt.   ♯ **West.WL 5092**
(*No. 23*)

No. 19, C major K 465 "Dissonant"
Guilet Qtt.   ♯ **CHS.CHS 1130**
(*No. 21*)

Nos. 20-23 COMPLETE
Roth Qtt. (4ss)   ♯ **Mer.MG 10133/4**

No. 20, D major K 499
No. 21, D major K 575
Stuyvesant Qtt.   ♯ **Phil. 105**

No. 21, D major K 575 [1]
Aeolian Qtt.   ♯ **Allo.ALG 3036**
(*No. 23*)
Guilet Qtt.   ♯ **CHS.CHS 1130**
(*No. 19*)

No. 22, B flat major K589
Roth Qtt. (in collection, *above*)

No. 23, F major K 590
Amadeus Qtt.   ♯ **West.WL 5092**
(*No. 18*)
Aeolian Qtt.   ♯ **Allo.ALG 3036**
(*No. 21*)

QUARTETS: "Milanese Quartets" (doubtful)
B flat major K.Anh. 210   C major K.Anh. 211
A major K.Anh. 212   E flat major K.Anh. 213
Barchet Qtt.   ♯ **E. & AmVox.PL 7480**

QUINTET, cl. & str. qtt., A major K 581
A. de Bavier & New Italian Qtt. ♯ **D.LXT 2698**
     (♯ Lon.LL 573)
L. Wlach & Vienna Konzerthaus Qtt.
     ♯ **West.WL 5112**
R. Kell & Fine Arts Qtt.   ♯ **B.AXTL 1007**
     (♯ AmD.DL 9600)
B. Goodman & American Art Qtt.
     ♯ **AmC.ML 4483**

☆ S. Forrest & Galimir Qtt. (♯ *Eur.LPG 620*)

QUINTET, pf., ob., cl., hrn., bsn., E flat major
   K 452
R. Veyron-Lacroix, P. Pierlot, J. Lancelot,
   G. Coursier, P. Hongne   ♯ **OL.LD 51**
(*Cassation*)

QUINTETS, 2 vlns., 2 vlas., vlc.
C minor K 406
(ARR. Mozart from Serenade K 388)
☆ Budapest Quintet   ♯ **C.CX 1031**
(*Quintet, D major, K 593*)

☆ Stross Quintet (*Pol. 15556/8*)

G minor K 516
Amadeus Qtt. & C. Aronowitz ♯ **West.WL 5086**
☆ Budapest Qtt. & M. Katims ♯ **AmC.ML 4469**
(*below*)

D major K 593
☆ Budapest Quintet   ♯ **C.CX 1031**
(*Quintet, C minor, K 406*)

E flat major K 614
Budapest Qtt. & M. Katims   ♯ **AmC.ML 4469**
(*above*)

SONATA, bsn. & vlc., B flat K 292
☆ B. Kohon & J. Schuster (*JpV.ND 737*)

SONATAS, pf. & vln.
COLLECTIONS
   No. 22, A major   K 305
   No. 24, F major   K 376
   No. 34, A major   K 526
R. Kirkpatrick (hpsi.) & A. Schneider
     ♯ **AmC.ML 4617**

   No. 17, C major   K 296
   No. 18, G major   K 301
   No. 21, E minor   K 304
P. Badura-Skoda & W. Barylli ♯ **West.WL 5130**

   No. 18, G major   K 301
   No. 21, E minor   K 304
A. Heksch (18th Cent. pf.) & N. de Klijn
(1s. each)   ♯ *Phi.A 00112R*

   No. 21, E minor   K 304
   No. 22, A major   K 305
☆L. Mittman & O. Shumsky in ♯ **EA.ALX 112**

   No. 22, A major   K 305
   No. 25, F major   K 377
   E flat major K 58 (Not by Mozart) (New K.Anh. 209f)
P. Badura-Skoda & W. Barylli ♯ **West.WL 5145**

   No. 26, B flat major   K 378
   No. 27, G major   K 379
A. Heksch (18th Cent. pf.), N. de Klijn (vln.)
     ♯ *Phi.A 00614R*

   No. 27, G major   K 379
   No. 32, B flat major   K 454
P. Badura-Skoda & W. Barylli ♯ **West.WL 5109**

No. 6, G major, Op. 3, No. 2 K 11
A. Heksch (18th Cent. pf.) & N. de Klijn
     Phi.A 11155G

No. 18, G major K 301
☆ S. Frykberg & O. Kyndel (*May.MR 504/5*)

No. 20, C major K 303
M. Michailov & E. Milzkott   ♯ *CdM.LD 8018*
(*F.-X. Murschhauser: Hpsi. music*)

No. 24, F major K 376
J. Antonietti & J. Martzy   *PV. 36035/6S*
(3ss—last blank)

No. 27, G major K 379
A. Nissen & D. Zsigmondy   **PV. 72109**
(2ss)

No. 32, B flat major K 454
W. Rosé & M. Elman   ♯ **Vic.LM 1208**
(*Paganini: Caprice 24*)   (4ss, ♭ set WDM 1634)
☆ E. Bay & J. Heifetz (*JpV. set JAS 238*)

No. 34, A major K 526
J. Goodman & J. de la Fuente   ♯ **SRC. 1**
(*Tartini*)

TRIOS, piano, vln., vlc.
COMPLETE RECORDING
☆A. Jambor, V. Aitay, J. Starker
   Nos. 1 & 2 on ♯ Clc. 6072
   Nos. 3 & 5 on ♯ Clc. 6135
   Nos. 4 & 6 on ♯ Clc. 6066

---

[1] The disc of this Qtt. & No. 22 by the Stradivarius Qtt. listed in WERM, p. 808 (♯ Strad.STR 605) was apparently withdrawn before issue.

No. 2, G major   K 496
  E. Rubbra, E. Gruenberg, W. Pleeth
  (*Rubbra: Trio*)   **♯ Argo.ARS 1005**

TRIO, pf., cl., vla., E flat major   K 498
  M. Horszowski, R. Kell, L. Fuchs
                            ♯ B.AXTL 1011
  (*Beethoven: Trio*)   (♯ AmD.DL 9543)
  J. Arnold, C. Brody, E. Lifschey   **♯ Ox.OR 106**
  (*Haydn*)
  ☆ E. Balogh, S. Forrest, C. Cooley (♯ Eur.LPG 622)

Variations on "Hélas, j'ai perdu mon amant"
  (*Albanèse*)   K 360   pf. & vln.
  A. Heksch (18th Cent. pf.) & N. de Klijn
                          Phi.A 11246G
  2ss   (*PhM.A 11246S*)

II. C. DIVERTIMENTI, CASSATIONS
& SERENADES

CASSATIONS

No. 2, B flat major   K 99
  Salzburg Festival—P. Walter   **♯ Per.SPLP 528**
  (*below*)   (♯ Clc. 6067; ♯ Nix.PLP 528)

E flat major (unid.)[1] ob., cl., hrn., bsn.
  New Art Wind Qtt.   in ♯ **CEd. set CE 2010**
  (*Stamitz, Danzi, Reicha*)
  P. Pierlot, J. Lancelot, G. Coursier, P. Hongne
  (*Quintet*)   **♯ OL.LD 51**

DIVERTIMENTI, 2 basset-hrns. & bsn.   K 439b
No. 2, B flat major
  ☆ L. Wlach, F. Bartosek (cl.), K. Öhlberger (Sel.LPG 8336)

No. 3, B flat major
  ☆ L. Wlach, F. Bartosek (cl.), K. Öhlberger (Sel.LPG 8317)

DIVERTIMENTO, vln., vla., vlc., E flat   K 563
  Pasquier Trio (n.v.)   **♯ DFr. 45**

DIVERTIMENTO, Orch., D major K 131 "No. 2"
  London Mozart Players—H. Blech
                          ♯ D.LXT 2753
  (*Haydn: Symphony No. 49*)   (♯ Lon.LL 586)
  ☆Royal Phil.—Beecham [2] **♯ Vic.LHMV 1030**
  (*Handel: Great Elopement Suite*)   (♭ set WHMV 1030)
  ☆Cha.—Goldschmidt   † **♯ AS. 3001LD**
  (*Les Petits Riens*)

DIVERTIMENTI, 2 fls., 5 trpts., 4 drums
C major K 187; **C major** K 188 ("Nos. 5 & 6")
  ☆Salzburg Brass Ens.—v. Zallinger
                       ♯ Nix.PLP 520
  (*Schubert: Sym. No. 2*)

DIVERTIMENTI, 2 obs., 2 hrns., 2 bsns.
F major   K 213   "No. 8"
E flat major   K 252   "No. 12"
F major   K 253   "No. 13"
B flat major   K 270   "No. 14"
  Vienna Sextet   **♯ West.WL 5103**

DIVERTIMENTI, Strings & 2 hrns.
D major   K 205   "No. 7"
  Salzburg Festival—P. Walter **♯ Per.SPLP 528**
  (*below*)   (♯ Clc. 6067; ♯ Nix.PLP 528)

F major   K 247   "No. 10"
  Stuttgart Ton-Studio—Lund **♯ Per.SPLP 545**
  (*March, K 248, & Sym. 24*)   (♯ Nix.PLP 545)
  Lamoureux—Goldschmidt   **♯ Clc. 6059**
  (*Fl. Concerto, K 314*)

  ... **Minuets I & II** : *See* Minuets & Gavotte, Sec. II. D. 2,
infra

D major   K 251   (with Oboe) "No. 11"
  M. Tabuteau & Perpignan Festival—Casals
                        ♯ AmC.ML 4566
  (*Oboe Qtt.*)   (& in set SL 170)
  ☆Dumbarton Oaks—Schneider **♯ Clc. 6029**
  (*Vivaldi: Concerto, Op. 3, No. 11*)

B flat major   K 287   "No. 15"
  Cha. orch.—Hewitt   **♯ DFr. 41**
  ☆N.B.C.—Toscanini   **♯ G.FBLP 1027**

D major   K 334   "No. 17"
  ☆ Vienna State Op.—Fekete (♯ Eur.LPG 610)

  ... **3rd movt. Minuetto,** only — ARR. VLN. & PF.
  ☆ J. Heifetz & E. Bay (in ♯ Vic.LM 1166; ♭ G.7RF 249)

MARCHES

D major   K 249   (for the Haffner Serenade)
  Salzburg Mozarteum Orch.—P. Walter
                        ♯ Per.SPLP 534
  (½s.—*Organ Sonatas*)   (♯ Clc. 6062; Nix.PLP 534)
  Berlin Phil.—F. Lehmann   **♯ Phi.A 00111R**
  (½s.—*Symphony 35*)

D major   K 335, No. 2   (for Serenade K 320)
  Naples Scarlatti Orch.—Paumgartner
                        ♯ Csm.CLPS 1035
  (*Aria; & A. Scarlatti*)

F major   K 248   (for Divertimento K 247)
  Stuttgart Ton-Studio—Lund **♯ Per.SPLP 545**
  (*Divertimento, K 247 & Sym.24*)   (♯ Nix.PLP 545)

(Ein) Musikalischer Spass   K 522   2 hrns. & str.
  Berlin Radio Ens.—M. Lange **♯ CdM.LDX 8017**
  (*Janáček: Youth*)

SERENADES, orch.

No. 4, D major   K 203
  Naples Scarlatti Orch.—Paumgartner
                        ♯ Csm.CLPS 1033

No. 5, D major   K 204
  ☆ Vienna Sym.—Swoboda (♯ Sel.LPG 8322)

No. 6, D major   K 239   (Serenata Notturna)
  Haydn Orch.—Newstone   **♯ Mon.MWL 301**
  (*Symphony No. 41*)

No. 7, D major   K 250   "Haffner"
  Bamberg Sym.—Leitner (8ss)   ♮ **PV. 72165/8**
  (D. Zsigmondy, vln.) (♯ Pol. 18041; ♯ AmD.DL 9636)
  Vienna Sym.—Krauss   **♯ AmVox.PL 6850**
                          (♯ Clc. 6043)
  Bamberg Sym.—Keilberth   **♯ Mer.MG 10117**

No. 9, D major   K 320   "Posthorn"
  Suisse Romande—Maag   **♯ D.LXT 2671**
  (2ss)   (♯ Lon.LL 502)
  Lamoureux—Goldschmidt   **♯ Pat.DTX 104**
  ☆Vienna State Op.—Sternberg ♯**Nix.HLP 1012**

No. 10, B flat major   K 361   (Gran Partita)
  13 insts.
  Los Angeles Wind Ens.—Steinberg
                        ♯ DCap.CTL 7030
                          (♯ Cap.P 8181)
  Vienna Sym. Wind Ens.   **♯ AmVox.PL 7470**
  ☆ Hewitt Cha. Ens. (♯ DFr. 9)

No. 11, E flat major   K 375
  2 obs., 2 cls., 2 hrns., 2 bsns.
  London Baroque Ens.—Haas   **P.R 20610/2**
  (6ss)   (♯ PMB 1002)

(*continued on next page*)

---

[1] Pub. 1936, Andraud, Cincinnati . No evidence of origin (said to have been "discovered" 1910).
[2] Omits 1st Minuet, plays 5th movt. before 4th and interpolates Minuet from Divertimento, K 287.

No. 11, E flat major (*continued*)

Kell Chamber Players   **♯ B.AXTL 1013**
(*No. 12*)   (♯ AmD.DL 9540)
Vienna Sym. Wind Ens.   **♯ AmVox.PL 7490**
(*No. 12*)

☆ Hewitt Cha. Ens. (♯ DFr. 10)
    Vienna Phil. Wind Group (♯ Sel.LPG 8345)

No. 12, C minor   K 388
   2 obs., 2 cls., 2 hrns., 2 bsns.
Kell Chamber Players   **♯ B.AXTL 1013**
(*No. 11*)   (♯ AmD.DL 9540)
Vienna Sym. Wind Ens.   **♯ AmVox.PL 7490**
(*No. 11*)

☆ Hewitt Cha. Ens. (♯ DFr. 10)
    Vienna Phil. Wind Group (♯ Sel.LPG 8345)

No. 13, G major   K 525   Str. orch.
   (*Eine kleine Nachtmusik*)
Stuttgart Cha.—Münchinger   **♯ D.LX 3061**
(*Divertimento, D major*)   (♯ Lon.LPS 385)
   (also, 4ss, D.K 28487/8: K 23218/9)
Perpignan Festival—Casals   **♯ AmC.ML 4563**
(*Symphony No. 29*)   (in set SL 170)
Berlin Cha.—Stross   **♯ Sat.LDG 8008**
(*Bach: Brandenburg Concerto No. 6*)
Sydney Civic Sym.—Beck   **♯ Dia.DPM 1**
(*Schubert, Grainger, etc.*)
Cha. orch.—Hewitt   (2ss)   **V♯ DFr. 38**
Vienna Phil.—Böhm   **♯ AmVox.PL 7760**
(*Symphony 41*)
☆Vienna Phil.—Furtwängler   **♯ G.FALP 117**
(*Sym. 40*)
(*Haydn: Sym. 94 on* ♯ Vic.LHMV 1018: ♭ set WHMV 1018)
(also, 4ss, ♭ G.7R 122/3)
Homburg Sym.—Schubert (♯ Rgt. 5011)
Berlin Sym. (♯ Roy. 1275, ♯ Var. 6933, etc.)

☆ Danish Radio—Busch (Attn. 27057/8)
   Vienna Sym.—Scherchen (AusT.E 1152/3)
   Salzburg—Weidlich (♯ Mrt. 1-5, d.c.)

II. D. ORCHESTRAL MUSIC
1. CONCERTOS

BASSOON & ORCH., B flat major   K 191
K. Bidlo & Czech Phil.—Ančerl   ♮ **U.H 24205/7**
☆L. Sharrow & N.B.C.—Toscanini

         ♯ G.FALP 164
(*Symphony 41*)

CLARINET & ORCH., A major   K 622
L. Cahuzac & Danish Radio—Wöldike

         ♯ HSLP. 1047
(*Haydn: Symphony 61*)
(*Haydn: Symphony 6, on* ♯ Nix.HLP 1047)
U. Delecluse & Cha. Sym.—Oubradous

         ♯ Pat.DTX 112
(*Horn Concerto*)
L. Wlach & Vienna Phil.—Karajan

         C.LWX 445/8S
(*7ss—last blank*)   (GQX 11484/7S)
☆R. Kell & Zimbler Sinfonietta

         ♯ B.AXL 2002
         (♯ D.AXT 233046)
☆ F. Etienne & Cha.—Hewitt (♯ DFr. 2)[1]

FLUTE & ORCH.
No. 1, G major   K 313
J. Wummer & Perpignan Festival—Casals

         ♯ AmC.ML 4567
(*Pf. Concerto, K 449*)   (& in set SL 170)

No. 2, D major   K 314 (see also Oboe Concerto)
J.-P. Rampal & Lamoureux—Goldschmidt

         ♯ Clc. 6059
(*Divertimento, K 247*)

FLUTE, HARP & ORCH., C major   K 299
K. F. Mess, D. Wagner, Stuttgart Ton-Studio
   Orch.—Lund   **♯ Per.SPLP 544**
(*Horn Concerto*)   (♯ Nix.PLP 544)
(Cadenza by K. Thomas)

HORN & ORCH.
No. 1, D major   K 412
G. Görmer & Stuttgart Ton-Studio—Lund

         ♯ Per.SPLP 544
(*Fl. & Harp Concerto*)   (♯ Nix.PLP 544)

No. 2, E flat   K 417
☆ D. Brain & Philharmonia—Süsskind (C.GQX 11480/1)

No. 3, E flat major   K 447
M. Jones & Nat. Gallery Orch.—Bales

       in **♯ WCFM. 8**
(*Exsultate, etc.*)
L. Thevet & Cha. Sym.—Oubradous

         ♯ Pat.DTX 112
(*Clar. Concerto*)

Rondo, E flat major   K 371
— ARR. HORN & PF.
J. Stagliano & P. Ulanowsky   **♯ Bo.L 200**
(*Beethoven, Schubert, Schumann*)

OBOE & ORCH.
C major   K 314a (later fl. & orch.)
P. Pierlot & Lamoureux—Goldschmidt
   (4ss)   **Pat.PDT 263/4**
☆M. Sailliet & Salzburg Mozarteum—
   Paumgartner   **♯ Ren.X 29**
(*Concerto, pf. K 175*)

PIANO & ORCH.
D major   K 175
☆A. Balsam & Sym.—Gimpel   **♯ Ren.X 29**
(now with *Oboe Concerto, C major*)

B flat major   K 238
C major   K 246
A. Balsam & Winterthur Sym.—Goehr

         ♯ CHS.CHS 1120
       (♯ Clc. 6083; ♯ Nix.CLP 1120)
(K 246 with cadenza by Mozart)

E flat major   K 271
M. Hess & Perpignan Festival—Casals

         ♯ AmC.ML 4568
       (& in set SL 170)
☆ L. Kraus & Philharmonia—Süsskind (♯ AmD.DL 9525)

A major   K 414
F. Jensen & Danish Radio Cha.—Wöldike

         ♯ HSLP. 1054
(*below*)   (cadenzas by Mozart)   (♯ Nix.HLP 1054)
A. Sandford & Rome Sym.—Guenther

         ♯ Roy. 1379
(*Concerto for 2 pfs., K 365*)

C major   K 415
☆A. Balsam & orch.—Swoboda

         ♯ CHS.CHS 1116
(*Pf. Sonata*)   (♯ Clc. 6060)

E flat major   K 449
E. Istomin & Perpignan Festival—Casals

         ♯ AmC.ML 4567
(*Fl. Concerto, K 313*)   (& in set SL 170)

B flat major   K 450
A. B. Michelangeli & Milan Afternoon Chamber
   Concerts—Gracis   (6ss)   **G.DB 11348/50**

---

[1] Originally this disc was 12-inch but re-issued on *10-inch* with the same number.

D major K 451
A. Balsam & Winterthur Sym.—Desarzens
♯ CHS.CHS 1405
(*Variations*) (♯ Clc. 6061; Nix.CLP 1405)
J. Haien & Nat. Gallery Orch.—Bales
♯ WCFM. 101

G major K 453
☆ R. Kirkpatrick & Dumbarton Oaks—Schneider
(♯ Eur.LDE 3001)

F major K 459
▽L. Kraus & Vienna Sym.—Moralt
♯ AmVox.PL 6890
(*Concerto K 488, and not Rondo*)
☆ C. Haskil & Winterthur Sym.—Swoboda
(♯ Sel.LPG 8329)

D minor K 466
A. Schnabel & Philharmonia—Süsskind
♯ Vic.LHMV 1012
(*K 491*) (Cadenzas by Schnabel) (♭ set WHMV 1012)
R. Serkin & Philadelphia—Ormandy
♯ AmC.ML 4424
(*Cadenzas by Beethoven*)
J. Iturbi & Victor Sym. **♯ Vic.LM 1717**
(*Concerto, 2 pfs.*) (♭ set WDM 1717)
F. Pelleg & Sym.—Goehr **♯ MMS. 9**
M. Huttner & Berlin Sym.—Rubahn (♯ Roy. 1341)
☆ C. Haskil & Winterthur—Swoboda (♯ Sel.LPG 8329)
F. Weidlich & Salzburg Festival Orch. (♯ Mrt. 200-13)

C major K 467
F. Jensen & Danish Radio—Wöldike
♯ HSLP. 1054
(*above*) (Cadenzas by F. Jensen) (♯ Nix.HLP 1054)
☆ R. Casadesus & N.Y.P.S.O.—Münch (♯ C.FC 1009)

E flat major K 482
L. Kraus & Vienna Sym.—Moralt
♯ AmVox.PL 7290
(*Rondo, K 382*)
R. Serkin & Perpignan Festival—Casals
♯ AmC.ML 4569
(& in set SL 170)

A major K 488
W. Gieseking & Philharmonia—Karajan [1]
C.LX 1510/3S
(7ss—last blank) (2ss—♯ C.FC 1013)
(*Franck: Symphonic Variations* on ♯ AmC.ML 4536)
L. Kraus & Vienna Sym.—Moralt
♯ AmVox.PL 6890
(*Concerto, K 459*)
M. Yudina & State Sym.—Gauk
USSR. 014983/9
(7ss—*Sonata K 457, Finale*)
(7ss—*Moussorgsky: Scherzo*, on ♮ U.H 24273/6)
E. Kilenyi & orch.—P. Walter **♯ Rem. 199-61**
(*Liszt*)
☆A. Rubinstein & St. Louis Sym.—
Golschmann **♯ G.FALP 112**
(*Falla*) (QALP 112)

C minor K 491
A. Schnabel & Philharmonia—Süsskind
♯ Vic.LHMV 1012
(*K 466*) (cadenzas by Schnabel) (♭ set WHMV 1012)
P. Badura-Skoda & Vienna Sym.—Prohaska
♯ West.WL 5097
(*below*)
S. Biro & Austrian Sym.—Loibner ♯ **Rem. 199-70**
(*Figaro Overture*)
▽L. Kraus & Vienna Sym.—Moralt
♯ AmVox.PL 6880
(1½ss—*Sonata No. 15*)

C major K 503
☆E. Fischer & Philharmonia—Krips
♯ Vic.LHMV 1004
(*Bach: Concerto, 3 claviers*) (♭ set WHMV 1004)
☆ C. Seemann & Munich Phil.—Lehmann
(♯ Pol. 16014; AmD.DL 9658)

D major K 537 "Coronation"
G. Bachauer & New London—Sherman
G.C 4151/4
(7ss—*Scarlatti-Tausig: Pastorale & Capriccio*)
(*Liszt: Spanish Rhapsody* on ♯ Vic.LM 9000:
♭ set WDM 9000)
L. Kraus & Vienna Sym.—Moralt
♯ E. & AmVox.PL 7300
(1½ss—*Adagio, K 540*) (♯ PaV.VP 170)
☆ W. Landowska & orch.—Goehr
(♯ Vic.LCT 1029: ♭ set WCT 44)

▽ It appears doubtful whether the Thyrion recording on
♯ AmVox.PL 6270 was ever in fact on sale.

B flat major K 595
P. Badura-Skoda & Vienna Sym.—Prohaska
(*above*) **♯ West.WL 5097**
M. Horszowski & Perpignan Festival—Casals
♯ AmC.ML 4570
(& in set SL 170)

Rondo, D major K 382
L. Kraus & Vienna Sym.—Moralt
♯ AmVox.PL 7290
(*Concerto, K 482*)
☆W. Kempff & Dresden Phil.—v. Kempen
♯ AmD.DL 9535
(*Symphony 38*)

CONCERTOS after French & other composers
F major K 37 [2, 3]
B flat major K 39 [2, 4]
A. Balsam & Winterthur Sym.—Goehr
♯ CHS.CHS 1119
(♯ Nix.CLP 1119)

D major K 40 [3, 6, 5]
G major K 41 [2, 3]
A. Balsam & Winterthur Sym.—Ackermann
♯ CHS.CHS 1163

CONCERTOS after J. C. Bach K 107 (New K 21b)
No. 1, D major
No. 2, G major
No. 3, E flat major
A. Balsam & Winterthur Sym.—Goehr
♯ CHS.CHS 1164

CONCERTO, 2 pfs. & orch., E flat major K 365
R. Gianoli, P. Badura-Skoda & Vienna State
Op.—Scherchen **♯ West.WL 5095**
(*below*)
J. & A. Iturbi & Vic. Sym. ♯ **Vic.LM 1717**
(*Pf. Concerto, K 466*) (♭ set WDM 1717)
C. Vidusso, A. Sandford & Rome Sym.—
Guenther **♯ Roy. 1379**
(*Pf. Concerto, K 414*)

CONCERTO, 3 pfs. & orch., F major K 242
— ARR. 2 PFS. & ORCH. Mozart
R. Gianoli, P. Badura-Skoda & Vienna State
Op.—Scherchen **♯ West.WL 5095**
(*above*)

——— *END OF PF. CONCERTOS* ———

---

[1] Cadenza by Mozart.
[2] After Raupach [3] After Honauer. [4] After Schobert. [5] After C. P. E. Bach.
[6] After Eckard.

CONCERTOS, Violin & Orch.
No. 1, B flat major   K 207
No. 2, D major   K 211
   D. Erlih & Lamoureux—Goldschmidt
               ♯ **G.FALP 152**
   A. Stücki & Ton-Studio—Lund ♯ **Nix.PLP 549**
                 (♯ Per.SPLP 549)

No. 3, G major   K 216
   S. Goldberg & Philharmonia—Süsskind
               ♯ **P.PMA 1003**
   (below)   (♯ AmD.DL 9609; ♯ Od.ODX 105)
   ☆ I. Stern & Cha. Orch. (C.LZX 271/3)

No. 4, D major   K 218
   S. Goldberg & Philharmonia—Süsskind
               ♯ **P.PMA 1003**
   (above)   (♯ AmD.DL 9609; ♯ Od.ODX 105)
   R. Barchet & Stuttgart Pro Musica—R.
     Reinhardt   ♯ **AmVox.PL 7240**
   (below)   (♯ PaV.VP 250; EVox. 250)
   ☆ J. Heifetz & Royal Phil.—Beecham
               ♯ **G.FALP 136**
   (Mendelssohn)   (QALP 136)
   ☆ J. Szigeti & L.P.O.—Beecham (♯ AmC.ML 4533)
   A. Schneider & Dumbarton Oaks (♯ Era.LDE 3001)

No. 5, A major   K 219
   E. Morini & Perpignan Festival—Casals
               ♯ **AmC.ML 4565**
                 (& in set SL 170)
   J. Heifetz & L.S.O.—Sargent ♯ **Vic.LM 9014**
   (Beethoven: Romances)   (♭ set WDM 9014)

No. 6, D major   K 271a
   A. Stücki & Stuttgart Ton-Studio—Lund
               ♯ **Per.SPLP 548**
   (below)   (♯ Clc.6095)
   H. Airoff & Austrian Sym.—Wöss
   (Dances)   ♯ **Rem. 199-46**

No. 7, E flat major   K 268 (new K 365b)
   R. Barchet & Stuttgart Pro Musica—R.
     Reinhardt   ♯ **AmVox.PL 7240**
   (above)   (♯ PaV.VP 250; EVox. 250)

D major K.Anh. 294a "Adelaide" (doubtful)
   L. Kaufmann & Netherlands Phil.—Ackermann
   (Symphonies 17 & 26)   ♯ **CHS.G 10**

Adagio, E major   K 261
Rondo, B flat major   K 269
Rondo, C major   K 373
   G. Swärdström & Stuttgart Ton-Studio Orch.—
     Lund   ♯ **Per.SPLP 548**
   (above)   (♯ Clc. 6095)

Adagio, E major   K 261
   ☆ N. Milstein & Vic. Sym.—Golschmann
           (♭ G.7RF 187; ♭ Vic.WEPR 11)

Rondo, C major   K 373
   ☆ N. Milstein & Vic. Sym.—Golschmann
           (♭ G.7RF 230; ♭ Vic.WEPR 11)

Concertone, 2 vlns. & orch., C major   K 190
   ☆ Vienna Sym.—Swoboda (♯ Sel.LPG 8321, 1½ss)

————*END OF VLN. CONCERTOS*————

SINFONIE CONCERTANTE
E flat major   K 297b   ob., cl., hrn., bsn., orch.
   F. Fischer, E. Flackus, G. Görmer, H. Gehring,
     Stuttgart Pro Musica—Reinhardt
   (below)   ♯ **E. & AmVox.PL 7320**
   Anon. soloists & Austrian Sym.—Wöss
               ♯ **Rem. 199-54**
   ☆ H. Kamesch, L. Wlach, G. v. Freiberg, K. Öhlberger,
     Vienna State Op.—Swoboda (♯ Sel.LPG 8317)
   Czech Phil.—Talich (♯ Eur.TAI 713/6)

E flat major   K 364   vln., vla. & orch.
   I. Stern, W. Primrose, Perpignan Festival—
     Casals   ♯ **AmC.ML 4564**
   (2ss)   (& in set SL 170)
   W. Barylli, P. Doktor & Vienna State Op.—
     Prohaska   *(2ss)*   ♯ **West.WL 5107**
   J. & L. Fuchs & Zimbler Sinfonietta
     (2ss)   ♯ **AmD.DL 9596**
   R. Barchet, H. Kirchner & Stuttgart Pro Musica
     —Seegelken   ♯ **E. & AmVox.PL 7320**
   (above)

————*END OF CONCERTOS*————

II. D. 2. DANCES

COLLECTION

Contretänze	K 534	Das Donnerwetter;
	K 609	complete
Ländler	K 606	... Nos. 1-5 only
Deutsche Tänze	K 600	... Nos. 1-5 only
	K 602	... No. 3, Der Leiermann
	K 605	complete

   Vienna State Op.—Litschauer   ♯ **Van.VRS 426**

CONTRETÄNZE
(5) K 609
   London Baroque Ens.—Haas   **P.R 20597**

... Nos. 1, 2, 4
   Danish Radio—Busch   **G.C 4124**
   (Haydn: Sinfonia Concertante, s.5)
               (idem, s.1, on DB 20134)

... Nos. 1, 2, 3, 5
   Suisse Romande—Blech   **D.K 28383**
   (Gluck: Iphigénie en Aulide Ov. s. 3)

DEUTSCHE TÄNZE
(21) K 509, 571, 600, 605, complete
   Frankenland Sym.—Kloss   ♯ **Lyr.LL 31**

(6) K 509
   French Radio—Leibowitz   ♯ **Eso.ES 512**
   (Beethoven, Schubert)   (♯ Cpt.MC 20003)
   Bamberg Sym.—Keilberth   ♯ **OL.LD 37**
   (below)

(6) K 536 ... No. 1   — ARR. HPSI.
   ☆ A. Ehlers (in ♯ AmD.DL 8019)

(6) K 571
   Bamberg Sym.—Keilberth   V♯ **DO.LD 4**
   (also on ♯ OL.LD 37 with *Dances, K 509,* & *Sym. 29)*

(6) K 600 ... Nos. 1 & 5
   Winterthur Sym.—Goehr   in ♯ **MMS. 1**

... Nos. 3 & 5
   Berlin State Op.—Schüler   **Imp. 014112**
   (K 602-3 & K 605-3)

(4) K 602
... No. 3, "Der Leiermann"
   Berlin State Op.—Schüler   **Imp. 014112**
   (above)

(3) K 605
... No. 3 only, "Der Schlittenfahrt"
   Berlin State Op.—Schüler   **Imp. 014112**
   (above)
   ☆ Sym. Orch.—Stokowski (in ♯ Vic.LM 1238: ♭ 49-0553)

(12) MINUETS, K 585
   Cha. Orch.—Hewitt   ♯ **DFr. 66**

(2) Minuets & Gavotte
   (Divertimento K 247, Minuets ; & Les Petits Reins, No. 9)
   Austrian Sym.—Wöss   ♯ **Rem. 199-46**
   (Vln. Concerto 6)

♯ = Long-playing, 33⅓ r.p.m.   ♭ = 45 r.p.m.   ♮ = Auto. couplings, 78 r.p.m.

II. D. *3. SYMPHONIES*

No. 1, E flat major K 16
No. 2, B flat major K 17 [1]
No. 5, B flat major K 22
No. 6, F major K 43
Winterthur Sym.—Ackermann ♯ **CHS.CHS 1165**

No. 1, E flat major K 16
Lamoureux—Colombo **V♯ *DO.LD 2***

No. 6, F major K 43
Lamoureux—Colombo **V♯ *DO.LD 3***

No. 4, D major K 19
No. 10, G major K 74
No. 11, D major K 84
No. 14, A major K 114
Winterthur Sym.—Ackermann ♯ **CHS.CHS 1166**

No. 17, G major K 129
Netherlands Phil.—Ackermann ♯ **CHS.G 10**
(No. 26, & Vln. Concerto)

No. 19, E flat major K 132
Stuttgart Ton-Studio—Michael
No. 21, A major K 134
Stuttgart Ton-Studio—Lund ♯ **Per.SPLP 538**
                              (♯ Clc. 6086; ♯ Nix.PLP 538)

No. 22, C major K 162
☆ Vienna Sym.—Swoboda (♯ Sel.LPG 8322)

No. 23, D major K 181
☆ Vienna Sym.—Swoboda (♯ Sel.LPG 8321, ⅓s).

No. 24, B flat major K 182
Stuttgart Ton-Studio—Michael ♯ **Per.SPLP 545**
(Divertimento, K 247 & March, K 248) *(♯ Nix.PLP 545)*

No. 25, G minor K 183
Danish Radio Cha.—Wöldike ♯ **HS.HSL 1055**
(No. 29)
  ☆ Pro Musica—Klemperer (♯ Pol. 545001)

No. 26, E flat major K 184
Netherlands Phil.—Ackermann ♯ **CHS.G 10**
(No. 17, & Vln. Concerto)
Bamberg Sym.—Lehmann **PV. 72234**
(No. 35, in ♯ Pol. 18066) *(♯ AmD.DL 4045)*

No. 27, G major K 199
Mozart Sym. Soc. ♯ **Roy. 1229**
(Symphony No. 31) *(& ♯ Roy. 6093)*

No. 28, C major K 200
Salzburg Mozarteum—P. Walter ♯ **Rem. 199-56**
(Haydn: Symphony 104)

No. 29, A major K 201
Bamberg Sym.—Keilberth ♯ **OL.LD 37**
(Deutsche Tänze)
Perpignan Festival—Casals ♯ **AmC.ML 4563**
(Serenade K 525) *(& in set SL 170)*
Danish Radio Cha.—Wöldike ♯ **HS.HSL 1055**
(Symphony No. 25)
Concert Hall Sym.—Swoboda ♯ **CHS.F 1**
(No. 34)
Austrian Sym.—Singer ♯ **Rem. 199-112**
(Weber: Symphony No. 2)
Mozart Sym. Soc. ♯ **Roy. 1230**
(Beethoven Overtures) *(& ♯ Roy. 6091)*

No. 31, D major K 297 "Paris"
L.S.O.—Krips ♯ **D.LXT 2689**
(No. 39) *(♯ Lon.LL 542)*
Royal Phil.—Beecham ♯ **AmC.ML 4474**
(Schubert: Sym. 8)
Minneapolis Sym.—Dorati ♯ **Vic.LM 1185**
(Bartók: Divertimento) *(♭ set WDM 1595)*

[1] New K.Anh. 223a. Not by Mozart.

Hastings Sym.—Bath ♯ **Allo.ALG 3049**
(Beethoven: Sym.No. 8)
Mozart Sym.—Soc. ♯ **Roy. 1229**
(No. 27) *(& ♯ Roy. 6092)*

No. 32, G major K 318
Orch.—Hewitt **V♯ *DFr. 63***
(Overture, K 311a)

No. 33, B flat major K 319
Amsterdam—v. Beinum ♯ **D.LXT 2686**
(Haydn) *(also, 6ss, D.K 23278/80)* *(♯ Lon.LLP 491)*
Cha. Orch.—Hewitt ♯ **DFr. 49**
(No. 34)
Bamberg Sym.—Weisbach ♯ **Mer.MG 10077**
(Haydn)
Austrian Sym.—Heger ♯ **Rem. 199-71**
(Haydn)
☆Vienna Phil.—v. Karajan ♯ **C.FCX 145**
(No. 39) *(♯ C.QCX 145)* *(also ♮ C.LVX 84/6)*

No. 34, C major K 338
Cha. Orch.—Hewitt ♯ **DFr. 49**
(No. 33)
Concert Hall Sym.—Swoboda ♯ **CHS.F 1**
(No. 29)

No. 35, D major K 385
R.I.A.S. Sym.—Fricsay **PV. 72267/8S**
(3ss—last blank) *(No. 26, on ♯ Pol. 18066)*
Berlin Phil.—F. Lehmann ♯ **Phi.A 00111R**
(1½ss—March, K 249)
☆Austrian Sym.—Wolf ♯ **Rem. 199-79**
(Haydn: Vlc. Concerto)
  (also ▽ ♯ Rem. 149-33; Mrt. 1-11; 2ss)
Berlin Sym.—Balzer (♯ Roy. 1365)
  ☆ N.B.C. Sym.—Toscanini (♯ G.FALP & QALP 124)

No. 36, C major K 425 "Linz"
Winterthur Sym.—Goehr ♯ **MMS. 1**
(Dances)
Berlin Sym.—Balzer (♯ Roy. 1365)
  ☆ Danish Radio—Busch
            (♯ Vic.LHMV 1019; ♭ set WHMV 1019)
  Pro Musica—Klemperer (♯ Pol. 545001)

No. 37, G major K 444: by J. M. Haydn, *q.v.*

No. 38, D major K 504 "Prague"
USSR. Radio Sym.—Samosud
(10ss) **USSR. 20491/500**
Mozart Sym. Soc. Orch. (♯ Roy. 1231)
etc.

No. 39, E flat major K 543
☆Vienna Phil.—v. Karajan ♯ **C.FCX 145**
(No. 33) *(QCX 145)*
☆L.S.O.—Krips ♯ **D.LXT 2689**
(No. 31) *(♯ Lon.LL 542)*
Berlin Sym.—Balzer (♯ Roy. 1309)
etc.

No. 40, G minor K 550
Minneapolis Sym.—Dorati ♯ **Mer.MG 50010**
(Mendelssohn)
Cha. Orch.—Hewitt ♯ **DFr. 64**
(No. 41)
☆Vienna Phil.—Furtwängler ♯ **G.FALP 117**
(Serenade, K 525)
      (Brahms, on ♯ Vic.LHMV 1010: ♭ set WHMV 1010)
USSR. Sym.—Samosud **USSR. 018272/7**
(6ss)
French Nat. Sym.—Tomasi ♯ **Pde. 2001**
                              (o.n. Pde.SY 301)
Berlin Sym.—Guthan (♯ Roy. 1222)
etc.
  ☆ Amsterdam—Jochum (♯ *T.LS 6004*)
    Italian Radio—v. Karajan (P.RR 8184/6)
    Salzburg Fest.—P. Walter (♯ Mrt. 1-9)

No. 41, C major K 551 "Jupiter"
Vienna Phil.—Böhm (n.v.)   ♯ **AmVox.PL 7760**
(Serenade, K 525)

Cha. Orch.—Hewitt   ♯ **DFr. 64**
(No. 40)

☆Royal Phil.—Beecham   ♯ **C.C 1002**

☆N.B.C. Sym.—Toscanini   ♯ **G.FALP 164**
(Bassoon Concerto)

Haydn Orch.—Newstone   ♯ **Mon.MWL 302**
(Serenade No. 6)

Berlin Sym.—Balzer (♯ Roy. 1321), etc.

☆ Vienna Phil.—Böhm (o.v.)
            (♯ BB.LBC 1018: ♭ set WBC 1018)
Viennese Sym.—Wöss (♯ *Mrt. 1-10*)

B flat major K 74g [1]
    (old K.Anh. 216: B & H. No. 54) 1771
Mozart Sym. Soc. Orch.   ♯ **Roy. 1231**
(No. 38)

II. D. 4. OTHER ORCHESTRAL WORKS

Maurerische Trauermusik K 477
Indiana Univ. Orch.—Hoffmann in ♯ **MR. 101**

☆ Vienna Phil.—v. Karajan (C.LFX 950)
  Hewitt Cha. Orch. (♯ *DFr. 2*) [2]

Overture, B flat major K 311a
Vienna State Academy—Swarowsky ♯**Lyr.LL 32**
(Haydn)

Orch.—Hewitt   V♯ *DFr. 63*
(Sym. 32)

SONATAS, organ & orch.
COLLECTIONS
    No. 1, E flat major K 67
    No. 2, B flat major K 68
    No. 3, D major K 69
    No. 6, B flat major K 212
    No. 14, A major K 225
    No. 16, C major K 329
    P. Messner & Salzburg Mozarteum—P. Walter
                                ♯ **Per.SPLP 534**
(1½ss—March)   (♯ Clc. 6062; Nix.PLP 534)

    No. 1, E flat major K 67
    No. 15, C major K 328
    No. 17, C major K 336
    H. Wismeyer & orch.—Kugler ♯ **Mer.MG 10086**
(Buxtehude)

No. 17, C major K 336 (ed. Duvauchelle)
H. Roget & Paris Cha.—Duvauchelle
(2ss)   *Lum. 2.08.016*

MISCELLANEOUS

Mozart, his story & his music
(Spoken story with short vocal & instrumental selections)
☆ J. Ferrer (speaker), E. Morgan (B) & Sym. Orch.—
  Goberman   ♯ *AmVox.VL 2150*

MUDARRA, Alonso de   (XVIth Cent.)
    SEE : † HARP MUSIC
          † SEGOVIA RECITAL

MÜLLER, Paul (b. 1898)

Symphony for Strings, Op. 40
Zürich Collegium—Sacher   ♯ **D.LXT 2702**
(Burkhard: Toccata)   (♯ Lon. LL 596)

MUNDY, John (c. 1554-1630)
    SEE : † TRIUMPHS OF ORIANA

MURRILL, Herbert Henry John
            (1909-1952)

Postlude on a ground   organ
E. P. Biggs   in ♯ **AmC.ML 4603**
(Marcello, Buxtehude, etc.)

MURSCHHAUSER, Franz Xaver Anton
            (1663-1738)

Aria pastoralis variata hpsi.
Variations on "Lass uns das Kindlein wiegen"
E. Harich-Schneider   ♯ *CdM.LD 8018*
(Mozart: Vln. Sonata, No. 20)

NANINI, Giovanni Maria (c. 1545-1607)
    SEE : † ITALIAN MADRIGALS (Fait)

NÁPRAVNÍK, Edward (1839-1916)

DON JUAN, Op. 54 Soli, cho., orch.
Inc. music to A. Tolstoy's play
Don Juan's Serenade
P. Lisitsian (B)   *USSR. 11934*
(Rechkunov: Spanish serenade)

DUBROVSKY, Op. 58 Opera, 4 acts 1895
Masha's aria   S
N. Shpiller   *USSR. 08079*
(Rubinstein: Demon, Tamara's aria)

NARVAEZ, Luis de (fl. XVIth Cent.)
    SEE : † HARP MUSIC

NAUDOT, Jean Jacques (d. 1762)
    SEE : † ♯ AS. 3002LD

NAUMANN, Johann Gottlieb (1741-1801)

(12) SONATAS   Glass harmonica
No. 5, D major 1786
No. 8, G major 1792
B. Hoffmann   **Pol. 6003**

NICHOLSON, Richard (d. 1639)
    SEE : † TRIUMPHS OF ORIANA

NICOLAI, Carl Otto Ehrenfried
            (1810-1849)

(Die) LUSTIGEN WEIBER VON WINDSOR
    Opera, 3 acts 1849
COMPLETE RECORDING
(omitting spoken dialogue & Aria No. 10)
    Frau Fluth ...   .   I. Beilke (S)
    Falstaff ...   .   W. Strienz (Bs)
    Fenton ...   .   W. Ludwig (T)
    Herr Fluth ...   .   G. Hann (B)
    Frau Reich ...   ...   M. L. Schilp (M-S)
    Anna ...   .   L. Hoffmann (S)
etc., Berlin Municipal Op. Cho. & Radio Orch.
—Rother (6ss)   ♯ **Ura. set 214**

---

[1] Labelled F major. May be F major, K 75, 76 or 98 (B & H 42, 43, 48). It has not been possible to check.
[2] Originally this disc was 12-inch; re-issued on *10-inch.*

Overture
Vienna Phil.—Furtwängler   **G.DB 21502**
(in ♯ Vic.LHMV 1020: ♭ set *WHMV 1020*)
Philharmonia—Schuechter   **C.DX 1827**
(CQX 16663: DWX 5079)

Philharmonia—Fistoulari   **♯ MGM.E 120**
(*Reznìček, Rimsky-Korsakov, & Wolf-Ferrari*
in ♭ *K 120* only)
Rhineland Sym.—Federer (♯ *Rgt. 5054*)

☆ L.P.O.—Boult (♭ *G.7R 109: 7RF 133*)
Columbia Sym.—Beecham
(♯ *AmC.AAL 5*: ♭ *4-73051D*)
Suisse Romande—Olof (♯ *Lon.LD 9012*)

Als Büblein klein Bs & cho. (Act II)
W. Strienz & Berlin Radio Cho. in ♯ **Ura. 7026**

E. List & pf. (*Phi.N 41049H*)
W. Lang (*Imp. 19177*)

Horch, die Lerche singt im Hain   T (Act II)
W. Ludwig   (n.v.)   *PV. 36009*
(*Bartered Bride, No. 20*)

SONG: (Des) Trinkers Wunsch
W. Strienz (Bs) & orch.   in ♯ **Ura. 7026**

NIEDHART VON REUENTHAL (*c.* 1180-1240)
SEE: † XIITH & XIIITH CENTURY MUSIC

NIELSEN, Carl August (1865-1931)

Concerto, Vln. & orch., Op. 33 1911
Y. Menuhin & Danish State Radio—Wöldike
♯ G.KBLP 1

MASQUERADE Opera, 3 acts   1906
Overture
Dance of the Cockerels, Act III
Danish Radio—Grøndahl   **G.DB 10510**
(Dance only, with *Symphony No. 4, s. 1* on DB 20156)

(3) Piano pieces, Op. 59 pf.   1928
A. S. Rasmussen   (2ss)   **Tono.A 179**

Quintet, A major, Op. 43 fl., ob., cl., hrn., bsn. 1922
New Art Wind Quintet   **♯ CEd. 2001**
(*Français*)

(29) SMALL PRELUDES, Op. 51 org.   1929
... Nos. 4, 5, 14, 27
F. Viderø (Sorø Chu. org.)   *Fdn.NC 1503*

SONGS
Bow thy head, Op. 21, No. 4 (J. Jørgensen)
(*Saenk kun dit Hoved*)
I know a lark's nest (H. Bergsteelt)
(*Jeg ved en Laerkerede*)
P. Torntoft (Tr), H. E. Knudsen (pf.)
(1 side each)   *Tono.K 8076*

See you on a Summer's day (Aakjaer)
(*Se dig ud en Sommerdag*)
A. Schiøtz (T), G. Kordt (pf.)   **G.X 7291**
(*Aargaard: Song*)
(This disc was recorded in 1950 and announced for issue
in 1951, but it is doubtful whether it was ever on sale.)

With a smile I bear my burden (Aakjaer)
(*Jeg baerer med Smil min Byrde*)
Wondrous evening breezes (Oehlenschläger)
(*Underlige Aftenlufte*)
E. Nørby (Bs), G. Nørby (pf.)   *Tono.K 8074*
(1s. each)

Wondrous evening breezes (Oehlenschläger)
☆ A. Schiøtz (*G.AL 3151*, d.c.)

SYMPHONIES
No. 1, G minor, Op. 7 1891-2
Danish State Radio—T. Jensen   **♯ D.LXT 2748**
(♯ Lon.LL 635)

No. 3, D minor, Op. 27 (Sinfonia espansiva)
S, B, orch.   1911
☆I. L. Hassing, E. Sjøberg & Danish Radio—
Tuxen   **♯ D.LXT 2697**
(♯ Lon.LLP 100)

No. 4, Op. 29 (The Inextinguishable) 1914-6
Danish Radio—Grøndahl   ♮ **G.DB 20156/60**
(9ss—*Masquerade, Dance*)
(♯ *G.ALP 1010*; Vic. LHMV 1006: ♭ set *WHMV 1006*)

No. 6 (Sinfonia semplice) 1925
Danish State Radio—Jensen   ♮ **Tono.Y 30012/5**
(8ss)   (♯ Mer.MG 10137)

Theme & Variations, Op. 40 pf.   1916
A. S. Rasmussen   (4ss)   ♮ **Tono.A 177/8**

NIKOLAYEVA, Tatiana

Concerto No. 1, pf. & orch.
T. Nikolayeva & USSR. State Sym.—
Kondrashin (6ss)   **USSR. 019217/22**

NIN Y CASTELLANO, Joáquin
(1879-1949)

(5) COMENTARIOS vln. & pf.   1929
No. 3, Sur un thème de R. ANGELÈS (1730-1816)
— ARR. VLC. & PF.
J. Serres & A. Leyvastre in **V♯** *Sat.MSA 5004*

Suite espagnole (ARR. Kochanski) 1929
— ARR. VLC. & PF.
J. Serres & A. Leyvastre in **V♯** *Sat. MSA 5004*
(*Granados*)

Homenaje a la jota
Serenata
G. Copeland (pf.)   in ♯ *MGM.E 87*
(♮ set 87: ♭ *K 87*)

SONGS
Cantilena asturiana — ARR. VLN. & PF. Levy
☆ J. Heifetz & E. Bay (in ♯ Vic.LM 1166; ♭ *G.7RF 250*)

Granadina
Paño murciano
(El) Vito
A. M. Iriarte (M-S), R. Machado (pf.)
♯ Pat.DT 1007
(½s.—*Vives: 3 songs; & Falla*)

Paño murciano
J. Tourel (M-S), G. Reeves (pf.)
in ♯ *AmC.ML 2198*

(10) VILLANCICOS 1932
Villancico Gallego
Villancico Vasco
Villancico Castellano
Villancico Catalan
Jesus de Nazareth
M. Haes (M-S), N. Newby (pf.) **Argo.S 1005**
(Announced but probably never issued)

Villancico vasco
Vocal Trio & pf.   in *Vic.set E 100*
(♭ set *WE 100*)

☆ = Re-issue of a recording to be found in WERM or Supplement I.

NIN-CULMELL, Joaquin Maria (b. 1908)
SEE: † GUITAR RECITAL

NIXON, Roger (b. 1921)

Quartet No. 1 Str.
☆California Qtt.   ♯ **ML. 7005**

NORCOME, Daniel (1576-c. 1625)
SEE: † TRIUMPHS OF ORIANA

NOVÁK, Vitĕzslav (1870-1949)

(The) Eternal Longing, Op. 33 Sym. Poem 1904
Czech Phil.—Šejna   ♮ **U.H 24187/9**

In the Tatra, Op. 26 Sym. Poem   1902
☆Czech Phil.—Ančerl   ♯ **Sup.LPM 13**
(Fibich)

Reisl's Polka, Op. 55, No. 21 orch.
Film Sym.—Strníštĕ   **U.H 23992**
(Foerster: Czech Dance)

Sonata eroica, Op. 24 pf.   1900
F. Rauch   (6ss)   ♮ **U.H 24208/10**

NYSTROEM, Gösta (b. 1890)

Sinfonia del Mare S & orch.   1949
☆ I. Eksell & Swedish Radio—Mann (♯ Mtr.CLP 504)

SONG: Mon - mon ikke
▽ E. Sigfuss (A) & orch. *(Tono.Z 18191)*

Valse solennelle orch.   1944
Swedish Radio—Rybrant   *Cup. 4443*
(Ch. W l iams: Dream of Olwen)

OBOUSSIER, Robert (b. 1900)

SONGS
Mittagsruh; Zeichen (Eichendorff)
☆ G. Baum (B), F. Leitner (pf.) *(Pol. 26517)*

(Die) Weihe der Nacht (Hebbel)
☆ G. Baum (B), F. Leitner (pf.) (Pol. 15555)

OBRECHT, Jakob (c. 1450-1505)
SEE: † OLD NETHERLANDS MASTERS
      † ♯ AS. 2501LD

OFFENBACH, Jacques (1819-1880)

I. OPERETTAS
(Abridged listings only)

BARBE-BLEU 3 acts   1866
Overture
L.P.O.—Martinon (in ♯ D.LXT 2590: ♯ Lon.LLP 350)
Paris Cons.—Dupré (in ♯ T.LCSK 8012)

Tous les deux   (Rondo)
J. Tourel (M-S)   in ♯ AmC.ML 4608

(La) BELLE HÉLÈNE 3 acts   1865
COMPLETE RECORDING
Hélène   ...   .   J. Linda (S)
Paris   ...   .   A. Dran (T)
Menelaus ...   .   R. Giraud (T)
Agamemnon ...   .   J. Linsolas (B)
etc., Paris Phil.—Leibowitz   ♯ **Ren.SX 206**
(4ss)   (♯ Nix.PLP 206-1/2)
(Abridged, in ♯ Ren.X 51)

ABRIDGED RECORDING (with *Fr. narration*)
Hélène   ...   .   Déva Dassy (S)
Paris   ...   .   C. Devos (T)
Oreste   ...   .   L. Berton (A)
Agamemnon ...   .   W. Clément (B)
Menelaus ...   .   Duvaleix (T)
etc., R. St. Paul Cho. & Lamoureux Orch.—
Gressier   ♯ **Pat.DTX 118**
(2ss)   (♯ AmVox.PL 20500)

Overture
L.P.O.—Martinon (in ♯ D.LXT 2590;
                              ♯ Lon.LLP 350 & *LD 9004*)
Paris Cons.—Dupré (in ♯ T.LCSK 8012)
Vienna Radio—Nilius (Vien.L 6090: ♯ *1011*)
☆ Boston Prom.—Fiedler (G.FKX 138; ♭ Vic. 49-1172)

Au Mont Ida   (Jugement de Paris)   T
☆ M. Lichtegg (*Ger*) (in ♯ Lon.LLP 55)

Dis-moi, Vénus   S
J. Tourel (M-S)   in ♯ AmC.ML 4608

(La) CHANSON DE FORTUNIO 1 act   1861
Si vous croyez que je vais dire . . .
(Fortunio's air)
J. Tourel (M-S)   in ♯ AmC.ML 4608
☆ M. Lichtegg (T, *Ger*) (in ♯ Lon.LLP 55)

GENEVIÈVE DE BRABANT 2 acts 1859-75
Overture   Rhineland Sym.—Federer (in ♯ *Rgt. 5047*)

(La) GRANDE DUCHESSE DE GEROLSTEIN
1867
Overture
L.P.O.—Martinon (in ♯ D.LXT 2590; ♯ Lon.LLP 350)
Paris Cons.—Dupré (in ♯ T.LCSK 8012)

Dites-lui qu'on l'a remarqué
J'aime le militaire
J. Tourel (M-S)   in ♯ AmC.ML 4608
Galop (Entr'acte Act III)   "À la can-can"
M.G.M. Orch.—Marrow   in ♯ *MGM.E 539*

(Le) MARIAGE AUX LANTERNES 1 act   1858
COMPLETE RECORDING in *English*
E. McGariby & V. Thomas (S), B. Wolf (M-S),
L. Chelsi (T) & orch.—Kramer
                              ♯ **MTR.MLP 1005**
Overture
L.P.O.—Martinon (in ♯ D.LXT 2590: ♯ Lon.LLP 350)

ORPHÉE AUX ENFERS 2 acts 1858-74
COMPLETE RECORDING (Overture omitted)
B. Demigny, J. Mollien, C. Collart, M. Chalot,
etc., Paris Phil. Cho. & orch.—Leibowitz
                              ♯ **Ren. set SX 204**
(4ss)   (♯ Clc.C 6103/4; ♯ Nix.PLP 204-1/2)
(Abridged, on ♯ Ren.X 51)

Overture (by C. Binder)
L.P.O.—Martinon   ♯ in **D.LXT 2590**
(also, 2ss, D.K 23212)   (♯ Lon.LLP 350 & *LD 9004*)
Munich Phil.—Leitner   **Pol. 57444**

♯ = Long-playing, 33⅓ r.p.m.   ♭ = 45 r.p.m.   ♮ = Auto. couplings, 78 r.p.m.

158

ORPHÉE—Overture (*continued*)

Philharmonia—Weldon   **C.DX 1823**
                              (DWX 5077: GQX 16654)

Strauss Orch.—F. Lanner (in ‡ *MGM.E 139*: ♭ *set K 139*)
Radio Luxemburg—Pensis (in ‡ FestF.FLD 3)
Vienna Radio—Nilius
              (Vien.L 6023; in ‡ AmVien.VLNP 1007)

☆ Berlin Sym.—Buschkötter (P.DPX 41)
Berlin State Op.—L. Ludwig
                              (G.SL 176: ♭ *7BF/BQ 1001*)
Col. Sym.—Rodzinski
     (in ♭ *AmC. set A 1003* & ‡ *AAL 2*, d.c.)
Boston Prom.—Fiedler (♭ *Vic. 49-0288*)

Couplets des baisers J. Tourel (M-S) (in ‡ AmC.ML 4608)

(La) PÉRICHOLE   2 acts   1868
Tu n'es pas beau;
Je t'adore, brigand

     ☆ G. Swarthout (M-S) (in ♭ *Vic. set WDM 1562*)

VERT-VERT   3 acts   1869
The Song of my love ☆ M. Lichtegg (*Ger*) (in ‡ Lon.LLP 51)

(La) VIE PARISIENNE   5 acts   1866
Overture   Paris Cons.—Dupré (in ‡ T.LCSK 8012)

Can can — ARR. 2 PFS. Gearhart
   V. Morley & L. Gearhart in ‡ *AmC.ML 2197*

(Les) CONTES D'HOFFMANN   3 or 4 acts 1881
COMPLETE RECORDINGS
   ☆R. Jobin (T), R. Doria (S), V. Bovy (S),
   Géori-Boué (S), F. Revoil (M-S), L. Musy
   (B), A. Pernet (Bs), C. Soix (Bs), R.
   Bourdin (Bs), etc., Opéra-Comique—
   Cluytens (6ss)   ‡ **C.FCX 137/9**
Soloists, Dresden State Op. Cho. & Orch.—Rubahn (*Ger*)
                                   Roy. 1269/71
(Excerpts, ‡ Roy. 1322: also ‡ Roy. 1213; ♭ *set EP 150*, etc.)

ABRIDGED RECORDING in *German*
E. Berger, A. Müller, P. Anders, Berlin Radio
   Cho. & Orch.—Rother   ‡ **Ura. set 224**
(4ss) (Excerpts also on ♭ *UREP 23*)

Orch. excerpts (Minuet, Intermezzo, Barcarolle) &
Scintille diamant

P. Schoeffler (B, *Ger*) & orch.—Schönherr
(*Delibes*)   ‡ **Rem. 149-39**

ACT I

Students' Chorus: Drig, drig, drig
San Francisco Op. Cho.   **ML. 47**

Il était une fois à la cour d'Eisenach   T
   (*Lied vom Kleinzack*)
W. Ludwig (*Ger*)   **PV. 36001**
(*Eugene Oniegin—Lenski's aria*)

J. Patzak (*Ger*)   in ‡ **D.LXT 2672**
(*below on D.K 28546*)   (‡ *Lon.LLP 427*)

ACT II (Olympia)

Allons ! courage et confinace . . . C'est elle
Ah ! vivre deux   T
J. Patzak (*Ger*)   in ‡ **D.LXT 2672**
(*above, on D.K 28546*)   (‡ *Lon.LLP 427*)

Les Oiseaux dans la charmille   S
   (*Doll Song*)
E. Spoorenberg   **Phi.N 11172G**
(*Pardon de Ploërmel—Ombre légère*) (*PhM.N 09006S*)

N. Kazantseva (*Russ*) (*USSR. 10469*)

ACT III (Giulietta)

Belle Nuit, O nuit d'amour S, M-S, Cho.
G. Brouwenstijn & L. v. d. Veen **Phi.N 11176G**
(*Trovatore—Miserere*)   (*PhM.N 09007S*)

R. Stevens (M-S), M. Elman (vln.) & pf.
                              in ‡ **Vic.LM 1703**
                              (♭ *set WDM 1703*)

N. Kazantseva, V. Gagarina (*Russ*) (*USSR. 10470*)

Ḥ G. Farrar & A. Scotti (B)
     (in ‡ Vic.LCT 1037*: ♭ *set WCT 57**)

— ARR. ORCH.
Strauss Orch.—F. Lanner (in ‡ *MGM.E 139*: ♭ *set K 139*)
S. Romberg Orch. (in ‡ Vic.LM 9019)
R. Crean Orch. (in ‡ *D.LF 1082*; *Lon.LPB 424*)
etc.

Scintille, diamant   B
T. Baylé   **Phi.N 11179G**
(*Faust—Avant de quitter* . . .)   (*PhM.N 09011S*)
P. Schoeffler   in ‡ **MSL.MW 44**
(*Verdi, Borodin, Mozart; & Lieder*)

ACT IV

Elle a fui, la tourterelle   S
   ☆ E. Noréna (*JpV.NF 4177*)

Ḥ C. Muzio (in ‡ Eso.ES 508; Cpt.MC 20010*)[1]

MISCELLANEOUS

GAÎTÉ PARISIENNE   Ballet
   ☆Boston Prom.—Fiedler   **G.C 4147/50**

OGINSKI, Michael Cleophas (1765-1833)
SEE: † POLISH KEYBOARD MUSIC

OKEGHEM, Jean de (*c.* 1430-1495)
SEE: † OLD NETHERLANDS MASTERS

ORBÓN, Julián (b. 1925)
SEE: † GUITAR RECITAL

ORFF, Carl (b. 1895)

(Die) KLUGE   Opera   12 Scenes   1942
O hätt' ich meiner Tochter...(Sc. 1) Bs
G. Frick
Als die Treue ward geboren (Sc. 7) T, B, Bs
L. Fehenberger, H. Löbel & K. Böhme
                              ▽Pol. 68151

ORTHEL, Léon (b. 1905)

Sonatina No. 3   pf.
T. v. d. Pas   ‡ *Phi.N 00126R*
(*Fauré, Pijper, Voormolen*)

OSTROVSKY, Fredy (b. 1922)

Capriccio orientale vln. unacc.
Impromptu vln. unacc.
Je pense à mon amour vln. unacc.
F. Ostrovsky   ‡ **CEd. 1029**
(*Geminiani & Stravinsky*)

---

[1] Recorded from Edison cylinder.

OWEN, Morfydd (1892-1918)
  SEE: † WELSH RECORDED MUSIC SOCIETY

PACHELBEL, Johann (1653-1706)
  SEE: † BAROQUE ORGAN MUSIC
        † MAÎTRES D'ORGUE DE J. S. BACH

PADEREWSKI, Ignace Jan (1860-1941)

Minuet, G major, Op. 14, No. 1
M. Flipse   **Phi.N 11236G**
(Rachmaninoff: Prelude)   *(PhM.N 09048S)*

— ARR. ORCH.   Col. Orch (in ‡ *AmC.GL 510*)

PAGANINI, Niccolo (1782-1840)

(24) CAPRICES, Op. 1, unacc. vln.
No. 6, G minor "Tremolo"
No. 9, E major "La Chasse"
— ARR. VLN. & PF.   Montbrun
R. G. Montbrun & G. Joy   **JpV.SD 3078**

No. 13, B flat major "Le rire du diable"
G. Garay *(Qual.QKM 5006)*

— ARR. VLN. & PF.
M. Wilk & F. Kramer   in ‡ *MTR.MLP 1002*
☆ F. v. Vecsey *(P.LL 3004)*

— ARR. VLC. & PF.   Kreisler
M. Wallerson & I. Rossican   **Phi.N 12042G**
(Popper: Spinnlied, Op. 55, No. 1; & Handel)
                         (PhM.N 12042G)

No. 14, E flat major
M. Wilk   in ‡ *MTR.MLP 1002*

No. 15, G major
No. 21, A major
— ARR. VLN. & PF.   Pilati
☆ Z. Francescatti & A. Balsam *(C.LF 283)*

Nos. 17-24
R. de Barbieri   (8ss)   *G.DA 11328/31*

No. 24, A minor
T. Spivakovsky   in ‡ *AmC.ML 4402*

— ARR. VLN. & PF.   Elman
M. Elman & W. Rosé   ♭ *Vic.set WDM 1625*
(3ss—Elman: Tango) (Mozart, in ‡ *LM 1208*)

CONCERTOS, Violin & Orch.
No. 1, E flat major, Op. 6
K. Brandt & Berlin Sym.—Rubahn ‡ **Roy. 1339**
(Chausson: Poème)
☆Z. Francescatti & Philadelphia—Ormandy
                       ‡ **C.FCX 140**
(Saint-Saëns: Concerto) (also C.LZX 274/6: LVX 181/3)

No. 2, B minor, Op. 7
R. Odnoposoff & Utrecht Sym.—P. Hupperts
(Mendelssohn)   ‡ **CHS.G 13**
☆Y. Menuhin & Philharmonia—Fistoulari
(2ss)   ‡ *G.FBLP 1006*
(Vieuxtemps: Concerto,
         on ‡ *Vic.LHMV 1015*:♭ *set WHMV 1015)*
(3rd Movt. only, G.DB 20406)

... **3rd movt. Ronde à la clochette**
☆ Vlns. of Boston Pops—Fiedler
     (G.C 4173: GB 75: ♭ 7BF 1028: 7P 120)

— — ARR. VLN & PF. (*La Campanella*)
H. Szeryng & pf. (Orf. 4004)
☆ R. Odnoposoff & pf. (G.ED 470)

Moto perpetuo, Op. 11   vln. & orch.
Metropole Orch.—v. d. Linden   *PhM. 1009S*
(Debussy: Clair de lune)
            (& in ‡ *Phi.P 10000R* & D.XP 6134)
☆Vlns. of Boston Pops—Fiedler   **G.C 4173**
(above)   (GB 75: ♭ *7BF 1028: 7P 120*)
Y. Sitkovetsky & pf. *(USSR. 17549)*

Quartet, String, E major
Guilet Qtt.   ‡ **CHS.F 14**
(Arriaga)

SONATAS, Vln. & guitar
No. 8, G major, Op. 3, No. 2 — ARR. VLN. & PF.
T. Spivakovsky & A. Balsam in ‡ **AmC.ML 4402**
(Beethoven, Sarasate, etc.)

Unspec. Sonata ... Andantino variato
— ARR. GUITAR SOLO   Ponce
A. Segovia   in ‡ **AmD.DL 9647**
(† Segovia program)

Sonatina (Grande)   Guitar
... **Romance**
▽ A. Segovia *(AmD. 24145 in set A 596:* ‡ *DL 5257)*

Variations on: (for vln.)
Dal tuo stellato soglio, from Rossini's "Mosé"
J. Kawaciuk & F. Vrána (pf.)   **U.H 23993**
(Kreisler: Tambourin chinois)

Nel cor più, from Paisiello's "La Molinara"
☆ V. Prihoda & C. Cerné *(P.OR 5098)*

PAISIELLO, Giovanni (1741-1816)

SEE ALSO: † ITALIAN SONGS

CONCERTO, C major pf. & orch. (ed. Brugnoli)
O. P. Santoliquido & Rome Coll. Musicum—
Fasano   **P.BB 25286/8**
(5ss—Respighi: Suite No. 3—Siciliana)

PALADILHE, Émile (1844-1926)

PATRIE   Opera, 5 acts   1886
Overture
▽ Pasdeloup Orch. (Pat.X 5519/20)

Pauvre martyre obscur   B
G. London   ‡ **AmC.ML 4489**
(Demon, Prince Igor, Don Quichotte)
▽ R. Couzinou (Pol. 516571: o.n. 566013, d.c.), etc.

Psyché (Corneille)   Song
▽M. Teyte (S), G. Moore (pf.)   *G.DA 1779*
(Duparc: Chanson triste)   *(Vic. 10-1003)*
▽ A. Endrèze (B)   *Pat.PG 88*
  J. Palmer (S)   in ‡ *Csm.CLPS 1001*
  G. Moore (S)   in *Vic. set M 918*
  L. Lehmann (S)   in *Vic. set M 1342*
  etc.

PALAU BOIX, Manuel (b. 1893)

Marche burlesque
Seguidillas (Hommage à Debussy)
☆Valencia Sym.—Iturbi   ♭ *G.7RF 186*
               (♭ *Vic. 49-3185/6,* d.cs.)

---

‡ = Long-playing, 33⅓ r.p.m.   ♭ = 45 r.p.m.   ♮ = Auto. couplings, 78 r.p.m.

PALERO,
SEE : † HARP MUSIC

PALESTRINA, Giovanni Pierluigi da
(1525-1594)

(Roman figures refer to Volumes of the complete edition)

COLLECTION
MOTETS :   Dies Sanctificatus VII 8vv.
                          Exsultate Deo IV 5 vv.
                          Hodie Christus natus est III 8 vv.
                          Pueri Hebraeorum V 4 vv.
                          Super flumina Babylonis V 4 vv.
                          Tribulationes civitatum—
                            Peccavimus IV 5 vv.
OFFERTORIES :   Bonum est confiteri IX
                          Exaltabo te, Domine IX
                          Laudate Dominum IX all 5 vv.
SONG OF SOLOMON :   Tota pulchra es IV
                          Vox dilecti mea IV 5 vv.
IMPROPERIUM :   Popule meus XXXI
Sistine Chapel Cho.—Bartolucci   ♯ Ren.X 55

MOTETS & OFFERTORIES

Adoramus te V (by F. Rosselli)
Wesley Chapel Cho.—Cleall   *Argo.R 1002*
(*Ricercare*)   (announced but prob. not issued)
Cho.—Wilhousky   ♯ *DCap.LC 6576*
(*Bach, Victoria, Rubinstein, etc.*)
                   (♯ Cap.L 9015: ♮/♭ set CD/CDF 9015)
☆ De Paur Infantry Cho. (in ♯ AmC.ML 4144)

Hodie Christus natus est III 8 voices
Rorate coeli desuper II 5 voices
Dies sanctificatus V 4 voices
Welch Chorale   in ♯ Lyr.LL 35
(*Byrd, Gibbons, etc.*)

Hodie Christus natus est III
St. Olaf Cho.—O. C. Christiansen in ♯ StO. 3
(*Grieg, Bach, Milhaud, Schreck, etc.*)

Improperium exspectavit Offertory IX 5 voices
Monaco Cath. Cho.—H. Carol in † ♯ SM. 33-01

O bone Jesu
Vocal Octet   in ♯ *Vic.set E 101*
                                 (♭ set *WE 101*)
☆ De Paur Infantry Cho. (in ♯ AmC.ML 4144)

Sicut cervus V 4 voices
International Boys' Cho.—Maillet **Pat.PDT 273**
(*Berchem: O Jesu Christe*) (3000 voices)
(recorded during Mass at St. Peter's, Rome, 1st April, 1951)

Tristis est anima mea 4 voices
☆Milan Madrigalists—Fait ♯ Csm.CLPS 1027
(† Italian Madrigals)

MASSES

Brevis XII 4 voices 1570
... Introit, Kyrie & Agnus Dei only
Trapp Cho.   Orf. 1003

Papae Marcelli XI 6 voices 1567
Netherlands Cha. Cho.—de Nobel
                               ♯ *Phi.A 00105L*

VARIOUS SACRED SETTINGS

Hymn : Veni creator spiritus VIII 4 voices
UOS Cho.—McConnell   in ♯ *UOS.pte*
(*Caplet, Holst, etc. & Anon.: Alle psallite*)

Magnificat quarti toni XXVII
Harvard Univ. Cho.—Russell in ♯ *Fest. 70-202*
(† Pre-baroque sacred music)

Magnificat (unspec.)
Lassus Vocal Qtt., Speyer   **Chr. 325B**
(2ss)

MADRIGALS (XXVIII)

Ahi, che quest' occhi miei
Da cosi dotta man sei stato fatto
Vassar Madrigal Singers—Geer
                               ♯ **Allo.ALG 3029**
(† Italian Madrigals)

PALMER, R. (b. 1915)
SEE : † AMERICAN MUSIC

PALMGREN, Selim (1878-1951)

CINDERELLA Music for a fairy play
(*Askungen: Tuhkimo*)
☆ Sym. Orch.—Järnefelt (*Od.PLD 18*)

PIANO MUSIC
Barcarolle, Op. 27, No. 6
May Night, Op. 27, No. 4   (*Toukokuun yö*)
☆ S. Palmgren (*Od.PLD 8*)

SONG
Where is the end of the road, Op. 70, No. 1 (Knape)
(*Var är vägens mål?*)
E. Holmström (T), J. Tolonen (pf.) *Täh.RW 455*
(*below*)

Tempo di menuetto vlc. & pf. *c.* 1950
G. Cassadò & pf.   **Täh.EW 701**

Violoncello vlc. & pf. *c.* 1950
G. Cassadò & T. Wiberg   *Täh.RW 455*
(*above*)

PANUFNIK, Andrzei (b. 1914)

Ancient Polish Airs & Dances Orch. suite
Warsaw Radio Orch.—Kolczkowski
                               ♯ **Van.VRS 6001**
(*Polish Folk Music*)

PARADIES, Pietro Domenico (1710-1792)

SONATAS, hpsi.
No. 3, E major ... Aria only
No. 6, A major ... Toccata only
O. Frugoni (pf.)   in ♯ **AmVox.PL 7700**
(*Scarlatti, Boccherini, etc.*)

PARADIES, Marie Thérèse von
(1759-1824)

Sicilienne
— ARR. VLN. & PF. Dushkin
I. Richards & Y. Fisher   **Croy.CX 2**
(⅓s.—*Boulanger & Handel-Harty*)
E. Nielsen & L. Christiansen   *G.DA 5265*
(*Porpora: Aria*)
T. Magyar & W. Hielkema   **Phi.N 11194G**
(*Kreisler: Sicilienne & Rigaudon*)   (*PhM. 09013S*)

— ARR. VLC. & PF.
E. Mainardi & M. Raucheisen   *Pol. 26521*
(*Stuck: Melodie*)
☆D. Shafran & pf.   in ♯ **Csm.CRLP 114**

☆ = Re-issue of a recording to be found in WERM or Supplement I.

PARRY, Sir Charles Hubert Hastings
(1848-1918)

CHORALE-PRELUDE   organ
Melcombe, Op. 186, No. 5
E. P. Biggs   in # AmC.ML 4603
(Murrill, Marcello, etc.)

Jerusalem, Op. 208   (Blake)   unison song
Sheffield Schools Cho. & pf.—Hall **G.B 10310**
(Quilter: Non nobis Domine)

SONG: Love is a bable, Op. 152, No. 3   (Anon.)
F. Smith (B), M. Carr (pf.)   **Croy.CX 3**
(½s.—Hurlstone & Stanford)

SONGS OF FAREWELL, Op. 206   unacc. cho.
1. My soul, there is a country   (Vaughan)
3. Never weather-beaten sail   (Campian)
Sale & District Musical Soc.—Higson **G.C 4180**
(1s. each)

PASQUINI, Bernardo (1637-1710)
SEE: † ITALIAN ART SONGS

PASSEREAU (fl. c. 1510)
SEE: † RENAISSANCE MASTERPIECES

PEERSON, Martin (c. 1580-1650/1)
SEE: † EARLY ENGLISH KEYBOARD MUSIC

PEIKO, Nikolai (b. 1916)
Moldavian Suite   orch.
USSR. Radio—Rakhlin   # **West.WL 5132**
(Prokofiev)   (USSR. 019187/90, 4ss)

PEPPING, Ernst (b. 1901)
SEE: † ORGAN MUSIC—HEITMANN

PERGOLESI, Giovanni Battista
(1710-1736)

SEE ALSO: † ITALIAN ART SONGS

(6) CONCERTINOS   Str. orch.[1]
No. 1, G major   No. 3, A major
No. 4, F minor   No. 5, E flat major
Winterthur Sym.—Ephrikian # **West.WL 4001/2**
(4ss)

No. 5, E flat major
Virtuosi di Roma—Fasano # **AmD.DL 9598**
(Cirri, Marcello, Albinoni)

SONG: Se tu m'ami   (Rolli)   (doubtful)
M. Laszlo (S), F. Holletschek (pf.)
                             # **West.WL 5119**
(† Italian Songs)
A. Yakovenko (Russ) (USSR. 19242)
Ħ C. Muzio (S) (in # Eso.ES 508*; Cpt.MC 20010*) [2]

PERI, Jacopo (1561-1633)

Lift up the voice   (unspec.) [3]
Vocal Sextet & pf.   in **Vic.set E 101**
                              (♭ set WE 101)

PÉROTIN-le-Grand (fl. XIIth Cent.)
SEE ALSO: † XIITH & XIIITH CENTURY MUSIC
          † ANCIENT MUSIC OF THE CHURCH

COLLECTION (only 2 items actually by Pérotin)
Alle, Psallite Motet (Anon.)
Bon vin Motet (Fr, Anon.)
Nobilis humilis (Gymel, attrib. Pérotin)
Salvatoris hodie
Vetus abit littera Conductus, 4 voices (attrib. Pérotin)
Viderunt omnes 4 voices
Dessoff Cho. & N.Y. Brass Ens.—Boepple
                              # **CHS.CHS 1112**
                              (# Nix.CLP 1112)

PERRUCHOT, Mgr.
SEE: † MONACO CATHEDRAL

PETER, Johann Friedrich (1746-1813)
QUINTETS, String   1789
No. 1, D major   No. 2, A major
No. 3, G major   No. 4, C major
No. 5, B flat major   No. 6, E flat major
Moravian Quintet   (6ss)   # **NRI. 2013/5**

PETERSON-BERGER, Wilhelm
(1867-1942)

SONGS
Marit's Songs, Op. 12   (Björnson)   1896
1. The goat came to the boy
2. The sun is shining bright at even
3. Do you love me?
I. Eksell (S), Y. Flyckt (pf.)   **D.F 44159**

My inheritance is longing   (Karlfeldt)
Aspåker Polka   (Karlfeldt)
Nothing like waiting   (Karlfeldt)
I. Eskell (S), Y. Flyckt (pf.)   **D.F 44160**

Nothing like waiting   (Karlfeldt)
(Intet är som längtans tider)
A. Ohlson (T), S. Ehrling (pf.)   **Od.SD 5600**
(Lindblad: Post-boy on the way home)

PFITZNER, Hans (1869-1949)

OPERAS & STAGE MUSIC

CHRIST-ELFLEIN, Op. 20   2 acts   1917
Overture
Berlin Radio—Rother   # **Ura. 7050**
(below)

KÄTHCHEN VON HEILBRONN, Op. 17a
Inc. music to Kleist's drama   1904
Overture
Vienna Phil.—Pfitzner   # **Ura. 7050**
(above, & Reger)
Bamberg Sym.—Lehmann   **PV. 72195**
                                     (in # AmD.DL 4017)

---

[1] Attributed to Pergolesi, but true authorship doubtful.
[2] Recorded from Edison cylinder.
[3] Perhaps Gioite al canto mio.

SONGS

ALTE WEISEN, Op. 33   (Keller)   1923
1. Mir glänzen die Augen
2. Ich fürcht' nit Gespenster
3. Du milchjunger Knabe
4. Wandl' ich dem Morgentau
5. Singt mein Schatz wie ein Fink
6. Röschen bisst den Apfel an
7. Tretet ein, hoher Krieger
8. Wie glänzt der helle Mond
    E. Berger (S), M. Raucheisen (pf.)   **PV. 72251**

(Die) Einsame, Op. 9, No. 2   (Eichendorff)
Im Herbst (unid.)
Nachts, Op. 26, No. 2   (Eichendorff)
Zum Abschiede meiner Tochter, Op. 10, No. 3
   (Eichendorff)
    M. Klose (A), M. Raucheisen (pf.) in ♯ **Ura. 7053**
   (Jensen, R. Strauss, Grieg, etc.)

Es fällt ein Stern herunter, Op. 4, No. 3   (Heine)
Klage, Op. 25, No. 2   (Eichendorff)
   ☆ G. Hüsch (B) & pf. (JpV.NF 4171)

SYMPHONIES
C sharp minor   1932
   German Op. House—Schmidt-Isserstedt
               ♯ **Ura. 7056**

Kleine Sinfonie, Op. 44   1939
   Leipzig Gewandhaus—Abendroth
Symphony, C major, Op. 46   1941
   Saxon State Orch.—Böhm   ♯ **Ura. 7044**

PHILIPS, Peter (c. 1560-1634, or 1628 ?)

Pavana Dolorosa   (FVB. 80)
Galliarda Dolorosa   (FVB. 81)
   T. Dart (hpsi.)   **D.X 542**
   († Early English Keyboard Music)

MOTETS
Ascendit Deus
Hodie sanctus benedictus
Surgens Jesus
   Purcell Performing Soc.—J. R. King
               ♯ **Allo.ALG 3038**
  (Gibbons & Locke)

PIERNÉ, Henri Constant Gabriel
(1863-1937)

CYDALISE ET LE CHÈVRE-PIED   Ballet 1923
Marche des petits faunes
   ▽ Boston Pops—Fiedler (n.v.) (♭ Vic. 49-1430)

   ☆ Carnegie Pops—Hendl
     (in ♯ AmC.ML 4118: ♭ set A 1013: ♭ A 1549)

Divertissement sur un thème pastoral orch. 1931
   Concerts Colonne—Fournet   **C.LFX 1007/8**
   (3ss—G. Dupont: La Farce du cuvier, Ov.)

Marche des petits soldats de plomb, Op. 14, No. 6 pf.
— ARR. ORCH.
   Boston Pops.—Fiedler (n.v.)   ♭ **G.7BF 1008**
   (Schubert: Marche militaire)
                (♭ Vic. 49-1432 & in ♭ WEPR 27)

   ☆ Carnegie Pops—Hendl
     (in ♯ AmC.ML 4118: ♭ A 1549 & in ♭ set A 1013)

— ARR. BAND   ☆ Kneller Hall Band (in ♯ D.LF 1013)

Serenade, A major, Op. 7   pf.   1875
— ARR. ORCH.
   Vienna Radio—Nilius   **Vien.P 6097**
   (Quattro Rusteghi, Intermezzo)   (in ♯ 1013)

PIJPER, Willem (1894-1947)

SONATINAS   piano
No. 2   1925
   J. Antonietti   **PV. 36019**
   (Badings: Sonatina)

No. 3   1925
   T. v. d. Pas   ♯ **Phi.N 00126R**
   (Fauré, Voormolen, Orthel)

PILKINGTON, FRANCIS (d. c. 1638)
SEE: † XVIth & XVIIth Century Songs

PISTON, Walter (b. 1894)

Concertino, pf. & cha. orch.   1937
   A. Jenner & Vienna State Academy—Strickland
                 ♯ **AmVox.PL 7750**
   (Copland, Barber, etc.)

Sonata, flute & piano   1930
   D. Anthony & B. Korn   ♯ **Cmt. 1205**
   (I. Dahl: Variations on a Swedish folk tune)

Sonata, violin & pf.   1939
   J. Fuchs & A. Balsam   ♯ **AmD.DL 9541**
   (Lopatnikoff)

Sonatina, violin & hpsi.   1945
   A. Schneider & R. Kirkpatrick ♯ **AmC.ML 4495**
   (Cage: Qtt.)

Symphony No. 2   1943
   A.R.S. Orch.—Dixon   ♯ **ARS. 1**

PITTALUGA, Gustavo (b. 1906)
SEE: † Harp Music

PIZZETTI, Ildebrando (b. 1880)

Concerto dell' Estate   orch.   1928
   Vienna State Op.—Krueger   ♯ **NRI. 106**

PLANQUETTE, Jean Robert
(1848-1903)

(Les) CLOCHES DE CORNEVILLE   1877
Abridged Recording (with Narrator: P. Hiégel)
   M. Angelici (S), N. Renaud (S), M. Dens (B),
   J. Peyron (B), cho. & Lamoureux Orch.—
   Gressier   ♯ **AmVox.PL 20100**
                       (♯ Pat.DTX 107)

   ▽ Many older recordings, including one on 20ss.
                     (Od. 166407/16)

PLATTI, Giovanni (c. 1690-1762)

Sonata, No. 1, E minor   vln. & cont.
   S. Caratelli (fl.) & P. Miguel (pf.) ♯ **NRI. 402**
   (Enesco, Karg-Elert)

☆ = Re-issue of a recording to be found in WERM or Supplement I.

PONCE, Manuel (b. 1886)

SEE: † SPANISH GUITAR MUSIC

▽ Older recordings include:

Theme & Variations, Folies d'Espagne
   A. Segovia (G.DB 1567/8; JpV.ND 825/6)

Mazurka: Petite valse A. Segovia (*G.DA 1552*)

Sonata A. Segovia (G.AB 656)

SONG: Estrellita—many recordings

PONCHIELLI, Amilcare (1834-1886)

(La) GIOCONDA 4 acts 1876
COMPLETE RECORDING
Gioconda	...	...	... A. Corridori (S)
Laura	...	...	M. Pirazzini (M-S)
La Cieca	...	...	R. Cavallari (M-S)
Enzo	...	...	G. Campora (T)
Barnaba	...	...	A. Colzani (B)
Alvise	...	...	F. Corena (Bs)

etc., La Scala Cho. & Orch.—Parodi
                      ♯ Ura. set 229
(8ss)
(Overture & Danza delle ore, also on ♭ *Ura.UREP 1*,
        & Vocal excerpts on ♭ *UREP 18*)

Highlights
  ♯ P. Amato (B), G. de Luca (B), G. Zenatello
    (T), E. Mazzoleni (S), A. Pertile (T), G.
    Baklanoff (B), C. Boninsegna (S)
(2ss)   ♯ **Ete.O-483***

ACT I

Voce di donna   A or M-S
C. Elmo   ♭ *Vic. 49-3450*
(*Ballo in Maschera*)

Enzo Grimaldo, Principe di Santafior T & B
  ♯ J. McCormack & G. M. Sammarco
              (G.VB 33*: o.n. DB 608*)

O monumento   B
  ☆ P. Silveri (C.GQX 11464)

ACT II

Pescator, affonda l'esca (Barcarola) B & cho.
  ☆ L. Warren & Victor Cho. (in ♯ Vic.LM 1168)

Cielo e mar   T
G. Prandelli   in ♯ **D.LXT 2688**
(*Gounod, Donizetti, etc.*)   (♯ *Lon.LL 534*)

K. Baum   in ♯ **Rem. 199-63**
(*Carmen, Manon Lescaut, etc.*)

  ☆ M. Lanza (♭ *G.7RF 142*; ♭ *Vic. 49-3202*, d.c.)
    J. Peerce (♭ *Vic.WEPR 36* & ♯ *LM 1169*)

  ♯ E. Caruso & pf. (*G.VA 29**: o.n. *DA 547**;
    also with orch. in ♯ *Vic.LCT 1007**: ♭ *set WCT 11**)

ACT III

Danza delle ore (Ballet: Dance of the hours)
Bavarian Sym.—Graunke   **PV. 56008**
(*Dohnányi: Veil of Pierrette, Waltz*)

Covent Garden—Rignold   **P.E 11489**
(in ♯ *AmD.DL 9549* & *DL 4019*; ♯ Od.ODX 1061;
                     ♯ *P.PMC 1001*)

Covent Garden—Braithwaite in ♯ **MGM.E 3003**

Boston Prom.—Fiedler (n.v.)   **G.C 4206**
(Vic. 12-1059: ♯ LM 9005: ♭ 49-0676; ♭ *G.7BF/BQ 1007*)

☆Col. Sym.—Beecham   **C.LX 1554**
          (♯ *AmC.AAL 5*: ♭ *4-73052D*)

ACT IV

Suicidio !   S
M. Vitale   **P.CB 20533**
(*Don Carlos—Tu che la vanita*)

D. Giannini   **IRCC. 3115**
(*Bloch: Psalm 114*)

  ♯ C. Boninsegna (in ♯ Ete.O-468* & O-483*)
    E. Destinn (in ♯ Vic.LCT 1039*: ♭ *WCT 62**)

Così mantieni . . . Ebbrezza ! Delirio ! S & B
  ♯ E. Mazzolini & P. Amato (in ♯ Ete.O-482* & O-483*)

POOT, Marcel (b. 1901)

Allegro symphonique   orch.
Brussels Radio—André in ♯ *DT.LGM 65002*
(*Chabrier, Debussy, etc.*)   (in ♯ *T.LS 6016*)

☆ Berlin Municipal—Schuricht (Pol. 15519)

Ouverture joyeuse   orch.
Berlin Phil.—F. Lehmann   **Phi.A 11161G**
(*Sibelius: Valse triste*)   (*PhM.A 9001S*)
(*Sibelius, Cherubini, etc.* in ♯ *Phi.A 00115R*)

PORPORA, Niccolo (1686-1767)

Aria, E major — ARR. VLN. & PF. Corti
E. Nielsen & K. L. Christiansen *G.DA 5265*
(*Paradies: Sicilienne*)

POULENC, Francis (b. 1899)

(Le) BAL MASQUÉ Secular Cantata 1932
  ☆ W. Galjour (B) & Cha. Ens.—Fendler
                    (♯ *Cpt. MC 20004*)

(Les) BICHES Ballet cho. & orch. 1923
Orch. Suite re-orch. 1939-40
Paris Cons.—Désormière   ♯ **D.LXT 2720**
(*Scarlatti-Tommasini: Donne di buon umore*) (♯ Lon.LL 624)

Concerto, piano & orch. 1949
A. Haas-Hamburger & Pasdeloup—Dervaux
                        ♯ **Clc. 6099**
(*Pf. pieces & Milhaud*)   (♯ *Per.SPL 563*)

Concerto, G minor org. & orch. 1938
  ☆ E. P. Biggs & Col. Sym.—Burgin (JpC.Z 119/21)

Humoresque pf. 1935
Improvisation No. 5, A flat major 1932
A. Haas-Hamburger   ♯ **Clc. 6099**
(*Concerto & Valse; & Milhaud*) (♯ *Per.SPL 563*)

(4) MOTETS POUR UN TEMPS DE PÉNITENCE 1938-9
No. 2, Vinea mea electa
Concordia Cho.—Christiansen in ♯ **Cdia. 2**
(*Bach & Carols*)

No. 3, Tenebrae factae sunt
Shaw Chorale   in ♯ **Vic. LM 1201**
(*Easter Songs*)   (♭ *set WDM 1623*)

Mouvements perpetuels pf. 1918
F. Poulenc (n.v.)   in ♯ **AmC.ML 4399**
(*below, & Satie*)
L. Thyrion   in ♯ *Phi.N 00601R*
(*Satie, Auric, Honegger*)

— ARR. 2 PFS. Poulenc
V. Morley & L. Gearhart in ♯ *AmC.ML 2197*

---

¹ Attributed in French lists to Irving but probably in error.

Napoli, Suite pf. 1926
  A. Schier-Tiessen   **PV. 72140**
  (Berg: Sonata, Op. 1)   (FPV. 5032)

... Caprice italien only
  M. Panzéra   in ♯ **Mer.MG 10098**
  (Song, below; & Ravel, Milhaud, etc.)

NOCTURNES pf. 1929-35
No. 2, D major
  F. Poulenc   in ♯ **AmC.ML 4399**
  (below; & Satie)

"No. 8", unid.
  G. Gorini   **P.AT 0273**
  (Clementi: Sonata, Op. 26 No. 3, s. 3)

PARTSONGS
(4) Petites prières Male cho. unacc. 1948
  (St. Francis of Assisi)
  Maastricht Royal Male Cho.—Koekelkoven
                 Phi.N 12045G
                 (PhM.N 12045S)

Pilons l'orge
(La) Reine de Saba (Legrand)
  French Nat. Scout Cho.—Geoffray
                 Lum. 2.04.020
  (½s. each—Geoffray: L'arbre du Paradis)

Presto, B flat major pf. 1935
  ☆ V. Horowitz   (G.DB 6971)

— ARR. VLN. & PF. Heifetz
  Z. Francescatti & A. Balsam   ♯ **AmC.ML 4534**
  (Kreisler, Valle, Massenet, etc.)
  ☆ J. Heifetz & E. Bay   **G.DA 1915**
  (Ravel: Valses nobles 6 & 7)

Sextet, pf., fl., ob., cl., hrn., bsn. 1930-32
  C. Rosen & Fairfield Quintet   ♯ **REB. 7**
  (below)

Sonata, 2 pfs. 1918
  A. Whittemore & J. Lowe   in ♯ **Vic.LM 1705**
  (Bax, Stravinsky, etc.)   (♭ set WDM 1705)

Sonata, hrn., tpt., tbn. 1922
  A. Berr, H. Glanz, G. Pulis   ♯ **Strad.STR 605** [1]
  (Saint-Saëns)

Sonata, clarinet & bassoon 1922
  D. Weber & L. Sharrow   ♯ **REB. 7**
  (above & below)

SONGS
COLLECTIONS
Calligrammes (Apollinaire) 1948
(La) Main dominée par le coeur (Éluard) 1947
(4) Poèmes de Guillaume Apollinaire 1931
Tu vois le feu du soir (Éluard) 1938
  P. Bernac (B), F. Poulenc (pf.)   ♯ **AmC.ML 4484**
  (Chabrier, Debussy, Satie)

BANALITÉS (Apollinaire) 1940
  1. Chanson d'Orkenise
  2. Hôtel
  3. Fagnes de Wallonie
  4. Voyage à Paris
  5. Sanglots
CHANSONS VILLAGEOISES (Fambeure) 1942
  1. Chanson du clair tamis
  2. Les gars qui vont à la fête
  3. C'est le joli printemps
  4. Le mendiant
  5. Chanson de la fille frivole
  6. Le retour du sergent
  ☆ P. Bernac (B), F. Poulenc (pf.)   ♯ **C.FCX 141**
  (Ravel)

(Le) Bestiaire (Apollinaire) 1919
  ☆ C. Croiza (M-S), F. Poulenc (pf.)   (JpC.SW 277)

Nous voulons une petite soeur (Jabonne)
  "Colinette" & pf.   **CdM.PM 1605**
  (Colinette: Song)

Priez pour paix (Charles d'Orléans) 1938
  C. Panzéra (B), M. Panzéra (pf.)
            in ♯ **Mer.MG 10098**
  (Ravel, Milhaud, Honegger, etc.)

Suite française pf. 1935
  F. Poulenc   ♯ **AmC.ML 4399**
  (above, & Satie)

Trio, pf., ob., bsn.   1926
  C. Rosen, N. Shulman, L. Sharrow   ♯ **REB. 7**
  (above)
  H. D. Koppel, W. Wolsing, C. Bloch
  (4ss)   **Mtr.CL 3000/1**

Valse (from *Album des six*) pf. 1926
  A. Haas-Hamburger   ♯ **Clc. 6099**
  (above & Milhaud)   (♯ Per.SPL 563)

POWELL, John (b. 1882)

Rhapsodie nègre pf. & orch. 1918
  Anon. soloist & A.R.S.O.—Dixon   ♯ **ARS. 20**
  (Mason)

PRAETORIUS, Michael (1571-1621)

Es ist ein Rös' entsprungen
  Vienna State Opera Cho.—Rossmayer
             in ♯ **D.LX 3065**
                 (♯ Lon.LPS 486)
  Cho.—Wasner   in **PV. 72256**
  Randolph Singers (*Eng.*)   in ♯ **West.WL 5100**
  Trapp Family Cho.   in ♯ **AmD.DL 9553**
  St. Eustache Singers—Martin (*Fr*)   *Pat.PD 151*
  Maastricht Male Cho.   in Phi.N 11188G
                 (*PhM.N 09005S*)
  Barmen Singers   *Chr. 324A*
  Y.M.C.A. Cho.—Lidstam (*Swed*)   *G.X 7856*
  Karlskoga Cha. Cho. (*Swed*)   *D.F 44182*
  Copenhagen Acad. Cho.—Asmussen (*Dan*)
                 Felix.F 45

In natali Domini   Cho.
  Regensburg Cath.—Schrems   **G.EG 7642**
  (½s.—Trad. Carols)

Singet dem Herrn
  Harvard Univ. Cho.—Russell   in ♯ **Fest. 70-202**
  († Pre-baroque sacred music)

PROKOFIEV, Serge (1891-1953)

I. PIANO

Contes de la vieille grand'mère, Op. 31 1918
(4) Pieces, Op. 32   1918
  ☆ A. Földes (in ♯ EVox. 180; PaV.VP 180)

Legend, Op. 12, No. 6 1908-13
Scherzo humoristique, Op. 12, No. 9
  ☆ H. Graf (in ♯ Clc. 6090)

March, F minor, Op. 12, No. 1
  P. Spagnolo   **P.PE 159**
  (½s.—below; & MacDowell: pieces)

---

[1] This number was originally announced as MOZART: Str. Qtts 21 & 22 (see WERM. p. 808) but that disc was withdrawn before issue and this substituted.

Prelude, C major, Op. 12, No. 7
G. Scherzer   **P.R 3437**
(*Marx: Prelude, E flat*)
V. Warlev   **Tono.A 174**
(⅓s.—*Rachmaninoff & Schubert*)
☆ H. Graf (in ♯ Clc. 6090)

SONATAS
No. 2, D minor, Op. 14   1913
No. 5, C major, Op. 38   1925
R. Cornman   **♯ D.LXT 2691**
(1s. each)   (♯ Lon.LL 553)

No. 5, C major, Op. 38 ☆ H. Graf (in ♯ Clc. 6090)

No. 8, B flat major, Op. 84   1939-1944
J. di Bonaventura   **♯ CEd. 1032**

Suggestion diabolique, Op. 4, No. 4
B. Moiseiwitsch (n.v.)   **G.C 4101**
(⅓s.—*Vallier: Toccatina; & Weber*)
P. Spagnolo   **P.PE 159**
(*above, & MacDowell*)

Toccata, D minor, Op. 11   1912
A. Uninsky   **Phi.A 11210G**
(*Debussy: Reflets dans l'eau*)   (*PhM. 09708S*)
V. Horowitz (n.v.)   ♭ **G.7RF 200**
(*Scriabin: Study, Op. 2, No. 1*)
(also, d.c., in ♭ Vic. set WDM 1605: & ♯ LM 1171)
☆ V. Horowitz (o.v.)   G.DB 6971
M. Lympany   G.S 10582

Visions fugitives, Op. 22   1915-17
A. Borowsky   **♯ Pol. 540001**

II. CHAMBER MUSIC

(5) Melodies, Op. 35a vln. & pf. 1925
R. Posselt & A. Sly   in ♯ **Acad.ALP 304**
(*Villa-Lobos, etc.*)

... No. 1, only
G. Knudsen & E. Garcia   in ♯ **ML. 5003**
(*Tveit, Fauré, Knudsen, etc.*)

... No. 3, only
☆ D. Oistrakh (in ♯ Csm.CRLP 110)

QUARTET, String
No. 2, F major, Op. 92   1941
Hollywood Qtt.   **♯ DCap.CTL 7016**
(*Hindemith*)   (♯ Cap.P 8151)

SONATAS, vln. & pf.
No. 1, F minor, Op. 80   1938-46
☆ J. Szigeti & J. Levine (♯ JpC.WL 5005)
No. 2, D major, Op. 94a   1944
☆ J. Szigeti & L. Hambro (♯ JpC.WL 5005)

Sonata, vlc. & pf., C major, Op. 119 1948
R. Garbousova & D. Stimer   **♯ CHS.F 15**
(*Strauss*)

III. ORCHESTRAL

CONCERTOS, pf. & orch.
No. 1, D flat major, Op. 10   1912
☆ A. Földes & Lamoureux—Martinon
                                 ♯ EVox. 180
                                    (♯ PaV.VP 180)
No. 5, G major, Op. 55   1932
☆ A. Brendel & Vienna State Op.—Sternberg
                                    (♯ Clc. 6090)

CONCERTOS, vln. & orch.
No. 1, D major, Op. 19   1913
R. Odnoposoff & Zürich Radio—Hollreiser
                                 ♯ Nix.CLP 1160
(*Stravinsky*)   (♯ CHS. CHS 1160)

☆ J. Szigeti & L.P.O.—Beecham
(*Mozart*)   **♯ AmC.ML 4533**
☆ D. Oistrakh & USSR—Kondrashin
                                 ♯ Per.SPLP 539[1]
(*Miaskovsky*) (also ♯ Csm.CRLP 123) [1]
(also 5ss, ♮ U.H 23947/9)

No. 2, G minor, Op. 63   1935
H. Stanske & Berlin Radio—Konwitschny
                                 ♯ CdM.LD 8014

Lyrical Waltzes, Nos. 1 & 2   orch.
USSR State Radio—Samosud **USSR. 018978/9**

March, Op. 99   Band
— ARR. ORCH. Kurtz
☆ N.Y.P.S.O.—Kurtz   **C.DX 1860**
(*Shostakovitch & Rimsky*)   (GFX 187)

Peter and the Wolf, Op. 67 Narrator & orch.
V. Matetskaya & State Sym.—Golovanov
                                 USSR. 014385/91
(*7ss—Love for 3 Oranges, Nos. 3 & 4*)
B. D. Walker (*Eng*) & Orch.—Leopold
                                 ♯ Roy. 1246
(*Debussy: Children's Corner*)   (& ♯ 6111: ♭ set 14576)
G. Soriano (*Sp*) & Philharmonia—Markevitch
                                 G.DB 4312/4
M. Wieth (*Dan*) & Philharmonia—Markevitch
                                 G.Z 7038/40
☆ (*Eng*) W. Pickles & Philharmonia—Markevitch
      (♯ G.DLP 1001; BB.LBC 1015: ♭ set WBC 1015)
☆ (*Fr*) C. Dauphin & Berlin Phil.—Lehmann
                                 (♯ Pol. 540000)
A. Reybaz & Philharmonia—Markevitch
                                 (♯ G.FMLP 1001)
☆ (*Ger*) M. Wieman & Berlin Phil.—Lehmann
                                 (♯ Pol. 16038)
... Theme & March — ARR. VLN. & PF. ☆ R. Odnoposoff
                                 (G.ED 470)
... March — ARR. 4 PFS. ☆ Phil. Qtt. (♭ AmC.A 1548)

Russian Overture, Op. 72   1936
Berlin Phil.—Steinkopf   **♯ Ura. 5005**
(*below*)   (& ♭ UREP 16)

Scythian Suite, Op. 20 1914 (*Ala and Lolly*)
Vienna Sym.—Scherchen   **♯ West.WL 5091**
(*Lt. Kije Suite*)   (♯ Sel.LPG 8486)

SYMPHONIES
No. 1, D major, Op. 25 "Classical" 1916-7
N.B.C.Sym.—Toscanini   **♯ Vic.LM 9020**
(*Gershwin*)   (also, 4ss, ♭ set WDM 9020)
☆ Boston Sym.—Koussevitzky   G.DB 6951/2
(*Buffoon, No. 6*)
(*Rachmaninoff, in ♯ Vic.LM 1215*)
☆ Philadelphia—Ormandy   **♯ C.FC 1007**
(*Rimsky-Korsakov: Easter Overture*)
☆ Berlin Phil.—Celibidache   **♯ BB.LBC 1009**
(*Ravel: Ma Mère l'oye*)   (♭ set WBC 1009)

No. 5, B flat major, Op. 100   1944
☆ Boston Sym.—Koussevitzky **♯ G.FALP 139**

No. 6, E flat major, Op. 111   1946
Suisse Romande—Ansermet   **♯ D.LXT 2667**
(2ss)   (♯ Lon.LL 527)

IV. FILM, OPERA, BALLET

(The) BUFFOON, Op. 21 (*Chout*) Ballet 1921
Suite No. 1, Op. 21a
... No. 6, Danse finale
☆ Boston Sym.—Koussevitzky (G.DB 6952)

---

[1] Probably a dubbing of the USSR issue in WERM, though listed by Per. as cond. Gauk & by Csm. as cond. Prokofiev.

CINDERELLA, Op. 87 Ballet 1941
Mazurka; The Winter Fairy
— ARR. VLN. & PF.
☆ D. Oistrakh (in ‡ Csm.CRLP 110)

Excerpts with Narration in *English*
Anon. artists (4ss, ♮ & ♭ *CRG. set 201*)

LIEUTENANT KIJE Film 1935
Suite, Op. 60
French Nat. Sym.—Désormière
          ‡ DCap.CTL 7017
(below)   (‡ Cap.P 8149)
Vienna Sym.—Scherchen **‡ West.WL 5091**
(above)   (‡ Sel.LPG 8486)
Royal Phil.—E. Kurtz   **‡ AmC.ML 4482**
(Roussel) (Announced but perhaps not issued)

Berlin Sym.—Rubahn, with A. Kessel (B) (‡ Roy. 1324)

(The) LOVE FOR THREE ORANGES, Op. 33
    Opera 4 acts 1919 (f.p. 1921)
Orchestral Suite, Op. 33a
French National Sym.—Désormière
          ‡ DCap.CTL 7017
(Lieut. Kije)   (‡ Cap.P 8149)
Copenhagen Opera—Malko ♮ **G.DB 20151/2**
(4ss)
Berlin Radio—Rother   **‡ Ura. 5005**
(Russian Overture)   (& ♭ UREP 7)

... Nos. 3 & 4, Marche & Scherzo
☆ Col. Sym.—Rodzinski (in ♭ *AmC. set A 1003*)
  ⌊Bolshoi Th.—Golovanov (USSR. 014641, d.c.)

... No. 3 only
Suisse Romande—Ansermet in **‡ D.LX 3072**
(Ravel, Stravinsky, Debussy) (‡ Lon.LS 503)

—— ARR. PF.
☆ A. Földes (in ‡ Rem. 149-4)

—— ARR. VLN. & PF. Heifetz
J. Heifetz & E. Bay   in **‡ B.LAT 8020**
(Valle, Tchaikovsky, etc) (‡ AmD.DL 8521)

ROMEO & JULIET, Op. 64 Ballet 1935/6
Orchestral Suite No. 1, Op. 64a
☆ Bolshoi Theatre—Fayer (in ‡ Csm.CRLP 108/9)

Orchestral Suite No. 2, Op. 64b
Leningrad Phil.—Mravinsky **‡ Van.VRS 6004**
(Shostakovitch: Ballet Suite)
Rhineland Sym.—Federer   **‡ Rgt. 5046**
☆ Moscow Phil.—Prokofiev (♮ U.C 23879/84)

V. CHORAL

On Guard for Peace, Op. 124 Oratorio
Narration, Soli., cho., orch. 1951
  (Marshak)
Z. Dolukhanova (A), E. Talanov (Tr), etc;
USSR State Cho. & Orch.—Samosud
          ‡ Van.VRS 6003
           (‡ USSR. D 05/6)

... Lullaby only on USSR. 020043/4

Winter holiday
Children's Cho. & USSR Radio—Samosud
          ‡ West.WL 5132
(Peiko)   (Excerpts on *USSR. 19203/4*)

PUCCINI, Giacomo A. D. M. S. M.
(1858-1924)

Crisantemi Elegy Str. Qtt. 1892
La Scala Qtt.   **‡ Ura. 7074**
(Boccherini & Giardini)

Inno a Roma (Salvatori) 1919
Anon. Cho. & Orch. *(Dur.A 10100)*

OPERAS

(La) BOHÈME 4 acts 1896
COMPLETE RECORDINGS
Set J
  (i) Mimi ... ... R. Tebaldi (S)
  (ii) Musetta ... ... H. Gueden (S)
  (iii) Rodolfo ... ... G. Prandelli (T)
  (iv) Marcello ... ... G. Inghilleri (B)
  (v) Colline ... ... R. Arié (Bs)
  (vi) Schaunard ... ... F. Corena (Bs)
  (vii) Benoit ... ... M. Luise (Bs)
Santa Cecilia Cho. & Orch.—Erede **(4ss)**
          ‡ D.LXT 2622/3
           (‡ Lon.LLP 462/3)
Set K
  Mimi ... ... L. Albanese (S)
  Musetta ... ... A. McKnight (S)
  Rodolfo ... ... J. Peerce (T)
  Marcello ... ... F. Valentino (B)
  Colline ... ... N. Moscona (Bs)
  Schaunard ... G. Cehanovsky (B)
  Benoit ... ... S. Baccaloni (Bs)
etc; N.B.C. Cho. & Orch.—Toscanini
          ‡ Vic. set LM 6006
(4ss—Recorded Feb. 1946) (18ss, ♭ *set WDM 1646*)
Set L
  Mimi ... ... R. Carteri (S)
  Musetta ... ... E. Ramella (S)
  Rodolfo ... ... F. Tagliavini (T)
  Marcello ... ... G. Taddei (B)
  Schaunard ... P. L. Latinucci (B)
  Colline ... ... C. Siepi (Bs)
etc; Italian Radio Cho. & Orch.—Santini
(4ss)   **‡ Sor set 1237**

Set M
D. Ilitsch (i), R. Boesch (ii), R. Delorco (iii),
T. Baylé (iv), G. Oeggl (vi), etc. Vienna State
Opera Cho. & Austrian Sym.—Loibner (6ss)
          ‡ Rem. set 199-80
(Highlights on Rem. 199-104; *see below* for Hma. issues)

Set N
F. Schimenti (i), M. Micheluzzi (ii),
G. Lauri-Volpi (iii), G. Ciavola (iv), etc. Rome
Opera Cho. & Orch.—Paoletti (6ss) ‡ Rem. set 199-96

Highlights
L. Albanese, G. di Stefano, P. Munsel, L. Warren
          ‡ Vic.LM 1709
(& see below for individual issues of excerpts from this
set)   (♭ *set WDM 1709*)
Anon. Artists (in ‡ Roy. 1346; ♮ Wde. 20204; &
‡ *Pde. 1005;* &, with narration, ‡ Pde. OP 106)

ACT I

Scene, Mimi—Rodolfo, complete
(Che gelida manina; Si, mi chiamano Mimi; O soave
fanciulla)
E. Shumskaya, I. Kozlovsky, And. Ivanov *(Russ)*
(4ss)   **USSR. 018466/9**

Che gelida manina   T
G. di Stefano (from Highlights) **G.DB 21518**
(*O Mimi, tu più non torni*) (♭ *Vic.WEPR 18*)
J. Björling (n.v.)   in **‡ Vic.LM 105**
(*Carmen, Africaine, etc.*) (♭ *set WDM 1546*)

    R. Delorco (from set M) Hma. 15007: ‡ *LM 803*
    I. Kozlovsky *(Russ)*   USSR. 9178/9
  ☆ M. Lanza in ‡ *Vic.LM 86:* ♭ *set WDM 1330*
      also in ‡ *LM 1202:* ♭ *set WDM 1626*

  H V. Herold   AF. 41 *
    E. Caruso in ‡ Vic. LCT 1007 *: ♭ *set WCT 11* *
    R. Tauber *(Ger)*   in ‡ Ete. O-466 *

Si, mi chiamano Mimi   S
L. Albanese (from Highlights set)
        in **‡ Vic.LM 1148**
         (♭ *set WDM 1542*)
(continued on next page)

☆ = Re-issue of a recording to be found in WERM or Supplement I.

Si, mi chiamano Mimi (*continued*)

Géori-Boué   **Sat.C 702**
(*Tosca—Vissi d'arte*)

M. Minazzi   **P.PE 170**
(*La Wally—Ebben, ne andro lontano*)
(*Traviata—Addio del passato, on P.PE 171*)

R. Carteri (from set L)   **P.CB 20542**
(*Donde lieta*)

E. Arizmendi   **ArgC. 307001**
(*Madama Butterfly—Un bel dì*)

M. Santreuil (*Fr*)   **Pac. 6785**
(*Louise—Depuis le jour*)

☆ C. Muzio   in ‡ AmC.ML 4404
   M. Carosio   ♭ G.7RF 130
   L. Bori   ♭ Vic. 17-0187
   R. Tebaldi   in ‡ AmD.DL 4005

⊞ L. Bori   IRCC. 3129 *
   R. Ponselle   in ‡ Gol. 1201 *
   P. Donalda   G.VB 10 *: o.n. 053104 *

O soave fanciulla   T. & S
K. Grayson & R. Atchison (*Eng*)   (*BrzMGM. 9001*)

ACT II

Quando m'en vo   S
R. Boesch (from set M)   **Hma. 15007**
(*Che gelida manina*)   (in ‡ LM 803)

P. Munsel, from Highlights (in ♭ Vic. WEPR 18)
I. Maslennikova (*Russ*) (*USSR. 16680*)

ACT III

Mimi ? Son io   S. & B.
A. Bolechowska & A. Hiolski (*Pol*)   **Muza. 1768**

Mimi è una civetta!   Trio
... Tenor part only
R. Delorco (from set M)   **Hma. 15008**
(*Donde lieta*)   (in ‡ LM 803)

⊞ L. Slezak (*Ger*) (HRS. 1114 *)

Donde lieta usci S (*Addio di Mimi*)
D. Ilitsch (from set M)   **Hma. 15008**
(*Mimi è una civetta!*)   (in ‡ LM 803)

R. Carteri (from set L)   **P.CB 20542**
(*Si, mi chiamano Mimi*)

C. Carroll   in ‡ **Rem. 149-41**
(*Turandot, Ballo, Pagliacci, etc.*)

M. Angelici (*Fr*)   **G.DB 11253**
(*Louise—Depuis le jour*)

L. Albanese (from Highlights)
                ♭ Vic. WEPR 18 & 49-3366
☆ E. Schwarzkopf   ♭ C.SCB 101: C.GQ 7246
   R. Tebaldi   in ‡ AmD.DL 4005
   A. Roselle   in ‡ Ete. 0-478
   etc.

Addio, dolce svegliare   Ens.
L. Albanese (S), G. di Stefano (T), L. Warren (B),
P. Munsel (M-S)   **G.DB 9777**
(*Death of Mimi, s. 1*) (from Highlights)

ACT IV

In un coupé ... O Mimi, tu più non torni T & B
G. di Stefano & L. Warren   **G.DB 21518**
(*Che gelida manina*) (from Highlights) (♭ Vic. WEPR 18)

J. Björling & R. Merrill   **G.DB 21311**
(*Forza—Solenne in quest'ora*)   (♭ G. 7R 124)
                (in Vic. ‡ LM/ ♭ set WDM 7007)

I. Kozlovsky & A. Ivanov (*Russ*)   (*USSR. 18340/1*)

Vecchia zimarra   Bs
G. Neri   **P.AT 0269**
(*Mefistofele—Son lo spirito*)

W. Strienz (*Ger.*)   in Ura. 7026
☆ M. Szekely (*Hung*)   Qual. QKM 5012
⊞ D. Gilly   G.VA 66 *

Sono andati ? Ens.   (*Death of Mimi*)
L. Albanese, G. di Stefano, G. Cehanovsky,
L. Warren, P. Munsel, N. Moscona (from
Highlights) (3ss, *above*)   ♮ **G.DB 9777/8**

D. Ilitsch & R. Delorco (2ss)   **Hma. 15009**
(from set M)   (in ‡ LM 803)

(La) FANCIULLA DEL WEST 3 acts 1910
Or son sei mesi   T (Act II)
R. Turrini   **P.PE 178**
(*Ernani—Come rugiada al cespite*)

☆ J. Schmidt (*Ger*) (P.DPW 62)

Ch'ella mi creda libero   T (Act III)
M. del Monaco   in ‡ **D.LX 3094**
(*below, & Verdi*)   (‡ Lon.LS 670)

   E. Holmström & pf.   Täh.RW 456

☆ J. Peerce   in ‡ Vic.LM 1169
   A. Piccaver   [in ‡ Ete. O-478
   J. Schmidt (*Ger*)   P.DPW 62

GIANNI SCHICCHI 1 act 1918
Complete Recording
☆ G. Taddei, G. Rapisardi, G. del Signore, R. Ferrari, etc.
   Turin Radio—Simonetto (‡ FSor.CS 509)

O mio babbino caro   S
D. Kirsten   in ‡ **AmC.ML 2200**
                              (♭ set A 1015)

☆ L. Albanese (♭ Vic. 49-1487)

⊞ C. Muzio (HRS. 1068 *)

MADAMA BUTTERFLY 2 acts 1904
Complete Recordings
Set G
   Madama Butterfly...   ...   R. Tebaldi (S)
   Suzuki   ...   ...   N. Rankin (M-S)
   Kate Pinkerton ...   ...   G. Diozzi (M-S)
   Lt. Pinkerton   ...   ...   G. Campora (T)
   Sharpless   ...   ...   G. Inghilleri (B)
etc., Santa Cecilia Academy Cho. & Orch.—
Erede   ‡ **D.LXT 2638/40**
(6ss)   (‡ Lon. set LLPA 8)

Set H
D. Ilitsch, R. Delorco, H. Rössl-Majdan,
Austrian Sym.—Loibner   ‡ **Rem. 199-81**
(6ss—Highlights on ‡ Rem. 199-100)

Highlights
Anon. Soloists, Berlin Op. Cho. & Orch. (‡ Roy. 1347)
Anon. Artists (‡ Wde. 20207; ‡ Pde. 1010; & with
narration, ‡ Pde.OP 104)

ACT I

Ancora un passo ... Spira sul mar S
☆ L. Albanese   **G.DB 21406**
(*Tu, tu, piccolo iddio!*)   (in ♭ Vic.WEPR 17)

☆ L. Lehmann (*Ger*) (in ‡ AmD.DL 9523)

⊞ C. Muzio (HRS. 2009 *; also in ‡ Eso.ES 502 *;
                         Cpt.MC 20009 * [1])

Love Duet: Viene la sera ... Bimba dagli occhi
                              S & T
R. Peters & J. Peerce   in ‡ **Vic.LM 7016**
(*Tonight we sing, Film music*)   (♭ set WDM 7016)

D. Ilitsch & R. Delorco   **Hma. 15010**
(from set H)

   E. Shumskaya & I. Kozlovsky (*Russ*)
                              (*USSR. 018709/12*)
   M. Cebotari & W. Ludwig (*Ger*) (in ‡ Ura. 7036)

☆ E. Malbin & M. Lanza (G.DB 21509)
   L. Albanese & J. Melton (in ‡ Vic.LM 1162)

⊞ G. Farrar & E. Caruso (in ‡ Vic.LCT 1037 *:
                         ♭ set WCT 57 *)

---

[1] Recorded from Edison cylinder.

MADAMA BUTTERFLY (*continued*)

ACT II, Sc. I

Un bel dì, vedremo   S
M. P. Putzolu   **P.CB 20529**
(*Manon Lescaut—In quelle trine*)
D. Kirsten   in ♯ *AmC.ML 2200*
              (♭ set A 1015)
E. Arizmendi   **ArgC. 307001**
(*Bohème*)
M. Santreuil (*Fr*)   **Pac. 6786**
(*Thaïs—Dis-moi que je suis belle*)
▽ M. Cebotari (*Ger*)   Pol. 67805

☆ E. Schwarzkopf   C.GQX 11456: ♭ SCB 102
   D. Ilitsch (o.v.)   Eur.TGB 149
   L. Albanese   in ♭ Vic.WEPR 17
   G. Moore   in ♯ AmD.DL 9593
   L. Bori   ♭ Vic. 17-0187
       & in ♯ Vic.LCT 1039: ♭ set WCT 62

♬ R. Ponselle   in ♯ Gol. 1201*
   E. Destinn   IRCC. 3124*

**Letter Duet: Sai cos' ebbe cuore
... Sop. part only**
♬ E. Destinn (*Ger*)   in ♯ set CEd. 7001*

ACT II, Sc. II

Intermezzo
☆ Berlin State Op.—Ludwig (Pol. 15530; P.RR 8174)

Non ve l'avevo detto ... Addio, fiorito asil   T & B
J. Peerce & E. Dunning   in ♯ Vic.LM 7016
(*Tonight we sing, film music*)   (♭ set WDM 7016)
☆ A. Piccaver & T. Scheidl   in ♯ Ete. O-478

... Tenor part only
☆ J. Melton, from set D(WERM) ♭ Vic.WEPR 17
♬ R. Tauber   in ♯ Ete. O-466*

Con onor ... Tu, tu, piccolo iddio!   S [& T]
☆ L. Albanese   **G.DB 21406**
(*Ancora un passo*)   (in ♭ Vic.WEPR 17)
▽ M. Cebotari (*Ger*)   Pol. 67805
☆ A. Guerrini & A. Ferracuti   C.GFX 186
   A. Roselle   in ♯ Ete. O-478
♬ E. Destinn (*Ger*)   in ♯ set CEd. 7001*

MANON LESCAUT   4 acts   1893
COMPLETE RECORDING
   Manon   ...   ...   M. Zamboni (S)
   Des Grieux...   ...   F. Merli (T)
   Lescaut ...   ...   L. Conati (B)
☆ etc.; Cho. & Orch. of La Scala—Molajoli
(4ss)   ♯ AmC. set SL 111

ACT I

Donna non vidi mai   T
M. del Monaco   **G.DA 11332**
(*Leoncavallo: Bohème—Testa adorata*)
A. Vernetti   **P.AT 0281**
(*Tosca—Recondita armonia*)
K. Baum   in ♯ Rem. 199-63
(*Andrea Chénier, Aïda, etc.*)
♬ E. Caruso   G.VA 33*: o.n. DA 106*
   F. de Lucia   in ♯ CMS. 201*

Choruses (unspec.)
San Francisco Op. Cho.   **ML. 45**

ACT II

In quelle trine morbide   S
M. P. Putzolu   **P.CB 20529**
(*Madama Butterfly—Un bel dì*)

A. Guerrini   **C.GQ 7245**
(*Tosca—Vissi d'arte*)
A. Varnay   in ♯ Rem. 199-53
(*Hérodiade, Fliegende Holländer, etc.*)
☆ L. Albanese   **G.DB 21505**
(*Louise—Depuis le jour*)
♬ R. Ponselle   in ♯ Gol. 1201*
   C. Ferrani   IRCC. 3095*
   A. Agostinelli   HRS. 1099*
   C. Boninsegna & pf.   G.VA 4*: o.n. 53372*

Ah! Manon, mi tradisce   T
☆ G. Zenatello   **AF.AGSA 3**
(*Tosca—O dolci mani*)

Intermezzo
☆ Berlin Municipal—Haarth (Pol. 15502)

ACT III

Ah! non v'avvicinate ... No! pazzo son!   T [& B]
M. del Monaco   in ♯ *D.LX 3094*
(*Fanciulla, Tosca, etc.*)   (♯ Lon.LS 670)

ACT IV

Sola, perduta, abbandonata   S
D. Kirsten   in ♯ *AmC.ML 2200*
              (♭ set A 1015)

   ☆ A. Guerrini (C.GFX 186)

(La) RONDINE   2 acts   1917
Chi il bel sogno di Doretta   S
M. Minazzi   **P.RO 30004**
(*Manon—Adieu, notre petite table*)   (FB 752)
(*Lodeletta—Flammen, perdonami, on FB 751*)

Ore liete, divine   S
D. Kirsten   in ♯ *AmC.ML 2200*
              (♭ set A 1015)

(Il) TABARRO   1 act   1918
Perchè, non m'ami più   B & S
Nulla! Silenzio!   B
☆ G. Inghilleri & E. Tegani (G.S 10591)

Scorri fiume   B
♬ ☆ D. Gilly (G.VA 66*)

TOSCA   3 acts   1901
COMPLETE RECORDINGS
Set F
   Cavaradossi   ...   ...   G. Poggi (T)
   Tosca   ...   ...   A. Guerrini (S)
   Scarpia   ...   ...   P. Silveri (B)
   Angelotti   ...   ...   J. Emanuel (B)
   Sacristan   ...   ...   C. Badioli (B)
   Spoletta   ...   ...   A. Benzi (T)
   Sciarrone   ...   ...   E. Coda (Bs)
   Shepherd Boy   ...   E. R. Pralungo (A)
etc., Italian Radio Cho. & Orch.—Prandelli
              ♯ Sor set 1230
(4ss)   (♯ FSor.CS 501/2)

Set G
   Cavaradossi   ...   ...   N. Scattolini (T)
   Tosca   ...   ...   S. dall'Argine (S)
   Scarpia   ...   ...   S. Colombo (B)
   Angelotti   ...   ...   A. Poell (B)
   Sacristan   ...   ...   K. Dönch (B)
   Spoletta   ...   ...   W. Kmentt (T)
   Sciarrone   ...   ...   H. Pröglhöff (Bs)
   Shepherd Boy   ...   H. Breitschopf (A)
etc., Vienna Academy Cho. & State Op. Orch.—
Quadri   ♯ West.WL 5115/7
(6ss)   (set WAL 302; ♭ Sel.LPG 8553/5)
(*continued on next page*)

☆ = Re-issue of a recording to be found in WERM or Supplement I.

TOSCA—COMPLETE (*continued*)

Set H

Tosca	... ...	R. Tebaldi (S)
Cavaradossi	... ...	G. Campora (T)
Scarpia	... ...	E. Mascherini (B)
Angelotti	... ...	D. Caselli (Bs)
Sacristan	... ...	F. Corena (B)
Spoletta	... ...	P. de Palma (T)
Shepherd Boy	...	G. Volante (Boy A)

etc., Cho. & Orch. of Santa Cecilia Acad., Rome—Erede ♯ **D.LXT 2730/1**
(4ss) (♯ Lon.LL 660/1)

Set I

V. Petrova (S), E. Ruhl (T), P. Campolonghi (B), etc. Florence Cho. & Orch.—Tieri
(6ss) ♯ **Rem. set 199-62**

Set A

Tosca	... ...	M. Caniglia (S)
Cavaradossi	... ...	B. Gigli (T)
Scarpia	... ...	A. Borgioli (B)

☆ etc., Rome Opera Cho. & Orch.—de Fabritiis ♯ **G.ALP 1020/1**
(4ss) (♯ Vic. set LCT 6004; ♭ *set WCT 82*)
(Highlights on ♯ Vic.LCT 1102; ♭ *set WCT 1102*)

Highlights

Salzburg Fest. Orch.—P. Walter ♯ **Rem. 149-24**
(*Cavalleria Rusticana*) (♯ *Mrt. 1-17*)

ACT I

Recondita armonia T
M. del Monaco in ♯ **D.LX 3094**
(*Fanciulla, etc; & Verdi*) (♯ *Lon.LS 670*)
G. Poggi [& C. Badioli (B)] **P.AT 0271**
(*E lucevan le stelle*) (also P. CB 20537)
A. Vernetti **P.AT 0281**
(*Manon Lescaut—Donna non vidi mai*)
F. Vroons **Phi.N 11174G**
(½s.—*Rigoletto & Pagliacci*) (*PhM.A 9010S*)
P. Munteanu **Pol. 62875**
(*E lucevan ...*)
K. Baum in ♯ **Rem. 199-63**
L. Melchior in ♯ **MGM.E. 109**
(♮ *set 109: ♭ set K 109*)

☆ J. Schmidt *Od. O-25986*
M. Lanza ♭ *G.7R 129: 7RF 141;*
♭ *Vic. 49-3204*
F. Tagliavini ♭ *G.7RF 131;* in ♯ *Vic.LM 1164*
J. Peerce in ♯ *Vic.LM 1169:* ♭ *WEPR 36*

Mario! Mario! (Duet—Tosca & Cavaradossi) S & T
☆ F. Quartararo & R. Vinay (in ♯ *Vic.LM 1162*)

Tre sbirri, una carrozza (Te Deum) B & Cho.
H P. Amato (in ♯ *Ete. O-482**)

ACT II

Vissi d'arte, vissi d'amore S
A. Guerrini **C.GQ 7245**
(*Manon Lescaut—In quelle trine morbide*)
G. Brouwenstijn **Phi.N 11169G**
(*Cavalleria Rusticana—Voi lo sapete*) (*PhM.A 09004S*)
D. Kirsten in ♯ **AmC.ML 2200**
(♭ *set A 1015*)
Géori-Boué **Sat.C 702**
(*La Bohème—Si, mi chiamano Mimi*)

☆ D. Ilitsch *Eur. TBG 149*
G. Moore in ♯ *AmD.DL 9593*
L. Albanese ♭ *Vic. 49-1487*

H C. Muzio in ♯ *Eso.ES 502**; ♭ *Cpt.MC 20009** [1]
R. Ponselle in ♯ *Gol. 1201**
F. Kaschowska *IRCC. 3120**
O. Fremstad *AF. 380/3**

[1] Recorded from Edison cylinder

ACT III

O dolci baci ... ; E lucevan le stelle T
M. del Monaco in ♯ **D.LX 3094**
(*above, below, & Verdi*) (♯ *Lon.LS 670*)
G. Poggi **P.AT 0271**
(*Recondita armonia*) (also on P.CB 20537)

S. Lemeshev (*Russ*) *USSR. 18386*
F. Klarwein (*Ger*) *Imp. 19069*
▽ R. Schock (*Ger*) ☆ *G.DA 5511*
☆ F. Tagliavini in ♯ *Vic.LM 1164:*
♭ *set WDM 1542*
G. di Stefano ♭ *G.7R 116*
& in ♯ *Vic. LM 1202:* ♭ *set WDM 1626*
J. Peerce in ♯ *Vic.LM 1169:* ♭ *WEPR 36*

H E. Caruso & pf. *G.VA 29**: *o.n. DA 547**
E. Caruso & orch. in ♯ *Vic.LCT 1034**:
♭ *set WCT 35**; also *IRCC 3121**
J. McCormack in ♯ *Ete. O-469**
L. Muratore (*Fr*) *IRCC. 3123**

Ah! franchigia ... O dolci mani S & T
... **Tenor part only**
☆ G. Zenatello **AF.AGSA 3**
(*Manon Lescaut—Ah! Manon*)

TURANDOT 3 acts 1926

ACT I

Signore, ascolta! S
☆ E. Schwarzkopf (*C.GQ 7246:* ♭ *SCB 101*)

Non piangere, Liù T
M. del Monaco in ♯ **D.LX 3094**
(*above, & Verdi*) (♯ *Lon.LS 670*)
A. Fügel (*Ger*) *Pol. 62831*
☆ A. Piccaver in ♯ *Ete. O-478*
R. Tauber (*Ger*) *HRS. 2016*

ACT II

In questa reggia S
J. Hammond (2ss) **G.DA 1988**
▽ A. Roselle (n.v. in ♯ *Rem.PL 2-149;* also, in *Ger*,
☆ in ♯ *Ete. O-478*)

ACT III

Nessun dorma T
K. Baum in ♯ **Rem. 199-63**
(*Pagliacci, Gioconda, etc.*)

A. Fügel (*Ger*) *Pol. 62831*
☆ B. Gigli ♭ *G.7R 127: 7RF 114;*
Vic. 10-3761: ♭ *49-3761, d.c.*
A. Piccaver in ♯ *Ete. O-478*
J. Björling ♭ *G.7R 106*
A. Salvarezza *P.PO 195;* *Od. O-4854*
R. Tauber (*Ger*) *HRS. 2016*

Principessa, l'amore S
☆ B. Kiurina (*IRCC. 3085*)

Tu che di gel sei cinta S (*Death of Liù*)
D. Kirsten in ♯ **AmC.ML 2200**
(*Rondine, etc.*) (♭ *set A 1015*)
C. Carroll in ♯ **Rem. 149-41**
(*Ballo, Pagliacci, Don Giovanni, etc.*)
☆ B. Kiurina (*Ger*) (*IRCC. 3085*)

Del primo pianto S
▽ A. Roselle (n.v. in ♯ *Rem.PL 2-149;* &, in *Ger*,
☆ in ♯ *Ete. O-478*)

PURCELL, Henry (1658-1695)

I. INSTRUMENTAL

A. HARPSICHORD

Fanfare, C major (Voluntary) [68]
— ARR. ORGAN
   E. P. Biggs   in ‡ **AmC.ML 4603**
   (*J. Clarke, Parry, etc.*)

Ground, C minor [39]
☆ W. Landowska (in ‡ *Vic.LM 1217*; ♭ *G.7RF 216*)

Hornpipe, (unspec.)
   G. Novães (pf.)   in ‡ **AmVox.PL 7500**
   (*Gluck, Bach, Saint-Saëns, etc.*)

(A) New Irish tune [31]
Minuet; Jig (unspec.)
— ARR. GUITAR
☆ A. Segovia (in ‡ *AmD.DL 5257*)

(A) New Irish tune (in *Vic. set E 97*: ♭ *WE 97*)

(8) SUITES
COMPLETE RECORDING
   I. Nef   ‡ **OL.LD 46**

No. 7, D minor ... Hornpipe only
☆ A. Ehlers (in ‡ *AmD.DL 8019*)

Trumpet Tunes & Air — ARR. ORG. Ley
☆ R. Foort (*G.MH 153*)

I. B. CHAMBER MUSIC

Chacony, G minor (orig. 4 viols.)
   New Music Str. Qtt.   ‡ **BRS. 913**
   (*below*)
   Vienna Cha. Orch.—Litschauer ‡ **Van.VRS 420**
   (*below*)

Chaconne, "London", unid.[1]
   Vienna Cha. Orch.—Litschauer ‡ **Van.VRS 419**
   (*below; & Beethoven*)

FANTASIAS   1680
(3) Three-part
   London Str. Trio   ‡ *Allo.AL 119*
   (*below*)   (‡ *EA.ALY 119A*)
   Vienna Cha.—Litschauer ‡ **Van.VRS 419**
   (*above; & Beethoven*)

(9) Four-part
   Aeolian Qtt.   ‡ *Allo.AL119/20*
   (*above & below*)   (‡ *EA.ALY 119 A|B*)
   Vienna Cha.—Litschauer ‡ **Van.VRS 420**
   (*Chacony*)
   Concert Hall Str. Orch.—Goehr ‡ **CHS.F 13**

Five-part (on one note)
   Aeolian Quintet   in ‡ *Allo.AL 119*
                  (‡ *EA.ALY 119A*)

Pavan, G minor (orig. 4 viols.)
   New Music Str. Qtt.   ‡ **BRS. 913**
   (*above; & Gibbons & Locke*)

II. VOCAL MUSIC

COLLECTION
OEDIPUS: Music for awhile (Dryden) 1692
A FOOL'S PREFERMENT: I'll sail upon the Dog Star 1688
The Knotting Song (Sedley)
COME YE SONS (Ode) ... Strike the viol
Evening hymn (Fuller)
The Queen's Epicedium
   J. Langstaff (B), H. Chessid (hpsi), D. Soyer (vlc.)
                 ‡ **Nix.PLP 227**
   (*Dowland*)   (‡ *Ren.X 27*)

II. A. DRAMATIC MUSIC

ABDELAZER 1695
Nos. 2, 6 & 8 *SEE:* Suite, *below*

BONDUCA 1695
Overture excpt. *SEE:* Suite, *below*

DIDO & AENEAS Opera, Prol. & 3 Acts 1689
Set C [2]
   Dido   ...   .   K. Flagstad (S)
   Belinda   ...   ...   E. Schwarzkopf (S) [3]
   Sorceress ...   ...   A. Mandikian (M-S)
   Aeneas   ...   ...   T. Hemsley (B)
   etc., Mermaid Theatre Singers & Orch.—
      G. Jones   ‡ **G.ALP 1026**
         (‡ *Vic.LHMV 1007*: ♭ *set WHMV 1007*)

Set D
   Dido   ...   .   E. Houston (S)
   Belinda   ...   .   A. Leigh (S)
   Sorceress ...   ...   E. Cuthill (M-S)
   Aeneas   ...   .   H. Cummings (B)
   etc., Stuart Cha. Cho. & orch.—Gregory
                 ‡ **Per.SPLP 546**
         (‡ *Clc. 6087*; ‡ *Nix.PLP 546*)

No. 37, When I am laid in earth
   E. Wysor (A)   in ‡ **Rem. 199-30**
   C. Rubio (S) & Madrid Cha. Orch.—Argenta
                 SpC.RG 16174
   (*Nozze di Figaro*)
   ☆ S. Danco (D.KX 28313)

— ARR. HARMONICA: L. Adler (in ‡ *CHS.CHS 1161*)

DISTRESSED INNOCENCE 1690
No. 3, Slow Air *SEE:* Suite, *below*

(The) FAIRY QUEEN Opera, 5 Acts 1692
Nos. 4, 22, 23, 43, 49, 51, 54
   M. Ritchie (S) & Ens.—Lewis   ‡ **OL.LD 16**
   (*below*)

KING ARTHUR Opera, Prol. & 5 Acts 1691
COMPLETE RECORDING [4]
   J. Ellsperman (S), M. Milton ( ),
      M. Bleiberg ( ), L. Chelsi (T), R. Harris ( ),
      Hammond org. & pf.   ‡ **Mtr.MLP 1006**

Chaconne See below, footnote to Section III

(The) LIBERTINE 1692
Nymphs and Shepherds, Act IV   S
   Sheffield Schools' Cho. & pf.—Hall *G.B 10309*
   (*Thiman: A Breton Fishing*)
   Kirkintilloch Junior Cho. (*P.R 3474*)

TIMON OF ATHENS 1694
Nos. 1, 7, 10 & Curtain tune on a ground
   M. Ritchie (S) & Ens.—Lewis   ‡ **OL.LD 16**
   (*Fairy Queen*)

(The) VIRTUOUS WIFE 1694
No. 4, Air
   See footnote to Dido & Aeneas, *above*.

II. B.1 ODES

Come, ye sons of art, away 1694
... **Strike the viol**
   J. Langstaff (B)   in ‡ **Nix.PLP 227**
   (*Collection, above*)   (‡ *Ren.X 27*)

Hail, bright Cecilia (for St. Cecilia's Day) 1692
... **Soul of the World** 8 voices
   Festival Cho. & Orch.—Boult   **G.DB 21273**
   (*Anon: All people that on earth do dwell*)

---

[1] Said to be from same MS as Fantasias; possibly one of the two *In Nomine's*.
[2] Includes (at end of Act II): (a) Chorus: *Then since our charms are sped,* sung to *Then would we conclude ...* (from Ode: *The Summer's absence,* 1682); (b) Air, No. 4 from *The Virtuous Wife,* 1694.
[3] Also singing parts of Second Lady & Attendant Spirit. First Lady is sung by E. McNab (S) & A Sailor by D. Lloyd(T).
[4] According to *New Records,* "distorted".

ODES (*continued*)

(The) Summer's absence unconcerned we bear 1682
... Then would we conclude that our isle ...
See footnote to Dido & Aeneas, *above*

II. B.2 ANTHEMS & SACRED SONGS

Evening Hymn (Fuller)
   A. Deller (C-T), G. Jones (org.)   **G.C 4144**
   (*Humphrey: A Hymne to God the Father*)

O sing unto the Lord   4 voices, cho., str., orch.
   1688
Rejoice in the Lord alway   A, T, B, cho. orch.
Te Deum & Jubilate, D major   1694
   Cleveland Purcell Soc. Cho. & orch.—King
                              ♯ **Allo.ALG 3027**

III. MISCELLANEOUS

Suite for Strings — ARR. A. Coates
1. Abdelazer, No. 2—Rondeau
2. Distressed Innocence, No. 3—Slow Air
3. Abdelazer, No. 6—Air
4. Abdelazer, No. 8—Minuet
5. Bonduca, Overture—Allegro quasi assai
   Sydney Civic Str. Orch.—Beck in ♯ **Dia.DPM 4**

(2) Bourrées (unid.) — ARR. SAX. & PF. Rascher [1]
   S. Rascher & D. Tudor   in ♯ **CHS.CHS 1156**

Chaconne, F major [2]
   F. Heitmann   in † ♯ **T.LSK 7010/1**

QUANTZ, Johann Joachim (1697-1773)

   SEE Also: † AS. 166 & † ♯ 3002LD

Concerto, No. 17, D major   fl. & orch.
   K. Wanausek & Vienna Philharmonia—Adler
   (*Friedrich II*)   ♯ **SPA. 23**

QUILTER, Roger (1877-1953)

SONGS
COLLECTION
Fair house of joy, Op. 12, No. 7 (Anon.)
Now sleeps the crimson petal, Op. 3, No. 2 (*D.M 680*)
FOLKSONG ARRS.
Drink to me only with thine eyes (*D.M 679*)
Over the mountains and over the waves
Ye banks and braes of bonnie Doon (*D.M 679*)
   K. Ferrier (A), P. Spurr (pf.) in ♯ **D.LX 3098**
   (*Folk-Songs*)   (♯ Lon.LPS 538)
   (Issues on 78 r.p.m. in brackets after the titles above)

Go, lovely rose, Op. 24, No. 3 (Waller)
   W. Midgley (T), G. Moore (pf.)   **G.DA 2014**
   (*To Daisies*)

It was a lover and his lass, Op. 23, No. 3
   (Shakespeare)
   H. Nash (T), G. Moore (pf.)   **G.B 10265**
   (*Trad.: The road to the Isles*)

Non nobis Domine (Kipling)
   Sheffield Schools Choir—Hall   **G.B 10310**
   (*Parry: Jerusalem*)

To Daisies, Op. 8, No. 3 (Herrick)
   W. Midgley (T), G. Moore (pf.)   **G.DA 2014**
   (*Go, lovely rose*)
   K. Ferrier (A), P. Spurr (pf.)   **D.M 680**
   (*Now sleeps the crimson petal*)

---

[1] First published by A. Moffatt for pf.
[2] Unspec. but probably from *King Arthur*.

RAASTED, Niels Otto (b. 1888)

How wonderful it is to walk ... (Kingo)
   (*Hvor lifligt er det dog at gaa*)
   T. Kraft (S), G. Krarup (org.)   **G.X 8037**
   (*Knudsen: Every day is a sure gift*)

RACHMANINOFF, Sergei Vassilievitch
(1873-1943)

ALEKO Opera, 1 act 1893
No. 10, The moon is high in the sky Bs
   B. Gmyria (2ss)   **USSR. 17418/9**

(The) BELLS, Op. 35 (Poe, trs. Balmont)
   ("Symphony") S, T, B, Cho., Orch.
   O. Moscucci, C. Anthony, L. Malfatti, Rome
   Cho. & Orch.—Rachmilovich (*Eng*) ♯ **RS. 8**

CONCERTOS, pf. & orch.
No. 2, C minor, Op. 18
   J. Katchen & New Sym.—Fistoulari
                              ♮ **D.AX 535/9**
   (*9ss—Chopin*)   (♯ D.LXT 2595; Lon.LLP 384)
      F. Everett & Berlin Sym. (♯ Roy. 1316)

   ☆ A. Rubinstein & N.B.C.—Golschmann (♯ G.FALP 161)
      J. Karolyi & Munich Phil.—Rosbaud (Pol. 68357/61S;
                               P.RR 8167/71; ♯ Pol. 18053)
      T. Nikolayeva & Czech Phil.—Ivanov (♯ Sup.LPM 1)
      F. Karrer & Austrian Sym.—Wöss (♯ Mrt .200-12)

... 1st movt. only
   ☆ L. Pennario & Col. Sym.—Rodzinski
                              (in ♭ AmC. set A 1002)

No. 3, D minor, Op. 30
   V. Horowitz & Vic. Sym.—Reiner
                              ♯ **G.ALP 1017**
      (♯ G.FALP 180; ♯ Vic.LM 1178; ♭ set WDM 1575)
   M. Lympany & New Sym.—Collins
                              ♯ **D.LXT 2701**
                              (♯ Lon.LL 617)

   ☆ W. Malcuzynski & Philharmonia—Kletzki
                              (♮ C.LVX 116/20S)

Danse orientale, Op. 2, No. 2 vlc. & pf.
   M. Rostropovich & A. Dedyukhin
   (2ss)   **USSR. 021124/5**

ÉTUDES TABLEAUX   pf.
C minor, Op. 39, No. 1
   ☆ E. Gilels (U.C 24117; in ♯ Csm.CRLP 115)

Five, unspec.
   — ARR. ORCH. Respighi
   Rome Sym.—Rachmilovich   in ♯ **RS. 9**
   (*below*)

One, unspec., from Op. 39: L. Rostchina (U.H 24038)

(The) Isle of the Dead, Op. 29 orch. 1907
   ☆ Boston Sym.—Koussevitzky ♯ **Vic.LM 1215**
   (*Prokofiev*)

MASQUERADE Inc. music (Lermontov)
Abrenin's monologue
   A. Pirogov (B)   **USSR. 15632**
   (*At the monastery gate*)

(The) MISERLY KNIGHT Opera, 3 Scenes 1906
Scene II, In the cellar   Bs
COMPLETE RECORDING
   C. Siepi (*Eng*) & Little Orch. Soc.—Scherman
   (*Arensky*)   ♯ **AmC.ML 4526**

Moment musical, Op. 16, No. 4, E minor [1] pf.
M. Yestchenko U.H 24041
(Scriabin: Valse)

Nocturne, Op. 10, No. 1 pf.
A. Goldenweiser USSR. 015655
(Sonata, Op. 19, s. 9)

PRELUDES pf.
Op. 3, No. 2, C sharp minor 1892
A. Rubinstein (n.v.) ♭ *G.7RF 159*
(Mendelssohn: Song without words, No. 34)(♭ *Vic.WEPR 41*)
(Schubert, etc. in ♯ *Vic.LM 1153:* ♭ *set WDM 1558)*
M. Flipse Phi.N 11236G
(Paderewski: Minuet) *(PhM.N 09048S)*
J. v. Karolyi *PV. 36018*
(below)
B. Böttner T.E 3921
(Khachaturian)
☆ J. Iturbi (in ♯ Vic.LM 1167: ♭ *set WDM 1604:* ♭ *ERA 53*)
V. Schiøler (in ♯ Mer.MG 10099)

— ARR. ORCH. Cailliet
☆ Philadelphia—Ormandy (C.LX 1464: GQX 11492:
LVX 179)

— ARR. ORCH.
Boston Pops—Fiedler (n.v.) ♭ *Vic. 49-1442*
(below)

Op. 23 1901
No. 1, F sharp minor
☆ J. Zak U.H 23969
(Chopin: Concerto, No. 1, s. 1)

No. 2, B flat major
☆ P. Serebriakov *USSR. 16398*
(Tchaikovsky: Waltz, Op. 40-9)

No. 4, D major
No. 6, E flat major
No. 9, E flat minor
C. Keene in ♯ Mer.MG 10113
(Chopin, Liszt, Albeniz, etc.)

No. 5, G minor
V. Schiøler G.DB 10508
(Sibelius: Romance)
J. v. Karolyi (n.v.) *PV. 36018*
(above) (also ☆ o.v. P.RR 8171)

— ARR. 2 PFS.
Sisters J. Madeleine & F. Therese
in ♯ Cln.SF 1
(also ♮ & ♭)

— ARR. ORCH.
Boston Pops—Fiedler, n.v. (♭ *Vic. 49-1442*)
▽ Carnegie Pops—O'Connell (in ♯ *AmC.ML 2176*:
♭ *set A 1001*)

No. 6, E flat major
No. 7, C minor
☆ E. Joyce (in ♯ AmD.DL 9528)

Op. 32 1910
No. 5, G major
A. Brailowsky ♭ *G.7RF 220*
(Chopin: Étude, Op. 10, No. 3)
(Franck: Variations in ♭ *Vic. set WDM 1572)*
V. Sofronitsky *USSR. 12440*
(below)

— ARR. ORCH. Cailliet
☆ Philadelphia—Ormandy (C.LX 1464: GQX 11492:
LVX 179)

No. 7, F major
No. 8, A minor
T. Nikolayeva *USSR. 15804/5*

No. 12, G sharp minor
V. Sofronitsky *USSR. 12449*
(No. 5)

QUARTET, String, No. 1 (unfinished)
... Romance & Scherzo
Beethoven Qtt. *USSR. 16230/1*
(2ss each) & 16314/5

Rhapsody on a theme of Paganini, Op. 45
W. Kapell & Robin Hood Dell—Reiner
♯ *Vic.LM 126*
(♭ *set WDM 1576*)
☆ A. Rubinstein & Philharmonia—Süsskind
(♯ *G.FBLP 102?*
S. Rachmaninoff & Philadelphia—Stokowski
(¶ ♮ G.DB 7812/4)

(The) ROCK, Op. 7 Sym. poem for orch., after
Lermontov
(3) Russian Songs, Op. 41 Cho. & orch.
Rome Cho. & Sym.—Rachmilovich ♯ *RS. 9*
(above)

Sonata No. 1, D minor, Op. 28 pf.
W. P. Thew ♯ *RS.6*
(Song—Powder & Paint)

Sonata, G minor, Op. 19 vlc. & pf.
S. Knushevitsky & A. Goldenweiser
USSR. 015646/54
(9ss—Nocturne, Op. 10, No. 1)

SONGS [2]
COLLECTION
All once I gladly owned, Op. 26, No. 2 (Merezhkovsky)
(or: *Everything is taken from me*)
Come, let us rest, Op. 26, No. 3 (Tchekhov) (or: *We will rest*)
Day to night comparing, Op. 34, No. 4 (Balmont)
(or: *The Changing Wind*)
Discord, Op. 34, No. 13 (Polonsky) (or: *Dissonance*)
(The) Fountains, Op. 26, No. 11 (Tyutchev)
Fragment from Nuit de Mai (A. de Musset)
How fair this spot, Op. 21, No. 7 (Galina)
(or: *It is pleasant here*)
Let me rest here alone, Op. 26, No. 9 (Bunin-Shevchenko)
(or: *I am alone*)
(The) Muse, Op. 34, No. 1 (Pushkin)
(The) Ring, Op. 26, No. 14 (Koltzov)
Two Partings, Op. 26, No. 4 (Koltzov) (Duet)
What wealth of rapture, Op. 34, No. 12 (Fet)
(or: *What happiness*)
When yesterday we met, Op. 26, No. 13 (Polonsky)
M. Kurenko (S), V. Gontzoff (B, in the duet)
L. Rosenthal (pf.) ♯ *RS. 5*

(The) Answer, Op. 21, No. 4 (Hugo, trs. Mey)
Z. Dolukhanova (A) *USSR. 18582*
(Morning)
S. Lemeshev (T) *USSR. 16272*
(½s.—*Sleep, & In the silent night*)

Arion, Op. 34, No. 5 (Pushkin)
V. Kilchevsky (T) *USSR. 17700*
(Schumann: An den Sonnenschein)

As fair as day in blaze of noon, Op. 14, No. 9
(Minsky)
B. Gmyria (Bs) *USSR. 18496*
(I wait for thee)

At the monastery gate (Lermontov) 1890
A. Pirogov (B) *USSR. 15631*
(Masquerade, Abrenin's monologue)

Before my window, Op. 26, No. 10 (Galina)
G. Zhukovskaya (S) *USSR. 10852*
(Lilacs)
V. Firsova (S) *USSR. 17290*
(Rimsky-Korsakov)
I. Kozlovsky (T) *USSR. 19451*
(Tchaikovsky: Disappointment)

[1] Listed as F minor but this is probably meant.
[2] The identification of some of the USSR discs is conjectural.

Daisies, Op. 38, No. 3
— ARR. PF. Rachmaninoff
☆ E. Gilels (in ♯ Csm.CRLP 115)

— ARR. VLN. & PF. Kreisler
D. Oistrakh & pf.   *USSR. 17371*
(*Taneiev: Romance*)

Do not depart, Op. 4, No. 1   (Merezhkovsky)
A. Pirogov (B)   *USSR. 14038*
(*Taneiev: It is not the wind*)

Floods of spring, Op. 14, No. 11   (Tyutchev)
N. Shpiller (S), Stuchevsky (pf.)   *USSR. 11567*
(*So many hours*)
S. Lemeshev (T)   *USSR. 16076*
(*How fair this spot*)

(The) Flower's faded   (Rathaus)   1893
T. Lavrova   *USSR. 19587*
(*Tchaikovsky: Song*)

How fair this spot, Op. 21, No. 7   (Galina)
S. Lemeshev (T)   *USSR. 16075*
(*Floods of spring*)
N. Kazantseva (S)   *USSR. 18859*
(*Rimsky-Korsakov: In the silence of the night*)
☆ L. Pons (S) & orch.   (C.LX 1539)

How few the joys, Op. 14, No. 3   (Fet)
V. Borisenko (M-S)   *USSR. 16200*
(½s.—*Sorrow in spring & The Soldiers' wife*)

I'll not tell you anything   (Fet)
S. Shaposhnikov   *USSR. 20063*
(*Tchaikovsky: Tears*)

I wait for thee, Op. 14, No. 1   (Davidova)
B. Gmyria (Bs)   *USSR. 18497a*
(*As fair as day*)

In the silent night, Op. 4, No. 3   (Fet)
R. Merrill (B), Y. Menuhin (vln.) C. Hollister
(pf.) (*Eng*)   in ♯ **Vic.LM 1703**
("*Great Combinations*")   (♭ set WDM 1703)
S. Lemeshev (T)   *USSR. 16273*
(*The Answer, & Sleep*)

Lilacs, Op. 21, No. 5   (Beketova)
G. Zhukovskaya (S)   *USSR. 10853*
(*Before my window*)
Z. Dolukhanova (A)   *USSR. 18399*
(*Tchaikovsky: O child, beneath thy window*)
S. Lemeshev (T)   *USSR. 17268*
(*Tchaikovsky: First meeting*)

Morning, Op. 4, No. 2   (Janov)
Z. Dolukhanova (A)   *USSR. 18581*
(*The Answer*)

O cease thy singing, maiden fair, Op. 4, No. 4
    (Pushkin)
S. Lemeshev (T)   *USSR. 017267*
(*Glinka: The forest murmurs*)

Powder and paint   (Folksong arr. Rachmaninoff)
N. Plevitzkaya (M-S), S. Rachmaninoff (pf.)
(*Sonata No. 1*)   ♯ **RS. 6**

Sleep, Op. 38, No. 5   (Sologub)
S. Lemeshev (T)   *USSR. 16272*
(½s.—*Answer & In the silent night*)

So many hours, so many fancies, Op. 4, No. 6
    (Golenishchev-Kutuzov)
N. Shpiller (S), S. Stuchevsky (pf.)
    USSR. 11577
(*Floods of spring*)

The Soldier's Wife, Op. 8, No. 4   (Shevchenko,
    trs. Pleshcheev)
V. Borisenko (M-S)   *USSR. 16200*
(*How few the joys & Sorrow in spring*)
N. Obukhova (M-S)   *USSR. 20587*
(*Varlamoff: Why sit you till midnight?*)
Ħ M. Kouznetzoff (S) (IRCC. 3130*)

Sorrow in Spring, Op. 21, No. 12   (Galina)
V. Borisenko (M-S)   *USSR. 16200*
(½s.—*How few the joys, & The Soldier's Wife*)
S. Lemeshev (T)   *USSR. 19454*
(*Tchaikovsky: No response or word of greeting*)

Twilight, Op. 21, No. 3   (Guyot)
E. Katulskaya (S)   *USSR. 15775*
(*Rubinstein: Night*)

(The) Water Lily, Op. 8, No. 1   (Heine,
    trs. Pleshcheev)
Z. Dolukhanova (A), B. Kozel (pf.)
    USSR. 20391
(*Tchaikovsky: Love's beginning*)

Vocalise, Op. 34, No. 14
☆ L. Pons (S) & orch.   (in ♯ AmC.ML 2181: ♭ set A 1006
)
— ARR. VLC. & PF.
☆ G. Piatigorsky & R. Berkowitz
    in ♯ **AmC.RL 3015**
(*Rimsky, Cui, etc.; & Shostakovitch*)

———— *END OF SONGS* ————

SUITES, 2 pfs.
No. 2, C major, Op. 17
☆ P. Sellick & C. Smith (C.GQX 11476/8)

SYMPHONIES
No. 1, D minor, Op. 13   (1895: reconstructed 1945)
Stockholm Radio—Rachmilovich
    ♯ **Mer.MG 10111**
    (♯ Clc. 6113; ♯ Mtr.CLP 508)

No. 2, E minor, Op. 27   1907
Philadelphia—Ormandy   ♯ **AmC.ML 4433**

No. 3, A minor, Op. 44   1936
USSR State Sym.—Golovanov ♮ **U.H 23927/31**
(10ss)   (♯ Sup.LPM 37/8, 3ss)

Trio, G minor   pf., vln., vlc.
A. Goldenweiser, D. Tziganov, S. Shirinsky
(4ss)   *USSR. 15960/3*

VARIATIONS   pf.
On a theme of Chopin, Op. 22
B. Weiser   ♯ **RS. 4**
(*below*)
R. Goldsand   ♯ **CHS.CHS 1149**
(*Liszt: Études*)

On a theme of Corelli, Op. 42
B. Weiser   ♯ **RS. 4**
(*above*)
B. Segáll   ♯ **NRI. 404**
(*Villa-Lobos*)

♯ = Long-playing, 33⅓ r.p.m.   ♭ = 45 r.p.m.   ♮ = Auto. couplings, 78 r.p.m.

RAKOV, Nicolai (b. 1908)

Concerto, E minor, vln. & orch.
☆ D. Oistrakh & USSR—Kondrashin
(♯ Csm.CRLPX 2 & ♯ Griff. 1004)

Dance Suite
Intermezzo on Kazakh airs; Tartar dance; Tadjik dance; Finale
☆ Moscow Phil.—Ivanov (4ss) *USSR. 8902/3*
(o.n. ▽ *D.M 528* & *M 534*; *C.MC 3313/2*) & *8906/7*

Humoresque & Serenade　　vlc. & pf.
☆ D. Shafran (in ♯ Csm.CRLP 114)

Poem　　　　　　vln. or vlc. & pf.
D. Oistrakh (vln.) & pf.　　*USSR. 16477/8*
☆ S. Knushevitzky (vlc.) & N. Rakov (in ♯ Csm.CRLP 114)

RAMEAU, Jean Philippe (1683-1764)

I. STAGE WORKS

(Les) INDES GALANTES Opera. Prol. &
4 Entrées　1735
ABRIDGED RECORDING
☆ Soloists, Cho. & Cha. Orch.—Hewitt (♯ DFr. 6)

Air grave pour deux polonais　(Prologue)
W. Landowska (hpsi)　　♯ **Vic.LM 1186**
(† Anthology)　　　　(in ♭ set *WDM 1586*)

PLATÉE Opera　Prol. & 3 acts　1745
Orch. Suites Nos. 1 & 2
Lausanne Sym.—Desarzens　　♯ **CHS.F 3**
(*below*)

Menuet dans le goût de vièle; Rigaudon
☆ Brussels Radio—André　♯ *DT.LGM 65002*
(*Debussy, Chabrier, etc.*)　　　(♯ *T.LS 6011*)

II. INSTRUMENTAL

A. CHAMBER MUSIC

(6) CONCERTS EN SEXTUOR　Str. & hpsi.
COMPLETE
Cha. Orch.—Hewitt (n.v.)　　♯ **DFr. 1**

PIÈCES DE CLAVECIN EN CONCERT　1741
Concert No. 1 ... Le Vézinet
Concert No. 2 ... Le Boucon
Concert No. 3 ... Tambourin en rondeau
— ARR. PF. VLN. VLC., Saint-Saëns
Trieste Trio　　　　♯ **D.LX 3106**
(*Vivaldi: Sonata*)　　　(♯ *Lon.LS 600*)

Concert No. 3 ... La Timide—*SEE* Sec. III, Miscellaneous

II. B. HARPSICHORD

SUITES (ed. Riemann)
No. 1, A minor
... 6, Sarabande; 7, Gavotte; 8, La Vénitienne
G. Copeland (pf.)　　in ♯ *MGM.E 151*

... 1, Prelude & Gigue; 8, La Vénitienne
C. J. Chiasson (hpsi.)　　in ♯ **Lyr.LL 19**
(† French Masters)

No. 2, E minor

1. Allemande	5. Rigaudons I & II
2. Courante	6. Musette en rondeau
3. Gigue en rondeau	7. Tambourin
4. Le rappel des oiseaux	8. La Villageoise

No. 4, A minor

1. Allemande	5. Fanfarinette
2. Courante	6. La Triomphante
3. Sarabande	7. Gavotte & 5 doubles
4. Les Trois Mains	

F. Valenti　　　　　♯ **West.WL 5128**

No. 2, E minor
T. Sack (omitting Courante)　　♯ **CHS.F 3**
(*above*)

... **No. 6, Musette en rondeau** only
☆ A. Ehlers (in ♯ AmD.DL 8019)

No. 4 ... No. 7, Gavotte & 5 Doubles
No. 5 ... No. 3, La Poule
☆ S. Marlowe　　　in ♯ *MGM.E 538*
(*Couperin*)

II. C. MISCELLANEOUS

(La) Dauphine
☆ W. Landowska (♭ G. 7RF 254; in ♯ Vic.LM 1217:
♭ set *WDM 1181*)

Minuet (unspec.) — ARR. GUITAR
▽ A. Segovia (*AmD. 24146* in set A 596: ♯ *DL 5257*)

(La) Timide
(from *5 Pièces extraites des pièces en concert*)
C. J. Chiasson (hpsi.)　　in ♯ **Lyr.LL 19**
(† French Masters)

RANGSTRÖM, Ture (1884-1947)

(3) Legends from the Mälar
(for Strindberg's play "*Town Journey*")
S. Ribbing (pf.)　　　　**T.E 19809/10**
(*Wiklund: Lyric pieces*)

Symphony No. 1, C sharp minor　1914
(*In memoriam A. Strindberg*)
Stockholm Concert Soc.—Mann ♯ **D.LXT 2665**
(♯ *Lon.LL 514*)

RAPHLING, Sam (b.　　)

(An) American Album　　　pf.
... **Three pieces**
S. Raphling　　　　　♯ **Circ. 51-102**
(*Goeb & Starer*)

RASCH, Kurt (b. 1902)

Toccata, Op. 27　　　orch.
Berlin Municipal—Meyer　　**Pol. 15510**
(2ss)　　　　　　(o.n. 57219)

RATNER, Leonard (b. 1916)

Serenade, oboe, horn, Str. Qtt.
Cha. Mus. Ens.—Salgo　　　♯ **ML. 7023**

☆ = Re-issue of a recording to be found in WERM or Supplement I.

RAVEL, Maurice (1875-1937)

CLASSIFIED: I. PIANO
             II. CHAMBER MUSIC
             III. ORCHESTRAL
             IV. STAGE WORKS
             V. SONGS

I. PIANO

COMPLETE RECORDING OF THE PIANO WORKS

À la manière de ... 1913	ML 4518
GASPARD DE LA NUIT	ML 4519
Habanera (pf. duet) 1895	ML 4519
Jeux d'eau	ML 4519
MA MÈRE L'OYE (pf. duet)	ML 4519
Menuet antique 1895	ML 4519
Menuet sur le nom d'Haydn 1909	ML 4520
MIROIRS	ML 4518
Pavane pour une infante défunte	ML 4518
Prelude, A minor 1913	ML 4520
Sonatina, F sharp minor	ML 4518
(Le) TOMBEAU DE COUPERIN	ML 4520
Valses nobles et sentimentales	ML 4520

R. Casadesus (with G. Casadesus in the duets)
(6ss)   ♯ AmC.ML 4518/20

GASPARD DE LA NUIT 1908

1. Ondine   2. Le Gibet   3. Scarbo

L. Pennario   ♯ DCap.CTL 7019
(Miroirs)   (♯ Cap.P 8152)

G. Scherzer   (6ss)   P.R 3516, 3615 & E 11509

Jeux d'eau   1901

M. Panzéra   in ♯ Mer.MG 10098
(Songs; & Poulenc, Milhaud, etc.)

MA MÈRE L'OYE

— PF. DUET VERSION   1908

G. Gorini & S. Lorenzi (4ss)   Dur.SA 144/5
(Debussy: Epigraphes antiques, in ♯ Csm.CLPS 1026)

E. Bartlett & R. Robertson   ♯ MGM.E 161
(Debussy: Petite suite)

— ORCH. VERSION   1912

☆ Boston Sym.—Koussevitzky   ♯ G.ALP 1003

☆ L.S.O.—Previtali (♯ BB.LBC 1009: ♭ set WBC 1009)

MIROIRS   1905

1. Noctuelles   4. Alborada del gracioso
2. Oiseaux tristes   5. La vallée des cloches
3. Une barque sur l'océan

COMPLETE RECORDING

L. Pennario   ♯ DCap.CTL 7019
(Gaspard de la nuit)   (♯ Cap.P 8152)

No. 4, Alborada del gracioso

— ORCH. VERSION Ravel

Minneapolis Sym.—Dorati   ♯ Mer.MG 50005
(below; & Debussy)

Suisse Romande—Ansermet   ♯ D.LX 3072
(Stravinsky, Prokofiev, Debussy)   (♯ Lon.LS 503)

Pavane pour une infante défunte   1889

— ORCH. VERSION   1912

Minneapolis Sym.—Dorati   ♯ Mer.MG 50005
(above; & Berlioz & Debussy)

Residentie—v. Otterloo   Phi.N 12046H
                        (PhM.N 09036S)

— ARR. VLN. & PF.

C. Ferras & P. Barbizet   D.GAB 15097
(Debussy: Vln. Sonata, s. 1)

Sonatina, F sharp minor   1905

K. Long   in ♯ D.LK 4043
(below & Chabrier)   (♯ Lon.LL 452)

C. Haskil   ♯ Phi.A 00143L
(D. Scarlatti)

E. Passani   ♯ Pat.DT 1010
(Valses nobles et sentimentales)

(Le) TOMBEAU DE COUPERIN   1914-7

K. Long   in ♯ D.LK 4043
(Sonatina, & Chabrier)   (♯ Lon.LL 452)

— ORCH. VERSION   1918

Lamoureux—Fournet   C.LFX 1002/3
(4ss)

N.B.C. Sym.—Reiner   ♯ Vic.LM 1724
(Mendelssohn & Debussy)   (♭ set WDM 1724)

Valses nobles et sentimentales   1911

E. Passani   ♯ Pat.DT 1010
(Sonatina)

M. Schwalb   ♯ Acad.ALP 307
(Liszt: Spanish Rhapsody)

— ORCH. VERSION   1912   ("Adelaide" Ballet)

☆ Brussels Radio—André   ♯ DT.LGM 65003
(below)   (♯ T.LS 6010)

... Nos. 6 & 7   — ARR. VLN. & PF.   Heifetz

☆ J. Heifetz & E. Bay   G.DA 1915
(Poulenc: Presto)

II. CHAMBER MUSIC

Berceuse sur le nom de Fauré   vln. & pf.   1922

J. Martzy & J. Antonietti   PV. 36015
(below; & Falla & Milhaud)

Introduction & Allegro, G flat major   1906
(Septet) hp., fl., cl., & str. qtt.

A. Stockton, A. Gleghorn, M. Lurie,
& Hollywood Qtt.   ♯ DCap.CCL 7509
(Debussy: Danses, sacrée et profane)   (♯ Cap.L 8154)

P. Berghout & Amsterdam Cha. Music Soc. Ens.
                            ♯ D.LX 3097
(Debussy: Danses, sacrée et profane)   (♯ Lon.LS 621)

Pièce en forme de habanera   1907

— ARR. VLN. & PF. Catherine

Y. Menuhin & A. Baller   JpV.SD 3046
(Dvořák-Kreisler: Sym. 5, excpt.)

J. Martzy & J. Antonietti   PV. 36015
(Berceuse; & Falla & Milhaud)

I. Haendel & G. Moore   G.B 10135
(Grieg: Scherzo-Impromptu)

E. Nielsen & L. Christiansen   G.DA 5268
(Stravinsky: Danse Russe)

T. Magyar & W. Hielkema   Phi.N 11157G
(Kreisler: Variations) (also in PhM.N 09009S: &
                             ♯ Phi.N 00125R)

— ARR. 2 PFS.   Gearhart

V. Morley & L. Gearhart   in ♯ AmC.ML 2197

— ARR. VLC. & PF.

P. Fournier & E. Lush   G.DA 2005
(L. Boulanger: Nocturne)

S. Knushevitzky (in ♯ Csm.CRLP 114)

☆ R. Krotschak (in ♯ Eur.LPG 631)

Quartet, Strings, F major   1903

Juilliard Qtt.   (2ss)   ♯ AmC.ML 2202

Pascal Qtt.   ♯ CHS.CHS 1123
(Sonata)

Champeil Qtt.   (2ss)   ♯ Sat.LD 7001

Stuyvesant Qtt.   (Debussy)   ♯ Phil. 104

Fine Arts Qtt.   ♯ Mer.MG 10105
(Hindemith)

☆ Paganini Qtt.   (2ss)   ♯ Vic.LM 146
                           (♭ set WDM 1645)

Sonata, vln. & vlc.   1920-2
(Pour le Tombeau de Debussy)

B. Urban & M. Herbert   ♯ CEd. 1005
(Milhaud, Debussy, Ibert)

☆ O. Shumsky & B. Greenhouse (♯ CHS.CHS 1123)

♯ = Long-playing, 33⅓ r.p.m.   ♭ = 45 r.p.m.   ♮ = Auto. couplings, 78 r.p.m.

Trio, A minor,   pf., vln., vlc.   1915
  ▽ Albeneri Trio   ♯ **Mer.MG 10089**
  (Fauré: Trio)

  ☆ A. Rubinstein, J. Heifetz, G. Piatigorsky
                                ♯ **G.ALP 1009**
  (Mendelssohn: Trio)   (♯ FALP 111)

Tzigane   vln. & pf. (or orch.)   1924
  T. Magyar & W. Hielkema   ♯ *Phi.N 00125R*
  (Pièce en forme ...; & Kreisler, Bloch)

III. ORCHESTRAL

Boléro   1928
  ☆ Paris Cons.—Münch   ♯ **D.LXT 2677**
  (Berlioz: Overtures)   (♯ Lon.LL 466)
  ☆ Czech Phil.—Désormière   ♯ *Sup.LPM 31*
  (Karajev: Seven Beauties)
  ☆ Boston Sym.—Koussevitzky ♮ **G.DB 9601/2**
  (Ma Mère l'oye on ♯ G.ALP 1003)
  Berlin Sym.—List (♯ Roy. 1313: also ♯ *6135*)
  ☆ Brussels Radio—André (♭ *Cap. set KBM 8092*)
  Paris Cons.—Giardino (♮ *Pat.PM 4016/7*)

CONCERTOS
G major, pf. & orch.   1931
  M. Long & Paris Cons.—Tzipine ♯ **C.FCX 169**
  (Fauré: Ballade)

D major, pf. (left hand) & orch.   1931
  ☆ R. Casadesus & Philadelphia—Ormandy
                              · (C.GQX 11461/2)

Ma Mère l'oye: *SEE:* Section I, Piano

Rapsodie espagnole   1907
  Suisse Romande—Ansermet   ♯ **D.LXT 2637**
  (Debussy: Nocturnes)   (♯ Lon.LL 530)
  Boston Sym.—Münch   ♯ **Vic.LM 1700**
  (below; & Lalo)   (♭ set WDM 1700)
  French Nat. Radio—Cluytens   ♯ *Pat.DT 1005*
  (La Valse)   (♯ QT 1005)

(La) Valse   Poème chorégraphique   1920
  French Nat. Radio—Cluytens **Pat.PDT 259/60**
  (4ss)   (MDT 14/15: ♯ *Pat.DT 1005: QT 1005*)
  Brussels Radio—André   ♯ *DT.LGM 65003*
  (Valses nobles et sentimentales)   (♯ *T.LS 6010*)
  (Daphnis et Chloë, Suite No. 2, on Cap. L 8145)
  (3ss—*Damnation de Faust, Menuet*, on T.E 3885/6)
  (also ▽ ♭ *Cap.set KBM 8083*)
  ☆ Boston Sym.—Münch   ♯ **Vic.LM 1700**
  (above; Saint-Saëns, Berlioz, etc.) (♭ set WDM 1700)
                                     (& ♭ G.7RF 257)

— ARR. 2 PFS.
  A. Whittemore & J. Lowe (in ♯ Vic.LM 1705:
                                   ♭ set WDM 1705)

IV. STAGE WORKS

(L') HEURE ESPAGNOLE   Opera   1 act   1911
COMPLETE RECORDING
  Concepción   ...   ...   J. Linda (S)
  Gonzalve ...   .   A. Dran (T)
  Torquemada   ...   ...   J. Mollien (T)
  Ramiro   ...   .   J. Hoffman (B)
  Don I. Gómez   ...   ...   L. Mans (Bs)
  Paris Radio Sym. Orch.—Leibowitz
                         ♯ **E. & AmVox.PL 7880**

DAPHNIS ET CHLOË   Ballet   1910
Orchestral Suite No. 2
  Brussels Radio—André   ♯ **DT.LGX 66001**
  (Debussy: Images, Set III—Ibéria)   (♯ T.LSK 7015)
  (La Valse on ♯ Cap.L 8145)

V. SONGS & PART-SONGS

(3) Chansons (Ravel)   S, A, T, B   1915
  Couraud Ensemble   V♯ *DFr. 21*

... Nos. 1 & 2 only
  G. Carrillo Vocal Qtt (*Span*)   **Orf. 22002**
  (Wolf)

... **Nos. 1 & 3 only**
  ☆ Pro Musica Cho.—Calder (in ♯ *CID. 33007*)

(3) Chansons madécasses (Paray) voice, fl., vlc., pf.
  J. Tourel (M-S), J. Wummer, L. Vargo,
  G. Reeves   ♯ *AmC.ML 2184*
  (Debussy)
  M. Singher (B),   S. Baron,   D. Soyer,
  P. Ulanowsky   ♯ **CHS.CHS 1124**
  (below)

(4) Chants populaires   1910
  M. Singher (B), P. Ulanowsky (pf.)
                               ♯ **CHS.CHS 1124**
  (above & below)
  C. Panzéra (B), M. Panzéra (pf.)
                               ♯ **Mer.MG 10098**
  (below; Jeux d'eau; & Poulenc, etc.)

... **No. 4, Hébraïque (Méjerke)** only
  ☆ P. Bernac (B), F. Poulenc (pf.) (in ♯ C.FCX 141)

Histoires naturelles (Renard)   1906
  M. Singher (B), P. Ulanowsky (pf.)
  (above)   ♯ **CHS.CHS 1124**
  G. Souzay (B), J. Bonneau (pf.) ♯ *D.LX 3077*
  (Falla: 7 Popular songs)   (♯ Lon.LS 563)
  ☆ P. Bernac (B), F. Poulenc (pf.) ♯ **C.FCX 141**
  (below & Poulenc)

(2) Mélodies hébraïques   1914
      1. Kaddisch   2. L'énigme éternelle
  ☆ P. Bernac (B), F. Poulenc (pf.) ♯ **C.FCX 141**
  (above & Poulenc)

(5) Mélodies populaires grecques   1907
      (Calvocoressi)
  I. Kolassi (M-S), J. Bonneau (pf.)
                            in ♯ *D.LX 3060*
  (Fauré, Aubert, etc.)   (in ♯ Lon.LS 568)
  C. Panzéra (B), M. Panzéra (pf.)
                               ♯ **Mer.MG 10098**
  (Jeux d'eau; above; Poulenc, etc.)

Noël des jouets (Ravel)   1905
  J. Wilson (S), G. Trovillo (pf.)
                            in ♯ **AmD.DL 9554**
  (Respighi, Rossini, etc.)

Vocalise en forme de habanera   1907
  D. Pantofel-Nechetskaya (S)   *USSR. 16644*
  (Saint-Saëns: Cygne)

RAWSTHORNE, Alan (b. 1905)

Concerto No. 2, pf. & orch.   1951
  C. Curzon & L.S.O.—Sargent   ♯ *D.LX 3066*
  (2ss)   (♯ Lon.LS 513)

Theme and Variations   Str. Qtt.
  Hirsch Qtt.   in ♯ **Argo.ARS 1002**
  (Debussy & Arensky)

REDFORD, John (c. 1485-1548)

  SEE: † RENAISSANCE MASTERPIECES

REGER, Max (1873-1916)

Ballet Suite, Op. 130   orch.
  Dresden Phil.—Schrader   ♯ **Ura. 7050**
  (Pfitzner)

Benedictus, Op. 59, No. 9   org.
  ▽ W. Bäumer   **Chr. 310B**
  (Bruhns: Prelude)

☆ = Re-issue of a recording to be found in WERM or Supplement I.

CHORALE-PRELUDES, Op. 135a organ
Grosser Gott, wir loben dich
Herr Jesu Christ, dich zu uns wend
Meinen Jesum lass ich nicht
Was mein Gott will, das g'scheh allzeit
Wer nur den lieben Gott lässt walten
Pastorale, Op. 59, No. 2 organ
R. Noehren in ♯ **Aphe.AP 2**
(Vierne & Liszt)

Intermezzo, Op. 45, No. 2 pf.
L. Podolsky in ♯ **Cmt. 1204**
(Scriabin, Kortchmaryev, etc.)

Serenade, G major, Op. 95 orch.
Berlin Phil.—Jochum ♯ **Ura. 7052**

(4) SONATINAS, Op. 89 pf.
N. Dayton ♯ **NRI. 407**

SERENADES, fl., vln., & vla.
D major, Op. 77a
G major, Op. 141a
Caratelli, Figueroa, di Piazza ♯ **NRI. 202**
(below)

SONG
Mariä Wiegenlied, Op. 76, No. 52 (Boelitz)
I. Seefried (S), W. Schneiderhan (vln.),
E. Werba (pf.) **Pol. 62893**
(Wolf: Schlafendes Jesuskind)
G. Catley (S, *Eng*) & pf. **G.B 10186**
(Woodgate: Jubilate)
E. Berge (S), Cho. & orch. **Felix. 51**
(Brahms: In stiller Nacht)

▽ D. Dame (T, *Eng*) *MGM. 30265*
☆ E. Berger (S) *Pol. 26502*
M. Lanza (T), Cho. & orch. *BrzV. 10-1582*

— ARR. CHO.
Wiltener Sängerknaben—Gerholdt *Tono.K 8083*
(Gounod: Ave Maria)

Suite, Op. 103a vln. & pf.
... Aria only
G. Knudsen & E. Garcia ♯ **ML. 5002**
(Eccles, Knudsen, Gjerstrøm)

TRIOS, vln., vla., vlc.
A minor, Op. 77b
D minor, Op. 141b
Figueroa Trio ♯ **NRI. 202**
(above)

Variations on a theme of J. A. Hiller, Op. 100 orch.
Berlin Phil.—v. Kempen (6ss) ♮ **PV. 72091/3**

Variations on a theme of Mozart, Op. 132 orch.
☆ Amsterdam—v. Beinum (♯ AmD.DL 9565)

Variations & Fugue on a theme of Telemann,
Op. 134 pf.
E. Then-Bergh (4ss) ♮ **PV. 72186/7**
(♯ *Pol. 16018)*

REGNART, Francis (fl. end XVIth Cent)
SEE: † COURTLY MUSIC

REICHA, Antonin (1770-1836)

QUINTETS, fl., ob., cl., hrn., bsn.
No. 2, E flat major, Op. 88, No. 2
New Art Wind Quintet ♯ **CEd. set CE 2010**
(Mozart, Danzi, Stamitz)

No. 22, E minor, Op. 100, No. 4
French Wind Quintet (2ss) ♯ **OL.LD 23**

REICHARDT, Johann Friedrich
(1752-1814)

Grazioso, G major Glass harmonica 1786
B. Hoffmann **Pol. 6002**
(Beethoven & Mozart)

REICHEL, Bernard (b. 1901)

Concertino, pf. & orch. 1949
C. Montandon & Suisse Romande—Appia
♯ **D.LXT 2703**
(Beck: Viola Concerto) (♯ Lon.LL 601)

REINAGLE, Alexander (1756-1809)

Sonata, E major pf.
A. Loesser (xviiith. century pf.) ♯ **NRI. 2006**
(† American Inst. Music)
J. Behrend ♯ **Allo.ALG 3024**
(† American Music)

RESPIGHI, Ottorino (1879-1936)

Concerto gregoriano vln. & orch. 1922
☆ P. Richartz & Berlin Municipal—Heger (Pol. 15511/4S)

Feste Romane Sym. Poem Orch. 1929
☆ N.B.C. Sym.—Toscanini **G.DB 21487/9**
(♯ *G.BLP 1011; FBLP & QBLP 1009)*
☆ Berlin Phil.—de Sabata (P.RR 8014/7S)

(Le) Fontane di Roma Sym. Poem orch. 1917
☆ [1] Augusteo, Rome—de Sabata ♯ **G.FALP 178**
(Debussy: Jeux)

Sonata, B minor vln. & pf. 1917
J. Heifetz & E. Bay ♯ **G.FALP 165**
(Debussy: Sonata)
(♯ Vic.LM 1184: & 6ss, ♭ *set WDM 1576)*
▽ L. Kaufman & T. Saidenberg
♯ **Tem.MTT 2078**
(Saint-Saëns: Concerto)

SONGS
Crepuscolo (Rubino) 1917
Pioggia (Pompilj) 1909
C. Williams (S), B. Bazala (pf.)
in ♯ *MGM.E 140*
(Carpenter, Dougherty, Debussy, etc.)

Noël ancien (Anon) 1912
J. Wilson (S, *Fr*), G. Trovillo (pf.)
♯ **AmD.DL 9554**
(Rossini, Byrd, etc.)

Romance (unspec.) M. Mey-Figner (S) (*USSR 18246*)

Trittico Botticelliano Small orch. 1927
Vienna State Op.—Litschauer ♯ **Van.VRS 418**
(Locatelli)

ARRANGEMENTS for orchestra
SUITE No. 3 ... No. 3, Siciliana (Anon.)
Rome Coll. Mus.—Fasano **P.BB 25285**
(Vivaldi: Concerto, P. 434, s. 3)
(Paisiello: Pf. Concerto, s. 5 on BB 25288)
(Vivaldi: Concerto, Op. 3, No. 10, s. 3 on BB 25292)
(Bach: Concerto for 4 claviers, s. 3 on BB 25294)

(La) Boutique fantasque 1919
(Ballet Suite, after Rossini)
Covent Garden—Rignold ♯ *P.PMD 1002*
(♯ *Od.OD 1006; ♯ AmD.DL 7518)*

---

[1] This orch. is now catalogued as "Santa Cecilia Academy, Rome."

(La) Boutique fantasque (*continued*)

Covent Garden—Braithwaite (excerpts)
in ♯ **MGM.E 3006**
(*Chopin, Delibes, etc.*)
☆ Santa Cecilia—Serafin (G.DB 4299/301)

Rossiniana—Suite after Rossini
Berlin State Op.—Steinkopf ♯ **Ura. 7030**
(*Janáček: Sinfonietta*)
(2 movts. only on ♭ *Ura.UREP 10*)

SEE also: Rachmaninoff—Études tableaux; Vitali; etc.

REUBKE, Julius (1834-1858)

Sonata, C minor (on Psalm 94) org.
C. Crozier (org. of Rochester Univ.) ♯ **Ken.2552**
▽ E. P. Biggs **Vic. 11-8560/2**
(5ss—*Clarke: Trumpet Voluntary*) (set M 961)
... Intro. & Finale only
▽ G. D. Cunningham (C.DX 457), etc.

REUSNER, Esajas (1636-1679)

Suite, C minor Lute 1676
W. Gerwig **Pol. 6001**

REYER, Ernest (1823-1909)

SIGURD Opera 4 acts 1884
Et toi, Freïa B (Act II)
Ⓗ M. Renaud (IRCC. 3049*)

Salut! splendeur du jour S (Act II)
G. Lubin (2ss) *IRCC. 3099*
(o.n. ▽ *Od. 188724*)

Un souvenir poignant T (Act IV)
Ⓗ A. Alvarez (HRS. 1078*)

REZNIČEK, Emil Nikolaus von
(1860-1945)

DONNA DIANA Opera 3 acts 1894
Overture
Brussels Radio—André **T.E 3922**
(*Hellmesberger: Ball Scene*)
Philharmonia—Fistoulari ♯ *MGM.E 120*
(*Nicolai, Rimsky;* also *Wolf-Ferrari* in ♭ *K 120*)
Vienna Radio—Nilius **Vien.L 6051**
(*Tchaikovsky: Sleeping Beauty Waltz*)
☆ Vienna Phil.—Karajan (C.LFX 1013: M 15141)
Boston Pops—Fiedler (♭ *G.BF 1040*)
Chicago Sym.—Stock (in ♯ AmC.RL 3002)

RHEINBERGER, Joseph (1839-1901)

SONATAS organ
No. 11, D minor, Op. 148
... Cantilène only
F. Asma **Phi.N 11168G**
(*J. Grison: Toccata*) (*PhM.N 09002S*)
(also, with *Grison, Bach & Mendelssohn,* in ♯ *N 00118L*)

▽ Older recordings include:
SONATAS: No. 6, *G.B 4015*
No. 8, excpts. *G.B 3316*
CONCERTO: No. 2 Pol. 66445/7; B.80005/7
Vision, from Op. 156: Tema variato from Op. 167
D.CA 8239; Pol. 27128
Other organ works on Pol. 27127; Vocal on Pol. 27107;
Chr. 44; etc.

RIEGGER, Wallingford (b. 1885)

Quartet, String, No. 2, Op. 43 1948
New Music Qtt. ♯ **AmC.ML 4494**
(*Moore*)

RIISAGER, Knudåge (b. 1897)

Concertino, Tpt. & str. orch. Op. 29 1938
Little Overture Str. orch.
☆ G. Eskdale & Danish Radio—Jensen
(*Schierbeck*) ♯ **Mer.MG 15041**

Monument for Kingo orch. 1944
Torgutik Dance orch. 1939
Copenhagen Royal Op.—Frandsen **C.DDX 31**

NIELS EBBESEN 1945
(Inc. music to play by Kai Munk)
Prelude
Copenhagen Royal Op.—Hye-Knudsen
Pol.Z 60149
(*K. N. Andersen: The Silken Castle—Funeral March*)

Palavas vln. & pf. 1951
W. Tworek & H. Aurvig (*Pol.HA 70039*)

SONGS
April (Jensen)
Winter verse (Lorentzen)
A. Schiøtz (T), H. D. Koppel (pf.) *G.X 8010*

Denmark's Freedom song (Kristensen)
▽ A. Schiøtz (T) & orch. (*G.X 6982*, 2 d.cs)

Lullaby (Lorentzen) 1929 — ARR. VLN. & PF.
(*Sovesang*)
W. Tworek & E. Vagning *Pol.HA 70036*
(*Suk: Burlesque*)

RIMSKY-KORSAKOV, Nicholas
Andreievitch (1844-1908)

I. ORCHESTRAL & INSTRUMENTAL

Capriccio espagnol, Op. 34 orch.
French Nat. Sym.—Désormière
♯ **DCap.CTL 7020**
(*Golden Cockerel, suite*) (♯ Cap.P 8155)
Paris Cons.—Cluytens ♯ **Pat.DTX 116**
(*below, Moussorgsky, Borodin, etc.*) (♯ AmVox.PL 7670)
Boston Prom.—Fiedler (n.v.) ♯ *Vic.LM 164*
(*Mendelssohn, Tchaikovsky*) (♭ set WDM 1647)
Philharmonia—Schuechter ♯ *MGM.E 138*
(*Tchaikovsky: Marche slave*)
Austrian Sym.—Mehlich ♯ **Rem. 149-45**
(*Delibes*)
(*Sibelius: Finlandia,* on ♯ *Mrt. 1-8*)
Berlin Sym.—Hermann ♯ **Roy. 1294**
(*Khachaturian*) (also on ♯ *Roy. 6125*)
☆ Danish Radio—Malko (G.DB 4304/5: GB 56/7)
A. Kostelanetz Orch. (♮ C.CQX 7000/1)
Sym.—Kondrashin (♯ *CdM. LD 8010*)

— ARR. 4 PFS.
First Piano Qtt. (in ♯ Vic.LM 1227: ♭ set WDM 1624)

Concerto on a Russian theme pf. & orch. 1882-3
S. Richter & Moscow Youth Sym.—Kondrashin
(4ss) **USSR. 017956/9**
F. Jacquinot & Philharmonia—Fistoulari
(*Liszt*) ♯ *MGM.E 182*

☆ = Re-issue of a recording to be found in WERM or Supplement I.

Concerto, trombone & Military Band 1877
 D. Shuman & Band—Serly
Khorovod (from *Jour de fête*) Str. Qtt.
 Radio Artists Qtt.
(3) Russian Folksongs
— ARR. FL., OB., CL., BSN. Rimsky & Nazarov
 Shuman Ensemble   ‡ **Circ.L 51-103**
 (Glazounov, Liadov, & Folksongs)

Easter Overture, Op. 36 ("*Grande Pâque Russe*")
 Philharmonia—Dobrowen (4ss) ♮ **G.C 7916/7**
 Paris Cons.—Cluytens   ‡ **Pat.DTX 116**
 (Borodin, Moussorgsky, etc.)   (‡ AmVox.PL 7670)
 ☆ Philadelphia—Ormandy   ‡ **C.FC 1007**
 (Prokofiev: Sym. No. 1)

Quartet, Strings, F major, Op. 12
... **Scherzo**
 Bolshoi Theatre Qtt.   (2ss)   **USSR. 18448/9**

Scheherazade, Op. 35 1888
 Minneapolis Sym.—Dorati   ‡ **Mer.MG 50009**
                         (♭ set X 50009)
 French Nat. Radio—Cluytens ‡ **Pat.DTX 122**
 Rhineland Sym.—Federer   ‡ **Rgt. 5044**
 ▽ Bolshoi Theatre—Golovanov
                         ♮ **U.H 23935/40**
 (D. Oistrakh, vln. solo)   (USSR. 014691/702)
 Berlin Radio—Rucht   ‡ **CdM.LDX 8016**
 Berlin Sym.—Balzer   ‡ **Roy. 1260**
 ☆ Paris Cons.—Ansermet (D.K 23151/6)
 L.P.O.—Dorati (‡ BB.LBC 1006: ♭ set WBC 1006)
 Philadelphia—Ormandy (‡ C.FCX & QCX 134)
 Viennese Sym.—Brown (‡ Mrt. 200-15)
... 3rd movt. Col. Sym.—Rodzinski (in ♭ AmC. set A 1003)

Sinfonietta on Russian themes, A minor, Op. 31
 Berlin Radio—Ludwig   ‡ **Ura. 7045**
 (above)

Symphony No. 2, Op. 9 (Antar)
... **3rd movt. only**
 Brussels Radio—André   **T.E 3196**
 (Prince Igor—Dances, s. 3)

Tati-tati: Paraphrases on *Chopsticks* pf. duet
Theme, 24 variations & finale [1]
Berceuse, Tarantella, Fughetta on B.A.C.H.
Carillon
— ARR. & ORCH. N. Tcherepnin 1937
 Col. Sym.—Janssen   ‡ **AmC.ML 4480**
 (Cui, Liszt, Borodin, etc.)

II. SONGS

Anchar, Op. 49, No. 1 (Pushkin) (*The Upas-Tree*)
 A. Krivchenia   (2ss)   **USSR. 16365/6**

At last the dark clouds, Op. 42, No. 3 (Pushkin)
 ▽ S. J. Lemeshev (T), F. Stutchevsky (pf.) (*USSR. 4874*)

(The) Echo, Op. 27, No. 2
 (Coppé, trs. Andreyevsky)
 V. Borisenko (M-S)   **USSR. 15855**
 (Tchaikovsky: First meeting)

(The) Fir and the Palm, Op. 3, No. 1
 (Heine, trs. Mikhailov)
 A. Pirogov (B)   **USSR. 15234**
 (Tchaikovsky: O thou moonlight night)

Hebrew Song, Op. 7, No. 2 (Mey)
 (*I sleep, but my heart ...*)
**In the dark grove the nightingale is silent, Op. 4,
 No. 3** (Nikitin)
 V. Viktorova (S)   **USSR. 15242/3**

In the silence of the night, Op. 56, No. 2 (Maikov)
 N. Obukhova (M-S)   **USSR. 17880**
 (Bulakhov: I have not forgotten you)
 N. Kazantseva (S)   **USSR. 18858**
 (Rachmaninoff: How fair this spot)

It is not the wind, Op. 43, No. 2 (Tolstoy)
 A. Nezhdanova (S)   **USSR. 8361**
 (Masquerade—Nina's romance)

On the hills of Georgia, Op. 3, No. 4 (Pushkin)
 I. Kozlovsky (T)   **USSR. 18091**
 (Tchaikovsky: Frenzied nights)
 P. Nortsov (B)   **USSR. 4579**
 (½s.—*What is my name to you & Dargomijsky: Oriental
 ballad*)

(The) Prophet, Op. 49, No. 2 (Pushkin)
 M. Reizen (Bs) (2ss)   **USSR. 17453/4**

(The) Rose and the Nightingale, Op. 2, No. 2
 (Koltsov)
 ☆ L. Pons (S) & orch. (in ‡ AmC.ML 2181: ♭ set A 1006)

Sun of the sleepless, Op. 41, No. 1 (Byron, trs.
 A. Tolstoy)   (Or: *Star awakening ...*)
 V. Viktorova (S)   **USSR. 15244**
 (Zuleika's song)

What is my name to you? Op. 4, No. 1 (Pushkin)
 P. Nortsov (B)   **USSR. 4579**
 (½s.—*On the hills of Georgia & Dargomijsky: Oriental
 Ballad*)

When the yellowing cornfield blows, Op. 40, No. 1
 (Lermontov)
 Z. Dolukhanova (A), B. Kozel (pf.)
                          USSR. 021240
 (Mozart: Ridente la calma)

Zuleika's Song, Op. 26, No. 4 (after Byron)
 V. Viktorova (S)   **USSR. 15245**
 (Sun of the sleepless)

III. OPERAS

CHRISTMAS EVE 4 acts 1895
Orchestral Suite—ARR. Rimsky-Korsakov
 Berlin Radio—Ludwig   ‡ **Ura. 7045**
 (below)

(The) GOLDEN COCKEREL 3 acts 1910
Orchestral Suite
 Royal Phil.—Beecham   ‡ **AmC.ML 4454**
 (Franck: Chasseur maudit)
 French Nat. Sym.—Désormière
                          ‡ **DCap.CTL 7020**
 (Capriccio espagnol)   (‡ Cap.P 8155)
 Vienna Artists Sym.—Fekete [2] ‡ **Etu. 706**
 (Tchaikovsky: Tempest)
 USSR Radio—Golovanov   ‡ **Van.VRS 6000**
 (Moussorgsky) (excerpts on USSR. 018436/7)
 ☆ Austrian Sym.—Singer   ‡ **Rem. 199-55**
 (Tchaikovsky)   *(Grieg, in ‡ Rem. 199-68)*
 (also on ‡ Mrt. 1-6, 2ss)
 ☆ L.S.O.—Goossens (♮ G. JOX 7018/20)

... **Bridal procession only**
 L.S.O.—Weldon   in ‡ **MGM.E 145**

Hail to thee, Sun! (Hymn to the Sun) S Act II
 K. Grayson (*Eng*)   **MGM. 9070**
 ☆ D. J. Pantofel-Nechetskaya in ‡ Csm.CLPS 121
 E. Norena (*Fr*)   JpV.ND 4177

— ARR. VLN. & PF. Kreisler
 L. Kaufman & P. Ulanowsky
                       in ‡ **DCap. CCL 7513**
 (Schumann, Dvořák, etc.)   (‡ Cap.L 8165)

---

[1] Jointly with Cui, Liadov & Borodin.
[2] In a letter to *Saturday Review*, M. Fekete stated that he had never recorded this music for any company.

Hail to thee, Sun! (*continued*)
T. Magyar & W. Hielkema   **Phi.N 11230G**
(*Handel: Te Deum, excpt.*) (*PhM. 09045S &*
in ♯ *Phi.N 00605R*)
P. Sanchez & F. Doreau   **Sat.M 509**
(⅓s.—*Tsar Saltan—Bumble bee; & Monti: Czardas*)

(The) IMMORTAL KASHCHEY 1 act 1902
Kashcheyevna's Aria (unspec.)
☆ S. Preobrazhenskaya (M-S) (in ♯ Csm.CLPS 121)

(A) MAY NIGHT 3 acts 1880
COMPLETE RECORDING in *Russian*
Levko   ...   ...   S. Lemeshev (T)
Hanna   ...   ...   V. Borisenko (M-S)
Pannochka ...   ...   I. Maslennikova (S)
Golova   ...   ...   S. Krasovsky (B)
Bolshoi Theatre Cho. & Orch.—V. Nebolsin
(30ss)   **USSR. 021132/61**
(6ss, ♯ Van.VRS 6006/8; stated to be cond. Melik-Pashayev)

Overture
Philharmonia—Fistoulari   in ♯ *MGM.E 120*
(*Nicolai, Reznicek; also Wolf-Ferrari in ♭ K 120 only*)
Bolshoi Theatre—Orlov   **USSR. 010120/1**

The Sun descends (Levko's first aria, Act I)   T
☆ S. J. Lemeshev (in ♯ Csm.CLPS 121; or may be n.v.)

Duet, Hanna & Levko: Does she sleep? (Act I)
V. Borisenko, S. Lemeshev (from set)
      USSR. 17349
(*Gounod: Faust—Flower song, V. Borisenko*)

Cooper, stop the holes! (*Song on Village Mayor*)
Ens.—Alexandrov (*U.D 26116*)

Sleep, my beauty (Levko's second song, Act III) T
I. Kozlovsky   (2ss)   **USSR. 9176/7**
      (in ♯ Csm.CLPS 121)
ⱨ L. Sobinoff (AF. 49*)

Mayor's song (unspec.)
W. Pushkow (*Pol*) (*Muza. 1837*)

MLADA Opera-ballet 4 acts 1892
Procession of the nobles orig. cho. & orch.
☆ L.S.O.—Weldon   in ♯ *MGM.E 145*

PAN-VOYEVODA 4 acts 1904
Mazurka
USSR Radio—Golovanov   **USSR. 015497/8**
(2ss)

SADKO 7 Scenes 1898
Ho! Ye merchant guests   T
(Sadko's recit. & Aria, Sc. 1)
G. Nelepp   (2ss)   **USSR. 15679/80**

Ah! now I know   M-S (Sc. 3)
V. Borisenko   **Muza. X 1555**
(*Snow Maiden—Aria*)

Song of the Viking guest   Bs.   (Sc. 4)
B. Gmyria   **USSR. 18749**
(*Boris Godounov—Vaarlam's Song*)
B. Freitkov   in ♯ **Csm.CLPS 121**
☆ B. Christoff (♭ *G.7RF 163: 7R 150*)

Song of the Indian Guest   T   (Sc. 4)
H. Rosenberg (B, *Ger*) (*Imp. 19102*)
☆ S. J. Lemeshev (in ♯ Csm.CLPS 121)
A. Galli-Curci (S, *Fr*) (in ♯ Vic.LCT 1039:
      ♭ set WCT 62)
ⱨ R. Ponselle (in ♯ Gol. 1201*)

— ARR. ORCH.
Boston Pops—Fiedler (in ♭ *Vic.WEPR 20: ♭ 49-1445*)

— ARR. VLC. & PF.
☆ G. Piatigorsky & R. Berkowitz
      in ♯ **AmC.RL 3015**
(*Cui, Tchaikovsky, etc. & Shostakovitch*)

Sleep went along the river   S   (Lullaby, Sc. 7)
☆ N. Kazantseva (in ♯ Csm.CLPS 121)

SERVILIA 5 acts 1902
Servilia's aria (unspec.)   S
N. Shpiller   (2ss)   **USSR. 12740/1**

(The) SNOW-MAIDEN Prol. & 4 acts 1882
Orchestral Suite
USSR Radio Sym.—Gauk   ⱨ U.H 23902/3
(3ss—*Tchaikovsky: Mazeppa, Gopak*)

Introduction (Prologue)
☆ Philharmonia—Collingwood (in ♯ BB.LBC 1026:
      ♭ set WBC 1026)

ACT II
O my father   S & T
Full of wonders   T
Mizgir's aria (unspec.)   Bs
☆ S. Lemeshev, A. Ivanova & A. P. Ivanov
      (in ♯ Csm.CLPS 121)

ACT III
Joyous day departs   T
ⱨ ☆ L. Sobinoff (AF. 49*)

Ballet Music (including *Dance of the Tumblers*)
Berlin Radio—L. Ludwig   ♯ **Ura. 7035**
(*Moussorgsky*)   (& ♭ UREP 20)

Dance of the Tumblers   orch.
Concert Orch.—C. Williams (C.DX 1829: CQX 16652)
☆ Philharmonia—Collingwood (in ♯ BB.LBC 1026:
      ♭ set WBC 1026)

Clouds plotted with thunder   S or M-S
M. Maksakova   **USSR. 16241**
(*Joyous day departs*)
V. Borisenko   **Muza.X 1555**
(*Sadko, aria*)

(The) TALE OF TSAR SALTAN Prol. & 4 acts
      1900
Orchestral Suite
Netherlands Phil.—Spruit   ♯ **Nix.CLP 1155**
(*Massenet: Le Cid, ballet*)   (♯ CHS.CHS 1155)

Flight of the bumble-bee   orch.   Act III
☆ N.Y. Phil. Sym.—Kurtz   **C.DX 1860**
(¼s.—*Shostakovich & Prokofiev*)   (GFX 187)
      (♭ AmC.A 1509)
Metropole—v. d. Linden   in ♯ *Phi.P 10000R*
☆ Philharmonia—Malko (♭ G.7P 128: 7BF 1019;
      in ♯ BB.LBC 1026: ♭ set WBC 1026)
Carnegie Pops—Abravanel (in ♭ AmC. set A 1013)
Kostelanetz Orch. (C.DX 1845)

— ARR. VLN. (or VLC.) & PF.   Hartmann
P. Sanchez & F. Doreau   **Sat. M 509**
(¼s.—*Golden Cockerel—Hail to thee, Sun & Monti: Czardas*)
J. Heifetz & E. Bay   ♭ **G.7RF 171**
(*Sarasate & Castelnuovo-Tedesco*)   (♭ Vic. 49-1294)
W. Tworek & E. Vagning   **Pol.HA 70027**
(*Polakin: Le Canari*)
H. Szeryng & pf. (Orf. 4002)
☆ P. Casals (vlc.) (in ♯ Vic.LCT 1050: ♭ set WCT 72)

Intro. to Act IV, Sc. 2 (*The Three Wonders*)
USSR Radio Sym.—Golovanov
(2ss)   **USSR. 015749/50**

☆ = Re-issue of a recording to be found in WERM or Supplement I.

(The) TSAR'S BRIDE 3 acts 1899
Overture
  Bolshoi Theatre—Golovanov   *USSR. 14732/3*

ACT I

Gryazny's aria   B
  And. Ivanov (2ss)   **USSR. 014477/8**
  M. Grishko (2ss)   **USSR. 20015/6**

Scene & Duet: Lyubasha & Gryazny S & B
  A. Rudenko & M. Grishko   *USSR. 19914/5*

Darkling lowered the storm   T
  ☆ S. J. Lemeshev (in ♯ Csm.CLPS 121)

ACT II

In Novgorod (Martha's aria)   S
  I. Maslennikova (2ss)   *USSR. 17336/7*
  A. Nezhdanova   *USSR. 16033*
  (Arensky: Nal & Damayanti, Cradle song)
  E. Chavdar (2ss)   *USSR. 19906/7*
  ☆ N. D. Shpiller (in ♯ Csm.CLPS 121)

You will pay S or M-S (*Lyubasha's aria*)
  S. Preobrazhenskaya   *USSR. 17179*
  (Verdi: Trovatore, excpt.)
  ☆ M. Maksakova (in ♯ Csm.CLPS 121)

ACT III

Mad Scene: Ivan Sergeïch, Come into the garden
  I. Maslennikova   **USSR. 017335**
  (Borodin: Prince Igor, duet)

RODRIGO, Joaquin (b. 1902)

À l'ombre de Torre Bermeja pf. 1945
  (Homenaje a Ricardo Viñes)
  J. Rodrigo (2ss)   *G.AA 658*

Concerto, guitar & orch. 1939
  (Concierto de Aranjuez)
  R. S. de la Maza & Spanish Nat.—Argenta
  (6ss)   **SpC.RG 16066/8**

Concierto de estio, vln. & orch. 1943
  (Concerto d'été)
  C. Ferras & Paris Cons.—Enesco ♯ **D.LXT 2678**
  (Semenoff: Double Concerto)   (♯ Lon.LL 546)

Homenaje a la Tempranica   orch.
  ☆ Valencia Sym.—Iturbi   **G.DB 21456**
  (Palau-Boix: Marcha burlesca)

Pastoral pf. 1926
Preludio al gallo mañanero pf. 1928
  J. Rodrigo (1 side each)   *G.AA 647*

SONGS
Con qué la laveré (Trad.) 1947 (½s.)
De los alamos vengo, madre (Trad.) 1947 (½s.)
Cántico de la esposo (San Juan de la Cruz) 1934
  C. P. Durias (S), J. Rodrigo (pf.)
                   SpC.RG 16179

Coplas del pastor enamorado (Lope de Vega) 1935
(Un) home San Antonio (Rosalia de Castro) 1950
  C. P. Durias (S), J. Rodrigo (pf.) **SpC.RG 16176**

Serranilla (Montañesa) (Marques de Santillana)
  ▽ C. Supervia (M-S), A. Vilalta (pf.) *(Od. 184246)*

Zarabanda leyana   guitar
  R. de la Torre   in ♯ **Phil. 106**
  († Guitar Recital)

ROMAN, Johann Helmich (1694-1758)

Sinfonia No. 16, D major
  ☆ Danish Radio Cha.—Wöldike   **C.DX 1828**

Sonata, G minor   2 obs., cont.
  ☆ R. Lannerholm, A. Arnholm, I. Kjellström
  (hpsi)   ♮ **G.DB 11066S/7**

ROPARTZ, Guy (b. 1864)

(La) Cloche des Morts orch. 1902
... Paysage breton ▽ Sym.—Ropartz (Pat. X 5540)

(La) Mer ▽ C. Panzéra (B) & orch. (G.D 2082: W950)

Nocturne No. 3; Scherzo   pf.
  ▽ A. Vidal   **Lum. 3.06.010**
  (1 side each)   o.n. 32073

(Un) Prélude dominical et 6 pièces à danser pour
  chaque jour de la semaine   orch.
... Mardi; Mercredi ▽ Pierné—Ruhlmann (*AA. 3*)

Rondo   pf.
  M. Panzéra   in ♯ **Mer.MG 10098**
  (Tremois: Le Voyage; & Ravel, Poulenc, etc.)

ROSA, Salvator (1615-1673)

Star vicino al bell'idol
  Vocal Trio (*Eng*) & pf.   in *Vic. set E 100*
  (Schumann, Arne, etc.)   (♭ *set WE 100*)

ROSENBERG, Hilding (b. 1892)

Quartet No. 4, Op. 74 Strings 1939
  ☆ Garaguly Qtt.   ♮ **G.DB 11071/3**

ROSENMÜLLER, Johann (1619-1684)

Welt, ade!   Chorale
  Copenhagen Cha. Cho.—Bertelsen (*Dan*)
  (Schein: Chorale)   *Felix.F 50*

ROSSETER, Philip (c. 1575-1623)

What then is love but mourning ? (Campian)
  A. Deller (C-T), D. Dupré (lute)   **G.C 4178**
  (½s.—Campian: It fell on a summer day
         & Dowland: Sorrow, stay)

ROSSINI, Gioacchino (1792-1868)

I. INSTRUMENTAL

(La) Boutique fantasque, ARR. Respighi, *q.v.*

Matinées musicales, ARR. Britten, *q.v.*

(6) QUARTETS, fl., clar., hrn., bsn.
COMPLETE RECORDING
  New Art Wind Qtt. (4ss)   ♯ **CEd.CE 1010**

♯ = Long-playing, 33⅓ r.p.m.   ♭ = 45 r.p.m.   ♮ = Auto. couplings, 78 r.p.m.

182

II. SONGS

(La) Regata Veneziana
... **No. 3, Anzoleta dopo la regata**
G. Lavrova (*Russ*)　　　　***USSR. 18562***
(*Chopin: My sweetheart*)

(La) Separazione (Uccelli)
♓ C. Muzio (S) (in ♯ *Eso.ES 508**; ♯ *Cpt.MC 20009** [1])

SOIRÉES MUSICALES 1835
No. 6, Tirolese: La pastorella della Alpi
N. Kazantseva (*S. Russ*)　　***USSR. 19144***
(*Bulakhov: Valse*)

No. 8, La Danza (Pepoli)
▽ A. Galli-Curci (S), H. Samuels (pf.)　*G.VA 8*
(*Manon Lescaut, aria*)

J. Peerce (T) (o.v.) (in ♯ *Roy. 1278* & ♯ *6020*: ♭ *set 14540*)

☆ R. Tucker (T) (♭ *AmC.A 1540*)

Tu viens à nous (Abbé Maris)
J. Wilson (S), R. Baker (org.)
　　　　　　　　　　in ♯ **AmD.DL 9554**

(*Byrd, Bax, etc.*)

III. SACRED WORKS

MESSE SOLENNE 1820
Crucifixus
♓ ☆ E. Caruso (in ♯ *Vic.LCT 1034**: ♭ *set WCT 35**)

Domine Deus
♓ ☆ E. Caruso (in ♯ *Vic.LCT 1121**: ♭ *set WCT 1121**)

Pietà, Signore (often attrib. Stradella)
♓ E. Caruso (T) (in ♯ *Vic.LCT 1121** ♭ *set WCT 1121**)

STABAT MATER S, A, T, B, Cho., Orch. 1842
COMPLETE RECORDINGS
I. Steingruber, D. Herrmann, A. Dermota,
P. Schoeffler, Academy Cho. & Vienna State
Opera Orch.—Sternberg (2ss) ♯ **Oce.OCS 24**
I. Seefried (S), R. Anday (A), L. Fehenberger (T),
F. Frantz (B), Salzburg Cath. Cho. &
Mozarteum Orch.—Messner
(4ss)　　　　　　　♯ **Rem. set 199-111**

IV. OPERAS

(Il) BARBIERE DI SIVIGLIA 2 acts 1816
(*The Barber of Seville*)
COMPLETE RECORDINGS
Figaro　...　...　...　G. Bechi (B)
Rosina　...　...　V. de los Angeles (S)
Il Conte Almaviva...　...　N. Monti (T)
Don Basilio...　...　N. Rossi-Lemeni (Bs)
Dr. Bartolo...　...　...　M. Luise (B)
etc., Cho. & Milan Sym.—Serafin
　　　　　　　　　　♯ **G.ALP 1022/4**
(6ss)　　　(♯ *G.QALP 10001/3*; ♯ *Vic. set LM 6104*)

☆ G. Simionato (M-S), L. Infantino (T),
G. Taddei (B), C. Badioli (Bs), etc. Italian
Radio Cho. & Orch.—Previtali　(6ss)
　　　　　　　　　　♯ **FSor.CS 506/8**

Highlights
Rome Opera Soloists—Questa (♯ *Roy. 1208* & ♯ *Roy 6071*)
Anon. Soloists & Berlin State Op. Orch. (♯ *Roy. 1323*;
　　　　　　　　♯ *Var. 2008* & *6960, etc.*)

Overture
Berlin Municipal Op.—Rother　in ♯ **Ura. 7057**
　　　　　　　　　　　(& ♭ *UREP 3*)

☆ N.B.C. Sym.—Toscanini　in ♯ **G.ALP 1007**
(♯ *FALP 125*: ♭ *7R 138: 7RF/RQ 126*; ♭ *Vic. 49-1423* &
WEPR 14)

☆ Florence May Festival—Serafin　　*G.C 4136*

☆ Suisse Romande—Olof (♯ *Lon.LD 9012*)
　Berlin State Op.—v. Kempen (Pol. 15487)
　Florence May Fest.—Ghiglia (in ♯ *Rem. 149-18*)

[1] Recorded from Edison cylinder.

ACT I

No. 2, Ecco ridente in cielo　　　T
P. Munteanu　　　　　　**Pol. 68468**
(*Elisir d'Amore—Una furtiva lagrima*)
♓ F. de Lucía　　　　in ♯ *Ete.O-464**
H. Jadlowker　　G.VB 54*: o.n. 052385*

No. 4, Largo al factotum　　　B
I. Petroff & orch. (n.v.)　in ♯ **Rem. 199-93**

M. Grishko (*Russ*)　　　*USSR. 10530/1*
☆ T. Gobbi　　　♭ *G.7R 107*: ♭ *7RF 107*
L. Warren　　　　in ♯ *Vic.LM 1168*

No. 5, Se il mio nome　(*Serenata*)　T
C. Valletti　　　　　　*P.AT 0243*
(*Marta—Ach so fromm*)
♓ A. Bonci (HRS. 1113*)

No. 6, All' idea ... Numero quindici　T & B
♓ A. Bonci & F. Corradetti (in ♯ *GAR. 101**)
J. McCormack & G. Sammarco (G.VB 33*:
　　　　　　　　　　　o.n. DB 608*)

No. 7, Una voce poco fa　　　S
E. M. Pralungo　　　　　*P.AT 0277*
A. Noni　　　　　　　**P.CB 20536**
V. Maximova (*Russ*)　　　**U.H 23860**
V. Barsova (*Russ*) (? n.v.)　*USSR. 06340/1*
V. Firsova (*Russ*)　　　*USSR. 16334/5*
☆ C. Supervia　　in ♯ *AmD.DL 9523*
L. Pons　　　　　♭ *AmC.A 1510*
♓ S. Arnoldson　　G.VA 57*: o.n. 53517*
L. Tetrazzini　　　　*IRCC. 3091**
G. Fabbri　　　　　HRS. 1098*

No. 8, La calunnia è un venticello　Bs
G. Neri　　　　　　　P.R 30051
(*Simone Boccanegra—Il lacerato ...*)　(BB 25295)
R. Arié　　　　　in ♯ *D.LX 3041*
(*Boris, Sonnambula, Don Carlos*)　(♯ *Lon.LPS 98*)
E. List　　　　　in ♯ **Rem. 199-73**
(*Juive, Caïd, etc.*)
I. Petrov (*Russ*)　　　**USSR. 016464**
(*Bizet: Carmen—Air de fleur*)
W. Strienz (*Ger*)　　in ♯ *Ura. 7026*
M. Popov (*Pol*, 2ss)　　*Muza. 1772*
A. Majak (*Pol*)　　　*Muza. 1724*
E. Haken (*Cz*)　　　U.H 24236
☆ I. Tajo　in ♯ *Vic.LM 1148*: ♭ *set WDM 1542*
♓ A. Didur　　　in ♯ *Ete. O-467**

No. 9, Dunque io son　　　S & B
M. Tauberova & Z. Otava (Cz)　**U.H 24193**
(*Rigoletto—Duet, Act II*)
V. Firsova & D. Gamrekeli (*Russ*) (*USSR. 16059/60*)

No. 10, A un dottor della mia sorte　Bs
F. Corena　　　　in ♯ **D.LXT 2688**
(*Donizetti, Gounod, etc.*)　(in ♯ *Lon.LL 534*)

ACT II

Contro un cor　　　　S & T
☆ C. Supervia & G. Manuritta (in ♯ *AmD.DL 9533*)

No. 17, Storm Music　　　Orch.
☆ Berlin Municipal—Haarth (Pol. 15528)

No. 18, Ah! qual colpo inaspettato　S, T, Bs
♓ J. Huguet, De Lucia & A. Pini-Corsi (G.VB 1*:
　　　　　　　　　　o.n. DB 388*)

(La) CAMBIALE DI MATRIMONIO　1 act 1810
Overture
Royal Phil.—Beecham　(2ss)　**C.LX 1458**
(*Chabrier: España, in* ♯ *AmC.AAL 11*) (C.GQX 11498;
　　　　　　　　　　♭ *AmC. 4-73284D*)

(La) CENERENTOLA 2 acts 1817
Overture
☆ N.B.C. Sym.—Toscanini in ♯ **G.ALP 1007**
   (♯ FALP & QALP 125; ♭ *Vic. WEPR 13*)

ACT I

C'era una volta [1]   M-S & T
Z. Dolukhanova & A. Orfenov (*Russ*)
(*Rondo finale*)   **USSR. 18513**

Signore, una parola   M-S & Bs
☆ C. Supervia & V. Bettoni (in ♯ AmD.DL 9533)

ACT II

Nacqui all'affanno ... Non più mesta   M-S
  (*Air & Rondo finale*)
Z. Dolukhanova (*Russ*)   **USSR. 18512**
(*above*)

☆ C. Supervia (in ♯ AmD.DL 9533)

(La) GAZZA LADRA 2 acts 1817
Overture
Amsterdam—v. Beinum   in ♯ **D.LXT 2733**
        (in ♯ Lon.LL 358)

Rhineland Sym.—Federer   ♯ *Rgt. 5040*

☆ N.B.C. Sym.—Toscanini in ♯ **G.ALP 1007**
       (♯ FALP & QALP 125)

☆La Scala—Marinuzzi (AusT.E 1169)
  Philharmonia—Galliera (C.DWX 5063: GQX 11479)
  Berlin Municipal—Haarth (Pol. 15552/3), etc.

GUILLAUME TELL 4 acts 1829
COMPLETE RECORDING in *Italian*

Tell ...	...	...	G. Taddei (B)
Mathilde	...	...	R. Carteri (S)
Arnold	...	...	M. Filippeschi (T)
Walter	...	...	G. Tuzzi (Bs)
Melchtal	...	...	P. Clabassi (Bs)

etc., Italian Radio Cho. & Orch.—Rossi
(8ss)   **♯ Sor. set 1232**

"Complete Arias"
P. Malgarini (S), G. Gatti (S),
A. Marcangeli (S), G. Tomei (Bs), J. Soler (T),
E. Brino (T), Rome Op. House Cho. & Orch.—
Questa (2ss) (*It*)   **♯ Roy. 1212**
(Highlights from above on ♯ *Roy. 6072*)

Overture
Amsterdam—v. Beinum   in ♯ **D.LXT 2733**
        (in ♯ Lon.LL 358)

☆ N.B.C.—Toscanini   ♭ *G.7RF 189/90*

Berlin Phil.—v. Kempen   **PV. 72115**
(on ♯ *AmD.DL 4002*, attrib.—Fricsay) (FPV. 5031)
Berlin Municipal Op.—Rother in ♯ **Ura. 7057**
Covent Garden—Braithwaite in ♯ *MGM.E 149*
Austrian Sym.—Wöss   in ♯ *Rem. 149-18*
        (also ♯ *Mrt. 1-7* d.c.)

Anon. Orchs. (in ♯ *Var. 2009, 2021* & *6936*)

☆ Col. Sym.—Rodzinski (in ♭ *AmC. set A 1002*)
  Chicago Phil.—H. Weber (♯ Clc. 6040)

Ballet Music, Acts I & III
Covent Garden—Braithwaite ♯ *MGM.E 149*
(*above & below*)   (also on ♯ MGM.E 3003)

ACT I

No. 2, Ah! Mathilde   T & B
 H ☆ G. Martinelli & M. Journet (in ♯ Vic.LCT 1037*:
              ♭ *set WCT 57*)

No. 5, Pas de six (*Passo a sei*)
☆ Orch.—Kostelanetz   **C.DX 1824**
(*Samson et Dalila—Bacchanale*)

ACT II

No. 9, Sombre forêt (*Mathilde's Cavatina*) S
J. Hammond (2ss)   **G.DB 21549**
A. Guerrini (*It*)   **G.GQX 11497**
(*Forza—Pace, pace ...*)
 H C. Muzio (*It*) (IRCC. 3084* & in ♯ Eso.ES 502*:
              ♯ Cpt.MC 20009*) [2]

ACT III

No. 18, Je te bénis ... Sois immobile B
 H M. Battistini (*It*) (in ♯ *Ete. 451*)

(L') INGANNO FELICE 1 act 1812
Overture
Austrian State Sym.—Gui   ♯ **MSL.MW 41**
(*Cherubini & Verdi*) (also in ♯ *MW 50*)

(L') ITALIANA IN ALGERI 2 acts 1813
Overture
Austrian State Sym.—Gui in ♯ **MSL.MW 50**
(*above, below, & Cherubini, etc.*)
☆ New Sym.—Erede (♯ *Lon.LD 9010*)
  Berlin Phil.—Fricsay (in ♯ *AmD.DL 4010*)

ACT I

Languir per una bella   T
B. Finelli, G. Sas (pf.) in ♯ **Mon.MWL 300**

ACT II

O che muso   M-S & Bs
Per lui che adoro   M-S, T, B, Bs
☆ C. Supervia, N. Ederle, C. Scattola, V. Bettoni
              (in ♯ AmD.DL 9533)

(La) SCALA DI SETA 1 act 1812
Overture
Amsterdam—v. Beinum   in ♯ **D.LXT 2733**
        (in ♯ Lon.LL 358)

Florence May Festival—Serafin **G.S 10576**
☆ Berlin Phil.—Fricsay (in ♯ *AmD.DL 4002*)

SEMIRAMIDE 2 acts 1823
Overture
Amsterdam—v. Beinum   in ♯ **D.LXT 2733**
        (♯ Lon.LL 358)

R.I.A.S. Sym.—Fricsay   *PV. 46004*
(2ss)   (in ♯ *AmD.DL 4010*)

ACT I

Ah! quel giorno   M-S
Z. Dolukhanova (2ss)   **USSR. 018007/8**

Bel raggio lusinghier   S
 H A. Galli-Curci   G.VB 5*: o.n. DB 812*
  L. Tetrazzini   G.VB 15*: o.n. DB 537*
  M. Sembrich   AF. 44*

ACT II

Giorno d'onore   S, M-S
G. Sakharova, Z. Dolukhanova
(*Russ*, 2ss)   **USSR. 018786/7**

(Le) SIÈGE DE CORINTHE 3 acts 1826
    (*Assiedo di Corinto*)
Overture
Austrian State Sym.—Gui   ♯ **MSL.MW 50**
(*above: & Cherubini & Wolf-Ferrari*)

(Il) SIGNOR BRUSCHINO 1 act 1813
Overture
Covent Garden—Braithwaite ♯ *MGM.E 149*
(*above*)

---

[1] Labelled merely *Duet, Cenerentola-Romiro* but probably this.
[2] Recorded from an Edison cylinder.

SIGNOR BRUSCHINO Overture (*continued*)
  R.I.A.S.—Fricsay   *PV. 36049*
  (*Tancredi*)
  (*Guillaume Tell & Scala di Seta* on ‡ *AmD.DL 4002*)

  ☆N.B.C.—Toscanini   in ‡ **G.ALP 1007**
  (*above*)   (‡ FALP & QALP 125)

Ah, donate al caro sposo   S
  A. Noni   **P.R 30500**
  (*Cimarosa: Matrimonio Segreto, Aria*) (CB 20535)

TANCREDI 2 acts 1813
Overture
  R.I.A.S. Sym.—Fricsay   *PV. 36049*
  (*Signor Bruschino Overture*)
  Rhineland Sym.—Federer   ‡ **Rgt. 5050**
  (*Suppé & Massenet*)

———

ROUSSEL, Albert (1869-1937)

Andante & Scherzo, Op. 51 fl. & pf. 1934
  ☆ J. P. Rampal & R. Veyron-Lacroix
                      ‡ **Clc. 6032**

  (*Bach, Beethoven, Hindemith, etc.*)

BACCHUS ET ARIANE, Op. 43 Ballet 1930
Symphonic Suite No. 2
  Berlin Radio—Rucht   ‡ **Ura. 7037**
  (*Symphony No. 3*)
  Royal Phil.—E. Kurtz[1]   ‡ **AmC.ML 4482**
  (*Prokofiev: Lieut. Kijé*)

Concerto for small orchestra, Op. 34 1927
  Concert-Hall Sym.—Swoboda ‡ **CHS.F 16**
  (*Martinů*)

(Le) Festin de l'araignée, Op. 17 Ballet 1912
(Le) Marchand de sable qui passe, Op. 13 Ballet 1908
  French Radio Sym.—Leibowitz ‡ **Eso.ES 511**
                      (‡ Cpt.MC 20002)

Petite Suite, Op. 39 orch. 1929
  Berlin Radio—Celibidache ‡ **Ura. 5006**
  (*Debussy: Petite suite*)

Quartet, Str., D major, Op. 45 1931-2
  Loewenguth Qtt.   ♮ **PV. 72094/5**
  (4ss)   (‡ *AmD.DL 4026*)

Song: Jazz dans la nuit, Op. 38 (Dommange)
  ☆ C. Croiza (M-S) (JpC.SW 278)

Symphony No. 3, G minor, Op. 42 1930
  Leipzig Radio—Borsamsky ‡ **Ura. 7037**
  (*Bacchus et Ariane*)

———

ROY, Adrian le (d. *c.* 1589)

  SEE: † XVITH & XVIITH CENTURY SONGS

———

ROZSA, Miklos (b. 1907)

Concerto, Op. 17   Str. Orch.
  London Str. Orch.—Rozsa ‡ **AmVox.PL 7690**
  (*below*)

QUO VADIS Film music 1951
Orchestral Suite (from the sound track)
  Sym. Orch.—Rozsa   ♮ **MGM. set 103**
  (8ss on *Brz MGM. 9065/8*) (‡ *E 103:* ♭ set *K 103*)
  (4ss also on *MGM. 460/1*)

Serenade for Orchestra
  La Jolla (Cal.) Festival—Sokoloff ‡ **CHS.G 4**
  (*Lopatnikoff*)

Theme, variations & Finale, Op. 13 Orch.
  Royal Phil.—Rozsa   **AmVox.PL 7690**
  (*above*)

Older recordings of his film music include:
  Jungle Book (1942): in ♮ Vic. set DM 905
  Lost Weekend (1945): in Vic. 46-0000
  Lydia (1941): in Vic. 46-0003
  Madame Bovary (1949): in ♮ *MGM.* set 43
  (The) Red House (1947): on ♮ Cap. set CB 48
  Spellbound (1946): in ‡ *Rem.LP 1* & ‡ *AmC. RL 3029*; etc.

———

RUBBRA, Edmund Duncan (b. 1901)

Improvisations on virginal pieces, Op. 50 Orch. 1951
... No. 4, Loth to depart (Farnaby)
  Hallé—Barbirolli   **G.DB 21384**
  (*Symphony No. 5, s. 7*)

Missa in honorem Sancti Dominici, Op. 66 1950
  Fleet Street Cho.—Lawrence[1] ‡ **Arg.ARS 1003**
  (*Berger & Milhaud*)

Quartet, String, No. 2, E flat major, Op. 73 1952
  Griller Qtt.   ‡ **D.LX 3088**
  (2ss)   (‡ *Lon.LS 657*)

Symphony No. 5, B flat major, Op. 63 1948
  Hallé—Barbirolli   **G.DB 21384/7**
  (7ss—*Loth to depart*)
  (*Sibelius: Symphony No. 7* on ‡ Vic. LHMV 1011:
                ♭ set *WHMV 1011*)

Trio, Op. 68 pf., vln., vlc. 1950
  E. Rubbra, E. Gruenberg, W. Pleeth
  (*Mozart: Trio*)[2]   ‡ **Argo.ARS 1005**

(The) Virgin's Cradle Hymn unacc. cho. 1925
  (Coleridge)
  Randolph Singers   in ‡ **West.WL 5100**
  Columbia Choristers—Engel
               in ‡ **AmC.ML 2199**

———

RUBINSTEIN, Anton (1830-1894)

CLASSIFIED: I. INSTRUMENTAL &
                           ORCHESTRAL
           II. OPERAS
        III. SONGS

———

I. INSTRUMENTAL & ORCHESTRAL

Concerto No. 4, D minor, Op. 70 pf. & orch. 1864
  O. Levant & N.Y.P.S.O.—Mitropoulos
                    ‡ **AmC.ML 4599**

  F. Wührer & Vienna Philharmonia—Moralt
                    ‡ **AmVox.PL 7780**

Kammenoi-Ostrow, Op. 10   pf.
... No. 22, Rêve angélique — ARR. ORG.
  V. Fox   in ‡ **AmC.ML 4401**
              (♭ set *A 1008:* ♭ *A 1518*)

Melody in F, Op. 3, No. 1   pf.
  G. Axelrod   **U.H 23854**
  (*Liszt: Funérailles, s. I*)

— ARR. ORCH.
  Metropole—v. d. Linden   *PhM.P 01006S*
  (*Godard: Jocelyn—Berceuse*)

  Columbia Orch. (in ‡ *AmC.GL 513*)
  R. Crean Orch. (in ‡ *D.LF 1082; Lon.LPB 424*)
  Bolshoi Th.—Ginsburg (*USSR. 16586*)
                    (*continued on next page*)

———

[1] Announced but probably not issued.
[2] Originally announced with coupling—*Beethoven: Trio, Op. 70 No. 1.*

Melody in F, Op. 3, No. 1 (*continued*)
— ARR. VLC. & PF.
G. Cassadò & O. Schulhof   in ♯ MSL.MW 45
☆ R. Krotschak (in ♯ Eur.LPG 631)
G. Piatigorsky & R. Berkowitz (in ♯ AmC.RL 3015)
— VOCAL ARR.: H. E. Groh (T, *Ger*) (in ♯ *D.LM 4549*)

Polka (Bohème) Op. 82, No. 7   pf.
☆ J. Flier (in ♯ Csm.CRLP 115)

Romance, E flat, Op. 44, No. 1   pf.
— VOCAL ARR. "Night" (to words by Pushkin)
E. Smolenskaya (S)   *USSR. 17291*
(*Verstovsky: The old husband*)
☆ J. MacDonald (*Eng*) & Orch. (*G.DA 1939*)

— ARR. VLC. & PF.
G. Piatigorsky & R. Berkowitz (in ♯ Vic.LM 1187:
♭ *set WDM 1578*)

Trot de cavalerie, Op. 64   pf.
— ARR. ORCH.
Bolshoi Theatre—L. Ginsburg   *USSR. 16585*
(*Melody in F*)

Valse caprice, E flat major   pf.
— ARR. ORCH.
Bolshoi Theatre—L. Ginsburg   *USSR. 16583/4*
(2ss)

II. OPERAS

(The) DEMON   3 acts   1875

ACT I

Accursed World!   Bs
A. Ivanov   *USSR. 15308*
(*Tchaikovsky: Mazeppa—Three Treasures*)

Invocation to the Night   Cho.
Cho.—Wilhousky   in ♯ *DCap. LC 6576*
(*Bach, Victoria, Palestrina, etc.*) (♯ *Cap.L 9015;*
♭/♭ *CD/CDF 9015*)

On desire's soft, fleeting wing   T
I. Kozlovsky   (2ss)   *USSR. 018502/3*

ACT II

Do not weep, my child   Bs
G. London   in ♯ AmC.ML 4489
(*Prince Igor, Don Quichotte, etc.*)
P. Lisitsian   *USSR. 11940*
(*I am he whom you called*)

ACT III

Calm and clear is the night   S
E. Katulskaya   (2ss)   *USSR. 16453/4*
N. Shpiller   *USSR. 08078*
(*Napravnik: Dubrovsky—Masha's aria*)
A. Siergiejev   *Muza. 1836*
(*Serov: Enemy Power—Jeranka's Song*)

I am he whom you called   Bs
P. Lisitsian   *USSR. 11941*
(*Do not weep, my child*)

NERO   4 acts   1879
Epithalamium, Act I   Bs
A. Ivanov (? n.v. or d.c.)   *USSR. 20893*
(*Tchaikovsky: Eugene Onegin, Act III, aria*)

III. SONGS

(The) Bard, Op. 115, No. 10   (Pushkin)
Z. Dolukhanova (A)   *USSR. 18912*
(*Balakirev: I loved him*)

Be not coy, Op. 34, No. 11   (Mirza-Schaffy)
B. Gmyria (Bs)   *USSR. 17420*
(*Rose & Sign of wisdom*)

[1] Labelled *The Bird.*

Bow, fair bud, Op. 34, No. 8   (Mirza-Schaffy)
B. Gmyria (Bs)   *USSR. 17423*
(*When I look upon thy feet*)

Draw the Tchadra back, Op. 34, No. 7
(Mirza-Schaffy)
B. Gmyria (Bs)   USSR. 017545
(*Zuleika*)

Gold rolls here below, Op. 34, No. 9 (Mirza-Schaffy)
(Or: *Persian Love song*)
A. Pirogov (B)   *USSR. 08268*
(*Ballad*)
A. Majak (Bs., *Pol*)   *Muza. 1724*
(*Rossini: Barbiere—La calunnia*)
¶ F. Chaliapin (G.DB 1525)

Lied der Vöglein (unid.) [1]   (Schultze)
Vocal Trio (*Eng*) & pf.   in *Vic. set E 100*
(*Arne, Grieg, etc.*)   (♭ *set WE 100*)

Longing, Op. 27, No. 9   (Lermontov)
M. Romensky   *USSR. 13895*
(*Tchaikovsky: Courage*)

(The) Rose, Op. 34, No. 4   (Mirza-Schaffy)
B. Gmyria (Bs)   *USSR. 17421*
(½s.—*Sign of wisdom & Be not so coy*)

(The) Sign of wisdom, Op. 34, No. 5 (Mirza-Schaffy)
B. Gmyria (Bs)   *USSR. 17421*
(½s.—*Rose & Be not so coy*)

(Die) Träne, Op. 83, No. 8   (after T. Moore)
☒ L. Slezak (T) (in ♯ *Ete. 453**)

When I look upon thy feet, Op. 34, No. 3
(Mirza-Schaffy)
B. Gmyria (Bs)   *USSR. 17422*
(*Bow, fair bud*)

Zuleika, Op. 34, No. 1   (Mirza-Schaffy)
B. Gmyria (Bs)   USSR. 017544
(*Draw the Tchadra back*)

SAEVERUD, Harald (b. 1897)

Galdreslåtten, Op. 20
(*Danza sinfonica con Passacaglia*)
Danish Radio—Malko   G.DB 10505
Oslo Phil.—Fjeldstad   Nera.SK 15539

Kjæmpevise-slåtten, Op. 22, No. 5   pf.
S. Ribbing   T.E 19807
(*Sinding & Backer-Grøndahl*)

PEER GYNT   Inc. music to Ibsen's play
Orchestral Suite
☆ Danish Radio—Tuxen (G.ZN 551/3)

Rondo amoroso, Op. 14, No. 7   pf.
— ARR. ORCH. Saeverud
Sinfonia dolorosa
Oslo Phil.—Fjeldstad   ♮ Nera.SK 15540/1

SAINT-SAËNS, Charles Camille
(1835-1921)

I. PIANO, ORGAN, HARP

Allegro appassionato, Op. 70   orig. pf. & orch.
☆ J. Iturbi (in ♯ Vic.LM 1167: ♭ *set WDM 1604* &
♭ *ERA 53*)

Caprice sur des airs de ballet d'Alceste (Gluck) pf.
G. Novães (n.v.)   in ♯ AmVox.PL 7500
(*Bach, Brahms, etc.*)

ÉTUDES   pf.
Op. 52, No. 6, D flat major
   (*Étude en forme de valse*)
   J. Bolet   in ♯ **Bo.B 301**
   (*Moszowski, Mendelssohn, etc.*)

Op. 111, No. 6, F major
   (*Toccata d'après le 5ᵉ Concerto*)
   ☆ J. M. Darré (JpV.SD 3068)

Prelude & Fugue, E flat maj., Op. 99, No. 3   org.
  ... Prelude only   ☆ M. Dupré (*JpV.NF 4179*)

II. CHAMBER MUSIC

Allegro appassionato, Op. 43   vlc. & pf.
   J. Pacey & F. Kramer   in ♯ *MTR. MLP 1003*

Élégie, Op. 143   vln. & pf.
— ARR. PF. SOLO
  ☆**H** C. Saint-Saëns (in ♯ AudA.LA 1203*)

Septet, E flat maj., Op. 65   pf., tpt., str. qtt., cbs.
   B. Smith, H. Glantz, Stradivarius Qtt. &
   P. Sklar   ♯ **Strad.STR 605** ¹
   (*Poulenc*)

Sonata, E flat major, Op. 167   cl. & pf.
   H. Tichman & R. Budnovich   ♯ **CHS.G 18**
   (*Henri VIII*)

SONATA, vln. & pf.
No. 1, D minor, Op. 75
   J. Heifetz & E. Bay   ♯ **Vic.LM 9007**
   (*Bruch*)   (♭ set WDM 1658)

SONATA, vlc. & pf.
No. 1, C minor, Op. 32
   G. Schwarz & G. Kuhn   ♯ **Sat.LDG 8002**
   (*Boëllmann*)

III. ORCHESTRAL

(Le) Carnaval des animaux   Orch. & 2 pfs.
... Le Cygne   vlc. & pf.
   G. Piatigorsky & R. Berkowitz   ♭ *G.7RF 229*
   (*Granados: Goyescas—Intermezzo*)
   (*Granados, Tchaikovsky, etc.* in ♯ Vic.LM 1187:
           set ♭ *WDM 1578*)

    G. Cassadò & O. Schulhof   in ♯ MSL.MW 45
    J. Pacey & F. Kramer   in ♯ MTR.MLP 1003
    L. Rose & orch.   in ♯ Long.LW 121
    ☆ R. Krotschak   in ♯ Eur.LPG 631
    P. Casals   in ♯ Vic.LCT 1050: ♭ set WCT 72

— ARR. VLN. & PF.
   J. Heifetz & E. Bay   in ♯ **B.LAT 8020**
   (*Prokofiev, Chopin, etc.*)   (♯ AmD.DL 8521)

— ARR. 2 PFS.
   Sisters J. Madeleine & F. Therese (in ♯ Cln.SF 1; also ♮ & ♭)

— ARR. 4 PFS.
   First Piano Qtt. (in ♯ Vic.LM 1227: ♭ set WDM 1624)

— ARR. ORCH.
   ☆ Kostelanetz Orch. (C.DX 1819)
   etc.

CONCERTO, pf. & orch.
No. 2, G minor, Op. 22
   M. Lympany & L.P.O.—Martinon
               ♯ *D.LX 3064*
              (♯ Lon.LPS 408)
   A. Sandford & Hastings Sym.—Bath
              ♯ **Allo.ALG 3028**
   (*Henri VIII*)   (♯ EA.ALX 3028)
   C. Vidusso & Berlin Sym.—Günther
               ♯ **Roy. 1273**

CONCERTO, vln. & orch.
No. 3, B minor, Op. 61
   ☆ Z. Francescatti & N.Y.P.S.O.—Mitropoulos
               C.LX 1526/8
   (6ss) (*Paganini,* on ♯ C.FCX 140)

CONCERTO, vlc. & orch.
No. 1, A minor, Op. 33
   M. Gendron & Vienna State Opera—Sternberg
   (*Haydn*)   ♯ **Oce.OCS 23**
   G. Piatigorsky & Victor Sym.—Reiner
              ♯ **Vic.LM 1187**
   (*Cello encores*)   (♭ set WDM 1538)
   L. Rose & N.Y.P.S.O.—Mitropoulos
   (*Bloch*)   ♯ **AmC.ML 4425**

Danse macabre, Op. 40
   Sydney Sym.—Goossens   **G.ED 1213**
   Danish Radio—Malko   **G.DB 10505**
       (in ♯ BB.LBC 1019: ♭ set WBC 1019)
   Brussels Radio—André   ♯ *Cap.H 8169*
   (*Moussorgsky*)
   ☆ N.B.C. Sym.—Toscanini   **G.DB 21432**
   (2ss) (*Dukas & Smetana,* in ♯ G.FALP 130: QALP 130)
   (2ss, ♭ G.7RF 181; also, 1 side, ♭ Vic.WEPR 15 with *Grofé*)
   ☆ French Nat. Radio—Lindenberg **P.R 20598**
                (BX 611)
   ☆ Amsterdam—Münch (♭ D. 71013)
   N.Y.P.S.O.—Mitropoulos (♯ AmC.AAL 8:
               ♭ 4-13150/1D)
   L.S.O.—Weldon (in ♭ MGM. set K 58)
   etc.

— ARR. 4 PFS.
   First Piano Qtt. (in ♯ Vic.LM 1227: ♭ set WDM 1624)

Havanaise, Op. 83   vln. & orch.
   J. Heifetz & Vic. Sym.—Steinberg **G.DB 21552**
       (♭ G.7RF 169; ♭ Vic. 49-3634)
   (*Sarasate & Bizet,* in ♯ Vic.LM 163: ♭ set WDM 1642)

Introduction & Rondo Capriccioso, Op. 28
   vln. & orch.
   Z. Francescatti & Philadelphia—Ormandy
              ♯ *AmC.ML 2194*
   (*Chausson*)   (♯ C.FC 1017)
   J. Heifetz & Vic. Sym.—Steinberg **G.DB 21516**
   (2ss)   (Vic. 12-3443; ♭ G.7R 133: 7RF/RQ 161)
   (*Bizet & Sarasate,* in ♯ Vic.LM 163: ♭ set WDM 1642)
   H. Krebbers & Residentie—v. Otterloo
   (2ss)   **Phi.N 11234G**
                (PhM.N 09049S)
   D. Oistrakh & USSR State Sym.—Kondrashin
   (2ss)   **USSR. 016274/5**
                (U.H 24271)
   M. Piastro & Longines Orch. (in ♯ Long.LW 121)

Morceau de concert, Op. 154   hp. & orch.   1918
   J. Helmis & Berlin Radio—Mahlke ♯ **Ura. 7039**
   (*Massenet*)

(Le) Rouet d'Omphale, Op. 31
   ☆ N.Y.P.S.O.—Mitropoulos (♯ AmC.AAL 8:
               ♭ 4-13150/1D)

Suite algérienne, Op. 60
... No. 3, Rêverie du soir   (Blidah)
... No. 4, Marche militaire française
— ARR. PF.   ☆**H** C. Saint-Saëns (in ♯ AudA.LA 1203*)

SYMPHONIES
No. 3, C minor, Op. 78   with org. & 2 pfs.
   ☆ A. Cellier, D. Herbrecht & L. Petitjean, Sym.—
        Coppola (JpV. set JAS 231)

IV. SONGS

(La) Brise, Op. 26, No. 1   (Renaud)
  H M. Gay (S) (IRCC. 3093*)

(Le) Solitaire, Op. 26, No. 3   (Renaud)
   S. Couderc (?) & orch.   *Sat.IM 901*
   (*J.-L. Cartier: Invocation à Brama*)   (o.n. C 901)

¹ This number was originally announced as *Mozart: Str. Qtts. 21* & *22* (see WERM p. 808), but that disc was withdrawn before issue and this substituted.

V. CHURCH MUSIC

(Le) DÉLUGE, Op. 45 Oratorio 1876
Prelude   vln. & orch.
— ARR. VLN. & PF.
☆**H** G. Willaume & C. Saint-Saëns (in ♯ AudA.LA 1203*)

Oratorio de Noël, Op. 12 1863
Soloists, Cho. & San José State Sym.—Downey
(*Eng*)   ♯ **ML.7008**

VI. OPERAS

HENRI VIII 4 acts 1883
Ballet-divertissement, Act II
Hastings Sym.—Bath   ♯ **Allo.ALG 3028**
(*Concerto*) (♯ EA.ALX 3028)   (also, 4ss, Ori.SA 503/4)
Netherlands Phil.—Spruit   ♯ **CHS.G 18**
(*Sonata*)

(La) PRINCESSE JAUNE, Op. 30 1 act 1872
Overture
Opéra-Comique—Wolff   in ♯ **D.LXT 2625**
(*Berlioz, Lalo, Massenet*)   (♯ Lon.LLP 355; & LD 9020)
Boston Sym.—Münch   ♯ **Vic.LM 1700**
(*Berlioz, etc.*)   (♭ set WDM 1700)

SAMSON ET DALILA, Op. 47 3 acts 1877

ACT I

Dieu d'Israël (Opening Cho.)
San Francisco Op. Cho. (2ss)   **ML. 43/4**

Arrêtez, o mes frères   T & Cho.
... Tenor part only
H F. Tamagno (*Ital*) (*G.VA 62*: o.n. DR 101*)

Printemps qui commence   A or M-S
J. Tourel   **C.LX 1555**
(*Mon coeur s'ouvre*)
G. Simionato (*Ital*)   **C.GQX 11488**
(*Amour, viens aider*)
R. Siewert (*Ger*)   **G.EH 1429**
(*Kienzl: Evangelimann excpt*)
☆ G. Swarthout (in ♭ Vic. set WDM 1562)
G. Ripley (*Eng*) (G.JOX 17)

ACT II

Amour, viens aider ma faiblesse A or M-S
G. Simionato (*Ital*)   **C.GQX 11488**
(*above*)
E. Nicolai (*Ital*)   **P.R 30049**
(*Fedora—O grandi occhi*)   (CB 20512)
S. Preobrazhenskaya (*Russ*)   **USSR. 17155/6**
☆ G. Swarthout (in ♭ Vic. set WDM 1562)
M. Anderson (in ♯ Roy. 1278 & 6001: ♭ set 14516)
H. Bouvier (& P. Cabanel, Bs), from set (Pat.PN 5015)

J'ai gravi la montagne ... La victoire facile
A or M-S & Bs
☆ L. Ribacchi & R. Panerai   (*Ital*) **P.R 30033**

Mon coeur s'ouvre à ta voix A or M-S
J. Tourel   **C.LX 1555**
(*above*)
E. Wysor   in ♯ Rem. 199-30
☆ G. Swarthout   in ♭ Vic. set WDM 1562
B. Thebom   in ♭ Vic. set WDM 1542
L. Homer   in ♯ Vic.LCT 1039: ♭ set WCT 62
H. Bouvier (from set)   Pat.PN 5015
H M. Gay   G.VB 31*: o.n. 033041*

ACT III

Vois ma misère, hélas!   T & Cho.
☆ P. Franz & Cho. (HRS. 1120)

Bacchanale
☆ Florence Festival—Serafin (2ss) **G.C 4155**
                                 (♭ BF 1045)
☆ Carnegie Pops—O'Connell (in ♭ AmC. set A 1013)
L.S.O.—Weldon (in ♭ MGM. set K 58)
A. Kostelanetz Orch. (C.DX 1824)

SALZEDO, Carlos (b. 1885)

Variations (unspec.)   Harp
O. Erdeli   **USSR. 17338/9**

SAMMARTINI, Giuseppe (1693-c. 1750)

Sonata, No. 5, F major recorder, vln. & hpsi.
D. Barnett, E. Kelly & N. Salas **C.DO 3475**
(2ss)

Sonata, A minor, Op. 1, No. 4 vln. & cont.
... 3rd movt., Andante "*Canto amoroso*"
A. Mus & D. Colacelli   **ArgOd. 57008**
(*Sarasate: Miramar*)

SAMSON, Joseph (b. ?)

SEE: † FRENCH NOËLS & CHANSONS

SANDOVAL, Miguel (b. 1903)

SONGS
Cantiga; Copla bailable; Copla leonesa; Copla malagueña;
El mercado de los esclavos; Soléa; Zamorana
L. de Ibarrondo (M-S), M. Sandoval (pf.)
(*Falla*)   ♯ **AmC.ML 2189**

SARASATE y NAVASCUES, Pablo
Martin Meliton de (1844-1908)

(All for vln. & pf. unless otherwise stated)

Caprice basque, Op. 24
☆ I. Stern & A. Zakin (♭ AmC.A 1517)

Carmen fantasia, Op. 25
☆ D. Oistrakh & A. D. Makarov (in ♯ Csm.CRLP 105)
— ARR. VLN. & ORCH.
L. Kogan & Radio Orch.—Nebolsin
(4ss)   **USSR. 17980/3**
(*Rimsky-Korsakov: Capriccio espagnole* in ♯ CdM.LD 8010)
☆ J. Heifetz & Vic. Sym.—Voorhees (in ♯ Vic.LM 163:
                           ♭ set WDM 1642: ♭ 49-0130)

DANZAS ESPAÑOLAS
No. 1, Malagueña, Op. 21, No. 1
No. 2, Habañera, Op. 21, No. 2
Y. Menuhin & A. Baller   **JpV.SD 3047**
(1 side each)   (in set JAS 230)

No. 2, Habañera, Op. 21, No. 2
☆ Y. Menuhin & G. Moore   ♭ **G.7RF 224**
(*Wieniawski: Scherzo tarantelle*)

No. 3, Romanza andaluza, Op. 22, No. 1
Y. Menuhin & A. Baller   **JpV.SD 3048**
(*Wieniawski: Scherzo Tarantelle*) (in set JAS 230)
A. Brugman & B. Linderud   **Tono. A 181**
(*Monti: Czardas*)
A. Mus & D. Colacelli   **ArgOd. 64003**
(*No. 5*)
☆ B. Huberman (Qual.QMN 7041)

No. 4, Jota Navarra, Op. 22, No. 2
☆ V. Prihoda & M. Raucheisen (Pol. 57392)

No. 5, Playera, Op. 23, No. 1
A. Mus & D. Colacelli (*No. 3*) **ArgOd. 64003**

♯ = Long-playing, 33⅓ r.p.m.   ♭ = 45 r.p.m.   ♮ = Auto. couplings, 78 r.p.m.

No. 6, Zapateado, Op. 23, No. 2
J. Heifetz & E. Bay (n.v.)   ♭ *G.7RF 171*
(*Castelnuovo-Tedesco & Rimsky-K*) (♭ *Vic. 49-1294 &*
                                         ♭ *ERA 71*)

D. Oistrakh & pf. (in ♯ Csm.CRLP 105; *USSR. 12457*)

No. 7, A minor, Op. 26, No. 1
M. Wilk & F. Kramer   in ♯ *MTR.MLP 1002*

Introduction & Tarantelle, Op. 43
T. Spivakovsky & A. Balsam
                    in ♯ *AmC.ML 4402*

Miramar (Zortzico), Op. 42
A. Mus & D. Colacelli   *ArgOd. 57008*
(*Sammartini: "Canto amoroso"*)

Navarra, Op. 33   2 vlns. & orch.
D. & I. Oistrakh & pf. (?)   *USSR. 17637/8*
(2ss)

Zigeunerweisen, Op. 20, No. 1   vln. & orch.
J. Heifetz & Vic. Orch.—Steinberg   *G.DB 21560*
(*Bizet & Saint-Saëns, in ♯ LM 163: ♭ set WDM 1642:*
                           ♭ *49-3782*)

E. Telmanyi & Danish Radio—Jensen (n.v.
   same no.)   *Tono. X 25005*
W. Tworek & Danish Radio—Reesen
                      Pol.HM 80018
                       (Pol. 516812)
A. Mozi & Ens. (U.H 23834)
M. Polyakin & pf. (*USSR. 10460/1*)
☆ V. Prihoda & pf. (*P.LL 3000*)

SARTI, Giuseppe (1729-1802)
SEE: † ITALIAN SONGS

SATIE, Erik Alfred Leslie (1866-1925)

PIANO MUSIC COLLECTION
Avant-dernières pensées   1915
Croquis et agaceries d'un gros-bonhomme en bois
   1913
Descriptions automatiques   1912-13
Gnossienne No. 3   1890
Gymnopédie No. 1   1888
Sarabande No. 2   1887
F. Poulenc (pf.)   ♯ *AmC.ML 4399*
(*Poulenc*)

(3) Gnossiennes   pf.   1890
... **No. 2** only
L. Thyrion   in ♯ *Phi.N 00601R*
(*below & Auric, Honegger, Poulenc*)

(3) Gymnopédies   pf.   1888
... **No. 3** only
G. Copeland   in ♯ *MGM.E 151*
... **Nos. 1 & 3**
— ARR. ORCH. Debussy
   ☆ Boston Sym.—Koussevitzky (♭ *G.7RF 185; Vic. 49-0771*)

Messe pour les pauvres   org. [or pf.] & cho.   1895
M. Mason & Cho.—Randolph   ♯ *Eso. 507*
(*Variations; & Schönberg*)   (♯ Cpt.MC 20013)

(5) NOCTURNES   pf.   1919
... **No. 3** only
L. Thyrion   in ♯ *Phi.N 00601R*
(*above & Auric, Honegger, Poulenc*)

SOCRATE   Symphonic drama   4 S & orch. 1919
V. Journeaux, J. Lindenfelder, S. Pebordes,
   A. M. Carpenter, French Radio Sym.—
   Leibowitz   ♯ *Eso.ES 510*
                       (♯ Cpt.MC 20006)

SONGS
(La) Diva de l'Empire
"Colinette" & self pf. acc.   *CdM.PM 1606*
(*Colinette: Song*)

(3) Mélodies   1916
1. **Daphénéo**   (Fargue)
2. **La Statue de Bronze**   (God)
3. **Le Chapelier**   (Chalupt)
P. Bernac (B), F. Poulenc (pf.) ♯ *AmC.ML 4484*
(*Chabrier, Debussy, Poulenc*)

   ☆ J. Bathori (S), D. Milhaud (pf.) (JpC.SW 276)

SCANDELLI, Antonio (1517-1580)

Ein Hennlein weiss
Trapp Family Cho.—Wasner
                  in ♯ *CHS.CHS 1101*

SCARLATTI, Alessandro (1660-1725)

I. INSTRUMENTAL

CONCERTI GROSSI, Str. Orch.
No. 3, F Major [1] (ed. Fasano)   pub. 1740
   Virtuosi di Roma   ♯ *B.AXTL 1004*
   (*Bach, Tartini, Albinoni*)   (♯ AmD.DL 9572)

Gavotte & Sarabande — ARR. GUITAR
   ☆ A. Segovia (in ♯ *AmD.DL 5257*)

SONATAS   hpsi.[2]
A major; C major
   W. Schatzkamer (pf.)   ♭ *Vic. 49-3626*
   (*Mozart: Pf. Sonata No. 17*)   (in ♭ *set WDM 1650*)

Sonata a quattro, D minor
   New Music Str. Qtt.   ♯ *BRS. 911*
   (*Boccherini & Tartini*)

II. VOCAL

CANTATA: Sulle sponde del Tebro   S, tpt., str.
   T. Stich-Randall & Naples Scarlatti Orch.—
     Paumgartner   ♯ *Csm.CLPS 1035*
   (*Mozart*)

Exsultate Deo   Motet
   Hamline Singers—Holliday   in ♯ *NRI. 305*
   (*Schütz, etc.*)

OPERAS
(La) DONNA ANCORA È FEDELE   3 acts 1698
Se Florindo è fedele
   E. Brems (M-S), vln., hpsi., vlc.   *Fdn.NC 3502*
   (*below*)
   ☆ H. Spani (S)   *G.VA 60*
   (*Caccini: Amarilli*)

(Il) FLAVIO   3 acts   1688
Chi vuole innamorarsi
   ☆ E. Pinza (Bs.) & pf. (in ♯ Vic.LCT 1031: ♭ *set WCT 47*)

(Il) PIRRO E DEMETRIO   3 acts   1694
Rugiadose, odorose, violette graziose
   E. Brems (M-S), vln., hpsi., vlc.   *Fdn.NC 3502*
   (*above*)

---

[1] Labelled No. 6.
[2] The recording is attributed to A. Scarlatti, but probably in error for D. Scarlatti. No sonatas by A. Scarlatti have been traced.

OPERAS (continued)

(II) TRIONFO DELL'ONORE 3 acts 1718
COMPLETE RECORDING   (ed. Mortari)

Doralice Rosetti ...	...	R. Zerbini (S)
Leonora Dorini ...	...	A. Pini (M-S)
Cornelia Buffacci ...	...	O. Rovero (M-S)
Rosina Caruccia ...	...	E. Zareska (M-S)
Riccardo Alberori ...	...	A. Berdini (T)
Flaminio Castravacca ...	...	S. Messina (T)
Capitano Bombarda ...	...	A. Poli (B)

etc., Italian Radio—Giulini   # Sor. set 1223
(4ss)

UNIDENTIFIED ARIA
Tutto accesso a quel rai
M. Laszlo (S), F. Holletschek (pf.)
                              # West.WL 5119
(† Italian Songs)

SCARLATTI, Domenico (1685-1757)

SONATAS, hpsi.
COLLECTIONS
VOL. I

L.37, G major;	L.204, G major;	L.252, C major;
L.262, D major;	L.279, F major;	L.345, A major;
L.395, A major;	L.415, D major;	L.429, A minor;
L.430, E major;	L.449, B minor;	L.500, B flat major

F. Valenti   # West.WL 5106

VOL. II

L.8, C major;	L.14, D major;	L.23, E major;
L.104, C major;	L.127, G major;	L.126, G minor;
L.232, G major;	L.263, B minor;	L.413, D minor;
L.422, D minor;	L.465, D major;	L.486, G major

F. Valenti   # West.WL 5116

VOL. III

L.10, C minor;	L.25, E major;	L.33, B minor;
L.58, D minor;	L.165, D major;	L.241, A minor;
L.352, C minor;	L.365, D major;	L.419, D major;
L.420, D minor;	L.432, F major;	L.433, F major

F. Valenti   # West.WL 5139

L.33, B minor;	L.142, E flat major;	L.171, F minor;
L.255, C major;	L.256, C sharp minor;	
L.386, G minor;	L.388, G major;	L.457, C major;
L.475, F minor;	L.479, F major;	L.483, A major

C. Haskil (pf.)   # West.WL 5072

L.23, E major;	L.33, B minor;	L.58, D minor;
L.344, A major;	L.423, D minor;	L.429, A minor;
L.449, B minor;	L.463, D minor;	L.468, A minor;
L.475, F minor;	L.487, G major;	L.498, B flat major
L.499, G minor;		

☆ M. Meyer (pf.)   # DFr. 15

L.10, C minor;	L.142, E flat major;	L.223, A minor;
L.292, A major;	L.294, F sharp minor;	L.315, D major;
L.325, E minor;	L.382, F minor	

K. Long (pf.)   # D.LX 3073
                            (# Lon.LS 524)

L.33, B minor;   L.142, E flat major; L. 171, F minor
C. Haskil (pf.)   # Phi. A00143R
(Ravel)

L.23, E major
D. Lipatti (pf.)   C.LB 113
(L.413)   (GQ 7247)

L.239, A minor
V. Horowitz (pf.)   G.DB 21359
(L. 483)   (♭ G.7RF 201)

L.352, C minor — ARR. GUITAR
☆ A. Segovia (in # AmD.DL 5257)

L.413, D minor
D. Lipatti (pf.)   C.LB 113
(L.23)   (GQ 7247)

O. Frugoni (pf.)   in # AmVox.PL 7700
(Boccherini, Galuppi, etc.)

F. Chapiro (pf.)   in # Ox.OR 105
(Bach, Mozart, etc.)

L.418, D major
L.423, D minor
☆ W. Landowska (in # Vic.LM 1217: ♭ set WDM 1181)

L.483, A major
V. Horowitz (pf.)   G.DB 21359
(L.239)   (♭ G.7RF 201)

L.499, G minor   ("Cat's Fugue")
— ARR. STR. ORCH.   Kramer
☆ Str. Orch.—Serly (in # BRS. 905, n.n.)

L.503 [Supp. 3], C major (Pastorale)
O. P. Santoliquido (pf.)   in # AmD.DL 9649
(Vivaldi, Torelli, etc.)

MISCELLANEOUS

"Pastorale & Capriccio" L.413 & 375
— ARR. PF. Tausig
G. Bachauer   G.C 4154
(Mozart: Concerto, K537, s. 7)
V. Schiøler   G.DB 20163
(Beethoven: 32 Variations, s. 1)

... Capriccio only—ARR. ORCH.
Stradivari Orch. (D.F 44138)

(Le) DONNE DI BUON UMORE
    (L.388, 361, 33, 463, 385, ARR. Tommasini)
    (The Good-humoured Ladies)
Paris Cons.—Désormière   # D.LXT 2720
(Poulenc: Les Biches)   (# Lon.LL 624)

SCHEIDT, Samuel   (1587-1654)
SEE: † MAÎTRES D'ORGUE DE J. S. BACH

SCHEIN, Johann Hermann (1586-1630)

Die mit Tränen säen Motet
St. Olaf Cho.—O. C. Christiansen in # StO. 6

Mein Herz ruht und ist stille Motet
Copenhagen Cha. Cho.—Bertelsen (Dan)
                                  Felix.F 50
(Rosenmüller: Welt, ade!)

SCHIBLER, Armin (b. 1920)

CANTATA: Weil alles erneut sich begibt, Op. 23
    (Bergengruen) A, vla., pf.
L. Fischer, R. Nel & A. Schibler Od. 210710/1
(3ss—below)

(Der) HÄUSLICHE PSALTER, Op. 13
... Excerpts
M. Stader (S), H. Erismann (pf.)   C.LZX 15

SUITE, Op. 9c unacc. vlc.
... Konzertantes Allegro
P. Grümmer   Od. 210711
(above)

= Long-playing, 33⅓ r.p.m.   ♭ = 45 r.p.m.   ♮ = Auto. couplings, 78 r.p.m.

SCHIERBECK, Poul (1888-1949)

Fête Galante, Overture, Op. 25   Orch.   1931
  ☆ Danish Radio—Grøndahl   **♯ Mer.MG 15041**
  (*Riisager*)

SCHMIDT, Franz (1874-1939)

NOTRE DAME   Opera   2 acts   1914
Intermezzo
  Brussels Radio—André   **T.E 3915**
  (*Sibelius: Valse Triste*)   (in ♯ *LB 6022*)
  ☆ Württemberg State Op.—Leitner (Pol. 15542)
  Berlin Phil.—Schmidt-Isserstedt (AusT.E 1162)
  etc.

Quintet, G major   pf. (left hand) & str. qtt.   1927
  J. Demus & Barylli Qtt.   **♯ West.WL 5158**

SCHNABEL, Artur (1882-1951)

(7) Piano Pieces
Youth Piece   pf.
  H. Schnabel
Piece in seven movements   pf.   pub. 1947
  D. Newlin   **♯ SPA. 13**

Rhapsody ʹor orch.   1946-7
  Philharmonia—Karajan   (4ss)   ♮ **C.LX 8843/4**

SCHOECK, Othmar (b. 1886)

DON RANUDO DE COLIBRADOS   1919
  Opera. 4 acts
Intermezzo (Serenade)
  ☆ Berlin Municipal—Meyer (Pol. 15534 & ▽ 15242)

Toccata, A flat major, Op. 29, No. 2   pf.
  W. Frey   in ♯ **D.LXT 2658**
  (*Binet & Brunner*)   (in ♯ Lon.LL 498)

SCHOENBERG, Arnold (1874-1951)

COLLECTION: COMPLETE PIANO WORKS
(3) Klavierstücke, Op. 11   1909
(6) Klavierstücklein, Op. 19   1911
(5) Klavierstücke, Op. 23   1922
Suite für Klavier, Op. 25   1925
(2) Klavierstücke, Op. 33   1932
  E. C. Krauss   (2ss)   **♯ Esq.TW 14-001**

Concerto, Op. 42   pf. & orch.   1943
  C. Helfer & French Radio Sym.—Leibowitz [1]
  (*below*)   **♯ Ren.X 48**

Erwartung, Op. 17   S & Orch.   1909
  (*Pappenheim*)
  D. Dow & N.Y.P.S.O.—Mitropoulos
                ♯ AmC.ML 4524
  (*Křenek*)

Pierrot lunaire, Op. 21   (Georg) Recit. & Ens. 1912
  E. Adler & Paris Cha. Ens.—Leibowitz **♯ Dial. 16**
  H. Anderson & L.S.O. Cha. Ens.—Stadlen [1]
                ♯ Argo.ATC 1001

  ☆ E. Stiedry-Wagner & Ens.—Schoenberg
                ♯ AmC.ML 4471

Serenade, Op. 24   B & Septet   1924
  ☆ W. Galjour & Ens.—Mitropoulos (♯ Cpt.MC 20005)

SONGS, Opp. 1, 2, 6, 14—COMPLETE [2]
  I. Steingruber (S), H. Haefner (pf.)   **♯ SPA. 32**

(The) Survivor from Warsaw, Op. 46   1947
  Cho. & French Radio Orch.—Leibowitz [1]
    & Narrator   **♯ Ren.X 48**
  (*above*)

Verklärte Nacht, Op. 4   Str. sextet or Str. orch. 1899
  ☆ Hollywood Str. Qtt., A. Dinkin (vla.) & K. Reher (vlc.)
                   (♯ *T.LCB 8118*)

Variations on a recitative, Op. 40   org.   1943
  C. Watters   **♯ CEd. 1004**
  (*Messiaen*)
  M. Mason   **♯ Eso. 507**
  (*Satie*)   (♯ Cpt.MC 20013)

SCHOOP, Paul (b. 1909)

Fata Morgana
March Ballet   orch.
  Frankenland Sym.—Kloss   **♯ Lyr.LL 29**
  (*La Violette, Delmar, Laszlo*)

SCHUBERT, Franz Peter (1797-1828)

CLASSIFIED: I. INSTRUMENTAL
            A. Piano   B. Chamber Music
            C. Dances   D. Orchestral
       II. VOCAL
            A. Stage Works   B. Church Music
            C. Part Songs   D. Songs (Lieder)

I. INSTRUMENTAL

A. PIANO & PIANO DUET

Allegretto, C minor   D.915
  ☆ A. Schnabel   **G.DB 21357**
  (*Sonata No. 21, s. 9*)

Allegro, A minor, Op. 144   D.947   pf. duet
  (*Lebensstürme*)   1828
  P. Badura-Skoda & J. Demus   **♯ West.WL 5147**
  (*below*)

Andantino varié, B minor, Op. 84, No. 1   D.823
 — ARR. PF. SOLO   Tausig   [pf. duet
  E. Petri   **♯ AmC.ML 4436**
  (*Schubert-Liszt: Transcriptions*)

Grand Duo   SEE Sonatas, pf. duet

IMPROMPTUS
(4) Impromptus, Op. 90   COMPLETE   D.899
  A. Schnabel   (2ss)   **♯ G.BLP 1007**
  (*Op. 142* in ♯ Vic.LHMV 1027: ♭ *set WHMV 1027*)
       No. 1 on G.DB 21320
       Nos. 2 & 3 on G.DB 21335
       No. 4 on G.DB 21351
  R. Goldsand   **♯ CHS.CHS 1146**
  (*Op. 142*)   (♯ Nix.CLP 1146)
  P. Badura-Skoda   in ♯ **West. set WAL 205**
  (*Op. 142 & Sonata 13*)
  R. Firkusny   **♯ AmC.ML 4527**
  (*Op. 142*)

No. 2, E flat major
  A. d'Arco   **Pat.PDT 274**
  (*Mendelssohn: Étude No. 2*)
  ☆ E. Joyce (in ♯ AmD.DL 9528)

---

[1] Announced but probably not issued.
[2] Also stated to contain Op. 3 instead of Op. 1.

IMPROMPTUS—*continued*

No. 3, G major
G. Scherzer   **P.E 11504**
(*Op. 142, No. 2*)

☆A. Rubinstein   ♭ *G. 7RF 247*
(*below*)

No. 4, A flat major
A. Rubinstein   in ♯ **Vic.LM 1153**
(*Chopin, etc.*)   (♭ *WDM 1558*)
(*above,* ♭ *G. 7RF 247*)

(4) Impromptus, Op. 142 COMPLETE D.935
A. Schnabel   ♯ **Vic.LHMV 1027**
(*Op. 90*)   (♭ *set WHMV 1027*)
     No. 1 on G.DB 21382
     No. 2 on G.DB 21500
     No. 4 on G.DB 21557
R. Goldsand   ♯ **CHS.CHS. 1146**
(*Op. 90*)   (♯ *Nix.CLP 1146*)
P. Badura-Skoda   ♯ **West. set WAL 205**
(*Op. 90 & Sonata 13*)
R. Firkusny   ♯ **AmC.ML 4527**
(*Op. 90*)
M. Schwalb   (2ss)   ♯ *Acad.ALP 306*
L. Pattison   (2ss)   ♯ **Cmt. 1201**

No. 2, A flat major
G. Scherzer   **P.E 11504**
(*Op. 90, No. 3*)

No. 3, B flat major
V. Warlev   **Tono.A 174**
(*Khachaturian & Prokofiev*)

Lebensstürme *SEE* Allegro, A minor

MARCHES (MILITAIRES) Op. 51 D.733
No. 1, D major
— ARR. ORCH.
Boston Prom.—Fiedler   (n.v.)   ♭ *G.7BF 1008*
(*Pierné: Marche*)   (in ♭ *Vic.WEPR 27: 49-1432*)
Amsterdam—v. Kempen   **PhM.N 09039S**
(*J. Strauss I: Radetzky March*)
     Vienna Radio—Nilius (Vien.L 6120: ♯ *1003*)
     A. Bernard Str. Orch. (*Pac. 2863*)
☆ Amsterdam—Mengelberg (FT.T 177)

MOMENTS MUSICAUX, Op. 94 D.780
     1. C major   2. A flat major
     3. F minor   4. C sharp minor
     5. F minor   6. A flat major
R. Goldsand   ♯ **CHS.CHS 1148**
(*Sonata 13*)   (♯ *Nix.CLP 1148*)
Y. Nat   **V♯** *DFr. 72*

Nos. 2 & 4   G. Scherzer (P.E 11501)

Nos. 3, 5, 6   F. Karrer (*Vien.P 6060:* ♯ *1015*)

Nos. 3 & 6   P. Browne (*Pax.PR 487*)

No. 3   J. Battista (in ♯ *MGM.E 141*)

— ARR. VLC. & PF.
G. Cassadò & O. Schulhof (in ♯ MSL.MW 45)
☆ P. Casals & pf. (in ♯ Vic.LCT 1050: ♭ *set WCT 72;*
                 ¶ *G.DA 776*)
G. Piatigorsky & pf. (in ♯ Vic.LM 1187:
etc.   ♭ *set WDM 1578*)

— ARR. STR. ORCH.
A. Bernard Str. Orch. (*Pac. 2863*)
Sydney Civic—Beck (in ♯ Dia.DPM 1)

Scherzo, B flat major D.593
G. Puchelt   **G.EH 1404**
(*Sonata No. 13, s. 3*)

SONATAS, Piano solo
No. 13, A major, Op. 120 D.664
R. Goldsand   ♯ **CHS.CHS 1148**
(*Moments musicaux*)   (♯ *Nix.CLP 1148*)

P. Badura-Skoda   in ♯ **West. set WAL 205**
(*Impromptus*)
G. Puchelt   **G.EH 1403/4**
(*3ss—Scherzo*)

No. 18, G major, Op. 78   (Fantasia)   D.894
☆ E. Balogh   ♯ **Eur.LPG 625**

... **3rd movt., Minuetto** — ARR. GUITAR Segovia
A. Segovia   in ♯ **B.AXTL 1005**
(† *Segovia Recital*)   (♯ *AmD.DL 9633*)

No. 20, A major D.959
☆ A. Schnabel   (9ss)   **G.DB 21418/22S**

No. 21, B flat major D.960
☆ A. Schnabel   **G.DB 21353/7**
(*9ss—Allegretto, C minor*)
C. Haskil   ♯ **Phi.A 00108L**
(*1½ss—Schumann*)
J. Demus   ♯ **Rem. 199-39**
☆ W. Kempff   (8ss,   ♮ D.GAG 519/22)

SONATAS, Pf. duet
C major, Op. 140   D.812   "*Grand Duo*"
P. Badura-Skoda & J. Demus   ♯ **West.WL 5093**

— ARR. ORCH. Joachim
Vienna State Opera—Prohaska   ♯ **Van.VRS 417**
     (♯ *Nix.VLP 417*)

— ARR. ORCH. Oeser   "*Gastein Symphony*"
Salzburg Mozarteum Orch.—Fekete
     ♯ **Csm.CLPS 1013**
     (♯ *Eur.LPG 607*)

VARIATIONS, Pf. duet
A flat major, Op. 35   D.813
B flat major, Op. 82, No. 2   D.603
P. Badura-Skoda & J. Demus   ♯ **West.WL 5147**
(*above*)

I. B. CHAMBER MUSIC

Nocturne, E flat major, Op. 148 pf., vln., vlc. D.897
L. Mannes, B. Gimpel, L. Silva   ♯**B.AXTL 1014**
(*Schumann: Trio No. 1*)   (♯ *AmD.DL 9604*)

Octet, F major, Op. 166 cl., hrn., bsn., str. qtt., cbs.
     D.803
Vienna Konzerthaus Ens.   ♯ **West.WL 5094**
Berlin Phil. Ens.   (8ss)   ♮ **PV. 72220/3**
(*o.n. PV. 72149/52*)   (♯ *Pol. 16030/1,* 4ss)
☆ Vienna Chamber Group (♯ *Clc. 6044*)

QUARTETS, String
No. 7, D major D.94
No. 8, B flat major, Op. 168   D.112
Vienna Konzerthaus Qtt.   ♯ **West. WL 5110**

No. 10, E flat major, Op. 125, No. 1   D.87
... **4th movt., Allegro, only**
Paganini Qtt. (in † ♯ Vic.LM 1192: ♭ *set WDM 1611*)

No. 12, C minor   (one movt.)   D.703
Amadeus Qtt.   ♯ **West.WL 5084**
(*Brahms*)
Koeckert Qtt.   **PV. 72067**
(*Wolf: Italian Serenade*)   (♯ *AmD.DL 4044*)
Fine Arts Qtt.   ♯ **Mer.MG 10104**
(*No. 15*)
☆ New Italian Qtt.   ♯ **D.LXT 2679**
(*Beethoven*)   (♯ *Lon.LL 321*)

No. 13, A minor, Op. 29   D.804
Vegh Qtt.   ♯ **D.LXT 2709**
     (♯ *Lon.LL 587*)
Vienna Konzerthaus Qtt.   ♯ **West.WL 5115**
Cumberland Fest. Qtt (♯ *Pte. recording*)

♯ = Long-playing, 33⅓ r.p.m.   ♭ = 45 r.p.m.   ♮ = Auto. couplings, 78 r.p.m.

No. 14, D minor D.810 ("*Tod und das Mädchen*")
Hungarian Qtt.   ♯ **CHS.CHS 1152**
           (♯ Nix.CLP 1152)

☆ Vienna Konzerthaus Qtt. (♯ Sel.LPG 8333)
   Koeckert Qtt. (♯ AmD.DL 9567; ♯ Pol. 18043)

No. 15, G major, Op. 161 D.887
Fine Arts Qtt.   ♯ **Mer.MG 10104**
(*No. 12*)
Amadeus Qtt.   ♮ **PV. 72132/4**
(6ss)   (♯ Pol. 18010)
Philharmonic Qtt.   ♯ **Rgt. 5005**

☆ Vienna Konzerthaus Qtt. (♯ Sel.LPG 8334)

Quartet, G major, fl., vla., vlc., guit. D.96
(A trio by M. W. Matiegka (1773-1820) to which Schubert
added a vlc. part & Trio)

☆ Mess, Kirchner, Barchet, Faiss (♯ Clc. 6097)

QUINTETS
A major, Op. 114 pf., vln., vla., vlc., cbs. D.667
(*The Trout—Forellen*)
A. Gabrielyan & Ens.   ***USSR. 10884/90***
(12ss)   **& *10947/51***
☆ M. Horszowski, Budapest Trio, G. Moleux
               C.LX 1521/5S
(9ss, last blank)   (LVX 202/6S)
For practice—recorded with one instrument missing, in
   turn (♯ CEd.MMO 11/15)

... **4th movt., Variations** — ARR. 4 PFS.
First Pf. Qtt. (in ♯ Vic.LM 1227: ♭ set *WDM 1624*)

C major, Op. 163 2 vlns., vla., 2 vlcs. D.956
Pascal Qtt. & A. Navarra   ♯ **AmVox.PL 7030**
☆ Budapest Qtt. & B. Heifetz (♯ AmC.ML 4437)
   Vienna Konzerthaus Quintet (♯ Sel.LPG 8335)

Rondo, A major vln. & str. qtt. D.438
M. Solovieff & Vienna State Opera—Swoboda
(*Lalo*)   ♯ **CHS.CHS 1143**

Sonata, A minor, Arpeggione & pf. D.821
— ARR. VLC. & PF.
G. Ricci & L. Mittman   ♯ **Strad.STR 612**
(*Schumann: Concerto*)

Sonata, A major, Op. 162 vln. & pf. D.574
("*Duo*")
S. Borries & E. Michel   **G.DB 11505/7**
(5ss—below)
Y. Menuhin & A. Baller   ♯ ***Vic.LM 140***
(5ss—*Sonatina excpt.*, in ♭ set *WDM 1593*)

(3) SONATINAS, Op. 137 vln. & pf.
☆ M. Mischakoff & E. Balogh (♯ Eur.LPG 626)

No. 1, D major D.384
... **2nd movt., Andantino,** only
Y. Menuhin & A. Baller
(*above*)   in ♭ *Vic. set WDM 1593*
S. Borries & E. Michel   **G.DB 11507**
(*Sonata, Op. 162, s. 5*)

TRIOS, pf., vln., vlc.
No. 1, B flat major, Op. 99 D.898
Albeneri Trio   ♯ **Mer.MG 10106**
☆ A. Cortot, J. Thibaud, P. Casals (♮ G.DB 7419/22)

No. 2, E flat major, Op. 100 D.929
Albeneri Trio   ♯ **Mer.MG 10107**
P. Badura-Skoda, J. Fournier & A. Janigro
             ♯ **West.WL 5121**

Variations on Trock'ne Blumen, Op. 160 fl. & pf.
   D.802   1824
H. Barwahser & F. de Nobel   **Phi.A 11148/9G**
(*Gaubert & Caplet, in ♯ A 00104L*)

I. C. DANCES
Collection—Piano
Wiener Deutscher Tanz D.128, No. 6 (played twice)
Waltzes (Originaltänze) Op. 9 D.365, Nos. 33 & 34
Ecossaise D.299, No. 5
Waltzes, Op. 18 D.145, Nos. 6 & 10
Deutscher Tanz D.971, No. 2
Ländler (unid.)
Écossaises D.977 Nos. 2 & 6; D.735, Nos. 5, 7 & 8
Galop D.735 (Op. 49)

E. Krauss (2ss)   **Esq.TW 4-010**

---

(16) Deutsche Tänze, Op. 33 pf. D.783
— ARR. ORCH. Goehr
Concert Hall Sym.—Goehr   in ♯ **CHS.F 6**

— ARR. ORCH. Stokowski (with 2 Écossaises)
☆ Sym.—Stokowski (in ♯ Vic.LM 1238: ♭ 49-0814;
                   ♭ *G.7RF 245*)

(6) Deutsche Tänze D.820 pf.
— ARR. ORCH. von Webern
French Radio—Leibowitz   ♯ **Eso.ES 512**
(*Beethoven, Mozart*)   (♯ Cpt.MC 20003)

(17) Deutsche Tänze (unspec.) (perhaps D. 366)
Vienna Sym.—Moralt   ♯ **AmVox.PL 7280**
(*Symphony No. 5*)

(12) Ländler, Op. 171 pf. D.790 1823
A. Cortot (n.v.)   **G.DB 21492**

I. D. ORCHESTRAL
Overture in the Italian Style, C major, Op. 170
   D.591   1817
Orch.—Hewitt   V♯ *DFr. 71*
(*Rosamunde Overture*)
Concert Hall Sym.—Goehr   in ♯ **CHS.F 6**

SYMPHONIES (*See also* Sonata, pf. duet)
No. 1, D major D.82 1813
☆ Winterthur Sym.—Swoboda   ♯ *MMS. 2*

No. 2, B flat major D.125
Salzburg Mozarteum—Sternberg   ♯ *OL.LD 18*
(2ss)
Pittsburg Sym.—Steinberg   ♯ *DCap.CCL 7512*
(2ss)   (♯ Cap.L 8161)
(also with *Sym. 8* on ♯ Cap.S 8162)
Stuttgart Phil.—v. Hoogstraten ♯ **Per.SPLP 517**
(*Sym. 3*)   (♯ Clc. 6106)
(*Mozart: Divertimenti*, on ♯ Nix. PLP 520)
☆ Boston Sym.—Münch (2ss)   ♯ *G.FBLP 1013*
☆ C.B.S.—Barlow   ♯ **AmC.RL 3010**
(*Humperdinck*)

No. 3, D major D.200
Cincinnati Sym.—Johnson   ♯ **D.LXT 2604**
(*J. C. Bach*)   (♯ Lon.LLP 405)
Berlin Sym.—Friedl (2ss)   ♯ **Roy. 1236**
Austrian Sym.—Singer   ♯ **Rem. 199-110**
(*Haydn: Sym. 93*)
☆ Stuttgart Phil.—v. Hoogstraten
               ♯ **Per.SPLP 517**
(now with *Sym. 2*)   (♯ Clc. 6106)

No. 4, C minor D.417 ("Tragic")
Orch.—Hewitt   ♯ *DFr. 50*
(*Symphony No. 8*)
Salzburg Mozarteum—Freilassing ♯ *Ofo.LP 10*
☆ Lamoureux—Klemperer
             ♯ **E. & AmVox.PL 7860**
(*Mendelssohn: Symphony No. 4*)
Austrian Sym.—Wöss (♯ Rem. 199-37; ♯ Mrt. 200-18)

☆ = Re-issue of a recording to be found in WERM or Supplement I.

SYMPHONIES—*continued*

No. 5, B flat major   D.485
Amsterdam—v. Beinum   ♮ **D.AX 451/3**
        (♯ *D.LX 3082*; ♯ *Lon.LPS 253*)
Vienna Sym.—Moralt   ♯ **AmVox.PL 7280**
(Deutsche Tänze)
Salzburg Mozarteum—Sternberg   ♯ *OL.LD 19*
Munich Phil.—Rieger   ♯ *Mer.MG 15029*
Austrian Sym.—Paulmüller   ♯ **Rem. 199-86**
(Mendelssohn)
 ☆ Winterthur Sym.—F. Busch   ♯ **Nix.CLP 61**
                    (♯ Clc. 6056)

No. 6, C major   D.589
 ☆ Austrian Sym.—Wöss (♯ *Mrt. 1-23*)

No. 7, E major   D.729   (completed Weingartner)
Vienna State Op.—Litschauer   ♯ **Van.VRS 427**

No. 8, B minor   D.759   "Unfinished"   1822
R.P.O.—Beecham   (6ss)   ♮ **C.LX 8942/4**
    (*Mozart: Symphony 31* on ♯ AmC.ML 4474)
Pittsburg Sym.—Steinberg   ♯ *DCap.CCL 7511*
(2ss)   (♯ *Cap.L 8160*; ♯ *T.LCS 8162*)
(& with *Sym. 2*, ♯ Cap.S 8162)
Amsterdam—Jochum   (2ss)   ♯ *Phi.A 00604R*
Orch.—Hewitt   ♯ *DFr. 50*
(No. 4)
French Nat. Radio—Lindenberg ♯ *Od.ODX 102*
(Rosamunde)
  Rome Sym.—Günther (♯ *Roy. 1220*), etc.
 ☆ Vienna Phil.—Furtwängler (♯ *G.FBLP 1005*;
              ♯ *Vic.LHMV 1020*; ♭ set *WHMV 1020*)
  Conservatoire—Cluytens (♯ *C.FC 1011*)
  Sym.—H. A. Brown (♯ *Mrt. 1-1*)

No. 9, C major   (old No. 7)   D.944   1828
Amsterdam—Krips   ♯ **D.LXT 2719**
                  (♯ Lon.LL 619)
Berlin Phil.—Furtwängler (8ss)   ♮ **PV. 72153/6**
    (3ss, ♯ Pol. 18015/6; AmD. set DX 119)
Austrian Sym.—Wöss (♯ Rem. 199-48; ♯ Mrt. 200-17)
 ☆ N.B.C.—Toscanini (♯ *G.FALP 170*)
  Chicago Sym.—Stock (♯ AmC.RL 3008)

II. VOCAL

A. STAGE WORKS

ALFONSO UND ESTRELLA, Op. 69   D.732
  3 Acts, 1822   (f.p. 1854)
Overture
Concert Hall Sym.—Goehr   in ♯ **CHS.F 6**

ROSAMUNDE VON CYPERN, Op. 26   D.797
  Inc. music to v. Chezy's play
COLLECTIONS
Overture (orig. *Die Zauberharfe*)
No. 1, Entracte I, B minor   (in ♭ set only)
No. 5, Entracte III, B flat major
Nos. 2 & 9, Ballets: I, B minor; II, G major
Covent Garden—Braithwaite   ♯ *MGM.E 96*
                  (♭ set K 96)

Overture & Nos. 1, 2, 9
French Nat. Radio—Lindenberg ♯ *Od.ODX 102*
(Symphony No. 8)
(Overture only on Od. 123940: O-3704; Nos. 2 & 9 on
                   O-3705)

Nos. 1, 2, 3a (Entracte II), 5, 9
 ☆ Czech Phil.—Meylan   ♯ *Sup. LPM 23*

Nos. 5 & 9
Residentie—v. Otterloo   ♯ *Phi.N 00107R*
(Bruch: Concerto)
 ☆ Vienna Phil.—Furtwängler (♭ *G.7R 121*: ♭ *7RF 145*;
    in ♯ *Vic.LHMV 1020*; ♭ set *WHMV 1020*

Overture ("Die Zauberharfe")   D.644
Concert Hall Sym.—Goehr   in ♯ **CHS.F 6**
Orch.—Hewitt   V♯ *DFr. 71*
(Overture in Italian Style)
Residentie—v. Otterloo   **Phi.N 11220G**
               (PhM.N 09038S)

No. 5 only
 ☆ Carnegie Pops—O'Connell (♭ *AmC.A 1532*:
               in ♭ set A 1001)

No. 9, Rome Sym.—Questa (in ♯ *Roy. 1227* & ♯ *Roy. 6066*, etc.)

SCHNEEWITTCHEN   1941
  (compiled Weingartner)
Ballet Music   (ARR. Fekete)
Salzburg Mozarteum—Fekete
                 ♯ **Csm.CLPS 1011**
 (*Fekete: Caucasus Ballet Suite*)
 (*Handel: Jephtha*, Suite, on ♯ *Eur.LPG 605*)

II. B. CHURCH MUSIC

MASSES
No. 2, G major   D.167   1815   S, T, B, Cho., Orch.
L. Dutoit, A. Planyavsky, H. Buchsbaum,
Academy Cho. & Vienna Sym. Orch.—
Grossmann   ♯ **AmVox.PL 7510**
(Partsongs)   (♯ EVox. 260; PaV.VP 260)

No. 6, E flat major   S, A, T, B, Cho., Orch.   D.950
 ☆ Soli, Cho. & Vienna Sym.—Moralt
    (♯ Clc. 6045/6; & n.n., ♯ AmVox.PL 7840, 2ss)

DEUTSCHE MESSE, F major   D.872   1827
— MALE VOICE VERSION, A flat major
Vienna Teachers Cho.—Drexler   *G.GA 5056/7*
(4ss)

… Heilig, Heilig
Cologne Male Cho.—Trunk   *Chr. 604A*
(Griesbacher: Pange lingua)

OFFERTORIES   S, Cho., Orch.
Salve Regina, A major, Op. 153   D.676
Salve Regina, F major, Op. 47   D.223
Totus in corde langueo, Op. 46   D.136
C. Lorand & Orch.—Fekete   ♯ **Mer.MG 10081**
(Mozart: Exsultate)   (♯ Eur.LPG 612)

Psalm 23: *See* Partsong collections, *below*

II. C. PARTSONGS

COLLECTION
(Das) Dörfchen, Op. 11, No. 1   (Bürger)   D.641
Geist der Liebe, Op. 11, No. 3   (Matthisson)   D.747
(Der) Gondelfahrer, Op. 28   (Mayrhofer)   D.809
Im gegenwärtigen Vergangenes   (Goethe)   D.710
Liebe, Op. 17, No. 2   (Schiler)   D.983
Nachthelle, Op. 34   (Seidl)   D.892
(Die) Nachtigall, Op. 11, No. 2   (Unger)   D.724
Psalm 23, Op. 132   D.706
Widerspruch, Op. 105, No. 1   (Seidl)   D.865
Academy M.V. Cho.—Grossmann [1]
              ♯ **AmVox.PL 6870**

An die Sonne   (Uz)   D.439   S, A, T, B, & pf.
 1816
Mirjams Siegesgesang, Op. 136   (Grillparzer)
  D.942   S, Cho. & pf.   1828
A. Neulinger, Academy Cho. & N. Scherlich-
Grossmann   ♯ **AmVox.PL 7510**
(Mass)   (♯ PaV.VP 260; ♯ EVox. 260)

Gesang der Geister über den Wassern, Op. 167
  D.714   (Goethe)
 ☆ Vienna State Op. Cho. & Vienna Sym.—
Krauss   ♯ **EVox. 110**
(Beethoven: Fantasia)   (♯ PaV.VP 110)

---

[1] *Liebe* unacc.; Op. 11 with guitar; the rest with pf.

(La) Pastorella (Goldoni) D.513 1817
[3] Vienna Boys' Cho.—Lacovitch
Phi.A 00606R
(below; & Mozart, J. Strauss)

Ständchen, Op. 135 (Grillparzer) D.921
A & female Cho.
[3] Vienna Boys' Cho.—Lacovitch
Phi.A 00606R
(above, Mozart & J. Strauss) (also Phi.A 11224G:
PhM.A 09717S)
☆ M. Nussbauer & Vienna Academy Cha. Cho.—
Grossmann (in # Sel.LPG 8238)

II. D. SONGS (LIEDER)
(for pf. transcriptions, see LISZT)

CYCLES

(Die) SCHÖNE MÜLLERIN, Op. 25 (Müller)
D.795 1823

1. Das Wandern	2. Wohin
3. Halt!	4. Danksagung an den Bach
5. Am Feierabend	6. Der Neugierige
7. Ungeduld	8. Morgengruss
9. Des Müllers Blumen	10. Tränenregen
11. Mein!	12. Pause
13. Mit dem grünen	14. Der Jäger
Lautenbande	15. Eifersucht und Stolz
16. Die liebe Farbe	17. Die böse Farbe
18. Trock'ne Blumen	19. Der Müller und der Bach
20. Des Baches Wiegenlied	

COMPLETE RECORDINGS
D. Fischer-Dieskau (B), G. Moore (pf.)
(16ss)　　　　　　　　　G.DB 21388/95
W. Ludwig (T), M. Raucheisen (pf.)
PV. 72189/93
(9ss—Vor meiner Wiege & Fischerweise)
(4ss, # Pol. 18031/2; 2ss, # AmD.DL 9648)
M. Singher (B), P. Ulanowsky (pf.)
CHS.CHS 1114
☆ A. Schiøtz (T), G. Moore (pf.) (# Vic.LCT 1048:
♭ set WCT 78)

... Nos. 2, 4, 6, 10, 16, 20
L. Lehmann (S) (in † # Pembroke. set)

SCHWANENGESANG D.957 1828

1. Liebesbotschaft	2. Kriegers Ahnung
3. Frühlingssehnsucht	4. Ständchen
5. Aufenthalt	6. In der Ferne
7. Abschied	8. Der Atlas
9. Ihr Bild	10. Das Fischermädchen
11. Die Stadt	12. Am Meer
13. Der Doppelgänger	14. Die Taubenpost

COMPLETE RECORDINGS
G. Hüsch (B), M. Gurlitt (pf.)　JpV.SD 3073/5
(14ss) (set JAS 249)　　　　　　　　& SF 715/8
P. Munteanu (T), F. Holletschek (pf.)
West.WL 5165

WINTERREISE, Op. 89　D.911 1827

1. Gute Nacht	2. Die Wetterfahne
3. Gefror'ne Tränen	4. Erstarrung
5. Der Lindenbaum	6. Wasserfluth
7. Auf dem Flusse	8. Rückblick
9. Irrlicht	10. Rast
11. Frühlingstraum	12. Einsamkeit
13. Die Post	14. Der greise Kopf
15. Die Krähe	16. Letzte Hoffnung
17. Im Dorfe	18. Der stürmische Morgen
19. Täuschung	20. Der Wegweiser
21. Das Wirthshaus	22. Muth!
23. Die Nebensonnen	24. Der Leyermann

COMPLETE RECORDINGS
B. Boyce (B), J. Germain (pf.)　　# OL.LD 24
(2ss)
V. Carne (T), G. Moore (pf.) # West.WL 5087/8
(4ss)　　　　　　　　　　　　　(set WAL 203)
☆ H. Hotter (B), M. Raucheisen (pf.)
(4ss)　　　　　　　　　# AmD. set DX 111

[3] ARR. Keldorfer.

COLLECTIONS

(Die) SCHÖNE MÜLLERIN: Nos. 2, 7, 15
WINTERREISE: Nos. 4, 8, 11, 13, 15
Gott im Frühlinge (Uz) D.448
Im Frühling (Schulze) D.882
(Der) Kreuzzug (Leitner) D.932
(Das) Lied im Grünen, Op. 115, No. 1 (Reil) D.917
(Der) Musensohn, Op. 92, No. 1 (Goethe) D.764
Todtengräber-Weise (Schlechta) D.869
(Der) Wanderer an den Mond, Op. 80, No. 1 (Seidl)
D.870
H. Schey (Bs), M. Reymers (pf.)
Polym.PRLP 1009

(Der) Goldschmiedsgesell (Goethe) D.560
Tischlerlied (Anon.) D.274
Tischlied, Op. 118, No. 3 (Goethe) D.234
W. Strienz (Bs), M. Raucheisen (pf.)

Heimliches Lieben, Op. 106, No. 1 (Klenke) D.922
T. Lemnitz (S), M. Raucheisen (pf.)

Hoffnung (Goethe) D.295
(Der) Jüngling an der Quelle (Salis) D.300
Nachtstück, Op. 36, No. 2 (Mayrhofer) D.672
K. Erb (T), H. Reuter (pf.)　　# Ura. 7047
(Schumann)

(Die) SCHÖNE MÜLLERIN: Nos. 11, 16
SCHWANENGESANG: Nos. 1, 13
WINTERREISE: No. 5
Auf dem Wasser zu singen, Op. 72 (Stolberg) D.774
Heidenröslein, Op. 3, No. 3 (Goethe) D.257
Nacht und Träume, Op. 43, No. 2 (Collin) D.827
C. Mauranne (B), L. Bienvenue (pf.)
Pat.DT 1003

(Die) SCHÖNE MÜLLERIN: No. 2
SCHWANENGESANG: Nos. 4, 8, 10, 11
WINTERREISE: Nos. 1, 5, 11, 13
(Der) Musensohn, Op. 92, No. 1 (Goethe) D.764
Sei mir gegrüsst, Op. 20, No. 1 (Rückert) D.741
☆ H. Schlusnus (B), S. Peschko (pf.)
D.LXT 2539
(# Lon.LLP 106)

SCHWANENGESANG: Nos. 4, 8, 14
Alinde, Op. 81, No. 2 (Rochlitz) D.904
(Die) Forelle, Op. 32 (Schubert) D.550
Frühlingsglaube, Op. 20, No. 2 (Uhland) D.686
Im Frühling (Schulze) D.882
Nachtstück, Op. 36, No. 2 (Mayrhofer) D.672
☆ H. Schlusnus (B), S. Peschko (pf.)
(Wolf)　　　　　　　　in # Pol. 18059
(# AmD.DL 9620)

WINTERREISE: No. 5
An Schwager Kronos, Op. 19, No. 1 (Goethe) D.369
Im Abendroth (Lappe) D.799
(Der) Jüngling an der Quelle (Salis) D.300
☆ H. Schlusnus (B) & pf.　　in # Pol. 18029
(# AmD.DL 9621)

(Die) SCHÖNE MÜLLERIN: No. 2
(Der) Musensohn, Op. 92, No. 1 (Goethe) D.764
(Der) Wanderer, Op. 4, No. 1 (Schmidt) D.493
☆ H. Schlusnus (B)　　　in # AmD.DL 9623

[1,2] Ave Maria, Op. 52, No. 6 (Scott) D.839
[1] Erlkönig, Op. 1 (Goethe) D.328
[1,2] (Die) Forelle, Op. 32 (Schubart) D.550
Gretchen am Spinnrade, Op. 2 (Goethe) D.118
Liebesbotschaft (Rellstab) D.957
Ständchen (Rellstab) D.957
[2] (Der) Tod und das Mädchen, Op. 7, No. 3 (Claudius)
D.531
M. Anderson (A), F. Rupp (pf.)　# *Vic.LM 98*
(Songs marked [1] also on　　(♭ set WDM 1530)
♭ Vic.WEPR 19 and [2] on ♭ G.7RF 251)

Fragment aus dem Aeschylus (Mayrhofer) D.450
(Der) Geistertanz (Matthisson) D.116
Iphigenia, Op. 98, No. 3 (Mayrhofer) D.573
(Der) König in Thule, Op. 5, No. 5 (Goethe) D.367
Nachtgesang (Kosegarten) D.314
(Dem) Unendlichen (Klopstock) D.291
Verklärung (Pope, trs. Herder) D.59
M. Klose (A), M. Raucheisen (pf.) # Ura. 7017
(Gluck, etc.)

(continued on next page)

COLLECTIONS—*continued*

SCHWANENGESANG: Nos. 1, 14
Am Grabe Anselmos, Op. 6, No. 3 (Claudius) D.504
Im Abendroth (Lappe) D.799
(Die) Junge Nonne, Op. 43, No. 1 (Craigher) D. 828
(Das) Lied im Grünen, Op. 115, No. 1 (Reil) D.917
H. Mott (S), E. Lush (pf.) in ‡ **Mon.MWL 301**
(*Brahms & Weber*)

Auf dem Wasser zu singen (Stolberg) D.774
Dithyrambe (Schiller) D.801
Du liebst mich nicht (Platen) D.756
Ihr Bild (SG 9—Heine)
Lachen und Weinen (Rückert) D.777
Nacht und Träume (Collin) D.827
(Das) Wirthshaus (W 21—Müller)
T. Niemela (S), P. Koskimies (pf.) ‡ **WCFM.10**
(*Haydn: Songs*)

Erster Verlust, Op. 5, No. 4 (Goethe) D.226
(Der) Jüngling an der Quelle (Salis) D.300
Nacht und Träume, Op. 43, No. 2 (Collin) D.827
(Der) Schmetterling, Op. 57, No. 1 (Schlegel) D.633
M. Ribbing (S), S. Ribbing (pf.)   **G.DB 10512**

(Der) Blumen Schmerz, Op. 173, No. 4 (Mayláth) D. 731
(Die) Blumensprache, Op. 173, No. 2 (Platner) D.519
Viola, Op. 123 (Schober) D.786
T. Lemnitz (S), M. Raucheisen (pf.) ‡ **Ura. 7013**
(*Cornelius, Wolf*)

Frühlingsglaube, Op. 20, No. 2 (Uhland) D.686
Heidenröslein, Op. 3, No. 3 (Goethe) D.257
Ungeduld (SM. 7)
☆ R. Tauber (T) & Orch. in ‡ **AmD.DL 9547**

(Der) Musensohn, Op. 92, No. 1 (Goethe) D.764
(Der) Doppelgänger (SG.13—Heine)
(Die) Stadt (SG.11—Heine)
P. Schoeffler (B), O. Schulhof (pf.)
in ‡ **MSL.MW 43**
(*Beethoven, Loewe, Schumann, Wagner*)

Erlkönig, Op. 1 (Goethe) D.328
(Der) Lindenbaum (W.5)
(Der) Tod und das Mädchen, Op. 7, No. 3 (Claudius)
▽ K. Branzell (A)   in ‡ **Rem. 149-6**

INDIVIDUAL SONGS
(SM—From Schöne Müllerin;
SG—From Schwanengesang;
W—From Winterreise;
those marked ☐ are also in collections, *above*)

Am Meer (SG.12) ☐
D. Fischer-Dieskau (B), G. Moore (pf.)
G.DB 21491
(*Der Doppelgänger*)

An die Laute, Op. 81, No. 2 (Rochlitz) D.905
— ARR. VOCAL QTT. & PF. (in *English*)
Victor Qtt., R. Viola (pf.)   in *Vic. set E 101*
(♭ *set WE 101*)

An die Leyer, Op. 56, No. 2 (Bruchmann) D.737
▽ J. Greindl (Bs), H. Klust (pf.) **G.DB 11504**
(*Der Wanderer*)

☆ H. Schlusnus (B) (in ‡ AmD.DL 9622)

An die Musik, Op. 88, No. 4 (Schober) D.547
G. Hüsch (B), M. Gurlitt (pf.)   *JpV.SF 719*
(*Das Rosenband*)
(in set JAS 275)
L. Lehmann (S)   in † ‡ **Pembroke set**
(*Unfinished*)
☆ H. Schlusnus (B) (*Pol. 62848*)

An die Nachtigall, Op. 98, No. 1 (Claudius) D.497
E. Berger (S), M. Raucheisen (pf.)
in ‡ **Ura. 7060**
(*below, Mozart, Brahms, etc.*)

(Der) Atlas (SG.8—Heine) ☐
K. Schmitt-Walter (B), M. Raucheisen (pf.)
T.A 11300
(*Ihr Bild*)

Auf dem See, Op. 92, No. 2 (Goethe) D.543
☆ H. Günter (B) (Pol. 15479)

Auf dem Strom, Op. 119 (Rellstab) (with horn)
D.943
M. Stagliano (S), J. Stagliano & P. Ulanowsky
‡ **Bo.L 200**
(*Beethoven, Mozart, Schumann*)

Auf dem Wasser zu singen, Op. 72 (Stolberg)
D.774 ☐
W. Ludwig (T), M. Raucheisen (pf.) *Pol. 62884*
(*Fischerweise*)
H. Marten (T), F. Albes (pf.)   *Imp. 19140*
(*Fischerweise*)
☆ I. Seefried (S), G. Moore (pf.) (*C.LW 56*)

Auf der Bruck, Op. 93, No. 2 (Schulze) D.853
P. Pears (T), B. Britten (pf.)   **G.DB 21423**
(*Im Frühling*)

Auf der Riesenkoppe (Körner) D.611
K. Erb (T), H. Altmann (pf.)   **G.DB 11538**
(*Das Zügenglöcklein*)

Aufenthalt (SG. 5—Rellstab) ☐
M. Reizen (Bs., *Russ*)   **USSR. 017775**
(*Alnaes: Last voyage*)   (& 07520, d.c.)

Ave Maria, Op. 52, No. 6 (Starck, after Scott)
D.839
R. Ponselle (S), M. Elman (vln.) & pf. **G.VB 74**
(*Bishop: Home, sweet home*) (in ‡ *Vic.LCT 10*: ♭ *WCT 55*:
& AF. 387/2)
T. Lemnitz (S) & orch.   **T.A 11153**
(*Gounod: Ave Maria*)
☆ T. Rossi (T, *Lat*) (in ‡ *AmC.FL 9544*: ♭ set F 4-41)
H. Traubel (S) (in ‡ *Vic.LM 118*)
C. Lynch (T) & org. (in ‡ AmC.RL 3016)
Ⅱ J. McCormack (T) (in ‡ Vic.LCT 1121*:
♭ set WCT 1121*)

— ARR. VLN. & ORCH. Anderson
☆ N. Milstein & Vic. Sym.—Fiedler (♭ *G.7RF 210*)
— ARR. VLN. & ORCH. Wilhelmj
Krips & Boston Pops—Fiedler   ♭ *G.7BF 1035*
(*Franck: Panis Angelicus*)   (♭ *Vic. 49-1447*)
— ARR. VLN. & PF.
L. Kaufman & P. Ulanowsky   in ‡ *DCap.CCL 7513*
(‡ *Cap.L 8165*)
☆ J. Heifetz & E. Bay (in ‡ *Vic.LM 1166*)
I. Haendel & G. Moore (in ‡ BB.LBC 1013:
♭ set WBC 1013)
etc., etc.
— ARR. VLC. & PF. E. Mainardi & F. Lehmann (*PV. 46008*)
etc.
— ARR. ORG. G. Mertens (*C.BF 5006*)
— ARR. CHO. R. Shaw Chorale (in ‡ *Vic.LM 96*:
♭ set WDM 1528: also in ♭ WEPR 43 & 49-3448)

(Der) Doppelgänger (SG.13—Heine) ☐
(*Le Sosie* or *Le Double*)
D. Fischer-Dieskau (B), G. Moore (pf.)
G.DB 21491
(*Am Meer*)
N. Rossi-Lemeni (Bs) & pf.   **P.R 30046**
(*Wolf: Verborgenheit*)   (AB 30012)
A. Ivanov (B, *Russ*), A. Holeček (pf.)
U.H 23858
(*Borodin: To distant shores*)
J. Chalud-ben-Baruch & orch. (*Fr*) *Sat. S 1001*
(*Fauré: Les Berceaux*)
M. Reizen (Bs, *Russ*)   **USSR. 07521**
(*Aufenthalt*)

---

‡ = Long-playing, 33⅓ r.p.m.   ♭ = 45 r.p.m.   ♮ = Auto. couplings, 78 r.p.m.

Du bist die Ruh', Op. 59, No. 3 (Rückert) D.776
D. Fischer-Dieskau (B), G. Moore (pf.)
(Ständchen)   **G.DB 21349**
☒ J. McCormack ᶜG.VB 32*: o.n. DB 766*)

Erlkönig, Op. 1 (Goethe) D.328 ☐
D. Fischer-Dieskau (B), G. Moore (pf.)
                                             G.DB 21350
(Schumann: Die beiden Grenadiere)
A. Mestral (B, *Fr*), I. Aïtoff (pf.)
                                             PhM.A 77500S
(Fauré: Clair de lune)
☆ B. Sonnerstedt (B), G. Moore (pf.) *(G.EH 1337)*

(Das) Fischermädchen (SG.10—Heine) ☐
K. Schmitt-Walter (B), M. Raucheisen (pf.)
(Die Stadt)   *T.A 11327*

Fischerweise, Op. 96, No. 4 (Schlechta) D.881
W. Ludwig (T), M. Raucheisen (pf.) *Pol. 62884*
(Auf dem Wasser ...)   *(& in PV. 72193, d.c.)*
H. Marten (T), F. Albes (pf.)   *Imp. 19140*
(Auf dem Wasser ...)

(Die) Forelle, Op. 32 (Schubart) D.550 ☐
E. Berger (S), M. Raucheisen (pf.) *PV. 36040*
(⅓s.—La Pastorella & Die Junge Nonne)

Frühlingsglaube, Op. 20, No. 2 (Uhland) D.686 ☐
J. Vincent (S), F. de Nobel (pf.)
                                   in ♯ *Phi.A 00610R*
(Grieg, Tchaikovsky, etc.)

Gretchen am Spinnrade, Op. 2 (Goethe) D.118 ☐
E. Berger (S), M. Raucheisen (pf.) *Pol. 62889*
(Nacht und Träume)
☆ M. Anderson (A), F. Rupp (pf.) *(G.DA 2016)*

Gruppe aus dem Tartarus, Op. 24, No. 1 (Schiller)
    D.583   1817
¶ T. Schnabel (S), A. Schnabel (pf.) **G.DB 1835**
(Der Kreuzzug)

Heidenröslein, Op. 3, No. 3 (Goethe) D.257 ☐
E. Berger (S), G. Schick (pf.) in ♯ *Vic.LM 133*
(Mozart: Songs)   *(♭ set WDM 1589)*

Heimliches Lieben, Op. 106, No. 1 (Klenke) D.922
☆ H. Günther (B) *(Pol. 15479)*

(Der) Hirt auf dem Felsen, Op. 129
    (Müller & Chezy) D.965   1828 S, cl., pf.
(The Shepherd on the Rock)
☆ D. Maynor, D. Oppenheim, G. Schick *(G.ED 1205)*

Horch! horch! die Lerch! D.889 (after Shakespeare)
M. Morley (treb.), J. Wills (pf.)   *D.F 9782*
(Arne: Lass with the delicate air) (in ♯ *LM 4543;*
                                  ♯ *Lon.LPS 399)*

Ihr Bild (SG.9—Heine) ☐
K. Schmitt-Walter (B), M. Raucheisen (pf.)
(Der Atlas)   *T.A 11300*

Im Abendroth (Lappe) D.799 ☐
W. Ludwig (T), M. Raucheisen (pf.) *Pol. 62885*
(Jüngling und der Tod)
☆ L. Lehmann (S), E. Balogh (pf.) *(JpV.NF 4196)*

Im Frühling (Schulze) D.882 ☐
P. Pears (T), B. Britten (pf.)   **G.DB 21423**
(Auf der Bruck)

(Die) Junge Nonne, Op. 43, No. 1 (Craigher) ☐
    D. 828
E. Berger (S), M. Raucheisen (pf.) *PV. 36040*
(La Pastorella & Die junge Nonne)
☒ S. Strong (S) & orch.[1] (G.VB 13*, o.n. 043078*)

(Der) Jüngling an der Quelle (Salis) D.300 ☐
☆ H. Schlusnus (B) *(Pol. 62800)*

(Der) Jüngling und der Tod (Spaun) D.545
W. Ludwig (T), M. Raucheisen (pf.) *Pol. 62885*
(Im Abendroth)

(Die) Krähe (W.15) ☐
E. Laider (T), P. Alsfelt (pf.)   *Pol.X 51401*
(Die Post)

(Der) Kreuzzug (Leitner) D.932 ☐
¶ T. Schnabel (S), A. Schnabel (pf.) **G.DB 1835**
(Gruppe aus dem Tartarus)

Lachen und Weinen, Op. 59, No. 4 (Rückert)
    D.777 ☐
E. Berger (S), M. Raucheisen (pf.) in ♯ *Ura. 7060*
(above, & Mozart, Brahms, etc.)

(Der) Leyermann (W.24) ☐
Y. Ciannella &/or L. Winter (S) & pf.
                              in *Vic. set E 100*
                                   (♭ set WE 100)

Liebesbotschaft (SG.1—Rellstab) ☐
☆ M. Anderson (A), F. Rupp (pf.) *(G.DA 2016)*

Lied der Mignon III, Op. 62, No. 4
    (Goethe—*Nur wer die Sehnsucht kennt*) D. 877-4
M. Maddox (S) & pf.   in ♯ *MTR.MLO 1009*

Lied eines Schiffers an die Dioskuren, Op. 65, No. 1
    (Mayrhofer) D.360
☆ H. Schlusnus (B)   *Pol. 62848*
(now has d.c.—An die Musik)   *(& in ♯ AmD.DL 9622)*

(Der) Lindenbaum (W.5) ☐
— ARR. CHO. Neeber-Schüler Cho.—Zoll *(T.A 11151)*

Litaney (Jacobi) D.343
    (Auf das Fest Aller Seelen)
K. Borg (Bs) & orch.   **Felix.Ø 65**
(Gounod: Mors et Vita—Judex)
— ARR. ORGAN
E. P. Biggs   in ♯ **AmC.ML 4603**
(R. Strauss, J. Clarke, etc.)

(Des) Müllers Blumen (SM.9) ☐
T. Pyle (B, *Eng*), R. Viola (pf.) in *Vic. set E 100*
(Handel)   *(♭ set WE 100)*

(Der) Musensohn, Op. 92, No. 1 (Goethe) D.764 ☐
H. Schlusnus (B), O. Braun (pf.)   *Pol. 62880*
(Wohin?)
☆ K. Ferrier (A), P. Spurr (pf.) (in ♯ *Lon.LPS 402)*
                          (announced but not issued)

Nacht und Träume, Op. 43, No. 2 (Collin) D.827 ☐
D. Fischer-Dieskau (B), G. Moore (pf.)
                                   G.DB 21517
(Schumann: Mondnacht)
E. Berger (S), M. Raucheisen (pf.)   *Pol. 62889*
(Gretchen am Spinnrade)
☆ I. Seefried (S), G. Moore (pf.) *(C.LW 56)*

Nachtstück, Op. 36, No. 2 (Mayrhofer) D.672 ☐
K. Erb (T), H. Altmann (pf.)   **G.DB 11539**
(Wer nie sein Brot ...)

(Der) Neugierige (SM.6) ☐
C. Rubio (S), C. D. Martin (pf.) **SpC.RG 16181**
(Schumann: Der Nussbaum)

(La) Pastorella (Goldoni) D.528
    (Die junge Schäferin)
E. Berger (S), M. Raucheisen (pf.)   *PV. 36040*
(⅓s.—Die Forelle & Die Junge Nonne)

[1] ARR. ORCH. Liszt. (G. 667, No. 1)

(Die) Post (W.13) □
E. Laider (T), P. Alsfelt (pf.)   *Pol.X 51401*
(*Die Krähe*)

Prometheus (Goethe) D.674
☆ B. Sönnerstedt (B), G. Moore (pf.) (G.EH 1337)

(Das) Rosenband (Klopstock) D.280
G. Hüsch (B), M. Gurlitt (pf.)   *JpV.SF 719*
(*An die Musik*)   (in set JAS 275)

(Die) Stadt (SG.11—Heine) □
K. Schmitt-Walter (B), M. Raucheisen (pf.)
    T.A 11327
(*Das Fischermädchen*)

Ständchen (SG.4—Rellstab) □
D. Fischer-Dieskau (B), G. Moore (pf.)
    G.DB 21349
(*Du bist die Ruh'*)
☆ R. Crooks (T, *Eng*)   *G.DA 1952*
(*Grieg: A Dream*)
☆ R. Ponselle (S) & orch. (in ♯ Vic.LCT 10: ♭ se. WCT 55)
J. Schmidt (T) & pf. (*P.DPW 60*)
L. Slezak (T) & pf. (Pol. 15546)
J. Peerce (T, *Eng*) (in Vic.set ♮ DM/♭ WDM 1514)
G. Moore (S, *Eng*) (in ♯ AmD.DL 9593)
▽ L. Homer (S) (G.DB 1151)

— ARR. VLN. & ORCH. Anderson
☆ N. Milstein & Vic. Sym.—Fiedler (♭ G.7RF 210)

(Der) Tod und das Mädchen, Op. 7, No. 3
(Claudius) D.531 □
P. Schoeffler (B), O. Schulhof (pf.)
    ♯ **MSL.MW 44**
(*below; & Schumann, Loewe, etc.*)

Todtengräbers Heimwehe (Craigher) D.842
E. List (Bs), O. Schulhof (pf.) in ♯ **Rem. 199-73**
(*Ziehrer, Moussorgsky, etc.*)

Ungeduld (SM.7) □
☆ L. Slezak (T) (Pol. 15546)
L. Lehmann (S) (in ♯ Vic.LCT 1108: ♭ set WCT 1108;
    JpV.NF 4196)
J. Schmidt (T) (*P.DPW 60*)

Verklärung (Herder, after Pope) D.59 □
I. Baillie (S, *Eng*), G. Moore (pf.)   *C.DB 2999*
(*Wohin*)

Vor meiner Wiege, Op. 106, No. 3 (Leitner) D.927
W. Ludwig (T), M. Raucheisen (pf.) **PV. 72193**
(⅓s.—*Fischerweise & Schöne Müllerin No. 20*)

(Der) Wanderer, Op. 4, No. 1 (Schmidt) D.493 □
▽ J. Greindl (Bs), H. Klust (pf.)   **G.DB 11504**
(*An die Leyer*)
P. Schoeffler (B), O. Schulhof (pf.)
    ♯ **MSL.MW 44**
    above; Schumann, Loewe, etc.

Wanderers Nachtlied, Op. 4, No. 3 (Goethe) D.224
P. Gavert (T) & pf.   in ♯ **MTR.MLO 1009**

Wer nie sein Brot, Op. 12, No. 2 (Goethe) D.480
K. Erb (T), H. Altmann (pf.)   **G.DB 11539**
(*Nachtstück*)

Wiegenlied, Op. 98, No. 2 (Claudius) D.498
J. Vincent (S), F. de Nobel (pf.) **Phi.A 11242G**
(*Grieg & Mendelssohn*)(*PhM.A 11242S* & in ♯ *Phi.A 00610R*)

(Der) Winterabend (Leitner) D.938
K. Erb (T), H. Altmann (pf.)   **G.DB 11540**
(2ss)

Wohin? (SM.2—Müller) □
H. Schlusnus (B), O. Braun (pf.)   *Pol. 62880*
(*Der Musensohn*)

I. Baillie (S, *Eng*), G. Moore (pf.)   *C.DB 2999*
(*Verklärung*)
☆ M. Anderson (A) (in ♭ Vic.WEPR 19)

(Das) Zügenglöcklein, Op. 80, No. 2 (Seidl) D.871
K. Erb (T), H. Altmann (pf.)   **G.DB 11538**
(*Auf der Riesenkoppe*)

MISCELLANEOUS
Schubert, his story & his music
☆ J. Ferrer (narrator) & Sym. Orch.—Goberman
    (♯ *AmVox.VL 2540*)

SCHUBERT, Heinz (1908-*c.* 1942)

Concertante Suite   vln. & cha. orch.
☆ H. Stanske & Berlin Phil.—H. Schubert (Pol. 15537)

SCHÜTZ, Heinrich (1585-1672)

COLLECTION
MOTETS: Also hat Gott …
    Das ist je …
    Der Engel sprach
    Ich sterbe …
    Selig sind die Toten
(Die) SIEBEN LETZTEN WORTE
    ☆ Soloists & Vienna Academy Cho. (♯ *BàM.LD 02*)

À jamais béni (unid.)
Lausanne Youth Cho. (*Fr*)   *G.JK 44*
(*Bach: Johannes Passion, No. 68*)

Also hat Gott die Welt geliebt (GK.1636)
So fahr' ich hin (GC.1648)
Barmen Singers   *Chr. 323A*

(Die) AUFERSTEHUNGS-HISTORIE   Oratorio
    1623
Soloists, Cho., Munich Viol Quintet & org.—
    Schleiffer   ♯ **Mer.MG 10073**

… No. 2, Marienszene am Grabe
Soloists, Zürich Str. Orch.—Huber, hpsi. & org.
    G.HEX 128

Ehre sei Dir, Christe
Shaw Chorale   in ♯ **Vic.LM 1201**
(*Easter Songs*)   (♭ set WDM 1623)

Eile mich, Gott, zu erretten (GK.1636)
W. Warfield (B), A. Tietjen (org.)
    in ♯ **AmC.ML 4545**
(† *Ancient Music of the Church*)

Frohlocket mit Händen (SS) 1647
Lobet den Herrn (SS) 1647
M. Meili (T), 2 vlns. & org. **V♯** *CdM.LDY 8031*
(*Matthäus-Passion, below*, in ♯ *Van.BG 520*)

Ich weiss, dass mein Erlöser lebet (GC) 1648
    7 voices
(Die) Worte der Abendmahleinsetzung (GG) 1657
Stuttgart Cho. Soc.—Grischkat
    ♯ **Ren.set SX 203**
(*Matthäus-Passion*)   (♯ *Nix.PLP 203-1*)

♯ = Long-playing, 33⅓ r.p.m.   ♭ = 45 r.p.m.   ♮ = Auto. couplings, 78 r.p.m.

198

Musikalische Exequien ("German Requiem") 1636
J. Brainerd & C. Bloecher (S), P. Pierce (A),
A. Squires & W. Hess (T), P. Matthen &
L. Cass (B), Cantata Singers—Mendel
(J. Beaven, org.)   ♯ REB. 9

PASSION-MUSIC

JOHANNES-PASSION T, T, B, Cho.
☆ C. Stemann, W. Hohmann, B. Müller, Stuttgart Cho.—
Grischkat (♯ Clc. 6075)

MATTHÄUS-PASSION
COMPLETE RECORDINGS
M. Meili, H. Rüngenhagen, B. Michaelis,
H. Wilhelm, R. Patzke, G. Räker, L. Möller-
Jarmer, etc. Berlin Radio Chos.—H. Koch
(4ss)   ♯ CdM.LD 8029/30
(3ss—above, on ♯ Van.BG 519/20)
C. Stemann & G. Jelden, B. Müller,
M. Mangold, Stuttgart Cho. Soc.—Grischkat
                                           ♯ Ren.set SX 203
(3ss—Motets)   (♯ Nix.PLP 203-1/2)
(subsequently re-issued, complete, on ♯ Ren.X 49, 2ss)

... Final Chorus
Hamline Singers—Holliday   ♯ NRI. 305
(Britten, etc.)

Weihnachts-Historie Oratorio 1664
N. Filacuridi, M. Rizzo, P. Gablassi, Cho. &
Naples Scarlatti Orch.—Caracciolo (Ital)
                                           ♯ Csm.CLPS 1034

SCHULZ, Johann Abraham Peter
(1749-1800)

Abendlied (Claudius) (Der Mond ist aufgegangen)
S. Mervild Qtt. (Dan) (Felix.F 49)

SCHUMAN, William Howard (b. 1910)

Quartet, Strings, No. 4 1950
Juilliard Qtt.   ♯ AmC.ML 4493
(Dahl: Concertino)

American Festival Overture Orch. 1939
A.R.S. Orch.—Hendl   ♯ ARS. 28
(Harris: Symphony)

Symphony No. 3 1941
Philadelphia—Ormandy   ♯ AmC.ML 4413

SCHUMANN, Clara (1819-1896)

Trio, G minor, Op. 17   pf., vln., vlc.
J. Mannes, B. Gimpel, L. Silva ♯ AmD.DL 9555
(Beethoven)

SCHUMANN, Robert (1810-1856)

CLASSIFIED: I. PIANO
             II. CHAMBER MUSIC
            III. ORCHESTRAL
             IV. SONGS

I. PIANO

Abendlied, Op. 85, No. 12   pf. duet
— ARR. VLC. & PF.
E. Mainardi & F. Lehmann   PV. 46008
(Schubert: Ave Maria)
E. Mainardi & S. Legrenzi   Pol. 57408
(Träumerei)
☆ R. Krotschak (in ♯ Eur.LPG 631)

— ARR. VLC. & ORCH. Machula
T. de Machula & Residentie—v. Otterloo
                                    Phi.N 12047G
(Träumerei)   (PhM. 09037S)

— ARR. ORCH. McDonald
Boston Prom.—Fiedler (G.C 4137; ♭ Vic. 49-1084)

ALBUM FÜR DIE JUGEND, Op. 68
Nos. 8, 10, 11, 13, 16
E. Beckman-Shcherbina   (2ss)   USSR. 6441/2

Arabeske, Op. 18
W. Kempff   ♯ D.LXT 2670
(Papillons; & Liszt)   (♯ Lon.LL 515)
R. Lev   ♯ CHS.CHS 1104
(Davidsbündlertänze)
V. Horowitz   (2ss)   (n.v.)   ♭ Vic. 49-3304
M. Pressler   ♯ MGM.E 119
(below)
☆ A. Rubinstein (♭ G.7R 113)
J. Iturbi (in ♯ Vic.LM 1167: ♭ set WDM 1604)

BUNTE BLÄTTER, Op. 99
Nos. 1 to 8
C. Haskil   ♯ Phi.A 00108L
(½s.—Schubert: Sonata)

CARNAVAL, Op. 9
(Scènes mignonnes sur quatre notes)
W. Gieseking   (6ss)   ♮ C.LCX 5013/5
N. Magaloff   ♯ D.LX 3074
                                    (♯ Lon.LS 528)
V. Schiøler   ♯ G.KBLP 2
A. Brailowsky   ♯ Vic.LM 9003
(Fantasia)   (♭ set WDM 9004)
G. Sandor   ♯ AmC.ML 4452
P. Badura-Skoda   ♯ West.WL 5105
(Sonata No. 1)
☆ G. Novães   ♯ PaV.VP 230
(Papillons)   (♯ AmVox.PL 7830)
☆ S. Rachmaninoff (♯ Vic.LCT 12: ♭ set WCT 66)

... No. 1, Préambule; No. 4, Valse noble;
No. 11, Chiarina; No. 12, Chopin;
No. 13, Estrella
M. Pressler   ♯ MGM.E 119
(Arabeske, etc.)

— ARR. ORCH. Jacob
Covent Garden—Rignold (2ss) ♯ P.PMD 1001
(Gounod, in ♯ AmD.DL 9548)   (♯ Od.OD 1005)

— ARR. ORCH. Glazounov
☆ L.P.O.—Goossens   ♮ G.JOX 7015/7

... Nos. 1; 14, Reconnaissance; 15, Pantalon et
Columbine, only
Covent Garden—Braithwaite   ♯ MGM.E 3006
(Tchaikovsky, Respighi, etc.)

Davidsbündlertänze, Op. 6
A. Aeschbacher   ♮ PV. 72112/3
(4ss)   (♯ Pol. 16016; ♯ AmD.DL 7531)
R. Lev   ♯ CHS.CHS 1104
(Arabeske)

☆ = Re-issue of a recording to be found in WERM or Supplement I.

199

Études symphoniques, Op. 13
L. Kolessa   ♯ CHS.CHS 1111
(*Toccata*)

G. Anda (n.v.)   T.E 3899/901
(6ss—includes the 5 posthumous études)

E. Kilenyi   ♯ Rem. 199-91
(*Brahms: Variations*)

☆ M. Lympany   ♯ G.CLP 1002
(*Franck: Variations symphoniques*) (♯ Vic.LHMV 1013:
                              ♭ set WHMV 1013)

☆ A. Földes (Pol. 566290/1; omits the 5 posth. études)

Fantasia, C major, Op. 17
A. Brailowsky   ♯ Vic.LM 9003
(*Carnaval*)   (7ss—*Traumeswirren*, in ♭ set WDM 9003)

J. Demus   ♯ West.WL 5157
(*Fantasiestücke*)

L. Pattison   ♯ Cmt. 1202
(*Fantasiestück*)

FANTASIESTÜCKE, Op. 12
COMPLETE RECORDING
J. Demus   ♯ West.WL 5157
(*Fantasia*)

Nos. 1, 2 & 8 (Des Abends; Aufschwung;
Ende vom Lied)
S. Richter (4ss)   USSR. 15876/7 & 15879/80

No. 3, Warum
☆ W. Backhaus   in ♯ D.LXT 2754
                              (♯ Lon.LL 603)

No. 7, Traumeswirren
A. Brailowsky   in ♭ Vic. set WDM 9003
(*Fantasia, s. 1*)

— ARR. 4 PFS.
First Piano Qtt. (in ♯ Vic.LM 1227: ♭ set WDM 1624)

FANTASIESTÜCKE, Op. 111
No. 2, A flat major
L. Pattison   ♯ Cmt. 1202
(*Fantasia*)

Faschingsschwank aus Wien, Op. 26
J. Blancard   ♯ Van.VRS 416
(*Brahms*)

KINDERSZENEN, Op. 15
W. Gieseking (4ss)   ♭ C.LX 8913/4
(*Brahms: Intermezzi* on ♯ AmC.ML 4540)

A. Ferber   ♯ D.LM 4544
(*Mendelssohn*)   (♯ Lon.LPS 453)

E. Dohnányi   ♯ Rem. 199-43
(*Dohnányi*)

Y. Nat   V♯ DFr. 77

☆ V. Horowitz   ♯ G.FALP 113
(*Chopin: Mazurkas*)

☆ A. Cortot   ♯ Vic.LHMV 1009
(*Debussy*)   (♭ set WHMV 1009)

... **No. 7, Träumerei**
O. Frugoni   in ♯ AmVox.PL 7700
(*Weber, Debussy, etc.*)

M. Pressler   in ♯ MGM.E 119

☆ V. Horowitz (♭ G.7RF 232; in ♯ Vic.LM 1171:
etc.   ♭ set WDM 1605)

—— ARRANGEMENTS (*inter alia*)
Vln. & pf.
L. Kaufman (in ♯ DCap.CCL 7513: Cap.L 8165)

☆ M. Elman (♭ Vic.WEPR 29)
V. Prihoda (P.LL 3001, & 3009 d.c.)

Vln. & orch.
F. Akos & Berlin Mun. Op. Ens. (*T.A 11187*)

Vlc. & orch.
T. Machula & Residentie (Phi.N 12047G: *PhM. 09037S*)

Vlc. & pf.
E. Mainardi & S. Legrenzi (Pol. 57408)
S. Knushevitzky (*USSR. 18968*)
G. Cassadò & O. Schulhof (in ♯ MSL.MW 45)
☆ P. Casals (in ♯ Vic.LCT 1050: ♭ set WCT 72)
R. Krotschak (in ♯ Eur.LPG 631)

Orch.
Concert Orch. (in ♯ Roy. 1233)
☆ Boston Prom.—Fiedler (G.C 4137)

2 pfs. in ♯ Conl.SF 1

4 pfs. in ♯ Vic.LM 1227: ♭ set WDM 1624

Kreisleriana, Op. 16
J. Demus   ♯ West.WL 5142
(*Toccata*)

Midsummer Night (unspec.)
—— ARR. VOCAL DUET & PF.
Y. Ciannella & L. Winter (S), R. Honte (pf.)
                              in *Vic. set E 98*
                              (♭ set WE 98)

Papillons, Op. 2
W. Kempff   ♯ D.LXT 2670
(*Arabeske; & Liszt*)   (♯ Lon.LL 515)

L. Cifarelli (4ss)   P.PE 167/8

☆ G. Novães   ♯ PaV.VP 230
(*Carnaval*)   (♯ AmVox.PL 7830)

(3) ROMANCES, Op. 28
G. Manley   ♯ NRI. 104
(*Symphony No. 4*)

No. 2, F sharp major, only
J. Demus   ♯ West.WL 5142
(*above & below*)

A. Previn (in ♯ Vic.LPM 3045: ♭ EPB 3045)

Schlummerlied, Op. 124, No. 16
— ARR. ORCH. Anon. Orch. (*Scd. 5008*)

SONATAS
No. 1, F sharp minor, Op. 11
P. Badura-Skoda   ♯ West.WL 5105
(*Carnaval*)

L. H. Behrendt (2ss)   ♯ SPA. 3

No. 2, F minor, Op. 14 "*Concert sans orchestre*"
R. Goldsand   ♯ CHS.CHS 1147
(*Brahms: Variations*)   (♯ Nix.CLP 1147)

No. 3, G minor, Op. 22
V. Yankoff   ♯ Pat.DTX 108
(*Brahms: Klavierstücke*)

STUDIES in Canon-form, Op. 56 Pedal-pf.
No. 5, B minor — ARR. ORGAN
C. Snyder   in ♯ KR. 15
(*Buxtehude, Franck, etc.*)

Toccata, C major, Op. 7
J. Demus   ♯ West.WL 5142
(*Kreisleriana*)

L. Kolessa   ♯ CHS.CHS 1111
(*Études symphoniques*)

A. Földes (2ss)   *Tono. K 8081*
                              (in ♯ Mer.MG 10122)

Variations on the name "Abegg", Op. 1
C. Haskil (n.v.)   Phi.A 11213G
                              (*PhM. 09700S*)

A. Földes (2ss)   *Tono.A 169*
                              (in ♯ Mer.MG 10122)

♯ = Long-playing, 33⅓ r.p.m.   ♭ = 45 r.p.m.   ♮ = Auto. couplings, 78 r.p.m.

200

WALDSCENEN, Op. 82
No. 7, Vogel als Prophet
No. 8, Jagdlied
S. Feinberg   *USSR. 18808/9*

No. 7 only
J. Battista   in ♯ *MGM.E 141*
(*Schubert, Liszt, etc.*)

—— ARR. VLN. & PF.
J. Heifetz & E. Bay   in ♯ *B.LAT 8020*
(*Weill, Aguirre, etc.*)   (♯ AmD.DL 8521)

II. CHAMBER MUSIC

Adagio & Allegro, A flat, Op. 70 hrn. (or vlc.) & pf.
J. Stagliano (hrn.) & P. Ulanowsky ♯ **Bo.B 200**
(*Beethoven, Mozart, Schubert*)

Andante & Variations, B flat major, Op. 46
2 pfs. 2 vlcs., hrn.
☆ V. Appleton & D. Field, vlcs. & hrn.
                               ♯ **AmVox.PL 7740**
(*Konzertstück*)

QUARTETS, String, Op. 41
No. 1, A minor
No. 3, A major
Curtis Qtt.   ♯ **West.WL 5166**

No. 1, A minor
... 2nd & 4th movts.   (Scherzo & Intermezzo; Presto)
Paganini Qtt. (in † ♯ Vic.LM 1192: ♭ set WDM 1611)

No. 2, F major
New Italian Qtt.   ♯ **D.LXT 2591**
(*Verdi: Quartet, E minor*)   (♯ Lon.LLP 323)

QUARTET, pf. & str., E flat major, Op. 47
R. Lev, D. Guilet, W. Schoen, D. Soyer
                               ♯ **CHS.F 9**

QUINTET, pf. & str., E flat major, Op. 44
C. Curzon & Budapest Qtt.   ♯ **AmC.ML 4426**
☆ A. Rubinstein & Paganini Qtt.   (♯ G.FALP 140)

(3) ROMANCES, Op. 94   ob. & pf.
J. Marx & I. Rosenberg   ♯ **CHS.G 5**
(*Vlc. Concerto*)

SONATAS, vln. & pf.
No. 1, A minor, Op. 105
J. Tryon & J. di Bonaventura   ♯ **CEd. 1028**
(*below*)

No. 2, D minor, Op. 121
G. Enesco & C. Chailley-Richez   (2ss)
                               ♯ **Rem. 149-50**
J. Tryon & J. di Bonaventura   ♯ **CEd. 1028**
(*above*)

TRIOS, pf., vln., vlc.
No. 1, D minor, Op. 63
L. Mannes, B. Gimpel, L. Silva ♯ **B.AXTL 1014**
(*Schubert: Nocturne*)   (♯ AmD.DL 9604)

III. ORCHESTRAL
(inc. Stage Works)

CONCERTO, pf., & orch., A minor, Op. 54
G. Nováes & Vienna Sym.—Klemperer
                               ♯ **AmVox.PL 7110**
                               (♯ PaV.VP 310)

M. Haas & Berlin Phil.—E. Jochum
                               ♮ **PV. 72089/90**
(4ss)   (2ss, ♯ Pol. 16007; ♯ AmD.DL 7522)
C. Haskil & Residentie—v. Otterloo
                               ♯ **Phi.A 00134L**
C. Chailley-Richez & Austrian Sym.—Heger
                               ♯ **Rem. 199-65**
C. Vidusso & Rome Sym.—Günther ♯ **Roy. 1358**
☆ D. Lipatti & Philharmonia—v. Karajan
(8ss)   ♮ **C.LCX 8012/5**
                  (2ss, ♯ C 1001: FC/QC 1016)
(*Grieg: Concerto* on ♯ AmC.ML 4525; also announced
as 2ss, ♯ AmC.ML 2195, which appears to have been
issued in Canada, if not in U.S.A.)

CONCERTO, vln. & orch., D minor ("Op. 134")
P. Rybar & Lausanne Sym.—Desarzens
                               ♯ **CHS.CHS. 1128**
                               (♯ Nix.CLP 1128)

CONCERTO, vlc. & orch., A minor, Op. 129
A. Navarra & Colonne—Cluytens ♯ **C.FC 1006**
(2ss)
B. Michelin & Utrecht Sym.—P. Hupperts
(*Romances*)   ♯ **CHS.G 5**
G. Ricci & Rome Sym.—Vittori
                               ♯ **Strad.STR 612**
(*Schubert: Sonata*)
M. Dorner & Stuttgart Pro Musica—
  R. Reinhardt   ♯ **AmVox.PL 7680**
(*below*)
S. Seidler & Berlin Sym.   ♯ **Roy. 1312**

Fantasia, C major, Op. 131   vln. & orch.
A. Stücki & Stuttgart Pro Musica—
  R. Reinhardt   ♯ **AmVox.PL 7680**
(*above & below*)

GENOVEVA, Op. 81   Opera 4 acts   1850
Overture
Boston Sym.—Münch   ♯ **Vic.LM 7009**
(*Mozart & Handel*)   (♭ set WDM 7009)

Introduction & Allegro, G major, Op. 92 pf. & orch.
☆ E. Erdmann & Munich Radio—Görlich (♯ Clc. 6076)

Introduction & Allegro, D minor, Op. 134
pf. & orch.
W. Bohle & Stuttgart Pro Musica—
  R. Reinhardt   ♯ **AmVox.PL 7680**
(*Concerto & Fantasia*)

Konzertstück, F major, Op. 86   4 horns & orch.
Görmer, Krumbein, Hühne, Himmer &
Stuttgart Pro Musica—Reinhardt
                               ♯ **AmVox.PL 7740**
(*Andante & Variations*)

MANFRED, Op. 115   Inc. music to Byron's Play
Overture
Vienna Phil.—Furtwängler
                           in ♯ **Vic.LHMV 1023**
                               (♭ set WHMV 1023)
Bamberg Sym.—Lehmann   ♯ **Pol. 16024**
(*Brahms: Tragic Overture*)   (& 2ss, PV. 36056)
(*Pfitzner* on ♯ AmD.DL 4017)

Overture, Scherzo & Finale, Op. 52   1841-5
Munich Phil.—Mennerich   ♯ **Mer.MG 10115**
(*Liszt*)

SYMPHONIES
No. 1, B flat major, Op. 38   "Spring"
Suisse Romande—Ansermet   ♯ **D.LXT 2602**
(also 8ss, D.K 28472/5: X 53099/102)   (♯ Lon.LLP 391)
Boston Sym.—Münch   ♯ **G.FALP 175**
(♯ G.QALP 175; ♯ Vic.LM 1190: ♭ set WDM 1608)
Berlin Sym.—List   ♯ **Roy. 1334**

☆ = Re-issue of a recording to be found in WERM or Supplement I.

SYMPHONIES—*continued*

No. 2, C major, Op. 61
Paris Cons.—Schuricht   ♯ **D.LXT 2745**
                                     (♯ Lon.LL 638)
Sym.—Stokowski   ♯ **Vic.LM 1194**
                                     (♭ set WDM 1614)
Berlin Sym.—Guthan   ♯ **Roy. 1361**

No. 3, E flat major, Op. 97 "Rhenish"
Munich Phil.—R. Albert   ♯ **Mer.MG 15034**
Berlin Sym.—Guthan   ♯ **Roy. 1366**
☆ N.Y.P.S.O.—Walter (♯ C.FCX 147)

No. 4, D minor, Op. 120
San Francisco Sym.—Monteux   ♯ **Vic.LM 1714**
(*Beethoven: Symphony No. 4*)   (♭ set WDM 1714)
Vienna State Op.—Krüger   ♯ **NRI. 104**
(*Romances*)
Sonor Sym.—Ledermann   ♯ **Pde. 2002**
Berlin Sym.—Guthan   ♯ **Roy. 1234**

IV. SONGS & DUETS

SONG CYCLES

DICHTERLIEBE, Op. 48 (Heine)
G. Souzay (B), J. Bonneau (pf.)   ♯ **D.LXT 2734**
(*Wolf*)   (♯ Lon.LL 535)
W. Ludwig (T), M. Raucheisen (pf.)
(4ss)   **PV. 72117/8**
                      (♯ Pol. 16029; AmD.DL 7525)
P. Bernac (B), R. Casadesus (pf.)
                                     ♯ **AmC.ML 2210**

FRAUENLIEBEN UND -LEBEN, Op. 42
(Chamisso)
☆ E. Höngen (A), F. Leitner (pf.)
(*Loewe*)   ♯ **AmD.DL 9610**

COLLECTIONS
   Familien-Gemälde, Op. 34, No. 4   (Grün)
   Unter'm Fenster, Op. 34, No. 3   (Burns)
   Wiegenlied, Op. 78, No. 4   (Hebbel)
T. Lemnitz (S), P. Anders (T),
                          M. Raucheisen (pf.)

   Frühlingsnacht, Op. 39, No. 12   (Eichendorff)
   (Die) Kartenlegerin, Op. 31, No. 2   (Chamisso)
   Lust der Stürmnacht, Op. 35, No. 1   (Kerner)
M. Klose (A), M. Raucheisen (pf.)

   Märzveilchen, Op. 40, No. 1   (Andersen)
   Schneeglöckchen, Op. 79, No. 26   (Rückert)
T. Lemnitz (S), M. Raucheisen (pf.) ♯ **Ura. 7047**
(*Schubert*)

(9) Lieder und Gesänge aus Wilhelm Meister, Op. 98a
   (Goethe)
   No. 2, Ballade des Harfners
   No. 4, Wer nie sein Brot
   No. 5, Heiss mich nicht reden
   No. 7, Singet nicht in Trauertonen
   No. 8, An die Türen
P. Gavert (T), M. Maddox (S) & pf.
                          in ♯ **MTR.MLO 1009**
(*Schubert, Beethoven, Wolf*)

   O ihr Herren, Op. 37, No. 3   (Rückert)
   Ständchen, Op. 36, No. 2   (Reinick)
   Wer machte dich so krank;
     Alte Laute, Op. 35, Nos. 11 & 12   (Kerner)
   Widmung, Op. 25, No. 1   (Rückert)
L. Lehmann (S)   in † ♯ **Pembroke set**

   DICHTERLIEBE, Op. 48: Nos. 1, 2, 3, 13   (Heine)
   (Die) Lotosblume, Op. 25, No. 7   (Heine)
   Mondnacht, Op. 39, No. 5   (Eichendorff)
   (Der) Nussbaum, Op. 25, No. 3   (Mosen)
☆ R. Tauber (T), P. Kahn (pf.)
                          in ♯ **AmD.DL 9547**

An den Sonnenschein, Op. 36, No. 4 (Reinick)
V. Kilchevsky (T, *Russ*)   **USSR. 17701**
(*Rachmaninoff: Arion*)

Auf das Trinkglas, Op. 35, No. 6 (Kerner)
W. Strienz (Bs) & Orch.   in ♯ **Ura. 7026**
(*Loewe, Nicolai, etc.*)

Aufträge, Op. 77, No. 5 (L'Egru)
E. Schwarzkopf (S), G. Moore (pf.)   **C.LB 122**
(*Nussbaum*)   (LW 58: LV 16)

(Die) Beiden Grenadiere, Op. 49, No. 1 (Heine)
D. Fischer-Dieskau (B), G. Moore (pf.)
                                     G.DB 21350
(*Schubert: Erlkönig*)
P. Schoeffler (B), O. Schulhof (pf.)
                          in ♯ **MSL.MW 44**
(*Schubert, etc.; Verdi, etc.*)
A. Mestral (B, *Fr*), I. Aïtoff (pf.) **PhM.A 77501S**
(*Fauré: Les berceaux*)

Flutenreicher Ebro, Op. 138, No. 5 (Geibel)
— ARR. GUITAR Segovia (*Romanza*)
A. Segovia   in ♯ **AmD.DL 9647**
(† Segovia Program)

Ich grolle nicht (Dichterliebe No. 7)
A. Ivanov (B, *Russ*)   **U.H 23835**
(*Beethoven: Scottish Song*)

(Die) Lotosblume, Op. 25, No. 7 (Heine)
P. Schoeffler (B), O. Schulhof (pf.)
                                     ♯ **MSL.MW 43**
(*Schubert, etc. & Wagner*)
N. Obukhova (M-S, *Russ*)   **USSR. 17112**
(*Brahms: Sapphische Ode*)
— ARR. VOCAL TRIO in *Vic. set E 100*: ♭ WE 100

Mondnacht, Op. 39, No. 5 (Eichendorff)
D. Fischer-Dieskau (B), G. Moore (pf.)
                                     G.DB 21517
(*Schubert: Nacht und Träume*)
J. Vincent (S), F. de Nobel (pf.)
                          in ♯ **Phi.A 00610R**
(*Beethoven, Mendelssohn, etc.*)

(Der) Nussbaum, Op. 25, No. 3 (Mosen)
V. de los Angeles (S), G. Moore (pf.)
                                     G.DB 21457
(*Brahms: Von ewiger Liebe*)
E. Schwarzkopf (S), G. Moore (pf.)   **C.LB 122**
(*Aufträge*)   (LW 58: LV 16)
J. Vincent (S), F. de Nobel (pf.)
                          in ♯ **Phi.A 00610R**
(*Beethoven, Mendelssohn, etc.*)
C. Rubio (S), C. D. Martin (pf.) **SpC.RG 16181**
(*Schubert: Neugierige*)
▽ G. Farrar (S, *Eng*) & pf. (IRCC. 1)

Provençalisches Lied, Op. 139, No. 4 (Uhland)
Talismane, Op. 25, No. 8 (Goethe)
H. Schlusnus (B), O. Braun (pf.)   **Pol. 62883**

Schmetterling, Op. 79, No. 2 (Anon.)
— ARR. VOCAL TRIO
Victor Trio (*Eng*) & pf.   in *Vic. set E 100*
(*Grieg, Arne, etc.*)   (♭ WE 100)

Volksliedchen, Op. 51, No. 2 (Rückert)
K. Ferrier (A)   in ♯ **Lon. LPS 402**
(*announced but not issued*)

Wanderlust, Op. 35, No. 3 (Kerner)
H. Rosenberg (B) & orch.   **Imp. 19013**
(*R. Strauss: Heimliche Aufforderung*)
☆ H. Schlusnus (B) (in ♯ AmD.DL 9623)

♯ = Long-playing, 33⅓ r.p.m.   ♭ = 45 r.p.m.   ♮ = Auto. couplings, 78 r.p.m.

Weihnachtslied, Op. 79, No. 16   (Andersen)
J. Wilson (S), G. Trovillo (pf.)
              in ♯ **AmD.DL 9554**
(*Grieg, Humperdinck, etc.*)

Widmung, Op. 25, No. 1   (Rückert)
K. Ferrier (A)   in ♯ *Lon.LPS 402*
(announced but not issued)

— ARR. PF.   Liszt, *q.v.*

MISCELLANEOUS
Schumann, his story & his music
A. Moss (narrator) & Sym. Orch.—Gobermann
              ♯ *AmVox.VL 2550*

NOTE: Psalm 23 on ♯ *StO. 5*, is by Georg Schumann.

SCOTT, Cyril Meir (b. 1879)

Danse nègre, Op. 58, No. 3   pf.
P. Spagnolo   **P.PE 157**
(‡s.—*Sinding: Danse orientale; & Mompou*)

SONG: (The) Unforeseen, Op. 74, No. 3   (Watson)
M. Searle (S), B. Idle (pf.)   **Croy.CX 4**
(*L. Lehmann & E. Thiman: Songs*)

SCRIABIN, Alexander Nicolaevitch
(1872-1915)

I. PIANO SOLO

Album leaf, Op. 58
L. Podolsky   in ♯ **Cmt. 1204**
(*Kortchmaryev: Fairy Tale; Infante, etc.*)

Nocturne, F sharp minor, Op. 5, No. 1
— ARR. VLN. & PF.
 ☆ D. Oistrakh (in ♯ Csm.CLPS 110)

Nocturne for the left hand, D flat, Op. 9, No. 2
 ☆ V. Schiøler   in ♯ **Mer.MG 10099**
(*Mendelssohn, Grieg, Chopin, etc.*)

POEMS
Op. 32, No. 1, F sharp major
Op. 32, No. 2, D major
Op. 59, No. 1
G. Neuhaus   *USSR. 8309/10*

Polonaise, B flat minor, Op. 21
V. Sofronitsky (2ss)   **USSR. 018954/5**

PRELUDES
Op. 11, No. 2, A minor
Op. 11, No. 4, E minor
V. Sofronitsky   *USSR. 19583/4*

Op. 11, No. 5, D major; No. 17, A flat major
Op. 11, No. 20, C minor
V. Sofronitsky   *USSR. 19585/6*

Op. 11, No. 7, A major; No. 8, F sharp minor
Op. 11, No. 19, E flat major; No. 22, G minor
V. Sofronitsky   *USSR. 19975/6*

Op. 11, No. 9, E major; No. 10, C sharp minor
 ☆ G. Neuhaus   *U.C 24111*

Op. 11, No. 14, E flat minor
Op. 17, No. 4, D flat major
V. Sofronitsky   *USSR. 13094*
(*Study*)

Op. 13, No. 6, D major
Op. 31, No. 3, G flat major
V. Sofronitsky   *USSR. 13081*
(*Study, Op. 8-12*)

Op. 31, No. 4, C major
Op. 39, No. 2, D major
Op. 48, No. 2, C major
V. Sofronitsky   *USSR. 20974/5*

SONATA No. 4, F sharp major, Op. 30
 ☆ W. Schatzkamer   ♯ *Vic. LM 156*
(*Mozart: Sonata, K 576*)
S. Feinberg (2ss)   **USSR. 08515/6**

STUDIES
Op. 2, No. 1, C sharp minor
V. Horowitz   ♭ *G.7R*   *200*
(*Prokofiev: Toccata, Op. 11*)
(*Clementi: Sonata excpt., on* ♭ *Vic. 49-3303*)

Op. 8, No. 9, G sharp minor
V. Sofronitsky (2ss)   *USSR. 12450/I*

Op. 8, No. 11, B flat minor
 ☆ V. Sofronitsky (in ♯ Csm.CRLP 115)

Op. 8, No. 10, D flat minor
Op. 42, No. 5, C sharp minor
M. Yestchenko   **U.H 24042**

WALTZES
A flat major, Op. 33
M. Yestchenko   **U.H 24041**
(*Rachmaninoff: Moment musical, F minor*)

II. ORCHESTRAL

Concerto, F sharp major, Op. 20   pf. & orch. 1894
S. Feinberg & Sym.—Gauk   **USSR. 018864/9**
(6ss)

Rêverie, Op. 24
USSR Radio Sym.—Golovanov
(2ss)   *USSR. 12591/2*

SYMPHONIES
No. 2, C minor & major, Op. 29   1897-1903
USSR Radio—Golovanov   **USSR. 018722/31**
(12ss)

No. 3, C minor & major, Op. 43   1903
USSR Radio—Golovanov   **USSR. 019749/60**
(12ss)

SEIBER, Matyas (b. 1904)

SEE ALSO: † SPANISH CHORAL MUSIC

Fantasy, vlc. & pf.
▽ W. Pleeth & M. Good   *D.M 565*

SEIDEL, Jan (b. 1908)

People behold!   Cantata
(on Julius Fucik's *Report from the Gallows*)
Singers & Children's Cho. Czech Phil.—Šejna
(20ss)   ♮ **U.H 23839/48**
             (♯ Sup.LPV 28/9)

☆ = Re-issue of a recording to be found in WERM or Supplement I.

SEMENOFF, Ivan (b. 1917)

Double Concerto   vln., pf. & orch.
  C. Ferras, P. Barbizet & Paris Cons.—
  Semenoff   **♯ D.LXT 2678**
  (Rodrigo: Vln. Concerto)   (♯ Lon.LL 546)

SENALLIÉ, Jean-Baptiste (1687-1730)

SONATA, D minor   vln. & hpsi. (Bk. II, No. 5)
... 4th movt., Allegro — ARR. BAND   D. Wright
  Band—H. Mortimer *(Pax.PR 574)*

SENFL, Ludwig (c. 1490-1555)

  SEE: † SPANISH CHORAL MUSIC

SERLY, Tibor (b. 1901)

Sonata in modus lascivus   vln. unacc.
  F. Magnes   **♯ BRS. 908**
  (Stravinsky)

SERMISY, Claudin de (c. 1490-1562)

  SEE: † COURTLY MUSIC
      † RENAISSANCE MASTERPIECES

SESSIONS, Roger Huntington (b. 1896)

(The) BLACK MASKERS
  Inc. music to Andreyev's play
Orchestral Suite   1923
  A.R.S. Orch.—Hendl   (2ss)   **♯ ARS. 11**

From my diary   pf. 1937-40
  B. Weiser   **♯ NE. 1**
  (Shapero, etc.)
  B. Abramovitch   **♯ ML. 7003**
  (below) (also announced as *♯ ML 5000)*

Sonata, No. 2   pf. 1946
  ☆ B. Abramovitch   **♯ ML. 7003**
  (above) (also announced as *♯ ML 5000)*

SÉVERAC, Déodat de (1873-1921)

Ma poupée chérie   Song (de Séverac)
  O. Laure & Inst. Ens. *(Sat.R 1)*

SHAPERO, Harold (b. 1920)

Sonata No. 1, pf. *"Amateur"* 1944
  B. Weiser   **♯ NE. 1**
  (Berger)

SHAPORIN, Yuri Alexandrovitch (b. 1889)

ORATORIO: On the field of Kulikovo   (Blok)
... Aria of Dmitri Donskoy
  A. Pirogov (B) & USSR Sym.—Gauk
  (2ss)   *USSR. 17153/4*
          (o.n. or o.v., *USSR. 10102/3)*

SHAPOSHNIKOV, Adrian (b. 1888)

Sonata, D minor, fl. & harp   pub. 1928
  S. Caratelli & A. Sacchi   **♯ NRI. 406**
  (Ibert, Milhaud, Hindemith, etc.)

SHEPHERD, Arthur (b. 1880)

Triptych (Tagore) S & Str. Qtt. 1927
  M. Kraft & Walden Qtt.   **♯ SPAM. 1**
  (Koutzen)   *(Bergsma on ♯ ARS. 18)*

SHOSTAKOVITCH, Dmitri (b. 1906)

(The) AGE OF GOLD, Op. 22   Ballet 1930
... Polka
  ☆ N.Y.P.S.O.—Kurtz (C.DX 1860: GFX 187;
                    ♭ *AmC.A 1509)*

—— ARR. PF.   ☆ A. Földes (in *♯ Rem. 149-4)*

Ballet Suite No. 1   Orch. 1950
  USSR State Sym.—Gauk   **♯ Van.VRS 6004**
  (Prokofiev: Romeo & Juliet)

(The) FALL OF BERLIN   film music
... Finale
  Cho. & Sym.—Gauk   *USSR. 18361/2*
  (2ss)

(3) Fantastic Dances, Op. 5   pf. 1922
  L. Rostchina   **U.H 24258**
  (Bach: Chromatic Fantasy & Fugue, s. 1)
  ☆ M. Lympany (G.S 10582)

... No. 1 only   ☆ A. Földes (in *♯ Rem. 149-4)*
—— ARR. VLN. & PF.   ☆ J. Heifetz & E. Bay (♭ *G.7RF 250)*

MEETING ON THE ELBE   film music
Song of Peace (Dolmatovsky)
  Red Banner Ens.   *USSR. 019200*
  (Song of the Forests, s. 9)

PIROGOV   film music
Waltz
  Orch.—Knushevitsky   *USSR. 17096*
  (Dunayevsky: Film music excpt.)

(24) PRELUDES, Op. 34   pf.
No. 10, C sharp minor; No. 24, D minor
— ARR. VLN & PF.
  M. Wilk & F. Kramer   in *♯ MTR.MLP 1002*

QUARTET, Strings, No. 2, Op. 69
  R. Schulz Qtt.   **♯ Ura. 7040**

QUINTET, G minor, Op. 57   pf. & str. 1940
  Chigi Quintet   **♯ D.LXT 2749**
                (♯ Lon.LL 500)
  V. Aller & Hollywood Qtt. **♯ DCap.CTL 7024**
                (♯ Cap.P 8171)

(The) Song of the Forests (Dolmatovsky)
  T, Bs, Cho. 1951
  ☆ Petrov, Kilichevsky, Choirs & USSR State
  Sym.—Mravinsky   *USSR. 019191/9*
  (▽ 9ss—*Meeting on the Elbe—Song)*
        (♯ Van.VRS 422 & ♯ Csm.CRLP 118)

SONATA, D minor, Op. 40   vlc. & pf. 1934
  ☆ G. Piatigorsky & V. Pavlovsky
                ♯ AmC.RL 3015
  (Cui, Rubinstein, etc.)

  ♯ = Long-playing, 33⅓ r.p.m.   ♭ = 45 r.p.m.   ♮ = Auto. couplings, 78 r.p.m.

SONG: The Country hears (Dolmatovsky)
N. Postavnicheva & Cho.   *USSR. 19120*
(*Dunayevsky: Song of the young builders*)

SYMPHONIES
No. 1, F major, Op. 10   1924-5
Bolshoi Theatre—Kondrashin
(8ss)   **USSR. 020617/24**

No. 5, D major, Op. 47   1937
Vienna Sym.—Horenstein   ♯ **AmVox.PL 7610**
Harvard-Radcliffe—Stanger   ♯ **XTV 14451**
                    (Pte. rec.)

No. 7, C major, Op. 60 "Leningrad" 1942
Berlin Phil.—Celibidache (4ss) ♯ **Ura. set 601**
☆ Buffalo Phil.—Steinberg ♯ **Allo.ALG 3041**
(4ss)

Trio, E minor, Op. 67 pf., vln., vlc. 1944
☆ D. Oistrakh, D. Shostakovitch, M. Sadlo
               (Eur.TAI 721/3)

(The) WAYFARER film music
Song of the Wayfarer
State Radio Ens.   *USSR. 21043*
(*Pokrass: Moscow*)

SIBELIUS, Jean Julian Christian (b. 1865)

Canzonetta, Op. 62, No. 1 str. orch.
☆ Curtis Ens.—Bailly (in JpV. set JAS 236)

Concerto, D minor, Op. 47 vln. & orch.
I. Stern & Royal Phil.—Beecham
(7ss)   ♮ **C.LX 8947/50S**
   (2ss, ♯ *C.C 1008*) (*below*, ♯ AmC. ML 4550)
E. Telmanyi & Danish State Radio—Jensen
         ♮ **Tono.Y 30003/6**
           (♯ Mer.MG 10131)
C. Wicks & Stockholm Radio—Ehrling
         ♯ **DCap.CTL 7026**
      (♯ Cap.P 8175; ♯ Mtr.CLP 510)
A. Eidus & Vienna Orch. Soc.—Hummel [1]
(*Brahms*)   ♯ **Strad.STR 611**

Finlandia, Op. 26 (Tableau) orch.
B.B.C. Sym.—Sargent   **G.DB 21522**
L.S.O.—Fistoulari   in ♯ *MGM.E 166*
☆ Philharmonia—Malko   ♭ *G.7R 101*
  (G.TH 30; in ♯ BB.LBC 1028: ♭ set WBC 1028)
☆ Philadelphia—Ormandy ♯ *AmC.AAL 9*
(*below*)   (& 2ss, ♭ 4-13131D)
 Berlin Sym.—List (in ♯ *Roy. 6114* & ♯ *Roy. 1259*)
☆ Austrian Sym.—Wöss (♯ Mrt. 1-8, d.c.)
 Boston Pops—Fiedler (♭ *G.7BF 1015*;
           ♭ Vic. 49-0698 & WEPR 1)

... **Excerpt** —ARR. CHO.
Helsinki Polytechnic Cho. *Täh.RW 468*
(*Kuula & Genetz: Partsongs*)

— — VOCAL ARR. "The Star's Song": O. Werner (B)
            (Od.ND 7013)

KARELIA, Op. 11 (Tableaux) Orch.
1. Intermezzo   2. Ballade   3. Alla marcia
Danish State Radio—Jensen ♯ **D.LXT 2744**
(*Symphony No. 5*)   (♯ Lon.LL 634)
Berlin Radio—J. Blomstedt ♯ **Ura. 7038**
(*Pelléas*)

KING CHRISTIAN II, Op. 27
   (Inc. music to Paul's play)
Fool's Song: The Spider (*Ristilukki*)
— ORCH. VERSION
  ☆ Concert Orch.—Similä   **G.TJ 112**
  (*Linsén: Song*)

March of the Finnish Infantry, Op. 91, No. 1 orch.
☆ Helsinki Orch.—Kajanus (*G.TJ 103*)

Mazurka, Op. 81, No. 1 vln. & pf.
E. B. Nielsen & L. Christiansen **G.DA 5276**
(*Dvořák: Songs my mother taught me*)

PARTSONGS   Male cho.
Boat-journey, Op. 18, No. 3 (Kalevala)
  (*Venematka*)
Finlandia Cho.—Klemetti   *Od.PLD 9*
(*T. Kuula: Partsong*)

PELLÉAS AND MÉLISANDE, Op. 46
  (Inc. mus. to Maeterlinck's play)
1. At the Castle gate   2. Mélisande
3. On the sea shore   4. A Spring in the park
5. The Three Blind Sisters 6. Pastorale
7. Mélisande at the spinning-wheel 8. Entr'acte
9. Death of Mélisande

COMPLETE RECORDING
  Winterthur Sym.—Desarzens ♯ **CHS.F 18**
  (*Weber*)

... Nos. 1, 2, 4, 5, 6, 7, 9
  Berlin Radio—J. Blomstedt ♯ **Ura. 7038**
  (*Karelia*)

PIANO MUSIC
Berceuse, Op. 40, No. 5 (*Kehtolaulu*)
Polonaise, Op. 40, No. 1
— ARR. ORCH.
  ☆ Helsinki Odeon Orch.—Cronvall (*Od.PLD 12*)

Romance, D flat major, Op. 24, No. 9
V. Schiøler   **G.DB 10508**
(*Rachmaninoff: Prelude, Op. 23, No. 5*)

(A) Saga, Op. 9   orch.
☆ Philharmonia—Kletzki (C.M 15163/5)

SCÈNES HISTORIQUES   orch.
Op. 25: No. 3, Festivo
Op. 66: No. 1, The Chase
        No. 2, Love Song
        No. 3, At the drawbridge
Royal Phil.—Beecham   ♯ **AmC.ML 4550**
(*Vln. Concerto*)

Op. 25, No. 3, Festivo, only
L.S.O.—Fistoulari   in ♯ *MGM.E 166*

SONGS
COLLECTION
In the fields a maiden sings, Op. 50, No. 3 (Dehmel)
Spring is flying, Op. 13, No. 4 (Runeberg)
To Evening, Op. 17, No. 6 (Forsman)
Was it a dream, Op. 37, No. 4 (Wecksell)
  T. Niemela (S), P. Koskimies (pf.) ♯ **WCFM. 5**
  (*Grieg, Kilpinen*)

And is there a thought? Op. 86, No. 4
  (Tavaststjerna)   (*Och finns det en tanke*)
  E. Holmström (T), J. Tolonen (pf.) *Täh.RW 456*
  (*Puccini: Fanciulla, aria*)

Come away, death, Op. 60, No. 1 (Shakespeare)
  M. Lehtinen (B), J. Tolonen (pf.) *Täh.RW 460A*
  (*below*)   (also, in *Swed.* on RW 460B)

(The) Maiden came from her lover's tryst,
    Op. 37, No. 5 (Runeberg)
  K. Derzhinskaya (S) (*Russ*) *USSR. 10032*
  (*Bizet: Chanson d'avril*)

---

[1] A combination of 2 tape recordings made on different occasions.

To Evening, Op. 17, No. 6 (Forsmann) (*Illalle*)
M. Lehtinen (B), J. Tolonen (pf.)
Täh. RW 460A & B
(*Come away, death*)

Suite champêtre, Op. 98b   Str. orch. 1921
Finnish Radio—Jalas   *Symf.L 2011/2*
(*Ryt.R 6149/50*)

(The) Swan of Tuonela, Op. 22, No. 2   Sym. Poem
L.S.O.—Fistoulari   in ‡ *MGM.E 166*
Sym.—Stokowski   **G.DB 21555**
(in ‡ *Vic.LM 151:* ♭ *49-0461*)
☆ Chicago Sym.—Stock (in ‡ *AmC.RL 3002*)
  Philadelphia—Ormandy (‡ *AmC.AAL 9:* ♭ *4-13130 D*)
  Janssen Sym.—Janssen (in ‡ *Atst. 504*)

SYMPHONIES
No. 1, E minor, Op. 39
L.S.O.—Collins   ‡ **D.LXT 2694**
(‡ *Lon.LL 574*)
Stockholm Radio—Ehrling   ‡ **Mer.MG 10129**

No. 2, D major, Op. 43
Boston Sym.—Koussevitzky (n.v.)
‡ **G.FALP 168**
(‡ *G.QALP 168;* ‡ *Vic.LM 1172:* ♭ *set WDM 1602*)
Berlin Sym.—Balzer   ‡ **Roy. 1258**
☆ Stockholm Concert Soc.—Mann (T.SK 19017/21)

No. 3, C major, Op. 52
Stockholm Radio—Ehrling   ‡ **Mer.MG 10125**
(*below*)

No. 5, E flat major, Op. 82
Danish State Radio—Tuxen ‡ **D.LXT 2744**
(1½ss—*Karelia Suite*)   (‡ *Lon.LL 634*)

No. 7, C major, Op. 105
Stockholm Radio—Ehrling   ‡ **Mer.MG 10125**
(*above*)
☆ Hallé—Barbirolli   ‡ **Vic.LHMV 1011**
(*Rubbra*) (also ♮ G.TH 7005/7) (♭ *set WHMV 1011*)

(The) TEMPEST, Op. 109   Inc. music
No. 7, Berceuse
☆ Sym.—Stokowski   **G.DB 21334**
(*below*) (♭ *7R 101: 7RF/7RQ 160;* in ‡ *Vic.LM 1238*)

Valse triste, Op. 44   (from *Kuolema*)
Brussels Radio—André   **T.E 3915**
(*Schmidt: Notre Dame—Intermezzo*)
L.S.O.—Fistoulari   in ‡ *MGM.E 166*
☆ Sym.—Stokowski   **G.DB 21334**
(*above*) (♭ *7R 101: 7RF/RQ 160;* in ‡ *Vic.LM 1238*)
Berlin Phil.—F. Lehmann   **Phi.A 11161G**
(*M. Poot: Ouverture joyeuse*) (*PhM.A 9001S &*
in ‡ *A 00115R*)
A. Bernard Str. Orch. (*Od. 282479*)
Vienna Radio—Nilius (*Vien.L 6091:* in ‡ *1009*)
A. Sciascia Orch. (*Fnt. 13876*)
☆ Berlin Phil.—Schmidt-Isserstedt (AusT.E 1162)
  Philharmonia—Kletzki (C.M 15165)
  etc.

Waltz, Op. 81, No. 3   vln. & pf.
☆ ▽ E. Cronvall & A. Andström   *Od.PLD 15*
(*Kilpinen: In the evening*)

SIEGEL, Paul (b. 1914)

Concerto between two worlds   pf. & orch.
G. Radluker & Vienna Sym.—Moralt
‡ **Abbey. 3**

SILVA, Giulio (b. 1875)

MYSTERIES OF THE ROSARY
Symphonic meditation with biblical narration &
passages in Gregorian chant, ed. Silva.
R. Hartung (narrator), C. Dolan &
W. Brisbois (S), M. Sargent (pf.),
M. Silva (vln.), Dominican College Cho. &
Str. Ens.—G. Silva   ‡ **ML. 7010/2**
(6ss)   (also, 20ss, ♮ MLR 100/19)

SIMON, Johann Kaspar   (fl. *c.* 1750)
SEE: † BAROQUE ORGAN MUSIC

SINDING, Christian (1856-1941)

Danse orientale, Op. 33, No. 5   pf.
P. Spagnolo   **P.PE 157**
(½s.—*Scott: Danse nègre;* & *Mompou*)

Rustle of Spring, Op. 32, No. 3   pf.
W. Gieseking   **C.LX 1506**
(*Grieg: Concerto, s. 7*)   (*Chopin,* on C.LNX 7)
(*Debussy: Clair de lune,* on C.LDX 13)
C. de Groot   **Phi.N 11158G**
(*Grieg: To Spring;* & *Liszt*)   (*PhM.N 9000S*)
— ARR. PF. & ORCH.
B. Norman & Berlin Sym.—Buschkötter (*Od.O-28088*)
— ARR. ORCH.
Vienna Radio—Nilius (*Vien.P 6095:* in ‡ *1013*)
etc.

Serenade, D flat major, Op. 33, No. 4 pf.
S. Ribbing   **T.E 19807**
(½s.—*Backer-Grøndahl: Elves' Game:* & *Saeverud*)

Waltz, G major, Op. 59, No. 3   pf.
— ARR. ORCH.
Stavanger Ens.—Andersen   *C.GN 1150*
(*Backer-Grøndahl*)

SJÖGREN, Emil (1853-1918)

Erotikon, Op. 10   Suite, pf.
... No. 1   only
O. Wibergh   **Symf.RT 1023**
(*Stenhammar: Fantasy*)

SMETANA, Bedřich (1824-1884)

I. OPERAS

(The) BARTERED BRIDE   3 acts   1866
COMPLETE RECORDING in *German*
Mařenka   ...   .   T. Richter (S)
Jeník   ...   .   S. Hauser (T)
Micha   ...   .   W. Lang (B)
Kruščina ...   .   R. Koffmane (B)
Kečal   ...   .   K. Böhme (Bs)
etc., Berlin Municipal Opera Cho. & Orch.—
Lenzer   (6ss)   ‡ **Ura. set 210**

Highlights
☆ Czech Nat. Theatre Soloists   ‡ **Syc.SR 3**

Orchestral Suite
Overture; Polka; Furiant; Dance of the Comedians
Los Angeles Phil.—Wallenstein ‡ *AmD.DL 4014*
Excerpts "Nat. Op. Orch." (in ‡ *Var. 6937*)

‡ = Long-playing, 33⅓ r.p.m.   ♭ = 45 r.p.m.   ♮ = Auto. couplings, 78 r.p.m.

Overture
Philharmonia—Kubelik   **G.DB 21463**
(1½ss—*No. 13*)   (♭ *G.7RF 236*)
Bamberg Sym.—Leitner   **PV. 72213**
(*Nos. 13 & 24*)
Bolshoi Theatre—Kondrashin **USSR. 019527/8**
☆ Chicago Sym.—Defauw (♭ *Vic. 49-0667*)

ACT I

No. 3, If such a thing ...   S
H E. Destinn (in ♯ CEd. set 7001*)

No. 9, Polka   Cho.
— ARR. ORCH. Riešenfeld
☆ Royal Phil.—Beecham   ♭ *G.7R 102*
(*No. 24*)

ACT II

No. 13, Furiant
Philharmonia—Kubelik   **G.DB 21463**
(½s.—*Overture*)   (♭ *7RF 236*)
Bamberg Sym.—Leitner   **PV. 72213**
(½s.—*No. 24 & Overture*)
☆ Bavarian State—Eichhorn (*Pol. 26514*)

No. 17, Each man praises his own ...
I know a girl   T & Bs
G. Nelepp & N. Shchegodkov (*Russ*)
    USSR. 16524/5
☆ J. Schmidt & M. Bohnen (*Ger*) (in ♯ *Ete. 460*)

No. 20, How could he believe ...   T
W. Ludwig (*Ger*)   **PV. 36009**
(*Lustigen Weiber von Windsor—Horch die Lerche*)
H R. Tauber (*Ger*) (in ♯ Ete. O-466*)

ACT III

No. 24, Dance of the Comedians
Philharmonia—Kubelik   **G.DB 21464**
(2ss)   (♭ *7RF 237*)
Bamberg Sym.—Leitner   **PV. 72213**
(½s.—*No. 13 & Overture*)
Aarhus Municipal—Jensen   *Tono.L 28044*
(*Khachaturian: Gayaneh—Sabre Dance*)
    (in ♯ *Mer.MG 15045*)
Vienna Radio—Schönherr   *Vien.P 6121*
(*Prophète—Coronation March*)
☆ Royal Phil.—Beecham (♭ *G.7R 102*)
Philadelphia—Ormandy (♭ *AmC.A 1519*)

No. 29, Oh, what sorrow ... The Dream of love   S
I. Maslennikova (*Russ*)   *USSR. 19114/5*

(The) BRANDENBURGERS IN BOHEMIA
3 acts 1866
Dechana's aria (unspec.)
V. Krylova   *USSR. 18195*
(*Dvořák: Songs my mother taught me*)

DALIBOR 3 acts 1868
(The) DEVIL'S WALL 3 acts 1882
LIBUŠE 3 acts 1872-81
(The) TWO WIDOWS 3 acts 1874
Highlights
☆ Czech Nat. Theatre Soloists   ♯ Syc.SR 5

DALIBOR
Didst thou hear, friend?   T   (Act I)
H H. Winkelmann (*Ger*) (*IRCC. 3096**)

How do I feel?   (*Jak je mi?*)   S   (Act II)
H E. Destinn (in ♯ set CEd. 7001*)

LIBUŠE
Eternal Gods!   S   (Act I)
My fathers   S   (Act II)
☆ M. Podvalová, from set (U.G 22870)

II. PARTSONGS etc.

(The) Czech Song Cantata 1868
(5) Evening Songs (Halek) 1879
(5) First Songs 1846
☆ Anon. Soloists, Prague Cho. & Orch.
    ♯ **Syc.SR 2**

III. INSTRUMENTAL & CHAMBER MUSIC

QUARTETS, String
No. 1, E minor (From my life) 1876
Stradivari Qtt.   ♯ **Strad.STR 613**
(*Dvořák*)
☆ Koeckert Qtt. (2ss)   ♯ *Pol. 16008*
(*Dvořák: Qtt. No. 6 on* ♯ AmD.DL 9637)

Wedding Scenes   pf.
— ARR. ORCH.
F.O.K. Sym.—Vostrak   ♮ **U.H 24036/7**

IV. DANCES

BOHEMIAN DANCES pf. 1878
BOOK I
No. 2, Moderato, A minor
No. 3, Allegro, F major
No. 4, Lento, B flat major
BOOK II
No. 2, Slepička (Moderato, B flat major)
S. Askenase (2ss)   **PV. 72204**
BOOK II
No. 2, The little hen (Slepička)
No. 5, The little onion (Cibulička)
No. 10, Skočná ("*Circus*")
— ARR. ORCH. Byrns
Chamber Sym.—Byrns   ♯ **DCap.CTL 7025**
(*Suk: Serenade*)   (♯ Cap.P 8174)
Unspec. — ARR. 4 PFS.
☆ First Pf. Qtt. (in ♯ Vic.LM 1165)

V. ORCHESTRAL

Hakon Jarl, Op. 16 Sym. Poem 1861
☆ Czech Phil.—Kubelik   ♯ **Syc.SR 1**
(*Wallenstein's Camp*)

MY COUNTRY (*Ma Vlast*) 1874-9
COMPLETE RECORDING
☆ Czech Phil.—Šejna (6ss)   ♯ *Sup.LPM 2/4*

No. 2, Vltava
No. 4, From Bohemia's meadows & forests
Bamberg Sym.—Keilberth   ♯ *DT.LGM 65006*
    (♯ *T.LS 6014*; ♯ *Cap.L 8166*)

... No. 2, Vltava
Vienna Phil.—Furtwängler   ♯ **Vic.LHMV 1023**
(*R. Strauss & Schumann*)   (♭ set WHMV 1023
☆ N.B.C. Sym.—Toscanini   **G.DB 21496/7**
(*3ss—Gluck: Orphée—Dance*)
(*Dukas & Saint-Saëns in* ♯ G.FALP & QALP 130)
Los Angeles Phil.—Wallenstein
(*Enesco*)   ♯ *AmD.DL 4012*
Rhineland Sym.—Federer   ♯ **Rgt. 5033**
(*Beethoven: Overture*)
Austrian Sym.—Singer   ♯ *Rem. 149-52*
(*Enesco*)   (♯ *Mrt. 1-22, d.c.*)
Berlin Sym.—List   ♯ **Roy. 1311**
(*Hindemith: Vla. Concerto*)
☆ Amsterdam—v. Beinum (♮ D.AX 354/5)

☆ = Re-issue of a recording to be found in WERM or Supplement I.

Triumphal Symphony, E major   1854
... Scherzo
Czech Phil.—Šejna   (3ss)   ♮ **U.H 24246/7S**

Wallenstein's Camp, Op. 14   1858
☆ Czech Phil.—Kubelik   # **Syc.SR 1**
(*Hakon Jarl*)   (also on Eur.TAI 710/11)

SMITH, John Christopher (1712-1795)

(The) FAIRIES, Opera 1754
(after Shakespeare's *A Midsummer Night's Dream*)
... You spotted snakes
(The) TEMPEST Inc. music 1756
... No more dams I'll make for fish
L. Chelsi (T), F. Kramer (pf.)
in # **MTR.MLO 1010**

SMITH, Robert (c. 1648-1675)
SEE: † CATCHES AND GLEES

SMITH, Russel (b. 1927)

Eclogue   vln. or vla. & pf.
B. Earle or A. Loft & B. Weiser   in # **NE. 3**
(*Babbitt, Berger, Flanagan*)

SOR, Fernando (c. 1778-1839)

GUITAR PIECES

Andantino, Op. 24, No. 1
T. Usher   *Deci.C 1644*
(*Haydn: Andantino quasi minuetto*)

Menuet (unspec.)
A. Segovia   in # **AmD.DL 9647**
(† Segovia Program)

Petites variations sur un air français
L. Walker   **Phi.N 11223G**
(*Tarrega: Capricho arabe*)   (*PhM.N 09040S*)

Preludio (unspec.) ☆ V. Gomez (in # AmD.DL 8017)

Sonata (unspec.) . . . Allegro
A. Segovia   in # **B.AXTL 1005**
(† Segovia Recital)   (# AmD.DL 9633)

STUDIES
Nos. 1, 2, 3, 4, 6, 8, 10, 11, 13, 14, 16, 20
(Segovia edn.)
R. de la Torre   # **SMC. 517**

Variations on a theme of Mozart, Op. 9 [1]
A. Segovia   in # **B.AXTL 1010**
(† Segovia Concert)   (# AmD.DL 9638)

SOWERBY, Leo (b. 1895)
SEE ALSO: † AMERICAN CHURCH MUSIC

From the Northland   Suite 1922
Prairie Sym. Poem 1925
A.R.S. Orch.—Dixon   # **ARS. 14**

SPOHR, Louis (1784-1859)

Concerto, clarinet & orch., F minor   No op. no.
F. Hammerle & Linz Sym.—L. G. Jochum
Concerto, Str. Qtt. & orch., A minor, Op. 131 1850
Linz Sym.—L. G. Jochum   # **Ura. 7021**

CONCERTOS, vln. & orch.
No. 7, E minor, Op. 38   1815
R. Schulz & Berlin Radio—Heger
No. 8, A minor, Op. 47 (*Gesangsscene*) 1815
K. Stiehler & Leipzig Gewandhaus—Schmitz
Ura. 7049

Fantasia, C minor, Op. 35   hp.
O. Erdeli   (2ss)   **USSR. 020338/9**

FAUST Opera 2 acts 1816
Overture
JESSONDA Opera 3 acts 1823
Overture
Berlin Radio—Görlich   # **Ura. 7028**
(*Gluck*)

Nonet, F major, Op. 31   1813
fl., ob., cl., hrn., bsn., vln., vla., vlc., cbs.
Stradivari Ens.
(6) Songs, Op. 103 S, cl. & pf.   1837
A. Howland, D. Weber, L. Mittman
Strad.STR 609

Symphony No. 3, C minor, Op. 78   1828
Frankfurt Radio—Schlemm   # *Ura. 5008*

SPONTINI, Gasparo Luigi Pacifico
(1774-1851)

OPERAS
FERNAND CORTEZ 3 acts 1809 (orig. *Fr*)
... Prisoners' Cho.; Danse barbare (Act I)
MILTON 1 act 1804 (orig. *Fr*)
... Charlotte's Aria; Emma's Romance
OLIMPIE 3 acts 1819 (*Fr*)
... Overture; Auprès d'un amant (Act I)
(La) VESTALE 3 acts 1807
... Overture: Vestals' Morning & Evening hymns.
M. Flery (S), R. Ferrigno (M-S), A. Pirino (T),
Cho. & Naples Scarlatti Orch.—Caracciolo
(2ss) (*Ital & Fr*)[2]   # **Csm.CLPS 1030**

(La) VESTALE (orig. *French*)
COMPLETE RECORDING (in *Italian*)

Giulia	M. Vitale (S)
High Priestess	E. Nicolai (M-S)
Licinio	R. Gavarini (T)
Cinna	A. Fineschi (B)
High Priest	G. Ferrein (Bs)

Italian Radio Cho. & Orch.—Previtali
(6ss)   # **Sor. set 1224**

Tu che invoco & O nume tutelar S (Act II)
☆ R. Ponselle (in # *Vic.LCT 10:* ♭ *set WCT 10*)

STAINER, Sir John (1840-1901)

(The) CRUCIFIXION Oratorio 1887
... God so loved the world ... Cho.
Canterbury Cho.   in # *MGM.E 102*
(♭ *set K 102*)
☆ Shaw Chorale & orch. (♭ *Vic.WEPR 44*)

---

[1] Theme from *Die Zauberflöte*.   [2] Only the *Olimpie* aria is sung in *French*.

STAMITZ, Carl (1746-1801)

CONCERTOS, fl. & orch.
D major; G major
  K. Redel & Oiseau-Lyre Orch.   **# OL.LD 44**

CONCERTO, vla. & orch., D major
  H. Wigand & Stuttgart Pro Musica Orch.—
    Reinhardt   **# AmVox.PL 7540**
  (Telemann)

QUARTET, E flat major, Op. 8, No. 2
  cl. or ob. & str. or wind
  New Art Wind Qtt.   **# CEd. set CE 2010**
  (Mozart, Danzi, Reicha)

STAMITZ, Johann Wenzel Anton
(Stamič, Jan Václav) (1717-1757)

Allemande (unspec.)
  Stuttgart Cha. Soc. Trio   **# Ren.X 40**
  (Haydn, Milandre, Cervetto, etc.) (# Nix.PLP 240;
                        Clĉ. 6124)

STANFORD, Sir Charles Villiers
(1852-1924)

MORNING SERVICE, B flat major, Op. 10
... Jubilate Deo
  Choirs of Royal School of Church Music—
    Dykes Bower   **C.DX 1780**
  (Anon: All people that on earth do dwell)

TRADITIONAL MELODIES (ARR. Stanford)
Molly Brannigan
  F. Smith (B), M. Carr (pf.)   **Croy.CX 3**
  (½s.—Hurlstone & Parry)

STARER, Robert (b. 1924)

(5) Miniatures for Brass
  Shuman Ens.—Starer   **# Circ. 51-102**
  (Goeb & Raphling)

STENHAMMAR, Vilhelm Eugen
(1871-1927)

(3) Fantasies, Op. 11   pf.
  O. Wibergh   ♮ **Symf.RT 1023/4**
  (3ss—Sjögren: Erotikon, No. 1)

(A) PEOPLE Cantata 1905 (Heidenstam)
... No. 5, Sweden *(Sverige)* Cho.
  ☆ J. Björling (T) (♭ *Vic. 53-5004*)

QUARTET, String, No. 5, C major, Op. 29
  ☆ Garaguly Qtt.   ♮ **G.DB 11068S/70**

Sentimental Romance, F minor, Op. 28, No. 2
  vln. & orch.
  O. Kyndel & Stockholm Radio—Frykberg
                 Rtj. RC 303

STEPHAN, Rudi (1887-1915)

Musik für Orchester
  ▽ Berlin Municipal orch.—Schuricht
                   Pol. 15543/5S
  (5ss—last blank)   (o.n. 57364/6S)
  ▽ Berlin State Op.—Lehmann (Od.O-9132/3)

STILL, William Grant (b. 1895)

Afro-American Symphony 1931
  Vienna State Op.—Krueger   **# NRI. 105**
  (below)

Lennox Avenue, Suite ... Blues
Here's One (Negro spiritual)
  — ARR. VLN. & PF. Kaufman
  L. & T. Kaufman   **# CHS.CHS 1140**
  (Copland, McBride, Carpenter)

PIANO PIECES—COLLECTION
(7) Traceries 1940
  ... No. 1, Cloud cradles   No. 2, Mystic pool
  No. 3, Muted laughter   No. 4, Out of the silence
  No. 5, Woven silver
Lennox Avenue Suite ... Blues 1937
(3) Visions 1935
    1. Dark Horsemen   2. Summerland
    3. Radiant pinnacle
  G. Manley   **# NRI. 105**
  (above)

STRAUSS, Eduard (1835-1916)

Bahn frei! Op. 45 (Polka schnell)
  Austrian State Sym.—O. Straus
               in **# MSL.MW 48**
  Philadelphia—Ormandy   in ♭ *AmC.A 1543*
           (in ♭ *set A 1031:* # *ML 4589*)

Doctrinen Waltz, Op. 79
  Vienna Radio—Schönherr   **Vien.L 6050**
  (2ss)   (in # *AmVien.VNLP 1004*)

STRAUSS, Johann I (1814-1849)

Donaulieder, Op. 127 Waltz
  — VOCAL ARR.
  E. Roon (S) & Vienna Sym.—Pauspertl
              in **# AmVox.PL 20900**

Loreley-Rheinklänge, Op. 154 Waltz
  Vienna Radio—Nilius (2ss)   ***Vien.P 6094***

Radetzky March, Op. 228
  Amsterdam—v. Kempen   ***Phi.N 09039S***
  (Schubert: Marche Militaire)
  Austrian State Sym.—O. Straus
               in **# MSL.MW 48**
  Austrian Sym.—Wöss (in # *Rem. 149-27*)
  Aarhus Municipal—Jensen (*Tono.L 28043;*
                in # *Mer.MG 15045*)
  Lower Austrian Police Band—Neusser (*Phi.P 41236H;*
      & *D.F 43233:* in # *LF 1074;* # *Lon.LPS 561*)
  Vienna Radio—Nilius (*Vien.A 6061:* in # *1008*)
  etc.
  ☆ Boston Pops—Fiedler (*G.AA 692:* ♭ *7BF 1029*)
  Vienna Sym.—Stolz (*D.M 662*)

☆ = Re-issue of a recording to be found in WERM or Supplement I.

STRAUSS, Johann II (1825-1899)

CLASSIFIED: A. INSTRUMENTAL
  1. Marches
  2. Polkas, Mazurkas, etc.
  3. Waltzes
  4. Other Inst. Works
B. OPERETTAS & STAGE WORKS
C. MISCELLANEOUS

A. 1. MARCHES

Egyptischer Marsch, Op. 335
Vienna Phil.—Krauss   in # D.LXT 2645
(also on D.K 28584: K 23310)   (# Lon.LLP 484)
Philharmonia—Schuechter   in # MGM.E 145

Persischer Marsch, Op. 289
Philharmonia—Schuechter   in # MGM.E 145
Austrian Sym.—Wöss   in # Rem. 149-27

Vienna Radio—Schönherr (Imp. 19228)
etc.

Russischer Marsch, Op. 426
Vienna Radio—Schönherr   Vien.L 6048
(Romanze)   (in # 1007)

A. 2. POLKAS, MAZURKAS, ETC.

COLLECTIONS
"POLKAS, Vol. II".
Brautschau, Op. 417 (themes from Zigeunerbaron)
Furioso, Op. 260 (Polka quasi Galop)
Ritter Pázmán, Op. 441 (themes from Operetta)
Fledermaus-Polka, Op. 362 (themes from Operetta)
Im Krapfenwald'l, Op. 336
Um Sturmschritt, Op. 348 (P-schnell, from Indigo)
Boston Pops—Fiedler   # Vic.LM 1226
(Waldteufel)   (♭ set WDM 1520)
(Ritter Pázmán & Im Krapfenwald'l also on G.B 10387)

Im Krapfenwald'l, Op. 336 (K 23310 & 28584)
Eljen a Magyar, Op. 332 (M 38127)
Pizzicato (Jointly with Jos. Strauss) (M 38128)
Vergnügungszug, Op. 281 (M 38128)
Vienna Phil.—Krauss   in # D.LXT 2645
(also on 78 r.p.m., nos. above)   (# Lon.LLP 484)

Eljen a Magyar, Op. 332 (P-schnell)
Stadt und Land, Op. 322 (P-Mazurka)
Vergnügungszug, Op. 281 (P-schnell)
Vienna Phil.—Krauss   in # AmVox.VL 3140

Annen-Polka, Op. 117
Lower Austrian Artists—Günther
(Frauenherz)   AusT.C 3046
Vienna Radio—Nilius   Vien.P 6086
(Indigo—Intermezzo)   (in # 1007)

Auf der Jagd, Op. 373
(P-schnell; themes from Cagliostro)
Vienna Phil.—Krauss   in # D.LXT 2755
(New Year Concert 2)   (# Lon.LL 683)

Electrophor, Op. 297 (P-schnell)
Vienna Radio—Schönherr   Vien.P 6066
(Husarenpolka)

Freikugeln, Op. 326 (P-schnell)
Vienna Radio—Schönherr (in # AmVien.VNLP 1001)

Husarenpolka, Op. 421 (from Zigeunerbaron)
Vienna Radio—Schönherr   Vien.P 6066
(Electrophor P.)   (in # 1007)

Leichtes Blut, Op. 319 (P-schnell)
Austrian Sym.—Wöss   in # Rem. 149-34
Lower Austrian Artists—Wöss   AusT.M 5150
(Sängerlust)
Vienna Radio—Schönherr   in # Vien. 1003

Pizzicato-Polka Str. orch.
(jointly with Jos. Strauss)
Vienna Sym.—Paulik   # FestF.FLD 2
(below; & Waltzes & Overtures)
Stockholm Phil.—Ehrling   in # Rgt. 5052
☆ Vienna Phil.—Furtwängler (♭ G.7R 134: ♭ 7RF 148)
   Vienna Phil.—Szell (in # BB.LBC 1008: ♭ set WBC 1008)
   Berlin State Op.—Melichar (Pol. 57416)

— ARR. 2 PFS.
M. Rawicz & W. Landauer (C.DB 2899: DD 559)

Sängerlust, Op. 328 (P-française)
Lower Austrian Artists—Wöss   AusT.M 5150
(Leichtes Blut)
Vienna Sym.—Paulik   in # FestF.FLD 2

Stadt und Land, Op. 322 (P-Mazurka)
Vienna Phil.—Krauss   in # D.LXT 2755
(New Year Concert 2)   (# Lon.LL 683)

Tik-tak, Op. 365 (P-schnell from Fledermaus)
Lower Austrian Artists—Wöss   AusT.M 5146
(Ziehrer: Lolassen, & Jos. Strauss: Jockey)

— ARR. 2 PFS.   M. Rawicz & W. Landauer (C.DB 3040)

Tritsch-tratsch, Op. 214
Vienna Phil.—Karajan   C.LB 128
(Perpetuum mobile)   (LW 62: GQ 7251)
Vienna Radio—Nilius (Vien.P 6083: in # 1002)
Berlin Municipal Op. (Pal. 1301)
Aarhus Municipal—Jensen (Tono.L 28043;
                              in # Mer.MG 15045)
Lower Austrian Sym.—Wöss (in # Rem. 149-27;
                              AusT.M 5149)
☆ N.B.C.—Toscanini (♭ G.7RF 127; ♭ Vic. 49-1082)
   Carnegie Pops—Abravanel (in ♭ AmC. set A 1013)
   Vienna Phil.—Szell (in # BB.LBC 1008: ♭ set WBC 1008)

Unter Donner und Blitz, Op. 324 (P-schnell)
Vienna Phil.—Karajan   C.LV 15
(Perpetuum mobile)
Boston Prom.—Fiedler (n.v.)   G.B 10290
(Gioielli della Madonna, Dance) (Vic. 10-3255: ♭ 49-1430)
S. Torch Orch. (P.R 3488: ♭ DSP 4001)

— ARR. 2 PFS.   M. Rawicz & W. Landauer (C.DB 3302)

Vergnügungszug, Op. 281 (P-schnell)
Lower Austrian Artists—Günther AusT.M 5149
(Tritsch-tratsch)

Vom Donaustrande, Op. 356
(P-schnell from Carneval in Rom)
Vienna Radio—Schönherr   Vien.P 6085
(Millöcker: Rasch wie der Blitz) (in # 1002;
                              in # AmVien. 1004)

Zepperl-Polka (unid.)
Vienna Radio—Schönherr   Vien.P 6045
(Jos. Strauss: Feuerfest)   (in # 1016)

A. 3. WALTZES

Accelerationen, Op. 234
Philadelphia—Ormandy   in # AmC.ML 4589
                              (in ♭ set A 1031)
Vienna State Op.—Schönherr   Phi.P 41039H
(Jos. Strauss: Nilfluten)   (# P 10300R)
Vienna Radio—Nilius (2ss)   Vien.L 6027
Rhineland Sym.—Federer   in # Rgt. 5049
Berlin Sym.—Ludwig (in # Roy. 1201)
etc.
☆ Vienna Sym.—Baltzer (Eur.TPV 105)
   Minneapolis—Ormandy (in # Vic.LM 9025:
                              ♭ WDM 262)
   Austrian Sym.—Wöss (in # Rem. 199-97)

= Long-playing, 33⅓ r.p.m.   ♭ = 45 r.p.m.   ♮ = Auto. couplings, 78 r.p.m.

An der schönen, blauen Donau, Op. 314
Vienna Sym.   Moralt   **Phi.A 11238G**
       (*PhM. 09722S:* & in ‡ A *00139L*)
Vienna Sym.—Paulik   in ‡ **FestF.FLD 2**
Vienna Phil.—Günther   in ‡ *Phi.P 10300R*
Munich Phil.—Rieger   in ‡ **Mer.MG 10024**

Berlin Sym.—Ludwig (in ‡ *Roy. 1201*)
Strauss Orch.—F. Lanner (in ‡ *MGM.E 133: ♭ set K 133*)

▽ Austrian Sym.—Wöss (in ‡ *Rem. 149-3* & *199-97*)

☆ Vienna Sym.—Krauss (*Eur.TGV 111*)
  R. Stolz Orch. (in ‡ *D.AM 233032: ‡ AmD.DL 5008*)
  Sym.—Stokowski (*G.DB 21346: ♭ 7RQ 182*)
  Minneapolis—Ormandy (in ‡ *Vic.LM 9025:*
                       ♭ set WDM 262)
  Berlin Phil.—Fricsay (*FPV. 5027; ‡ AmD.DL 4009*)
  Philadelphia—Ormandy (‡ *AmC.AAL 13*)
  Vienna Phil.—Szell (in ‡ *BB.LBC 1008: ♭ set WBC 1008*)
  etc.

— ARR. PF.
B. Janis (in ‡ *BB.LBC 1030: ♭ WBC 1030*)
L. Pennario [1] (in ‡ *DCap.CCL 7514: ‡ Cap.H 8167*)
— ARR. VLC. & PF.   (Improvisations)   Cassadò
G. Cassadò & O. Schulhof (in ‡ *MSL.MW 45*)
— VOCAL ARRS.
P. Munsel (S) (in ‡ *Vic.LM 139: ♭ set WDM 1601*)
E. Sack (S) (*T.E 3926*), etc.

Bei uns z'Haus, Op. 361
Vienna Sym.—Krauss   **‡ Rem. 149-26**
(*Seid umschlungen ...*)   (also, ☆ *Eur.TSV 142*)
☆ H. Horlick Orch. (in ‡ *AmD.DL 5208*)

Donauweibchen, Op. 427   (from *Simplicius*)
☆ H. Horlick Orch. (in ‡ *AmD.DL 5208*)

— VOCAL (FILM) ARR.
☆ J. Schmidt (T) (*P.DP 7;* in ‡ AmD.DL 9538)

Du und Du, Op. 367
Munich Phil.—Rieger   in ‡ **Mer.MG 10024**

M. Marrow Orch. (in ‡ *MGM.E 94*)
A. Bernard Str. Orch. (*Od. 282481*)
Pallas Orch. (*Pal. 1343*)
Vienna Radio—Schönherr (*Vien.P 6013; AmVien.V 4007*
                   & in ‡ *VNLP 1003*)
Vienna Waltz—Pauscher (*Hma. 16035:* in ‡ *LM 802*)
Orch.—Michaelof (in ‡ *Nix.LPY 118*)
etc.

☆ R. Stolz Orch. (in ‡ *D.AM 233032; ‡ AmD.DL 5008*)
  Hollywood Bowl—Stokowski (♭ *Vic. 49-0279*)

— ARR. PF.   Dohnányi
M. Schwalb   **‡ Acad.ALP 302**
(*below*)

— ARR. PF.   Godowsky
D. Saperton   in ‡ **CPf. 1201**

Freut euch des Lebens, Op. 340
Berlin Sym.—Ludwig   in ‡ **Roy. 1201**
Vienna State Op.—Schönherr   **Pol. 48525**
(*Lanner: Schönbrunner*)
Vienna Radio—Schönherr (*Vien.P 6032;*
              in ‡ *AmVien.VNLP 1004*)
Vienna Sym. (in ‡ *Roy. 6101*) etc.

Frühlingsstimmen, Op. 410
R.I.A.S. Sym.—Fricsay   **PV. 72247**
(*Rosen aus dem Süden*)   (in ‡ *Pol. 18050*)
Vienna Sym.—Moralt   **Phi.A 11239G**
        (*PhM. 09723S:* & in ‡ A *00139L*)
Munich Phil.—Rieger   **‡ Mer.MG 10024**

Strauss Orch.—F. Lanner (in ‡ *MGM.E 133: ♭ set K 133*)
Berlin Sym.—Friedl (in ‡ Roy. 1202)
Berlin Sym.—Buschkötter (*BrzOd.X 3359*)
etc.

☆ Vienna Sym.—Krauss (*T.E 3861; AusT.E 1075*)
  Vienna Sym.—Szell (in ‡ *BB.LBC 1008: ♭ set WBC 1008*)
— VOCAL VERSION
E. Roon & Vienna Sym.—Pauspertl
        in ‡ **AmVox.PL 20900**

☆ E. Sack (in ‡ *T.LB 6001* & *6020*)

G'schichten aus dem Wiener Wald, Op. 325
Vienna Phil.—Krauss   in ‡ **D.LXT 2645**
(Zither solo: A. Karas)   (‡ *Lon.LLP 484*)
(also, 3ss, on *D.K 28581/2*)
Bamberg Sym.—Leitner   **PV. 72259**
(Zither solo: R. Knabl)
Vienna Sym.—Moralt   in ‡ **Phi.A 00139L**
(with zither solo)
Strauss Orch.—F. Lanner   in ‡ *MGM.E 139*
(probably with zither solo)   (♭ *set K 139*)
Austrian Sym.—Wöss   **‡ Rem. 149-49**
(*Morgenblätter*)   (‡ *Mrt. 1-15*)

D. Bela Orch. (*P.DP 278*)
Bavarian State Operetta Orch. (*Tpo. 3539*)
Vienna Radio—Günther (*Phi.P 41076H: ‡ P 10300R*)
Orch.—Eisele (*Vien.A 4902/3, 2ss*)
Viennese Sym. (*CGD.PV 1563*)
Berlin Sym.—Friedl (in ‡ Roy. 1202)
etc., etc.

☆ Vienna Phil.—v. Karajan (*C.LFX 1014: LVX 137*)
  Sym.—Stokowski (*G.DB 21346: ♭ 7RQ 182*)
  Philadelphia—Ormandy (‡ *AmC.AAL 13*)
  Boston Pops—Fiedler (*BrzV. 12-3276; ‡ G.DLP 1005*)
  R. Stolz Orch. (in ‡ *D.AM 233032; AmD.DL 5008*)

— VOCAL ARRANGEMENTS
☆ L. Pons (S., *Ital*)   **C.LX 1462**
(*Bishop: Pretty mocking bird*)
E. Roon (S) & Vienna Sym.—Pauspertl
        in ‡ **AmVox.PL 20900**

E. Sack (S) (in ‡ *T.LB 6001* & *LB 6020*)
H. E. Groh (T) (*Od.O-4668*)
P. Munsel (S) (in ‡ *Vic.LM 139: ♭ set WDM 1601*)

Juristenballtänze, Op. 177
Vienna Radio—Schönherr   *Vien.P 6110*
(*Künstlerleben*)   (in ‡ *1002*)

Kaiserwalzer, Op. 437
Vienna Sym.—Paulik   in ‡ **AmC. set SL 119**
(in *Nacht in Venedig* as ballet) (also in ‡ FestF.FLD 2, d.c.)
Philadelphia—Ormandy   in ‡ **AmC.ML 4589**
                 (♭ *set A 1031*)
Berlin Phil.—F. Lehmann   **Phi.A 11178G**
                 (*PhM. 09703S*)
Schneider Str. Ens   in ‡ *AmC.ML 2179*
[2] Berlin Municipal Op.—Vack   **P.DPW 45**
                (*Od.O-28083*)
Strauss Orch.—F. Lanner   in ‡ *MGM.E 133*
                (♭ *set K 133*)

Berlin Sym.—Ludwig (in ‡ Roy. 1201)
Vienna State Op.—Schönherr (*Phi.P 41077H: ‡ P 10300R*)
Orch. Continentale (in ‡ *Nix.LPY 118*)
M. Marrow Orch. (in ‡ *MGM.E 94*)
M. Lanner Orch. (*G.EG 7750: HE 3062*)
Orch.—Foster (*VIS.VI 4607*)

☆ Vienna Phil.—Furtwängler (♭ *G.7RF 104: ♭ 7RQ 104*)
  Boston Pops—Fiedler (‡ *Vic.LM 9025: ♭ set WDM 445*)
  S. Romberg Orch. (in ‡ *Vic.LM 91*)
  R. Stolz Orch. (in ‡ *D.AM 233032: ‡ AmD.DL 5002*)
  etc.

— ARR. PF.   Pennario
L. Pennario   **‡ DCap.CCL 7514**
(*Blue Danube*)   (‡ *Cap.H 8167*)
— VOCAL ARR. in *Eng*
L. Melchior (T) (in ‡ *MGM.E 109:* ♮ *set 109* &
                    & MGM.E 3003)
P. Munsel (S) (in ‡ *Vic.LM 139: ♭ set WDM 1601:*
                    ♭ *WEPR 35*)

Klangfiguren, Op. 251
Vienna Phil.—Krauss   in ‡ *AmVox.VL 3140*

Künstlerleben, Op. 316
Vienna State Op.—Schönherr   *Phi.P 41072H*
(*Wiener Blut*) (in ‡ *Phi.P 10300R*)   (& *P 44167H*)
Bavarian Radio—Schmidt-Boelcke
        in ‡ **Mer.MG 10022**

(*continued on next page*)

[1] ARR. Schulz-Evler.
[2] ARR. Weninger.

Künstlerleben, Op. 316—*continued*
 Schneider Str. Ens in ♯ *AmC.ML 2179*

D. Bela Orch. (*ArgOd. 55288*)
Orch.—Schönherr (*Vien.P 6110*: ♯ *1007* & *Imp. 19183*, etc.)
Viennese Waltz—Pauscher (Hma. 16035: in ♯ *LM 802*)
Orch. Continentale (in ♯ *Nix.LPY 118*)
H. Zacharias Orch. (*Pol. 48580*), etc.

 ☆ Boston Pops—Fiedler (G.JOX 44; in ♯ Vic.LM 9025:
           ♭ *set WDM 445*)
 R. Stolz Orch. (in ♯ *D.AM 233032*: ♯ *AmD.DL 5008*)

— ARR. PF. Godowsky
 D. Saperton   in ♯ *CPf. 1202*

— VOCAL ARR.
 P. Munsel (S) (in ♯ *Vic.LM 139*: ♭ *set WDM 1601*:
           ♭ *WEPR 35*)

Kuss-Walzer, Op. 400 (from *Lustige Krieg*)
 Orch. Continentale—Michaelof (in ♯ *Nix.LPY 118*)

Lagunen-Walzer, Op. 411 (from *Nacht in Venedig*)
 Berlin Sym.—Friedl   in ♯ **Roy. 1202**

Vienna Sym. (in ♯ *Roy. 6101*), etc.

 ☆ H. Horlick Orch. (in ♯ *AmD.DL 5208*)

Liebeslieder, Op. 114
— VOCAL ARR.
 E. Roon (S) & Vienna Sym.—Pauspertl
      in ♯ **AmVox.PL 20900**

Märchen aus dem Orient, Op. 444
 Vienna Radio—Nilius (2ss) **Vien.L 6081**

Morgenblätter, Op. 279
 Vienna Phil.—Krauss in ♯ **D.LXT 2755**
 (*New Year Concert 2*)   (♯ *Lon.LL 683*)
 Bavarian Radio—Schmidt-Boelcke
      in ♯ **Mer.MG 10022**
 Austrian Sym.—Wöss ♯ *Rem. 149-49*
 (*G'schichten ...*)   (♯ *Mrt. 1-15*)
 (also on ♯ Rem. 199-97)

  Vienna Radio—Schönherr (*Vien.P 6013; AmVien. 4007*:
           ♯ *VNLP 1003*)
  Pallas Orch. (*Pal. 1343*), etc.

 ☆ Royal Phil.—Beecham (♯ *AmC.AAL 6*: ♭ *4-73053D*)
 Vienna Phil.—Böhm (G.GB 29; in ♯ **BB.LBC 1008**:
           ♭ *WBC 1008*)

O schöner Mai, Op. 375
 Schneider Str. Ens in ♯ *AmC.ML 2179*

 ☆ Vienna Sym.—Krauss (T.E 3874)

Promotionen, Op. 221
 ☆ H. Horlick Orch. (in ♯ *AmD.DL 5208*)

Rosen aus dem Süden, Op. 388
 R.I.A.S. Sym.—Fricsay **PV. 72247**
 (*Frühlingsstimmen*)   (in ♯ *Pol. 18050*)
 Bavarian Radio—Schmidt-Boelcke
      in ♯ **Mer.MG 10022**
 Lusson-St. Croix Phil.—Monteverdi
      in ♯ McG. 3303
 Vienna State Op.—Schönherr *Phi.P 41071H*
 (*Wein, Weib und Gesang*) (in ♯ *P 10300R*)
 Bavarian State Operetta Orch. (*Tpo. 3539*)
 Vienna Radio—Schönherr (*Vien.P 6032*: ♯ *1003*;
         AmVien.V 3002: ♯ *VNLP 1003*)
 etc.

 ☆ Vienna Phil.—Böhm (G.EH 1374: GB 19: ♭ *7BF 1005*)
 Boston Pops—Fiedler (♭ *Vic. 49-1189*)
 R. Stolz Orch. (in ♯ *D.AM 233032*; ♯ *AmD.DL 5008*)

— ARR. CHO. & PF.
 Vienna Boys Cho.—Brenner ♯ *Phi.A 00606R*
 (*Jos. Strauss & Mozart*, etc.) (also Phi.A 11224G:
           PhM.A 09717S)

— VOCAL ARR.
 H. E. Groh (T) (*Od.O-4668*)
 E. Sack (S) (T.E 3926), etc.

Schatz-Walzer, Op. 418 (from *Zigeunerbaron*)
 Aarhus Municipal—Jensen *Tono.L 28045*
       (in ♯ *Mer.MG 15045*)

 ☆ Boston Prom.—Fiedler   **G.C 4179**
 (in ♯ G.DLP 1005; ♭ Vic. WEPR 24; BrzV. 886-5005)
 Vienna Radio—Schönherr (*Vien.P 6035*: ♯ *1011*;
        AmVien V 3003: ♯ *VNLP 1006*)
 Lusson-St. Croix Phil.—Monteverdi (in ♯ McG. 3303)
 Orch. Continentale (in ♯ *Nix.LPY 24*)
 A. Bernard Str. Orch. (*Od. 282457; P.DPF 42*), etc.

— ARR. PF. Dohnányi
 M. Schwalb   ♯ **Acad.ALP 302**
 (*above & Brahms*)

— VOCAL ARR.
 P. Munsel (in ♯ *Vic.LM 139*: ♭ *set WDM 1601*: ♭ *WEPR 35*)

Seid umschlungen, Millionen, Op. 443
 Vienna Sym.—Krauss ♯ *Rem. 149-26*
 (*Bei uns z'Haus*)   (also ☆ Eur.TSV 142)
 Berlin Sym.—Friedl   in ♯ **Roy. 1202**

Viennese Waltz Orch (in ♯ *Hma.LM 802*)

Solonsprüche, Op. 128
 Schneider Str. Ens. in ♯ *AmC.ML 2179*

Tausend und eine Nacht, Op. 346
 Concert Orch. (in ♯ Roy. 1249: *6134*), etc.

 ☆ H. Horlick Orch. (in ♯ *AmD.DL 5208*)

Wein, Weib und Gesang, Op. 333
 Philadelphia—Ormandy in ♯ **AmC.ML 4589**
      (♭ *AmC.A 1543*: ♭ *set A 1031*)
 Vienna State Op.—Schönherr *Phi.P 41071H*
 (*Rosen aus dem Süden*) (in ♯ *Phi.P 10300R*)

  Vienna Radio—Schönherr (*Vien.P 6035*:
       AmVien.V 3001: ♯ *VNLP 1003*)
  Berlin Sym.—Ludwig (in ♯ Roy. 1201)
  Various Orchs. (in ♯ *Roy. 6132*: 1249: etc.)

 ☆ Vienna Phil.—v. Karajan (C.LFX 1013: M 15141)
 R. Stolz Orch. (in ♯ *D.AM 233032*: ♯ *AmD.DL 5008*)
 L.S.O.—Krips (♯ *Lon.LD 9013*)
 Württemberg State—Leitner (IPV. 8198)
 Boston Pops—Fiedler in ♯ Vic.LM 9025:
           ♭ *set WDM 445*
 Berlin Municipal Op.—Vack (*Od. 275003*)

— VOCAL ARR.
 P. Munsel (S) (in ♯ *Vic.LM 139*:
       ♭ *set WDM 1601* & ♭ *WEPR 35*)

 ☆ M. Lichtegg (T) (in ♯ Lon.LLP 55)

Wiener Blut, Op. 354
 Vienna Sym.—Moralt   **Phi.A 11237G**
     (*PhM. 09721S* & in ♯ *A00139L*)
 Munich Phil.—Rieger in ♯ **Mer.MG 10024**
 Vienna St. Op.—Schönherr *Phi.P 41072H*
 (*Künstlerleben*) (♯ *P 10300R*) (& *P 44167H*)
 Orch. Continentale (in ♯ *Nix.LPY 118*)
 M. Lanner Orch. (*G.EG 7750: HE 3062*)
 Sym. Orch. (*Tpo. 3649*)
 H. Zacharias Orch. (*Pol. 48580*)
 Viennese Waltz.—Pauscher (Hma. 16037: ♯ *LM 802*)
 Wiener Bohème Orch. (*Od.O-28113*)
 etc., etc.

 ☆ Vienna Phil.—Karajan (C.LFX 1023: LVX 167)
 L.S.O.—Krips (♯ *Lon.LD 9013*)
 Berlin Phil.—Fricsay (FPV. 5027; ♯ *AmD.DL 4009*)
 Boston Pops—Fiedler (in ♯ Vic.LM 9025:
           ♭ *set WDM 445*)
 S. Romberg Orch. (in ♯ *Vic.LM 91*)
 R. Stolz Orch. (in ♯ *D.AM 233032*; ♯ *AmD.DL 5008*)

— ARR. 2 PFS. W. Rawicz & W. Landauer (*C.DB 2975*)

Wiener Bonbons, Op. 307
 H. Bund Orch. (*Pol. 47590*)
 M. Schönherr Orch. (*Imp. 19183* & *BrzOd. 8231*)

♯ = Long-playing, 33⅓ r.p.m.   ♭ = 45 r.p.m.   ♮ = Auto. couplings, 78 r.p.m.

Wo die Zitronen blühn, Op. 364
Stockholm Phil.—Ehrling   in ♯ Rgt. 5052

— VOCAL ARR.
E. Roon (S) & Vienna Sym.—Pauspertl
          in ♯ AmVox.PL 20900

A. 4. OTHER ORCHESTRAL WORKS

Perpetuum Mobile, Op. 257
Vienna Phil.—Karajan   *C.LB 128*
(Tritsch-Tratsch)   *(LW 62: GQ 7251)*
(Unter Donner und Blitz, Polka on LV 15)
Vienna Phil.—Krauss   in ♯ D.LXT 2755
          (♯ Lon.LL 683)
Philadelphia—Ormandy   in ♯ AmC.ML 4589
          (♭ set A 1031: & ♭ A 1543)
Stockholm Phil.—Ehrling   in ♯ Rgt. 5052
Vienna Radio—Schönherr   in ♯ *Vien. 1007*
☆ Boston Prom.—Fiedler *(♭ Vic. 49-1434)*

Romanze, Op. 243 (? orig.) vlc., hp., orch.
B. Reichert, O. Skala, Vienna Radio—Nilius
          Vien.L 6048
(Russischer Marsch)   *(in ♯ 1008)*

B. OPERETTAS & STAGE WORKS

ASCHENBRÖDEL Ballet [1] 1901
... **Waltz** — ARR. PF.
F. Kramer   in ♯ *MTR.MLP 1001*

(Die) FLEDERMAUS 1874

Vocal Excerpts (Nos. 5B, 11B, 11C)
☆ L. Lehmann, R. Tauber, etc. ♯ AmD.DL 9524
(Nozze di Figaro, Freischütz, etc.)

Vocal Selections
R. Anday, R. Bösch, E. Funk, H. Meyer-Welfing,
G. Oeggl, etc.   AusT.E 1108/9
          (♯ Rem. 199-41; ♯ Mrt. 200-24; ♭ Ply. 12-24)
R. Streich, E. Trötschel, P. Anders, W. Hoffmann,
W. Schneider, etc.   PV. 58612
          (♯ Pol. 45025)
H. Tolksdorf, C. Spletter, etc.   *Imp. 19024*

☆ E. Berger, E. Friedrich, A. Frind, C. Müller, P. Anders,
E. Fuchs, etc.   in ♯ T.LSK 7002
☆ A. Kern, F. Völker, etc. (Pol. 57430/4)

Overture
Vienna Phil.—Krauss   in ♯ D.LXT 2634
(2ss, in D.K 23112)   *(♯ Lon.LLP 454 & ♯ LD 9008)*
R.I.A.S. Sym.—Fricsay   *PV. 46009*
          (in ♯ Pol. 18050)
☆ Vienna Phil.—Karajan   *C.LX 1546*
          (LFX 989: LVX 152)
Stockholm Phil.—Ehrling   in ♯ Rgt. 5052
Vienna Sym.—Paulik   in ♯ FestF.FLD 2
Austrian State Sym.—O. Straus (in ♯ MSL.MW 47)
Strauss Orch.—F. Lanner (in ♯ MGM.E 133: ♭ set K 133)
▽ Austrian Sym.—Schönherr, formerly listed as
          Vienna Sym.—Stolz (in ♯ Rem. 149-1)
☆ Berlin Phil.—Karajan (Pol. 516817)
Minneapolis—Ormandy (in ♯ Vic.LM 9025:
          ♭ set WDM 262)
Boston Pops.—Fiedler (♭ Vic. 49-0900)

No. 5A, Trinke Liebchen, trinke schnell (Act I)
... **Glücklich ist, wer vergisst** (T. part only)
☆ M. Lichtegg (in ♯ Lon.LLP 51)

No. 8B, Mein Herr Marquis S (Act II)
E. Spoorenberg & Cho.   **Phi.N 11173G**
(Suppé: Schöne Galathée, excpt.)   *(PhM.N 09026S)*
P. Munsel *(Eng)* *(G.JO 287: EA 4033;*
          Vic. 20-4255: ♭ 47-4255)
☆ E. Sack (in ♯ T.LB 6001 & LB 6020)
E. Mayerhofer (in ♯ D.LM 4548; Lon.LPS 41)

INDIGO UND DIE 40 RÄUBER 1871
ABRIDGED RECORDING
(in the Reiterer version of 1906—*Tausend und eine Nacht*)
          Wally   ...   .   R. Seegers (S)
          Mossu ⎫   ...   ...   H. E. Groh (T)
          Sultan ⎭
etc., Berlin Radio Cho. & Orch.—Dobrindt
(4ss)   ♯ Ura. set 203
(Overture & Waltz song on ♭ UREP 4)
Vocal excerpts (in *Eng*; actual performance, 1946)
▽ C. Williams (A), T. Owen (T), A. Turner Op. Co.
          (Buckland pte. rec.)

Overture
Vienna Radio—Schönherr   *Vien. P 6122*
(2ss)

Intermezzo
Vienna Radio—Schönherr   *Vien.P 6086*
(Annen-Polka)   (in ♯ 1011; in ♯ AmVien.VNLP 1006)
H. Bund Orch. *(Imp. 19098)*

Nun lachst du wieder   T
K. Friedrich   **D.K 28566**
(Nacht in Venedig—Treu sein)
          (in ♯ D.LX 3068; Lon.LPS 428)

Launisches Glück T (interpolated)
K. Riemann *(Imp. 19263)*

(Der) LUSTIGE KRIEG 1881
ABRIDGED RECORDING
          Violetta   ...   .   E. Roon (S)
          Else   ...   ...   G. Scheyred (S)
          Artemisia   ...   ...   E. Hofstätter (M-S)
          Umberto   ...   ...   W. Kmentt (T)
          Marchese   ...   ...   R. Kreuzberger (T)
          Balthasar   ...   ...   G. Oeggl (Bs)
Academy Cho. & Vienna Sym.—von Pauspertl
(2ss)   ♯ AmVox.PL 20600

Overture
Vienna Radio—Nilius   *Vien.P 6080*
          (in ♯ 1002)

No. 11, Nur für Natur   T
E. Kunz (B)   **C.LX 1544**
(Nacht in Venedig—Komm' in die Gondel)
H. E. Groh   **Od.O-3695**
(Zeller: Obersteiger—Sei nicht bös)
☆ J. Patzak *(Pol. 48500)*

(Eine) NACHT IN VENEDIG 1883
COMPLETE RECORDING
          Annina   ...   ...   E. Rethy (S)
          Duke of Urbino   ...   ...   K. Friedrich (T)
          Pappacoda ...   ...   H. M. Gansbacher (B)
          Caramello   ...   ...   K. Preger (T)
etc. Bregenz Festival Cho. & Vienna Sym.—
          Paulik   ♯ AmC. set SL 119
(4ss—Kaiser-W. played as ballet)

Vocal Selection
☆ F. E. Engels (T), German Opera House Orch. & Cho.
          —Schüler (in ♯ T.LSK 7002)

[1] Only Act I was completed by Strauss; the sketches for the remainder were completed after his death by J. Bayer.

Overture
Philadelphia—Ormandy   in ♯ AmC.ML 4589
(♭ set A 1031)

Austrian State Sym.—O. Straus (in ♯ MSL.MW 48)
Vienna Radio—Schönherr (Vien.P 6096: ♯ 1007;
♯ AmVien.VNLP 1005)
Berlin Sym.—Liebe (Od.O-26986: P.B 547)
"Nat. Op. Orch." (in Roy. 6132)
etc.

Ach! wie so herrlich (Lagunen Waltz) T
E. Kurz (Imp. 19196)

☆ M. Lichtegg (in ♯ Lon.LLP 55)
J. Patzak (Pol. 10782)

Komm' in die Gondel   T
E. Kunz (B)   C.LX 1544
(Lustige Krieg—Nur für Natur)
R. Schock   G.EH 1421
(Zigeunerbaron—Als flotter Geist)   (GB 70)
☆ J. Patzak (Pol. 10782)
K. Schmitt-Walter (B) (AusT.M 5157)

Sei mir gegrüsst, du mein holdes Venetia T
☆ M. Lichtegg (in Lon.LLP 51)
♮ R. Tauber (in ♯ Ete. 459*)

Treu sein, das liegt mir nicht   T
E. Kunz (B)   C.LB 117
(Zeller: Der Vögelhändler—Wie mein ...) (LW 60)
K. Friedrich   in ♯ D.LX 3068
(Indigo—Nun lachst ... in D.K 28566) (in ♯ Lon.LPS 428)
♮ R. Tauber (in ♯ Ete. 459*)

PRINZ METHUSALEM 1877
Overture
Austrian State Sym.—O. Straus
in ♯ MSL.MW 47
Vienna Radio—Schönherr (Vien.P 6078: ♯ 1002;
♯ AmVien.VNLP 1005)

RITTER PÁZMÁN Comic Opera 1892
Ballet Music
Vienna Radio—Nilius   Vien.P 6099
(in ♯ 1012; in ♯ AmVien. 1004)

... Csárdás only
Vienna Phil.—Krauss   in ♯ D.LXT 2755
(New Year Concert 2)   (♯ Lon.LL 683)

... Waltz only — ARR. STR. ORCH. Bernard
☆ A. Bernard Str. Orch. (BrzOd.X 3356)

(Das) SPITZENTUCH DER KÖNIGIN 1880
Overture
Vienna Radio—Schönherr   Vien.P 6079
(in ♯ 1007; in ♯ AmVien.VNLP 1005)

Du Märchenstadt im Donautal   T
☆ M. Lichtegg (in ♯ Lon.LLP 55)

Sei mir gegrüsst, du schöne Frau T
☆ M. Lichtegg (in ♯ Lon.LLP 52)

WALDMEISTER 1895
Overture
☆ German Op. House—Lutze (in ♯ T.LSK 7002)

(Der) ZIGEUNERBARON 1885
COMPLETE RECORDING
Graf Peter Homonay ...   A. Poell (B)
Comte Carnero   ...   K. Dönch (Bs)
Sandor Barinkay   ...   J. Patzak (T)
Kalmar Zsupan   ...   K. Preger (T)
Arsena   ...   ...   E. Loose (S)
Czipra   ...   ...   R. Anday (A)
Saffi ...   .   H. Zadek (S)
etc., Vienna State Op. Cho. & Vienna Phil.
Orch.—Krauss   ♯ D.LXT 2612/3
(4ss) (also 24ss, D.K 28526/37)   (♯ Lon.LLP 418/9)

Highlights
E. Funk (S), B. Seidl (A), H. Meyer-Welfing (T),
Cho. & Austrian Sym.—Schönherr
♯ Rem. 199-47
(also 8ss, AusT.E 1144/7)
Anon. Soloists & Cho. (♯ Roy. 1266, 1360, 6116)
etc.

Vocal Selections
E. Trötschel (S), P. Anders (T), etc. PV. 58613
(♯ Pol. 45025)

☆ A. Gura, P. Anders, etc. (in ♯ T.LSK 7002)
M. Reiner, J. Patzak, etc. (Pol. 57415)

Overture
Vienna Phil.—Krauss   in ♯ D.LXT 2634
(♯ Lon.LLP 454 & LD 9008)
Stockholm Phil.—Ehrling   in ♯ Rgt. 5052
Vienna Sym.—Paulik   in ♯ FestF.FLD 2

Vienna Radio—Schönherr (in ♯ Vien. 1001)
▽ Austrian Sym.—Schönherr (in ♯ Rem. 149-7)
☆ Minneapolis—Ormandy (in ♯ Vic.LM 9025:
♭ set WDM 262)
Berlin Phil.—Karajan (Pol. 57424)
Boston Pops.—Fiedler (♭ Vic. WEPR 23: 49-0898)

ACT I

No. 2, Als flotter Geist ... Ja, das Alles auf Ehr' T
E. Kurz   Imp. 19196
(Nacht in Venedig, excpt)
R. Schock   G.EH 1421
(Nacht in Venedig—Komm' in die Gondel) (GB 70)
J. Patzak (from set) (D.K 28527)

No. 3, Ja, das Schreiben ... Mein idealer
Lebenszweck   Bs
H. Reinmar (B)   Od.O-28138
(Millöcker: Bettelstudent, aria)
☆ G. Hann (Pol. 57440)

ACT II

No. 11, Wer uns getraut?   S & T
☆ L. della Casa & H. Roswaenge (D.GAH 15055;
in ♯ Lon.LPS 11)
C. V. & R. Tauber (Od.O-9174)

No. 12, Das war kein rechter Schifferknecht
R. Anday & A. Jaresch (from set) (D.K 28527)

No. 13A, So voll Fröhlichkeit   S
☆ V. Schwarz   in ♯ Ete. 459

ACT III
Prelude
☆ Bavarian Sym.—Nick (Pol. 57440)

No. 17, Hurrah! Die Schlacht! Cho. & Orch.
— ORCH. ONLY
☆ Berlin St. Op. Orch.—H. G. Otto T.A 11177
Suppé: Boccaccio, March)
Austrian Sym.—Wöss   in ♯ Rem. 149-27

C. MISCELLANEOUS

OPERETTA PASTICHES
CASANOVA (ARR. Benatzky)
Nuns' Cho.   S, Cho. & Orch.
J. Candel (Dutch), Cho. & Orch.—H. de Groot
Phi.A 17901G
(Gounod)   (PhM.A 02900S)
Nuns' Cho. & Spanish Romance
☆ A. Frind & Cho. (♭ G.7P 106)

♯ = Long-playing, 33⅓ r.p.m.   ♭ = 45 r.p.m.   ♮ = Auto.   r.p.m.

(Die) TÄNZERIN FANNY ELSSLER
(ARR. Weninger)
Draussen in Sievering   S
   E. Roon   in ‡ AmVox.PL 20900
   M. Thoma   in *Phi.P 41002H*
 ☆ E. Sack   in ‡ *T.LB 6020*
   etc.

WIENER BLUT   (ARR. Müller)   1899
COMPLETE RECORDING
I. Beilke (S), T. Richter (S), R. Streich (S),
    S. Hauser (T), Berlin Municipal Opera Cho.
    & Orch.—Lenzer (4ss)   ‡ **Ura. set 209**
(Overture & Waltz song on ♭ *UREP 5*)

Vocal Selections
 ☆ T. Richter & S. Hauser (*Od.O-28012*)
   E. Schwarzkopf (S), R. Glawitsch (T) (AusT.E 1160)

Es hat dem Grafen nicht benützt das Warnen
 ☆ V. Schwarz (S)   in ‡ *Ete. 459*

J. Strauss & His Music
Narration & orch.   ‡ *AmVox.VL 2590*
                (♮ set 259)

STRAUSS, Josef (1827-1870)

POLKAS
Feuerfest, Op. 269   P-schnell
   Vienna Phil.—Krauss   in ‡ D.LXT 2755
                    (‡ Lon.LL 683)
   Philadelphia—Ormandy   in ‡ **AmC.ML 4589**
              (♭ *set A 1013*: ♭ *A 1543*)
   Vienna Radio—Schönherr (*Vien.P 6045*: in ‡ *1008*)

Frauenherz, Op. 166   P-Mazurka
   Vienna Sym.—Paulik   in ‡ **FestF.FLD 2**
   Lower Austrian—Wöss   **AusT.C 3046**
   (*J. Strauss II: Annen-Polka*)   (& in ‡ *Rem. 149-35*)

Jockey, Op. 278   Polka (Gallop)
   Vienna Phil.—Krauss   in ‡ D.LXT 2645
   (also *D.M 38127*)   (‡ Lon.LLP 484)
   Lower Austrian—Wöss   *AusT.M 5146*
   (½s.—*Ziehrer: Loslassen* &   (& in ‡ *Rem. 149-34*)
      J. Strauss II: Tik-tak)

(Die) Lachtaube, Op. 117   P-Mazurka
   Vienna Radio—Schönherr   *Vien.P 6083*
   (*J. Strauss: Tritsch-tratsch*) (in ‡ *1002*;
              in ‡ *AmVien.VNLP 1004*)

(Die) Libelle, Op. 204   P-Mazurka
   Vienna Phil.—Krauss   in ‡ D.LXT 2645
   (& *D.K 28582*)   (‡ Lon.LLP 484)
   Vienna Phil.—Krauss   in ‡ *AmVox.VL 3140*

Moulinet, Op. 57   P-française
   Vienna Phil.—Krauss   in ‡ D.LXT 2755
                    (‡ Lon.LL 683)

Ohne Sorgen, Op. 271   P-schnell
   Vienna Phil.—Krauss   in ‡ D.LXT 2755
                    (‡ Lon.LL 683)
   Vienna Phil.—Krauss   in ‡ *AmVox.VL 3140*

Plappermäulchen, Op. 245   P-schnell
   Vienna Radio—Nilius (in ‡ *AmVien.VNLP 1004*;
                    ‡ *Vien. 1008*)

WALTZES
Aquarellen, Op. 258
   Bavarian Radio—Görlich   in ‡ **Mer.MG 10022**

    M. Schönherr Orch. (*Imp. 19206*; *BrzOd. 8180*)
  ☆ Vienna Sym.—Baltzer (Eur.TPV 106)

Delirien, Op. 212
   Bavarian Radio—Görlich   in ‡ **Mer.MG 10022**
   Vienna Radio—Nilius (*Vien.L 6082*: in ‡ *1008*)
   Vienna Radio—Schönherr (*Phi.P 41077H*)
   Berlin Sym.—Friedl (in ‡ Roy. 1202)
   etc.

Dorfschwalben aus Österreich, Op. 164
   Vienna Phil.—Krauss   in ‡ **D.LXT 2755**
                    (‡ Lon.LL 683)
   Austrian State Sym.—O. Straus
                 in ‡ **MSL.MW 47**
   Berlin Sym.—Friedl (in ‡ Roy. 1202)
   H. Zacharias Orch. (*Pol. 48605*)
   Orch.—Foster (*VIS.VI 4606*)
   etc.

 — VOCAL. ARRS.
   E. Roon (S) & Vienna Sym.—Rauspertl
               in ‡ **AmVox.PL 20900**
  ☆ E. Sack (S) (in ‡ *T.LB 6001*)

Dynamiden (Geheime Anziehungskräfte), Op. 173
   Austrian Sym.—Günther   ‡ **Rem. 199-97**
   (*Acceleration, Blue Danube & Morgenblätter*)
  ☆ Vienna Sym.—Krauss (Eur.TSV 143)

(Die) Ersten und Letzten, Op. 1 [1]
   Schneider Str. Ens.   in ‡ *AmC.ML 2179*

Mein Lebenslauf ist Lieb' und Lust, Op. 263
   Vienna Phil.—Krauss   in ‡ **D.LXT 2645**
   (also on K 28583)   (‡ Lon.LLP 484)
   Vienna Phil.—Krauss   in ‡ *AmVox.VL 3140*
   Vienna Radio—Nilius (*Vien.L 6100*: in ‡ *1008*)

Nilfluten, Op. 275
   Vienna Radio—Schönherr   **Vien.L 6053**
   Vienna State Op.—Schönherr   *Phi.P 41039H*
   (*Accelerationen*)

Sphärenklänge, Op. 235
   Vienna Radio—Schönherr   **Vien.L 6024**
   Bavarian Radio—Görlich   in ‡ **Mer.MG 10022**
   Austrian State Sym.—O. Straus
                 in ‡ **MSL.MW 48**
   Berlin Sym.—Ludwig (in ‡ Roy. 1201)
  ☆ Vienna Phil.—Karajan (C.LFX 1027: M 15175)
   Vienna Phil.—Böhm (G.EH 1360: GB 49;
             in ‡ BB.LBC 1008: ♭ *WBC 1008*)
   Boston Pops.—Fiedler (♭ Vic. 49-0261)

 — ARR. CHO. & PF.
   Vienna Boys' Cho.—Brenner   ‡ *Phi.A 00606R*
   (*Joh. Strauss & Mozart, etc.*)
   (also 2ss, Phi.N 11221G; *PhM.N 09718S*)

Transaktionen, Op. 184
  ☆ Vienna Phil.—Karajan (C.LFX 1022)

STRAUSS, Richard (1864-1949)

CLASSIFIED: I. ORCHESTRAL
            II. INSTRUMENTAL & CHAMBER
                  MUSIC
           III. STAGE WORKS
           IV. LIEDER
           V. MISCELLANEOUS

I. ORCHESTRAL

(Eine) Alpensinfonie, Op. 64   1915
   Munich State Op.—Konwitschny   ‡ **Ura. 7064**

---

[1] This *may* be (*Die*) *Ersten nach die Letzten, Op. 12.*   It has not been possible to check.

Also sprach Zarathustra, Op. 30   1896
☆ Chicago Sym.—Rodzinski   ♯ **G.FALP 179**
(*Wagner: Tristan*)

Burleske   pf. & orch.   1883
F. Jacquinot & Philharmonia—Fistoulari
(*Dohnányi*)   ♯ **MGM.E 3004**

CONCERTO, vln. & orch., D minor, Op. 8   1883
S. Borries & Berlin Radio—Rother   ♯ **Ura. 7032**
(*Oboe Concerto*)

CONCERTO, oboe & orch.   1945
E. Ertel & Berlin Radio—Rother   ♯ **Ura. 7032**
(*above*)

Divertimento after Couperin, Op. 86   1940-1
Berlin Radio Orch.—Rother   ♯ **Ura. 7042**
(*Taillefer*)

Don Juan, Op. 20   1888
N.B.C. Sym.—Toscanini   ♯ **G.FALP 157**
(*Wagner: Götterdämmerung*) (♯ Vic.LM 1157:
                                    ♭ *set WDM 1563*)
Philharmonia—Karajan   ♮ **C.LX 8920/1**
(4ss)   (♮ C.GQX 8039/40)
(*Till, on ♯ C.CX 1001: FCX/QCX 159*)
Amsterdam—E. Jochum   ♯ *Phi.A 00608R*
(*Till*)
☆ Boston Sym.—Koussevitzky   ♯ **Vic.LM 1177**
(*Wagner: Siegfried Idyll*)
Berlin Sym.—Balzer   ♯ **Roy. 1344**
(*Borodin: In the Steppes …*)   (& in ♯ Roy. 1370)

Don Quixote, Op. 35   vlc. & orch.   1897
☆ O. Uhl & Bavarian State Orch.—Strauss
                              ♯ **AmD.DL 9539**

Festliches Praeludium, Op. 61   1913
— ARR. ORGAN   Reger & Biggs
E. P. Biggs   in ♯ **AmC.ML 4603**
(*J. Clarke, Vaughan Williams, etc.*)

Festmarsch, E flat major, Op. 1   1876
Bavarian Sym.—Graunke   in ♯ **Ura. set 602**
(*Josephs Legende & Rosenkavalier*)

(Ein) Heldenleben, Op. 40   1898
Vienna Phil.—Krauss   ♯ **D.LXT 2729**
                              (♯ Lon.LL 659)
☆ Bavarian State—Strauss   ♯ **AmD.DL 9602**

Macbeth, Op. 23   1887
☆ Vienna Sym.—Swoboda (♯ Sel.LPG 8546)

Sinfonia domestica, Op. 53   1903
Vienna Phil.—Strauss   ♯ **AmVox.PL 7220**
(*Actual performance, 1944*)
Vienna Phil.—Krauss   ♯ **D.LXT 2643**
(also, 10ss, ♮ D.AKX 28576/80)   (♯ Lon.LL 483)

Symphony, F minor, Op. 12   1884
Vienna Phil.—Haefner   ♯ **SPA. 17**

Till Eulenspiegels lustige Streiche, Op. 28   1895
Philharmonia—Karajan   ♮ **C.LX 8908/9**
(4ss)   (LVX 173/4: ♮ GQX 8037/8)
(*Don Juan, on ♯ C.CX 1001: FCX/QCX 159*)
Victor Sym.—Reiner   ♯ **G.FALP 177**
(*Tod und Verklärung*) (♯ Vic.LM 1180: 4ss, ♭ *set WDM 1580*)
Amsterdam—E. Jochum   ♯ *Phi.A 00608R*
(*Don Juan*)
Berlin Sym. (in ♯ Roy. 1370, also ♯ 1259)
☆ Vienna Phil.—Krauss, o.v. (in ♯ T.LSK 7003)

Tod und Verklärung, Op. 24   1889
Victor Sym.—Reiner   ♯ **G.FALP 177**
(*Till*) (♯ Vic. LM 1180: 6ss, ♭ *set WDM 1579*)
☆ Vienna Phil.—Furtwängler
                          ♯ **Vic.LHMV 1023**
(*Schumann & Smetana*)   (♭ *set WHMV 1023*)
☆ Amsterdam—Mengelberg (in ♯ T.LSK 7003)
Berlin Phil.—de Sabata (P.RR 8011/3)

II. INSTRUMENTAL & CHAMBER MUSIC

Sonata, vln. & pf., E flat major, Op. 18   1887
L. Kaufman & A. Balsam   ♯ **CHS.F 15**
(*Prokofiev*)
J. Tryon & J. La Montaine   ♯ **CEd. 1019**
(*Elgar: Sonata*)

Sonata, vlc. & pf., F major, Op. 6   1883
C. Stern & P. O'Neil   ♯ **SPA. 8**
(*Hindemith*)
… 2nd movt. only   S. Popoff & O. Schulhof (*Vien.P 3023*)

III. STAGE WORKS

ARABELLA, Op. 79   Opera   3 acts   1933
Mein Elemer   S   (Finale, Act I)
☆ L. Lehmann   in ♯ **AmD.DL 9524**
(*Fledermaus, Freischütz, etc.*)

Das war sehr gut   S   (Act III)
L. Rysanek   **C.LX 1559**
(*Albert: Tiefland—Ich weiss nicht*)

ARIADNE AUF NAXOS, Op. 60   1 act
Overture
Württemberg State Op.—Leitner
Es gibt ein Reich   (Ariadne's aria)   S
A. Kupper   **PV. 72238**

Sie lebt hier ganz allein … Es gibt ein Reich
In den schönen Feierkleidern   (Ariadne's aria)
♯ F. Leider (in ♯ Ete. O-477*)

(Der) BÜRGER ALS EDELMANN, Op. 60
(*Inc. music for Molière's Bourgeois gentilhomme*)
Orch. Suite
Vienna Phil.—R. Strauss   ♯ **Rgt. 5013**
☆ Berlin State Op.—Strauss (♯ AmD.DL 9576)

DAPHNE   Opera   1 act   1938
Verwandlung der Daphne: Wind, spiele …   S
A. Kupper   (2ss)   **PV. 72172**

ELEKTRA, Op. 58   Opera   1 act   1909
COMPLETE RECORDING
☆ A. Konetzni, M. Mödl, D. Ilitsch, F. Klarwein,
   H. Braun, Florence Cho. & Orch.—Mitropoulos
                              (♯ FSor.CS 519/20)

Allein!   Weh, ganz allein   (Elektra's Monologue) S
C. Goltz   (2ss)   *PV. 36045*

FEUERSNOT, Op. 50   Opera   1 act   1901
Love Scene   orch.
☆ R.P.O.—Beecham   **G.DB 21301**

JOSEPHS LEGENDE, Op. 63   Ballet   1914
Munich State Op.—Eichhorn   in ♯ **Ura. set 602**
(*above & below*)

♯ = Long-playing, 33⅓ r.p.m.   ♭ = 45 r.p.m.   ♮ = Auto. couplings, 78 r.p.m.

(Der) ROSENKAVALIER, Op. 59   Opera   3 acts
(1911)
COMPLETE RECORDING

Feldmarschallin	...	...	V. Ursuleac (S)
Sophie	...	...	A. Kern (S)
Oktavian	...	...	G. v. Milinkovic (A)
Baron Ochs...	...	...	L. Weber (Bs)
Faninal	...	...	G. Hann (B)

etc., Munich State Op. Cho. & orch.—C. Krauss
♯ **AmVox.set PL 7774**
(8ss—Recorded April 1944)

Highlights
U. Richter, T. Lemnitz, K. Böhme, Saxon State
Orch.—Kempe   ♯ **Ura. 7062**
Anon. Soloists, Berlin Op. Cho. (♯ Roy. 1352;
excpts. in ♯ 1370)

Orch. Suite — ARR.   Strauss   1946
☆ Hallé—Barbirolli   ♯ **BB.LBC 1017**
(*Peer Gynt Suites 1 & 2*)   (♭ *set WBC 1017*)

Waltzes   (Act II or unspec.)
Brussels Radio.—André   **T.E 3920**
(2ss)   (*Liszt: Les Préludes, on ♯ Cap.L 8173*)
Stadium Concerts—Smallens   ♯ **AmD.DL 4032**
(*Salome*)

▽ Berlin State—Schüler (Imp. 014113)

☆ M.G.M.—Marrow (in ♯ *MGM.E 539*)
L.P.O.—Collins (♯ *Lon.LD 9025*)
Boston Prom.—Fiedler (♭ *Vic.WEPR 5: 49-0307:*
in ♯ LM 9005)
Austrian Sym.—Brown (♯ Rem. 199-67;
& ♯ *Mrt. 1-15, d.c.*)

— ARR. VLN. & PF.
☆ V. Prihoda & O. A. Graef (P.LL 3002)

Preludes, Acts I & III
Saxon State Orch.—Kempe   in ♯ **Ura.set 602**
(*Festmarsch & Josephs Legende*)

ACT I

Di rigori armato   (Arie des Sängers)   T   (*Ital*)
Ⅱ R. Tauber (in ♯ *Ete. O-466**)

Kann mich auch an ein Mädel erinnern ...
Oh sei er gut, Quinquin
Leicht will ich's machen Dir und mir S & A or M-S
(Monolog der Marschallin)
T. Lemnitz & G. von Milinkovic **PV. 72147/8S**
(3ss—last blank)
(in ♯ Pol. 18011; AmD.DL 9606, commencing
Da geht er hin)
☆ L. Lehmann   in ♯ **AmD.DL 9524**
(*Arabella, etc.*)

ACT II

Herr Gott im Himmel!
Mir ist die Ehre   S & A or M-S
E. Trötschel & G. von Milinkovic   **PV. 72139**
(2ss)
V. Richter & T. Lemnitz   ♭ *Ura.UREP 14*
(from Highlights)
E. Berger & R. Stevens   ♯ **Vic.LM 9010**
(*below, Orphée, etc.*)   (♭ *set WDM 9010*)

Da lieg' ich Bs & A   (Finale)
K. Böhme & R. Michaelis   **PV. 72101**
(2ss)
E. List & E. Schurhoff   in ♯ **Rem. 199-73**
(*Barbiere, Juive, etc.*)

ACT III

Hab' mir's gelobt   Trio
Ist ein Traum   2 S
T. Lemnitz, E. Trötschel & G. von Milinkovic
PV. 72121
(in ♯ Pol. 18011; AmD.DL 9606, commencing earlier at
Mein Gott ... ; with anon. Bar.)

... Ist ein Traum only
E. Berger & R. Stevens   ♯ **Vic.LM 9010**
(*above, Figaro, etc.*)   (♭ *set WDM 9010*)

SALOME, Op. 54   Opera   1 act   1905
Salomes Tanz   Sc. 4   Orch.
(*Dance of the Seven Veils*)
Stadium Concerts—Smallens   ♯ *AmD.DL 4032*
(*Rosenkavalier Waltzes*)
☆ Royal Phil.—Beecham   ♭ *G.7R 103*
(2ss)   (♭ *Vic. 49-0899*)
☆ Philadelphia—Ormandy   ♯ *AmC.AAL 12*
(*Weinberger*)   (♭ *4-13162D, 2ss*)

Ah! Du wolltest mich ... (Finale)   S, M-S, T
G. Goltz, H. Plümacher, W. Windgassen
(2ss)   **PV. 72100**
M. Cebotari   (Solo)   in ♯ **Ura. 7036**
(*Entführung, Figaro, Butterfly*)

IV. LIEDER

Allerseelen, Op. 10, No. 8   (Von Gilm)
☆ J. McCormack (T) (*G.VA 72*)

Du meines Herzens Krönelein, Op. 21, No. 2 (Dahn)
G. Hüsch (B), M. Gurlitt (pf.)   *JpV.SF 721*
(*Morgen*)   (in set JAS 275)

Freundliche Vision, Op. 48, No. 1   (Bierbaum)
H. Schlusnus (B), O. Braun (pf.)   *Pol. 62876*
(*Traum durch die Dämmerung*)   (in ♯ AmD.DL 9622)
☆ L. Slezak (T) (*Pol. 26507*)

Geduld, Op. 10, No. 5   (von Gilm)
M. Klose (A), M. Raucheisen (pf.)
in ♯ **Ura. 7053**
(*Grieg, Jensen, etc.*)

Heimkehr, Op. 15, No. 5   (Schack)
H. Schlusnus (B), O. Braun (pf.)   *Pol. 62882*
(*Ständchen*)   (& in ♯ Pol. 18029; ♯ AmD.DL 9621)

Heimliche Aufforderung, Op. 27, No. 3   (Mackay)
H. Rosenberg (B) & orch.   *Imp. 19013*
(*Schumann: Wanderlust*)
▽ K. Branzell (A)   in ♯ *Rem. 149-6*
(*Brahms, Wolf, etc.*)
☆ H. Schlusnus (B) (in ♯ Pol. 18029)
K. Schmidt-Walter (B) (*G.DA 5510*)

Ich liebe dich, Op. 37, No. 2   (Liliencron)
☆ H. Schlusnus (B) (in ♯ Pol. 18029; ♯ AmD.DL 9621)

Morgen, Op. 27, No. 4   (Mackay)
P. Schoeffler (B), G. Cassadò (vlc.)
O. Schulhof (pf.)   *Hma. 14003*
(*Massenet: Élégie*)   (in ♯ MSL.MW 46)
G. Hüsch (B), M. Gurlitt (pf.)   *JpV.SF 721*
(*Du meines Herzens Krönelein*)   (in JAS 275)
☆ H. Schlusnus (B) & pf. (o.v.)   *Pol. 62714*
(now d.c., *Winterliebe*)

(Die) Nacht, Op. 10, No. 3   (von Gilm)
J. Moor (S), H. W. Haeusslein (pf.)   *Eli. 9037*
(*Ständchen*)

(Der) Nachtgang, Op. 29, No. 3   (von Gilm)
☆ H. Schlusnus (B) (in ♯ AmD.DL 9622)

☆ = Re-issue of a recording to be found in WERM or Supplement I.

Ophelia's Songs, Op. 67, Bk. 1 1919
1. Wie erkenn' ich mein Treulieb'
2. Guten Morgen, 's ist Sankt Valentinstag
3. Sie trugen ihn auf der Bahre bloss
  E. Berger (S), M. Raucheisen (pf.)
                  in ♯ **Ura. 7060**
  (Debussy, Handel, etc.)

Ruhe, meine Seele, Op. 27, No. 1 (Henckell)
♭ H. Schlusnus (B), R. Strauss (pf.)
  (below)   *IRCC. 3111* *

Ständchen, Op. 17, No. 2 (Schack)
  H. Schlusnus (B), O. Braun (pf.) *Pol. 62882*
  (Heimkehr)   (& in ♯ Pol. 18029; AmD.DL 9621)
  J. Moor (S), H. W. Haeusslein (pf.) *Eli. 9037*
  (Die Nacht)
  ☆ R. Tauber (T) & orch. (in ♯ AmD.DL 9547)
  ♭ L. Slezak (T) (in ♯ Ete. 453*)

Traum durch die Dämmerung, Op. 29, No. 1
  (Bierbaum)
  H. Schlusnus (B), O. Braun (pf.) *Pol. 62876*
  (Freundliche Vision)   (in ♯ AmD.DL 9623)
  ☆ L. Slezak (T) (*Pol. 26507*)

Waldseligkeit, Op. 49, No. 1 (Dehmel)
  ☆ K. Schmitt-Walter (B) (*G.DA 5510*)

Winterliebe, Op. 48, No. 5 (Henckell)
  H. Schlusnus (B), S. Peschko (pf.) *Pol. 62714*
  (Morgen)   (in ♯ AmD.DL 9623)

Zueignung, Op. 10, No. 1 (von Gilm)
♭ H. Schlusnus (B), R. Strauss (pf.)
  (above)   *IRCC. 3111* *

V. MISCELLANEOUS

Enoch Arden, Op. 38 (Tennyson) Narrator & pf.
  1904
  E. Rhodes & G. Manley   ♯ **NRI.set 501**
  (3ss—Liszt: Consolations)

Taillefer, Op. 52 (Uhland) S, T, B, Cho.,Orch.
  1903
  M. Cebotari, W. Ludwig, H. Hotter, R. Lamy
    Cho. & Berlin Radio Orch.—Rother
  (Divertimento)   ♯ **Ura. 7042**

Wanderers Sturmlied, Op. 14 (Goethe)
  Vienna Cha. Cho. & Sym.—Swoboda
                  ♯ **West.WL 5081**
  (Brahms)   (*Macbeth*, in ♯ Sel.LPG 8546)

STRAVINSKY, Igor (b. 1882)

  CLASSIFIED: I. PIANO
              II. CHAMBER MUSIC
             III. ORCHESTRAL
             IV. BALLET
             V. VOCAL
             VI. MISCELLANEOUS

I. PIANO

Piano Rag-music 1920
  P. Scarpini   **Dur.SA 138**
  (Sonata, s. 3)   (*Bartók*, in ♯ Csm.CLPS 1025)

(5) Pièces faciles 4-hands 1917
  ▽ A. Gold & R. Fizdale (☆ in ♯ *CHS.CHS 1089*
                      with *Sonata*)

Serenade, A major 1925
  C. Seemann   **PV. 72071**
  (2ss)

Sonata 1922
  P. Scarpini   **Dur.SA 137/8**
  (3ss—Piano Rag-music) (*Bartók* in ♯ Csm.CLPS 1025)

Sonata, 2 pfs. 1943-4
  A. Whittemore & J. Lowe in ♯ **Vic.LM 1705**
  (Bartók, Ravel, etc.)   (♭ set WDM 1705)

II. CHAMBER MUSIC

Duo concertant   vln. & pf. 1932
  ☆ J. Fuchs & L. Smit (♯ D.AXT 233048)

Élégie unacc. vla. (or vln.) 1946
  F. Ostrovsky (vln.)   ♯ **CEd. 1029**
  (Geminiani & Ostrovsky)
  ☆ B. Milofsky (vla.) (in ♯ Mtr.CLP 506)

Octet Wind Insts. 1923
  Wind Inst. Soc.—Oubradous ♯ *Pat.DT 1002*
  (Suites 1 & 2)

(3) Pieces for Clarinet solo 1919
  R. Kell   ♯ **AmD.DL 9570**
  (Hindemith & Debussy)

(3) Pieces for Str. Qtt. 1914
  ☆ New Music Qtt. (in ♯ Clc. 6119; BRS. 901, n.n.)

Russian Maiden's Song
  (Parasha's aria from *Mavra*)
— ARR. VLN. & PF. Stravinsky 1920-1
  ☆ J. Szigeti & I. Stravinsky (in ♯ AmC.ML 4398)

III. ORCHESTRAL

(Le) Chant du rossignol Suite 1919
  ☆ Cincinnati Sym.—Goossens (♮ G.DB 9339/41)

Circus Polka (after Schubert) 1942
  N.Y.P.S.O.—Stravinsky in ♯ **AmC.ML 4398**
  ☆ Suisse Romande—Ansermet in ♯ *D.LX 3072*
  (Debussy, Ravel, Prokofiev) (♯ Lon.LS 503)

— ARR. PF.
  A. Földes   **PV. 46002**
  (Thomson: Ragtime bass, & Albeniz: Tango)

CONCERTOS

D major Str. Orch. 1946
  ☆ Hallé—Barbirolli (G.TH 1/2)
    Victor Str. Orch.—Stravinsky (♯ G.FALP 132)

E flat major 16 insts. 1938
  ☆ Dumbarton Oaks—Stravinsky ♯ **Clc. 6030**
  (Falla)

Piano & Wind insts. 1923-4
  N. Mewton-Wood & Residentie
         Members—Goehr ♯ **Nix.CLP 1160**
  (Prokofiev)   (♯ CHS.CHS 1160)

Ebony Concerto Jazz orch. 1946
  ☆ Woody Herman Orch.—Stravinsky (C.LZX 262)

Danses concertantes 1942
  ☆ Victor Sym.—Stravinsky ♯ **G.FALP 159**
  (Baiser de la fée)

Fireworks, Op. 4 1904 (*Feux d'artifice*)
  ☆ N.Y.P.S.O.—Stravinsky (C.LFX 997;
                 in ♯ AmC.ML 4398)

♯ = Long-playing, 33⅓ r.p.m.   ♭ = 45 r.p.m.   ♮ = Auto. couplings, 78 r.p.m.

(4) Norwegian Moods 1942
☆ N.Y.P.S.O.—Stravinsky in ♯ **AmC.ML 4398**

Ode 1943
N.Y.P.S.O.—Stravinsky in ♯ **AmC.ML 4398**
(above)

SUITES Small Orch. (orig. *Pièces faciles*, pf.)
No. 1—1. **Andante**   2. **Napolitana**
     3. **Española**   4. **Balalaika** 1925-6
No. 2—1. **Marche**   2. **Valse**
     3. **Polka**   4. **Galop**   1921
Cha. Orch.—Oubradous   ♯ *Pat.DT 1002*
(Octet)
Little Orch. Soc.—Scherman   ♯ *B.AXL 2005*
(Hindemith)   (♯ *AmD.DL 7529*)

No. 1 only   ☆ N.Y. Cha.—Craft (in ♯ Mtr.CLP 506)

IV. BALLETS

APOLLON MUSAGÈTE 1927
☆ Victor Sym.—Stravinsky (♯ G.FALP 132)

(Le) BAISER DE LA FÉE 4 Scenes 1928
(on themes of Tchaikovsky)
☆ Victor Sym.—Stravinsky   ♯ **G.FALP 159**
(Danses concertantes)

(The) Card Party 1937
☆ Berlin Phil.—Stravinsky (♯ *T.LB 6006*)

(The) FIRE BIRD
Revised Suite 1919
Minneapolis—Dorati   ♯ **Mer.MG 50004**
(Borodin)
Danish Radio—Tuxen   ♮ **Tono.Y 30016/7**
☆ Philharmonia—Galliera   **C.DX 1757/9**
(6ss)
☆ Sym.—Stokowski (♯ *G.QBLP & FBLP 1020*)

... **Berceuse**—ARR. VLN. & PF.
☆ J. Heifetz & E. Bay (♮ *G. 7RF 250*)

New Orchestral Suite 1945
☆ N.Y.P.S.O.—Stravinsky (C.LFX 994/7: ♯ FCX 146)

Orpheus 1948
☆ Victor Sym.—Stravinsky   ♯ **G.FALP 181**

PETROUCHKA 4 Tableaux 1911
COMPLETE RECORDINGS
N.Y.P.S.O.—Mitropoulos   ♯ **AmC.ML 4438**
Sym.—Stokowski   ♯ **G.FALP 167**
     (♯ *Vic.LM 1175*: ♮ set *WDM 1568*)
Berlin Sym.—List   ♯ **Roy. 1342**
☆ Suisse Romande—Ansermet (D.K 28227/31)

... **Danse russe; Chez Petrouchka;**
La Semaine grasse — ARR. 2 PFS. Babin
V. Vronsky & V. Babin   ♯ **AmC.ML 4470**
(Debussy: En blanc et noir)

... **Danse russe** — ARR. VLN. & PF. Dushkin
E. Nielsen & L. Christiansen   *G.DA 5268*
(Ravel: Pièce en forme de habanera)

PULCINELLA 1 act 1920 (after Pergolesi)
Suite italienne vln. & pf. 1933
F. Magnes & D. Garvey   ♯ **BRS. 908**
(Serly)

Suite italienne vlc. & pf. 1934 (ed. Piatigorsky)
E. B. Bengtsson & H. D. Koppel
          ♮ **G.DB 20168/70**
(5ss—Milhaud: Élégie)

(The) Rite of Spring 1913 *(Sacre du Printemps)*
Philharmonia—Markevitch   ♯ **G.CLP 1003**
           (♯ G.FALP 189)
Boston Sym.—Monteux   ♯ **Vic.LM 1149**
           (♮ set WDM 1548)

V. VOCAL

MASS Male & Boys' Cho. & Wind Insts. 1948
☆ Cho. & Inst. Ens.—Stravinsky (♯ *G.FBLP 1012*)

RENARD Opera-ballet 1 act 1920
COMPLETE RECORDING (in *English*)
☆ Soloists & N.Y. Cha. Orch.—Craft (in ♯ Mtr.CLP 506)

SONGS: The Cats' Lullabies (Ramuz) 1917
☆ A. Carmin (A) & 3 cl. (in ♯ Mtr.CLP 506)

VI. MISCELLANEOUS

Song of the Volga Boatmen
— ARR. ORCH. Stravinsky
☆ N.Y. Cha. Orch.—Craft (in ♯ Mtr.CLP 506)

SUK, Josef (1874-1935)

Love Song, Op. 7, No. 1   pf.
— ARR. VLN. & PF. Mařák
G. Barinova & A. Dedyukhin   *USSR. 21038/9*

(4) Pieces, Op. 17   vln. & pf.
... **No. 4, Burlesque**
W. Tworek & E. Vagning   *Pol.HA 70036*
(Riisager: Lullaby)

Serenade, E flat major, Op. 6 Str. orch.
Chamber Sym.—Byrns   ♯ **DCap.CTL 7025**
(Smetana: Dances)   (♯ Cap.P 8174)
☆ Czech Phil.—Talich (♯ Sup.LPV 5)

SULLIVAN, Sir Arthur Seymour
(1842-1900)

Onward, Christian soldiers (Baring-Gould) Hymn
☆ Vic. Cho.—Shaw & org. (in ♯ *Vic.LM 85*:
      ♮ set WDM 1314: also ♮ Vic. 49-0493)

— ARR. BAND
Cities Service Band—Lavalle
         in ♯ *Vic. LPM 3022*
     (Sets P 315: ♮ WP 315; also ♮ 47-4155)

(The) GONDOLIERS 2 Acts 1889
Overture
☆ Sym. Orch.—Godfrey   in ♯ **D.LXT 2609**
(Sullivan Overtures)   (♯ Lon.LLP 398)

Vocal Selection
☆ Light Opera Co.—Godfrey (♮ *G.7P 110*)

H.M.S. PINAFORE 2 Acts 1878
Overture
☆ Sym. Orch.—Godfrey   in ♯ **D.LXT 2609**
           (♯ Lon.LLP 398)
Boston Pops—Fiedler   in ♯ *Vic.LM 7006*
           (♮ set WDM 7006)

☆ = Re-issue of a recording to be found in WERM or Supplement I.

IOLANTHE   2 acts   1882
COMPLETE RECORDING

Lord Chancellor	...	...	M. Green (B)
Earl of Mountararat		...	E. Thornton (B)
Earl Tolloller	...	...	L. Osborn (T)
Private Willis	...	...	F. Morgan (Bs)
Strephon	...	...	A. Styler (B)
Queen of the Fairies	...	E. Halman (A)
Iolanthe	...	A. Drummond-Grant (M-S)
Phyllis	...	...	M. Mitchell (S)

D'Oyly Carte Opera Co. Cho. & Orch.—
Godfrey (4ss)   ♯ **D.LK 4044/5**
                       (♯ Lon.LLP 469/70)

☆ A. Moxon, B. Lewis, D. Fancourt, etc. (♮ G.D 7708/18)

Overture
Boston Pops—Fiedler   in ♯ *Vic.LM 7006*
                             (♭ set *WDM 7006*)

(The) MIKADO   2 acts   1885
Vocal Selection
☆ Light Opera Co.—Godfrey (♭ *G.7P 109*)

Overture
☆ Sym. Orch.—Godfrey   in ♯ **D.LXT 2609**
                              (♯ Lon.LLP 398)

Boston Pops—Fiedler   in ♯ *Vic.LM 7006*
                             (♭ set *WDM 7006*)

PATIENCE   2 acts   1881
COMPLETE RECORDING

Patience	...	...	M. Mitchell (S)
Archibald Grosvenor	...	A. Styler (B)
Reginald Bunthorne	...	M. Green (B)
Col. Calverley	...	D. Fancourt (B)

etc., D'Oyly Carte Cho. & Orch.—Godfrey
(4ss)   ♯ **D.LK 4047/8**
               (♯ Lon.LLP 474/5)

(The) PIRATES OF PENZANCE 2 acts   1880
Highlights in *Yiddish*, Narration in *Eng*
Kadimah Group   ♮ **Ban.B 108**

Overture
☆ Sym. Orch.—Godfrey   in ♯ **D.LXT 2609**
                              (♯ Lon.LLP 398)

Boston Pops—Fiedler   in ♯ *Vic.LM 7006*
                             (♭ set *WDM 7006*)

RUDDIGORE   2 acts   1887
Overture
☆ Sym. Orch.—Godfrey   in ♯ **D.LXT 2609**
                              (♯ Lon.LLP 398)

TRIAL BY JURY   1 act   1875
COMPLETE RECORDING
Regent Light Opera Co.   ♯ **Rgt. 5006**
(reported as ☆ of Roy. set 42)

(The) YEOMEN OF THE GUARD   2 acts   1888
COMPLETE RECORDING
☆ E. Griffin, D. Gill, L. Sheffield, etc. (♮ G.D 7719/29)

Overture
☆ Sym. Orch.—Godfrey   in ♯ **D.LXT 2609**
                              (♯ Lon.LLP 398)

Boston Pops—Fiedler   in ♯ *Vic.LM 7006*
                             (♭ set *WDM 7006*)

Pineapple Poll   Ballet ARR. Mackerras 1951
Sadler's Wells Orch.—Mackerras
(12ss)   **C.DX 1765/70**
(2ss, ♯ C.SX 1001; ♯ AmC.ML 4439: ♭ set *A 1016*)
Covent Garden—Lanchberry   ♯ **AmD.DL 7521**
L.S.O.—Irving   ♯ **Vic.LM 1224**
                       (12ss, ♭ set *WDM 1653*)

SUPPÉ, Franz von (1819-1895)

OPERETTAS, etc.

BANDITENSTREICHE   1867
Overture
Berlin Sym.—Buschkötter   *P.DPW 59*
(2ss)   (*Od.O-28160; P.B 544*)
Rhineland Sym.—Federer   ♯ **Rgt. 5050**
(*below; & Massenet & Rossini*)
Bavarian Sym.—Graunke   in ♯ *AmD.DL 4021*

BOCCACCIO   3 acts   1879
Overture
Bavarian Sym.—Graunke   **PV. 58610**
(*Schöne Galathée Overture*)

Florenz hat schöne Frauen   (Act I)
☆ L. Claus & W. Ludwig (Pol. 57422)

March
☆ Berlin State Op.—H. G. Otto   *T.A 11177*
(*Zigeunerbaron, March*)
Austrian Sym.—Wöss   in ♯ *Rem. 149-27*

Hab' ich nur deine Liebe   (Act I)
☆ M. Lichtegg (in ♯ Lon.LLP 51)

DICHTER UND BAUER   (from Inc. Music)
Overture
L.P.O.—Solti   **D.X 570**
(in ♯ LXT 2589; Lon.LLP 352 & *LD 9006*)
Bavarian Sym.—Graunke   **Pol. 57447**
(*Leichte Kavallerie*, on ♯ *AmD.DL 4020*)
Boston Pops—Fiedler (n.v.)   ♭ *Vic. 49-1439*
☆ Berlin State Op.—Steeger (Pol. 57423)
Berlin Phil.—Schmidt-Isserstedt (*AusT.M 5151*)
Philadelphia—Ormandy (C.LFX 1004: DZX 57:
          GQX 11469; ♯ *AmC.AAL 10*)
Chicago Phil.—H. Weber (in ♯ Clc. 6041)

LEICHTE KAVALLERIE   1866
Overture
L.P.O.—Solti   in ♯ **D.LXT 2589**
(also 2ss, D.K 23209)   (♯ Lon.LLP 352 & in *LD 9005*)
Rhineland Sym.—Federer   ♯ **Rgt. 5034**
(*Thomas*)
Bavarian Sym.—Graunke   in ♯ *AmD.DL 4020*
☆ Boston Pops—Fiedler (G.DB 4318: ♭ *G.7BF 1009* :
          ♭ *Vic. 49-0286 & WEPR 3*)

Galop   Band—Freese (*Phi.P 44176H*)

**(Ein) MORGEN, EIN MITTAG, EIN ABEND
IN WIEN**
Overture
L.P.O.—Solti   in ♯ **D.LXT 2589**
(also 2ss, D.K 23259)   (♯ Lon.LLP 352 & in ♯ *LD 9005*)
☆ Royal Phil.—Beecham (C.GQX 11508:
          ♯ *AmC.AAL 6*: ♭ *4-73054D*)

PIQUE DAME   1864
Overture
L.P.O.—Solti   in ♯ **D.LXT 2589**
                      (♯ Lon.LLP 352 & *LD 9006*)
▽ ☆ Berlin Phil.—Schmidt-Isserstedt (in ♯ Cap.P 8108)

(Die) SCHÖNE GALATHÉE   1 act   1865
COMPLETE RECORDING
E. Roon (S), W. Kmentt (T), K. Preger (T)
O. Wiener (B), Vienna Academy Cha. Cho. &
State Philharmonia—Hagen
                      ♯ **AmVox.PL 20200**

♯ = Long-playing, 33⅓ r.p.m.   ♭ = 45 r.p.m.   ♮ = Auto. couplings, 78 r.p.m.

(DIE) SCHÖNE GALATHÉE (*continued*)

Overture
Vienna Radio—Schönherr   ***Vien.P 6114***
(2ss)   (in ‡ *1016*; in *AmVien.VNLP 1001*)
Bavarian Sym.—Graunke   **PV. 58610**
(*Boccaccio Overture*)
(*Banditenstreiche Overture* on ‡ *AmD.DL 4021*)
Rhineland Sym.—Federer   in ‡ **Rgt. 5050**
☆ Boston Prom.—Fiedler   ‡ **G.C 4120**
(G.FKX 154; ♭ *Vic.WEPR 33*)

Ja, wenn die Musik nicht wär'   S
E. Spoorenberg   **Phi.N 11173G**
(*Fledermaus—Mein Herr Marquis*)   (*PhM.N 09026S*)

Mein Oesterreich   March
Lower Austrian Police Band—Neusser (*Phi.P 41047H*)

SUSATO, Tielman   (d. *c.* 1561)
SEE: † MADRIGALS (‡ *AS. 2501 LD*)

SVENDSEN, Johan Severin (1840-1911)

Carnival in Paris, Op. 9   orch.
☆ Danish Radio—Malko (G.ZN 583/4)

Festival Polonaise, Op. 12   orch.
☆ Danish Radio—Malko   **G.C 4157**
(2ss)   (GB 66: ZN 564)
☆ Tivoli—Felumb (Son.K 9508)

Norwegian Artists' Carnival, Op. 16   orch.
Oslo Phil.—Fjeldstad   (2ss)   **Nera.SK 15513**

Romance, G major, Op. 26   vln. & orch.
M. Gardi & Hamburg Phil.—
  Brückner-Rüggeberg   **PV. 58605**
(*Bruch: Vln. Concerto No. 1—Adagio*)

Symphony No. 2, B flat major, Op. 15
Oslo Phil.—Grüner-Hegge   ♭ **Nera.SK 15509/12**
(8ss)

SWANSON, Howard (b. 1909)

(A) Short Symphony   (Symphony No. 2)   1948
A.R.S. Orch.—Dixon   ‡ *ARS. 7*
(*Diamond*)

(7) SONGS
1. The Negro speaks of Rivers   (L. Hughes)
2. Joy   (L. Hughes)
3. Ghosts in Love   (V. Lindsay)
4. Night Song   (L. Hughes)
5. Still Life   (C. Sandburg)
6. The Junk Man   (C. Sandburg)
7. The Valley   (E. Markham)
  H. Thigpen (S), D. Allen (pf.)   in ‡ **ARS. 10**
(*Goeb, B. Weber*)

SWEELINCK, Jan Pieterszoon (1562-1621)

Fantasia No. 11 in echo-style   org.
F. Peeters   in ‡ **Ren.X 39**
(† *Old Netherlands Masters*)   (‡ *Nix. PLP 239*)

Hodie Christus natus est   Motet
Welch Chorale   in ‡ **Lyr.LL 35**
(*Weelkes, Handl, etc.*)

Rozette   (Chanson française)
Dutch Vocal Qtt.—Raugel   † ‡ *AS. 2501LD*
Netherlands Cha. Cho.—de Nobel
(*below, etc.*)   ‡ ***Phi.N 00127R***

Tu as tout seul
Netherlands Cha. Cho.—de Nobel
                                          ‡ ***Phi.N 00127R***
(*above; & v. Delden, Voormolen & Dresden*)

Toccata, A minor   org.
F. Heitmann   in † ‡ **T.LSK 7010/1**

Variations on Mein junges Leben ...   org.
W. Supper (in † Baroque Organ Music)

SZYMANOWSKI, Karol (1883-1937)

Concerto No. 1, vln. & orch., Op. 35   1917
☆ E. Uminska & Philharmonia—Fitelberg
                                          ‡ *AmD.DL 7516*

HARNASIE, Op. 55   Ballet   1926
Highland Melody — ARR. VLN. & PF.   Kochanski
E. Uminska & I. Newton   **P.R 20603**
(⅓s.—*Bacewicz: Oberek, & Szymanowski: Polish Folksong*)

(4) MAZURKAS   1924-6
E minor, Op. 50, No. 1   ▽ Z. Drzwiecki (*Muza. 1194*)

Nocturne & Tarantella, Op. 28   vln. & pf.   1914
J. Martzy & J. Antonietti   *PV. 36006*

Polish Folksong from Kurpie   cho.
— ARR. VLN. & PF.   Kochanski
E. Uminska & I. Newton   **P.R 20603**
(*Harnasie, excpt., & Bacewicz*)

PRELUDES, Op. 1   pf.   1900
No. 2, D minor; No. 7, C minor
I. Podolsky   in ‡ **Cmt. 1204**
(*Medtner, Reger, etc.*)

QUARTET, Strings, C major, Op. 37   1917
Walden Qtt.   ‡ **Lyr.LL 22**
(*Kodály: Qtt. No. 2*)

TAFFANEL, Claude Paul (1844-1908)

QUINTET, G minor   fl., ob., clar., hrn., bsn.
☆ New York Quintet (in ‡ **Cpt.MC 20001**)

TAILLEFERRE, Germaine (b. 1892)

(Les) Jeux de plein air   2 pfs.
... Le Tirelitentaine
V. Morley & L. Gearhart   in ‡ *AmC.ML 2197*

TALLIS, Thomas (*c.* 1505-1585)

O nata Lux de lumine   5 voices   1575
San José State A Cappella Cho.—Erlendson
                                          ‡ **ML. 7007**
(*Corsi, Copland, Villa-Lobos, etc.*)

When shall my sorrowful sighing cease
Renaissance Singers—Engel   ‡ **AmC.ML 4517**
(† *Treasury of Madrigals*)

☆ = Re-issue of a recording to be found in WERM or Supplement I.

TANEIEV, Sergei Ivanovitch (1856-1915)

ORESTEIA   Opera   3 acts   1895
Overture
   Bolshoi Theatre—Samosud   ♮ U.H 23875/6
   (4ss)
   (*Rachmaninoff: Symphony No. 3, s. 1 on* ♯ *Sup.LPM 37*)

Romance   vln. & pf.
   D. Oistrakh & pf.   USSR. 17372
   (*Rachmaninoff-Kreisler: Daisies*)

SONGS
In the silence of the night, Op. 17, No. 10   (Fet)
   N. Shumskaya (S)   USSR. 15673
   (*My heart is throbbing*)

Music when soft voices die   (Shelley)
   S. Shaposhnikov   USSR. 14865
   (*Deutsch: I shall tell nothing*)

My heart is throbbing, Op. 17, No. 9   (Nekrassof)
   N. Shumskaya (S)   USSR. 15672
   (*In the silence of the night*)

Symphony No. 1, C minor, Op. 12   1892
   USSR State Radio—Gauk   USSR. 019989/98
   (10ss)

TANSMAN, Alexander (b. 1897)

Lyrical Song
   Female Vocal Qtt. & pf.   in *Vic. set E 101*
                       (♭ set WE 101)

Triptych   Str. orch.   1930
   Zimbler Sinfonietta   ♯ B.AXTL 1006
   (*Vaughan Williams*)   (♯ AmD.DL 9625)

TARP, Svend Erik (b. 1908)

(The) Battle of Jericho, Op. 51   orch.
Overture to my puppet-play, Op. 53 orch.
   Copenhagen Royal—Frandsen   C.DDX 32
   (1 side each)

TARREGA EIXEA, Francisco (1854-1909)

COLLECTION of Guitar pieces
PRELUDES: Nos. 1, 2, 3, 4, 5, 6, 7, 10 & 11
Endecha—Oremus
Lágrima
MAZURKAS: Marieta; Adelita
Minueto
STUDY: Tremolo (Recuerdos de la Alhambra)
   R. de la Torre   ♯ SMC. 516

Capricho arabe   (Serenata)
   L. Walker   Phi.N 11223G
   (*Sor: Variations*)   (PhM. 09040S)

ESTUDIOS
Tremolo
   U. Neumann   *Od.ND 7068*
   (*Mozart: Sym. 39, Minuet*)

Tremolo; Sueño
   L. Maravilla   in ♯ Sel.LPG 8495
   († Tañidos)   (♯ West.WL 5194)

(2) Mazurkas ☆ V. Gomez (in ♯ AmD.DL 8017)

TARTINI, Giuseppe (1692-1770)

CONCERTOS, vln. & str. orch.
D minor   (ed. Pente)
   P. Rybar & Winterthur—Dahinden
   (*Sonatas*)   ♯ West.WL 5118
   ☆ J. Szigeti & Str. Orch. (C.GQX 11516/7)

E major   (ed. Scherchen)
   L. Ferro & Virtuosi di Roma ♯ B.AXTL 1004
   (*Albinoni, Bach, A. Scarlatti*)   (♯ AmD.DL 9572)

Sinfonia pastorale
   German Opera House—Schrader ♯ Ura. 5007
   (*Telemann*)

SONATAS, vln. & cont.
A minor; B minor [1];
D major; G minor, Op. 2, No. 7
   P. Rybar & F. Holletschek (hpsi.)
                      ♯ West.WL 5141

B flat major
   ☆ L. Kaufman & A. Geoffroy-Dechaume (hpsi.)
                  (in ♯ Eur.LPG 627)

E minor; E major
   P. Rybar & F. Holletschek (hpsi.)
   (*Concerto*)   ♯ West.WL 5118

G minor, Op. 1, No. 10   (Didone abbandonata)
   T. Magyar & W. Hielkema   Phi.N 11231G
                    (PhM.N 09046S)
   ▽ A. Spalding & A. Kooiker ♯ Rem. 199-23
   (*Bach & Corelli*)

G minor   "Il trillo del diavolo"
   Y. Menuhin & A. Baller (pf.) [2] JpV.SD 3037/8
   (3ss—*Dvořák: Slavonic Dance No. 2*) (set JAS 206)
   J. de la Fuente & J. Goodman (?) ♯ SRC. 1
   (*Mozart: Sonata*)
   D. Oistrakh & V. Yampolsky (pf.)
   (4ss)   USSR. 017901/4
   ☆ V. Prihoda & O. A. Graef (pf.) (Pol. 15470/1)

Sonata a quattro, D major
   New Music Str. Qtt.   ♯ BRS. 911
   (*A. Scarlatti & Boccherini*)

TAYLOR, Raynor (c. 1747-1825)
SEE: † AMERICAN MUSIC, INST. & CHAMBER

TCHAIKOVSKY, Peter Ilich (1840-1893)

CLASSIFIED: I. INSTRUMENTAL
              A. Piano
              B. Chamber
              C. Orchestral
       II. VOCAL
              A. Opera
              B. Songs
              C. Choral

I. INSTRUMENTAL
A. PIANO

Album Leaf, Op. 19, No. 3
   E. Gilels   USSR. 18432
   (*Capriccioso*)

[1] Padua, No. 14.
[2] ARR. Kreisler.

Berceuse, A flat, Op. 72, No. 2
L. Rostchina   **U.H 24038**
(*Rachmaninoff: Étude, Op. 39*)

Capriccioso, B flat major, Op. 19, No. 5
E. Gilels   *USSR. 18433*
(*Album leaf*)

Chanson triste, Op. 40, No. 2
— ARR. VLC. & PF.
☆ G. Piatigorsky & R. Berkowitz
                              in ♯ **AmC.RL 3015**
(*Rubinstein, Cui & Shostakovitch, etc.*)

— ARR. ORCH.
Lusson-St. Croix Phil.—Monteverdi
                              in ♯ **McG. 3303**
R. Crean Orch. (in ♯ *D.LF 1082; Lon.LPB 424*)

Chant sans paroles, Op. 2, No. 3, F major
A. Goldenweiser   *USSR. 16594*
(*Children's Album, s. 9*)

☆ E. Gilels   *USSR. 18101*
(*Chopin: Étude, Op. 10, No. 6*)
              (*U.C 24117; in ♯ Csm.CRLP 115*)

— ARR. ORCH.
R. Crean Orch. (in ♯ *D.LF 1082; Lon.LPB 424*)
M. Marrow Orch. (in ♯ *MGM.E 510*)

CHILDREN'S ALBUM, Op. 39
COMPLETE RECORDING
A. Goldenweiser   *USSR. 16500/3*
(*9ss—Chant sans paroles*)   & *16589/93*

L'Espiègle, Op. 72, No. 12 — ARR. ORCH.
Radio Sym.—Orlov   *USSR. 7229*
(*Miniature March*)

Humoresque, Op. 10, No. 2 — ARR. ORCH.
R. Crean Orch. (in ♯ *D.LF 1082; Lon.LPB 424*)
M. Marrow Orch. (in ♯ *MGM.E 510*)
Rome Sym. (in ♯ *Var. 6921*, etc.)
Sydney Civic Str.—Beck (in ♯ *Dia.DPM 2*)

(The) MONTHS, Op. 37a
1. At the fireside   2. Carnival
3. Song of the lark   4. Snowdrop
5. May Night   6. Barcarolle
7. Reapers' Song   8. Harvest Song
9. Hunting Song   10. Autumn Song
11. Troïka en traineaux   12. Christmas
COMPLETE RECORDING
L. Oborin   (16ss)   *USSR. 18132/47*

COMPLETE — ARR. PF. & ORCH.   Gould
M. Gould & orch.   ♯ **AmC.ML 4487**

Nos. 5, 6, 7 & 10 ☆ K. Igumnov & J. Flier
                              (in ♯ Csm.CRLP 115)

Nos. 6 & 10 — ARR. ORCH. M.G.M. Orch.—Marrow
                              (in ♯ MGM.E 510)

No. 6 — ARR. ORCH.   Rome Sym. (in ♯ *Var. 6921;*
                              ♭ *Roy. set 14573*, etc.)
Hall Concert Orch. (in ♯ *Var. 6923*)
☆ Robin Hood Dell—Kostelanetz (C.DCX 105;
                              in ♭ *AmC.A 601*)

No. 8, Harvest song
P. Serebriakov   *USSR. 16400*
(*Glazounov: Valse*)

No. 11 — ARR. ORCH.
Hall Concert Orch. (in ♯ *Var. 6923;* ♭ *Roy. set 14530*)

Nocturne, C sharp minor, Op. 19, No. 4
— ARR. VLC. & PF.
☆ G. D. Tsomik & L. Fienstein (in ♯ Csm.CRLP 114)

(6) Pieces on a single theme, Op. 21   1873
... No. 2, Fugue, G sharp major
... No. 5, Mazurka, G sharp minor
L. Oborin   (1 side each)   *USSR. 020595/6*

(Un) Poco de Chopin, Op. 72, No. 15
Valse bluette, Op. 72, No. 11
— ARR. ORCH.   Inc. in *Swan Lake "Complete"* q.v.

Romance, F minor, Op. 5
I. Mikhanovsky   in ♯ **Csm.CRLP 115**

— ARR. VLN. & PF.
☆ V. Prihoda & C. Cerné (Pol. 57392)

— ARR. ORCH.
Metropole—v. d. Linden   in ♯ **Phi.P 10000R**
M. Skalka Orch. (*Eli. 8998*)

Romance, F major, Op. 51, No. 5
— ARR. ORCH.   Orch.—Marrow (in ♯ *MGM.E 510*)

Scherzo humoristique, Op. 19, No. 2   1873
E. Beckman-Shcherbina   *USSR. 18960*
(*Arensky: Étude, F sharp major*)

Tender reproaches, Op. 72, No. 3
Valse à cinq temps, Op. 72, No. 16
G. Fedorova   *USSR. 20172/3*

WALTZES
F sharp minor, Op. 40, No. 9
P. Serebriakov   *USSR. 16397*
(*Rachmaninoff: Prelude, Op. 23-2*)

F minor, Op. 51, No. 6 (Valse sentimentale)
— ARR. VLN. & PF.
H. Szeryng & L. Schwarz   **Orf. 4002**
(*Dvořák & Rimsky-Korsakov*)

— ARR. VLC. & PF.
G. Piatigorsky & R. Berkowitz   ♭ **G.7RF 190**
(*Weber: Sonata No. 3, excpt*) (in ♭ *Vic.set WDM 1578:*
                                    ♯ *LM 1187*)

G. Cassadò & O. Schulhof   **Hma. 14002**
(*Granados: Dance No. 5*)   (in ♯ *MSL.MW 45*)

L. McMorrow (in ♯ *AmC.GL 512*)

I. B. CHAMBER MUSIC

QUARTETS, Strings
No. 1, D major, Op. 11
Oistrakh Qtt.   **USSR. 019979/86**
(8ss; 2nd movt. only on USSR. 018266/7)

☆ Beethoven Qtt. (♯ *Csm.CRLP 119*)

... 2nd movt., Andante cantabile, only
Paganini Qtt.   in † ♯ **Vic.LM 1192**
                                (♭ *set WDM 1611*)

— — STRING ORCH. VERSIONS
Sydney Civic Sym.—Beck   in ♯ **Dia.DPM 2**
Stadium Concerts—Smallens   ♯ **AmD.DL 4033**
(*Eugene Oneigin, excpts*)
▽ Salzburg Festival—Weidlich   ♯ **Rem. 149-36**
(*below & Mozart: Serenade*)   (& ♯ *Mrt. 1-17*, d.c.)
Lusson St. Croix Phil.—Monteverdi
                                in ♯ **McG. 3303**
Royale Orch. (in ♯ *Roy. 1233*, etc.)
☆ Robin Hood Dell—Kostelanetz (C.DCX 105;
                                in ♭ *AmC.set A 601*)

▽ Sym.—Stokowski (Vic. 11-9574: ♭ *49-0296*)

— — ARR. VLN. & PF.
L. Kaufman & P. Ulanowsky
                                in ♯ **DCap. CCL 7513**
                                (♯ *Cap.L 8165*)

☆ F. Kreisler (in ♯ *Vic.LCT 1049:* in ♭ *set WCT 80*)

No. 2, F major, Op. 22
Beethoven Qtt.   *USSR. 8202/7* & *8226/31*
(12ss)

☆ = Re-issue of a recording to be found in WERM or Supplement I.

SEXTET, D minor, Op. 70　2 vlns., 2 vlas., 2 vlcs.
(Souvenir de Florence)
Vienna State Opera Strings—Swoboda
‡ **West.WL 5083**
(‡ Sel.LPG 8586)

Souvenir d'un lieu cher, Op. 42　vln. & pf.
No. 1, Meditation
D. Oistrakh & pf.　(n.v.)　　**USSR. 016044/5**
(2ss)

No. 3, Melody, E flat major　vln. & pf.
J. Heifetz & E. Bay　　　in ‡ *B.LAT 8020*
(in ‡ *AmD.DL 8521*)

— ARR. ORCH.
Orch.—Marrow (in ‡ *MGM.E 510*)
M. Skalka Orch. (*Eli. 8998*)
☆ Robin Hood Dell—Kostelanetz (in ♭ *AmC.set A 601*)

Trio, A minor, Op. 50　pf., vln., vlc.
☆ L. Oborin, D. Oistrakh, S. Knushevitsky
♮ **U.H 24125/30**

Valse-Scherzo, Op. 34　vln. & pf. or orch.
T. Spivakovsky & A. Balsam (pf.)
in ‡ **AmC.ML 4402**
D. Oistrakh　(& pf.?)　　**USSR. 16046/7**

I. C. ORCHESTRAL (inc. BALLET)

BALLETS

NUTCRACKER, Op. 71　(orig. Ballet)
SUITE NO. 2　(ARR. Fistoulari)
No. 3, Scène & Coda; No. 4, Pas de deux (Permission de dix heures); No. 5, Scène & Danse du Grossvater; No. 14, Pas de deux; No. 9, Valse des flocons de neige; No. 11, Scène; No. 12a, Le chocolat; No. 15, Valse finale et Apothéose.
Paris Cons.—Fistoulari　　**‡ D.LXT 2611**
(*below*)　　　　　　　　　　(‡ Lon.LLP 441)

... No. 14 only—See Suite 1, below (Markevitch)

... No. 15 only A. Kostelanetz Orch.　in ‡ AmC.ML 4546

... **Unspec. Excerpts.**　(prob. 1, 2, 12, 15)
☆ Bolshoi Theatre—Fayer　　in ‡ Csm.CRLP 108/9

SUITE, OP. 71A
Paris Cons.—Fistoulari　　**‡ D.LXT 2611**
(*above*)　(also, 6ss, D.K 23248/50)　(‡ Lon.LLP 441)
French Sym.—Désormière　**‡ *DCap.CCL 7508***
(2ss)　　　　　(‡ Cap.L 8141; also ♭ set KCM 8141)
(*Swan Lake*, on ‡ Cap.P 8140)
Philharmonia—Markevitch　　**G.C 4133/5**
(6ss)　　　　　　　　　　　　(EH 1406/8)
(also, with *Pas de Deux* from *Suite 2*, on ‡ BB.LBC 1015:
♭ set WBC 1015)
Covent Garden—Irving　　**‡ P.PMC 1001**
(*Ponchielli & Weber*)　　　　(‡ Od.ODX 106)
(*Chopin: Sylphides* on ‡ AmD.DL 9550)
French Nat. Sym.—Tomasi　　**‡ Pde. 2004**
(o.n. ‡ Pde.SY 302)
(also, with Narration, on ‡ Pde.SY 201)
Munich Phil.—Lehmann　　♮ **PV. 56002/3**
(4ss)　　　　(*Capriccio italien* on ‡ Pol. 18014)
Homburg Sym.—Schubert (‡ *Rgt. 5008*)
☆ Chicago Sym.—Stock (in ‡ AmC.RL 3002)
Sym.—Stokowski (‡ *G.FBLP 1002*; Nos. 1, 2a, 2b,3, on
♭ *Vic.WEPR 46*; & No. 2b only, ♭ *49-0553*)
A. Kostelanetz Orch. (♭ *AmC.set A 714*)
Austrian Sym.—Wöss (‡ *Rem. 199-87*, d.c. & *Mrt. 1-13*,
2ss)
Philadelphia—Stokowski (♮ *G.DB 7902/4*)

... **Nos. 2 (a-c) & 3 only**
☆ Chicago Phil.—H. Weber (in ‡ *Clc. 6041*)

... **No. 2a, March**
Leningrad Phil.—Mravinsky　　**U.C 23944**
(*Glier: Concerto for voice & orch., s. 1*)

... **No. 2c,** Polish Radio—Rachon　(*Muza. 1787*)

... **No. 3, Valse des fleurs, only**
Victor Sym.—Reiner　　　in ‡ *Vic.LM 103*
(♭ set WDM 1539)
Paris Opéra—Cloëz　　　　**Od. 123928**
(*Sleeping Beauty Waltz*)
Leningrad Phil.—Mravinsky　　**U.C 23934**
☆ Sym.—Stokowski (from set)　　**G.DB 21547**
(♭ *Vic. 49-3346: G.7RF 195*)
☆ Los Angeles Phil.—Wallenstein (in AmD.set A 912:
♭ set 9-300; ‡ D.AXT 233057)
Dresden Phil.—v. Kempen (Pol. 68014)
N.Y.P.S.O.—Rodzinski (♭ AmC.A 1508)

— — ARR. 4 PFS.
Phil. Pf. Qtt. (♭ *AmC.A 1548*)
☆ First Pf. Qtt. (in ‡ Vic.LM 1165: ♭ *WEPR 30*)

... **Unspec. excerpts**
Covent Garden—Braithwaite in ‡ MGM.E 3006

(The) SLEEPING BEAUTY, Op. 66　Ballet
COMPLETE RECORDING
Paris Cons.—Fistoulari　　**‡ D.LXT 2762/3**
(4ss)　　　　　　　　　　　　(‡ Lon.LL 636/7)

Intro. & Nos. 4, 6, 8, 8a, 17, 23
Paris Cons.—Désormière　　**‡ D.LXT 2610**
(*Ippolitov-Ivanov: Caucasian Sketches*)　(‡ Lon.LL 440)

Intro, & Nos. 1, 3, 6, 8, 9, 12e, 12b, 15a, 17, 21, 22, 23, 24, 25,
27, 28, 29b
☆ Sym.—Stokowski　　　　**‡ G.ALP 1002**
(‡ FALP 133)

Intro. & Nos. 3a, 3b, 4, 21, 22, 25, 27, 29a
☆ L.P.O.—Kurtz　　　　♮ G.JOX 7012/4

Unspec. Excerpts ☆ Bolshoi Theatre—Fayer
(in ‡ Csm.CRLP 108/9)

Unspec. Excerpts with Narration
Anon. artists (4ss)　　　(♮ & ♭) *CRG.set 202*

No. 2, Scene—Entrance of fairies　Act I
☆ Bolshoi Theatre—Fayer (*U.C 24296*)

No. 6, Waltz
Philharmonia—Weldon　　**C.DX 1807**
(*Cavalleria Rusticana—Intermezzo*)　(DWX 5073)
Victor Sym.—Reiner　　in ‡ *Vic.LM 103*
(♭ set WDM 1539)
Paris Opéra—Cloëz　　　**Od. 123928**
(*Nutcracker Waltz*)
☆ Danish Radio—Malko　　**‡ BB.LBC 1007**
(*Tchaikovsky: Romeo & Juliet Overture*) (♭ set WBC 1007)
A. Kostelanetz Orch.　　in ‡ AmC.ML 4546
Vienna Radio—Nilius (Vien.L 6051: in ‡ *1009*)
Hall Concert Orch. (in ‡ *Var. 6923*)
D'Artega Orch. (in ♭ *Roy.set 14511*)
☆ Chicago Phil.—H. Weber (in ♭ *Clc. 6041*)
Robin Hood Dell—Kostelanetz (in ♭ AmC.set A 601)
Los Angeles Phil.—Wallenstein (in AmD.set A 912:
♭ set 9-300; ‡ D.AXT 233057)
Str. Ens.—Selinsky (in ‡ *AmC.CL 6038*)
Salon Orch. (in ‡ *AmC.GL 511*), etc.

Marche　(unspec.)
Leningrad Phil.—Mravinsky　　**U.H 23947**
(*Prokofiev: Vln. Concerto No. 1, s. 1*)

(The) SWAN LAKE, Op. 20　Ballet
COMPLETE RECORDINGS
L.S.O.—Fistoulari [1]　　　**‡ D.LXT 2681/2**
(4ss)　　　　　　　　　　　　(‡ Lon.LL 565/6)
Prague Nat. Theatre—Škvor　　**U.H 23765/78**
(28ss)　　　　　　　　　　　　(‡ CdM.LD 8024/6)
Prague Nat. Theatre—Krombholc　**‡ Ura.set 404**
(4ss)　(*Waltzes on ♭ UREP 8; Excpts. Act II, on ♭ UREP 24*)

---

[1] Omits Nos. 3, 8, 23, 27, 29, 30; abridges other items; and includes orch. arrs. of pf. pieces Op. 72 Nos. 11 & 15.

SWAN LAKE, Op. 20 (*continued*)
Suite
  (Nos. 4, 9, 12, 13, 14, 16, 19, 20, 22, 24, 25, 31, 33)
  French Sym.—Désormière **‡ DCap.CTL 7015**
  (2ss)   (‡ T.LCSK 8142)
  (‡ Cap.P 8142; 6ss, in ♭ *set KCM 8143*)
  (Nos. 4, 9, 14, 16, 24, 33 with *Nutcracker* on ‡ Cap.P 8140)

Suite
  (Nos. 5, 7, 9, 11-14, 16, 19-22, 24, 25, 33)
  ☆ A. Kostelanetz Orch.   **‡ C.FCX 110**
                            (QCX 110)

Suite
  (Intro. & Nos. 2, 4, 6, 13, 14, 16, 17, 20, 22, 24, 25, 31, 33)
  ☆ St. Louis Sym.—Golschmann
  (10ss)   **♮ G.DB 9365/9**

Suite
  (Intro. & Nos. 2, 13, 14, 16, 17, 20, 22, 25, 31, 33)
  ☆ L.P.O.—Dorati   **‡ AmC.RL 3014**

Suite (Nos. 4, 9, 13, 14, 24)
  ☆ Hallé—Barbirolli   **‡ G.BLP 1004**
  (*Bizet: L'Arlésienne Suite*)

Suite (Nos. 1, 3, 5, 6, 7, 19, 20)
  ☆ Covent Garden Op.—Rignold (‡ BB.LBC 1016:
                   in ♭ *set WBC 1016*)

Unspec. Excerpts
  Covent Garden—Braithwaite in ‡ **MGM.E 3006**
  Berlin Sym.—Ludwig   in ‡ **Roy. 1216**
                    (& in ‡ *Roy. 6028*)
    Varsity Sym. Orch. (in ‡ *Var. 2030*)
    Berlin Sym.—List (‡ Roy. 1319, 2ss)
  ☆ Bolshoi Theatre—Fayer (‡ Csm.CRLP 108/9)

No. 4, Valse, only [1]
  Victor Sym.—Reiner   in ‡ *Vic.LM 103*
                  (♭ *set WDM 1539*)

No. 12, Waltz in A [1]
  ☆ Los Angeles Phil.—Wallenstein (in AmD.set A 912:
           ♭ *set 9-300*; ‡ D.AXT 233057)

No. 13, Scene (Queen of the Swans)
  ☆ Sym.—Stokowski (♭ *Vic. 49-3368*)

Capriccio italien, Op. 45
  Amsterdam—van Kempen **‡ Phi.A 00603R**
  (*1812 Overture*)
  ☆ Danish Radio—Malko **‡ G.FBLP 1004**
  (*Glazounov*)
  (*1812* on ‡ BB.LBC 1014: ♭ *set WBC 1014*)
  ☆ Columbia Sym.—Beecham ♮ **C.LX 8924/5**
  ☆ Munich Phil.—Lehmann **‡ Pol. 18014**
                      (FPV. 5024)
  (*Liszt: Les Préludes* on ‡ *AmD.DL 7530*)
  "Nat. Op. Orch." etc. (‡ *Var. 6925*; *Roy. 6065*, etc.)
  ☆ Philharmonia—Kletzki (C.GQX 11459/60: M 15161/2)
  Czech Phil.—Šejna (‡ *Sup.LPM 9*)

CONCERTOS, pf. & orch.
No. 1, B minor, Op. 23
  E. Gilels & Stockholm Radio—Ehrling
  (8ss)   ♮ **Mtr.CL 3004/7**
                    (‡ Rgt. 5055)
  N. Mewton-Wood & Sym. Orch.—Goehr
                    ‡ MMS. 12
  S. Cherkassky & Berlin Phil.—Ludwig
  (5ss)   ♮ **PV. 72129/31S**
                    (‡ Pol. 18013)
  M. de la Bruchollerie & Vienna State Phil.—
  Moralt   **‡ E. & AmVox.PL 7720**

A. Ciccolini & Paris Cons.—Cluytens
                  ‡ G.FALP 102
  (‡ BB.LBC 1020/ ♭ *WBC 1020*)[2]   (‡ QALP 102)
A. Uninsky & Residentie—v. Otterloo
                  ‡ Phi.A 00135L
H. Schwertmann & Austrian Sym.—Paulmüller
                  ‡ Rem. 199-76
M. Huttner & Berlin Sym.—Balzer ‡ **Roy. 1261**
☆ C. Solomon & Philharmonia—Dobrowen
                  ‡ G.CLP 1001
  (G.S 10578/81; ‡ Vic.LHMV 1028: ♭ *set WHMV 1028*)
☆ V. Horowitz & N.B.C.—Toscanini
                  ♮ **G.DB 8922/5**
☆ E. Gilels & USSR State Sym.—Samosud
                (♮ U.H 24088/91)
  E. Petri & L.P.O.—Goehr (‡ AmC.RL 3018)
  C. Hansen & Berlin Phil.—Mengelberg (FT.SK 76/9)
… **1st movt., Opening theme**
  A. Semprini & Melachrino Orch. (*G.B 10295*)

No. 2, G major, Op. 44
  N. Mewton-Wood & Winterthur Sym.—
  W. Goehr   **‡ Nix.CLP 1125**
                  (‡ CHS.CHS 1125)

No. 3, E flat major, Op. 75
  N. Mewton-Wood & Winterthur Sym.—
  W. Goehr   **‡ Nix.CLP 1126**
  (*below*)   (‡ CHS.CHS 1126)

Concert Fantasia, G major, Op. 56
  T. Nikolayeva & State Sym.—Kondrashin
  (8ss)   **USSR. 018768/75**
  N. Mewton-Wood & Winterthur Sym.—
  W. Goehr   **‡ Nix.CLP 1126**
  (*Concerto No. 3*)   (‡ CHS.CHS 1126)

Concerto, vln. & orch. D major, Op. 35
  F. Malachowsky & Berlin Sym.—Balzer
                  ‡ Roy. 1265
  (2ss)   (Excerpts on ‡ Roy. 1314)
  ☆ J. Heifetz & Philharmonia—Süsskind
              (‡ *G.FBLP/QBLP 1008*)
  D. Oistrakh & Moscow Phil.—Gauk (♮ U.H 24077/81)
… **1st & 3rd movts. only**
  Anon. Soloist & Nat. Op. Orch. (in ‡ *Roy. 6954*)

Elegy Str. orch. 1884
  Netherlands Phil.—Goehr   **‡ CHS.G 7**
  (*Fatum & Voyevoda*)

Fatum, Op. 77 Sym. poem 1868
  Netherlands Phil.—Goehr   **‡ CHS.G 7**
  (*Elegy & Voyevoda*)

Francesca da Rimini, Op. 32
  Leningrad Phil.—Mravinsky ♮ **U.H 23899/901**
  (6ss)
  ☆ N.Y.P.S.O.—Stokowski **‡ C.CX 1030**
  (*Romeo & Juliet*)
  ☆ Danish Radio—Dobrowen **‡ BB.LBC 1010**
  (*Brahms: Haydn Variations*) (♭ *set WBC 1010*)

Hamlet, Overture-Fantasia, Op. 67
  L.P.O.—Boult   **‡ D.LXT 2676**
  (*Ouverture solennelle, 1812*) (‡ Lon.LL 582)
  Philharmonia—Fistoulari **‡ MGM.E 3002**
  (*Romeo & Juliet*)
  Stockholm Radio—Rachmilovich
                  ‡ Mer.MG 10112
  (*below*)   (‡ Mtr.CLP 509; ‡ Clc. 6077)

Manfred, Op. 58 "Symphony"
  USSR Radio Sym.—Gauk **USSR. 019125/40**
  (16ss)
  ☆ N.B.C.—Toscanini (‡ G.FALP/QALP 150)

---

[1] The identification of these two items is conjectural.
[2] Originally announced as LBC/WBC 1000.

Marche slave, Op. 31
  Boston Prom.—Fiedler   ♭ *G.7BF 1042*
  (n.v., 2ss)   (& ♭ *Vic. WEPR 2*)
  (*Mendelssohn, Rimsky-Korsakov* in ♯ *Vic.LM 164:*
       ♭ *set WDM 1647*)
  Philharmonia—Schuechter   ♯ *MGM.E 138*
  (*Rimsky-Korsakov: Capriccio espagnole*)
  Amsterdam—van Kempen   **Phi.A 11156G**
        (*PhM. 09704S*)
  N.Y. Stadium—Smallens   ♯ *AmD.DL 4031*
  (*Overture, 1812*)
  Aarhus Municipal—Jensen   **Tono.X 25177**
        (in ♯ *Mer.MG 15045*)
  ☆ Chicago Phil.—H. Weber (in ♯ Clc. 6041)
    Moscow Radio—Golovanov (in ♯ Csm.CRLP 107)

  — ARR. 2 PFS. M. Rawicz & W. Landauer (C.DX 1791)

Marche solennelle, D major   1885
  Sym. Orch.—Tergowski   ♯ *MMS. 5*
  (*Valse, & 1812*)

Ouverture solennelle, 1812, Op. 49
  L.P.O.—Boult   ♯ *D.LXT 2696*
  (*Hamlet*)   (♯ *Lon.LL 582*)
  Amsterdam—van Kempen   ♯ *Phi.A 00603R*
  (*Capriccio Italien*) (also, 4ss, Phi.A 11195/6G)
  Berlin Sym.—Ludwig   in ♯ **Roy. 1216**
  Rome Sym.—Questa   in ♯ *Roy. 6065*
  Sym. Orch.—Tergowski   ♯ *MMS. 5*
  (*Marche & Valse*)
  ☆ Amsterdam—Mengelberg   ♯ *T.LB 6009*
  (*Berlioz*)   (also ▽ ♭ *Cap.set KBM 8022*)
  ☆ Austrian Sym.—Wöss   ♯ *Rem. 199-87*
  (*Nutcracker Suite*)   (♯ *Mrt. 200-22*)
  ☆ Philharmonia—Malko   ♯ **BB.LBC 1014**
  (*Capriccio Italien*)   (♭ *set WBC 1014*)
  "Nat. Op. Orch." (in ♯ *Var. 6925*; ♯ Var. 2021, etc.)

Pezzo capriccioso, Op. 62 vlc. & orch.   1887
  M. Rostropovich & Moscow Youth Sym.—
    Kondrashin (2ss)   **USSR. 018611/2**

Romeo and Juliet, Fantasy Overture
  Philharmonia—Cantelli   **G.DB 21373/5S**
  (*5ss—last blank*)   (♯ *Vic.LM 1719:* ♭ *set WDM 1719*)
  Amsterdam—v. Kempen   ♯ *Phi.A 00128R*
  Paris Cons.—Münch   **D.K 23214/7**
  (8ss)
  Philharmonia—Fistoulari   ♯ **MGM.E 3002**
  Bamberg Sym.—Lehmann   ♮ **PV. 72235/6**
  (*3ss—Ruslan & Ludmilla Overture*)
  (*Bruch: Vln. Concerto* on ♯ Pol. 18086)
  Rhineland Sym.—Federer   ♯ *Rgt. 5037*
  A. Kostelanetz Orch.   ♯ **AmC.ML 4546**
  (*Waltzes*)
  ☆ N.Y. Phil. Sym.—Stokowski   ♯ **C.CX 1030**
  (*Francesca da Rimini*)
  ☆ N.B.C.—Toscanini (*Berlioz*)   ♯ **G.FALP 155**
  ☆ Sym. Orch.—Lambert   ♯ **BB.LBC 1007**
  (*Sleeping Beauty Suite*)   (♭ *set WBC 1007*)
  Berlin Sym.—Ludwig   in ♯ **Roy. 1216**
        (in ♯ *Roy. 6028*)
  Varsity Sym. Orch. (in ♯ Var. 2030)
  ☆ Austrian Sym.—Wöss (♯ Mrt. 1-3 & ♯ Rem. 199-88, d.c.)

Serenade, C major, Op. 48   str. orch.
  Sydney Civic Sym.—Beck   ♯ **Dia.DPM 2**
  (*above*)
  Bamberg Sym.—Ludwig   ♯ *Mer.MG 15035*
  ☆ N.W.D.R. Sym.—Schmidt-Issersedt (P.RR 8191/4)

… **2nd movt. Waltz, only**
  M.G.M. Orch.—Marrow   in ♯ *MGM.E 510*
  A. Kostelanetz Orch.   in ♯ **AmC.ML 4546**

  ▽ Salzburg Festival—Weidlich   ♯ *Rem. 149–36*
  (*above, & Mozart: Serenade*)   (& ♯ *Mrt. 1-17, d. c.*)
  ☆ Vienna Phil.—Furtwängler (♭ *G.7R 134: 7RF 148*)
  Boston Sym.—Koussevitzky (♭ *Vic. WEPR 7*)
  Col. Sym.—Rodzinski (in ♭ *AmC.set A 1002*)
  Danish State Radio—Malko
      (in ♯ BB.LBC 1026: ♭ *set WBC 1026*)
  Los Angeles Phil.—Wallenstein (in AmD.set A 912:
       ♭ *set 9-300*; ♯ D.AXT 233057)
  N.W.D.R.—Schmidt-Issersedt (*PV. 46003;* ▽ Pol.
                                 68014)
  Vienna State Op.—Baltzer (*Vien. 5003*)

… **3rd movt., Elegy, only**
  Madrid Cha.—Argenta   **SpC.RG 16175**

… **4th movt., Finale, only**
  Vienna Phil.—Furtwängler   **G.DB 21172**
  (2ss)   (♭ *G.7R 140: 7RF 146*)
  ☆ Boston Sym.—Koussevitzky (♭ *Vic. WEPR 7*)

Sérénade mélancolique, B flat minor, Op. 26
  vln. & orch.
  ☆ D. Oistrakh & orch. (in ♯ Csm.CRLP 110)

SUITES
No. 1, D major, Op. 43
  Winterthur Sym.—Goehr   ♯ **CHS.CHS 1121**
        (♯ Nix.CLP 1121)

No. 2, C major, Op. 53
  Winterthur Sym.—Goehr   ♯ **CHS.CHS 1122**
        (♯ Nix.CLP 1122)

No. 3, G major, Op. 55
  Winterthur Sym.—Goehr   ♯ **CHS.CHS 1144**
        (♯ Nix.CLP 1144)
  Sym.—Samosud   *USSR. 9210/3,*
  (16ss)   *14188/90, 19044/52*
  (4th movt. in ♯ Csm.CRLP 107)

… **2nd movt., Valse mélancolique**
  A. Kostelanetz Orch.   in ♯ **AmC.ML 4546**
  Sym.—Tergowski   ♯ *MMS. 5*
  (*Marche; & Overture, 1812*)

… **4th movt., Theme & Variations**
  ☆ Philharmonia—Malko   ♯ **BB.LBC 1024**
  (*Borodin: Symphony No. 2*)   (♭ *set WBC 1024*)

No. 4, G major, Op. 61—Mozartiana
  Slovak Phil.—Talich   ♮ **U.H 23973/6**
  (*7ss—Mozart: Fugue, K.426*)

… **1st & 4th movts. only**
  USSR Radio Sym.—Gauk   *USSR. 18944/9*
  (6ss)

SYMPHONIES
No. 1, G minor, Op. 13   (*"Winter rêveries"*)
  Vienna Philharmonia—Haefner   ♯ **SPA. 11**

No. 3, D major, Op. 29
  Vienna State Op.—Swoboda   ♯ **CHS.CHS 1139**
        (♯ Nix.CLP 1139)
  Homburg Sym.—P. Schubert   ♯ *Rgt. 5012*
  ☆ USSR State Sym.—Ivanov (♮ U.H 24082/7)

No. 4, F minor, Op. 36
  Vienna Phil.—Furtwängler   **G.DB 21376/81S**
  (*9ss, last blank*)
  (2ss, ♯ G.ALP 1025; ♯ Vic.LHMV 1005:♭ *set WHMV1005*)
  Brussels Radio—André   ♯ **DT.LGX 66002**
        (♯ T.LSK 7009)
  R.I.A.S. Sym.—Fricsay   ♯ **Pol. 18039**
  Vienna State Op.—Scherchen   ♯ **West.WL 5096**
  Chicago Sym.—Kubelik   ♯ **Mer.MG 50003**
  Residentie—v. Otterloo   ♯ **Phi.A 00110L**
  Czech Phil.—Nyazi   ♮ **U.H 23825/9**
  (10ss)   (♯ *Sup.LPM 8/9, 3ss*)

♯ = Long-playing, 33⅓ r.p.m.   ♭ = 45 r.p.m.   ♮ = Auto. couplings, 78 r.p.m.

No. 4, F minor, Op. 36 (*continued*)
Austrian Sym.—H. A. Brown   ♯ **Rem. 199-64**
        (♯ Mrt. 200-1; Ply. 12-1)
Berlin Sym.—Balzer   ♯ **Roy. 1335**
☆ Boston Sym.—Koussevitzky (♯ G.FALP 138)
  Minneapolis Sym.—Mitropoulos (♯ AmC.RL 3007)

No. 5, E minor, Op. 64
Minneapolis—Dorati   ♯ **Mer.MG 50008**
Philadelphia—Ormandy   ♯ **AmC.ML 4400**
        (♭ *set A 1007*)
Amsterdam—v. Kempen   ♯ **Phi.A 00141L**
Leningrad Phil.—Mravinsky   ♮ **U.H 23865/70**
(12ss)
Rome Sym.—Questa   ♯ **Roy. 1224**
☆ La Scala—Cantelli   ♯ **G.ALP 1001**
        (♯ Vic.LHMV 1003: ♭ *set WHMV 1003*)
☆ Boston Sym.—Koussevitzky   ♮ **G.DB 9493/8**
        (♯ FALP 134)
☆ Viennese Sym.—Wöss (♯ Mrt. 200-2; Ply. 12-2)
  Berlin Phil.—Fricsay (IPV.RR 8187/90; ♯ Pol. 18012)
  L.P.O.—Lambert (♮ G.TH 7008/12)

... 2nd movt. only
Berlin Sym.—Guenther (in ♯ Roy. 1247)

... 3rd movt. Waltz, only
Victor Sym.—Reiner   in ♯ **Vic.LM 103**
        (♭ *set WDM 1539*)
☆ Los Angeles Phil.—Wallenstein (in ♯ AmD.set A 912:
        ♭ *set 9-300;* ♯ D.AXT 233057)

No. 6, B minor, Op. 74
Philadelphia—Ormandy   ♯ **AmC.ML 4544**
Amsterdam—v. Kempen   ♯ **Phi.A 00120L**
Chicago Sym.—Kubelik   ♯ **Mer.MG 50006**
Sonor Sym.—Ledermann   ♯ **Pde. 2006**
Rome Sym.—Questa   ♯ **Roy. 1226**
☆ Vienna Phil.—Karajan   ♯ **C.CX 1026**
(C.M 15147/52: LVX 87/92)   (♯ FCX 105)
☆ Philharmonia—Malko (♯ BB.LBC 1002: ♭ *set WBC 1002;*
        ♮ G.TH 7013/7)
  Viennese Sym.—Brown (♯ Mrt. 200-3; Ply. 12-3)

(The) Tempest, Op. 18
Stockholm Radio—Rachmilovich
        ♯ **Mer.MG 10112**
(*Hamlet*)   (♯ Mtr. CLP 509; ♯ Clc. 6077)
Vienna Sym.—Fekete   ♯ **Rem. 199-55**
(*Rimsky-K: Golden Cockerel Suite*)
(*Fekete: Caucasus Suite*, on ♯ Eur.LPG 606)
Vienna Artists' Sym.—Fekete [1]   ♯ **Etu. 706**
(*Rimsky-K: Golden Cockerel Suite*)
☆ Bolshoi Theatre—Melik-Pashayev
        (in ♯ Csm.CLPS 112/3)

(The) Voyevoda, Op. 78   Sym. ballad
Netherlands Phil.—Goehr   ♯ **CHS.G 7**
(*Fatum & Elegy*)
USSR State Sym.—Ivanov   **USSR. 20160/3**
(4ss)

II. VOCAL

A. OPERA & INCIDENTAL MUSIC

(The) ENCHANTRESS   4 acts   1887
My fate is strange (Love Duet, Act III)   S & T
  N. Shpiller (& unspec. T.?)   **USSR. 015506**
(*Gossip's aria*)

Where are you   S   (Act IV)
  E. Smolenskaya   **USSR. 17113**
(*Dargomijsky: Roussalka, Natasha's song*)

Gossip's aria   (unspec.) [2]
  N. Shpiller   **USSR. 015504**
(*Duet, Act III*)

EUGENE ONIEGIN, Op. 24   3 acts   1879
COMPLETE RECORDING
  ☆ Bolshoi Theatre Soloists, etc. (♯ Csm.CRLP 127/9)

ACT I

No. 3, Not mine to live in despair   M-S
  L. I. Andeyeva   *U.C 23863*
(*Pique Dame, Aria*)

No. 9, Tatiana's Letter Scene   S
  J. Vymazalova   **U.H 23805S/6**
(3ss)
  L. Albanese   *♯ G.FBLP 1025*
(*Villa-Lobos: Bachianas No. 8*) (♯ Vic.LM 142:
        ♭ *set WDM 1610*)
  E. Trötschel (*Ger*)   **PV. 72088**
(2ss)   (in ♯ Pol. 18057)

... Excerpt
  ℟ C. Muzio (*Ital*) (in ♯ Eso.ES 500*; ♯ Cpt.MC 20008*) [3]

No. 12, Written words   (Oniegin's aria)   B
  A. Hiolski   *Muza. 1721*
(*Rigoletto—Pari siamo*)

ACT II

No. 13, Waltz
  Philharmonia—Dobrowen   **G.C 4190**
(*No. 19*)
  Victor Sym.—Reiner   in ♯ *Vic.LM 103*
        (♭ *set WDM 1539*)
  Stadium Concerts—Smallens   ♯ *AmD.DL 4033*
(*No. 19; & Andante cantabile*)
  ☆ N.Y. Phil. Sym.—Kurtz (♭ AmC.A 1508)
  Berlin State—Ludwig (in ♯ BB.LBC 1026:
        ♭ *set WBC 1026*)
  Los Angeles Phil.—Wallenstein (in AmD.set A 912:
        ♭ *set 9-300;* ♯ D.AXT 233057)

— ARR. 2 PFS. M. Rawicz & W. Landauer (C.DB 2899)

No. 17, Faint echo of my youth   T
  B. Blachut   (2ss)   **U.H 24218**
  ☆ W. Ludwig (*Ger*)   *PV. 36001*
(*Contes d'Hoffmann—Légende de Kleinsack*)
  ☆ I. Kozlovsky (U.H 24282)
  ℟ D. Smirnoff (G.VB 39*; o.n. DB 581*;
        also JpC.SW 244*)

ACT III

No. 19, Polonaise
  Philharmonia—Dobrowen   **G.C 4190**
(*No. 13*)
  Stadium Concerts—Smallens   ♯ *AmD.DL 4033*
(*No. 13; & Andante cantabile*)
  ☆ Berlin State—Ludwig (in ♯ BB.LBC 1026:
        ♭ *set WBC 1026*)

No. 20a or 21—Oniegin's aria   (unspec.)
  J. S. Adamczewski (*Pol*)   *Muza. 1559*
(2ss)

No. 21, Alas, there is no doubt   B, M-S, Bs
  A. Ivanov, E. Kruglikova, M. Reizen
        USSR. 21205
(*Rubinstein: Nero—Epithalamium*)

... Bar. part only
  ℟ G. Baklanoff (G.VA 51*: o.n. DA 464*)

(The) GUARDSMAN   (Oprichnik)   4 acts   1874
Natasha's aria, Act I
  A. Ivanova   **USSR. 16466**
(*Mazeppa—Maria's lullaby*)

---

[1] In a letter to *Saturday Review*, M. Fekete stated he had never conducted for this Company.
[2] Presumably different from *USSR. 15505*—see WERM.
[3] Recorded from Edison cylinder.

IOLANTHE, Op. 69   1 act   1891
Duke Robert's aria   B
Al. Ivanov   *USSR. 17108*
(*Pique Dame—Tomsky's aria, Act III*)

Duet: Iolanthe and Vodemon   S & T
E. Shumskaya & V. Kilchevsky
(4ss)   **USSR. 018506/9**

Who can compare?   (King René, Sc. 4)   Bs
B. Gmyria   **USSR. 019977**
(*Ruslan & Ludmilla—Farlaf's Rondo*)

JOAN OF ARC   4 acts   1879
Farewell, forests   S or M-S   (Act I)
V. Borisenko   (2ss)   **USSR. 018681/2**
J. Tourel (*Fr*)   (2ss)   **C.LX 1547**
☆ M. Anderson (*Fr*) (in ♯ Roy. 1278: *6001*: etc.)

MAZEPPA   3 acts   1883
Cossack Dance   (Gopak)
State Sym.—Samosud   **U.H 23902**
(*Rimsky-K: Snow Maiden, Suite, s. 1*)
Czech Phil.—Nyazi (announced in ♯ *Sup.LPM 5/6*,
but perhaps not issued)

Maria's Lullaby   S
A. Ivanova   *USSR. 16465*
(*Guardsman—Natasha's aria, Act I*)

(The) Three Treasures   (Kochubey's aria)
B. Gmyria (Bs)   *USSR. 19035*
(*Moussorgsky: Boris Godounov—Coronation scene*)

PIQUE DAME, Op. 68   3 acts   1890
COMPLETE RECORDING
☆ Bolshoi Theatre Soloists, etc.
♯ Csm.CRLP 130/3

ABRIDGED RECORDING in *German*
Lisa ...   . E. Grümmer (S)
Pauline   ...   . M. Klose (A)
Hermann   ...   . R. Schock (T)
Yeletzky   ...   .H. H. Nissen (Bs)
etc., Berlin Municipal Op. Cho. & Berlin Radio
Sym.—Rother   (4ss)   ♯ Ura.set 207

ACT I

No. 7, Already shades of night   2S
K. Derzhinskaya, M. Maksakova
(*No. 8*)   *USSR. 16742*

No. 8, Dear friends, for whom I sing S (Pauline)
M. Maksakova   *USSR. 16743*
(*No. 7*)
L. Andeyeva   *U.C 23863*
(*Eugene Oniegin, No. 3*)

No. 10a, O burning tears   S   (Lisa)
E. Smolenskaya   **USSR. 017641**
(*Dargomijsky: Roussalka, Miller's aria*)

No. 10b, Forgive me, bright celestial visions   T
A. Frinberg (*Latv*)   *USSR. 19958*
(*Puccini: Tosca, aria*)

ACT II

No. 12, I love you, dear   Bs   (Yeletsky)
I. P. Alexeyev   *U.C 23859*
(*Faust—Avant de quitter...*)

ACT III

No. 20, 'Twill soon be midnight S (Lisa)
J. Hammond (*Eng*)   **G.DB 21451**
(*Dvořák: Rusalka—O Moon in the deep sky*)
L. Lobanova-Rogacheva   (2ss) *USSR. 19855/6*

E. Smolenskaya   (2ss)   *USSR. 16802/3*
☆ L. Welitsch (*Ger*)   **D.K 23235**
(*Ballo in Maschera—Ma dall' arido*)

No. 23, Darling maidens   B   (Tomsky)
Al. Ivanov   *USSR. 17107*
(*Iolanthe—Duke Robert's aria*)

SNOW-MAIDEN, Op. 12
Inc. music to Ostrovsky's play
Entr'actes, Acts II & IV   1873
USSR Radio Sym.—Gauk   *USSR. 21016/7*
(1 side each)

Shepherd Lehl's Songs (3)
Z. Dolukhanova (A)   (4ss)   *USSR. 19108/11*

VAKULA THE SMITH   4 acts   1876
(revised as: *The Little Slippers*, 3 acts   1887)

Overture
Bolshoi Theatre—Melik-Pashayev
(4ss)   *USSR. 18037/40*

Duet: Solokha & fiend, Act I   S & B
V. Davidova, Al. Ivanov (2ss) USSR. 016244/5

Vakula's aria, Act I   T
S. Lemeshev   *USSR. 8469*
(*Vakula's song, unspec.*)

Vakula's Song   (unspec.)   T
S. Lemeshev   *USSR. 8470*
(*Vakula's aria, Act I*)

Russian Dance
Ukrainian Dance
Bolshoi Theatre—Melik-Pashayev
(1 side each)   *USSR. 10515/6*

II. *B. SONGS*
(In the absence of copies of the records, the contents of
certain of the USSR and Muza discs are conjectural.)

Accept but once, Op. 16, No. 3   (Maikov)
A. Pirogov (B)   *USSR. 15233*
(*Dusk fell on the earth*)

Again, as before, alone, Op. 73, No. 6   (Rathaus)
I. Kozlovsky (T)   *USSR. 20164*
(*Arensky: Dozing*)

As o'er the burning ashes, Op. 25, No. 2 (Tyutchev)
G. Nelepp (T)   *USSR. 18580*
(*Balakirev: Song*)

(A) Ballroom meeting, Op. 38, No. 3 (A. K. Tolstoy)
(*At the ball: or, The tapers were flashing*)
B. Gmyria (Bs)   *USSR. 18405*
(*If I could express in one word*)
S. Migai (?)   *USSR. 9888*
(*No response or word of greeting*)
M. Mey-Figner (S) (*USSR. 18247*)

Behind the window in the shadow, Op. 60, No. 10
(Polonsky)
S. Shaposhnikov   *USSR. 18569*
(*My naughty girl*)
I. Kozlovsky (T)   *USSR. 20453*
(*Dargomijsky: Lonely and sad*)

Born to Sorrow, Op. 27, No. 5
(Mickiewicz, trs. Mey)
(Or: *Was it the mother who bore me ...*)
S. Preobrazhenskaya (M-S)   *USSR. 17168*
(*The fires in the rooms ...*)

♯ = Long-playing, 33⅓ r.p.m.   ♭ = 45 r.p.m.   ♮ = Auto. couplings, 78 r.p.m.

Courage, Op. 60, No. 11　(Khomyakov)
(or: *Exploit*)
M. Romensky　　　　　　　*USSR. 13894*
(*Rubinstein: Longing*)

Disappointment, Op. 65, No. 2　(Collin)
I. Kozlovsky (T)　　　　　　*USSR. 19452*
(*Rachmaninoff: Before my window*)

Does the day reign?　Op. 47, No. 6　(Apukhtin)
Z. Gaidai　　　　　　　　*USSR. 12410*
(*It was in early Spring*)

Don Juan's Serenade, Op. 38, No. 1 (A. K. Tolstoy)
Ⓗ E. Caruso (*G.VA 42*: o.n. DA 114**)

Dusk fell on the earth, Op. 47, No. 3
(Mickiewicz, trs. Berg)
A. Pirogov (B)　　　　　　*USSR. 15232*
(*Accept but once*)

Evening, Op. 27, No. 4　(Shevchenko, trs. Mey)
S. Lemeshev (T)　　　　　　*USSR. 19034*
(*None but the weary heart*)

Farewell, Op. 60, No. 8　(Nekrasov) (Or: *Forgive*)
S. Lemeshev (T)　　　　　　*USSR. 15083*
(*As o'er the burning ashes*)

(The) Fires in the rooms were already extinguished,
Op. 63, No. 5　(Gd. Duke Constantine)
N. Obukhova (M-S)　　　　　*USSR. 10979*
(*None but the weary heart*)

☆ S. Preobrazhenskaya (M-S)　*USSR. 17167*
(*Born to sorrow*)

Z. Dolukhanova (M-S)　　　　*USSR. 18849*
(*Dargomijsky: Evening Song*)

(The) First meeting, Op. 63, No. 4
(Gd. Duke Constantine)
V. Borisenko (M-S)　　　　　*USSR. 15854*
(*Rimsky-Korsakov: Echo*)

S. Lemeshev (T)　　　　　　*USSR. 17301*
(*Rachmaninoff: Lilacs*)

B. Gmyria (Bs)　　　　　　*USSR. 20380*
(*We sat together*)

Frenzied nights, Op. 60, No. 6　(Apukhtin)
I. Kozlovsky (T)　　　　　　*USSR. 18092*
(*Rimsky-Korsakov: On the hills of Georgia*)

M. Reizen (Bs)　　　　　　*USSR. 9601*
(*Nightingale*)

He loved me, Op. 28, No. 4　(Anon.)
T. Lavrova　　　　　　　　*USSR. 19588*
(*Rachmaninoff: Song*)

I do not please you, Op. 63, No. 3
(Gd. Duke Constantine)
☆ S. Preobrazhenskaya (M-S)　*USSR. 17165*
(*Only thou*)

I never spoke with her, Op. 25, No. 5　(Mey)
S. Migai　　　　　　　　*USSR. 10104*
(*No, I shall never name her*)

If I could express in one word　(Heine, trs. Mey)
B. Gmyria (B)　　　　　　*USSR. 18404*
(*Ballroom meeting*)

S. Lemeshev (T)　　　　　　*USSR. 15689*
(*Glinka: Song*)

In the garden, by the ford, Op. 46, No. 4
Duet (Surikov)
G. Sakharova (S), Z. Dolukhanova (A)
　　　　　　　　　　　USSR. 17783

(*Dargomijsky: Fair maidens*)

It was in early Spring, Op. 38, No. 2 (A. K. Tolstoy)
Z. Gaidai　　　　　　　　*USSR. 12539*
(*Does the day reign*)

Love's beginning, Op. 6, No. 3
(Gumbert, trs. Rostopchina)
(Or: *What torment*, or: *Painfully and sweetly*)
S. Lemeshev (T)　　　　　　*USSR. 7776*
(*Why?*)

Z. Dolukhanova (A), B. Kozel (pf.)
　　　　　　　　　　　USSR. 20403

(*Rachmaninoff: Water Lily*)

Lullaby in a storm, Op. 54, No. 10　(Plescheev)
A. Orfenov　　　　　　　*USSR. 14674*
(*Winter*)

Mid sombre days, Op. 73, No. 5　(Rathaus)
S. Lemeshev (T)　　　　　　*USSR. 20384*
(*So soon forgotten*)

(The) Mild stars shone for us, Op. 60, No. 12
(Polonsky)
V. Borisenko (M-S) & orch.　*Muza. 1556*
(*Glier: Oh, how great is my sorrow*)

My genius, my angel, my friend　(Fet)
M. Maksakova (S)　　　　　*USSR. 15806*
(*Dargomijsky: 2 songs*)

My naughty girl, Op. 27, No. 6
(Mickiewicz, trs. Mey) (Or: *My spoilt darling*)
S. Shaposhnikov　　　　　*USSR. 18570*
(*Behind the window ...*)

(The) Nightingale, Op. 60, No. 4　(Pushkin)
M. Reizen (Bs)　　　　　　*USSR. 9602*
(*Frenzied nights*)

No, I shall never name her, Op. 28, No. 1
(A. de Musset, trs. Grekov)
S. Migai　　　　　　　　*USSR. 10105*
(*I never spoke with her*)

No response or word of greeting, Op. 28, No. 5
(Or: *No word from you*; or: *No tidings*)　(Apukhtin)
S. Migai　　　　　　　　*USSR. 9887*
(*Ballroom meeting*)

S. Lemeshev (T)　　　　　　*USSR. 19453*
(*Rachmaninoff: Sorrow in spring*)

None but the weary heart, Op. 6, No. 6
(Goethe, trs. Mey)
S. Lemeshev (T)　　　　　　*USSR. 19101*
(*Evening*)

N. Obukhova (M-S)　　　　　*USSR. 10978*
(*Fires in the rooms ...*)

J. Vincent (S, *Ger*), F. de Nobel (pf.)
　　　　　　　in ‡ *Phi.A 00610R*
(*Grieg, Mendelssohn, etc.*)

E. Pinza (Bs, *Eng*), N. Milstein (vln.) & pf.
　　　　　　　in ‡ *Vic.LM 1703*
(*Offenbach, Massenet, etc.*)　(♭ set *WDM 1703*)

F. Ferrari (T, *Eng*)　　　　*P.R 3531*
(*Gounod: Ave Maria*)

☆ M. Lipton (A) & Col. Sym.—Rodzinski
　　　　　　　(in ♭ *AmC.set A 1002*)

— ARR. VLC. & PF.
☆ G. Piatigorsky & R. Berkowitz　in ‡ *AmC.RL 3015*
(*Cui, Rachmaninoff, Shostakovitch, etc.*)

— ARR. ORCH.
Orch.—Marrow (in ‡ *MGM.E 510*)
☆ Robin Hood Dell—Kostelanetz (in ♭ *AmC.set A 601*)

— ARR. ORGAN: V. Fox (in ‡ *AmC.AAL 18*), etc.

O bless you, forests, Op. 47, No. 5 (A. K. Tolstoy)
A. Ivanov (Bs)　(2ss)　　　*U.C 23857*

Oh if you knew, Op. 60, No. 3　(Pleshcheev)
I. Kozlovsky (T)　　　　　　*USSR. 18632*
(*Moussorgsky: Tell me why*)

M. Chubenko　　　　　　*USSR. 13187*
(*What then?*)

☆ = Re-issue of a recording to be found in WERM or Supplement I.

O thou moonlit night, Op. 73, No. 3   (Rathaus)
(Or: *In this summer night*)
A. Pirogov (B)   *USSR. 15235*
(*Rimsky-Korsakov: Fir and Palm*)

Only thou, Op. 57, No. 6   (Pleshcheev)
(Or: *All for you*; or: *'Twas you alone*)
S. Preobrazhenskaya (M-S)   *USSR. 17166*
(*I do not please you*)

Serenade, Op. 63, No. 6   (Gd. Duke Constantine)
(*O child, beneath thy window*)
Z. Dolukhanova (A)   *USSR. 18338*
(*Rachmaninoff: Lilacs*)
S. Lemeshev (T)   *USSR. 019987*
(*Wait*)

So soon forgotten   (Apukhtin)
S. Lemeshev (T)   *USSR. 20385*
(*Mid sombre days*)

Tears, Op. 65, No. 5   (Blanchecotte) (*Les Larmes*)
S. Shaposhnikov   *USSR. 20064*
(*Rachmaninoff: Song*)

Wait, Op. 16, No. 2   (Grekov)
S. Lemeshev (T)   *USSR. 019988*
(*Serenade*)

We sat together, Op. 73, No. 1   (Rathaus)
(Or: *Side by side*)
N. Obukhova (M-S)   *USSR. 17152*
(*Why?*)
B. Gmyria (Bs)   *USSR. 20381*
(*First meeting*)

What then? Op. 16, No. 5   (Tchaikovsky)
(Or: *Thy radiant image*)
N. Chubenko   *USSR. 13186*
(*O if you knew*)

Why? Op. 6, No. 5   (Heine, trs. Mey)
S. Lemeshev (T)   *USSR. 7775*
(*Love's beginning*)

Winter, Op. 54, No. 12   (Pleshcheev)
A. Orfenov   *USSR. 14673*
(*Lullaby in a storm*)

Zemfira's song   (Pushkin)
E. Kruglikova (S)   *USSR. 16566*
(*Bakhmetov: The Ring*)

II. C. CHORAL

MOSCOW Cantata 1883
... **Soldier's arioso**   (unspec.)
S. Preobrazhenskaya & Radio Sym.—Kovalev
(2ss)   *USSR. 17153/4*

MISCELLANEOUS

Tchaikovsky Fantasy
Melachrino Orch. (G.C 4174: S 10601)

Tchaikovsky & his music
☆ F. Mack (Narrator) & Vox Sym.—Gobermann
(♯ *AmVox.VL 2570*)

TCHEMBERDZHIE, Nicholas (b. 1903)

ARMENIAN SONGS
On the banks of Araz
Spring song
N. Shpiller (S)   *USSR. 15252/3*
(1 side each)

TCHEREPNIN, Nikolai Nikolaievitch
(1873-1945)

Tati-tati Symphonic variations on *Chopsticks*, 1937
—ORCH. ARR. of pieces by Borodin, Cui, Liadov,
Liszt, Rimsky-Korsakov, q.v.

TEJERA ABANADES
SEE: † TAÑIDOS

TEJERA FRANCO
SEE: † TAÑIDOS

TELEMANN, Georg Philipp (1681-1767)

CANTATA: Ihr Völker, hört   A, recorder, cont.
H. Hennecke, G. Scheck, F. Neumeyer (org.)
A. Wenzinger (gamba)   **PV. 5404**
(o.n. 4409)

CONCERTOS
E major, fl., oboe d'amore, viola d'amore & strings
H. P. Schmitz, H. Töttcher, E. Seiler, Cha. Ens.
& hpsi.   **PV. 4411/2S**

F major, vln. & orch.
L. Kaufman & Cha. Orch.—D. Stevens
(*below*)   ♯ **CHS.G 17**

G major, vla. & orch.
H. Wigand & Stuttgart Pro Musica Orch.—
Reinhardt   ♯ **AmVox.PL 7540**
(*Stamitz*)

FANTASIAS   hpsi.
No. 2, D minor; No. 8, G minor   (Bk. I)
I. Lechner   **G.C 4167**

Quartet, D minor   (Tafelmusik II-2) 3 fls. & cont.
M. Wittgenstein, T. Witt, S. Baron,
S. Marlowe (hpsi.), M. Hubert (vlc.)
♯ **West.WL 5076**
(*below & Loeillet*)

SONATAS
GAMBA & CONT.
G major
J. Koch & W. Gerwig (lute)   **PV. 4407**
(2ss)

OBOE & CONT.
C minor
E minor   (Partita No. 5)
H. Gomberg & C. Chiasson (hpsi.)
♯ **AmD.DL 9618**
(*Mozart: Oboe Qtt.*)

VIOLIN & CONT.
A minor; G minor
☆ L. Kaufman & A. Geoffroy-Dechaume (hpsi.)
(in ♯ *Eur.LPG 627*)

2 VIOLINS   (orig. 2 fls.)
DUOS: No. 1, D major
No. 4, E minor
No. 5, B minor
KANONISCHE SONATEN
No. 2, D major
S. Harth & T. Testa   ♯ **Allo.ALG 3039**

♯ = Long-playing, 33⅓ r.p.m.   ♭ = 45 r.p.m.   ♮ = Auto. couplings, 78 r.p.m.

SONATAS (*continued*)
'CELLO & CONT.

F minor
☆ H. Busch & Weiss-Mann (hpsi.)
        (♯ Ome. & CID.LX 33008)

SUITES
A minor   fl. & str. orch.
... Minuet & Réjouissance only
☆ M. Coppe (recorder) & Str. Ens.—Oubradous
        (Tono.A 175)

D major str. ("*Overture*")
Scheck-Wenzinger Ens. (viols)   ♯ **Ura. 7031**
(*Haydn: Concerto*)

D major vln., ob., tpt., str. (Tafelmusik II-1)
L. Kaufman, S. Zilverberg, F. Hausdorfer,
  Cha. Orch.—Stevens   ♯ **CHS.G 17**
(*Concerto*)

Don Quichotte
German Op. House Orch.—Schrader
(*Tartini*)   ♯ **Ura. 5007**

TRIO, E minor (Tafelmusik II-4) fl., ob., cont.
M. Wittgenstein, E. Brenner, S. Marlowe (hpsi.),
  M. Hubert (vlc.)   ♯ **West.WL 5076**
(*above & Loeillet*)

(Die) UNGLEICHE HEIRAT Opera 1725
  ("*Pimpinone*")
H. Fuchs (S), E. Lassner (B), Salzburg Str. Qtt.,
  J. Sternberg (hpsi.)—Messner ♯ **Oce.OCS 27**

———————

THIRIET, Maurice (b. 1906)

(Les) VISITEURS DU SOIR Film music
Deux ballades médiévales;
Complainte de Gilles (Prévert)
  J. Jansen (B), L. Laskine (hp.)   **D.GAF 15107**
(1½ss.—*Jaubert: Le marmitier*)

———————

THOMAS, Ambroise (1811-1896)

OPERAS

(Le) CAÏD 2 acts 1849
Air du Tambour-Major   Bs
  E. List, & O. Schulhof (pf.) in ♯ **Rem. 199-73**
(*Moussorgsky, R. Strauss, etc.*)

HAMLET 5 acts 1868
Vains regrets ... Doute de la lumière S & B (Act I)
  ☆ F. Heldy & M. Journet (G.VB 71)
  🎜 M. Sembrich & E. de Gogorza (G.VB 29*: o.n. 034019*)

O vin, dissipe la tristesse B (Act II)
Comme une pâle fleur B (Act V)
  C. Cambon   *G.DA 5053*
              (♭ *G.7RF 111*)
  🎜 M. Battistini (*Ital*) (in ♯ *Ete. 451*)

O vin, dissipe la tristesse, only
  🎜 E. Giraldoni (*Ital*) (HRS. 1074*)

Comme une pâle fleur, only
  🎜 G. de Luca (*Ital*) (in ♯ GAR. 100*)

MIGNON 3 acts 1866
Overture
  Berlin State Op.—Ludwig   **G.DB 11503**
  Vienna Sym.—Nilius   **Vien.L 6028**
              (in ♯ *1010*)

Radio-Luxemburg Sym.—Pensis ♯ FestF.FLD 3
(*Offenbach, Adam, Bizet, Gounod, etc.*)
Rhineland Sym.—Federer   ♯ *Rgt. 5038*
(*Hérold & Weber*)
"Nat. Op. Orch." (in ♯ *Var. 6932*)
☆ Dresden Phil.—v. Kempen (Pol. 15527)

ACT I

Connais-tu le pays?   S
  M. Guilleaume (*Ger*)   **T.E 3923**
  (*Marta—Letzte Rose*)
  D. Eustrati (*Ger*)   in ♯ **Roy. 1209**
  Anon. Artist (*Ger*)   in ♯ Var. 2014
  🎜 A. Patti   G.VB 53*: o.n. 03083*
  S. Arnoldson   G.VA 10*: o.n. 33612*
  E. Destinn (*Ger*)   in ♯ CEd.set 7001*

ACT II

Entracte (Gavotte)
  Columbia Orch. (in ♯ *AmC.GL 513*)

Je connais un pauvre enfant M-S or S
  G. Simionato (*Ital*)   **C.GQX 11503**
  (*Carmen—Habanera*)

Me voici dans son boudoir M-S
  ☆ B. Castagna   *G.DA 1951*
  (*Carmen—Chanson bohème*)

Adieu, Mignon, courage   T
  N. Monti (*Ital*)   **C.GQX 11475**
  (*Elle ne croyait pas*)
  🎜 R. Tauber (*Ger*) (in ♯ Ete. O-466*)

Je suis Titania S (*Polonaise*)
  ☆ L. Pons   **C.LX 1514**
  (*Puritani—Son vergin vezzosa*)

ACT III

Elle ne croyait pas (*Ah! non credevi tu*) T
  N. Monti (*Ital*)   **C.GQX 11475**
  (*Adieu, Mignon*)
  R. Schock (*Ger*) (in ♯ Roy. 1209 & 1256)
  🎜 J. Hislop (*Ital*) (AF. 45*)

RAYMOND 3 acts 1851
Overture
  Rhineland Sym.—Federer   ♯ *Rgt. 5034*
  (*Suppé*)

———————

THOMAS, David Vaughan (1873-1934)

SEE: † Welsh Recorded Music Society

———————

THOMPSON, Randall (b. 1899)

Alleluia 1940 Unacc. cho.
Odes of Horace 1925
... Montium custos nemorumque
Vitas hinnuleo me similis, Chloë
O fons Bandusiae unacc. cho.
  Vienna Academy Cha. Cho.—Grossmann
             ♯ **AmVox.PL 7750**
  (*Barber, V. Thomson, etc.*)

Symphony No. 2, E minor 1931
... 1st movt. only
  A.R.S. Orch.—Dixon   ♯ **ARS. 45**
  (*Moore*)

(The) Testament of Freedom (Jefferson) 1943
  Eastman Male Cho. & Eastman-Rochester
  Sym.—Hanson   ♯ **Mer.MG 40000**
  (*Hanson*)

———————

☆ = Re-issue of a recording to be found in WERM or Supplement I.

THOMSON, Virgil (b. 1896)

Capital, capitals (G. Stein) 4 male voices & pf. 1927
   J. Crawford & C. Turner (T), J. James (B),
   W. Smith (Bs), V. Thomson (pf.)
                                    ♯ AmC.ML 4491
   (*below*, & *L. Harrison*)

CONCERTO, vlc. & orch.   1945-6   (f.p. 1950)
   L. Silva & Janssen Sym.   ♯ AmC.ML 4468
   (*below*)

Fanfare   org.
   R. Ellsasser   in ♯ MGM.E 3005

Hymns from the old South
1. The Morning star   (Anon.)
2. Death, 'tis a melancholy day   (Watts)
   Vienna Academy Cha. Cho.—Grossmann
                                    ♯ AmVox.PL 7750
   (*Piston, Copland, etc.*)

Louisiana Story   Film music
... **Acadian songs & dances**   (Orch. suite No. 2)
   Little Orch. Soc.—Scherman   ♯ AmD.DL 9616
   (*Copland*)

Mother of us all   Opera   3 acts   1947   (G. Stein)
... **Orch. Suite**
   Janssen Sym.   ♯ AmC.ML 4468
   (*Concerto*)

(The) Plow that broke the Plains   Film music
... **Orch. Suite**   1937
   Little Orch. Soc.—Scherman   ♯ AmD.DL 7527
   (*Copland*)

Ragtime Bass   pf.
   A. Földes   PV. 46002
   (½s.—*Albeniz: Tango, & Stravinsky: Circus Polka*)

(The) River   Film music   1942
   A.R.S. Orch.—Hendl   ♯ ARS. 8
   (*Luening*)

Stabat Mater   (M. Jacob) M-S & str. qtt. 1931-2
   J. Tourel & New Music Qtt.   ♯ AmC.ML 4491
   (*above*)

TIESSEN, Heinz (b. 1887)

Allegro ritmico, Op. 52, No. 5
Amsel, Op. 31, No. 3   pf.
   A. Schier-Tiessen   Pol. 62877

TIPPETT, Michael Kemp (b. 1905)

Concerto, C major   Double Str. Orch.   1939
   Philharmonia—Goehr   (6ss)   ♮ G.C 7926/8

TISSERAND, F. J.   (fl. XV Cent.)
SEE: † FRENCH NOËLS & CHANSONS

TOCH, Ernest (b. 1887)

(3) Burlesques, Op. 31 ... 2 only   pf.
   P. Spagnolo   P.PE 158
   (*Longo: La burla del Pievano Arlotto*)

TOMÁŠEK, Vaclav Jan (1774-1850)
   (TOMASCHEK, Johann Wenzel)

Fantasia, E minor   Glass harmonica   1809
   B. Hoffmann   Pol. 6004

TOMASI, Henri (b. 1901)

Concert champêtre   ob., cl., bsn.
   French Radio Reed Trio   (2ss)   Pat.PDT 268

TOMKINS, Thomas   (c. 1573-1656)

SEE: † AMERICAN MUSIC—BAY PSALM BOOK
      † EARLY ENGLISH KEYBOARD MUSIC
      † TRIUMPHS OF ORIANA

TORELLI, Giuseppe (c. 1658-1708)

SEE also: † ITALIAN SONGS

Concerto à quattro, G major, Op. 8, No. 6
   (*In forma di Pastorale*)
   Virtuosi di Roma—Fasano   ♯ AmD.DL 9649
   (*Boccherini, Corelli, etc.*)

Concerto, vln. & orch., E minor, Op. 8, No. 3
   L. Kaufman & Str. Orch.—Dahinden
   (*Vivaldi, etc.*)   ♯ CHS.F 17

TOURNIER, Marcel   (b. 1879)
SEE: † HARP MUSIC

TRAPP, Max (b. 1887)

Allegro deciso, Op. 40   orch.
   Berlin Municipal—B. Lehmann   Pol. 15507
   (2ss)   (o.n. ▽ Pol. 57203)

TRAVIS, Roy Elihu (b. 1922)

Symphonic Allegro   orch.
   (*7th Gershwin Memorial Award*)
   N.Y.P.S.O.—Mitropoulos   ♯ AmC.AAL 16
   (*Couperin*)

TURINA, Joaquin (1882-1949)

(3) Danzas fantásticas   orch.   1920
   Hallé—Barbirolli   ♮ G.DB 9738/9
   (4ss)

Escena andaluza   vla., pf., str. qtt.   1912
   R. & L. Persinger & Strad. Qtt. ♯ Strad.STR 608
   (*Hindemith, Villa-Lobos, Handel*)

Fandanguillo   guit.   1926
   ☆A. Segovia   in ♯ C.CX 1020
   († *Spanish Guitar Music, & Castelnuovo-Tedesco*)
                                    (♯ FCX/QCX 127)

(La) Oración del Torero, Op. 8
   (orig. Lute qtt., ARR. Str. orch. Turina)
   Madrid Cha. Orch.—Argenta   SpC.RG 16180

♯ = Long-playing, 33⅓ r.p.m.   ♭ = 45 r.p.m.   ♮ = Auto. couplings, 78 r.p.m.

232

(La) Procession del Rocio, Op. 9 orch. 1913
☆ Paris Cons.—Jorda (D.GAG 2344)

Rapsodia sinfonica pf. & str. orch. 1932
☆ M. Lympany & Philharmonia—Süsskind (G.DB 4306;
   in ♯ Vic.LHMV 1025; ♭ G.7BF 1006)
E. Joyce & orch.—Raybould (in ♯ AmD.DL 9528)

Sacro-Monte, Op. 55, No. 5 pf. 1930
G. Copeland   in ♯ MGM.E 151

— ARR. CASTANETS, GUIT., PF. & DANCE
J. Toledano, C. Montoya, P. Miguel, etc.
                          in ♯ SMC. 513

Sinfonia Sevillana orch. 1920
Sydney Sym.—Goossens (6ss) ♮ G.ED 1210/2

SONGS
Cantares (Campoamor)
☆ V. de los Angeles (S) & orch. (♭ G.7RF 209)

Saeta en forma de salve a la Virgen de la Esperanza
C. Rubio (S), C. D. Martin (pf.) SpC.R 18237
(Tolibra: Madre, unos ojeulos vi)

☆ V. de los Angeles (S) (♭ G.7RF 209)

Triptico (Campoamor)
... Farruca only ☆ V. de los Angeles (S) (♭ G.7RF 147)

TRIOS, pf., vln., vlc.
No. 1, D minor, Op. 35 1926
J. Hill Trio   ♯ Argo.ARL 1004
(Announced but probably never issued)

TVEITT, Geirr (b. 1908)

BALDUR Ballet 1935
Dance (unspec.) — ARR. VLN. & PF. Knudsen
G. Knudsen & E. Garcia   in ♯ ML. 5003
(Prokofiev, Halvorsen, Fauré, etc.)

VACHON, Pierre (1731-1803)

Quartet, Strings, F minor, Op. 7, No. 3 1773
Loewenguth Qtt. (4ss)   † AS. 164/5

VALEN, Fartein (1887-1952)

(Le) Cimetière marin, Op. 20 orch. 1934
Oslo Phil.—Fjeldstad (2ss)   Nera.SK 15542

(La) Isla de las Calmas, Op. 21 orch. 1934
Oslo Phil.—Fjeldstad (2ss)   Nera.KN 7100

Sonetto di Michelangelo, Op. 17 orch. 1932
Oslo Phil.—Fjeldstad (2ss)   Nera.KN 7101

VAŇHAL, Jan Křtitel (1739–1813)

FUGUES org.
B flat major; C major
M. Šlechta   U.H 13133

VASILENKO, Sergei Nikiforovich
(b. 1872)

Ballet Suite, Op. 122
State Sym.—Vasilenko   USSR. 14850/3
(4ss)

(The) Gypsies, Ballet Suite, Op. 90 1936
State Sym.—Vasilenko   USSR. 15808/11
(4ss)

VAUGHAN WILLIAMS, Ralph (b. 1872)

Concerto accademico, D minor vln. & str. orch.
  1925
J. Fuchs & Zimbler Sinfonietta ♯ B.AXTL 1006
(Tansman)   (♯ AmD.DL 9625)
L. Kaufman & Zürich Radio—Dahinden
(Britten)   ♯ CHS.F 8

Concerto, 2 pfs. & orch.
  (orig. pf. solo, 1932; ARR. 2 pfs.[2] 1946)
A. Whittemore & J. Lowe & Robin Hood Dell
  —Golschmann   ♯ Vic.LM 135
                          (♭ set WDM 1597)

Fantasia on Greensleeves [1] 1929
New Sym.—Collins   in ♯ D.LXT 2699
(below)   (♯ Lon.LL 583)
☆ Boyd Neel Orch.   Lon. 12017
(Grainger: Handel in the Strand)   (♭ 40357)

Fantasia on a theme by Tallis Str. orch. 1910
New Sym.—Collins   ♯ D.LXT 2699
(above; & Elgar: Intro. & Allegro &   (♯ Lon.LL 583)
Serenade for Strings)

Flos campi vla., cho. & cha. orch. 1925
F. Tursi, Cornell A Cappella Cho. & Concert
  Hall Cha. Orch.—Hall   ♯ CHS.CHS 1151
(Johnson)   (♯ Nix.CLP 1151)

For all the Saints (Sine nomine) Hymn-tune
Shaw Chorale   in ♯ Vic.LM 108
(Hymns)   (♭ set WDM 1559)

(5) Mystical Songs (Herbert) B. & Cho. 1911
O how amiable Anthem Cho. & org.
H. Ronk (B) & Washington Presbyterian Chu.
  Cho.—Schaefer   ♯ Den.DR 2
(Buxtehude)

Prelude on Rhosymedre org. 1920
E. P. Biggs   in ♯ AmC.ML 4603
(Walond: Intro. & Toccata; Parry, etc.)
R. Ellsasser   in ♯ MGM.E 3005
(Marcello, etc.)

Romance harmonica & str. orch. 1952
L. Adler & Str. Orch.—Sargent   C.DX 1861

Serenade to Music (Shakespeare) 1938
Royal Festival Cho. & orch.—Boult
(4ss)   ♮ G.DA 7040/1

Song of Thanksgiving [3] S, Speaker, cho., orch.
  1945
B. Dolemore, R. Speaight, Luton Cho. Soc.,
  Section of Luton Girls Cho., L.P.O.—Boult
(4ss)   ♮ P.SW 8138/9

SYMPHONIES
No. 2, A London Symphony, G major 1914-20
L.P.O.—Boult   ♯ D.LXT 2693
                              (♯ Lon.LL 569)
(continued on next page)

---

[1] ARR. Graves from Sir John in Love.   [2] In collaboration with J. Cooper
[3] Original title: Thanksgiving for Victory.

Symphonies (*continued*)
No. 6, E minor 1947
☆ L.S.O.—Boult   **# G.BLP 1001**

(The) WASPS Inc. music to Aristophanes 1909
Overture
L.S.O.—Menges   **G.C 4195**
☆ Hallé—Sargent (C.GQX 11502)

FOLKSONG ARRANGEMENT
Wassail Song
Columbia Choristers—Engel in **# AmC.ML 2199**
M. Gould Orch. (in # *AmC.ML 2065*)

VAUTOR, Thomas (fl. *c.* 1620)
SEE: † TREASURY OF MADRIGALS

VECCHI, Orazio (1550-1605)
SEE: † ITALIAN MADRIGALS

VERACINI, Francesco (1690-*c.* 1750)

ROSELINDA Opera 1744
Meco sulla verrai ("*Pastorale*") S
H ☆ L. Tetrazzini (in # Vic.LCT 1039*: ♭ set WCT 62*)

VERDI, Giuseppe Fortunio Francesco
(1813-1901)

I. NON-OPERATIC

(4) PEZZI SACRI cho. 1898
1. Ave Maria (unacc.)   2. Stabat Mater (with orch.)
3. Te Deum (with orch.)   4. Laudi alla Vergine (unacc.)
Vienna Academy Cha. Cho. & State Op. Orch.—
Swoboda   **# CHS.CHS 1136**
Aachen Cath. Cho. & Aachen Municipal Orch.
—Rehmann (2ss)   **# AmD.DL 9661**
(Nos. 1 & 4, ☆ Pol. 68416; No. 2, PV. 72174;
                              No. 3, PV. 72194)

Quartet, Strings, E minor 1873
New Italian Qtt.   **# D.LXT 2591**
(*Schumann: Qtt. Op. 41, No. 2*)   (# Lon.LLP 323)

REQUIEM MASS 1873 S, A, T, B, Cho., orch.
COMPLETE RECORDINGS
L. Hunt, J. Moudry, P. Knowles, K. Smith,
Calvary Chu. Cho.—Ossewaarde
                          # CHS.set CHS 1131
(*org. acc.*—4ss)   (# Nix.CLP 1131-1/2)
S. Kaye, M. Pirazzini, G. Sinimberghi, A. Beuf,
Rome Op. Cho. & Orch.—Ricci
(4ss)   **# Ura.set 213**
H. Steingruber (S), R. Delorco (T), Cho. &
Austrian Sym.—Koslik   **# Rem.set 199-105**
(4ss)
Anon. Soloists, Berlin Cath. Cho. & Sym.
Orch.—Balzer (4ss)   **# Roy. 1377/8**
☆ Soloists, Rome Op. Cho. & Orch.—Serafin
                          (# Vic.LCT 6003: ♭ set WCT 68)
... **Ingemisco**   T
☆ A. Piccaver (Pol. 67540)

SONGS
COLLECTION
Ad una stella (Maffei)
Deh, pietoso (Goethe, trs. Balestri)
In solitaria stanza (Vittorelli)
(Il) Mistero (Romano)
(Il) Poveretto (Anon.)
Stornello (Anon.)
(Il) Tramonto (Maffei)
☆ I. B. Lucca (S), R. Malipiero (pf.)
                          # Csm.CLPS 1028

II. OPERAS

AÏDA 4 acts 1871
COMPLETE RECORDINGS
Set H
Aïda   ...   .   C. Mancini (S)
Amneris   ...   ...   G. Simionato (M-S)
Radames   ...   ...   M. Filippeschi (T)
Amonasro   ...   .   R. Panerai (B)
Ramfis   ...   .   G. Neri (Bs)
Italian Radio Cho. & Orch.—Gui
(6ss)   **# Sor.set 1228**

Set K
Aïda   ...   .   R. Tebaldi (S)
Amneris   ...   ...   E. Stignani (M-S)
Radames   ...   ...   M. del Monaco (T)
Amonasro   ...   .   A. Protti (B)
Ramfis   ...   ...   D. Caselli (Bs)
Rome St. Cecilia Acad. Cho. & Orch.—
Erede   **# D.LXT 2735/7**
(6ss)   (# Lon.set LLA 13)

Set L
S. Roman (S), S. Sawyer (M-S), G. Sarri (T),
A. M. Serra (B), V. Tatozzi (Bs), Rome Opera
Cho. & Orch.—Paoletti **# Cap.set PCR 8179**
(6ss)   (Highlights on # P 8177; # T.LCSK 8177)

"Aïda of Yesterday" [1]
B. Gigli, E. Rethberg, G. Martinelli, E. Pinza,
R. Ponselle, J. Gadski & P. Amato, L. Homer
& E. Caruso   **# Vic.LCT 1035**
                          (♭ set WCT 51)

Highlights
Anon. Artists (# Wde. 20201; Roy. 1206; & *Pde. 1003*;
          also with narration, # Pde.OP 103)
☆ N.Y. City Center Op. Co. (♭ MGM. set K 81)

ACT I
Prelude
Metropolitan Op.—Cleva in **# AmC.ML 4515**
(*below, & Faust*)
Berlin Municipal Op.—Rother in **# Ura. 7057**

Celeste Aïda   T
V. Campagnana   **P.PE 176**
(*Andrea Chénier—Un di ...*)
B. Blachut   **U.H 24221**
(*below*)
K. Baum   in **# Rem. 199-63**
(*Forza, Tosca, etc.*)
R. Schock   in **# Roy. 1206**
Y. Kiporenko-Domansky   **USSR. 20190/1**
(2ss)   (*Ukrainian*)
☆ R. Tucker   **C.LX 1508**
(*Cavalleria Rusticana—Addio alla madre*)
☆ M. del Monaco   ♭ Vic. 49-3676
  M. Lanza   in # Vic.LM 86 & ♭ 49-0632
  A. Miltschinoff   AusT.E 1098
  F. Völker (Ger)   Pol. 67159
H J. McCormack   in # Ete. O-469*
  F. de Lucia   in # Ete. O-464*
  E. Caruso   in # Vic.LCT 1007*: ♭ set WCT 11*
  E. Caruso & pf.   G.VA 12*: o.n. DA 549*

---

[1] Contains: ☆ Celeste Aïda, Ritorna vincitor, Temple Scene, O patria mia, Su, dunque*; Pur ti riveggo & La, tre foreste;
      Gia i sacerdoti & Aïda, a me*.

AÏDA: ACT I (continued)

Ritorna vincitor!   S
C. Martinis   **C.LX 1536**
(2ss)   (CQX 11515)

A. Varnay   in # **Rem. 199-45**
(Simone Boccanegra, Trovatore, Fidelio, etc.)

C. Goltz   **PV. 72116**
(O Patria mia)   (& Ger on 72119)

M. Corelli   in # **Roy. 1206**

L. Lobanova-Rogatcheva   **USSR. 020192/3**
(2ss—Ukrainian)

☆ D. Ilitsch   Eur.TGB 148
   R. Tebaldi   in # AmD.DL 9017

ℌ E. Destinn (Ger)   in # CEd.set 7001*

Dance of the Priestesses
Metropolitan Op.—Cleva   in # **AmC.ML 4515**
(below, & Faust)

☆ Berlin Municipal—Haarth (Pol. 15518)

ACT II

Dance of the Moorish Slave-boys
Metropolitan Op.—Cleva   in # **AmC.ML 4515**
(above, & Faust)

☆ Berlin Municipal—Haarth (Pol. 15518)

**Chi mai fra gli inni ...
Fu la sorte dell' armi**   S, M-S, Cho.
A. Kupper, E. Höngen, Württemberg State Op.
   Cho.—Leitner   **PV. 72099**
(2ss—Ger)   (in # Pol. 18009)

... M-S part only
M. Krasova [1]   **U.H 24221**
(Celeste Aïda)

Gloria all' Egitto!   (March & Cho.)
Hilversum Radio Cho. & Orch.—van Kempen
     # **Phi.A 00116L**
(½s.—Forza Overture & Lohengrin Excerpts)
(also, 2ss, Phi.N 12012G: PhM.N 09016S)

— ORCH. ONLY
Metropolitan Op.—Cleva   in # **AmC.ML 4515**
(above, & Faust)

☆ Boston Pops—Fiedler (♭ G.7BF 1030; ♭ Vic. 49-0616:
     in ♭ WEPR 27)

Ballabili   (Ballet Music)
Covent Garden—Braithwaite in # **MGM.E 3003**
(Rossini, Gounod, etc.)
Metropolitan Op.—Cleva   in # **AmC.ML 4515**
(above, & Faust)

☆ Berlin Municipal—Haarth   Pol. 15518
   Chicago Phil.—H. Weber   in # Clc. 6040

ACT III

O Patria mia   S
C. Martinis   **C.LX 1463**
(Otello—Ave Maria)   (GQX 11512)

R. Tebaldi   **Fnt. 22007**
(Mefistofele—L'altra notte)
(Otello—Ave Maria, on Fnt. 22009;
     also ☆ in # Lon.LD 9017)

C. Goltz   **PV. 72116**
(Ritorna vincitor!)   (Ger. on 72119)

N. Sokolova   (Russ, 2ss)   **USSR. 19116/7**

Ciel! Mio Padre! ... Rivedrai le foreste   S & B
☆ H. Kupper & H. Reinmar (Ger) (# Pol. 18009)
ℌ E. Mazzoleni & P. Amato (in # Ete.O-482*)

Pur ti riveggo ... Sovra una terra estrania   S & T
☆ A. Kupper & L. Fehenberger (Ger) (in # Pol. 18009)

ℌ R. Ponselle & G. Martinelli (G.VB 73*)
   G. Zenatello & M. Rappold (IRCC. 3109*)

[1] Listed as Amneris' Aria, Act III but probably part of this scene.

ACT IV

Morir! Si pura ... O terra addio   S & T
M. Corelli & R. Schock   in # **Roy. 1206**

Già i sacerdoti ... Di mia discolpa   M-S & T
ℌ S. Kalter & R. Tauber (Ger) (in # Ete.O-466*)

(Un) BALLO IN MASCHERA   3 acts   1859
COMPLETE RECORDINGS

Riccardo	...	...	J. Kerol (T)
Renato	...	...	J. Borthayre (B)
Amelia	...	...	E. Semser (S)
Ulrica	...	...	M-T. Cahn (A)
Oscar	...	...	L. Valdarnini (S)
Samuel	...	...	L. Mans (Bs)

etc. Paris Phil. Cho. & Radio Sym.—Leibowitz
(6ss)   # **Ren.set SX 207**

	(a)	(b)
Amelia ...	M. Caniglia (S)	D. Ilitsch (S)
Ulrica ...	C. Elmo (M-S)	M. Harshaw (M-S)
Riccardo ...	G. Masini (T)	J. Peerce (T)
Renato ...	C. Tagliabue (B)	L. Warren (B)

(a) Rome Opera Cho. & Orch.—Marinuzzi

(b) Metropolitan Op.—Antonicelli # **CEd. 5001**
(6ss—Advertised with artists (a); produced with artists (b)
but immediately withdrawn)

ACT I

La rivedrò nell' estasi   T part only
ℌ L. Slezak (Ger)   HRS. 1114*

Alla vita che t'arride   B
ℌ M. Battistini   Pol. 85061*; AF. 48*

Re dell' abisso   A
J. Watson   **C.DB 2912**
(Trovatore—Stride la vampa)

C. Elmo   ♭ **Vic. 49-3450**
(Gioconda)

☆ E. Wysor   in # Rem. 149-2

Di tu se fedele   T [& cho.]
A. Frinberg (Latvian)   **USSR. 19956**
(Otello—Dio! mi potevi ...)

☆ J. Björling   ♭ G.7RF 115

ℌ E. Caruso   in # Vic.LCT 1034*: ♭ set WCT 35*
   G. Zenatello   IRCC. 3109*

ACT II

Ma dall' arido stelo divulsa   S
C. Martinis   **C.LX 1548**
(2ss)   (GQX 11519)

A. Varnay   in # **Rem. 199-53**
(Manon Lescaut, Hérodiade, etc.)

☆ L. Welitsch   **D.K 23235**
(Tchaikovsky: Pique Dame—No. 20)

ℌ J. Gadski   G.VB 52*: o.n. DB 661*

Teco io sto ... O qual soave   S & T
ℌ C. Boninsegna & Del Ry   in # Ete.O-468*
   E. Burzio & G. Zenatello   HRS. 1020*, 2ss

Seguitemi, mio Dio ... Ve' se di notte
ℌ M. Battistini, Barbieri & Bettoni   AF. 48*

ACT III

Morrò, ma prima in grazia   S
L. Cervinkova   **U.H 24195**
(Carmen—Flower song, Blachut)

☆ M. Caniglia   BrzV. 886-5001

ℌ J. Gadski   G.VB 52*: o.n. DB 661*
   C. Boninsegna   in # Ete.O-468*

(continued on next page)

(Un) BALLO IN MASCHERA: ACT III (*continued*)

Eri tu, che macchiavi   B
I. Alexeyev (*Russ*)   **U.H 23837**
(*Tannhäuser—Abendstern, A. Ivanov*)

P. Nortsov (*Russ*)   **USSR. 09105**
(*Traviata—Di Provenza*)

☆ L. Warren   **G.DB 6895**
(*Otello*)   (in ♯ Vic.LM 1168)

☆ G. Inghilleri   *G.HN 2932*
R. Merrill   in ♯ *Vic.LM 111*

♄ M. Battistini   Pol. 85061*

Ma se m'è forza perderti   T
H. Roswaenge (*Ger*)   in ♯ Ura. 7027

☆ J. Schmidt (*Ger*)   in ♯ *T.LB 6007*

♄ J. Hislop   AF. 45*

Saper vorreste   S   (*Page's aria*)
C. Carroll   in ♯ *Rem. 149-41*
(*Pagliacci, Figaro, etc.*)

(La) BATTAGLIA DI LEGNANO   3 acts   1849
COMPLETE RECORDING
Lida   …   …   …   C. Mancini (S)
Arrigo   …   …   …   A. Berdini (T)
Rolando   …   …   R. Panerai (B)
Federigo Barbarossa   A. Gaggi (Bs)
Italian Radio Cho. & Orch.—Previtali
(6ss)   ♯ Sor.set 1220

Overture
Philharmonia—Markevitch   G.C 4181
(2ss)   (S 10592: ♭ 7P 117: 7BF 1048)

DON CARLOS   5 acts   1867   (later 4 acts)
COMPLETE RECORDING
Elisabeth di Valois…   …   M. Caniglia (S)
Principessa d'Eboli   …   E. Stignani (MS)
Don Carlos…   …   …   M. Picchi (T)
Rodrigo   …   …   …   P. Silveri (B)
Filippo II   …   …   N. Rossi-Lemeni (Bs)
Inquisitor   …   …   G. Neri (Bs)
Italian Radio Cho. & Orch.—Previtali
(8ss)   ♯ Sor.set 1234

ACT II
(ACT I in some versions)

Io t'ho perduto … Qual pallor   T, B & Bs
☆ J. Björling, R. Merrill & E. Markow (in ♯ Vic.LM 7007:
     ♭ set WDM 7007)

Nei giardin del bello saracin   M-S
(*Canzone del Velo*)
☆ B. Thebom   **G.DB 21494**
(*below*)

Dio, che nell' alma infondere   T & B
H. Roswaenge & H. Schlusnus (*Ger*)
     in ♯ Ura. 7027

ACT IV
(ACT III in some versions)

Ella giammai m'amo … Dormirò sol   Bs
E. Pinza (n.v.)   ♭ *Vic. WEPR 37*
(*Don Giovanni—Catalogue aria*)
P. Schoeffler   in ♯ MSL.MW 44
(*Offenbach, Mozart, etc. & Lieder*)
☆ R. Arié   in ♯ *D.LX 3041*
(*Boris, Sonnambula, etc.*)   (♯ Lon. LPS 98)
M. Reizen   (2ss, *Russ*)   **USSR. 018917/8**
♄ P. Knüpfer (*Ger*) (AF. 40*)

O don fatale   M-S or A
E. Nicolai   **P.CB 20511**
(*Cavalleria Rusticana—Voi lo sapete*)

M. Mödl (*Ger*)   **T.E 3897**
(*Orphée—J'ai perdu …*)
☆ B. Thebom   **G.DB 21494**
(*above*)

☆ G. Ripley (*Eng.*) (G.JOX 17)

ACT V

Tu che le vanità   S   (*Elisabeth's aria*)
J. Hammond   (2ss)   **G.DB 21510**
M. Vitale   **P.CB 20533**
(*Gioconda—Suicidio*)
♄ G. Russ (*IRCC. 3088**)

(I) DUE FOSCARI   3 acts   1844
Questa dunque è l'iniqua mercede   B
♄ P. Amato (in ♯ Ete.O-482*)

ERNANI   4 acts   1844
ABRIDGED RECORDING   (*Set A*)
Elvira   …   …   …   I. Pacetti (S)
Ernani   …   …   …   A. Melandri (T)
Don Carlo   …   …   G. Vanelli (B)
Don Silva   …   …   C. Zambelli (Bs)
☆ La Scala Cho. & Orch.—Molajoli
     ♯ AmC.ML 4407

ACT I

Come rugiada al cespite   T
R. Turrini   **P.PE 178**
(*Fanciulla del West—Or son sei mesi*)
♄ F. de Lucia (IRCC. 3108*)

Ernani, Ernani, involami   B
♄ C. Boninsegna (in ♯ Ete. O-468*)
C. Muzio (in ♯ Eso.ES 502*; ♯ Cpt.MC 20009 [1];
     & HRS. 2009*)

Chi mai vegg'io … Infelice! e tuo credevi   Bs
B. Christoff   **G.DB 21424**
(*below*)
♄ F. Chaliapin   G.VB 72*; & in ♯ AudA. 0077*
A. Didur   in ♯ Ete. O-467*

**L'offeso onor, signori … Infin, che un brando
     vindice**   Bs
B. Christoff   **G.DB 21424**
(*above*)

ACT II

Lo vedremo   B & Bs
☆ ♄ M. Battistini & A. Sillich (in ♯ Vic.LCT 1039*:
     ♭ set WCT 62*)

ACT III

Gran Dio! … O de' verd' anni miei
P. Silveri   **C.LX 1509**
(*Puritani—Ah per sempre*)   (CQX 11501)
♄ M. Battistini (in ♯ Ete. O-462*)

O sommo Carlo   B, Ens., Cho.
♄ D. Gilly & Ens. (*Fr*) (IRCC. 3108*)

FALSTAFF   3 acts   1893
COMPLETE RECORDING
☆ G. Taddei, R. Carteri, L. Pagliughi, A. Pini, E. Renzi,
     S. Meletti, etc., Turin Radio Cho. & Orch.—Rossi
     (♯ FSor.CS 513/5)

ACT I, Sc. 1

L'Onore! Ladri!   B
G. Bechi   **G.DB 11353**
(*Denza: Si vous l'aviez compris*)
♄ A. Scotti (in ♯ Vic.LCT 1039*: ♭ set WCT 62*)

---

[1] Recorded from Edison cylinder.

FALSTAFF (*continued*)

ACT II, Sc. 1

Reverenza! Bs & B
J. Metternich & D. Fischer-Dieskau (*Ger*)
(4ss) ♮ PV. 36016/7
(♯ *Pol. 18047*)

ACT III

Ehi! Taverniere! B
O. Edelmann (*Ger*) in ♯ D.LXT 2672
(*Tannhäuser* on D.K 23261: K 28552) (♯ *Lon.LL 427*)

ACT IV, Sc. 2

Sul fil d'un soffio etesio S
M. Minazzi P.PE 169
(*Otello—Ave Maria*)

(La) FORZA DEL DESTINO 4 acts 1862
COMPLETE RECORDINGS

Donna Leonora	...	...	A. Guerrini (S)
Preziosilla	...	...	M. Pirazzini (M-S)
Don Alvaro	...	...	G. Campora (T)
Don Carlo	...	...	A. Colzani (B)
Fra Melitone	...	...	F. Corena (Bs)
Padre Guardiano	...	...	G. Modesti (B)
Il Marchese di Calatrava	...	...	G. Calo (B)

etc., La Scala Cho. & Orch.—Parodi
(6ss) ♯ Ura.set 226

☆ M. Caniglia, G. Masini, C. Tagliabue, E. Stignani, etc.
Cho. & orch.—Marinuzzi, now 6ss (♯ Sor.set 1236)

NOTE: The following sides of the Cetra complete recording (with M. Caniglia, E. Stignani, C. Tagliabue, T. Pasero, etc.) have been issued in England by Parlophone:

s. 9, Viva la buona compagnia	P.R 30035
s. 10, Là e dovunque narrar	P.R 30035
s. 11, Son giunta! Grazie o Dio!	P.R 30036
s. 12, Non mi lasciar	P.R 30036
s. 13, Or siam soli	P.R 30037
s. 14, E l'amante?	P.R 30037
s. 15, Sull' alba il piede	P.R 30040
s. 16, Il santo nome di Dio	P.R 30040
s. 17, L'immonda cenere ... La Vergine	P.R 30029
s. 20, Al tradimento	P.R 30038
s. 23, E s'altra prova	P.R 30038
s. 24, Lorchè pifferi	P.R 30039
s. 27, E la ragion?	P.R 30039

Overture
Hilversum Radio—v. Kempen ♯ Phi.A 00116L
(½s.—*Aïda March & Lohengrin, excpts.*)
(also, 2ss, Phi.N 11151G: *PhM.N 09025S*)
Berlin Municipal Op.—Rother in ♯ Ura. 7057
(♭ *UREP 2*)
Rhineland Sym.—Federer in ♯ Rgt. 5047
Bamberg Sym.—Leitner PV. 56010
(*Traviata—Preludes, Acts I & III*) (in ♯ *AmD.DL 4016*)
☆ Berlin Sym.—Buschkötter P.DPW 42
☆ Philharmonia—Markevitch (G.EH 1390:
♭ *7BF 1014: 7P 125*)
Vienna Sym.—Swarowsky (T.E 3875)

ACT II

Scenes 5-7, COMPLETE
Son giunta! Grazie, o Dio
Venite fidente alla Croce ... Il santo nome ...
La Vergine degli Angeli
A. Kupper, G. Neidlinger & J. Greindl (*Ger*)
PV. 72225/6
(4ss) (♯ *Pol. 16020*)

Son giunta! ... Madre pietosa Vergine, only S
H. Traubel in ♯ Vic.LM 123
(*Mefistofele, etc.*) (♭ *set WDM 1584*)

Il santo nome di Dio Bs & Cho.
Alzatevi, e partite Bs
La Vergine degli Angeli S
N. Rossi-Lemeni & J. Hammond
♮ G.DB 9779/80
(3ss—*Sonnambula—Vi ravviso*)

ACT III

Scenes 2, 3, 4, 7, 8, 9 T, B, Cho.
Al tradimento ...; Nè gustare ...
H. Roswaenge, H. Schlusnus, Berlin State Op.
Cho. & Orch.—Steinkopf in ♯ Ura. 7027
(*Ger*) (Solenne ... & Pace, pace ... in ♭ *UREP 17*)

O tu che in seno T
K. Baum in ♯ Rem. 199-63
(*Tosca, Turandot, etc.*)
♬ F. de Lucia (in ♯ *CMS. 201*)

Solenne in quest'ora T & B
J. Björling & R. Merrill G.DB 21511
(*Bohème—Ah, Mimi*) (in ♯ *Vic.LM 7007: ♭ set WDM 7007*)
♬ F. de Lucia & A. Armentano (in ♯ *CMS. 201*)

Morir! ... Urna fatale del mio destin B
☆ P. Silveri (C.GQX 11464)

E s'altra prova ... Egli è salvo B
♬ M. Battistini (*G.VA 5*: o.n. DA 189*)

ACT IV

Pace, pace, mio Dio S
A. Guerrini C.GQX 11497
(*Guillaume Tell—Sombre forêt*)
H. Traubel in ♯ Vic.LM 123
(*Mefistofele, etc.*) (♭ *set WDM 1584*)
☆ C. Muzio (in ♯ *AmC.ML 4404*)
♬ C. Muzio (in ♯ *Eso.ES 508*; in ♯ Cpt.MC 20020*) [1]

(UN) GIORNO DI REGNO 2 acts 1840
COMPLETE RECORDING

Marchesa del Poggio	...	L. Pagliughi (S)
Cavaliere di Belfiore	...	R. Capecchi (T)
Baron di Kelbar	...	S. Bruscantini (B)

Italian Radio Cho. & Orch.—Simonetto
(4ss) ♯ Sor.set 1225

(I) LOMBARDI ALLA PRIMA CROCIATA
4 acts 1843
O Signore, dal tetto natio Cho.
☆ La Scala—Erede (FT.T 174; AusT.E 1096)
EIAR—Marinuzzi (♭ *P.BSP 3001*)
Se vano è il pregare S
♬ ☆ C. Muzio (in ♯ *Eso.ES 500*; ♯ Cpt.MC 20008*) [1]

LUISA MILLER 3 acts 1849
COMPLETE RECORDING

Luisa	...	... L. Kelston (S)
Federica	...	... M. T. Pace (M-S)
Rodolfo	...	G. Lauri-Volpi (T)
Count of Walter	...	G. Vaghi (B)
Wurm	...	D. Baronti (B)
Miller	...	... S. Colombo (Bs)

Italian Radio Orch.—Rossi ♯ Sor.set 1221
(6ss)

Overture
Philharmonia—Markevitch G.C 4097
(2ss) (G.EH 1416: S 10585: AA 678: ♭ *7P 116*: ♭ *7BF 1032*)

Quando le sere al placido T (Act II)
M. del Monaco in ♯ D.LX 3094
(*Traviata, Tosca, etc.*) (♯ *Lon.LS 670*)

---

[1] Recorded from Edison cylinder.

MACBETH 4 acts 1847

ABRIDGED RECORDING in *German*

Lady Macbeth	...	... E. Höngen (M-S)
Macbeth	...	... M. Ahlersmeyer (B)
Banquo	...	... H. Alsen (Bs)

Vienna State Opera Cho. & Vienna Phil.—
Böhm (6ss)   **# Ura.set 220**

ACT II

La luce langue   S
(*Nun sinkt der Abend*)
M. Mödl (*Ger*)   *T.E 3891*
(*Act IV, below*)

ACT IV

Ah! la paterna mano   T
M. del Monaco   in *# D.LX 3094*
(*above, & Traviata, etc.*)   (*# Lon.LS 670*)

Vegliammo invan due notte
Una macchia è qui tutt' ora M-S or S, B, S
E. Höngen, G. Grefe, H. Plümacher *PV.36004*
(2ss)   (*# Pol. 18047*)

... Una macchia è qui tutt' ora, only
(*Dieser Flecken kommt immer wieder*)
M. Mödl (*Ger*)   *T.E 3891*
(*Act II, aria*)

Pietà, rispetto, amore   B
G. Malaspina   *P.RO 30006*
(*Nabucco—Dio di Giuda*)   (*AT 0274*)
I. Petroff (n.v.)   in *# Rem. 199-93*
ꞟ ☆ M. Battistini (in # Ete. O-462*)

NABUCODONOSOR 4 acts 1842 (*Nabucco*)
Gli arredi festivi Cho. (Act I)
Dutch Op. Cho. & Hilversum Radio—
v. Kempen   **Phi.N 11175G**
(*below*)   (*PhM.N 09012S*)

Chi mi toglie? B (Act II)
ꞟ ☆ R. Stracciari (*HRS. 1103**)

Va pensiero sull'ali dorate Cho. (Act III)
Dutch Op. Cho. & Hilversum Radio—
v. Kempen   **Phi.N 11175G**
(*above*)   (*PhM.N 09012S*)
☆ La Scala—Erede (FT.T 174; AusT.E 1096)
EIAR—Tansini (♭ *P.BSP 3001*)

Dio di Giuda B (Act IV)
G. Malaspina   *P.RO 30006*
(*Macbeth—Pietà, rispetto, amore*)   (*AT 0274*)
ꞟ R. Stracciari (*HRS. 1103**)

OTELLO 4 acts 1887

COMPLETE RECORDING (Set B)
Soloists, Rome Op. Cho. & Orch.—Paoletti
(6ss)   **# Ura.set 216**

COLLECTED EXCERPTS (Set C)
(Contents indicated [C] below)
Soloists & Met. Op. Orch.—Cleva
                        # AmC.ML 4499

	Set B	*Set C*
Otello ...	G. Sarri (T)	R. Vinay (T)
Iago ...	... A. M. Serra (B)	F. Guarrera (B)
Desdemona ...	A. La Pollo (S)	E. Steber (S)

Excerpts (*Ital & Ger*)
L. Slezak (T), T. Pattiera (T), M. Battistini (B),
P. Amato (B), M. Seinemeyer (S),
G. Zenatello (T), etc. (2ss)   **# Ete. O-470**
(Some are *; others are ☆, for which see below)

ACT I

Inaffia l'ugola! (Brindisi) B & Cho.
☆ L. Warren, N. Sprinzena, etc. (in ♭ *Vic.set WDM 1542*)

Già nella notte densa ... Ed io vedea T & S [C]
B. & R. Gigli (2ss)   **G.DB 11345**
☆ C. Muzio & F. Merli (in # AmC.ML 4404)
M. Seinemeyer & T. Pattiera (in # Ete. O-470)

ACT II

Credo in un Dio crudel B [C]
A. Hiolski (*Pol*)   *Muza. 1774*
☆ L. Warren   **G.DB 6895**
(*Ballo in Maschera*)
☆ C. Tagliabue   **P.PXO 1070**
(*Carmen—Chanson du Toréador*)
☆ R. Merrill (in # *Vic.LM 111*)
ꞟ E. Giraldoni (HRS. 1074*)

Tu? Indietro! fuggi! ... ; Ora e per sempre T & B [C]
Era la notte (*Il sogno*)   B
☆ A. Sved   **P.SW 8124**
(*Rigoletto*)
☆ T. Gobbi (♭ *G.7R 107: 7RF 107*)

Si, pel ciel ...   T & B
J. Björling & R. Merrill   **G.DB 21426**
(*Pêcheurs de Perles—Au fond du temple ...*)
(in # *Vic.LM 7007*: ♭ *set WDM 7007*)

ACT III

Dio ti giocondi, o sposo S & T [C]
☆ C. Muzio & F. Merli (in # AmC.ML 4404)

Dio! mi potevi scagliar T [C]
A. Frinberg (*Latvian*)   *USSR. 19957*
(*Ballo in Maschera—Di tu si fedele*)

ACT IV

Salce, salce S (*Willow song*) [C]
C. Martinis (2ss)   **C.LX 1520**
R. Carteri (2ss)   *P.AT 0274*
                        (& CB 20537)
ꞟ R. Ponselle (in # *Vic. LCT 10**: ♭ *set WCT 55**)

Ave Maria S [C]
C. Martinis   **C.LX 1463**
(*Aida—O Patria mia*)   (GQX 11512)
R. Tebaldi   *Fnt. 22009*
(*Aida—O cieli azzurri*)
M. Minazzi   **P.PE 169**
(*Falstaff—Sul fil d'un soffio*)
H. Traubel   in # *Vic.LM 123*
(*Forza, Mefistofele, etc.*)   (♭ *set WDM 1584*)
ꞟ R. Ponselle (in # *Vic.LCT 10**: ♭ *set WCT 55**)

Niun mi tema T [C]
☆ M. del Monaco   **G.DB 21452**
(*Pagliacci—Vesti la giubba*)
☆ L. Slezak (*Ger*) (in # Ete. O-470)
ꞟ F. Tamagno (Pol. 78506S*)

RIGOLETTO 3 acts 1851
COMPLETE RECORDINGS
Set D (in *German*)

Gilda	...	...	E. Berger (S)
Maddalena	...	...	M. Klose (A)
Duca di Mantova	...	...	H. Roswaenge (T)
Rigoletto	...	...	H. Schlusnus (B)
Monterone	...	...	J. Greindl (Bs)
Sparafucile	...	...	G. Hann (Bs)

Berlin State Op. Cho. & Orch.—Heger
(4ss)   **# Ura.set 222**

= Long-playing, 33⅓ r.p.m.   ♭ = 45 r.p.m.   ꞟ = Auto. couplings, 78 r.p.m.

RIGOLETTO (*continued*)

Set E
O. Orlandini (S), L. Melani (M-S), G. Sarri (T),
I. Petroff (B), M. Frosini (Bs), Florence
Festival Cho. & Orch.—Ghiglia
(6ss)   **♯ Rem.set 199-58**
(Highlights on ♯ Rem. 199-103)

Set C
☆ E. Berger (S), J. Peerce (T), L. Warren (B),
etc., Robert Shaw Chorale, Victor Sym.—
Cellini   **♯ G.ALP 1004/6**

Highlights
Anon. Artists, Berlin Op. Cho. & Orch.
(2ss)   **♯ Roy. 1349**
(also in ♯ Roy. 1363)
Anon. Artists (in ♯ Wde. 20210 & ♯ Pde. 1007;
      also, with narration, ♯ Pde.OP 105)

ACT I

Questa o quella   **T**
P. Munteanu   *Pol. 62881*
(*Traviata—De' miei bollenti spiriti*)

☆ J. Björling   ♭ *G.7RF 115*
M. Lanza   ♭ *G.7RF 143: 7R 129*
J. Peerce   in ♯ Vic.LM 1169

♓ F. de Lucia   in ♯ Ete. O-464*

Pari siamo!   **B**
A. Hiolski (*Pol*)   *Muza. 1721*
(*Eugene Oniegin, No. 12*)
(*Carmen—Toreador song on Muza. 1719*)

☆ T. Gobbi   ♭ *G.7RF 192*

♓ T. Ruffo   in ♯ Vic.LCT 1039*: ♭ set WCT 62*
G. de Luca   in ♯ GAR. 100*
A. Magini-Coletti   HRS. 1111*
M. Ancona   HRS. 1088*

Figlia! Mio Padre!   **S, S, B**
M. Tauberová & Z. Otava (*Cz*)   **U.H 24223**
(2ss)

☆ L. Pagliughi, D. Mirto & A. Sved
                                       ♮ *P.SW 8124/5*
(3ss—*Otello—Era la notte*)

Ah! Veglia, o donna   **S & B**
L. Grani & G. Bechi   *G.DA 11334*
(*below*)

M. Tauberová & Z. Otava (*Cz*)   **U.H 24193**
(*Barbiere di Siviglia—Dunque io son*)

E il sol dell' anima   **S & T**
☆ E. Berger & J. Peerce (from set) (♭ *Vic. 49-3369*)

♓ G. Huguet & F. de Lucia (in ♯ CMS. 201*)

Caro nome   **S**
H. Gueden   in ♯ *D.LX 3067*
(*Tutte le feste on D.K 23277: K 28571*)   (♯ *Lon.LS 485*)
A. M. Alberghetti   **AmC. 73264D**
(*Flotow*) (C.GQX 11518)   (♯ 3/♭ 4-73264D)
V. Maximova (*Russ*) (2ss)   *U.C 23861*
☆ E. Berger, etc. (from set) in ♯ **Vic.LM 1148**
            (♭ 49-3367: in ♭ set WDM 1542)
☆ L. Pagliughi (AmD. 16009)
♓ M. Galvany (HRS. 2011*)

ACT II

Parmi veder le lagrime   **T**
R. Tucker   **C.LX 1545**
(*Pagliacci—Vesti la giubba*)
I. Kozlovsky (*Russ*—2ss)   *USSR. 10721/2*
S. Lemeshev (*Russ*—2ss)   *USSR. 17968/9*
☆ F. Tagliavini in ♯ Vic.LM 1164; ♭ *G.7RF 207*
J. Peerce (from set C)   ♭ *Vic. 49-3369*

Cortigiani, vil razza dannata   **B**
Z. Otava (*Cz*) (2ss) [1]   **U.H 24222**
(Cortigiani ... only, on U.H 24225)
I. Petroff & Ens. (from set E) [1] in ♯ **Rem. 199-93**
A. Hiolski (*Pol*—2ss)   *Muza. 1720*
▽ H. Schlusnus (*Ger*)   Pol. 67253
(*Barbiere—Largo al factotum*)
☆ R. Merrill   in ♯ *Vic.LM 111*
♓ M. Ancona   HRS. 1088*
P. Amato   in ♯ Ete. O-482*

Tutte le feste al tempio   **S**
H. Gueden   in ♯ *D.LX 3067*
(*Caro nome on D.K 23277: K 28571*)   (♯ *Lon.LS 485*)
☆ L. Pons   **C.LX 1418**
(*Linda di Chamounix—O luce ...*)

Ah! solo per me l'infamia ...
Piangi! piangi fanciulla ...
Si vendetta ...   **S, B, Bs**
☆ L. Pagliughi, A. Sved & G. Gallo **P.R 30042**

Si vendetta, tremenda vendetta   **S, B**
L. Grani & G. Bechi   *G.DA 11334*
(*above*)
♓ L. Hayes & M. Battistini (*G.VA 65**;
                          & in ♯ Ete. O-462*

ACT III

La donna è mobile   **T**
F. Vroons   **Phi.N 11174G**
(½s.—*Tosca—Recondita armonia*, &   (*PhM.A 9010S*)
Pagliacci)
G. Mattera   *P.AT 0289*
(*Manon—En fermant les yeux*)
J. Peerce   in ♯ Roy. 1278 & in ♯ Roy. 6028
R. Schock   in ♯ Roy. 1213
☆ M. Lanza   ♭ *G.7RF 143*
J. Peerce in ♯ Vic.LM 1202: in ♭ set WDM 1626
                        & in ♯ Vic.LM 1169
♓ E. Caruso   in ♯ Vic.LCT 1007*: ♭ set WCT 11*
J. McCormack in ♯ Ete. O-469*: & IRCC 3101*
F. de Lucia   in ♯ CMS. 201*
D. Smirnoff   G.VA 49*: o.n. DA 461*

Bella figlia dell' amore   **S, A, T, B**
☆ E. Berger, N. Merriman, J. Peerce, L. Warren, from set C
                                       (♭ Vic. 49-3367)

ACT IV

Lassù in cielo ...   **S & B**
M. Zvezdina, K. Laptev (*Russ*) *USSR. 18677/8*
(2ss)

SIMONE BOCCANEGRA   3 acts   1857
COMPLETE RECORDING
Maria (alias Amelia)   ...   M. A. Stella (S)
Gabriele   ...   .   C. Bergonzi (T)
Simone Boccanegra   ...   P. Silveri (B)
Fiesco   ...   .   M. Petri (Bs)
etc., Italian Radio Cho. & Orch.—
Molinari-Pradelli (6ss)   **♯ Sor. set 1231**

Il lacerato spirito   **Bs**
G. Neri   **P.R 30051**
(*Barbiere—La Calunnia*)   (BB 25295)

Come in quest'ora bruna (Amelia's Aria) **S**
A. Varnay   in ♯ **Rem. 199-45**
(*Trovatore, Fidelio, Walküre, etc.*)

---

[1] Including the preceding scene: *Povero Rigoletto ...* (or part).

(LA) TRAVIATA 3 acts 1853

COMPLETE RECORDINGS

Set A [1]

Violetta	...	...	...	L. Albanese (S)
Flora	...	...	...	M. Stellman (M-S)
Alfredo	...	...	...	J. Peerce (T)
Giorgio Germont	...	...	R. Merrill (B)

etc., N.B.C. Cho. & Sym. Orch.—Toscanini
　　　　　　　　　　　　G.DB 21360/72
(26ss)　　　　　　　　　　　(♭ *Vic. set WDM 1544*)
(4ss—♯ G.FALP 148/9; Vic. set LM 6003)
(Excerpts on ♭ *Vic.ERA 61*)

Set X

Alfred	...	...	...	A. Pola (T)
Violetta	...	...	...	F. Schimenti (S)
Flora	...	...	...	L. di Lelio (M-S)
Germont	...	...	...	W. M. Chesi (B)

etc., Rome Opera Co. & Orch.—Ricci
　　　　　　　　　　　　♯ Rem. set 199-98
(6ss)　(Highlights in ♯ Rem. 199-102)

Set Y

Violetta	...	...	...	R. Noli (S)
Flora	...	...	...	G. Olini (M-S)
Alfred	...	...	...	G. Campora (T)
Germont	...	...	...	C. Tagliabue (B)

etc., Italian Op. Cho. & Orch.—Berrettoni
(6ss)　　　　　　　　　　**♯ Rem. set 199-77**

Highlights
M. Cebotari (S), H. Roswaenge (T),
H. Schlusnus (B), Berlin State Opera Cho. &
Orch.—Steinkopf (*Ger*)　　　**♯ Ura. 7011**
Anon. Soloists & Berlin State Op. Orch.
　　　　　　　　　　　　in ♯ **Roy. 1323**
(also in ♭ Roy. 1363)　　　　　(♭ *set 14592*, 6ss)
Anon. Artists (in ♯ Wde. 20205: ♯ Roy. 1206; ♯ Pde. 1009;
　　　　　also, with narration ♯ Pde.OP 108)

Vocal Selection
☆ C. Ebers (S), J. Sabel (T), H. Wocke (B) (*Ger*) (P.DPX 44)

Preludes, Acts I & III
Czech Phil.—Pedrotti　　　　**U.H 23801**
Bamberg Sym.—Leitner　　　　**PV. 56010**
(½s. each—*Forza, Overture*)　　(in ♯ *AmD.DL 4016*)
Berlin Op.—Ludwig　　　　　in ♯ **Roy. 1206**

Anon. Orch.　　　　　　　　in ♯ *Roy. 6058*
"Nat. Op. Orch."　　　　　　in ♯ *Var. 2009*
La Scala—Toscanini (*sic*) [2]　　BrzV. 886-5000
☆ Berlin Municipal—Haarth　　　Pol. 15505

ACT I

Libiamo nei lieti calici　　　**T & S**
S. Lemeshev, I. Maslennikova (*Russ*)
(*below*)　　　　　　　　　**USSR. 14915**
☆ J. Peerce & L. Albanese (♯ Vic.LM 1148:
　　　　　　　　　　　　　♭ *set WDM 1542*)

H E. Caruso & A. Gluck (in ♯ Vic.LCT 1037*:
　　　　　　　　　　　　　♭ *set WCT 57*)

Un dì felice, eterea　　　**S & T**
M. Corelli & R. Schock　　in ♯ **Roy. 1206**
I. Maslennikova & S. Lemeshev (*Russ*)
(2ss)　　　　　　　　　　**USSR. 12118/9**
H (T. part only) F. de Lucia & pf. (*G.VA 15*: o.n. *52080*)

Ah! fors' è lui ...; Sempre libera　　**S**
M. Carosio (2ss)　　　　　　**G.DB 21306**
M. Corelli [& R. Schock (T)] in ♯ **Roy. 1206**
V. Firsova (*Russ*, 2ss)　　　**USSR. 017387/8**
☆ B. Sayão　　　　　　　in ♯ *AmC.AAL 3*
H A. Galli-Curci in ♯ Vic.LCT 1039*: ♭ *set WCT62*

[1] Of a radio performance in December 1946.
[2] Probably ☆ of NBC Sym.

... Ah! fors' è lui　only
☆ M. Caniglia　　　　　　BrzV. 886-5001
H G. Bellincioni　　　　G.VB 11*: o.n. 053019*

... Sempre libera　only
R. Peters　　　　　　in ♯ *Vic.LM 7016*
(*Tonight we sing, film music*)　(♭ *set WDM 7016*)
H Lilli Lehmann　　　　in ♯ Ete. O-463*

ACT II

De' miei bollenti spiriti　　　**T**
M. del Monaco　　　　in ♯ *D.LX 3094*
(*Luisa Miller, Macbeth, etc.*)　(♯ *Lon.LS 670*)
P. Munteanu　　　　　　*Pol. 62881*
(*Rigoletto—Questa o quella*)
R. Schock　　　　　in ♯ **Roy. 1206**
S. Lemeshev　　　　　**USSR. 14916**
(*Libiamo*)
☆ D. Georgevic　　　　　D.K 23211

H A. Giorgini　　　G.VB 16*: o.n. 052240*
R. Tauber (*Ger*)　　in ♯ Ete. O-466*
L. Muratore (*Fr*)　　IRCC. 3123*

Di Provenza il mar　　　**B**
H. Wocke　　　　　in ♯ **Roy. 1206**
P. Nortsov (*Russ*)　　　**USSR. 09106**
(*Ballo—Eri tu ...*)
I. Zidek (*Cz*)　　　　**U.H 24220**
(*below*)
H. Schlusnus (*Ger*)　　in ♯ Ura. 7027
J. S. Adamczewski (*Pol*)　*Muza. 1560*
☆ T. Gobbi　　　　　　♭ *G.7RF 192*
H G. de Luca　　　in ♯ GAR. 100*

ACT III

Addio del passato　　　**S**
R. Tebaldi　　　　　**Fnt. 22008**
(*Nozze di Figaro—Deh vieni non tardar*)
M. Minazzi　　　　　**P.PE 171**
(*Bohème—Sì, mi chiamano Mimi*)
M. Tauberova (*Cz*)　　**U.H 24220**
(*above*)
☆ C. Muzio　　　　in ♯ *AmC.ML 4404*
M. Carosio　　　　　♭ *G.7RF 130*
E. Schwarzkopf　　　C.GQX 11456: ♭ *SCB 102*

Parigi, o cara ...　　　**S & T**
M. Corelli & R. Schock　in ♯ **Roy. 1206**
I. Maslennikova & S. Lemeshev (*Russ*)
(2ss)　　　　　　　　**USSR. 14341/2**
E. Shumskaya & I. Kozlovsky (*Russ*)
(2ss)　　　　　　　**USSR. 019615/6**
H L. Bori & J. McCormack (in ♯ Vic.LCT 1037*:
　　　　　　　　　　♭ *set WCT 57*)

(IL) TROVATORE 4 acts 1853
COMPLETE RECORDINGS

Set A

Leonora	...	...	...	Z. Milanov (S)
Azucena	...	...	...	F. Barbieri (M-S)
Manrico	...	...	...	J. Björling (T)
Conte di Luna	...	...	L. Warren (B)

Shaw Chorale & Victor Sym.—Cellini
(4ss)　　　　　　　　**♯ Vic. set LM 6008**
　　　　　　　　　　　(♭ *set WDM 6008*)

Set B

Leonora	...	...	...	C. Mancini (S)
Azucena	...	...	...	M. Pirazzini (M-S)
Manrico	...	...	...	G. Lauri-Volpi (T)
Conte di Luna	...	...	C. Tagliabue (B)

Italian Radio Cho. & Orch.—Previtali
(6ss)　　　　　　　　**♯ Sor. set 1226**
　　　　　　　　　　　(♯ FSor.CS 503/5)

(IL) TROVATORE (*continued*)

Set C

Leonora	...	...	...	B. Scacciati (S)
Azucena	...	...	...	G. Zinetti (A)
Manrico	...	...	...	F. Merli (T)
Conte di Luna	...	...	E. Molinari (B)

☆ La Scala Cho. & Orch.—Molinari
(4ss) **♯ AmC. set SL 120**

Set E

Leonora	...	...	...	S. Roman (S)
Azucena	...	...	...	S. Sawyer (A)
Manrico	...	...	...	G. Sarri (T)
Conte di Luna	...	...	A. M. Serra (B)

Rome Op. Cho. & Orch.—Ricci
♯ Cap. set PCR 8180
(6ss) (Highlights on ♯ P 8178)

Highlights
Berlin Op. Soloists, Cho. & Orch. (in ♯ Roy. 1363:
♭ *set EP 149*)

ACT I

Tacea la notte S
Z. Milanov (from set A) ♭ *Vic. 49-3739*
(*below*)
H. Traubel in ♯ *Vic.LM 123*
(*Mefistofele, etc.*) (in ♭ *set WDM 1584*)
H C. Muzio in ♯ Eso.ES 508*: ♯ Cpt.MC 20010*1
E. Burzio HRS. 1059*
C. Boninsegna in ♯ Ete. O-468*

ACT II

Vedi! le fosche ... (*Anvil or Gypsy Cho.*)
Württemberg St. Op.—Leitner *Pol. 62879*
(*Pagliacci—Bell Cho.*) (*Ger*) (♯ *Pol. 18048*)
☆ La Scala Cho. (Pol. 15554)

Stride la vampa! M-S or A
J. Watson *C.DB 2912*
(*Ballo in Maschera—Re dell abisso*)
D. Eustrati (*Ger*) in ♯ *Roy. 1209*
(in ♭ *set 14593*)
☆ M. Krasova (*Cz*) U.H 24225
H M. Gay G.VB 31*: o.n. 2-034016*
M. Duchène *IRCC. 3106**

Condotta ell'era in ceppi M-S or A
E. Höngen (*Ger*) *PV. 72120*
(*below*) (in ♯ *Pol. 18047*)
D. Eustrati (*Ger*) in ♯ *Roy. 1209*
(in ♭ *set 14593*)
☆ C. Elmo (o.v.) *P.R 30034*
(*Carmen—Je dis que rien ...*)

Il balen del suo sorriso B
☆ L. Warren in ♯ Vic.LM 1168
R. Merrill in ♯ *Vic.LM 111*

Qual suono ... Per me ora fatale B & Cho
☆ L. Warren in ♯ Vic.LM 1168

ACT III

Or co' dadi (*Soldiers' Chorus*)
Grand Cho. *P.PO 192*
(*Faust—Soldiers' Chorus*)

Amor, sublime amore ... Ah! si ben mio T
K. Baum Hma. 15005
(*below; & Andrea Chénier—Un dì ...*)
R. Schock in ♯ *Roy. 1209*
(in ♭ *14593*)
H E. Caruso (in ♯ Vic.LCT 1034*: ♭ set WCT 35*)

Di quella pira!—T. solo only
K. Baum Hma. 15005
(*Ah! si ben mio & Andrea Chénier—Un dì ...*)
R. Schock in ♯ *Roy. 1209*
(in ♭ *set 14593*)

☆ A. Salvarezza *P.PO 195*
(*Turandot—Nessun dorma*) (*Od. O-4854*)
☆ B. Gigli in ♯ Vic.LM 1202: ♭ set WDM 1626
P. Anders (*Ger*) AusT.E 1170
H E. Caruso in ♯ Vic.LCT 1034*: ♭ set WCT 35*

ACT IV

Timor di me ... D'Amor sull'ali rosee S
Z. Milanov (from Set A) ♭ *Vic. 49-3738*
(*above*)
A. Varnay in ♯ *Rem. 199-45*
(*Fidelio, Walküre, Juive, etc.*)
☆ D. Ilitsch Eur.TGB 148
H C. Boninsegna & pf. G.VA 10*: o.n. 53375*
C. Boninsegna in ♯ Ete. O-468*
C. Muzio in ♯ Eso.ES 502*: ♯ Cpt.MC 20009 1*
R. Ponselle in ♯ Gol. 1201*
E. Destinn (*Ger*) in ♯ CEd set 7001*

Miserere—Ah! che la morte S, T, Cho.
G. Brouwenstijn, F. Vroons & Hilversum
Radio Cho. **Phi.N 11176G**
(*Contes d'Hoffmann—Barcarolle*) (*PhM.N 09007S*)
Z. Milanov, J. Peerce & Cho. ♭ *Vic. 49-3740*
(*below*) (from Set A)
M. Corelli & R. Schock in ♯ **Roy. 1209**
(in ♭ *set 14593*)
Anon. Artists in ♯ Var. 2014

Udiste? ... Mira, d'acerbe lagrime S & B
Z. Milanov & L. Warren ♭ *Vic. 49-3740*
(*above*) (From Set A)
H R. Ponselle & R. Stracciari in ♯ Gol. 1201*
F. Leider & H. Schlusnus (*Ger*) in ♯ Ete. O-477*

Se m'ami ... Ai nostri monti S & T
E. Höngen & W. Ludwig (*Ger*) *PV. 72120*
(*above*) (♯ *Pol. 18047*)
D. Eustrati & R. Schock in ♯ **Roy. 1209**
(in ♭ *set 14593*)

(LES) VÊPRES SICILIENNES 5 acts 1855
Overture
Czech Phil.—Pedrotti **U.H 23802S/3**
(3ss) (in ♯ *Sup.LPM 36*)
Lower Austrian—Gui Hma. 15001
(2ss) (in ♯ MSL.MW 41)
R.I.A.S. Sym.—Fricsay *PV. 36031*
(2ss)
☆ Santa Cecilia—Sabata (♭ Vic. 49-1143)

Ballet Music, Act III
Covent Garden—Braithwaite in ♯ **MGM.E 3006**
(*Ponchielli, Tchaikovsky, etc.*)

Mercè, dilette amiche S (Act V)
H S. Kurz (G.VB 48*: o.n. 053276*)
C. Muzio (☆ in ♯ Eso.ES 500*: ♯ Cpt.MC 20008*1

VICTORIA, Tomás Luis de (*c.* 1535-1611)

MASSES
O magnum mysterium (II)
O quam gloriosum (II)
Welch Chorale ♯ **Allo.ALG 3034**

MOTETS
Ave Maria
San Sebastian Cho.—Urteaga *SpC.R 14948*
(*below*)
Petits Chanteurs à la Croix de bois 2
Pat.PD 154
(*below*) (*Pat.MD 4*)
Cho.—Wilhousky2 in ♯ **DCap.LC 6576**
(*Palestrina, Bach, Rubinstein, etc.*)
(♯ *Cap.L 9015*: ♮/♭ *set CD/CDF 9015*)

---

1 Recorded from Edison cylinder.
2 The 4-voice setting from Vol. VIII.

MOTETS (continued)

Domine, non sum dignus (I)
Morriston Orpheus Cho.—Sims   *C.DB 3021*
(Trad. ARR. *Evans: Diniweidrwydd)*
San Sebastian Cho.—Urteaga   *SpC.R 14948*
(above)
Petits Chanteurs à la Croix de bois *Pat.PD 154*
(above)   *(Pat.MD 4)*

Gaudent in coelis (I)
Jesu, dulcis memoria (VIII)
Nonesuch Singers—R. D. Smith
   # Per.SPLP 535

(† Renaissance Masterpieces)

O magnum mysterium (I)
R. Shaw Chorale   in **Vic. set DM 1711**
   (♭ set WDM 1711: # LM 1711)
Welch Chorale   in **# Lyr.LL 35**
(below)
St. Olaf Cho.—Christiansen   in **# StO. 5**
(Berger, Schubert, Christiansen)
UOS Cho.—McConnell   in **# UOS.pte.**
(Palestrina, Caplet, etc.)

O quam gloriosum (I)
Welch Chorale   in **# Lyr.LL 35**
(Palestrina, Byrd, etc.)

O vos omnes (I)
R. Shaw Chorale   in **# Vic.LM 136**
(† XVIth Century Music)   *(in ♭ set WDM 1598)*
French Youth Cho.—Martini   *Pat.PD 149*
(2ss)
Pamplona Cha. Cho. (in † Spanish Cho. Music)

Popule meus (v)
Monaco Cath. Cho.—H. Carol in † **# SM. 33-01**

VIERNE, Louis (1870-1937)

ORGAN MUSIC
Carillon (unspec.)
R. Ellsasser   in **# MGM.E 3005**

(24) PIÈCES DE FANTAISIE, Opp. 51, 53, 54, 55
No. 18, Carillon de Westminster, Op. 54, No. 6
(24) PIÈCES, Op. 31
No. 11, Divertissement
No. 13, Légende
No. 14, Scherzetto
R. Noehren   in **# Aphe.AP 2**
(Reger & Liszt) *(Carillon & Légende, also Aphe.AP 3)*

Symphony No. 2, E major, Op. 20
... Scherzo only
V. Fox   in **# AmC.AAL 20**

VIEUXTEMPS, Henri (1820-1881)

CONCERTOS, vln. & orch.
No. 4, D minor, Op. 31 1853
Y. Menuhin & Philharmonia—Süsskind
   G.DB 21307/9
(6ss)   (also in ♭ Vic. set *WHMV 1015)*
(2ss on # G.BLP 1005;
   1s. with *Paganini* on # Vic. LHMV 1015)

(The) Nightingale, Op. 24, No. 2 vln. & pf.
(after Alabiev)
M. Erdenko & pf.   *USSR. 14500*
(Cui: Orientale)

VILLA-LOBOS, Heitor (b. 1887)

COLLECTION OF PF. MUSIC
(A) **Lenda do Caboclo** 1920
CIRANDAS
... No. 8, Vamos atraz de serra calunga
... No. 11, N'esta rua, n'esta rua
(A) **PRÓLE DO BÉBÉ**, No. 1
... No. 7, O Polichinello
CICLO BRASILEIRO
... No. 1, Plantio do Caboclo
... No. 3, Festa na Sertâo
... No. 4, Dansa do Indio branca
   ☆ E. Ballon   (2ss)   **# D.LX 3075**
   (# Lon.LS 531)

Ave Maria No. 20
San José State A Cappella Cho.—Erlendson
   # ML. 7007
(Corsi, Handl, Tallis, etc.)

BACHIANAS BRASILEIRAS
No. 1 Orch. 1930, f.p. 1932
Janssen Sym.   **# DCap.CTL 7014**
(Choros)   *(# Cap.P 8147)*

No. 5 S, 8 vlcs., cbs. 1938
L. Albanese & Ens.—Stokowski **# G.FBLP 1025**
(Eugene Oniegin aria) *(# Vic.LM 142: in ♭ set WDM 1610)*

... 1st movt., Aria, only
E. Spoorenberg & Ens.—v. Otterloo
   Phi.N 11171G

   ☆ L. Albanese & Ens.—Stokowski *(♭ G.7RF 180)*
   B. Sayâo & Ens.—Villa-Lobos *(# AmC.AAL 3)*

CHÔROS
No. 4 3 hrns., trombone 1926
No. 7 fl., ob., cl., sax., bsn., vln., vlc., gong 1924
Janssen Sym.   **# DCap.CTL 7014**
(Bachianas)   *(# Cap.P 8147)*

CICLO BRASILEIRO: COMPLETE   pf.
   1936-41, rev. 1948
(A) **PRÓLE DO BÉBÉ** No. 1: COMPLETE 1918
A. S. Schic   (some are ☆)   **# CdM.LDX 8004**

CIRANDAS 16 pieces, pf. 1926
No. 2, A Condessa
No. 5, Pobre céga
No. 6, Passa, passa, gavião
No. 7, Xô, xô, passarinho
(A) **Lenda do Caboclo** 1920   pf.
(As) **Tres Marias** 1939   pf.
B. Segáll   **# NRI. 404**
(Rachmaninoff)

Cisne negro (O canto do ...) vlc. or vln. & pf. 1917
Z. Francescatti (vln.), A. Balsam (pf.)
   # AmC.ML 4534
(Chabrier, Vitali, Kreisler, etc.)

Duo, violin & viola 1946
L. & R. Persinger   **# Strad.STR 608**
(Turina, Hindemith & Handel)

Étude No. 7, E major guitar 1929
A. Segovia   in **# B.AXTL 1010**
(† Segovia concert)   *(# AmD.DL 9638)*
(NOTE: C.LX 1229 contains Études No. 1, E minor & No. 7, C sharp minor)

Mass of Saint Sebastian 3 voices 1937
California Univ. Cho.—Janssen
   # AmC.ML 4516

Origin of the Amazon River Sym. poem
(or: Erosion) Orch. 1950
Louisville Sym.—Whitney   **# AmC.ML 4615**
(dello Joio)

= Long-playing, 33⅓ r.p.m.   ♭ = 45 r.p.m.   ♮ = Auto. couplings, 78 r.p.m.

Prelude guitar 1940
A. Segovia   in # AmD.DL 9647
(† Segovia Program)

SONATAS, vln. & pf. ("Fantasias")
No. 1 1912
R. Posselt & A. Sly   in # Acad.ALP 304
(Arbós, etc.)

No. 3 1915
R. Odnoposoff & L. Hambro # Allo.ALG 3025
(Debussy: Sonata)

SONGS
Miáu (A gatinha parda) (Modinha No. 4.) 1938
J. Tourel (M-S), G. Reeves (pf.)
     in # AmC.ML 2198

VIOLETTE, Wesley La (b. 1894)

Music from the High Sierras   orch.
Frankenland Sym.—Kloss   # Lyr.LL 29
(Delmar, Laszlo & Schoop)

VISÉE, Robert de (c. 1650-c. 1725)
SEE: † XVIᴛʜ & XVIIᴛʜ Cᴇɴᴛᴜʀʏ Sᴏɴɢs
      † Sᴇɢᴏᴠɪᴀ Cᴏɴᴄᴇʀᴛ

VITALI, Tommaso Antonio
             (c. 1665-c. 1735)

Ciacona, G minor   vln. & cont.
Z. Francescatti & A. Balsam (pf.)
         # AmC.ML 4534
(Chabrier, Poulenc, Valle, etc.)

— ARR. Respighi
J. Heifetz & R. Ellsasser (org.)   G.DB 4320
(2ss)   (♭ G.7RF 170; ♭ Vic. 49-3305)

VIVALDI, Antonio (c. 1675-1741)

I. CONCERTOS

CONCERTOS, Op. 3 (L'Estro armonico) 1712
Cᴏᴍᴘʟᴇᴛᴇ Rᴇᴄᴏʀᴅɪɴɢ
R. Barchet & Stuttgart Pro Musica Str. Orch.—
R. Reinhardt   # E. & AmVox.set PL 7423
(6ss) (o.n. # AmVox.set PL 7420; # EVox. 271/3;
                    PaV.set VP 273)

No. 6, A minor, vln. & orch.
☆ J. Bernstein & Concert Hall Ens. (# Clc. 6065)

— ARR. HARMONICA & ORCH.
L. Adler & Winterthur Sym.—Goehr
      in # CHS.CHS 1161

No. 8, A minor   2 vlns. & str.
R. Gendre & J. Dejean, Paris Cha.—
Duvauchelle   ♮ Lum. 2.08.011/3
(Concerto, 4 vlns., Op. 3, No. 10)   (# Lum.2LD 102)
☆ York Ensemble   # Rgt. 5051
(Boccherini)

No. 9, D major
☆ J. Fournier & Str. Orch. in † # AS. 2503LD

— ARR. VLC. & PF.   Maréchal
☆ J. Starker & M. Meyer (# Per.SPLP 540; # Clc. 6093)

No. 10, B minor   4 vlns. & strs.
A. Gramegna, Ferro, E. Malanotte, A. Pelliccia
& Rome Coll. Mus.—Fasano   P.BB 25291/2
(3ss—Respighi: Suite No. 3, Siciliana)
R. Gendre, S. Plazonich, J. Dejean,
D. Marchand & Paris Cha.—Duvauchelle
            ♮ Lum.2.08.011/3
(Concerto, No. 8, A minor)   (# Lum.2LD 102)

... Largo only
☆ Merckel, Schwartz, Dumont, Crut & Pro. Musica—
           Goldschmidt (in # Pol. 540002)

No. 11, D minor   2 vlns. & str.
Homburg Sym.—P. Schubert   # Rgt. 5015
(Corelli)
☆ Dumbarton Oaks—Schneider   # Clc. 6029
(Mozart: Divertimento, K 251)

CONCERTOS, Op. 8 1725
Nos. 1-4, Le Quattro Stagioni
Stuttgart Cha.—Münchinger   # D.LXT 2600
(also 12ss, D.K 28491/6)   (# Lon.LLP 386)

No. 1, E major (Primavera)
... Pastorale only
Virtuosi di Roma—Fasano in # AmD.DL 9649
(Torelli, Boccherini, etc.)

Nos. 5-12, Il Cimento dell' Armonia e
          dell' Invenzione   vln. & orch.
☆ L. Kaufman & Sym.—Dahinden (# Clc. 6054/5)

No. 9, D minor
E. Parolari (ob.) & Winterthur Sym.—Dahinden
(below)   # CHS.G 6
☆ L. Goossens (ob.) & Philharmonia—Süsskind
          (C.GQX 11457/8)

(12) CONCERTOS, Op. 9 (La Cetra) 1728
L. Kaufman & French National Radio Str.
Orch. (4ss)   # CHS.set CHS 1134

CONCERTOS, Op. 10, Flute & Orch. 1729/30
No. 1, F major (La tempesta di mare)
No. 2, G minor (La notte)
No. 3, D major (Il gardellino)
No. 4, G major
No. 5, F major (con sordini)
No. 6, G major
J-P. Rampal, Cha. Orch.—Froment;
R. V. Lacroix (hpsi.)   # AmVox.PL 7150

No. 3, D major, Il gardellino
☆ P. Kaplan & Boston Str. Orch.—Poto (# CID. 33004)

CONCERTOS, Op. 12, Vln. & Orch. 1729/30
No. 1, G minor
☆ P. Rybar & Vienna Sym.—Moralt (# Sel.LPG 8318)

CONCERTOS, No Op. no.
BASSOON
A minor (P 72)
E. Mucetti & La Scala—Valdinoci
         # Csm.CLPS 1015
(G mi, fl., ob., bsn.; E flat ma., vln.)

B flat major, La Notte (P 401)
☆ A. Montanari & La Scala—Ephrikian
         (# Csm.CLPS 1029)

D minor (P 282) (ed. Malipiero)
H. Helaerts & Suisse Romande—Ansermet
         # D.LX 3100
(A. Marcello: Oboe Concerto)   (# Lon.LS 591)

FLUTE
C minor (P. 440)
R. Meylan & Str. Orch.—Dahinden # CHS.F 17
(Albinoni, etc.)

☆ = Re-issue of a recording to be found in WERM or Supplement I.

FLUTE, OBOE, & BASSOON
G minor   (P 402)
   G. Peloso, F. Ranzani, E. Mucetti
                              ♯ **Csm.CLPS 1015**
   (A mi., bsn.; E flat ma., vln.)

FLUTE, OBOE, VIOLIN [1]*, BASSOON,
CONTINUO*
G minor   (P 360)   (ed. Veyron-Lacroix)
   J-P. Rampal, P. Pierlot, R. Gendre, P. Hongne,
      R. Veyron-Lacroix   ♯ *BàM.LD 01*
   (½s.—Sonata, below & Bach: Suite)

OBOE
F major   (P 306)
   E. Parolari & Winterthur Sym.—Dahinden
   (above & below)   ♯ **CHS.G 6**

TWO TRUMPETS
C major   (P 75); **E flat major**   (P 273) [2]
   F. Hausdorfer, H. Severnstern, & Sym.—
      Ackermann   ♯ **CHS.G 6**
   (Oboe concertos, above)

VIOLIN
B flat major   (P 405)
C major   (P 88)
   E. Magaziner & Paris Sym.—Bruck
   (below)   in ♯ **Polym. 1006**

E flat major   (P 429)
   E. Minetti & La Scala—Valdinoci
                              ♯ **Csm.CLPS 1015**
   (A mi. bsn; G mi. fl, ob. bsn.)
   ☆ P. Rybar & Vienna Sym.—Moralt (♯ Sel.LPG 8318)

VIOLA D'AMORE
A major   (P 233)
D minor   (P 287)
   H. Danks & London Ens.   ♯ *Nix.LPY 901*
                              (♯ HSLP. 1053)

D minor   (P 287)
   Virtuosi di Roma   ♯ **AmD.DL 9575**
   (Concertos for Str. Orch.)
                  (♯ B.AXTL 1020; ♯ D.UAT 233040)

D minor   (P 266)
   E. Seiler, W. Gerwig (lute) & Cha. Ens.
   (3ss)   **Pol. 4007/8S**

VIOLONCELLO
C minor   (P 434)
   B. Mazzacurati & Rome Coll. Mus.—Fasano
                              P.BB 25284/5
   (3ss—Respighi: Suite No. 3—Siciliana)

G major   SEE: Bach: Org. Concerto, No. 1

ORCHESTRA
C major "per la Solennità di S. Lorenzo"   (P 84)
   ☆ La Scala—Ephrikian (♯ Csm.CLPS 1029)

STRING ORCHESTRA
A major   (P 231)
G minor   (P 407)
G major   (P 143) "alla rustica"
   Virtuosi di Roma—Fasano   ♯ **AmD.DL 9575**
   (Vla. d'amore concerto)
                  (♯ B.AXTL 1020; ♯ D.UAT 233040)

E minor   (P 127)
F major   (P 279)
   Paris Sym.—Bruck   in ♯ **Polym. 1006**
   (above)

II. SINFONIE

B minor, "al Santo Sepolcro"   (P 21)
   Czech Phil.—Pedrotti   **U.H 23804**
   (2ss)   (in ♯ Sup.LPM 35)
   ☆ La Scala—Fanna (♯ Csm.CLPS 1029)

III. SONATAS

SONATAS, Op. 2   vln. & cont.
No. 2, A major
   ☆ J. Bernstein & R. Starer (pf.) (♯ Clc. 6065)
SONATAS, Op. 13   vln. & cont.
   ("Il Pastor Fido")
No. 4, A major
— ARR. VLN. & VLC.   Bazelaire
   A. Asselin & P. Bazelaire   **Od. 123921**

... *Pastorale only*
No. 6, G minor — ARR. FL. & CONT.   Bodky
   ☆ P. Kaplan, E. Bodky (hpsi.) & cont. (♯ CID. 33004)

SONATAS, Op. 14   vlc. & cont.
No. 2, F major
No. 6, B flat major
   ☆ S. Mayes & E. Bodky (hpsi.) (♯ CID. 33004)

No. 5, E minor — ARR. d'Indy
   J. Neilz & Pascal Qtt.   (4ss)   *Pat.PD 146/7*

SONATAS
D minor   fl. & cont.   (P.p.7)   (Upsala MS.)
   J-P. Rampal & R. Veyron-Lacroix (hpsi.)
                              ♯ *BaM.LD 01*
   (½s.—Concerto, above & Bach)

C minor   vln., vlc., cont.   (P.p.7)   (ed. Ghedini) [3]
   Trieste Trio (vln., vlc., pf.)   ♯ *D.LX 3106*
   (Rameau)   (♯ Lon.LS 600)

IV. VOCAL

Beatus vir (Psalm 111) S, S, T, B, B, Double Cho.,
   Double Orch.
   F. Sailer, L. Kiefer, H. Graf, B. Müller,
      H. Werdermann, Stuttgart State Academy
   Cho., Pro Musica Orch.—Grischkat
                              ♯ **E. & AmVox.PL 7140**
                              (o.n. ♯ EVox. 410)

Dixit Dominus (Psalm 109) S, S, A, T, B, Bs, Cho.
   R. Giancola, L. Piovesan, M. Amadini,
   E. Cristinelli, M. Cortis, G. Ferrein, Venice
   Cho. & Orch.—Ephrikian   ♯ **Per.SPLP 537**
                  (♯ Nix.PLP 537; ♯ Clc. 6115)

Juditha triumphans   Oratorio   1716
   S, A, T, Bs, Bs, Cho., Orch.
   R. Giancola, M. Amadini, E. Cristinelli,
   G. Ferrein, Venice Schola Cantorum & Orch.
   —Ephrikian (6ss)   ♯ **Per. set 533**
   (Abridged version, ♯ Per.SPLP 557) (♯ Nix.PLP 533-1/3;
                              ♯ Clc. 6107/9)

Laudate pueri, Nos. 1 & 2   S, & orch.
   (Psalm 112)
   R. Giancola & Venice Academy Cho. & Orch.—
   Ephrikian   ♯ **Ren.X 50**

Mass ... Gloria
   ☆ Soloists, Lecco Cho. & Milan Teatro Nuovo—Pedrollo
                              (♯ Clc. 6047)

Stabat Mater   A & orch.
   M. Amadini   ♯ **AmVox.PL 7180**
   (Carissimi: Jonas)

VLADIGEROV, Panchu (b. 1899)

Rachenica; Peasant's Dance   pf.
   E. Gilels   **USSR. 19029**
   (Vardar, s. 3)

September
   Radio Sofia Cho.—Obretenov   **USSR. 15163**
   (Folk-song)

Vardar, Op. 16   vln. & pf. version
   D. Oistrakh & pf.   **USSR. 19026/8**
   (3ss—*above*)

---

[1] Originally *Violetta*.   [2] Originally in F major, for two Corni di Caccia.
[3] The third movement has apparently been accidentally omitted and a repeat of the first item of the reverse side substituted.
This *may* have been remedied in later pressings.

VOCHT, Louis de (b. 1887)

CONCERTO, vln. & orch. E major 1943
C. van Neste & Belgian Nat.—de Vocht
♯ *D.LX 133018*

SONGS (in *Flemish*)
My little Queen (Cuypers)
E. de Deckers (Bs) & orch.   *C.DCB 46*
(*J. Broeckx: Song*)

My mother dear (Gezelle)
E. de Decker (Bs) & orch.   *C.DCB 45*
(*Verheyden: Song*)

Rodenbach's Reveillé (Rodenbach)
E. de Decker (Bs) & Orch.   *C.DCB 44*
(*Mestdagh: The Scheldt*)

VOORMOLEN, Alexander (b. 1895)

Sonata   pf.
... **Aria** only
T.v.d. Pas   ♯ *Phi.N 00126R*
(*Fauré, Pijper, Orthel*)

Wanderers Nachtlied (Goethe) Unacc. cho.
Netherlands Cha. Cho.—de Nobel
♯ *Phi.N 00127R*
(*Van Delden, Dresden & Sweelinck*)

VOŘÍŠEK, Jan Hugo (1791-1815)

Symphony, D major
☆ Czech Phil.—Ančerl   ♯ *Sup.LPM 33*

WAGENAAR, Bernard (b. 1894)

Symphony No. 4 1949
A.R.S. Orch.—Haefner   ♯ *ARS. 21*

▽ **Older recordings include**
Sonatina, vlc. & pf.; A Tale (pf. solo)
(in AmC.set X 49, o.n. M 223)

WAGNER, Richard (1813-1883)

I. NON-OPERATIC

Albumblatt, E flat major pf. 1875
▽ F. Karrer   ♯ *Rem. 199-26*
(*below*)

(Ein) Albumblatt, C major pf. 1861
— ARR. VLN. & PF. Wilhelmj
M. Kozolupova   *USSR. 10723*
(*Brahms: Hungarian Dance No. 1*)

— ARR. VLC. & PF.
G. Cassadò & O. Schulhof   in ♯ *MSL.MW 45*

Siegfried Idyll 1870
Suisse Romande—Münchinger   ♯ *D.LXT 2669*
(*Haydn: Symphony No. 45*)   (♯ Lon.LL 525)
(also D.K 28595/6, 4ss)
Philharmonia—Cantelli   ♮ *G.DB 9746/7*
(4ss)
Boston Sym.—Koussevitzky   ♯ *Vic.LM 1177*
(*R. Strauss*)   (in set ♮ *WDM 1571*)

☆ N.B.C. Sym.—Toscanini   ♯ **Vic.LCT 1116**
(*Götterdämmerung: Brünnhilde's Immolation*)
(♮ set WCT 1116)
French Nat. Radio—Lindenberg **Od. 123935/6**
(*Tannhäuser Overture on* ♯ *Od.OD 1001*)
Munich State Op.—Konwitschny   ♯ **Ura. 7063**
(*Ring excerpts*)
Berlin Sym.—List   ♯ **Roy. 1362**
(*Brahms: Variations*)

"Nat. Op. Orch." (♯ Roy. 6128)
☆ Vienna Phil.—Furtwängler (♯ G.FALP 110)
Vienna State Op.—Scherchen (AusT.E 1134/5)

SONATAS piano
B flat major 1831
E flat major (Album Sonata) 1853
▽ F. Karrer   ♯ **Rem. 199-26**
(*above*)

SONGS
(5) GEDICHTE (Wesendonck-Lieder)
T. Lemnitz (S), M. Raucheisen (pf.) ♯ **Ura. 7019**
(*Lohengrin, Tannhäuser*)

No. 5, Träume, only
L. Lehmann (S)   in † ♯ **Pembroke set**
J. Vincent (S), F. de Nobel (pf.)
in ♯ **Phi.A 00610R**
(*Schubert, Liszt, etc.*)
☆ J. McCormack (T) (in ♯ Vic.LCT 1036: ♮ set WCT 53)

II. OPERAS

(Die) FEEN 3 acts 1833
Overture
Munich State Op.—Konwitschny in ♯ **Ura. 7069**

(Der) FLIEGENDE HOLLÄNDER 3 acts 1847
Excerpts
T. Scheidl (B), E. Bettendorf (S), M. Bohnen (Bs)
E. Ohms (S)   ♯ **Ete. O-481**
(2ss) (Some are ☆, see below)
Anon. Soloists, Berlin Op. Cho. & Orch.
(2ss)   ♯ **Roy. 1354**

Overture
Philharmonia—Malko   **G.C 4176**
Munich State Op.—Konwitschny in ♯ **Ura. 7069**
Rhineland Sym.—Federer   in ♯ ***Rgt. 5047***
☆ Boston Sym.—Koussevitzky (♮ G.7RF 139)
Philharmonia—Kletzki (C.LVX 108/9)
Dresden Phil.—v. Kempen (Pol. 15498/9; P.OR 5112/3)
Vienna State Op.—Swarowsky (AusT.E 1117/8)

ACT I

Die Frist ist um   B
S. Björling (2ss)   **C.LX 1562**
☆ T. Scheidl   in ♯ Ete. O-481
W. Rode   in ♯ Ete. O-474

ACT II

Summ' und brumm' (*Spinning Cho.*)
Vienna State Op.—Karajan   **C.LX 1440**
(*below*)
Württemberg State Op.—Leitner   *PV. 46005*
(*below*)   (in ♯ Pol. 18048)

Jo-ho-hoe! Traft ihr das Schiff   S & Cho.
(*Senta's Ballad*)
A. Varnay & Cho   in ♯ **Rem. 199-53**
(*Oberon, Freischütz, etc.*)
☆ E. Bettendorf   in ♯ Ete. O-481
🄷 E. Destinn   in ♯ CEd. 7001*

Versank ich jetzt S & B (*Love duet*)
☆ E. Ohms & T. Scheidl (in ♯ Ete. O-481)

(*continued on next page*)

☆ = Re-issue of a recording to be found in WERM or Supplement I.

(Der) FLIEGENDE HOLLÄNDER (*continued*)

ACT III

Steuermann, lass' die Wacht (*Sailors' Cho.*)
Vienna State Op.—Karajan   **C.LX 1440**
(*above*)
Württemberg State Op.—Leitner   *PV. 46005*
(*above*)   (♯ Pol. 18048)

(Das) LIEBESVERBOT   2 acts   1836
Overture
Munich State Op.—Konwitschny in ♯ **Ura. 7069**

LOHENGRIN   3 acts   1850
COMPLETE RECORDINGS

Elsa ...	...	...	M. Schech (S)
Ortrud	...	...	M. Klose (A)
Lohengrin	...	...	G. Vincent (T)
Friedrich	...	...	A. Boehm (B)
König Heinrich	...	...	K. Böhme (Bs)

etc., Munich State Op. Cho. & Orch.—Kempe
(10ss)   ♯ **Ura. set 225**

T. Lemnitz (S), E. Leisner (A), W. Strienz (Bs),
H. H. Nissen (Bs), Berlin State Op.—
Furtwängler   ♯ **CEd. 5003**
(8ss) (Announced, but never issued)

Highlights
Anon. Artists (in ♯ Wde. 20206 & ♯ Pde. 1006; also with
narration, ♯ Pde. OP 110)

Excerpts, Act II
M. Olszewska (M-S), E. Schipper (B),
E. Bettendorf (S), K. Branzell (A)
        ♯ **Ete. O-472**
(2ss—one is ☆, see below; others are *)

Collected Excerpts
Prelude, Act I
Prelude, Act III
Wedding Chorus: Treulich geführt
Netherlands Opera Cho. & Hilversum Radio—
P. v. Kempen   ♯ **Phi.A 00116L**
(*Aïda, March, & Forza Overture*)
(also on Phi.N 11143/4G: PhM.N 0918/9S)

ACT I

Prelude
Royal Phil.—Beecham   **C.LX 1557**
Berlin Phil.—E. Jochum   *PV. 36007*
           (in ♯ *AmD.DL 4030*)
☆ Paris Opéra—Fourestier (Pat.MDT 21)
   Boston Sym.—Koussevitzky (♭ G.7RF 179)

SCENE 2
Einsam in trüben Tagen   S   (*Elsa's dream*)
A. Varnay   **C.LX 1535**
(*Tannhäuser—Dich, teure Halle*)
☆ V. de los Angeles   ♭ G.7R 132: 7RF 193
   L. Lehmann   in ♯ AmD.DL 9523
   H. Traubel   ♭ AmC.A 1550
⊞ R. Ponselle   in ♯ Gol. 1201*
   F. Labia (*Ital*)   HRS. 1099*

SCENE 3
Nun sei bedankt, mein lieber Schwan   T
⊞ F. de Lucia (*Ital*) (*G.VA 13** : o.n. 52650*)

Wenn ich im Kampfe ... Nie sollst du   S & T
⊞ E. Destinn & F. Krauss (*G.VB 25**: o.n. 044056*)

ACT II

SCENE 2
Euch Lüften, die mein Klagen   S
☆ L. Lehmann   in ♯ **AmD.DL 9523**
⊞ E. Destinn (in ♯ CEd.set 7001*)

Ortrud! Wo bist du?   2S
☆ E. Bettendorf & K. Branzell (in ♯ Ete. O-472)

ACT III

Prelude
Berlin Phil.—E. Jochum   ♯ *AmD.DL 4030*
(*Prelude Act I, & Walküre*)
Rhineland Sym.—Federer   ♯ *Rgt. 5043*
(*Liszt & Mozart*)
☆ Chicago Phil.—H. Weber (♯ Clc. 6040)
   Vienna Phil.—Karajan (C.GQX 11471: LVX 171:
                      LFX 1029)

— ARR. BAND   D. Wright
Band—H. Mortimer (*Pax.PR 577*)

SCENE 1
Treulich geführt   Wedding Cho.
☆ Vienna State Op. Cho.—Karajan (C.LFX 1029:
               LVX 171: GQX 11471)

— ARR. ORGAN: V. Fox (in ♯ AmC.AAL 18)

SCENE 2
Love duet: Das süsse Lied ...   S & T
T. Lemnitz & F. Völker   ♯ **Ura. 7019**
(*Tannhäuser, & Songs*)
⊞ E. Destinn & E. Krauss (*G.VB 25**: o.n. 044057*)

Höchstes Vertrau'n   T
☆ S. Svanholm (♯ Vic.LM 1155: ♭ set WDM 1561)

SCENE 3
In fernem Land   T
S. Lemeshev (*Russ*)   *USSR. 18872/3*
☆ S. Svanholm in ♯ Vic.LM 1155: ♭ set WDM 1561
⊞ V. Herold   AF. 41*
   G. Borgatti (*Ital*)   HRS. 1056*

===

(DIE) MEISTERSINGER VON NÜRNBERG
      3 acts   1868
COMPLETE RECORDINGS
Set F

Eva ...	...	...	T. Lemnitz (S)
Walther	...	...	B. Aldenhoff (T)
Beckmesser	...	...	H. Pflanzl (B)
Hans Sachs ...	...	...	F. Frantz (Bs)
David	...	...	G. Unger (T)
Pogner	...	...	K. Böhme (Bs)

Dresden State Op. Cho. & Orch.—Kempe
(12ss)   ♯ **Ura. set 206**

Set E
☆ O. Edelmann (Bs), F. Dalberg (Bs),
E. Kunz (B), H. Hopf (T), G. Unger (T),
E. Schwarzkopf (S), I. Malaniuk (M-S), etc.,
1951 Bayreuth Fest. Cho. & Orch.—v. Karajan
(10ss)   ♯ **C.CX 1021/5**
(ss. 23-26 of 78 r.p.m. set, on C.LVX 190/1)

Set C: Act III, COMPLETE RECORDING

Eva ...	...	...	M. Teschemacher (S)
Walther	...	...	T. Ralf (T)
Beckmesser	...	...	E. Fuchs (B)
Sachs	...	...	H. H. Nissen (Bs)

☆ Dresden Opera Co. & Orch.—Böhm
                ♯ **Vic. set LCT 6002**
(♮ G.DB 8643/57)   (♭ set WCT 50)

"Sachs' Scenes"
Wahn-Monolog; Euch macht ihr's leicht;
Verachtet mir die Meister nicht;
Preludes, Acts I & III; Lehrbubentanz
& Aufzug der Meister.
F. Frantz & Dresden Op.—Kempe ♯ **Ura. 7067**
(from Set F)

♯ = Long-playing, 33⅓ r.p.m.   ♭ = 45 r.p.m.   ♮ = Auto. couplings, 78 r.p.m.

246

(DIE) MEISTERSINGER VON NÜRNBERG (*continued*)
Prelude
  Württemberg State Op.—Leitner   *PV. 36032*
  (*Tannhäuser Overture on ‡ Pol. 16028; AmD.DL 4037, d.c.*)
  Bamberg Sym.—Keilberth ‡ *DT.LGM 65007*
  (*Brahms: Akademische Fest.-Ouvertüre*) (‡ *T.LB 6015*)
  Rome Sym.—Questa   in ‡ *Roy. 6065*
  ☆ N.B.C.—Toscanini   ♭ *G.7RF 138*
                    (♭ *Vic. 49-0297*)
  ☆ Vienna Phil.—Knappertsbusch (D.KX 28573)
                     (from Set D)
  Berlin Phil.—Knappertsbusch (P.RR 8031)

ACT I
SCENE 3
Das schöne Fest, Johannistag   Bs
  H W. Hesch   G.VB 12*: o.n. 042133*

Am stillen Herd   T
  ☆ S. Svanholm in ‡ Vic.LM1155: ♭ *set WDM 1561*

Fanget an! T (*Trial Song*)
  H L. Slezak   G.VA 3*: o.n. ER 141*

ACT II
SCENE 3
Was duftet doch der Flieder   Bs
  P. Schoeffler   in ‡ **MSL.MW 43**
  (*below, Tannhäuser & Lieder*)

ACT III
Prelude
  ☆ Vienna Phil.—Knappertsbusch **D.KX 28574**
                     (from Set D)

SCENE 1
Wahn! Wahn! Überall Wahn!   Bs
  ☆ J. Berglund   T.SK 19033

SCENE 5
Tanz der Lehrbuben
Aufzug der Meistersinger
  Württemberg State—Leitner ‡ *AmD.DL 4037*
  (*Prelude, Act I*)

Tanz der Lehrbuben
  ☆ Vienna Phil.—Furtwängler (♭ *G.7R 141*: ♭ *7RF 203*)

Morgenlich leuchtend
  ... **Tenor part only**
  G. Nelepp (*Russ,* 2ss)   *USSR. 21000/1*
  ☆ S. Svanholm (in ‡ Vic.LM 1202: ♭ *set WDM 1626*:
            & in ‡ LM 1155: ♭ *set WDM 1561*)
  H J. McCormack (G.VB 7*: o.n. DB 329*)
  — ARR. VLC. & PF.
  ☆ P. Casals & pf. (in ‡ Vic.LCT 1050: ♭ *set WCT 72*)

Verachtet mir die Meister nicht   Bs
  P. Schoeffler   Hma. 15003
  (*Tannhäuser—O du mein holder...*) (in ‡ MSL.MW 43)
  H M. Bohnen (in ‡ Ete. O-474*)

PARSIFAL 3 acts 1882
COMPLETE RECORDING
Gurnemanz	...	...	L. Weber (Bs)
Amfortas	...	...	G. London (B)
Parsifal	...	...	W. Windgassen (T)
Kundry	...	...	M. Mödl (S)
Klingsor	...	...	U. Uhde (B)
Titurel	...	...	A. v. Mill (Bs)

  Bayreuth Fest. Cho. & Orch.—Knappertsbusch
  (14ss)   ‡ D.LXT 2651/7
  (*Bayreuth actual performance 1951*) (‡ Lon. set LLPA 10)

ABRIDGED VERSION (26ss) from above set:
  Act I   on D.SX 63018/22
  Act II on D.SX 63023/5
  Act III on D.SX 63026/30

Prelude
  Munich State Op.—Konwitschny in ‡ **Ura. 7065**
                      (& ‡ set 603)
  ☆ N.B.C.—Toscanini   **G.DB 21270/1**
  (*3ss—below*)   (‡ *G.FBLP/QBLP 1007*)
  ☆ Vienna Phil.—Knappertsbusch
                      ‡ **Lon.LLP 451**
  (*below & Rienzi*)
  ☆ Vienna State Op.—Swarowsky (AusT.E 1140/1;
                     in ‡ *CdM.LD 8043*)

ACT I
Titurel, der fromme Held   Bs
  L. Weber (2ss)   C.LX 1441
  H M. Bohnen (in ‡ Ete. O-474*)

Transformation Scene — ARR. ORCH.
  Württemberg State Op.—Leitner   PV. 72211
  (*below*)
  ☆ Vienna Phil.—Knappertsbusch
                 in ‡ **Lon.LLP 451**
  (*above & Rienzi Overture*)

Zum letzten Liebesmahle Cho. & orch.
  Württemberg State Op. Cho. & Orch.—
    Leitner   PV. 72211
  (*above*)

ACT II
Flower Maidens' Scene   T & Cho.
  ☆ G. Treptow, Vienna State Op. Cho. & Vienna
    Phil.—Knappertsbusch   ‡ **D.LXT 2644**
  (*Walküre*)   (‡ Lon.LLP 447)

Ich sah' das Kind   S
  A. Varnay (2ss)   C.LX 1560

ACT III
So ward es uns verhiessen Bs [& T]
  (Sc. 1—*Good Friday Music*)
  J. Greindl   PV. 72212
  (*Walküre, Act I,* in ‡ Pol. 18023)

O Gnade! Höchstes Heil!   Bs
  L. Weber (2ss)   C.LX 1442

Charfreitagszauber —ORCH. ONLY
  Amsterdam—Jochum   T.SK 3712/3
  (*3ss—Beethoven: Ruinen von Athen, March*)
  ☆ N.B.C.—Toscanini   **G.DB 21271/2**
  (*Prelude, s. 3*)   (‡ *G.FBLP/QBLP 1007*)
  Munich State Op.—Konwitschny in ‡ **Ura. 7065**

RIENZI 5 acts 1842
Overture
  Munich State Op.—Konwitschny in ‡ **Ura. 7069**
  Rhineland Sym.—Federer   ‡ *Rgt. 5036*
  (*Weber*)
  Munich Phil.—Mennerich in ‡ **Mer.MG 10080**
  ☆ Vienna Phil.—Knappertsbusch
                      ‡ **Lon.LLP 451**
  (*Parsifal excerpts*)

Ihr Römer, hört die Kunde   Cho.
  Württemberg State Op. Cho. & Orch.—Leitner
                      PV. 72219
  (*Fidelio, No. 11*)

(Der) **RING DES NIBELUNGEN** Cycle 1876

(Das) **RHEINGOLD** 1 act 1869
Bin ich nun frei? (*Alberich's Curse*)
  H D. Zador (in ‡ Ete. O-474*)

(*continued on next page*)

☆ = Re-issue of a recording to be found in WERM or Supplement I.

RHEINGOLD (*continued*)

Weiche, Wotan, weiche! (Erda's Warnung—A only)
☆ E. Wysor (in ♯ *Rem. 149-2*)

Einzug der Götter in Walhall
— ORCH. ONLY
Munich State Op.—Konwitschny in ♯ **Ura. 7063**
(also in ♯ set 603)
☆ Berlin State Op.—Elmendorff (Pol. 15499)

Abendlich strahlt der Sonne Auge
♮ J. Schwarz (in ♯ *Ete. O-474**)

(Die) WALKÜRE 3 acts 1870
COMPLETE RECORDINGS OF ACT I
M. Müller (S), W. Windgassen (T),
J. Greindl (Bs), Württemberg State Op.
Orch.—Leitner ♯ **Pol. 18022/3**
(3ss—*Parsifal, Act 3, Sc. 1*) (*Götterdämmerung,*
in ♯ *AmD. set DX 121*)
(Scene 2 on PV. 36053, Scene 3 on PV. 72173 & 72188)

☆ L. Lehmann (S), L. Melchior (T), E. List (Bs),
Vienna Phil.—B. Walter ♯ **Vic.LCT 1033**
(♮ G.DB 8039/46) (♭ *set WCT 58*)

COMPLETE RECORDING OF ACT II
☆ L. Lehmann (S), M. Fuchs (S), M. Klose (A),
L. Melchior (T), H. Hotter (B), etc. Vienna
Phil.—Walter, etc. ♮ **G.DB 8737/46**

COMPLETE RECORDING OF ACT III
Brünnhilde ... ... A. Varnay (S)
Wotan ... ... S. Björling (B)
Sieglinde ... ... L. Rysanek (S)
etc., Bayreuth Festival Cho. & Orch.—Karajan
(16ss) **C.LX 1447/54**
(4ss, ♯ C.CX 1005/6: FCX/QCX 111/2; AmC. set SL 116)
(Actual performance, 12.VIII.1951)

ACT I

Der Männer Sippe S
A. Varnay in ♯ **Rem. 199-45**
(*Juive, Thaïs, Aïda, etc.*)

ACT II

Ho-jo-to-ho! S
♮ S. Krusceniski (*IRCC. 3095**)

Siegmund! sieh' auf mich S & T (Sc. 4)
☆ K. Flagstad & S. Svanholm ♯ **G.FALP 119**
(*Götterdämmerung*)

ACT III

Walkürenritt Orch. version
N.B.C. Sym.—Toscanini in ♭ *Vic. set WDM 1564*
Munich State Op.—Konwitschny in ♯ **Ura. 7063**
Württemberg State—Leitner ♯ *AmD.DL 4030*
(*Lohengrin Preludes*)
☆ Vienna Phil.—Furtwängler ♭ *G.7R 141*
(*Meistersinger—Tanz der Lehrbuben*) (7RF 203)
☆ Berlin Phil.—Knappertsbusch (P.RR 8032)

Wotans Abschied und Feuerzauber
☆ P. Schoeffler (B) & Vienna Phil.—Moralt
♯ **D.LXT 2644**
(*Parsifal*) (♯ Lon.LLP 447)
☆ J. Herrmann & Vienna Phil.—Moralt (G.DB 20404/5)

Feuerzauber only Orch.
Munich State Op.—Konwitschny in ♯ **Ura 7063**
(& ♯ set 603)

SIEGFRIED 3 acts 1876
Dass der mein Vater nicht ist T (Act II)
☆ F. Lechleitner in ♯ **D.LXT 2644**
(*Parsifal*) (♯ Lon.LLP 447)

Waldweben orch. only
☆ Paris Opéra—Fourestier (Pat.MDT 20)

Interlude, Act III, Sc. 3 (*Fire Music*)
Munich State Op.—Konwitschny in ♯ **Ura. 7065**
(& ♯ set 603)

Wache, Wala! ... Wotan's part only
♮ J. von Manowarda (in ♯ *Ete. O-474**)

Heil dir, Sonne! S & T
(*Awakening Scene*)
K. Flagstad, S. Svanholm & orch.
♯ **Vic.LHMV 1024**
(*Götterdämmerung*) (♭ *WHMV 1024*)

... Dann bist du mir
♮ F. Leider & F. Soot (in ♯ *Ete. O-477**)

(Die) GÖTTERDÄMMERUNG 1876
Prol. & 3 acts
Prologue: Siegfried's Rheinfahrt
N.B.C. Sym.—Toscanini ♯ **G.FALP 157**
(*R. Strauss*) (♯ Vic.LM 1157)
(3ss—*Walkürenritt* in ♭ *set WDM 1564*)
Munich State Op.—Konwitschny in ♯ **Ura. 7065**
(& ♯ set 603)
☆ Vienna Phil.—Furtwängler (♯ G.FALP 110: FALP 194)

ACT I

Hier sitz' ich zur Wacht Bs
L. Weber (n.v.) **C.LWX 449**
(*Tannhäuser—Gar viel und schön*)

Höre mit Sinn (*Waltraute's Narrative*) A
E. Wysor (n.v.) in ♯ **Rem. 199-30**

ACT II

Hoi-ho! (*Hagen's Call*) Bs & Cho.
J. Greindl & Bavarian State Op. Cho.
(2ss) **PV. 72224**
(*Walküre*, in ♯ *AmD. set DX 121*)

ACT III

Trauermusik orch.
Munich State Op.—Konwitschny in ♯ **Ura. 7065**
(includes Finale) (& ♯ set 603)
☆ Vienna Phil.—Furtwängler (♭ G.7RF 151:
in ♯ G.FALP 194)

Starke Scheite schichtet mir dort S
(*Finale—Brünnhilde's Immolation*)
☆ K. Flagstad & Philharmonia—Furtwängler
♯ **G.FALP 119**
(*Walküre*, Duet) (& ♯ FALP 194, d.c.)
(*Siegfried*, Duet, on ♯ Vic.LHMV 1023)
☆ H. Traubel & N.B.C.—Toscanini
♯ **Vic.LCT 1116**
(*Siegfried Idyll*) (♭ *set WCT 1116*)

TANNHÄUSER 3 acts 1845
COMPLETE RECORDING
Elisabeth ... ... M. Schech (S)
Venus ... ... M. Bäumer (S)
Tannhäuser... ... ... A. Seider (T)
Wolfram ... ... K. Paul (B)
Landgraf ... ... O. von Rohr (Bs)
etc., Munich State Op. Cho. & Orch.—Heger
♯ **Ura. set 211**
(8ss) (Excerpts on ♭ *UREP 13*)

Highlights
Anon. Artists (in ♯ *Roy. 1348*; ♯ *Wde. 20211*; & *Pde. 1011*)

♯ = Long-playing, 33⅓ r.p.m.   ♭ = 45 r.p.m.   ♮ = Auto. couplings, 78 r.p.m.

TANNHÄUSER (*continued*)

Overture
French Nat. Radio—Lindenberg   **Od. 123937/8**
(4ss)   (*Siegfried Idyll*, on ♯ *Od.OD 1001*)
Württemberg State Op.—Leitner   **PV. 72250**
(2ss)   (*Meistersinger Prelude* on ♯ *Pol. 16028*)
USSR Radio—Golovanov   **USSR. 021087/90**
(4ss)
☆ Vienna State Op.—Swarowsky (AusT.E 1115/6)

ACT II

Dich, teure Halle, grüss' ich   S
A. Varnay   **C.LX 1535**
(*Lohengrin—Einsam in trüben Tagen*)
T. Lemnitz   (n.v.)   in ♯ **Ura. 7019**
(*Lohengrin*)
☆ L. Lehmann   in ♯ *AmD.DL 9523*
   V. de los Angeles   ♭ *G.7RF 193: 7R 132*
   T. Lemnitz   (o.v.)   *Pol. 15079*
♭ F. Leider   in ♯ *Ete. O-477**
   O. Fremstad   *AF. 380/3**
   E. Destinn   in ♯ *CEd. set 7001**

Fest-Marsch & Einzug der Gäste   Cho. & Orch.
☆ Vienna State Op. Cho. & Vienna Phil.—Karajan
     (C.GQX 11463; M 15154: LVX 154: LFX 1021)
   B.B.C. Cho. (*Eng.*)—Pitt (C.DNX 31)

— ORCH. ONLY   (*Grand March*)
"Nat. Op. Orch." (in ♯ *Var. 6937*)
☆ Chicago Phil.—H. Weber (in ♯ *Clc. 6040*)

Gar viel und schön   Bs
O. Edelmann   in ♯ **D.LXT 2672**
(*Cornelius, Beethoven, etc.*)   (♯ *Lon.LL 427*)
(*Falstaff—Ehi, taverniere*, on D.K 23261: K 28552)
L. Weber   **C.LWX 449**
(*Götterdämmerung—Hier sitz' ich ...*)

Blick' ich umher   B
P. Schoeffler   ♯ **MSL.MW 43**
(*below; Meistersinger & Lieder*)
M. Dens (*Fr*)   **Pat.PDT 279**
(*O du mein holder Abendstern*)
♭ P. Amato (*Ital*) (HRS. 1094*)

ACT III

Pilgerchor: Beglückt darf nun
☆ B.B.C. Cho. (*Eng.*)—Pitt (C.DNX 31)

Allmächt'ge Jungfrau   S
☆ T. Lemnitz   *Pol. 15079*
   L. Lehmann   in ♯ *AmD.DL 9523*
   K. Flagstad   ♭ *Vic. 49-0783*: ♭ *G.7RF 194*
   H. Traubel   ♭ *Vic. WEPR 16*

O du mein holder Abendstern   B
P. Schoeffler   **Hma. 15003**
(*Meistersinger—Verachtet ...*)   (in ♯ *MSL.MW 43*)
And. Ivanov (*Russ*)   **U.H 23837**
(*Ballo in Maschera—Eri tu, Alexeyev*)
M. Dens (*Fr*)   **Pat.PDT 279**
(*Blick ich umher*)
♭ P. Amato (*Ital*) (HRS. 1094*)

— ARR. VLC. & PF.
A. Navarra & J. Dussot   **C.LFX 1009**
(*Liszt: Liebestraum*)
☆ P. Casals (in ♯ Vic.LCT 1050: ♭ *set WCT 72*)

Inbrunst im Herzen   T
☆ S. Svanholm (in ♯ Vic.LM 1155: in ♭ *WDM 1561*)

TRISTAN UND ISOLDE   3 acts   1865
Highlights
Anon. Artists (♯ Roy. 1353; ♯ Wde. 20212; &, 4ss,
              ♯ *Pde. set 1012*)

Symphonic Synthesis — ARR.   Stokowski
(*Prelude, Love duet, Liebestod*)
Sym.—Stokowski   ♯ **Vic.LM 1174**
         (8ss, ♭ *set WDM 1567*)

Prelude & Liebestod
Philharmonia—Dobrowen   **G.C 4111/3S**
(5ss—last blank)
Württemberg State—Leitner   ♯ *AmD.DL 4038*
☆ Chicago Sym.—Rodzinski   ♯ **G.FALP 179**
(*R. Strauss*)
☆ Berlin Phil.—de Sabata (P.RR 8008/10 ¹)
   Sym.—Leinsdorf (in ♯ Clc. 6040)

ACT I

Isolde's Narration   S & A
☆ K. Flagstad & E. Höngen   ♯ **Vic.LM 1151**

ACT II

O sink' hernieder   S, A, T
☆ K. Flagstad, C. Shacklock, S. Svanholm
              (in ♭ Vic.WDM 1550)
   H. Traubel, H. Glatz, T. Ralf (♭ C.LHX 8067/8)

... Einsam wachend   A
☆ E. Wysor (in ♯ *Rem. 149-2*)

Tatest du's wirklich?   Bs
L. Weber   ♮ **C.LX 8892/3**
(3ss—*Tot denn Alles, Act III*)

O König ...   T
Wohin nun Tristan scheidet
J. McCormack   in ♯ **Vic.LCT 1036**
          (♭ *set WCT 53*)

ACT III

Tot denn Alles!   S & Bs
E. Schwarzkopf & L. Weber   **C.LX 8892**
(*Tatest du's wirklich*)

Liebestod: Mild und leise   S
A. Varnay   **C.LX 1417**
☆ H. Traubel (♭ Vic.WEPR 16 & o.v., ♭ AmC.A 1550)
♭ F. Leider (in ♯ Ete. O-477*)

— ARR. 4 PFS.
First Pf. Qtt. (in ♯ Vic.LM 1227: ♭ *set WDM 1624*)

WALDTEUFEL, Emil (1837-1915)

WALTZES
Ange d'amour, Op. 241
Tout Paris, Op. 240
Orch. Continentale—Michaelof
          in ♯ *Nix.LPY 118*

Dolores, Op. 170
   A. Lutter Orch   *T.A 11155*
   Royale Concert Orch.   in ♯ *Roy. 1249*
   Varsity Salon Orch. in ♯ Var. 2004
            & in ♯ *Var. 6941*, etc.

España, Op. 236   (on themes of Chabrier)
Boston Pops—Fiedler (2ss, n.v.)   ♭ *G7.BF 1038*
(*Estudiantina, Très jolie*, &   (♭ Vic. 49-1443)
   Strauss: Polkas, in ♯ Vic.LM 1226: ♭ *set WDM 1522*)
Berlin Sym.—Buschkötter   *Od.O-28212*
(*Estudiantina*)
Berlin Municipal Op.—Otto (*T.A 11278*)
Vienna Radio—Schönherr (*Vien.P 6059; AmVien.V 3004*:
               in ♯ *VNLP 1008*)
☆ Carnegie Pops—Hendl (in ♭ AmC.set A 1013: ♭ A 1549)
   Munich Phil.—Nick (in ♯ Pol. 45011)

---

¹ Pol. 67496/7 now has fill-up, *Siegfried, Act III, Interlude.*

WALTZES (continued)

Estudiantina, Op. 191 (on theme of Lacôme)
Boston Pops—Fiedler (n.v.) ♯ **Vic.LM 1226**
(above & Strauss Polkas) (♭ *set WDM 1522*)
Berlin Sym.—Buschkötter *Od.O-28212*
(España)
International Concert Orch. (Vic. 42-0144: ♭ 27-0144)
Vienna Radio—Schönherr (*Vien.P 6014; AmVien.V 3004:*
in ♯ *VNLP 1008*)
Royale Concert Orch. (in ♯ Roy. 1249 & *6134*)
Orch.—Peters (Pol.Z 60132)
Pallas Orch. (*Pal. 1344*)

☆ Vienna Sym.—Stolz (in ♯ Lon.LLP 143 & D.K 28274)

— ARR. 4 PFS.
First Pf. Qtt. ♭ *AmC.A 1548*

Mon Rêve, Op. 151
Vienna Radio—Schönherr *Vien.P 6073*
☆ Vienna Tel. Orch.—Stolz *Vienna. 1009*
Vienna Sym.—Stolz in ♯ Lon.LLP 143

(Les) Patineurs, Op. 183
☆ N.B.C. Sym.—Toscanini **G.DB 21352**
(♭ *G.7RF 135;* ♭ *Vic. 49-0132 & WEPR 13*)
Vienna Radio—Schönherr *Vien.P 6014*
(*AmVien.V 3002:* in ♯ *VNLP 1003*)
Royale Concert Orch. in ♯ *Roy. 6134*
M. Marrow Orch. in ♯ *MGM.E 94*
Orch.—Peters Pol.Z 60132
Foster Orch. *VIS.VI 4612*
Pallas Orch. *Pal. 1344*
☆ Vienna Sym.—Stolz in ♯ Lon.LLP 143
International Concert Vic. 42-0144: ♭ 27-0144
Carnegie Pops—Brockman in ♭ *AmC.set A 1013*

Pluie de diamants, Op. 160
Vienna Radio—Schönherr *Vien.P 6073*
D. Bela Orch. *ArgOd. 56529*
☆ Vienna Sym.—Stolz in ♯ Lon.LLP 143

Pomone, Op. 155
E. Noblot Orch. *Od. 282648*

(Les) Sirènes, Op. 154
Foster Orch. *VIS.VI 4608*

Toujours ou jamais, Op. 156 (*Chantilly*)
☆ Vienna Tel. Orch.—Stolz *Vienna. 1009*

Très jolie, Op. 159 (alias: *Ganz allerliebst*)
Boston Prom.—Fiedler **G.B 10251**
(2ss) (in ♯ Vic.LM 1226: ♭ *set WDM 1522*)
Vienna Radio—Schönherr (*Vien.P 6074;*
in ♯ *AmVien.VNLP 1008*)

WALLACE, William Vincent (1812-1865)

MARITANA Opera 3 acts 1845
Overture
H. Bund Orch. *Imp. 19011*

Scenes that are brightest S
♬ R. Ponselle (in ♯ Gol. 1201*)

WALMISLEY, Thomas Attwood
(1814-1856)

Evening Service, D minor pub. 1857
R.S.C.M. Choirs—Dykes Bower **C.DX 1779**
(1½ss—*Knapp: Wareham*)

WALTHER, Johann Georg (1684-1748)

SEE: † BAROQUE ORGAN MUSIC
† CHRISTMAS ORGAN MUSIC

WALTON, Sir William (b. 1902)

FAÇADE (Orch. version) 1923
Nos. 8, 14, 16, 22
Philadelphia Pops—Hilsberg ♯ *AmC.AAL 17*
(Bernstein)

Scapino, Overture 1940 (revised 1950)
Philharmonia—Walton **G.DB 21499**

WARD, Robert (b. 1917)

Symphony No. 1 1941
A.R.S. Orch.—Dixon ♯ **ARS. 9**
(Haieff)

WARLOCK, Peter (1894-1930)

Balulalow (Trad.) Carol
UOS Cho.—McConnell in ♯ *UOS.pte*
(Victoria, Palestrina, etc.)

Corpus Christi (Trad.) T, A, Cho.
R. Soames, F. Nielsen & Festival Singers—
Woodgate **G.C 7934**
(The Curlew, s. 1)
Columbia Singers—Engel in ♯ *AmC.ML 2199*

(The) Curlew (Yeats) B, fl., cor anglais & Str. Qtt.
R. Soames (T), G. Gilbert, L. Goossens &
Aeolian Qtt. ♮ **G.C 7934/6**
(5ss—Corpus Christi)

(The) First mercy (Blunt) Song 1927
B. Neely (Tr.), G. Moore (pf.) *G.B 10373*
(Trad. arr. Moore: Coventry Carol)

Yarmouth Fair (Folksong arr.)
C. Williams (S), B. Bazala (pf.)
in ♯ *MGM.E 140*
(Carpenter, Debussy, Delibes, etc.)

WEBER, Ben (b. 1916)

Concert-Aria after Solomon, Op. 29 [1]
S, fl., ob., cl., hrn., bsn., pf. 1929
B. Beardslee (S) & Ens.—Brieff ♯ **ARS. 10**
(Goeb, Swanson)

WEBER, Carl Maria von (1786-1826)

Aufforderung zum Tanz, Op. 65 J.260 1819
(Rondo brillant, D flat major) pf.
☆ A. Brailowsky (♭ *G.7RF 129*)

— ARR. ORCH. Berlioz 1841
Covent Garden—Rignold (2ss) **P.E 11493**
(Od. O-3698)
(& in ♯ P.PMC 1001; ♯ Od.ODX 106; ♯ AmD.DL 9549
& DL 4019)
Bamberg Sym.—Leitner **PV. 72216**
(Jubel)
Residentie—v. Otterloo **Phi.N 12013G**
(2ss) (PhM.N 9015S)
"Nat. Op. Orch." (in ♯ Var. 2006)
"Radio Sym." (in ♯ Var. 6918)
☆ Philharmonia—Markevitch (♭ *G.7P 129: 7BF 1013;*
in ♯ BB.LBC 1028: ♭ *set WBC 1028*)
B.B.C.—Toscanini (♭ *G.7RF 101*)
Dresden Phil.—v. Kempen (Pol. 15497)

— ARR. 4 PFS.
☆ First Pf. Qtt. (in ♯ Vic.LM 1165)

---

[1] Text from The Song of Solomon, V 10-16.

CONCERTOS
Concertino, clar. & orch., C minor, Op. 26 J.109
1811
A. Bürkner & Berlin Phil.—Schrader
in ‡ **Ura. 7012**
(*Overtures & Symphony*)

Konzertstück, pf. & orch., F minor, Op. 79 J.282
1821
R. Casadesus & Cleveland—Szell
‡ **AmC.ML 4588**
(*Liszt: Concerto No. 2*)

Duo concertant, E flat major, Op. 48 cl. & pf.
J.204 1816
S. Forrest & L. Hambro   ‡ **WCFM. 12**
(*Variations*)

☆ L. Amodio & S. Schultze (Pol. 68060/2S, last side blank)

Jubel-Ouvertüre, E major, Op. 59 J.245 1818
Bamberg Sym.—Leitner   **PV. 72216**
(*Aufforderung zum Tanz*)

OPERAS
ABU HASSAN 1 act 1811 J. 106
COMPLETE RECORDING
Fatima ... ... E. Schwarzkopf (S)
Abu Hassan ... ... E. Witte (T)
Omar ... ... M. Bohnen (Bs)
Berlin Radio Cho. & Orch.—Ludwig
(2ss) ‡ **Ura. 7029**

Overture
Vienna Radio—Nilius *Vien.P 6029*
(in ‡ *Vien. 1013; AmVien.VNLP 1005*)
Winterthur Sym.—Desarzens ‡ **CHS.F 18**
(*Euryanthe Overture, & Sibelius*)
☆ Boston Pops—Fiedler ♭ *G.7BF 1040*
(*Rezniček: Donna Diana, Overture*)

EURYANTHE J.291 1823
Overture
Vienna Phil.—Böhm in ‡ **D.LXT 2633**
(*below*) (‡ *Lon.LLP 354* & in ‡ *LD 9002*)
(also 2ss, D.K 28561: K 23224)
Berlin Phil.—F. Lehmann ‡ *Phi.A 00115R*
(*Poot, Sibelius, etc.*)(also 2ss, Phi.N 11160G: *PhM. 09701S*)
Winterthur Sym.—Desarzens ‡ **CHS.F 18**
(*Abu Hassan & Sibelius*)
Berlin Radio—Rother in ‡ **Ura. 7012**
(*Concertino & Symphony*)
▽ Prussian State—Balzer ‡ *G.DB 7699*

☆ Concerts Colonne—Fournet (Pat.MDT 22)
Dresden Phil.—Kempen (P.OR 5028)
Vienna State Op.—Swarowsky (AusT.E 1112;
in ‡ *CdM.LD 8043*)

No. 5, Glöcklein im Tale, Act I A
ℍ B. Kiurina (IRCC. 3098*)

(Der) FREISCHÜTZ, Op. 77 1821 J.277
COMPLETE RECORDINGS
Set C
Agathe ... ... M. Cunitz (S)
Ännchen ... ... E. Loose (S)
Max ... ... H. Hopf (T)
Ottokar ... ... A. Poell (B)
Kuno ... ... F. Bierbach (Bs)
Kaspar ... ... M. Rus (Bs)
Hermit ... ... O. Edelmann (Bs)
Vienna State Opera Cho. & Orch.—Ackermann
(6ss) ‡ **D.LXT 2597/9**
(also D.KX 28512/25, 28ss) (‡ *Lon.set LLPA 5*)

Set D
Agathe ... ... E. Trötschel (S)
Ännchen ... ... I. Beilke (S)
Max ... ... B. Aldenhoff (T)
Ottokar ... ... K. Paul (B)
Kuno ... ... W. Faulhaber (Bs)
Kaspar ... ... K. Böhme (Bs)
Hermit ... ... H. Kramer (Bs)
Dresden State Op. Cho. & Orch.—Kempe
(6ss) ‡ **Ura. set 403**

Set E
Agathe ... ... D. Paludan (S)
Ännchen ... ... H. Löser (S)
Max ... ... K. Wehofschütz (T)
Ottokar ... ...K. H. Tuttner (B)
Kuno ... ... K. Duffek (Bs)
etc., Austrian State Cho. & Orch.—Doehrer
(6ss) ‡ **Rem. set 199-100**

ABRIDGED RECORDING (SET A)
☆ M. Müller, C. Spletter (S), A. Seider (T),
& Soloists, Cho. & Orch. of Berlin State
Opera—Heger (4ss) ‡ **AmD.set DX 112**

Vocal & Inst. Selection
T. Richter, S. Schöner, S. Hauser, G. Frei,
Berlin Municipal Op. Cho. & Orch.—Lutze
T.E 3898

Overture
Hallé—Barbirolli **G.DB 21504**
N.Y.P.S.O.—Szell (*below*) ‡ *AmC.AAL 19*
Copenhagen Royal Orch.—Frandsen C.DDX 30
☆ Philadelphia—Ormandy (‡ *AmC.AAL 10*)
Berlin State Op.—v. Kempen (in ‡ AmD. set DX 112)
N.B.C. Sym.—Toscanini (♭ *G.7RF/RQ 221*)
Vienna State Op.—Swarowsky (AusT.E 1111)

ACT I
Nein, länger trag' ich nicht ...
Durch die Wälder, durch die Auen T
P. Anders (2ss) **G.DA 5514**

Hier im ird'schen Jammertal Bs
☆ M. Bohnen (in ‡ *Ete. 460*)
ℍ A. Didur (*Ital*) (in ‡ *Ete. O-467**)

ACT II
Wie nahte mir der Schlummer ...
Leise, leise, fromme Weise S (*Agathe*)
M. Cunitz (from set C) **D.K 23268**
☆ L. Lehmann in ‡ **AmD.DL 9524**
(*Fledermaus, Rosenkavalier, etc.*)
ℍ E. Destinn (in ‡ *CEd. set 7001**)

ACT III
Und ob die Wolke S (*Cavatina*)
A. Varnay in ‡ **Rem. 199-53**
(*Cavalleria, Ballo, etc.*)
☆ T. Lemnitz (*G.DA 5509*)
ℍ E. Destinn (in ‡ *CEd.set 7001**)

Wir winden dir den Jungfernkranz Fem. cho.
(*Bridesmaids' Chorus*)
Was gleicht wohl auf Erden Male cho.
(*Huntsmen's Chorus*)
Württemberg State Op. Cho. & Orch.—Leitner
(1 side each) *Pol. 62888*
(in ‡ *Pol. 18048*)

OBERON 3 acts 1826 J.306
Overture
Vienna Phil.—Böhm in ‡ **D.LXT 2633**
(*Overtures*) (‡ *Lon.LLP 354*)
(also D.K 28562; & in ‡ *Lon.LD 9002*)

(*continued on next page*)

☆ = Re-issue of a recording to be found in WERM or Supplement I.

OBERON—Overture (continued)

Berlin Phil.—E. Jochum   *PV. 36002*
(2ss)   (in ‡ *AmD.DL 4006*)
N.Y.P.S.O.—Szell   · ‡ *AmC.AAL 19*
(above)
Hilversum Radio—v. Kempen   **Phi.N 11142G**
(*PhM.N 9017S* & in ‡ Phi.N 00119L)
Austrian State Sym.—Gui   ‡ **MSL.MW 42**
(*Beethoven, Gluck, Weber*)
Berlin Radio—Rother   in ‡ **Ura. 7012**
Rhineland Sym.—Federer   ‡ *Rgt. 5036*
(*Wagner*)
☆ Vienna Phil.—Furtwängler (in ‡ *Vic.LHMV 1020*:
   ♭ set *WHMV 1020*)
   Opéra-Comique—Cluytens (Pat.PM *4018*: MDT 8)
   Boston Sym.—Koussevitzky (♭ *Vic. 49-0706*)

ACT II

No. 13, Ocean, thou mighty monster! S
(*Ozean, du Ungeheuer!*)
G. Brouwenstijn (*Ger*)   in ‡ **Phi.N 00119L**
(above & *Mascagni, etc.*)   (2ss, A 12057G)
C. Goltz (*Ger*, 2ss)   *PV. 36052*
A. Varnay (*Ger*, 2ss)   **Hma. 15006**
   (in ‡ Rem. 199-53)

PETER SCHMOLL UND SEINE NACHBARN
  2 acts 1801
Overture, Op. 8 J.54 1807
Vienna Phil.—Böhm   in ‡ **D.LXT 2633**
(*above & below*)   (‡ Lon.LLP 354)
(also D.K 28564)

PRECIOSA, Op. 78 Inc. Music J.279 1821
Overture
Vienna Phil.—Böhm   in ‡ **D.LXT 2633**
(*Overtures*)   (‡ Lon.LLP 354)
(also 2ss, D.K 28563: K 23207)
☆ Dresden Phil.—v. Kempen (Pol. 15484)

TURANDOT, Op. 37
Inc. music to play by Schiller (after Gozzi) J.75 1809
Overture
Rhineland Sym.—Federer   ‡ *Rgt. 5041*
(*Boïeldieu, Pachernegg & Fiedler*)

PARTSONG
Wanderers Nachtlied (Goethe) (unid.)
(*Der du von dem Himmel bist*)
Neeber-Schüler Male Cho. & org.   *T.A 11147*
(*K. Lissmann: Beherzigung*)

Rondo brillante, E flat major, Op. 62 pf. J.252
G. Ginsburg (2ss)   *USSR. 20523/4*

SONATAS   pf.
No. 1, C major, Op. 24 J.138 1812
... 4th movt., Rondo ("*Perpetuum Mobile*")
B. Moiséiwitsch   *G.C 4104*
(*Prokofiev & Vallier*)
O. Frugoni   in ‡ **AmVox.PL 7700**
(*Debussy, Scuderi, etc.*)

— — ARR. ORCH.
Rhineland Sym.—Federer   ‡ *Rgt. 5038*
(*Hérold & Thomas*)

No. 2, A flat major, Op. 39 J.199 1816
☆ A. Cortot (JpV.ND 795/7)

No. 4, E minor, Op. 90 J.287 1822
H. Schnabel   ‡ **SPA. 15**
(*Malipiero*)

SONATAS, vln. & pf. Op. 10 1810
No. 3, D major J.101 ... 2nd movt., Rondo
— ARR. VLC. & PF. Piatigorsky
G. Piatigorsky & R. Berkowitz   ♭ *G.7RF 190*
(*Tchaikovsky: Valse sentimentale*)
   (in ♭ *Vic. set WDM 1578*: ‡ LM 1187)

SONGS
(**Das) Mädchen an das erste Schneeglöckchen** J.267 1819
   (v. Gerstenbergk)
(**Die) Gefangenen Sänger** J.197 ⎫
(**Die) Freien Sänger** J.198 ⎬ (v. Schenkendorf) 1816
Heimlicher Liebe Pein J.235 (Trad.) 1818
Unbefangenheit J.157 (Anon) 1813
H. Mott (S), E. Lush (pf.) in ‡ **Mon.MWL 301**
(*Brahms & Schubert*)

SYMPHONIES
No. 2, C major J.50 1807
Berlin Radio—Heger   ‡ **Ura. 7012**
(*Concertino & Overtures*)
Austrian State Sym.—Rabhuber ‡ **Rem. 199-112**
(*Mozart: Symphony 29*)

(7) Variations, B flat major, Op. 33 cl. & pf.
(*on a theme from Silvana*) J.128 1811
S. Forrest & L. Hambro   ‡ **WCFM. 12**
(*Duo concertant*)

WEBERN, Anton von (1883-1945)

Concerto, nine insts., Op. 24 1934
Quartet, ten. sax., cl., vln. & pf., Op. 22 1930
SONG CYCLE, Op. 12 1915
  1. Der Tag ist vergangen   2. Die geheimnisvolle Flöte
  3. Schein mir's   4. Gleich und gleich
J. L. Monod (pf.), B. Beardslee (S), & Inst.
  Ens.—Leibowitz   ‡ **Dial. 17**

WECKMANN, Matthias (1621-1674)

Suite No. 4, B minor
Toccata No. 4, A minor
L. Stadelmann (hpsi.)   *PV. 3411*

WEELKES, Thomas (c. 1575-1623)

SEE ALSO: † EARLY ENGLISH KEYBOARD MUSIC
          † TRIUMPHS OF ORIANA
          † TREASURY OF MADRIGALS

Gloria in excelsis; Sing, my soul
Welch Chorale   in ‡ **Lyr.LL 35**
(*Handl, Gregorians, etc.*)

WEILL, Kurt (1900-1950)

"Memorable Music"
(Selections from *Street Scene, One Touch of Venus,
Lost in the Stars, Love Life, Lady in the Dark, Marie
Galante*: ARR. PF. & ORGAN)
L. & J. Banan   ‡ **A 440.10-7**

(Die) DREIGROSCHENOPER 1928
... "Moderato assai" [1]
J. Heifetz (vln.), E. Bay (pf.) in ‡ **B.LAT 8020**
(*Aguirre, Valle, Tchaikovsky, etc.*) (in ‡ *AmD.DL 8521*)

KNICKERBOCKER HOLIDAY
September Song
A. Durand Cho. & Orch. (*Ger*) (*T.A 11180*)
— ARRANGEMENTS
The Dell Trio (in ‡ *AmC.CL 6185*: ♭ set B 266
             & ‡ *AmC.GL 513*)
M. Gould (pf.) & Orch. (in ‡ *AmC.ML 4451*: ♭ set A 1019)
etc., etc.

---

[1] A combination of *Lied von der Unzulänglichkeit menschlichen Strebens* and barrel-organ tune, *Morität vom Mackie Messer.*

WEINBERGER, Jaromir (b. 1896)

ŠVANDA THE BAGPIPER   Opera   2 acts 1927
Polka & Fugue   Orch.
  ☆ Philadelphia—Ormandy   ♯ *AmC.AAL 12*
  (*R. Strauss*)   (2ss, ♭ *4-12372D*)

WEINER, Leo (b. 1885)

Hungarian Peasant Songs, Op. 19   pf.
  M. Schwalb   ♯ **Acad.ALP 301**
  (*Dohnányi*)

WEIS, Flemming (b. 1898)

Serenade without serious intentions   1937
  Danish Wind Quintet of 1932 (n.v.) **G.DB 5293**
                           (o.v. ▽ G.DB 5276)

WEISS, Sylvius Leopold (1686-1750)

SEE: † SEGOVIA RECITAL

WELLESZ, Egon Joseph (b. 1885)

INCOGNITA, Op. 69   Opera (after Congreve)
  3 Acts   1951
COMPLETE RECORDING
    Lorenzo   ...   .   J. Slane (T)
    Orlando   ...   .   L. Fyson (T)
    Hippolito   ...   .   F. Loring (B)
    Juliana   ...   .   A. Mandikian (S)
    Leonora   ...   .   D. Murray (M-S)
  etc., Oxford Univ. Op. Club Cho. & Orch.—
    Westrup   **Isis.OC 1/16**
  (31ss—OCS 11 is single-sided)   (Pte. rec.)

WERT, Giaches de (c. 1536-1596)

SEE: † COURTLY MUSIC

WESLEY, Samuel (1766–1837)

Aria & Gavotte   organ
  H. Vollenweider   **G.C 4192**
  (*Bach: Cantata No. 147—Jesu, Joy*)

WESLEY, Samuel Sebastian (1810-1876)

Blessed be the God and Father   Anthem   1853
  Choirs of Royal School of Church Music—
    Dykes Bower   **C.DX 1781**

WEYSE, Christoph Ernst Friedrich
(1774-1842)

SONGS
Always cheerful   (Richardt)   (*Altid frejdig*)
  B. Löwenfalk (B), G. Krarup (org.)   **G.X 8038**
  (*Rung: Church bell*)
  Copenhagen Folk Music & School Cho.—
    Asmussen   *Felix.F 47*
  (*below*)

Among the stars of the night   (Jørgensen)
    (*Imellem Nattens Stjerner*)
  Copenhagen Folk Music School Cho.—
    Asmussen   *Felix.F 47*
  (*above*)

(The) Blessed Day   (Grundtvig)
    (to Norwegian text: God bless our Fatherland, Blix)
  Ø. Frantzen (B) & orch.   *Od.ND 7053*
  (*Paulsen: Song*)

(The) Blue sky is beautiful   (Grundtvig)
    (*Dejlig er den Himmel blaa*)
  B. Löwenfalk (B), G. Krarup (org.)   **G.X 8023**
  (*Grüber: Stille Nacht*)

Christmas has brought a blessed message(Ingemann)
    (*Julen har bragt velsigned Bud*)
  C. Brisson (T) & orch.   *Pol.X 51307*
  (*Hornemann: From the green tree's lofty top*)
  B. Löwenfalk (B) & Cho.   in **G.Z 356**

In the East the sun is rising   (Ingemann)
    (*I Østen stiger Solen op*)
Now peep at one another ...   (Ingemann)
    (*Na titte til hinanden de fogre Blomster smaa*)
  P. Torntoft (Tr.) H. E. Knudsen (pf.)
  (1 side each)   *Tono.K 8077*

Welcome again are God's little angels (Grundtvig)
    (*Velkommen igen Guds Engle smaa*)
  B. Löwenfalk (B) & Cho.   in **G.Z 356**

WHITE, Matthew (fl. c. 1603-1614)

SEE: † CATCHES AND GLEES

WIDOR, Charles Marie (1845-1937)

Symphony No. 5, F minor, Op. 42, No. 1   org.
  ... 5th movt., Toccata
    ☆ F. Germani   ♭ *G.7P 118*

WIENIAWSKI, Henryk (1835-1880)

Étude-caprice, A minor, Op. 18, No. 4
  ☆ Z. Francescatti & M. Lanner (♭ *AmC.A 1533*)

Mazurka, G major, Op. 19, No. 1—Obertass
  vln. & pf.
  L. Kogan & pf.   *USSR. 18627*
  (*Liszt: Canzonetta*)

Polonaise No. 1, D major, Op. 4   vln & pf.
  M. Wilk & F. Kramer   in ♯ *MTR.MLP 1002*

Polonaise (unspec.)
  O. Schumsky & orch.   in ♯ **Long.LW 121**

Scherzo Tarantelle, Op. 16   vln. & pf.
  Y. Menuhin & A. Baller   **JpV.SD 3048**
  (*Sarasate: Romanza andaluza*)   (in set JAS 230)
  ☆ Y. Menuhin & G. Moore   ♭ *G.7RF 224*
  (*Sarasate: Habañera*)
  ☆ H. Szeryng & M. Berthelier   *T.E 3887*
  (*Locatelli: Concerto 12—Labyrinthe*)

WIKLUND, Adolf (1879-1950)

Lyric pieces, Op. 14   pf.
  ... Allegro grazioso & Allegro energico, only
    S. Ribbing   *T.E 19810*
  (*Rangström: Legends from the Mälar, s. 3*)

☆ = Re-issue of a recording to be found in WERM or Supplement I.

WILBYE, John (1574-1638)
SEE: † TRIUMPHS OF ORIANA
† TREASURY OF MADRIGALS

WILLAERT, Adrian (*c.* 1490-1562)

Un giorno mi prego ... (Villotte)
Madonn', io non lo so (Villanesca)
O bene mio (Madrigal)
Dutch Vocal Qtt.—Raugel † #*AS. 2501 LD*

Ricercare org.
F. Peeters # **Ren.X 39**
(† *Old Netherlands Masters*) (# Nix. PLP 239)

WILLAN, Healey (b. 1880)

(An) Apostrophe to the Heavenly Hosts Cho.
Concordia—Christiansen # **Cdia. 2**
(*Bach, Poulenc & Carols*)

Concerto, C minor, pf. & orch. 1944
▽ A. Butcher & Canadian Radio Sym.—
J. Beaudet ♮ **Vic. set DM 1229**
(6ss) (*Canada*)

WILLIAMS, David McK. (b. 1887)
SEE: † AMERICAN CHURCH MUSIC

WILLIAMS, Meirion (b. 1901)
SEE: † WELSH RECORDED MUSIC SOCIETY

WIRÉN, Dag (b. 1905)

Quartet, Str., No. 2, C major, Op. 9 1935
☆ Kyndel Qtt. (5ss) ♮ **G.DB 11063S/5**

Serenade, Op. 11 Str. orch. 1937
Stockholm Radio—Westerberg # **D.LX 3086**
(*Larsson: Pastoral Suite*)

Sonatina, Op. 25 pf.
S. Ribbing **T.E 19808**

WISE, Michael (*c.* 1648-1687)
SEE: † CATCHES AND GLEES

WOLF, Hugo (1860-1903)

(Der) CORREGIDOR Opera 4 acts 1896
COMPLETE RECORDING
Doña Mercedes ... ... M. Fuchs (S)
Frasquita ... ... M. Teschemacher (S)
Don Eugenio ... ... K. Erb (T)
Tio Lukas ... ... J. Hermann (B)
Repela ... ... G. Hann (Bs)
Juan Lopez ... ... K. Böhme (Bs)
Tonuelo ... ... G. Frick (Bs)
Dresden Op. Cho. & Orch.—Elmendorff
(6ss) # **Ura. set 208**

Herz, verzage nicht geschwind (Scene II) T
Intermezzo (Act II)
W. Ludwig & Württemberg Sym.—Leitner
Pol. 62886

Italienische Serenade, G major 1887
Koeckert Qtt. **PV. 72067**
(*Schubert: Str. Qtt. No. 12*) (# AmD.DL 4044

PARTSONG: Ergebung (Eichendorff)
(No. 3 of 6 *Geistliche Lieder*, unacc. cho., 1881)
G. Carrillo Vocal Qtt. (*Span*) **Orf. 22002**
(*Ravel: Chansons*)

SONGS
(SL: Spanisches Liederbuch, 1889-90;
IL: Italienisches Liederbuch, 1890-6)
COLLECTIONS
(16) Songs from the Italienisches Liederbuch
Benedeit die sel'ge Mutter
Gesegnet sei, durch den die Welt entstund
Geselle, woll'n wir uns in Ketten hüll'n
Heb' auf dein blondes Haupt
Heut' Nacht erhob ich mich
Hoffärtig seid ihr, schönes Kind
(Der) Mond hat eine schwere Klag' erhoben
Nicht länger kann ich singen
Nun lass uns Frieden schliessen
Selig ihr Blinden
(Ein) Ständchen euch zu bringen
Sterb' ich, so hüllt in Blumen meine Glieder
Und steht ihr früh am Morgen auf
Und willst du deinen Liebsten sterben sehen
Was für ein Lied soll dir gesungen werden
Wie viele Zeit verlor' ich, dich zu lieben
☆ D. Fischer-Dieskau (B), H. Klust (pf.)
AmD.DL 9632

"An Hour of Lieder—H. Wolf"
Anakreons Grab (Goethe)
Auf eine Christblume (Mörike)
Blumengruss (Goethe)
Denk' es, o Seele (Mörike)
Du denkst mit einem Fädchen (IL)
Frühling uber's Jahr (Goethe)
(Der) Genesene an die Hoffnung (Mörike)
(Die) Geister am Mummelsee (Mörike)
Lied vom Winde (Mörike)
Mausfallensprüchlein (Mörike)
Morgentau (Anon.)
Nachtzauber (Eichendorff)
Nimmersatte Liebe (Mörike)
Und willst du deinen Liebsten sterben sehen (IL)
M. Bothwell (S), P. Meyer (pf.) # **Roy. 1310**

Denk' es, o Seele (Mörike)
(Der) Feuerreiter (Mörike)
Gesellenlied (Reinick)
Im Frühling (Mörike)
H. Roswaenge (T), P. Ulanowsky (pf.)

Gesang Weylas (Mörike)
Rat einer Alten (Mörike)
Über Nacht (Sturm)
M. Klose (A), P. Ulanowsky (pf.)

Elfenlied (Mörike)
Er ist's (Mörike)
In der Frühe (Mörike)
Mignon (Goethe)
Nixe Binsefuss (Mörike)
Sankt Nepomuks Vorabend (Goethe)
Tretet ein, hoher Krieger (Keller)
Wie glänzt der helle Mond (Keller)
A. Simon (S), P. Ulanowsky (pf.) # **Ura. 7025**

Auf dem grünen Balkon (IL)
Auf einer Wanderung (Mörike)
Cophtisches Lied II (Goethe)
Elfenlied (Mörike)
Schlafendes Jesuskind (Mörike)
Um Mitternacht (Mörike)
Verschling der Abgrund (IL)
Verschwiegene Liebe (Eichendorff)
☆ B. Thebom (M-S), W. Hughes (pf.)
Vic.LM 1203
(*Mahler: Lieder eines fahrenden Gesellen*)

= Long-playing, 33⅓ r.p.m. ♭ = 45 r.p.m. ♮ = Auto. couplings, 78 r.p.m.

COLLECTIONS (*continued*)

Herr, was trägt der Boden hier? (SL)
In der Frühe (Mörike)
Wenn du zu den Blumen gehst (Mörike)
Wer tat deinem Füsslein weh'? (SL)

G. Souzay (B), J. Bonneau (pf.) ♯ **D.LXT 2734**
(*Schumann*)   (♯ Lon.LL 535)

Citronenfalter im April (Mörike)
(Der) Knabe und das Immlein (Mörike)
Wiegenlied (Wette)

T. Lemnitz (S), M. Raucheisen (pf.) ♯ **Ura. 7013**
(*Cornelius, Schubert*)

(3) MICHELANGELO-LIEDER
1. Wohl denk' ich oft
2. Alles endet, was entstehet
3. Fühlt meine Seele

B. Sönnerstedt (B), F. Jensen (pf.)
          ♮ **G.DB 20161/2**
(*3ss—Anakreons Grab*)

Denk' es, o Seele (Mörike)
(Der) Gärtner (Mörike)
Heimweh (Eichendorff)
Verborgenheit (Mörike)

☆ H. Schlusnus (B)   in ♯ **Pol. 18059**
          (♯ AmD.DL 9620)

Abschied (Mörike)
Er ist's (Mörike)
Verschwiegene Liebe (Eichendorff)

☆ H. Schlusnus (B)   in ♯ **Pol. 18029**
          (♯ AmD.DL 9621)

Auch kleine Dinge (IL)
Fussreise (Mörike)

☆ H. Schlusnus (B)   in ♯ **AmD.DL 9622**

Anakreons Grab (Goethe)
B. Sönnerstedt (B), F. Jensen (pf.) **G.DB 20161**
(*above*)
P. Gavert (T) & pf.   in ♯ **MTR.MLO 1009**

Die ihr schwebet (SL)
▽ K. Branzell (A)   in ♯ **Rem. 149-6**
(*Schubert, Brahms, etc.*)

Fussreise (Mörike)
G. Hüsch (B), M. Gurlitt (pf.)   **JpV.SF 720**
(*below*)   (in set JAS 275)
T. Pyle (B, *Eng*), R. Viola (pf.) in **Vic. set E 101**
(*Cui*)   (♭ set WE 101)

(Der) Knabe und das Immlein (Mörike)
G. Hüsch (B), M. Gurlitt (pf.)   **JpV.SF 720**
(*above*)   (in set JAS 275)

Nimmersatte Liebe (Mörike)
J. Moor (S), H. W. Hauesslein (pf.)   **Eli. 9036**
(*below*)

Schlafendes Jesuskind (Mörike)
I. Seefried (S), W. Schneiderhan (vln.),
E. Werba (pf.)   **Pol. 62893**
(*Reger: Mariä Wiegenlied*)

Und willst du deinen Liebsten... (IL)
▽ K. Branzell (A)   in ♯ **Rem. 149-6**
(*above*)

Verborgenheit (Mörike)
N. Rossi-Lemeni (Bs), G. Favaretto (pf.)
          P.R 30046
          (AB 30012)
(*Schubert: Der Doppelgänger*)

(Das) Verlassene Mägdelein (Mörike)
J. Moor (S), H. W. Haeusslein (pf.)   **Eli. 9036**
(*above*)

Wer sich der Einsamkeit ergibt (Goethe)
P. Gavert (T) & pf.   in ♯ **MTR.MLO 1009**

WOLF-FERRARI, Ermanno (1876-1948)

OPERAS

(I) GIOIELLI DELLA MADONNA, Op. 4
3 acts 1911
Intermezzo, Act II orch. (No. 1 of Orch. Suite)
☆ L.S.O.—Bellezza (in ♯ BB.LBC 1028: ♭ set WBC 1028)

Sono un demonio buono, Act II   B
⌶ G. Sammarco (*G.VA 6**: o.n. 7-52028*)

Intermezzo, Act III orch. (No. 2 of Orch. Suite)
Philharmonia—Schuechter   in ♯ **MGM.E 131**
          (♭ set K 131)
☆ Württemberg State Op.—Leitner (Pol. 15542)
L.S.O.—Bellezza (in ♯ BB.LBC 1028: in ♭ set WBC 1028)

Danza dei Camorristi, Act III
Boston Prom.—Fiedler (n.v.)   **G.B 10290**
(*J. Strauss: Unter Donner und Blitz*)
          (♭ Vic. 49-1431, d.c. & in ♯ LM 9005)
☆ Carnegie Pops—Abravanel (♭ AmC.A 1549:
          in ♭ set A 1013)

(Der) LIEBHABER ALS ARZT 2 acts 1913
(*L'Amore Medico*, after Molière)
ABRIDGED RECORDING (*Dr. Cupid*)
Soloists & Punch Opera Co. & Orch.—Wilder
          ♯ **Abb. 5**

(I) QUATTRO RUSTEGHI 4 acts 1906
(*Die vier Grobiane: School for Fathers*)
Intermezzo, Act II
Philharmonia—Schuechter   in ♯ **MGM.E 131**
(*Intermezzi*)   (♭ set K 131)
Vienna Radio—Nilius   **Vien.P 6097**
(*Pierné: Serenade*)   (in ♯ 1010)

(II) SEGRETO DI SUSANNA 1 act 1909
Overture
Philharmonia—Fistoulari in ♭ **MGM. set K 120**
(*Nicolai, Rimsky-K, Reznıček*)
Austrian State Sym.—Gui   in ♯ **MSL.MW 50**
(*Rossini & Cherubini*)

Serenade for Strings, E flat major 1895
Berlin Radio—Lange   ♯ **Ura. 7043**
(*Busoni*)

WONDRATSCHECK, Francesco
          (1730-1780)

Concerto, F major, hpsi. & orch. 1757
F. Pelleg & Zürich Radio—Goehr ♯ **CHS.G 14**
(*Haydn: Symphony 46*)

WOOD, Charles (1866-1926)

SONG
Ethiopia saluting the colours (Whitman)
O. Brannigan (Bs), G. Moore (pf.)   **G.B 10252**
(*Hughes: The Palatine's Daughter*)

YARNOLD
SEE: † AMERICAN MUSIC (INST. & CHA.)

☆ = Re-issue of a recording to be found in WERM or Supplement I.

ZANDONAI, Riccardo (1883-1944)

FRANCESCA DA RIMINI   Opera   4 acts   1914
COMPLETE RECORDING
Francesca ...   . M. Caniglia (S)
Paolo   ...   . G. Prandelli (T)
Gianciotto ...   . C. Tagliabue (B)
etc., Italian Radio Cho. & Orch.—Guarnieri
(6ss)   ♯ Sor. set 1229

ZEISL, Eric (b. 1905)

Children's Songs
P. Beems (S), E. Zeisl (pf.)
Pieces for Barbara   pf.
E. Zeisl   ♯ SPA. 5

Sonata, vln. & pf.   ("Brandeis")
I. Baker & Yaltah Menuhin
Sonata, vla. & pf.
S. Reher & E. Schlatter   ♯ SPA. 10

ZELLER, Karl (1842-1898)

OPERETTAS

(Der) KELLERMEISTER
Lass dir Zeit
K. Schmitt-Walter   (n.v.)   *T.A 11269*
(*Abt: Gute Nacht*)
☆ F. Völker (Pol. 57441)

(Der) OBERSTEIGER   1894
Wo sie war, die Müllerin (Sei nicht bös)
H. E. Groh (T)   Od. O-3695
(*J. Strauss, II: Lustige Krieg—Nur für Natur*)

(Der) VOGELHÄNDLER   1891
Vocal Selection
W. A. Dotzer, M. Stelzer, E. Fez, F. Krenn,
Bregenz Fest. Cho. & Vienna Sym.—Paulik
                                      Phi.P 12044G

Grüss euch Gott   T
M. Lichtegg   in ♯ Lon.LLP 55
                                      (D.K 28163)

Schenkt man sich Rosen im Tirol   S & T
R. Krüger & F. Brückner   *Tpo. 3647*
(*below*)
    M. Wutz & F. Klarwein   *Imp. 19082*
    ▽ F. Völker   Pol. 19908
    ☆ L. Klaus & W. Ludwig   Pol. 57417

Wie mein Ahn'l zwanzig Jahr
E. Kunz (B)   *C.LB 117*
(*Strauss: Nacht in Venedig—Treu sein*)   (*LW 60*)
F. Brückner (T)   *Tpo. 3647*
(*above*)
F. Klarwein (T)   *Imp. 19076*

ZICH, Otakar (1879-1934)

Nonet, F minor
Czech Nonet Cha. Ens.   ♮ U.H 23797/800
(8ss)

ZIMBALIST, Efrem (b. 1889)

Fantasia on themes from Rimsky-Korsakov's
   "Coq d'Or"   vln. & pf.
I. Bezrodny   (2ss)   *USSR. 17221/2*

ANTHOLOGIES

(following L'ANTHOLOGIE SONORE, arranged in
Alphabetical order of titles. "Historical" and Acoustic
re-issues are listed in Summary form under "Vocal Re-issues")

L'ANTHOLOGIE SONORE

163:   *SEE* J. H. d'ANGLEBERT

164/5: *SEE* P. VACHON

166:   J. J. QUANTZ: Sonata, G major, Op. 1, No. 6
167:   J. A. HASSE: Sonata, D minor, Op. 1, No. 11
168:   FRIEDRICH II: Sonata, C minor
        J. P. Rampal (fl.), R. Veyron-Lacroix (hpsi.)

THE FOLLOWING ARE ALL ♯ DISCS:

☆ 3001 LD: MOZART: Divertimento, K131; Les petits
        riens (q.v.)

3002 LD: QUANTZ, HASSE, FRIEDRICH II, as 166/8
        (above)
        J.-J. NAUDOT: Sonata, B minor, Op. 4, No. 1
        (2 fls. unacc.)
        N. CHEDEVILLE: Sonata, C minor, Op. 8,
        No. 3 (2 fls. unacc.)
        J. C. de BOISMORTIER: Concerto, A minor,
        Op. 15, No. 2 (5 fls. unacc.)
        J. P. Rampal (playing all parts)

☆ 3003 LD: HAYDN: Trio No. 29 (5), E flat major, Op. 75,
        No. 3
        J. Février, J. Fournier, P. Fournier
        Trio, D major (Baryton, No. 74)
        BEETHOVEN: Trio, D major, Op. 9, No. 2
        Pasquier Trio

2501 LD: MADRIGALS & CHANSONS (15th & 16th
        Cent)
        OBRECHT: Ballade & Chanson de Nouvelan
        ISAAC: Chant de Pâques, Chanson tendre &
        Chant d'adieu
        JOSQUIN: Chanson du soldat
        T. SUSATO: Chanson de mai
        JOAN DE LATRE: Chanson à boire
        WILLAERT: Villotte, Villanesca & Madrigal
        SWEELINCK: Rozette
        Dutch Vocal Qtt.—Raugel

2502 LD: ITALIAN MADRIGALS at the end of the
        Renaissance
        A. AGAZZARI: Dimmi, donna gentile
        (6 voices)
        GIAN DOMENICO: Tri ciecoi siamo
        (Villanella, 3 voices)
        B. MARINI: O luci belle (Canzonetta, 3
        voices)
        L. MARENZIO: A Roma (2 parts, 5 voices)
        A. BANCHIERI: Il Festino della Sera del
        Giovedi Grasso (10 parts, 5 voices)
        L. Marenzio Vocal Ens.—Saraceni

☆ 2503 LD: J. S. BACH: Concerto, C major (2 clav. & orch.)
        (BWV 1061)
        R. Gerlin, M. Charbonnier (hpsis.) &
        Str. Orch.—Sachs
        A. VIVALDI: Concerto, D major, Op. 3, No. 9
        (vln. & orch.)
        J. Fournier & Str. Orch. & hpsi.
        J. S. BACH: Transcription of the above
        R. Gerlin (hpsi.)

2504 LD: MOZART: MOTETS & OFFERTORIES, *q.v.*
        Soloists, Cho. & orch.—Raugel

☆ V♯ 1801 LD: BACH: Cantatas 65 & 189, excerpts
        M. Meili (T), etc.

AMERICAN MUSIC

AMERICAN MUSIC, Vol. I
A. REINAGLE: Sonata, E major
L. M. GOTTSCHALK: March of the Gibaros
R. PALMER: 3 Preludes
C. T. GRIFFES: Sonata
    J. Behrend (pf.)   ♯ Allo.ALG 3024

AMERICAN CHURCH MUSIC
D.McK. WILLIAMS: The King's Highway
H. FRIEDELL: King of Glory
A. B. JENNINGS: Springs in the desert
    St. Bartholomew's Chu. Cho. N.Y.—Friedell
L. SOWERBY: Requiescat in Pace
G. EDMUNDSON: Toccata on Vom Himmel Hoch
    H. Friedell (organ)   ♯ Gco. 101

AMERICAN MUSIC OF EARLY ROMANTIC PERIOD
HOMANN: Overture
GOTTSCHALK: Symphony
BRISTOW: Symphony
    American Arts Orch.—Krueger   ♯ NRI. 2012

**INSTRUMENTAL & CHAMBER MUSIC IN COLONIAL
    AMERICA** (*SEE also:* PETER, J. F.)
J. C. MOLLER: Quartet, E flat major
J. GEHOT: Quartet, D major, Op. 7, No. 6
    New Music Str. Qtt.   ♯ NRI. 2002

R. TAYLOR: Sonatas, No. 4, D major & No. 6, C major
Chevalier de LEAUMONT: Duo concertant (1787)
    L. Silva (vlc.), A. Loesser (18th cent. pf.) ♯ *NRI. 2004*

G. FRANCESCHINI: Sonata, B flat major
    J. Figueroa, J. Margolies (vlns.), F. Valenti (hpsi.),
    J. Saunders (vlc.)
A. REINAGLE: Sonata, E major
    A. Loesser (18th cent. pf.)   ♯ NRI. 2006

HEWITT: Overture
CARR: The Archers, Overture 1796
YARNOLD: Overture
    American Arts Orch.—Krueger   ♯ NRI. 2008

MOLLER: Sinfonia
CLIFTON: Concertino, (pf. & orch.)
    A. Loesser (pf.) & idem.   ♯ NRI. 2010

J. ANTES: 3 Trios, Strings
    Moravian Trio   ♯ NRI. 2016

Other Recordings in this Series, summarised.
♯ NRI. 2007   The Bay Psalm Book (1640)
(& ♯ ARS. 32)   Harmonizations of Psalm-tunes, by R.
        Allison, T. Causton, J. Cosyn, W. Damon,
        J. Dowland, C. Goudimel, E. Hooper,
        G. Kirbye, J. Milton, R. Parsons,
        T. Ravenscroft, S. Stubbs, T. Tomkins,
        & Anon. (Scottish Psalter, 1635)
♯ *NRI. 2005* Ballads in Colonial America
♯ *NRI. 2001* Catholic Music of the South West (& ♯ ARS. 32)
♯ *NRI. 2003* Secular Part-Songs of 18th Cent.
♯ *NRI. 2009* Religious Music of European Protestants in
        America
♯ *NRI. 2011* Patriotic Music in Early America

ANCIENT MUSIC OF THE CHURCH

HAMMERSCHMIDT: De profundis
MONTEVERDI: Laudate Dominum
PEROTIN le grand: Homo vide (unacc.)
SCHÜTZ: Eile mich, Gott, zu erretten
    W. Warfield (B), A. Tietjen (org.)   ♯ AmC.ML 4545
    (*Loewe*)

BAROQUE ORGAN MUSIC

STEIGLEDER, WALTHER, PACHELBEL, SIMON,
    BRUHNS, BACH, BUXTEHUDE, SWEELINCK
☆ W. Supper (o.n. LP 224/5)   ♯ Nix.PLP 224-1/2

SEE: Buxtehude, Bach, Handel, for ♯ *Mer.MG 15036*

☆ = Re-issue of a recording to be found in WERM or Supplement I.

BYZANTINE LITURGICAL MUSIC
(Albanian Use of the Greek Church)

▽ Grottaferrata Abbey Cho.—Tardo (10ss)
  (Sor. set 12) **P.RDx 556/60**

CATCHES AND GLEES OF THE RESTORATION

ATTERBURY, Luffman: Hodge told Sue he loved her
BALDWIN, John: Adam catch'd Eve
BATTISHILL, Jonathan: Here on his back doth lie
CRANFORD, William: Here dwells a pretty maid
  Mark how these knavish rests
HILTON, John Jr.: She that will eat her breakfast in bed
LAWES, Henry: Man's life is but vain (Walton)
LENTON: Come, pretty wenches (or by Ives, Simon)
WISE, Michael: From twenty to thirty
WHITE, Matthew: My dame hath a lame tame crane
SMITH, Robert: Have you not in a chimney seen

☆ Male Voice Qtt. **♯ EA.ALX 3008**

CHRISTMAS ORGAN MUSIC

J. S. BACH: CHORALE-PRELUDES
  Von Himmel hoch, da komm ich her (BWV 606)
  In dulci jubilo (BWV 608)
  Lobt Gott, ihr Christen, allzugleich (BWV 609)
Pastorale, F major (BWV 590)
Canonic Variations on "Vom Himmel hoch, da komm ich
  her" (BWV 769)
BÖHM: Chorale Variations: Gelobet seist du, Jesu Christ
J. G. WALTHER: Chorale Variations: Lobt Gott, ihr
  Christen, allzugleich
BUXTEHUDE: Wie schön leuchtet der Morgenstern
J. S. BACH: Fantasia, G major

F. Heitmann (2ss) **♯ T.LSK 7016**

"COURTLY MUSIC OF XVITH CENTURY"

LASSUS: Ich waiss mir ein Meidlein
JANNEQUIN: Au joly bois
G. WERT: Un jour je m'en allai
JOSQUIN des Prés: Mille regretz
P. CERTON: Je ne l'ose dire
F. REGNART: Plus qu'il vous plait
N. GOMBERT: En aultre avoir
JACOTIN (Jacques Godebrye): Je suis désheritée
C. de SERMISY: Auprès de vous
H. ISAAC: Vergangen ist mir Glück und Heil

Harvard & Radcliffe Music Clubs Cho. **♯ Acad. 308**

EARLY ENGLISH KEYBOARD MUSIC

X 540 BYRD: The Carman's whistle (FVB. 58)
  T. Dart (hpsi.)
  The Earl of Salisbury's Pavan & Galliard
  E. Goble (virginals)
X 541 BULL: Walsingham Variations (2ss)
X 542 P. PHILIPS: Pavana dolorosa (1½ss)
  Galliarda dolorosa (½s.)
  T. Dart (hpsi.)

X 543 ANON: Irish Ochone (FVB. 26) *
  R. JOHNSON: Almain *
  T. Dart (clavichord)
  ANON: The Lord's Masque
  The New Noddy
  T. Dart (hpsi.), R. Donington (gamba)

♮ AX 544/5 BULL: Queen Elizabeth's Pavan (1½ss)
  T. TOMKINS: Pavan, A minor (FVB. 123) (1½ss)
  BULL: The King's Hunt

♮ AX 546/7 BYRD: Pavana Bray; Galliarda Bray (1½ss)
  O. GIBBONS: Fantasy (Glyn V-16)
  FARNABY: Woodycock (FVB. 141)
  E. Goble (hpsi.)

X 548 BULL: In Nomine (FVB. 119) * (2ss)
X 549 WEELKES: 2 Voluntaries (ed. Glynn) *
  O. GIBBONS: Fancy in A re (Glyn IV-6) (½s.)
  BYRD: Praeludium (Fellowes XVIII-2) (½s.)
  G. Jones (org.)

X 550 O. GIBBONS: Lord Salisbury's Pavan & Galliard
  (1½ss)
X 551 M. PEERSON: The fall of the leafe *
  O. GIBBONS: Prelude (Glyn IV-14) *
  FARNABY: Masque; His Dreame *; His Rest *;
  Tower Hill *; A Toye *
  E. Goble (virginals)

Also issued on **♯ D.LXT 2795/6**
  (4ss) **(♯ Lon.LL 712/3)**
  (The items marked * above are omitted)

FRENCH MASTERS OF THE HARPSICHORD

ATTAIGNANT (ed): 3 Court Dances
BALBÂTRE: Noel, D minor
CHAMBONNIÈRES: Chaconne; Rondeau, F major
DANDRIEU: La Favorite; Les Fifres; Les Tourbillons;
  Le Tympanon
DAQUIN: La Melodieuse
GERVAISE: Pavane & Basse Danse
GRIGNY: Dialogue
RAMEAU: Prelude; Gigue; La Timide; La Vénitienne

C. J. Chiasson (hpsi.) **♯ Lyr.LL 19**

FRENCH ORGAN MUSIC

J. ALAIN: Litanies, Op. 79
M. DUPRÉ: Variations sur un Noël, Op. 20
J. LANGLAIS: Hymne d'action de grâces (Te Deum) 1932
P. de MALEINGRAU: La tumulte au Prétoire, from Op. 24
MESSIAEN: Les Bergers; Le Banquet céleste

C. Crozier (Rochester Univ. organ) **♯ Ken. 2553**

FRENCH ORGAN MUSIC OF XVIIth & XVIIIth CENTURIES

L. C. DAQUIN: Noël No. 1 (with variations)
N. de GRIGNY: Récit de tierce en taille
L. MARCHAND: Basse de trompette
N. le BÈGUE: Les Cloches
L. COUPERIN: Chaconne, G minor
L. N. CLÉRAMBAULT: Suite No. 2, G minor

A. Marchal (org. St. Eustache, Paris) **♯ Lum.3LD 101**

FRENCH NOËLS & CHANSONS

Noëls: ARR. Samson & Gevaert
F. J. TISSERAND (XVth Cent): Grâces soient rendues
Folk Songs, ARR. Samson
ANON (XVIth Cent.): Branle de Bourgogne
  Margot, labourez les vignes
J. SAMSON: Changeons propos (Marot)

Beaune Collegiate Chu. Cho.—Samson **SM. 43/7**

GERMAN CHORAL MASTERPIECES

☆ LASSUS: Matona, mia cara
  HANDL: Hodie Christus natus est
  Ecce quomodo moritur
MOZART: Ave verum corpus, K618
  Venite populi, K260
☆ SCHUBERT: Ständchen, Op. 135 (M. Nussbauer, A Solo)
  BRAHMS: Liebeslieder Walzer, Nos. 1, 3, 5, 6, 9, 11,
  12, 13, 17, 18

Vienna Academy Cha. Cho.—F. Grossmann
  ♯ Sel.LPG 8238

GUITAR RECITAL

ALBENIZ: Torre Bermeja & Asturias (Leyenda)
FALLA: Homenaje
GRANADOS: Tonadilla No. 1; Danza española No. 5
J. NIN-CULMELL: Variations on a theme of Milán
J. ORBÓN: Preludio & Toccata
J. RODRIGO: Zarabanda leyana

R. de la Torre **♯ Phil. 106**

♯ = Long-playing, 33⅓ r.p.m. ♭ = 45 r.p.m. ♮ = Auto. couplings, 78 r.p.m.

HARP MUSIC

ANON: (XVIth Cent.) Villancete
CABEZON: Pavane with variations
MILAN: Pavane
MUDARRA: Fantasia
NARVAEZ: Variaciones populares
PALERO: Romanza
CAPLET: Divertissement à l'espagnole
HALFFTER: Three short pieces
PITTALUGA: Danza de la hoguera
TOURNIER: Lolita la danseuse

N. Zabaleta   ♯ Eso.ES 509
(♯ Cpt. MC 20012)

HEART OF THE STRING QUARTET

EXCERPTS FROM:
HAYDN: F major, Op. 3, No. 5
MOZART: D minor, K 421
BEETHOVEN: A major, Op. 18, No. 5
SCHUBERT: E flat, Op. 125, No. 1
MENDELSSOHN: No. 1, E flat, Op. 12
SCHUMANN: No. 1, A minor, Op. 41, No. 1
TCHAIKOVSKY: No. 1, D major, Op. 11
DVORAK: No. 6, F major, Op. 96

Paganini Qtt. (2ss)   ♯ Vic.LM 1192
(♭ set WDM 1611)

ITALIAN ART SONGS

ANON: Dolce Madonna
CACCINI: Amarilli, mia bella
CALDARA: Selve amiche
FALCONIERI: Bella fanciulla   Bk. I, No. 8.   1616
GIORDANI: Caro mio ben
LOTTI: Pur dicesti
PASQUINI: Con tranquillo riposo ...
       Susurrate intorno
PERGOLESI: Lo Frate 'nnamorato—D'ogni pena

☆ G. de Luca (B), P. Cimara (pf.)   ♯ B.AXL 2007
(♯ D.AK 233027; ♯ AmD.DL 7505)

ITALIAN MADRIGALS & GERMAN MOTETS

L. MARENZIO: Scaldava il sol (*Ital*)   1582
       Ti guardo negli occhi
C. GESUALDO: Ecco moriro dunque
       Ahi, gia mi discoloro
       Io tacerò
       In van dunque, O crudele   1611
H. L. HASSLER: Ach Herr, lass dein' lieb' Engelein
A. HAMMERSCHMIDT: Schaffe in mir, Gott

Bavarian Radio Cho.—Kugler   ♯ Mer.MG 10087
(all in *German* except where shown)

ITALIAN MADRIGAL—ARS NOVA & XVIth CENTURY

ANON: (XIVth Cent.): Io son pellegrin
J. CICONIA: Una panathera in compagnia de Marte
JACOPO DA BOLOGNA: Uscelletto selvaggio
F. LANDINO: Così pensoso ...
       De! dimmi tu ...
A. BANCHIERI: La Pazzia senile   (1598): 4 excerpts
       3 Villanelle
       Saviezza giovanile   (1628): Io son
       bella (Canzonetta)
C. FESTA: Amor che mi consigli?
PALESTRINA: Da così dotta
       Ahi che quest'occhi miei
O. VECCHI: Damon e Filli   1595

Vassar Madrigal Singers—Geer   ♯ Allo.ALG 3029

ITALIAN MADRIGALS

AZZAIOLO: Come t'aggio lasciata   Bk. I.   1557
       L'Amanza mia
DONATO: Chi la gagliarda   Bk. I
FALCONIERI: Folti, boschetti   Bk. I   1616
INGEGNERI: Tenebrae factae sunt
MONTEVERDI: Ecco mormorar l'onde
       Lamento di Arianna *

NANINI: Ahi, che debbo morire
       Come Fenice
       D'una donna gentil
       Io son farfalla   all Bk. I   1593
       Sonno soave
PALESTRINA: Tristis est anima mea

Milan Madrigalists—Fait   ♯ Csm.CLPS 1027
(all are ☆ except item marked *)

ITALIAN SONGS OF THE XVIIth & XVIIIth CENTURIES

MONTEVERDI: Partenza amorosa
       Arianna—Lasciatemi morire
A. SCARLATTI: Tutto accesso a quel rai
G. CACCINI: Amarilli, mia bella
G. CARISSIMI: Vittoria, vittoria mio core
B. MARCELLO: Quella fiamma che m'accende
G. B. BASSANI: Fuor dalle placid'onde
       La Serenata—Posate, dormite
(attrib.) PERGOLESI: Se tu m'ami
M-A. CESTI: Orontea—Intorno all'idol mio
A. CAMPRA: Fêtes Vénitiennes—Chanson du papillon

M. Laszlo (S), F. Holletschek (pf.)   ♯ West.WL 5119

BONONCINI: Camilla—Pupille nere
CAVALLI: Donzelle, fuggite
FALCONIERI: O bellissimi capelli   Bk. I,   1616
GIORDANI: Caro mio ben
LEGRENZI: Eteocle—Che fiero costume
PAISIELLO: La Molinara—Nel cor piu
SARTI: Armida—Lungi dal caro bene
TORELLI: Tu lo sai

☆ E. Pinza (Bs), F. Kitzinger (pf.)   ♯ Vic.LCT 1031
(♭ set WCT 47)

(*Handel, Monteverdi, Scarlatti, Mozart*)

LOTTE LEHMANN FAREWELL RECITAL

SCHUMANN: Widmung
       O Ihr Herren
       Ständchen
       Wer machte dich so krank
       Alte Laute
MENDELSSOHN: Der Mond
       Venetianisches Gondellied
CORNELIUS: Ein Ton
       Wiegenlied
WAGNER: Träume
FRANZ: Für Musik; Ständchen
       Gute Nacht; Weisst du noch
       Dies und das
SCHUBERT: Wohin; Danksagung an dem Bach;
       Der Neugierige; Tränenregen
       Die Liebe Farbe;
       Des Baches Wiegenlied
       An die Musik   (unfinished)

Lotte Lehmann (S), P. Ulanowsky (pf.)   ♯ Pembroke 1
(1—10 inch & 1—12 inch)
(Recorded Town Hall, N.Y. 16 Feb. 1951; includes
farewell speech)

(LES) MAÎTRES D'ORGUE DE J. S. BACH

G. BÖHM: Prelude & Fugue, C major
J. J. FROBERGER: Ricercare, G minor
J. PACHELBEL: Vom Himmel hoch
S. SCHEIDT: Cantilena Anglica Fortuna
BUXTEHUDE: Fugue, C major
       Ach Herr, mich armen Sünder
FRESCOBALDI: Fugue, Quadruple
F. COUPERIN: Messe pour les Convents:—
       Premier couplet du Kyrie
       5e couplet du Gloria
       Récit de cromorne en taille
N. de GRIGNY: Récit de tierce en taille (from *Gloria*)
       Dialogue sur les grands jeux (from
       Veni Creator)

G. Litaize (org. of St. Merri, Paris)   ♯ Sel.LPG 8234

(Das) MARIENLEBEN IM LIEDE

301A   XVII Cent: Freu' Dich, Du Himmelskönigin
       Trad: Ave Maria

(continued on next page)

☆ = Re-issue of a recording to be found in WERM or Supplement I.

(Das) MARIENLEBEN IM LIEDE (continued)

302A XVII Cent.: Sagt an, wer ist doch diese
XVIII Cent.: Maria durch ein Dornwald ging

303A XVII Cent.: Gegrüsset seist Du, Königin
Trad.: Glorwürd'ge Königin

304A XVII Cent.: O Maria noch so schön
XIX Cent.: Meerstern, ich dich grüsse

305A XIX Cent.: Über die Berge, Maria Maienkönigin

306B c. 1700: Wunderschön prächtige
XIX Cent.: Rosenkranzkönigin

∇ Cho., Wind Ens. & org.—Jakobi
Chr. 301/5A & 306B

MONACO CATHEDRAL CHOIR

VICTORIA: Popule Meus
PALESTRINA: Improperium exspectavit
LASSUS: Nos qui sumus
C. MORALES: Peccantem me
J. MAUDUIT: En son temple sacré
JANNEQUIN: Mass, La Bataille ... Benedictus; Osanna
G. AICHINGER: Regina coeli
Mgr. PERRUCHOT: Magnificat
Monaco Hymn: Domine salvum fac

Monaco Cath. Cho.—H. Carol   ♯ SM. 33-01
(also, 8ss, SM. 61/4)

MUSIC OF THE LITURGY IN ENGLISH

1. Gregorian Chant adapted to the Anglican Communion Service and Evening Prayer
2. Festal Responses and Anglican Chants for Morning Prayer
MERBECKE, J: Communion Service

Students of General Theological Seminary, New York
—Brown (s. 1); Mixed Choir—Gilbert (s. 2);
A. Tietjen (org.)   ♯ AmC.ML 4528

MUSICIANS OF THE PAST
(Acoustic re-issues, Instrumental)

♯ AudA.LA 1203   Musicians of the Past: pf.: C. Debussy;
C. Saint-Saëns; E. Grieg; F. Busoni
(playing Chopin & Liszt); with M.
Garden (S) & G. Willaume (vln.)

OLD NETHERLANDS MASTERS

CORNET: Fantasia in the 8th tone
DUFAY: Alma redemptoris mater
ISAAC: Herr Gott, lass dich erbarmen
JOSQUIN: Canzona
KERCKHOVEN: Prelude & Fugue, D major
MONTE: Canzona
OBRECHT: Ein fröhlich Wesen
OKEGHEM: Fuga trium vocum
SWEELINCK: Fantasia in Echo-style
WILLAERT: Ricercare

F. Peeters (org. of St. Jans, Gouda, 1736) ♯ Ren.X 39
(♯ Nix.PLP 239)

ORGAN MUSIC FROM SWEELINCK TO HINDEMITH

SWEELINCK: Toccata, A minor
BYRD: Fortune Variations
PURCELL: Chaconne, F major
HANFF: Chorale Prelude—Ach Gott, vom Himmel sieh darein
BÖHM: Chorale Variations—Wer nur den lieben Gott lässt walten
MICHEELSEN: Prelude & Fugue, D major
J. S. BACH: Prelude & Fugue, A minor (BWV 543)
Toccata & Fugue, D minor (BWV 565)
PEPPING: Chorale Preludes—
O Haupt voll Blut und Wunden
Erschienen ist der herrliche Tag
Heut' singt die liebe Christenheit
HINDEMITH: Sonata No. 1

F. Heitmann   ♯ T.LSK 7010/1
(4ss)   (org. of St. Paul's, Berlin)

POLISH KEYBOARD MUSIC
("LANDOWSKA plays for PADEREWSKI")

CATO. D: Chorea polonica
JACOB le POLONAIS: Gagliarda
LANDOWSKA. W.: Bourrée d'Auvergne
The Hop
OGINSKI. M.C.: Polonaises, A minor; G major
TRAD.: 3 Polish Dances (ARR. Landowska)

W. Landowska (hpsi.)   ♯ Vic.LM 1186
(Chopin, Couperin, Rameau)   (♭ set WDM 1586)

PRE-BAROQUE SACRED MUSIC

BYRD: Non nobis, Domine
JOSQUIN: Veni, Creator Spiritus
DUFAY: Magnificat octavi toni
INGEGNERI: O bone Jesu
LASSUS: Spiritus tuus
Auditui meo dabis gaudium
Non avertas faciem tuam a me
Ipsa te cogat pietas
PALESTRINA: Magnificat quarti toni
PLAIN CHANT: Veni Sancte Spiritus
PRAETORIUS: Singet dem Herrn

Harvard Univ. Cho. & Radcliffe Cho. Soc.—Russell
♯ Fest. 70-202

RENAISSANCE MASTERPIECES

JOSQUIN: Ave Maria; Ave verum corpus
VICTORIA: Jesu dulcis memoria
Gaudent in coelis
Nonesuch Singers—R. D. Smith
SERMISY: Vive la serpe et la serpette
Au joli bois
PASSEREAU: Il est bel et bon
JANNEQUIN: La plus belle de la ville
COSTELEY: Mignonne, allons voir ...
Bristol (U.S.A.) Univ. Fr. Circle—Banham
BYRD: Ave verum corpus
FARRANT: Hide not thy face
Call to remembrance
GIBBONS: Magnificat & Nunc dimittis
REDFORD: Rejoice in the Lord alway

Open Score Soc.—F. Cameron   ♯ Per.SPLP 535

SEGOVIA CONCERT

MILAN: Fantasia (vihuela) 1536
R. de VISÉE: Suite, D major
SOR: Variations on a theme of Mozart
HANDEL: Allegretto grazioso
Gavotte
BACH: Vlc. Suite No. 3—Courante
Vln. Sonata 2—Bourrée
M. GIULIANI: Sonata
FALLA: Homenaje
VILLA-LOBOS: Étude No. 7, E Major

A. Segovia   ♯ B.AXTL 1010
(♯ AmD.DL 9638)

SEGOVIA PROGRAM

MILAN: Pavana (unspec.)
HANDEL: Sarabande
Minuet
GLUCK: Orphée: Ballet excerpt (?)
BACH: Vln. Sonata No. 1—Sicilienne
Lute Suite, E minor—Bourrée
SOR: Minuet
CHOPIN: Prelude, A major
SCHUMANN: Romanze
PAGANINI, ARR. PONCE: Andantino variato
BRAHMS: Waltz, Op. 39, No. 2
MORENO TORROBA: Madronos
VILLA-LOBOS: Prelude

A. Segovia   ♯ AmD.DL 9647

♯ = Long-playing, 33⅓ r.p.m.   ♭ = 45 r.p.m.   ♮ = Auto. couplings, 78 r.p.m.

SEGOVIA RECITAL

MUDARRA: Romanesca, 1546
WEISS: Suite, A minor—Prelude, Ballet, Gigue
BACH: Vlc. Suite No. 1, G major—Prelude
Vlc. Suite No. 6, D major—Gavottes
SOR: Allegro (from Sonata)
MENDELSSOHN: Song without words, Op. 19, No. 6
SCHUBERT: Pf. Sonata, Op. 78—Minuet
MORENO TORROBA: Sonatina (Allegretto, Andante, Allegro)
ALBENIZ: Asturias (Leyenda)

A. Segovia ♯ **B.AXTL 1005**
(♯ AmD.DL 9633)

XVIth & XVIIth CENTURY SONGS

FRENCH:
P. ATTAIGNANT (ed.): Tant que vivrai
J.-B. BESARD: Beaux yeux; En quelque lieu
La voilà la nacelle
P. CERTON: Psalm 130
T. CREQUILLON: Quand me souvient
A. le ROY: Psalm 50
R. de VISÉE: Suite, D major (lute solo)

ENGLISH:
J. BARTLETT: What thing is love
When from my love
A pretty duck there was
J. DOWLAND: Flow my tears
I saw my lady weep
Fantasia (lute solo)
T. MORLEY: It was a lover and his lass
F. PILKINGTON: Rest, sweet nymphs

H. Cuénod (T), H. Leeb (lute) ♯ **West.WL 5085**

XVIth CENTURY MUSIC

MONTEVERDI: Lasciatemi morire
CLAUDE: Recevy venir du printans
MORLEY: Agnus Dei
BYRD: Christ rising again
LASSUS: Olà! O che bon eccho!
LEISRING: Lift up your heads
VICTORIA: O vos omnes

R. Shaw Chorale (2ss) ♯ **Vic.LM 136**
(♭ *set WDM 1598*)

SPANISH CHORAL MUSIC

LASERNA: Tumbayle que me voy contigo (Tonadilla)
attrib. **ALFONSO X:** Cantiga No. 96
ANON (XIV-XVth Cent.): 3 Canciones & 1 pregon
J. HIDALGO: Que dito pasito, que duerme
VICTORIA: O vos omnes
ARR. SENFL: Campanas
ARR. REBOUD, F. REMACHA, DONOSTI, VITAL, M. SEIBER, MASSA, MORONDO: Folk Songs
ARR. LEDESMA: Alborada

Pamplona Cha. Cho.—Morondo ♯ **Sel.LPG 8325**
(♯ West.WL 5195)

SPANISH GUITAR MUSIC

M. PONCE: Sonata Meridional
(also on ▽ *C.LX 1275*: 1st movt. only
also on *C.LB 130*)
J. GOMEZ CRESPO: Norteña (also on *C.LB 130*)
☆ **MORENO TORROBA:** Suite Castellana ...
Arada & Fandanguillo
☆ **TURINA:** Fandanguillo

A. Segovia ♯ **C.CX 1020**
(*Castelnuovo-Tedesco: Concerto*) (♯ FCX/QCX 127)

TAÑIDOS DE GUITARRAS

ANON: Huayno (Danza inca)
FALLA: Sombrero de tres picos—Farruca
Aragonesa (Jota)
LECUONA: Malagueñas (Andaluza)
ALBENIZ: Asturias (Leyenda)
L. TEJERA FRANCO: Aires Gallegos; Rondeña
L. TEJERA ABANADES: Brisas Malagueñas

[1] Of the Original Edition.

LOPEZ TEJERA: Burlerias; Alegrias por rosas;
Siguiriyas—Gitanas;
Soleariyas
TARREGA EIXEA: Recuerdos de la Alhambra (Study)
Sueño

L. Maravilla (Lopez Tejera) ♯ **Sel.LPG 8495**
(♯ West.WL 5194)

(A) TREASURY OF MADRIGALS

CLAUDE le jeune: Revecy venir du printans
COSTELEY: Allez, mes premières amours
LASSUS: Ne vous soit étrange
BERTANI: Ch'a mi la vita
GESUALDO: Tu m'uccide, o crudele
MONTEVERDI: Non piu guerra pietate
BATESON, T: Sister, awake Bk. I 1604
BYRD: I thought that love had been a boy 1589
GIBBONS: The Silver swan; What is our life?
T. GREAVES: Come away, sweet love 5 voices 1604
H. LICHFILD: I always loved to call my lady Rose Bk. I 1613
TALLIS: When shall my sorrowful sighing cease
WEELKES: To shorten Winter's sadness 5 vv. 1598
Hark all ye lovely saints 5 vv. 1598
WILBYE: Down in a valley Bk. II 1609
VAUTOR: Mother, I will have a husband 1619

Renaissance Singers—Engel ♯ **AmC.ML 4517**

(The) TRIUMPHS OF ORIANA Madrigals 1601

COMPLETE RECORDING [1]
M. EAST: Hence stars!
D. NORCOME: With Angel's face
M. EAST: Hence stars!
J. MUNDY: Lightly she whipped
E. GIBBONS: Long live fair Oriana
J. BENNET: All creatures now are merry-minded
J. HILTON: Fair Oriana, beauty's Queen
G. MARSON: The nymphs and shepherds danced
R. CARLTON: Calm was the air
J. HOLMES: Thus Bonny-boots
R. NICHOLSON: Sing, shepherds all
T. TOMKINS: The fauns and satyrs tripping
M. CAVENDISH: Come, gentle swains
W. COBBOLD: With wreaths of rose & laurel
T. MORLEY: Arise, awake
J. FARMER: Fair Nymphs, I heard
J. WILBYE: The Lady Oriana
T. HUNT: Hark! did ye ever hear
T. WEELKES: As Vesta was from Latmos Hill
J. MILTON: Fair Oriana, in the morn ...
E. GIBBONS: Round about her charret
G. KIRBYE: Bright Phoebus
R. JONES: Fair Oriana
J. LISLEY: Fair Citherea
T. MORLEY: Hard by a crystal fountain
E. JOHNSON: Come, blessed bird

Madrigal Guild—E. Washington (6ss) ♯ **ML. 7000/2**

XIIth & XIIIth CENTURY MUSIC

SACRED:
ANON: In saeculum artifex (Motet)
Alleluia psallat
Benedicamus Domino (organum duplum)
Ave verum corpus (Trope)
A la clarté (Hymn)
LÉONIN: Deum time (organum duplum)
attrib. **ALFONSO X:** Beneyto foi
attrib. **PEROTIN:** Deus misertus (organum triplum)

SECULAR:
ANON: La quinte estampie real
Belle Doette
En mai la rousée
In saeculum viellatoris
Entre copin et bourgeois
Stantipes
NIEDHART von REUENTHAL: Mayenzeit
BERNARD de VENTADORN: Can vei la lauzetta
MONOIT d'ARRAS: Ce fut en may
ADAM de la HALLE: Amours et ma dame
Li dous regards

Pro Musica Antiqua Ens.—Cape ♯ **EMS. 201**

VOCAL RE-ISSUES

"HISTORIC" & ACOUSTIC " Recital " Recordings

(Some items are electric)

Note : This list contains most of the important miscellaneous recitals in this class, other than Victor's *Collectors'* and *Treasury* discs, whose contents are entered under individual items where applicable, as are the H.M.V. *Archive* series, IRCC., and similar issues. In addition, discs containing collections of items from individual operas will be found under the main listings *supra*, and not here. See *e.g.*, under d'Albert, Bellini, Giordano, Goldmark, Halévy, Mahler (songs), Meyerbeer, Ponchielli, Puccini, Verdi and Wagner. Vocal collectors will also notice a number of USSR. issues (by, *e.g.*, Nezhdanova, Mey-Figner, etc.) which are probably **H**, though not so marked owing to the difficulty of obtaining exact information.

♯ *AudA. 0077* F. Chaliapin recital
(Ernani, Faust, Life for the Tsar, Sonnambula, etc.)

♯ *AudA. 0078* F. Chaliapin recital
(Lucrezia Borgia, Faust, & Songs)

♯ CEd. set 7001 E. Destinn Operatic recital
(4ss) (Bartered Bride, Pagliacci, Lohengrin, Mignon, Zauberflöte, Freischütz, Cavalleria Rusticana, Faust, Fliegende Holländer, Trovatore, Tannhäuser, Dalibor, Nozze di Figaro, Rusalka, Carmen, Madama Butterfly, Aïda, & Songs)

♯ CMS. 201 F. de Lucia Operatic recital
(Rigoletto, Forza, Huguenots, Amico Fritz, Lucia di Lammermoor, Manon Lescaut, Sonnambula)

▽ ♯ Eso.ES 500 [1] "The Duse of Song", Vol. I (C. Muzio)
(♯ Cpt.MC 20008) (Lombardi, Loreley, Hérodiade, Vêpres Siciliennes, Rinaldo, Eugene Oniegin, Africaine, Carmen)

♯ Eso.ES 502 [1] "The Duse of Song", Vol. II (C. Muzio)
(♯ Cpt.MC 20009) (Ernani, Trovatore, Mefistofele, Mme. Sans-Gêne, Pagliacci, Bianca e Fernando, Guillaume Tell, Butterfly, Tosca)

♯ Eso.ES 508 [1] "The Duse of Song", Vol. III (C. Muzio)
(♯ Cpt.MC 20010) (Trovatore, Forza, Adriana Lecouvreur, Contes d'Hoffmann, Andrea Chénier, Paride e Elena, Rossini, Pergolesi)

▽ ♯ *Ete. 451* M. Battistini Operatic recital
(Puritani, Guillaume Tell, Hamlet)

▽ ♯ *Ete. 452* L. Slezak Operatic recital
(Königin von Saba & Prophète)

▽ ♯ *Ete. 453* L. Slezak recital
(Mozart, Rubinstein, R. Strauss, Liszt, etc.)

♯ *Ete. 459* V. Schwarz & R. Tauber Operetta recital
(Zigeunerliebe, Nacht in Venedig, Zigeunerbaron)

♯ *Ete. 460* M. Bohnen & J. Schmidt Operatic recital
(Bartered Bride, Faust, Freischütz, Cavalleria Rusticana)

♯ *Ete. 461* L. Slezak Operatic recital (with Jokl, Jadlowker)
(La Juive, Manon, Alessandro Stradella)

♯ Ete. O-462 M. Battistini Operatic recital
(Pagliacci, Lucia di Lammermoor, Nozze di Figaro, Ernani, Macbeth, Rigoletto, Favorita, Don Sebastien)

[1] Recorded from Edison cylinders.

♯ Ete. O-463 Lilli Lehmann Operatic recital
(Traviata, Robert le Diable, Joshua, Norma, Entführung, Don Giovanni)

♯ Ete. O-464 F. de Lucia Operatic recital
(Huguenots, Barbiere, Rigoletto, Aïda, Werther, Amico Fritz, Carmen, Pêcheurs de Perles)

♯ Ete. O-466 R. Tauber Operatic recital
(Aïda, Bohème, Butterfly, Mignon, Rosenkavalier, Traviata, Bartered Bride)

♯ Ete. O-467 A. Didur Operatic recital
(Barbiere, Ernani, La Juive, Freischütz, Mefistofele, Boris Godounov, Faust)

♯ Ete. O-468 C. Boninsegna Operatic recital
(Ballo in Maschera, Trovatore, Ernani, Cavalleria Rusticana, Gioconda)

♯ Ete. O-469 J. McCormack Operatic recital
(Elisir d'amore, Aïda, Carmen, Tosca, Rigoletto, Favorita, Cavalleria Rusticana)

♯ Ete. O-474 Wagnerian Baritones
Bohnen, Rode, Schwarz, Zador, Manowarda

♯ Ete. O-477 F. Leider Operatic recital
(Siegfried, Tristan, Ariadne auf Naxos, Trovatore, Don Giovanni, Tannhäuser)

♯ Ete. O-479 Mozart Operatic Arias—G. Sammarco, M. Renaud, F. d'Andrade, G. Ritter-Ciampi, M. Ivogün, L. Slezak
(Figaro, Don Giovanni, Entführung, Zauberflöte, Re Pastore)

♯ Ete. O-482 P. Amato Operatic recital
(Rigoletto, Aïda, Due Foscari, Tosca, Gioconda)

♯ GAR. 100 G. de Luca Operatic recital
(Don Pasquale, Hamlet, Africaine, Traviata, Rigoletto)

♯ GAR. 101 A. Bonci Operatic recital
(Don Pasquale, Favorita, Lucia di Lammermoor, Puritani, Barbiere)

♯ Gol. 1201 R. Ponselle Operatic recital
(Tosca, Manon Lescaut, Butterfly, Trovatore, Cavalleria Rusticana, Lohengrin, Sadko, Maritana)

WELSH RECORDED MUSIC SOCIETY

D.K 2440 D. V. THOMAS: Berwyn (Cynddelw)
M. WILLIAMS: Gwynfyd (Crwys)
R. Jones (B), M. Williams (pf.)

D.K 2441 5 Folk Songs
A. Parry-Williams (M-S), M. Evans (B), O. Ellis (hp.)

D.K 2442 Penillion singing (poem by R. Williams Parry)
A. Parry-Williams & O. Ellis

D.M 673 W. DAVIES: Nant y Mynydd (Ceiriog)
O, Na byddai'n haf o hyd (Buddug)

D.M 675 M. OWEN: William (E. Hillier)
God made a lovely garden (M. Spence)
C. Rowlands (S), M. Williams (pf.)

D.M 674 Ballads
R. Roberts (T), M. Noel-Jones (pf.)